A DICTIONARY OF SCIENTIFIC TERMS

D0296023

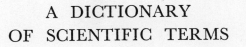

A DICTIONARY OF SCIENTIFIC TERMS

PRONUNCIATION, DERIVATION, AND DEFINITION OF TERMS IN BIOLOGY, BOTANY, ZOOLOGY, ANATOMY, CYTOLOGY, GENETICS, EMBRYOLOGY, PHYSIOLOGY

BY

I. F. HENDERSON, M.A.

AND

W. D. HENDERSON, M.A., B.Sc., Ph.D., F.R.S.E.

SEVENTH EDITION

BY

J. H. KENNETH, M.A., Ph.D., F.R.S.E., F.R.S.G.S.

[redacted]

D. VAN NOSTRAND COMPANY, INC.

PRINCETON, NEW JERSEY

TORONTO LONDON

NEW YORK

First Published 1920
Seventh Edition 1960

[redacted]

© 1960 Oliver and Boyd Ltd.

PRINTED IN GREAT BRITAIN BY
OLIVER AND BOYD LTD., EDINBURGH

Ref.
QH13
H4
1960

[redacted]

PREFACE

It was thought desirable that there should be available to students and others interested in the Biological Sciences an up-to-date work somewhat on the lines of Stormonth's *Manual of Scientific Terms* (1879, republished 1903). The subjects selected for treatment are Biology and its allies: Botany, Zoology, Cytology, Genetics, Embryology, Anatomy, Physiology; some terms in Bacteriology and Palæontology are included. Specific, generic, ordinal, and other systematic names of plants and animals have necessarily been omitted, nor could references to the sources of terms be listed in a volume of moderate size.

The method of spelling is in the main that used in Britain, but due attention is paid to American orthography, by means of cross-references or by reproducing in the original lettering terms culled from scientific literature published in the United States. Spelling, however, is not static, as may be illustrated by the tendency to substitute *e* for the diphthongs *ae* and *oe*, and by compound words which may be written as two separate words, or hyphenated, or integrated as one word.

In the statement of derivation of terms, Greek and Russian words have been transliterated, as science and medical students are seldom acquainted with those languages. On the advice of one authority on Greek, the transliteration of certain combinations of letters represents the sound rather than the exact letters of the original, hence the occurrence of such words as *brangchia*, *hydor*, etc.

Pronunciation, upon which there can never be universal agreement, is the least satisfactory portion, and is likely to remain so. Quite apart from natural differences in Scottish, English, and American utterance, pronunciation is subject to different fashions in different centres of learning. Moreover, the accepted position of the accent also varies in different localities and from one generation to another. Some of the alternative styles of pronunciation given will doubtless be regarded by the purist as faulty or definitely wrong, but their inclusion seems justified by the law of common usage.

SLS 3-27-62 12.50-11.25

This Dictionary now deals with more than fifteen thousand five hundred terms. As in previous editions, the text has been revised and amplified, numerous publications having been probed not only for new terms but for new meanings which have been attached to existing terms. However, as was pointed out in the Preface to the Second Edition, "a work of this nature must inevitably remain subject to limitations of time and resources".

The accretion of additional terms might have been dealt with in the form of Supplements, but with the generous consent of the Publishers, the work has been reset for each edition in order to retain the facility of reference afforded by an unbroken alphabetical arrangement.

Thanks are also due to many individuals who, during the past forty years, have furthered the work by suggestions and criticisms.

The preparation of each new edition has also been essentially facilitated by the courtesy of the staff of various libraries, particularly in Edinburgh and Glasgow. The helpfulness of the County Librarian and staff of the Argyll County Library during preparation of the present edition is gratefully appreciated.

J. H. K.

1960

EQUIVALENTS

One acre = 4840 square yards = 4046·873 square metres
One ångström = 0·0001 micron
One are = 119·6033 square yards = 0·02471 acre
One atmosphere = 14·7 pounds per square inch = 1033 grams per square centimetre
One bar = pressure of mercury column of 29·53 inches, one square centimetre in area, in latitude 45°
One British thermal unit = 251·99 calories
One centigram = 0·15432 grain
One centimetre = 0·39370 inch
One chain = 22 yards = 20·1168 metres
One cubic centimetre = 0·061 cubic inch
One cubic foot = 0·0283 cubic metre
One cubic inch = 16·387 cubic centimetres
One cubic metre = 1·308 cubic yards
One degree centigrade = 0·8 degrees Réaumur = 1·8 degrees Fahrenheit
One degree Fahrenheit = 0·5556 Centigrade
One degree of latitude at the equator = 68·704 statute miles
One degree of longitude at the equator = 69·65 statute miles
One degree Réaumur = 1·25 degrees Centigrade
One drachm = 60 grains = 3·88793 grams
One fathom = 6 feet = 1·828767 metres
One fluid drachm = 3·5515 millilitres
One fluid ounce = 28·4123 millilitres
One fluid scruple = 1·1838 millilitres
One foot = 12 inches = 30·4801 centimetres
One furlong = 10 chains = 201·168 metres
One gallon (Imperial) = 1·2 gallons (U.S.A.) = 4·54596 litres
One gallon (U.S.A.) = 0·8327 gallon (Imperial) = 3·785 litres
One grain (avoirdupois) = 0·0647989 gram
One gram = 0·035274 ounce = 15·432356 grains
One gram-calorie = 0·003968 British thermal units
One hectare = 2·47106 acres
One hundredweight = 112 pounds = 50·80 kilograms
One inch = 2·53995 centimetres
One inch (U.S.A.) = 2·54001 centimetres
One kilogram = 2·20462 pounds (avoirdupois)
One kilogram per square centimetre = 14·22 pounds per square inch
One kilometre = 0·62137 statute mile
One litre = 1·76077 pint (Imperial)
One metre = 3·28084 feet = 39·37011 inches
One microgram = 0·001 milligram = 0·00015 grain
One micron = 0·001 millimetre = 0·000039 inch
One mil = 0·001 inch
One mile (nautical) = 1·152 statute miles = 1·8532 kilometres
One mile (statute) = 1·6093 kilometres
One millibar = 0·001 bar

One milligram = 0·015432 grain
One millilitre = 0·001 litre = 0·0352 fluid ounce
One millimetre = 0·03937 inch
One millimicron = 0·000001 millimetre
One minim (British) = 0·05919 cubic centimetre
One minim (U.S.A.) = 0·00376 cubic inch = 0·06161 cubic centimetre
One ounce (apothecaries) = 8 drachms = 31·10347 grams
One ounce (avoirdupois) = 437·5 grains = 28·34954 grams
One ounce (troy) = 31·10347 grams
One pennyweight = 1·555 grams
One pint (Imperial) = 568·2454 cubic centimetres
One pound (avoirdupois) = 16 ounces = 453·59243 grams
One pound (troy) = 5760 grains = 373·24 grams
One pound per square inch = 70·308 grams per square centimetre
One quart (Imperial) = 1·13649 litre
One quart (U.S.A.) = 0·94636 litre
One quintal = 100 kilograms = 220·4621 pounds
One rood = 40 poles = 10·1168 ares
One scruple = 20 grains = 1·29598 grams
One square centimetre = 0·15498 square inch
One square foot = 929·034 square centimetres
One square inch = 6·4516 square centimetres
One square kilometre = 0·3861 square mile
One square metre = 1550 square inches
One square mile = 640 acres = 2·58998 square kilometres
One square millimetre = 0·00155 square inch
One square yard = 0·8361 square metre
One stere=35·3156 cubic feet
One stone = 14 pounds (avoirdupois) = 6·3503 kilograms
One yard = 0·9144 metre

Sound velocity (air), mean = 331·7 metres per second
Zero, absolute = −459·4° F. = −273° C. = − 218·4° R.
Zero, centigrade and Réaumur = +32° F.
Zero, Fahrenheit = −17·78° C.

ABBREVIATIONS

A . . androecium
A . . argon
a. . . anode
a. . . anterior
a. . . abundant (occurrence of species)
a. . . adjective
Å . . Ångström unit(s)
AA . . adenylic acid
aapm. . amphiapomict
A.C., a.c. alternating current
Ac . . actinium
ACTH . adrenocorticotrophic hormone
ADH . antidiuretic hormone
ADP . adenosine diphosphate
adv. . . adverb
aet. . . (*aetatis*) age(d)
Ag . . silver
alt. . . alternate
alt. . . altitude
Al . . aluminium
Am . . americium
Am . . ammonium
AMP. . adenosine monophosphate
amph. . amphimict
An . . actinon
an. . . anode
anal. . . analysis
anat. . . anatomical, anatomy
ant. . . anterior
APH . anterior pituitary hormone
APL . anterior-pituitary-like hormone
apm. . . apomict
appl. . . applied to
aq. . . water ; aqueous
Ar. . . Arabic
Ar . . argon
A.S. . . Anglo-Saxon
As . . arsenic
At . . astatine
atm. . . atmosphere, atmospheric
ATP . . adenosine triphosphate
Å.U. . Ångström unit(s)
Au . . gold
A-V . . atrioventricular
av. . . average
Az . . azote (nitrogen)
B . . boron
B. . . *Bacillus*
b. . . bicuspid
Ba . . barium
Bact., bact. Bacterium, bacterial
bar. . . barometric
Bé. . . Baumé
Be . . beryllium
Bi . . bismuth
B.I. . . buffer index
biol. . . biological, biology
Bk . . berkelium
B.M.R. . basal metabolic rate
B.N.A. . Basle Nomina Anatomica
B.O.D. . biochemical oxygen demand
bot. . . botanical, botany
B.P. . . blood pressure
B.P. . . British Pharmacopoeia
b.p. . . boiling point
B.R. . (British) Birmingham revision of B.N.A.
Br . . bromine
B.T.U. . British thermal unit
C . . carbon
C. . . centigrade ; Celsius
C . . (*centum*) hundred
C. . . century
C . . corolla
C^{14} . . radioactive carbon
c. . . canine tooth
c. . . (*circa*) approximately
c . . curie(s)
C.A. . . chronological age
Ca . . calcium
ca. . . cathode
ca. . . (*circa*) approximately
Cal. . . large calorie(s)
cal. . . small calorie(s)
c.c. . . cubic centimetre
Cd . . cadmium
Ce . . cerium
Cel. . . Celsius
cel. . . cellulose
cent. . . hundred ; centigrade

c.e.s. . central excitatory state
c.i.s. . . central inhibitory state
CF . . citrovorum factor
Cf . . californium
cf. . . compare
cg., cgm. centigram(s)
c.g.s. . centimetre-gram-second
Cl . . chlorine
c.l. . . corpus luteum
cm. . . centimetre(s)
Cm . . curium
c.mm. . cubic millimetre(s)
cm/s . . centimetres per second
CO . . cardiac output
Co . . cobalt
Co . . coenzyme
Co^{60} . . radioactive cobalt
col., cols . (bacterial) colony, colonies
conc. . . concentrated, concentration
conch. . conchology
C.O.V. . cross-over value
cpd. . . compound
c.p. . . candle-power
cpl. . . carpel
c.p.s. . cycles per second
Cr . . chromium
Cs . . caesium
c.s.f. . . cerebrospinal fluid
CU . . castrate's urine
Cu . . copper
cu., cub. . cubic
D . . deuterium
d. . . (*dexter*), right
d. . . dextrorotary
d. . . dominant (*appl.* species)
Dan. . . Danish
db. . . decibel(s)
D.C., d.c. direct current
DCA . desoxycorticosterone acetate
deg. . . degree(s)
dg. . . decigram(s)
diam. . diameter
dil. . . dilute
dim. . . diminutive
D : N . dextrose : nitrogen ratio
DNA . deoxyribonucleic acid
DNP . dinitrophenyl
DOPA . dihydroxyphenylalanine
doz. . . dozen
DPN . diphosphopyridine nucleotide
dr. . . drachm(s), dram(s)
Dut. . . Dutch
dwt. . . pennyweight
Dy . . dysprosium
E . . east
e . . . 2.71828
E.D. . . effective dose
EEG . electroencephalogram
eff. . . efferens, efferent
e.g. . . (*exempli gratia*) for example
embr. . embryological, embryology
E.M.F. . erythrocyte-maturing factor
e.m.f. . electromotive force
end. . . endosperm
entom. . entomological, entomology
eos . . eosinophil
equiv. . equivalent
Er . . erbium
ERG . electroretinogram
E.R.S. . erythrocyte sedimentation rate
Es . . einsteinium
E.S.P. . extrasensory perception
esp. . . especially
est. . . estimated, estimation
η . . . (*eta*) viscosity
et al. . . (*et alii*) and others
Eu . . europium
F . . fluorine
F. . . Fahrenheit
F. . . French
F_1, F_2, etc. 1st, 2nd, etc. filial generation
f. . . female
f. . . frequent (occurrence of species)
FAD . flavine-adenine-dinucleotide
F.D. . . focal distance
Fe . . iron
Fe^{59} . radioactive iron
flr(s) . . flower(s)
fm . . fathom
Fm . . fermium
f.p. . . freezing point
Fr . . francium
FSH . . follicle - stimulating hormone
ft. . . foot ; feet
fth. . . fathom
fur. . . furlong
G . . gravitation constant

G . . . gynoecium
g. . . . gram(s)
Ga . . gallium
gal. . . gallon(s)
γ . . . (*gamma*) microgram
Gd . . gadolinium
GDH . growth and development hormone
Ge . . germanium
gen. . . genus
geog. . geographical
geol. . . geological
Ger. . . German
Gk. . . Greek
gm. . . gram(s)
g.-mol. . gram-molecule
G.M.T. . Greenwich Mean Time
G : N . glucose : nitrogen ratio
gp. . . group
gr. . . grain(s), gram(s)
gr. n. . Gram-negative
gr. p. . Gram-positive
GSH . . glutathione
gt., gtt. . (*gutta*) drop, (*guttae*) drops
H . . hydrogen
H° . . hydrogen ion concentration
H^2 . . deuterium
H^3 . . tritium
Hb . . haemoglobin
He . . helium
herb. . . herbarium
Hf . . hafnium
h-f. . . high-frequency
Hg . . mercury
hg. . . hectogram(s)
Hgb . . hæmoglobin
Ho . . holmium
hor. . . horizontal
hr, hrs . hour, hours
H.W. . High Water
hyb. . . hybrid
hypoth. hypothetical
I. . . incisor
I . . iodine
I^{131} . radioactive iodine
i. . . incisor (deciduous)
IAA . β-indolyl acetic acid
ib., ibid. (*ibidem*) in the same place
Icel. . . Icelandic
ichth. . ichthyology
ICSH . interstitial cell-stimulating hormone
i.e. . . (*id est*) that is

in. . . inch(es)
In . . indium
inf. . . inferior
infl. . . inflorescence
i.q. . . (*idem quod*) the same as
Ir . . iridium
irid. . . iridescent
It. . . Italian
I.U. . . international unit(s)
I.W. . . isotopic weight
JH . . juvenile hormone
J.N.D. . just noticeable difference
K . . calyx
K . . potassium
ka. . . kathode
KC . . kilocycles
kg. . . kilogram(s)
km. . . kilometre(s)
Kr . . krypton
L. . . Latin
L. . . ligament(um)
L., Linn. Linnaean, Linnaeus
l. . . left
l. . . litre
l. . . laevorotary
λ . . (*lambda*) wave length
La . . lanthanum
Lam. . Lamarck
lat. . . latitude
lb. . . pound (weight)
LD . . lethal dose
l.f. . . low frequency
LH . . luteinising hormone
Li . . lithium
liq. . . liquid ; liquor
L.L. . . Late Latin
log. . . logarithm
long. . . longitude
l.p. . . low pressure
L.S. . . longitudinal section
l.t. . . low tension
LTH . luteotrophic hormone
LTPP . lipothiamide pyrophosphate
Lu . . lutetium
L.W. . . Low Water
M. . . Membrana, Musculus
M . . (*mille*) thousand
M . . molecular weight
m. . . male
m. . . metre(s)
m. . . mile(s)
m. . . minim(s)
m. . . minute(s)

m. . . molar
m. . . musculus, muscle
m- . . meta-
ma. . . milliampère
Mal. . . Malaysian
max. . . maximum
mb. . . millibar(s)
mc. . . millicurie(s)
Md . . mendelevium
M.E. . . Middle English
micr. . . microscopic
min. . . minimum
min. . . minute(s)
M.I.O. . minimum identifiable odour
Mg . . magnesium
mg., mgm. milligram(s)
ml. . . millilitre(s) ; c.c.
MLD . minimum lethal dose
mm. . . millimetre(s)
mμ . . millimicron
Mn . . manganese
Mo . . molybdenum
mo. . . month
mol. . . gram-molecule
mol. wt. . molecular weight
m.p. . . melting point
m.p.h. . miles per hour
m.p.s. . metres per second
mr. . . milliroentgen
mrad . millirad(s)
msec. . millisecond ; σ
MSH . melanocyte-stimulating hormone
m.s.l. . mean sea-level
M.U. . mouse unit
μ . . (*mu*) micron
μc . . microcurie(s)
μg. . . microgram(s)
μl . . microlitre(s)
μmm . micromillimetre(s)
$\mu\mu$c . . micromicrocurie(s)
$\mu\mu$g . . micromicrogram(s)
$\mu\mu$ . . micromicron (0·001 mμ)
Mv . . mendeleevium
mV . . millivolt(s)
myc. . . mycology
N . . nitrogen
N . . normal solution
N . . north
n. . . nasal
n. . . nervus, nerve
n. . . neutral, normal
n . . haploid number of chromosomes
2n . . diploid number
n . . refractive index
n. . . noun
Na . . sodium
Na^{24} . radioactive sodium
N.A.P . Nomina Anatomica, Paris
Nb . . niobium
Nd . . neodymium
Ne . neon
n.g. . . new genus
Ni . . nickel
No., no. . number
No . . nobelium
norm. . normal
Np . . neptunium
n.p. . . normal pressure
NPN . non-protein nitrogen
N.S. . not significant
n.sp. . . new species
NTP . . normal temperature and pressure
O . . oxygen
O_3 . . ozone
o- . . ortho-
o. . . occasional (occurrence of species)
obl. . . oblique, oblong
O.F. . . Old French
O.H.G. . Old High German
Ω . . . (*Omega*) ohm(s)
opp. . . as opposed to ; opposite
opt. . . optical
opt. . . optimal
org. . . organic
orig. . . original
orn., ornith. ornithology
Os . . osmium
O.T. . . old terminology
ov. . . ovary
Oz . . ozone
oz. . . ounce(s)
P . . perianth
P . . phosphorus
P. . . premolar
P . . . probability
P^{32} . . radioactive phosphorus
p . . posterior
p- . . para-
p.a. . . per annum
Pa . . protactinium
PABA . para-aminobenzoic acid
pal. . . palaeontology
P_1, P_2, etc. 1st, 2nd, etc., parental generation

PATH . pituitary adrenotrophic hormone
path. . . pathology
Pb . . lead
PBI . . protein-bound iodine
Pd . . palladium
Pe . . probable error
PμE . . precipitation: evaporation ratio
per. . . perennial
perp. . . perpendicular
pert. . . pertaining to
PGA . pteroylglutamic acid
*p*H . . hydrogen ion concentration
phys. . physics
physiol. . physiology
π . . (*pi*) 3·14159265
pigm. . pigment
Pl. . . plasma, Plasmodium
plu. . . plural
Pm . . promethium
pm. . . premolar
P-M-C . pollen mother-cell
PMS . pregnant mare's serum
PNA . pentose nucleic acid
Po . . polonium
POF . . pyruvate oxidation factor
pois. . . poisonous
pop. . . population
pot. . . potential
P-P . . pellagra-preventing
p.p. . . post partum
ppg. . . precipitating
p.p.m. . parts per million
ppt. . . precipitate
Pr . . praseodymium
p.sol. . . partly soluble
Pt . . platinum
pt. . . pint
pt. . . point
P.U. . . pregnancy urine
p.u. . . plant unit(s)
Pu . . plutonium
pulv. . . (*pulvis*) powder
Q_1 . . temperature coefficient
quad. . quadrilateral
ql . . quintal
qr. . . quarter
qt. . . quantity
qt. . . quart
q.v. . . (*quod vide*) which see
R. . . Réaumur
R . . electrical resistance
R . . rough (bacterial colony)
r. . . right
r. . . Roentgen unit(s)
r . . correlation coefficient
r. . . rare (*appl.* species)
Ra . . radium
rad. . . radius
rad. . . radix
Rb . . rubidium
Rbc . . red blood-cells
RBE . relative biological effectiveness
RE . . radium emanation
Re . . rhenium
rect. . . rectangular
refl. . . reflex
reg. . . regular
RES . . reticulo-endothelial system
ret. . . retarded
Rh . . rhesus factor
Rh . . rhodium
rh . . anti Rh agglutinin
R.I. . . refractive index
Rn . . radon
RNA . ribonucleic acid
rot. . . rotation, rotating
R.Q. . . respiratory quotient
RT . . reaction time
R.U. . . rat unit(s)
Ru . . ruthenium
Russ. . Russian
S . . smooth (bacterial colony)
S . . south
S . . sulphur
S^{35} . . radioactive sulphur
s. . . (*sinister*), left
Σ . . (*Sigma*) sum of
σ . . (*sigma*) 0·001 second; msec.
σ . . (*sigma*) standard deviation
S-A . . sinu-atrial
Sb . . antimony
Sc . . scandium
S.D.A. . specific dynamic action
Se . . selenium
sec. . . second, secondary
Si . . silicon
sin. . . sinus
sing. . . singular
sl. . . slightly
Sm . . samarium
sm. . . small
S-M-C . sperm or spore mother-cell
Sn . . tin
sol. . . soluble; solution

Sp. . . Spanish
sp., spp. . species
sp. gr. . specific gravity
sq. . . square
Sr . . strontium
s.s. . . *sensu stricto*
sta. . . stamen(s)
sta. . . station
std. . . standard
STH . somatotrophic hormone
sup. . . superior
Sw. . . Swedish
sym. . . symmetrical
syn. . . synonym
syst. . . system
syst. . . systole
T . . temperature
T . . tension
T . . tritium
T.A. . toxin-antitoxin
Ta . . tantalum
t° . . temperature
Tb . . terbium
T_b, t_b . . body temperature
Tc . . technetium
T.D.P. . thermal death-point
Te . . tellurium
temp. . temperature
tert. . . tertiary
t.g. . . type genus
Th . . thorium
Ti . . titanium
Tl . . thallium
Tm . . thulium
tot . . total
TPN . triphosphopyridine nucleotide
trop. . . tropical
TSH . . thyroid-stimulating hormone
TSP . . thyroid-stimulating hormone of prepituitary
U. . . unit(s)
U . . uranium
UDP . uridine diphosphate
uns. . . unsymmetrical
U.S.P. . United States Pharmacopoeia
U.V. . ultra-violet
V . . vanadium
V. . . vibrio
V. . . vision
v . . vision
v. . . volt(s)
v . . velocity
v. . . verb
var. . . variable, variety
ven. . . vena, vein
Vert. . . Vertebrata
vert. . . vertebra, vertebrate
vert. . . vertical
ves. . . vesica, vesicle
vet . . veterinary
V.F. . visual field
vic. . . vicinal
visc. . . viscous
vol. . . volume
v.s. . . (*vide supra*) see above
vs. . . versus
W . . tungsten
W . . west
w . . watt(s)
Wbc . white blood-cells
wh. . . white
wk(s). . week(s)
w.l. . . wave length, λ
wt. . . weight
x . . haploid generation
2*x* . . diploid generation
Xe . . xenon
Y . . yttrium
Yb . . ytterbium
yd(s). . yard(s)
yr(s). . . year(s)
Zn . . zinc
zool. . . zoological, zoology
Zr . . zirconium

SOUND-SYMBOLS USED IN PRONUNCIATION

The sound-symbols have been made as simple as possible, only the broader differences in vowel-sounds being included. The phonetic spelling following each term represents a general indication of the prevailing varieties of pronunciation rather than a critically exact reproduction.

ā	*as in*	rate	ō	*as in*	no
ă	,,	rat	ŏ	,,	not
â	,,	far	ô	,,	form
ch	,,	church	ö	,,	anatomy
ē	,,	he	oi	,,	toy
ĕ	,,	hen	oo	,,	good
ë	,,	her	ow	,,	cow
g	,,	go	s	,,	moss
gw	,,	guano	sh	,,	fish
ī	,,	pine	th	,,	thin
ĭ	,,	pin	ū	,,	pure
j	,,	gem	ŭ	,,	nut
k	,,	cat	y	,,	yard
kw	,,	queen	z	,,	maize
ng	,,	sing	zh	,,	vision

A DICTIONARY OF
SCIENTIFIC TERMS

abactinal (ăbăk'tĭnăl, ăbăktī'năl) *a.* [L. *ab*, from; Gk. *aktis*, ray.] *Appl.* area of echinoderm body without tube-feet and in which madreporite is usually included; abambulacral, antambulacral.

abambulacral (ăb'ămbūlā'krăl) *a.* [L. *ab*, from; *ambulare*, to walk.] Abactinal, *q.v.*

abapical (ăbăp'ĭkăl) *a.* [L. *ab*, from; *apex*, summit.] *Pert.* or situated at lower pole.

abaxial (ăbăk'sĭăl) *a.* [L. *ab*, from; *axis*, axle.] *Pert.* that surface of any structure which is remote or turned away from the axis; excentric. *Opp.* adaxial.

abaxile (ăbăk'sĭl) *a.* [L. *ab*, from; *axis*, axle.] *Appl.* embryo whose axis has not the same direction as axis of seed.

abbreviated (ăbrē'vĭātĕd) *a.* [L. *ad*, to; *brevis*, short.] Shortened; curtailed.

abcauline (ăbkôl'ĭn) *a.* [L. *ab*, from; *caulis*, stalk.] Outwards from or not close to the stem, *opp.* adcauline.

abdomen (ăbdō'mĕn) *n.* [L. *abdomen*, belly.] The belly; in vertebrates, part of body containing digestive organs; in Arthropoda and certain Polychaeta, posterior part of body; in Synascidiae, part of zooid below thorax.

abdominal (ăbdŏm'ĭnăl) *a.* [L. *abdomen*, belly.] *Pert.* abdomen; *appl.* structures, organs, or parts of organs situated in, on, or closely related to, the abdomen.

abdominal pores,—single or paired openings leading from coelom to exterior, in cyclostomes and certain fishes.

abdominal reflex,—contraction of abdominal wall muscles when skin over side of abdomen is stimulated.

abdominal regions,—nine areas into which the abdomen is divided by two horizontal and two vertical imaginary lines, viz., hypochondriac (2), lumbar (2), inguinal (2), epigastric, umbilical, hypogastric.

abdominal ribs,—ossifications occurring in fibrous tissue between skin and muscles of certain reptiles.

abdominal ring,—one of two openings in fasciae of abdominal muscles through which passes spermatic cord in male, round ligament in female; inguinal ring.

abducens (ăbdū'sĕnz) *n.* [L. *abducere*, to lead away.] The sixth cranial nerve, supplying the rectus externus muscle of the eyeball.

abduct (ăbdŭkt') *v.* [L. *abductus*, led away.] To draw away from median axis.

abduction (ăbdŭk'shŏn) *n.* [L. *abducere*, to lead away.] Movement away from the median axis, *opp.* adduction.

abductor (ăbdŭk'tŏr) *n.* [L. *abductus*, led away.] A muscle that draws a limb or part outwards.

aberrant (ăbĕr'ănt) *a.* [L. *aberrare*, to stray.] With characteristics not in accordance with type; *appl.* species, etc.

abience (ăb'ĭĕns) *n.* [L. *abire*, to depart.] Retraction from stimulus; avoiding reaction. *Opp.* adience.

abient (ăb'ĭĕnt) *a.* [L. *abire*, to depart.] Avoiding the source of stimulation. *Opp.* adient.

abiogenesis (ăbīōjĕn'ĕsĭs) *n.* [Gk. *a*, not; *bios*, life; *genesis*, birth.] The production of living from non-living matter; spontaneous generation. *Opp.* biogenesis.

abiology (ăbīŏl′öjĭ) *n.* [Gk. *a*, not; *bios*, life; *logos*, discourse.] The study of non-living things.

abjection (ăbjĕk′shŭn) *n.* [L. *abjicere*, to cast away.] The shedding of spores, as from sporophores.

abjunction (ăbjŭngk′shŭn) *n.* [L. *abjungere*, to unyoke.] The delimitation of spores by septa at tip of hypha.

ablactation (ăb′lăktā′shŭn) *n.* [L. *ab*, from; *lactare*, to give milk.] Cessation of milk secretion; weaning.

abomasum (ăbŏmā′sŭm) *n.* [L. *ab*, from; *omasum*, paunch.] The read or fourth chamber of stomach of ruminants.

aboral (ăbō′răl) *a.* [L. *ab*, from; *os*, *oris*, mouth.] Away from, or opposite to, the mouth.

abortion (ăbôr′shŭn) *n.* [L. *abortus*, premature birth.] Premature birth; arrest of development of an organ.

abranchiate (ăbrăng′kĭăt) *a.* [Gk. *a*, without; *brangchia*, gills.] Without gills.

abrupt (ăbrŭpt′) *a.* [L. *abrumpere*, to break off.] Appearing as if broken, or cut off, at extremity.

abruptly - acuminate, — having a broad extremity from which a point arises, *appl.* leaf.

abruptly-pinnate,—having the main axis of epipodium not winged, but bearing a number of secondary axes which are winged.

abscise (ăbsīz′) *v.* [L. *abscidere*, to cut off.] To become separated; to fall off, as leaves, fruit, etc.

absciss (ăb′sĭs) *a.* [L. *abscindere*, to cut off.] *Appl.* layer of meristematic cells just outside cork-layer, to whom fall of leaves, floral parts, fruits, and certain branches is due; abscissile.

abscission (ăbsĭsh′ŭn) *n.* [L. *abscindere*, to cut off.] The separation of parts.

absorption (ăbsôrp′shŭn) *n.* [L. *absorbere*, to suck in.] Intussusception of fluid by living cells or tissues; passage of nutritive material through living cells; of light when neither reflected nor transmitted.

abstriction (ăbstrĭk′shŭn) *n.* [L. *abstringere*, to cut off.] The process of detaching spores or conidia by rounding off of tips of sporophores, as in mildews; abjunction and abscission.

abterminal (ăbtĕr′mĭnăl) *a.* [L. *ab*, from; *terminus*, limit.] Going from the end inwards.

abyssal (ăbĭs′ăl) *a.* [Gk. *abyssos*, unfathomed.] *Pert.* depths of ocean; *appl.* organisms or material usually found there; abysmal.

abyssobenthic (ăbĭs′öbĕn′thĭk) *a.* Gk. *abyssos*, unfathomed; *benthos*, depths of sea.] *Pert.*, or found on, bottom of ocean at depths exceeding *ca.* 1000 metres.

abyssopelagic (ăbĭs′öpĕlăj′ĭk) *a.* [Gk. *abyssos*, unfathomed; *pelagos*, sea.] *Pert.*, or inhabiting, the ocean at depths exceeding *ca.* 1000 metres, *i.e.*, below the bathypelagic zone.

acanaceous (ăkănā′sëŭs) *a.* [Gk. *akanos*, thistle.] Prickly; bearing prickles, as leaves.

acantha (ăkăn′thă) *n.* [Gk. *akantha*, thorn.] Prickle; spinous process.

acanthaceous (ăkănthā′sëŭs) *a.* [Gk. *akantha*, thorn.] Bearing thorns or prickles.

acanthin (ăkăn′thĭn) *n.* [Gk. *akantha*, thorn.] Substance forming skeleton of some Radiolaria.

acanthion (ăkăn′thĭŏn) *n.* [Gk. *akanthion*, small thorn.] The most prominent point on the anterior nasal spine.

acanthocarpous (ăkăn′thökâr′pŭs) *a.* [Gk. *akantha*, thorn; *karpos*, fruit.] Having fruit covered with spines or prickles.

acanthocephalous (ăkăn′thökĕf′ălŭs, -sĕf-) *a.* [Gk. *akantha*, thorn; *kephale*, head.] With hooked proboscis.

acanthocladous (ăkăn′thöklăd′ŭs) *a.* [Gk. *akantha*, thorn; *klados* branch.] Having spiny branches.

acanthocyst (ăkăn′thösĭst) *n.* [Gk. *akantha*, thorn; *kystis*, bladder.] A sac containing lateral or reserve stylets in Nemertea.

acanthodion (ăkănthō′dĭŏn) *n.* [Gk. *akanthodes*, thorny.] A tarsal seta containing extension of a sensory basal cell, in Acarina. *Plu.* acanthodia.

acanthoid (ăkăn′thoid) *a.* [Gk. *akantha*, thorn; *eidos*, shape.] Resembling a spine or prickle; spiniform.

acanthophore (ăkăn′thöfōr) *n.* [Gk. *akantha*, thorn; *pherein*, to bear.] A conical mass, the basis of median stylet in Nemertea.

acanthopore (ăkăn′thöpōr) *n.* [Gk. *akantha*, thorn; *poros*, passage.] A tubular spine in certain Polyzoa.

acanthosphenote (ăkăn′thösfē′nōt) *a.* [Gk. *akantha*, thorn; *sphen*, wedge.] *Appl.* echinoid spine made of solid wedges separated by porous tissue.

acanthozooid (ăkăn′thözō′oid) *n.* [Gk. *akantha*, thorn; *zoon*, animal; *eidos*, form.] Tail part of proscolex of cestodes. *Opp.* cystozooid.

acapnia (ăkăp′nĭă) *n.* [Gk. *akapnos*, without smoke.] Condition of low carbon dioxide content in blood.

acarocecidium (ăk′ărösēsĭd′ĭŭm) *n.* [Gk. *akares*, tiny; *kekis*, gall.] A gall caused by gall-mites, as by Eriophytidae.

acarology (ăk′ărŏl′öjĭ) *n.* [Gk. *akares*, tiny; L.L. *acarus*, mite; Gk. *logos*, discourse.] The study of mites and ticks.

acaryote,—akaryote.

acaudate,—ecaudate.

acaulescent (ăkôlĕs′ĕnt) *a.* [Gk. *a*, without; *kaulos*, stalk.] Having a shortened stem.

acauline (ăkô′lĭn) *a.* [Gk. *a*, without; *kaulos*, stalk.] Having no stem; *appl.* certain fungi.

accelerator (ăksĕl′ĕrātŏr) *n.* [L. *accelerare*, to hasten.] *Appl.* muscle or nerve which increases rate of action.

acceptor (ăksĕp′tŏr) *n.* [L. *accipere*, to accept.] Body or substance which receives and unites with another substance, as in oxidation-reduction processes where oxygen acceptor is the substance oxidised, hydrogen acceptor the substance reduced.

accessorius (ăksĕsō′rĭŭs) *n.* [L. *accedere*, to support.] A muscle aiding in action of another; spinal accessory or eleventh cranial nerve.

accessory bodies,—minute argyrophil particles originating from Golgi substance in spermatocytes; chromatoid bodies.

accessory bud,—an additional axillary bud; a bud formed on a leaf.

accessory cells,—*see* auxiliary cells.

accessory chromosomes,—sex chromosomes.

accessory food factors,—vitamins.

accessory glands,—detached portions of glands; glands in relation with genital ducts.

accessory nerve,—the eleventh cranial nerve; spinal accessory nerve.

accessory pulsatory organs,—sac-like structures of insects, variously situated, pulsating independently.

acclimatation,—acclimation, acclimatisation.

acclimation (ăk′lĭmā′shŭn) *n.* [L. *ad*, to; Gk. *klima*, climate.] The habituation of an organism to a different climate or environment.

acclimatisation (ăklī′mătĭzā′shŭn) *n.* [L. *ad*, to; Gk. *klima*, climate.] Habituation of a species to a different climate or environment; acclimation under human management.

accommodation (ăk′ŏmödā′shŭn) *n.* [L. *ad*, to; *commodus*, fitting.] Adjustment of eye to receive clear images of different objects; adaptation of receptors to a different stimulus.

accrescent (ăkrĕs′ĕnt) *a.* [L. *accrescere*, to increase.] *Appl.* plants that continue to grow after flowering, or calyx growing after pollination.

accretion (ăkrē′shŭn) *n.* [L. *accrescere*, to increase.] Growth by external addition of new matter.

accumbent (ăkŭm′bĕnt) *a.* [L. *accumbere*, to lie on.] *Appl.* embryo having cotyledons with edges turned towards radicle, as in Cruciferae.

accumulators (ăkū′mūlātŏrz) *n. plu.* [L. *ad*, to ; *cumulus*, heap.] Plants with a relatively high concentration of certain chemical elements in tissues.

A-cells,—alpha cells of islets of Langerhans.

acelomate,—acoelomate.

acelous,—acoelous.

acentric (ăsĕn′trĭk) *a.* [Gk. *a*, without ; *kentron*, centre.] Having no centromere, *appl.* chromosomes and chromosome segments.

acentrous (ăsĕn′trŭs) *a.* [L. *a*, without ; *centrum*, centre.] With no vertebral centra, but persistent notochord, as certain fishes.

acephalocyst (ăkĕf′ălŏsĭst, -sĕf-) *n.* [Gk. *a*, without ; *kephale*, head ; *kystis*, bladder.] Hydatid stage of certain tapeworms.

acephalous (ăkĕf′ălŭs, -sĕf-) *a.* [Gk. *a*, not ; *kephale*, head.] Having no structure comparable to head ; *appl.* some molluscs ; *appl.* larvae of certain Diptera ; *appl.* ovary without terminal stigma.

acerate (ăs′ĕrāt) *a.* [L. *acer*, sharp.] Needle-shaped ; pointed at one end, *appl.* monaxon or oxeote spicules.

acerose (ăs′ĕrōs) *a.* [L. *acer*, sharp.] Narrow and slender, with sharp point, as leaf of pine.

acerous (ăs′ĕrŭs) *a.* [Gk. *a*, without ; *keras*, horn.] Hornless ; without antennae ; without tentacles.

acervate (ăsĕr′vāt) *a.* [L. *acervare*, to amass.] Heaped together ; clustered.

acervuline (ăsĕr′vūlĭn) *a.* [L.L. *dim.* of *acervus*, heap.] Irregularly heaped together, *appl.* foraminiferal tests.

acervulus (ăsĕr′vūlŭs) *n.* [L.L. *dim.* of *acervus*, heap.] A small heap or cluster, especially of sporogenous mycelium.

acervulus cerebri,—brain sand, *q.v.*

acetabular,—*pert.* acetabulum.

acetabulum (ăsētăb′ūlŭm) *n.* [L. *acetabulum*, vinegar-cup.] The cotyloid cavity or socket in pelvic girdle for head of femur ; in insects, cavity of thorax in which leg is inserted ; cavity in proximal end of spine, for articulation with mamelon, in echinoids ; large posterior sucker in leeches ; sucker on arm of cephalopod ; one of the cotyledons of placenta in ruminants.

achaetous (ăkē′tŭs) *a.* [Gk. *a*, without ; *chaite*, hair.] Without chaetae or bristles.

acheilary (ăkī′lărĭ) *a.* [Gk. *a*, without ; *cheilos*, lip.] Having labellum undeveloped, as some orchids.

achene (ăkēn′) *n.* [Gk. *a*, not ; *chainein*, to gape.] A one-seeded, dry, indehiscent fruit ; achenium.

achenial,—*appl.* one-seeded, dry, indehiscent fruits, as achene, cypsela, caryopsis, samara, and nut.

Achillis tendo (ăkĭl′ĭs tĕn′dō) *n.* [Gk. *Achilles* ; L. *tendo*, tendon.] The united strong tendon of gastrocnemius and solaeus muscles, tendo calcaneus.

achlamydeous (ăk′lămĭd′ēŭs) *a.* [Gk. *a*, without ; *chlamys*, cloak.] Having neither calyx nor corolla.

achondroplasia (ăkŏn′drŏplā′zĭă) *n.* [Gk. *a*, without ; *chondros*, cartilage ; *plasis*, a moulding.] Heritable dwarfism due to disturbance of ossification in the long bones of the limbs and of certain facial bones during development ; *cf.* ateleosis.

achroacyte (ăkrō′ăsīt) *n.* [Gk. *a*, not ; *chros*, colour ; *kytos*, hollow.] Colourless or lymph cell ; lymphocyte.

achroglobin (ăk′rōglō′bĭn) *n.* [Gk. *a*, not ; *chros*, colour ; L. *globus*, sphere.] A colourless respiratory pigment of some tunicates and molluscs.

achroic,—achroous.

achromasie (ăkrō′măsĭ) *n.* [Gk. *a*, not ; *chroma*, colour.] Emission of chromatin from nucleus ; *cf.* chromasie.

achromatic (ăk'rōmăt'ĭk) *a.* [Gk. *a*, without; *chroma*, colour.] *Appl.* threshold, the minimal stimulus inducing sensation of luminosity or brightness; *cf.* chromatic; *appl.* neutral colours; achromatinic, *q.v.*

achromatin (ăkrō'mătĭn) *n.* [Gk. *a*, without; *chroma*, colour.] The non-staining ground substance and linin of the nucleus.

achromatinic (ăkrō'mătĭn'ĭk) *a.* [Gk. *a*, without; *chroma*, colour.] *Pert.* achromatin, or resembling achromatin in properties.

achromic (ăkrō'mĭk) *a.* [Gk. *a*, without; *chroma*, colour.] Unpigmented; colourless; achromatous.

achromite,—centromere, *q.v.*

achroous (ăkrō'ŭs) *a.* [Gk. *a*, without; *chros*, complexion.] Unpigmented; colourless.

acicle (ăs'ĭkl) *n.* [L. *acicula*, small needle.] A thorn-shaped scaphocerite, as in Paguridae; acicula.

acicula (ăsĭk'ūlă) *n.* [L. *acicula*, small needle.] A small needle-like bristle, spine, or crystal; *plu.* of aciculum. *Plu.* aciculae.

acicular,—like a needle in shape; sharp-pointed.

aciculate (ăsĭk'ūlāt) *a.* [L. *acicula*, small needle.] Having acicles or aciculae.

aciculum (ăsĭk'ūlŭm) *n.* [L. *acicula*, small needle.] A stiff basal seta in parapodium of Chaetopoda.

acid-fast,—remaining stained with aniline dyes on treatment with acids; *appl.* bacteria.

acidic (ăsĭd'ĭk) *a.* [L. *acidus*, sour.] *Appl.* stains whose colour determinant plays the part of an acid, acting on protoplasm; *cf.* basic.

acidophil (ăs'ĭdōfĭl) *a.* [L. *acidus*, sour; Gk. *philein*, to love.] Oxyphil, *q.v.*; growing in acid media.

aciduric (ăs'ĭdū'rĭk) *a.* [L. *acidus*, sour; *durus*, hardy.] Tolerating acid media; acidophil.

aciform (ăs'ĭfôrm) *a.* [L. *acus*, needle; *forma*, shape.] Needle-shaped.

acinaciform (ăsĭnăs'ĭfôrm) *a.* [L. *acinaces*, short sword; *forma*, shape.] Shaped like a sabre or scimitar; *appl.* leaf.

acinarious (ăsĭnā'rĭŭs) *a.* [L. *acinarius*, *pert.* grapes.] Having globose vesicles, as some algae.

aciniform (ăsĭn'ĭfôrm) *a.* [L. *acinus*, berry; *forma*, shape.] Grape- or berry-shaped; *appl.* a type of silk gland in spiders.

acinus (ăs'ĭnŭs) *n.* [L. *acinus*, berry.] One of drupels composing fruit of bramble or raspberry; sac-like termination of branched gland.

acme (ăk'mē) *n.* [Gk. *akme*, prime.] The highest point attained, or prime, in phylogeny and ontogeny; *cf.* epacme, paracme.

acoelomate (ăsē'lōmāt) *a.* [Gk. *a*, without; *koilos*, hollow.] *Appl.* animals not having a true coelom; acoelomatous; acoelous, *q.v.*

acoelous (ăsē'lŭs) *a.* [Gk. *a*, without; *koilos*, hollow.] *Appl.* vertebrae with flattened centra; acoelomate, *q.v.*

acondylous (ăkŏn'dĭlŭs) *a.* [Gk. *a*, without; *kondylos*, knuckle.] Without nodes or joints.

acone (ăkōn') *a.* [Gk. *a*, without; *konos*, cone.] *Appl.* insect compound eye without crystalline or liquid secretion in cone cells.

acontia (ăkŏn'tĭă, ăkŏn'shĭă) *n. plu.* [Gk. *akontion*, small javelin.] Threadlike processes of mesenteric filaments armed with stinging cells, in actinians.

acotyledon (ă'kŏtĭlē'dŏn) *n.* [Gk. *a*, without; *kotyledon*, a cup-shaped hollow.] A plant without a cotyledon.

acoustic (ăkoo'stĭk) *a.* [Gk. *akouein*, to hear.] *Pert.* organs or sense of hearing; *appl.* meatus, nerve, etc.; *pert.* science of sound.

acquired character,—a modification or permanent structural or functional change effected during the lifetime of the individual organism and induced by use or disuse of a particular organ, by disease, trauma, or other functional or environmental influences.

acral (ăk'răl) *a.* [Gk. *akros*, tip.] *Pert.* extremities.

acraspedote (ăkrăs'pĕdōt) *a.* [Gk. *a*, without; *kraspedon*, border.] Having no velum.

acroblast (ăk'röblăst) *n.* [Gk. *akros*, tip; *blastos*, bud.] A body in spermatid and which gives rise to acrosome; outer layer of mesoblast.

acrobryous (ăkrŏb'rĭūs) *a.* [Gk. *akros*, tip; *bryein*, to swell.] Growing at the tip only.

acrocarpic (ăk'rökâr'pĭk) *a.* [Gk. *akros*, tip; *karpos*, fruit.] Having the fructification terminating the axis; acrocarpous; *appl.* mosses.

acrocentric (ăk'rösĕn'trĭk) *a.* [Gk. *akros*, tip; *kentron*, centre.] With centromere at end, *appl.* chromosome. *n.* A rod-shaped chromosome.

acrochordal (ăkrökôr'dăl) *a.* [Gk. *akros*, tip; *chorde*, cord.] *Appl.* a chondrocranial unpaired frontal cartilage in birds.

acrochroic (ăk'rökrō'ĭk) *a.* [Gk. *akros*, tip; *chros*, colour.] With coloured tips, as of hyphae.

acrocoracoid (ăk'rökŏr'ăkoid) *n.* [Gk. *akros*, tip; *korax*, crow; *eidos*, form.] A process at dorsal end of coracoid in birds.

acrocyst (ăk'rösĭst) *n.* [Gk. *akros*, tip; *kystis*, bladder.] The spherical gelatinous cyst formed by gonophores at maturation of generative cells.

acrodont (ăk'rödŏnt) *a.* [Gk. *akros*, tip; *odous*, tooth.] *Appl.* teeth attached to the summit of a parapet of bone, as in lizards.

acrodrome (ăk'rödrōm), **acrodromous** (ăkrŏd'römŭs) *a.* [Gk. *akros*, tip; *dramein*, to run.] *Appl.* leaf with veins converging at its point.

acrogenous (ăkrŏj'ĕnŭs) *a.* [Gk. *akros*, tip; *-genes*, producing.] Increasing in growth at summit or apex.

acrogynous (ăkrŏj'ĭnŭs) *a.* [Gk. *akros*, tip; *gyne*, female.] With archegonia arising from apical cell, *appl.* certain liverworts. *Opp.* anacrogynous.

acromegaly (ăk'römĕg'ălĭ) *n.* [Gk. *akros*, tip; *megalon*, great.] Gigantism due to excessive activity of part of pituitary gland.

acromial (ăkrō'mĭăl) *a.* [Gk. *akros*, summit; *omos*, shoulder.] *Pert.* acromion, *appl.* artery, process, ligament, etc.

acromio-clavicular (ăkrō'mĭöklăvĭk'ūlăr) *a.* [Gk. *akromion*, shoulder-summit; L. *clavicula*, *dim.* of *clavis*, key.] *Appl.* ligaments covering joint between acromion and clavicle.

acromion (ăkrō'mĭŏn) *n.* [Gk. *akros*, summit; *omos*, shoulder.] Ventral prolongation of scapular spine.

acron (ăk'rŏn) *n.* [Gk. *akron*, top.] Preoral region of insects; anterior, unsegmented part of young trilobite.

acropetal (ăkrŏp'ĕtăl) *a.* [Gk. *akros*, summit; L. *petere*, to seek.] Ascending; *appl.* leaves, flowers, or roots, developing successively from an axis so that youngest arise at apex. *Opp.* basipetal.

acrophyte (ăk'röfīt) *n.* [Gk. *akron*, peak; *phyton*, plant.] A plant growing at a high altitude; alpine plant.

acroplasm (ăk'röplăzm) *n.* [Gk. *akros*, tip; *plasma*, form.] Cytoplasm of the apex of an ascus.

acropodium (ăk'röpōdĭūm) *n.* [Gk. *akros*, tip; *pous*, foot.] Digits,—fingers or toes; *cf.* metapodium.

acrorhagus (ăkrörā'gŭs) *n.* [Gk. *akros*, summit; *rhax*, grape.] A tubercle near the margin of certain Actiniaria, containing specialised nematocysts.

acrosarc (ăk'rösârk) *n.* [Gk. *akros*, summit; *sarx*, flesh.] A pulpy berry resulting from union of ovary and calyx.

acroscopic (ăk'röskŏp'ĭk) *a.* [Gk. *akros*, tip; *skopein*, to view.] Facing towards the apex, *opp.* basiscopic.

acrosome (ăk'rösōm) *n.* [Gk. *akros*, tip; *soma*, body.] Body at apex of spermatozoon; apical body; perforatorium.

acrospire (ăk'röspīr) *n.* [Gk. *akros*, tip; *speira*, something twisted.] The first shoot or sprout, being spiral, at end of germinating seed.

acrospore (ăk'röspōr) *n.* [Gk. *akros*, tip; *sporos*, seed.] The spore at the apex of a sporophore.

acroteric (ăk′rötĕr′ĭk) *a.* [Gk. *akroterion*, topmost point.] *Pert.* outermost points, as tips of digits, nose, ears, tail.

acrotonic (ăk′rötŏn′ĭk) *a.* [Gk. *akros*, tip; *tonos*, brace.] Having anther united at its apex with rostellum; acrotonous. *Opp.* basitonic.

acrotrophic (ăk′rötrŏf′ĭk) *a.* [Gk. *akros*, tip; *trophe*, nourishment.] *Appl.* ovariole having nutritive cells at apex which are joined to oocytes by nutritive cords; telotrophic.

actinal (ăk′tĭnăl, ăktī′năl) *a.* [Gk. *aktis*, ray.] *Appl.* area of echinoderm body with tube-feet; *appl.* oral area with tentacles in Actiniaria.

actine (ăk′tĭn) *n.* [Gk. *aktis*, ray.] A star-shaped spicule.

actinenchyma (ăk′tĭnĕng′kĭmă) *n.* [Gk. *aktis*, ray; *en*, in; *chein*, to pour.] Cellular tissue having a stellate appearance.

actiniform,—actinoid.

actinobiology (ăk′tĭnöbīŏl′öjĭ) *n.* [Gk. *aktis*, ray; *bios*, life; *logos*, discourse.] The study of the effects of radiation upon living organisms.

actinoblast (ăk′tĭnöblăst) *n.* [Gk. *aktis*, ray; *blastos*, bud.] The mother-cell from which a spicule is developed, as in Porifera.

actinocarpous (ăk′tĭnökâr′pŭs) *a.* [Gk. *aktis*, ray; *karpos*, fruit.] *Appl.* plants with flowers and fruit radially arranged; actinocarpic.

actinochitin (ăk′tĭnökī′tĭn) *n.* [Gk. *aktis*, ray; *chiton*, tunic.] Anisotropic or birefringent chitin.

actinodrome (ăktĭn′ödrōm) *a.* [Gk. *aktis*, ray; *dromos*, course.] Veined palmately; actinodromous.

actinogonidial (ăk′tĭnögŏnĭd′ĭăl) *a.* [Gk. *aktis*, ray; *gonos*, offspring.] Having radiately arranged genital organs.

actinoid (ăk′tĭnoid) *a.* [Gk. *aktis*, ray; *eidos*, shape.] Rayed; star-shaped, stellate.

actinology (ăk′tĭnŏl′öjĭ) *n.* [Gk. *aktis*, ray; *logos*, discourse.] The study of the action of radiation; study of radially symmetrical animals; homology of successive regions or parts radiating from a common central region.

actinomere (ăktĭn′ömēr) *n.* [Gk. *aktis*, ray; *meros*, part.] A radial segment.

actinomorphic (ăk′tĭnömôr′fĭk) *a.* [Gk. *aktis*, ray; *morphe*, shape.] Radially symmetrical; actinomorphous.

actinopharynx (ăk′tĭnöfăr′ĭngks) *n.* [Gk. *aktis*, ray; *pharynx*, gullet.] The gullet of a sea-anemone.

actinospore (ăktĭn′öspōr) *n.* [Gk. *aktis*, ray; *sporos*, seed.] A spore of Actinomycetes.

actinost (ăk′tĭnŏst) *n.* [Gk. *aktis*, ray; *osteon*, bone.] Basal bone of fin-rays in teleosts.

actinostele (ăk′tĭnöstē′lē) *n.* [Gk. *aktis*, ray; *stele*, pillar.] Stele with xylem radiating outwards and forming ridges, as in certain Pteridophyta.

actinostome (ăktĭn′östōm) *n.* [Gk. *aktis*, ray; *stoma*, mouth.] The mouth of a sea-anemone; five-rayed oral aperture of starfish.

actinotrichia (ăk′tĭnötrĭk′ĭă) *n. plu.* [Gk. *aktis*, ray; *thrix*, hair.] Unjointed horny rays at edge of fins in many fishes.

actinotrocha (ăk′tĭnŏt′rökă) *n.* [Gk. *aktis*, ray; *trochos*, wheel.] Free-swimming larval form of Phoronis.

actinula (ăktĭn′ūlă) *n.* [Gk. *aktis*, ray.] A larval stage in some Hydromedusae.

action system,—behaviour pattern.

activator (ăktĭvā′tŏr) *n.* [L. *activus*, active.] A substance which promotes or protects enzyme action; a substance which stimulates development of any particular embryonic tissue or organ.

active centre,—the part of an enzyme protein structure which combines with the substrate where activation and reaction take place.

aculeate (ăkū′lēăt) *a.* [L. *aculeus*, prickle.] Having prickles, sharp points, or a sting.

aculeiform (ăkū'lēĭfôrm) *a.* [L. *aculeus*, prickle; *forma*, shape.] Formed like a prickle or thorn.

aculeus (ăkū'lēŭs) *n.* [L. *aculeus*, prickle.] A prickle growing from bark, as in rose; a sting; a hair-like projection; a microtrichium.

acuminate (ăkū'mĭnāt) *a.* [L. *acumen*, point.] Drawn out into long point; tapering; pointed.

acuminiferous (ăkū'mĭnĭf'ĕrŭs) *a.* [L. *acumen*, point; *ferre*, to carry.] Having pointed tubercles.

acuminulate (ăk'ūmĭn'ūlāt) *a.* [L. *acuminulus*, *dim.* of *acumen*, point.] Having a very sharp tapering point.

acute (ăkūt') *a.* [L. *acutus*, sharpened.] Ending in a sharp point; temporarily severe, not chronic.

acyclic (ăsĭk'lĭk) *a.* [Gk. *a*, without; *kyklos*, circle.] *Appl.* flowers with floral leaves arranged in a spiral.

adamantoblast (ăd'ămăn'töblăst) *n.* [Gk. *adamas*, diamond; *blastos*, bud.] Enamel cell; ameloblast.

adambulacral (ăd'ămbūlā'krăl) *a.* [L. *ad*, to; *ambulare*, to walk.] *Appl.* structures adjacent to ambulacral areas in echinoderms.

adaptation (ădăptā'shŏn) *n.* [L. *adaptare*, to fit to.] The process by which an organism becomes fitted to its environment; a structure or habit fitted for some special environment; the fitting of sensations to a point when discomfort ceases; adjustment of disturbance of nervous system without involving higher co-ordinating centres.

adaptive (ădăp'tĭv) *a.* [L. *adaptare*, to fit to.] Capable of fitting different conditions; adjustable; inducible, *appl.* enzymes formed when their specific substrates are available, *opp.* constitutive enzymes.

adaxial (ădăk'sĭăl) *a.* [L. *ad*, to; *axis*, axle.] Turned towards the axis. *Opp.* abaxial.

adcauline (ădkôl'ĭn) *a.* [L. *ad*, to; *caulis*, stalk.] Towards or nearest the stem, *opp.* abcauline.

ad-digital (ăd'dĭj'ĭtăl) *n.* [L. *ad*, to; *digitus*, finger.] A primary wing-quill connected with phalanx of third digit.

adduction (ăd'dŭk'shŏn) *n.* [L. *ad*, to; *ducere*, to lead.] Movement towards the median axis, *opp.* abduction.

adductor (ăd'dŭk'tŏr) *n.* [L. *ad*, to; *ducere*, to lead.] A muscle which brings one part towards another.

adeciduate (ă'dēsĭd'ūāt) *a.* [L. *a*, away from; *decidere*, to fall down.] Not falling, or coming away; *appl.* evergreens; *appl.* placenta.

adecticous (ădĕk'tĭkŭs) *a.* [Gk. *a*, without; *dektikos*, biting.] Without functional mandibles, *appl.* pupa. *Opp.* decticous.

adelocodonic (ăd'ēlökōdŏn'ĭk) *a.* [Gk. *adelos*, concealed; *kodon*, bell.] *Appl.* undetached medusome of certain Gymnoblastea, which degenerates after discharging ripe sexual cells. *Opp.* phanerocodonic.

adelomorphic (ăd'ēlömôr'fĭk) *a.* [Gk. *adelos*, concealed; *morphe*, shape.] Indefinite in form; *appl.* central cells of peptic glands; adelomorphous.

adelomycete (ăd'ēlömī'sēt) *n.* [Gk. *adelos*, concealed; *mykes*, fungus.] A fungus lacking the sexual spore stage; imperfect fungus.

adelophycean (ăd'ēllöfīsē'ăn) *a.* [Gk. *adelos*, concealed; *phykion*, seaweed.] *Appl.* stage or generation of many seaweeds when they appear as prostrate microthalli.

adelphogamy (ădĕlfŏg'ămĭ) *n.* [Gk. *adelphos*, brother; *gamos*, marriage.] Brother-sister mating, as in certain ants.

adelphous (ădĕl'fŭs) *a.* [Gk. *adelphos*, brother.] Joined together in bundles, as filaments of stamens; *cf.* monadelphous, diadelphous.

adendritic (ă'dĕndrĭt'ĭk) *a.* [Gk. *a*, not; *dendron*, tree.] Adendric; without dendrites or branches; *appl.* cells.

adendroglia (ădĕndröglī'ă) *n.* [Gk. *a*, not; *dendron*, tree; *gloia*, glue.] A type of neuroglia lacking processes.

adenine (ăd'ënĭn) *n.* [Gk. *aden*, gland.] A compound occurring in many cells, hydrolysed by adenase to hypoxanthine ; $C_5H_5N_5$.

adenoblast (ăd'ënöblăst) *n.* [Gk. *aden*, gland ; *blastos*, bud.] Embryonic glandular cell.

adenocheiri (ăd'ënökī'rī) *n. plu.* [Gk. *aden*, gland ; *cheir*, hand.] Elaborate accessory copulatory organs, outgrowths of atrial walls in Turbellaria.

adenocyte (ăd'ënösīt) *n.* [Gk. *aden*, gland ; *kytos*, hollow.] Secretory cell of a gland.

adenodactyli (ăd'ënödăk'tĭlī), *n. plu.* [Gk. *aden*, gland ; *daktylos*, finger.] Adenocheiri, *q.v.*

adenohypophysis (ăd'ënöhīpŏf'ĭsĭs) *n.* [Gk. *aden*, gland ; *hypo*, under ; *physis*, growth.] The glandular lobe or portions of the pituitary body, derived from Rathke's pouch.

adenoid (ăd'ënoid) *a.* [Gk. *aden*, gland ; *eidos*, shape.] *Pert.* or resembling a gland or lymphoid tissue.

adenophore (ăd'ënöfōr') *n.* [Gk. *aden*, gland ; *pherein*, to carry.] The stalk of a nectar gland.

adenophyllous (ăd'ënöfĭl'ŭs) *a.* [Gk. *aden*, gland ; *phyllon*, leaf.] Bearing glands on leaves.

adenopodous (ădënŏp'ödŭs) *a.* [Gk. *aden*, gland ; *pous*, foot.] Bearing glands on peduncles or petioles.

adenose (ăd'ënōs) *a.* [Gk. *aden*, gland.] Glandular.

adenostemonous (ăd'ënöstĕm'önŭs) *a.* [Gk. *aden*, gland ; *stemon*, spun thread.] Having glands on stamens.

adequate,—*appl.* stimulus which normally acts on a given receptor, and induces the appropriate sensation.

adermin, — vitamin B_6, rat antidermatitis factor ; pyridoxine.

adesmic (ădĕs'mĭk) *a.* [Gk. *adesmos*, unfettered.] *Appl.* cyclomorial scales made up of separate lepidomorial units ; *cf.* monodesmic, polydesmic.

adesmy (ădĕs'mĭ) *n.* [Gk. *adesmos*, unfettered.] A break or division in an organ usually entire.

adetopneustic (ăd'ëtŏnū'stĭk) *a.* [Gk. *adetos*, free ; *pnein*, to breathe.] Having dermal gills occurring beyond abactinal surface, as in certain stelleroids.

adfrontal (ădfrŭn'tăl) *a.* [L. *ad*, to ; *frons*, forehead.] *Appl.* oblique plates beside frons of certain insect larvae.

adherent (ădhē'rënt) *a.* [L. *ad*, to ; *haerere*, to stick.] Exhibiting adhesion, *q.v.* ; attached to substratum, *appl.* zooecia of polyzoan colony.

adhesion (ădhē'zhŭn) *n.* [L. *ad*, to ; *haerere*, to stick.] Condition of touching without growing together of parts normally separate, as between members of different series of floral leaves ; *cf.* cohesion.

adhesive cells,—various glandular or specialised cells for purposes of attachment ; as on tentacles of Ctenophora, on epidermis of Turbellaria, on pedal disc of Hydra.

adience (ăd'ĭëns) *n.* [L. *adire*, to approach.] Urge, or advance, towards stimulus ; approaching reaction. *Opp.* abience.

adient (ăd'ĭënt) *a.* [L. *adire*, to approach.] Approaching the source of stimulation. *Opp.* abient.

adipocellulose (ăd'ĭpösĕl'ūlōs) *n.* [L. *adeps*, fat ; *cellula*, small cell.] Cellulose with a large amount of suberin, as in cork tissue.

adipocyte (ăd'ĭpösīt) *n.* [L. *adeps*, fat ; Gk. *kytos*, hollow.] One of the cells forming the fat-body in insects.

adipoleucocyte (ăd'ĭpölū'kösīt, -loo-) *n.* [L. *adeps*, fat ; Gk. *leukos*, white ; *kytos*, hollow.] A leucocyte containing fat droplets or wax, in insects.

adipolysis (ădĭpŏl'ĭsĭs) *n.* [L. *adeps*, fat ; Gk. *lysis*, loosing.] Splitting or hydrolyis of fats by enzymes, as during digestion ; lipolysis.

adipose (ăd'ĭpōs) *a.* [L. *adeps*, fat.] *Pert.* animal fat ; fatty.

A-disc,—doubly refracting or anisotropic band in myofibrillae ; Q-disc.

aditus (ăd'ĭtŭs) *n.* [L. *aditus*, entrance,] Anatomical structure forming approach or entrance to a part, *e.g.* to antrum, larynx, etc.

adjustor (ădjŭs'tōr) *n.* [L.L. *adjustare*, to adjust, from L. *ad*, to; *justus*, just.] A muscle connecting stalk and valve in Brachiopoda; ganglionic part of a reflex arc, connecting receptor and effector.

adlacrimal (ădlăk'rĭmăl) *n.* [L. *ad*, to; *lacrima*, tear.] Lacrimal bone of reptiles.

admedial (ădmē'dĭăl) *a.* [L. *ad*, towards; *medius*, middle.] Near the middle, mediad; near the median plane, admedian.

adminiculum (ăd'mĭnĭk'ūlŭm) *n.* [L. *adminiculum*, support.] A locomotory spine of certain pupae; posterior fibres of linea alba attached to os pubis.

adnasal (ădnā'zăl) *n.* [L. *ad*, to; *nasus*, nose.] A small bone in front of each nasal in certain fishes.

adnate (ădnāt') *a.* [L. *ad*, to; *gnatus*, born.] *Pert.* or designating the condition of being closely attached to side of petiole or stalk, as stipules or leaves; designating condition of anther with back attached throughout its length to filament, or to its continuation the connective; conjoined.

adnephrine,—adrenaline.

adnexa (ădnĕk'să) *n. plu.* [L. *ad*, to; *nectere*, to bind.] Structures or parts closely related to an organ; extra-embryonic structures, as foetal membranes, placenta.

adnexed (ădnĕkst') *a.* [L. *ad*, to; *nectere*, to bind.] Reaching to the stem only.

adolescaria (ădōlĕskā'rĭă) *n.* [L. *adolescere*, to grow up.] Encysted stage, between cercaria and marita, in trematodes; metacercaria.

adoral (ădō'răl) *a.* [L. *ad*, to; *os*, mouth.] Near or *pert.* mouth.

adpressed (ăd'prĕst) *a.* [L. *ad*, to; *pressus*, pressed.] Closely applied to a surface; appressed.

adradius (ădrā'dĭŭs) *n.* [L. *ad*, to; *radius*, radius.] In coelenterates, the radius midway between perradius and interradius, a radius of third order.

adrectal (ădrĕk'tăl) *a.* L *ad* to; *rectum*, rectum.] Near to or closely connected with rectum.

adrenal (ădrē'năl) *a.* [L. *ad*, to; *renes*, kidneys.] Situated near kidneys; suprarenal, *appl.* glands, the endocrines secreting hormones affecting the sympathetic nervous system and blood pressure; *appl.* organs, the suprarenal and interrenal glands, and chromaphil bodies.

adrenaline (ădrĕn'ălĭn, ădrĕn'ălēn) *n.* [L. *ad*, to; *renes*, kidneys.] A hormone obtained from extract of suprarenal medulla; adrenalin, adrenin, suprarenin, epinephrin; $C_9H_{13}O_3N$.

adrenergic (ădrēnĕr'jĭk) *a.* [L. *ad*, to; *renes*, kidneys; Gk. *ergon*, work.] *Appl.* sympathetic nerves, which liberate sympathin or an adrenaline-like principle from their terminations; adrenalnergic; *cf.* cholinergic.

adrenin(e),—adrenaline.

adrenocortical (ădrē'nōkôr'tĭkăl) *a.* [L. *ad*, to; *renes*, kidneys; *cortex*, bark.] *Pert.*, or secreted in, the adrenal cortex.

adrenocorticotrophic (ădrē'nōkôr'tĭkōtrŏf'ĭk) *a.* [L. *ad*, to; *renes*, kidneys; *cortex*, bark; Gk. *trophe*, nourishment.] *Appl.* hormone secreted by anterior lobe of pituitary gland and which controls activity of adrenal cortex; ACTH.

adrenotropic (ădrēnōtrŏp'ĭk) *a.* [L. *ad*, to; *renes*, kidneys; Gk. *trope*, turn.] Adrenotrophic; *appl.* a pituitary hormone acting on the adrenal medulla.

adrostral (ădrŏs'trăl) *a.* [L. *ad*, to; *rostrum*, beak.] Near to or closely connected with beak or rostrum.

adsorption (ădsôrp'shŭn) *n.* [L. *ad*, to; *sorbere*, to suck in.] The adhesion of molecules to solid bodies; formation of unimolecular surface layer.

adtidal (ăd'tīdăl) *a.* [L. *ad*, to; A.S. *tid*, time.] *Appl.* organisms living just below low-tide mark.

adultoid,—*appl.* nymph having imaginal characters differentiated further than in normal nymph.

aduncate (ădŭng'kāt) *a.* [L. *aduncus*, hooked.] Crooked; bent in the form of a hook.

advehent (ad'vĕhĕnt) *a.* [L. *advehere*, to carry to.] Afferent; carrying to an organ.

adventitia (ădvĕntĭsh'ĭă) *n.* [L. *adventitius*, extraordinary.] External connective tissue layer of blood vessels; tunica adventitia.

adventitious (ădvĕntĭsh'ŭs) *a.* [L. *adventitius*, extraordinary.] Accidental; found in an unusual place; *appl.* tissues and organs arising in abnormal positions; secondary, *appl.* dentine.

aecia,—*plu.* of aecium.

aecial,—aecidial.

aecidia,—*plu.* of aecidium.

aecidial (ēsĭd'ĭăl) *a.* [L. *aecidium*, cup.] *Pert.* aecidia, or aecidium; *appl.* primordium.

aecidiosorus (ēsĭd'ĭŏsō'rŭs) *n.* [L. *aecidium*, cup; Gk. *soros*, heap.] A cluster or row of aecidiospores.

aecidiospores (ēsĭd'ĭŏspōrz') *n. plu.* [L. *aecidium*, cup; Gk. *sporos*, seed.] The spores produced in an aecidium; spring-spores.

aecidium (ēsĭd'ĭŭm) *n.* [L. *aecidium*, cup.] A cup-shaped structure containing simple sporophores, bearing rows of spores; cluster-cup of rusts.

aeciospores,—aecidiospores, *q.v.*

aecium,—aecidium, *q.v.*

aedeagus (ēdē'ăgŭs) *n.* [Gk. *aidoia*, genitals.] The male intromittent organ of insects; also aedoeagus.

aegithognathous (ē'jĭthŏg'năthŭs) *a.* [Gk. *aigithos*, hedge-sparrow; *gnathos*, jaw.] With maxillo-palatines separate, vomers forming a wedge in front and diverging behind; *appl.* a type of palate found in Passeres.

aeolian (ēōl'ĭăn) *a.* [L. *Aeolus*, god of the winds.] Wind-borne; *appl.* deposits.

aerenchyma (āĕrĕng'kĭmă) *n.* [Gk. *aer*, air; *engchyma*, infusion.] Tissue between spore mass and capsule wall in mosses; cortex of submerged roots of certain swamp plants; aerating cortical tissue in floating portions of some aquatic plants.

aerial (āē'rĭăl) *a.* [L. *aer*, air.] Inhabiting the air; *appl.* roots growing above ground, *e.g.* from stems of ivy, for purposes of climbing; also to small bulbs appearing in leaf-axils.

aero-aquatic (ā'ĕrŏăkwăt'ĭk) *a.* [L. *aer*, air; *aqua*, water.] *Appl.* or *pert.* fungi growing in water and liberating spores in the air.

aerobe (ā'ĕrōb) *n.* [Gk. *aer*, air; *bios*, life.] An aerobic organism, capable of living in presence of oxygen. *Opp.* anaerobe.

aerobic (ā'ĕrŏ̄b'ĭk) *a.* [Gk. *aer*, air; *bios*, life.] Thriving only in presence of free oxygen.

aerobiology (ā'ĕrŏbīŏl'ŏjĭ) *n.* [Gk. *aer*, air; *bios*, life; *logos*, discourse.] The study of airborne organisms and their distribution; biology of aeroplankton.

aerobiosis (ā'ĕrŏbīō'sĭs) *n.* [Gk. *aer*, air; *biosis*, manner of life.] Existence in presence of oxygen.

aerocyst (ā'ĕrŏsĭst) *n.* [Gk. *aer*, air; *kystis*, bladder.] An air vesicle of algae.

aerogenic (ā'ĕrŏjĕn'ĭk) *a.* [Gk. *aer*, air; *gennaein*, to produce.] Gas-producing; *appl.* certain bacteria.

aeromorphosis (ā'ĕrŏmôr'fōsĭs, -môrfō'sĭs) *n.* [Gk. *aer*, air; *morphosis*, form.] Modification of form or structure owing to exposure to air or wind.

aerophora (ā'ĕrŏf'ŏră) *n.* [Gk. *aer*, air; *pherein*, to bear.] Aerating outgrowth or pneumatophore in certain ferns.

aerophyte (ā'ĕrŏfīt) *n.* [Gk. *aer*, air; *phyton*, plant.] A plant growing attached to an aerial portion of another plant; epiphyte.

aeroplankton (ā'ĕrŏplăngk'tŏn) *n.* [Gk. *aer*, air; *plangktos*, wandering.] Living particles drifting in the air, as spores, pollen, bacteria, etc.; also applied to non-living particles.

aerostat (ā′ĕröstăt) *n.* [L. *aer*, air; *stare*, to stand.] An air-sac in insect body or in bird bone.

aerostatic (ā′ĕröstăt′ĭk), *a.* [L. *aer*, air; *stare*, to stand.] Pneumatic; containing air-spaces.

aerotaxis (ā′ĕrötăk′sĭs) *n.* [Gk. *aer*, air; *taxis*, arrangement.] The arrangement of bacteria and other micro-organisms towards or away from oxygen.

aerotropic (ā′ĕrötrŏp′ĭk) *a.* [Gk. *aer*, air; *trope*, turn.] *Appl.* curvature of a plant organ towards a higher concentration of oxygen.

aerotropism (āĕrŏt′röpĭzm) *n.* [Gk. *aer*, air; *trope*, turn.] Reaction to gases, generally to oxygen.

aesthacyte (ēs′thăsīt) *n.* [Gk. *aisthesis*, sensation; *kytos*, hollow.] A sensory cell of primitive animals.

aesthesis (ēsthē′sĭs) *n.* [Gk. *aisthesis*, sensation.] Sensibility; sense-percept; aesthesia.

aesthetasc (ēsthē′tăsk) *n.* [Gk. *aisthetes*, perceiver; *askein*, to exercise.] An olfactory receptor on antennule of daphnids.

aesthetes (ēsthē′tēz) *n. plu.* [Gk. *aisthetes*, perceiver.] Sense organs.

aestival (ĕstī′văl, ĕ̄s′tĭvăl) *a.* [L. *aestivus*, of summer.] Produced in, or *pert.* summer.

aestivation (ĕs′tĭvā′shŭn) *n.* [L. *aestivus*, of summer.] The mode in which different parts of flower are disposed in flower-bud; preefloration; torpor during summer, as in some animals; dormancy during heat and drought period, *opp.* hibernation.

aethalium (ēthā′lĭŭm) *n.* [Gk. *aithalos*, soot.] An aggregation of plasmodia or sporangia to form a compound fruit in Mycetozoa or Myxomycetes.

aethogametism (ā̆ē′thögămē′tĭzm) *n.* [Gk. *aēthes*, unaccustomed; *gametes*, spouse.] Gametal incompatibility or asynethogametism, *q.v.*; aëthogamety.

aetiology (ētĭŏl′öjĭ) *n.* [Gk. *aitia*, cause; *logos*, discourse.] The science of causation; or origin of causes; also etiology.

afferent (ăf′ĕrĕnt) *a.* [L. *afferre*, to bring.] Bringing towards; *appl.* nerves carrying impulses to nervous centres; *appl.* blood-vessels carrying blood to an organ or set of organs.

aflagellar (ă̄′flăjĕl′ăr) *a.* [Gk. *a*, without; L. *flagellum*, whip.] Without a flagellum.

afterbirth (âf′tĕrbĕrth) *n.* [A.S. *aefter*, behind; *beran*, to bring forth.] Placenta and foetal membranes expelled after offspring.

after-brain,—myelencephalon, *q.v.*

aftershaft (âf′tĕrshâft) *n.* [A.S. *aefter*, behind; O.E. *sceaft*, shaft.] A small tuft of down near superior umbilicus of a feather.

agameon (ăgămē′ŏn) *n.* [Gk. *a*, without; *gamos*, marriage, *on*, being.] A species comprising only apomictic individuals.

agamete (ăg′ămēt) *n.* [Gk. *a*, without; *gametes*, spouse.] An amoebula, or germ cell, which develops directly without syngamy into an adult.

agametoblast (ăgămē′töblăst) *n.* [Gk. *a*, not; *gametes*, spouse; *blastos*, bud.] A cytomere, *q.v.*, of Caryotropha.

agamic (ăgăm′ĭk), *a.* [Gk. *a*, without; *gamos*, marriage.] Asexual; parthenogenetic; agamous.

agamobium (ăg′ămŏb′ĭŭm) *n.* [Gk. *a*, without; *gamos*, marriage; *bios*, life.] The asexual stage in metagenesis; the sporophyte.

agamogenesis (ăg′ămöjĕn′ĕsĭs) *n.* [Gk. *a*, without; *gamos*, marriage; *genesis*, descent.] Asexual reproduction; parthenogenesis.

agamogenetic (ăg′ămöjĕnĕt′ĭk) *a.* [Gk. *a*, without; *gamos*, marriage; *genesis*, descent.] Asexual; produced asexually.

agamogony (ăg′ămŏg′önĭ) *n.* [Gk. *a*, without; *gamos*, marriage; *gonos*, generation.] Schizogony, or reproduction without sexual process.

agamont (ăg′ămŏnt) *n.* [Gk. *a*, without; *gamos*, marriage; *on*, being.] A schizont, or that stage which gives rise to agametes.

agamospecies (ăg'ămöspē'shēz) *n.* [Gk. *a*, without; *gamos*, marriage; L. *species*, particular kind.] Species without sexual reproduction, as in parthenogenetic aneuploids.

agamous,—agamic, *q.v.*

agar (âg'âr, ā'gâr) *n.* [Mal. *agar-agar*, a sea-weed.] A medium for bacterial and other cultures, prepared from agar-agar, a gelatinous substance, also of dietary utility, yielded by red algae.

age and area,—hypothesis of Willis that older species occur in a more extensive area than that occupied by more recent species.

agenesis (ăjĕn'ĕsĭs) *n.* [Gk. *a*, not; *genesis*, origin.] Failure to develop; agenesia.

agennesis (ăjĕn'ēsĭs) *n.* [Gk. *a*, without; *gennesis*, an engendering.] Sterility.

ageotropic,—apogeotropic, *q.v.*

agglomerate (ăglŏm'ĕrāt) *a.* [L. *ad*, to; *glomus*, ball.] Clustered, as a head of flowers; *appl.* adhering mass of protozoa, as in agglomeration of trypanosomes.

agglutinate (ăgloot'ĭnāt) *v.* [L. *agglutinare*, to glue on.] To cause or to undergo agglutination. *n.* The mass formed by agglutination. *a.* stuck together; obtect, *q.v.*

agglutination (ăg'lootĭnā'shŭn) *n.* [L. *ad*, to; *glutinare*, to glue.] The formation of clumps or floccules by pollen, bacteria, erythrocytes, spermatozoa, and some protozoa.

agglutinin (ăgloot'ĭnĭn) *n.* [L. *ad*, to; *glutinare*, to glue.] A substance or specific antibody which causes agglutination.

agglutinogen (ăglootĭn'öjĕn) *n.* [L. *ad*, to; *glutinare*, to glue; Gk. *gennaein*, to produce.] Substance or antigen that produces agglutinin.

aggregate (ăg'rëgāt) *a.* [L. *ad*, to; *gregare*, to collect into a flock.] Formed in a cluster; *appl.* a fruit or etaerio formed from apocarpous gynoecium of a single flower, as raspberry; *appl.* certain medullary rays; *appl.* a type of silk gland in certain spiders.

aggregation (ăgrëgā'shŭn) *n.* [L. *ad*, to; *gregare*, to collect.] A grouping or crowding of separate organisms; movement of protoplasm in tentacle or tendril cells of sensitive plants, which causes tentacle or tendril to bend towards the point stimulated.

aggressin (ăgrĕs'ĭn) *n.* [L. *aggressus*, attacked.] Toxic substance produced by pathogenic organisms, inhibiting defensive reactions of host.

aglomerular (ăglŏmĕr'ūlăr) *a.* [Gk. *a*, without; L. *glomerare*, to form into a ball.] Devoid of glomeruli, as kidney in certain fishes.

aglossate (ăglŏs'āt) *n.* [Gk. *a*, without; *glossa*, tongue.] Having no tongue.

agminated (ăg'mĭnātĕd) *a.* [L. *agmen*, a crowd.] Clustered; *appl.* glands, Peyer's patches.

agnathostomatous (ăgnăth'östŏm'-ătŭs) *a.* [Gk. *a*, without; *gnathos*, jaw; *stoma*, mouth.] Having mouth unfurnished with jaws, as lamprey; agnathous.

agon (ăg'ōn) *n.* [Gk. *agon*, contest.] The active principle of an enzyme; *cf.* pheron, symplex.

agonist (ăg'ōnĭst) *n.* [Gk. *agonistes*, champion.] A prime mover or muscle directly responsible for change in position of a part.

agranular (ăgrăn'ūlăr) *a.* [L. *a*, away; *granulum*, small grain.] Without granules; without a conspicuous layer of granular cells, *appl.* cortex of brain: the motor areas.

agranulocyte (ăgrăn'ūlösīt) *n.* [Gk. *a*, without; L. *granulum*, small grain; Gk. *kytos*, hollow.] A non-granular or lymphoid leucocyte.

agrestal (ăgrĕs'tăl) *a.* [L. *agrestis*, rural.] *Appl.* plants growing on arable land.

agriotype (ăg'rĭötīp) *n.* [Gk. *agrios*, wild; *typos*, image.] Wild or ancestral type.

agrostology (ăg'rŏstŏl'öjĭ) *n.* [Gk. *agrostis*, grass; *logos*, discourse.] That part of botany dealing with grasses.

aheliotropism,—apheliotropism, *q.v.*

A-horizon,—the upper, or leached, soil layers.

air-bladder (ăr′-blăd′ĕr) *n.* [L. *aer*, air; A.S. *blædre*, bladder.] The swim-bladder in fishes; hollow dilatation of thallus in bladder-wrack.

air-cells,—thin-walled cavities in ethmoidal labyrinth; numerous cavities in mastoid; alveoli of lungs; air spaces in plant tissue.

air chamber,—gas-filled compartment of Nautilus shell, previously occupied by the animal.

air-duct,—duct connecting the swim-bladder and gut of certain fishes.

air-pore,—stoma, *q.v.*, of plants.

air-sacs,—spaces filled with air and connected with lungs in birds; dilatations of tracheae in many insects; sacs representing tracheal system and having hydrostatic function in certain insect larvae.

air sinuses,—cavities in frontal ethmoid, sphenoid and maxillary bones, with passages to nasal cavities.

aitiogenic (ī′tĭöjĕn′ĭk) *a.* [Gk. *aitios*, causing; *gennaein*, to generate.] Resulting from causation; *appl.* reaction, as movement induced by an external agent.

aitionastic (ī′tĭönăs′tĭk) *a.* [Gk. *aitios*, causing; *nastos*, close-pressed.] *Appl.* curvature of part of a plant and induced by a diffuse stimulus.

akanth-,—*see* acanth-.

akaryocyte,—akaryote; an erythrocyte.

akaryote (ăkăr′ĭōt) *n.* [Gk. *a*, without; *karyon*, nut.] A cell in which nucleoplasm has not collected together to form a nucleus; a non-nucleated cell, condition present in many protista. *a.* Non-nucleated.

akene,—achene.

akinesis (ăkĭnē′sĭs) *n.* [Gk. *a*, not; *kinesis*, movement.] Absence or arrest of motion.

akinete (ăk′ĭnēt) *n.* [Gk. *a*, not; *kinein*, to move.] A resting cell in certain green algae, which will later reproduce.

ala (ā′lă, âlă) *n.* [L. *ala*, wing.] Any winglike projection or structure; lateral petal of papilionaceous flowers; membranous expansion on some seeds; basal lobe of moss leaves. *Plu.* alae.

alar (ā′lăr) *a.* [L. *ala*, wing.] Wing-like; *pert.* wings or alae; axillary; *appl.* ligaments, cartilages, etc.

alary (ā′lărĭ) *a.* [L. *ala*, wing.] Wing-like; *pert.* wings.

alate (ā′lāt) *a.* [L. *alatus*, winged.] Having a wing-like expansion, as of petiole or stem; broad-lipped, *appl.* shells; *appl.* a spicular system in Calcarea which is sagittal because of inequality of angles; winged.

albedo (ălbē′dö) *n.* [L. *albus*, white.] Diffused reflection, the ratio of the amount of light reflected by a surface to the amount of incident light; mesocarp of hesperidium, *cf.* flavedo.

albescent (ălbĕs′ĕnt) *a.* [L. *albescere*, to grow white.] Growing whitish.

albicant (ăl′bĭkănt) *a.* [L. *albicare*, to be white.] Tending to become white.

albinism (ăl′bĭnĭzm) *n.* [L. *albus*, white.] Absence of pigmentation in animals normally pigmented; state of having colourless chromatophores.

albino (ălbē′nö, ălbī′nö) *n.* [Sp. *albino*, white, from L. *albus*.] Any animal with congenital deficiency of pigment in skin, hair, eyes, etc.; a plant with colourless chromatophores, due to absence of chloroplasts or undeveloped chromoplasts.

albuginea (ălbūjĭn′ëă) *n.* [L. *albus*, white; *gignere*, to beget.] Tunica albuginea: white, dense connective tissue surrounding testis, ovary, corpora cavernosa, spleen, or eye.

albumen (ălbū′mĕn) *n.* [L. *albumen*, white of egg.] White of egg; nutritive material stored in seed.

albumin (ălbū′mĭn) *n.* [L. *albumen*, white of egg.] One of a group of heat-coagulable, water-soluble proteins occurring in egg-white, blood serum, milk, and many animal and vegetable tissues.

albuminoids (ălbū′mĭnoidz) *n. plu.* [L. *albumen*, white of egg; Gk. *eidos*, form.] Scleroproteins, *q.v.*

albuminous (ălbū′mĭnŭs) *a.* [L. *albumen*, white of egg.] *Pert.*, containing, or of nature of, albumen or an albumin.

albuminous cells,—parenchyma cells associated with sieve cells, as in pteridophytes and gymnosperms.

alburnum (ălbŭr′nŭm) *n.* [L. *albus*, white.] Sap-wood or splint-wood, soft white substance between inner bark and true wood; outer young wood of dicotyledon.

alecithal (ă̄lĕs′ĭthăl) *a.* [Gk. *a*, without; *lekithos*, yolk.] With little or no yolk; *appl.* ova; alecithic.

alepidote (ă̄lĕp′ĭdōt) *a.* [Gk. *a*, not; *lepidotos*, scaly.] Without scales.

aletocyte (ălē′tösīt) *n.* [Gk. *aletes*, wanderer; *kytos*, hollow.] Wandering cell.

aleurispore,—aleurospore.

aleuron (ăl′ūrŏn) *n.* [Gk. *aleuron*, flour.] *Appl.* protein grains found in general protoplasm and used as reserve food-material; *appl.* layer containing protein, of endosperm in monocotyledons; aleurone.

aleurospore (ăl′ūrōspōr) *n.* [Gk. *aleuron*, flour; *sporos*, seed. A lateral conidium of certain fungous parasites of skin; spore or tip early separated from hypha by a septum, or by contraction of protoplasm; aleuriospore, aleurispore, aleurium.

alexine (ălĕk′sĭn) *n.* [Gk. *alexein*, to ward off.] A substance in blood serum which combines with an amboceptor to produce lysis; alexin; complement.

algesis (ăljē′sĭs) *n.* [Gk. *algesis*, sense of pain.] The sense of pain.

algicolous (ăljĭk′ölŭs) *a.* [L. *alga*, seaweed; *colere*, to inhabit.] Living on algae.

algin (ăl′jĭn) *n.* [L. *alga*, seaweed.] A mucilaginous substance, alginic acid, obtained from certain algae.

algoid (ăl′goid) *a.* [L. *alga*, seaweed; Gk. *eidos*, shape.] *Pert.*, resembling, or of the nature of an alga.

algology (ălgŏl′öjĭ) *n.* [L. *alga*, seaweed; Gk. *logos*, discourse.] The study of algae; phycology.

Algonkian (ălgŏng′kĭăn) *a.* [*Algonquian* tribe of Indians.] *Pert.* late Proterozoic era.

aliform (ā′lĭfôrm) *a.* [L. *ala*, wing; *forma*, shape.] Wing-shaped; *appl.* muscles, as in insects.

alima (ăl′ĭmă) *n.* [Gk. *halimos*, *pert.* sea.] A larval stage of certain Crustacea.

alimentary (ăl′ĭmĕn′tărĭ) *a.* [L. *alimentarius*, *pert.* sustenance.] *Pert.* nutritive functions; *appl.* system, canal, tract, etc.

alimentation (ăl′ĭmĕntā′shŭn) *n.* [L. *alimentum*, nourishment.] The process of nourishing or of being nourished.

alisphenoid (ăl′ĭsfē′noid) *n.* [L. *ala*, wing; Gk. *sphen*, wedge; *eidos*, form.] Wing-like portion of sphenoid forming part of cranium; ala temporalis.

alitrunk (ăl′ĭtrŭngk) *n.* [L. *ala*, wing; *truncus*, trunk.] Thorax of insect when fused with first segment of abdomen.

alkaline gland,—a gland opening at base of sting of certain Hymenoptera; Dufour's gland.

alkaloid (ăl′kăloid) *n.* [Ar. *al*, the; *qali*, ash; Gk. *eidos*, form.] Basic nitrogenous organic substance with poisonous or medicinal properties, as caffeine, morphine, nicotine, strychnine, ptomaine, etc.

allaesthetic (ăl′ēsthĕt′ĭk) *a.* [Gk. *allos*, other; *aisthetes*, perceiver.] *Appl.* characters effective when perceived by other organisms.

allantochorion (ălăn′tökō′rĭŏn) *n.* [Gk. *allas*, sausage; *chorion*, skin.] Foetal membrane formed of outer wall of allantois and the primitive chorion; true chorion.

allantoid (ălăn'toid) *a.* [Gk. *allas*, sausage; *eidos*, form.] Sausage-shaped; botuliform.

allantoin (ălăn'töĭn) *n.* [Gk. *allas*, sausage.] The end-product of purine metabolism, occurring in allantoic fluid and urine of certain mammals; $C_4H_6O_3N_4$.

allantois (ălăn'töĭs) *n.* [Gk. *allas*, sausage.] An embryonic organ, a membranous sac arising from posterior part of alimentary canal in higher vertebrates, and acting as an organ of respiration or nutrition or both.

allassotonic (ălăs'ötŏn'ĭk) *a.* [Gk. *allassein*, to change; *tonos*, strain.] Induced by stimulus, *appl.* movements of grown plants; *cf.* auxotonic.

allatectomy (ălātĕk'tömĭ) *n.* [L. *allatum*, aided; Gk. *ektome*, a cutting out.] Excision or removal of corpora allata.

allele (ălēl') *n.* [Gk. *allelon*, one another.] Allelomorph.

allelism (ălē'lĭzm) *n.* [Gk. *allelon*, one another.] The relationship between two alleles; allelomorphism.

allelocatalysis (ălē'lökătăl'ĭsĭs) *n.* [Gk. *allelon*, one another; *katalysis*, dissolution.] Allelocatalytic or mutually accelerating or retarding effect of contiguous cells; *e.g.* acceleration of rate of fission with increase in number of individual protozoa present.

allelomorph (ălē'lömôrf) *n.* [Gk. *allelon*, one another; *morphe*, form.] One of any pair of alternative hereditary characters; gene which can occupy the same locus as another gene in a particular chromosome; allele.

allelopathy (ălēlŏp'ăthĭ) *n.* [Gk. *allelon*, one another; *pathos*, suffering.] The influence or effect of one living plant upon another.

allergen (ăl'ërjĕn) *n.* [Gk. *allos*, other; *ergon*, activity; *-genes*, producing.] A substance which induces allergy; atopen.

allergy (ăl'ërjĭ) *n.* [Gk. *allos*, other; *ergon*, activity.] Changed reactivity on second or subsequent infection or poisoning; exaggerated or unusual susceptibility; anaphylaxis; atopy, *q.v.*

allesthetic,—allaesthetic, *q.v.*

alliaceous (ălĭā'shŭs) *a.* [L. *allium*, garlic.] *Pert.* or like garlic; *appl.* a class of odours.

allobiosis (ăl'öbīō'sĭs) *n.* [Gk. *allos*, other; *biosis*, manner of life.] Changed reactivity of an organism in a changed internal or external environment.

allocarpy (ăl'ökârpĭ) *n.* [Gk. *allos*, other; *karpos*, fruit.] The production of fruit after cross-fertilisation.

allocheiral (ăl'ökī'răl) *a.* [Gk. *allos*, other; *cheir*, hand.] Having right and left sides reversed; *pert.* reversed symmetry.

allochroic (ăl'ökrō'ĭk) *a.* [Gk. *allos*, other; *chros*, colour.] Able to change colour; with colour variation.

allochronic (al'ökrŏn'ĭk) *a.* [Gk. *allos*, other; *chronos*, time.] Not contemporary; *appl.* species, etc. *Opp.* synchronic.

allochthonous (ălŏk'thönŭs) *a.* [Gk. *allos*, other; *chthon*, the ground.] Exotic; not aboriginal; acquired. *Opp.* autochthonous.

allocortex (ăl'ökôr'tĕks) *n.* [Gk. *allos*, other; L. *cortex*, bark.] The primitive cortical areas or cortex of olfactory brain, *opp.* isocortex.

allogamous (ălŏg'ămŭs) *a.* [Gk. *allos*, other; *gamos*, marriage.] Reproducing by cross-fertilisation, *opp.* autogamous.

allogamy (ălŏg'ămĭ) *n.* [Gk. *allos*, other; *gamos*, marriage.] Cross-fertilisation, *opp.* autogamy.

allogene (ăl'öjēn) *n.* [Gk. *allos*, other; *genos*, descent.] A recessive allele; *opp.* protogene.

allogenic (ălöjĕn'ĭk) *a.* [Gk. *allos*, other; *genos*, descent.] Caused by external factors; *appl.* plant successions; *pert.* allogenes; derived from elsewhere, *opp.* autogenic; allogenous or exogenous, *opp.* endogenous; allochronic, *q.v.*

alloheteroploid (ăl′öhĕt′ëröploid) *n.* [Gk. *allos*, other; *heteros*, other; *aploos*, onefold; *eidos*, form.] Heteroploid derived from specifically distinct genomes.

alloiogenesis (ăl′oiöjĕn′ĕsĭs) *n.* [Gk. *alloios*, different; *genesis*, descent.] The alternation, in a life-history, of a sexual and a non-sexual form; alternation of generations.

alloiometron (ăl′oiöm′ĕtrŏn) *n.* [Gk. *alloios*, different; *metron*, measure.] Measurable change of proportion or intensity of development within species or races, *e.g.* head, limb, tooth, etc. proportions.

allokinesis (ăl′ökīnē′sĭs) *n.* [Gk. *allos*, other; *kinesis*, movement.] Reflex, or passive, movement; involuntary movement.

allometry (ălŏm′ĕtrĭ) *n.* [Gk. *allos*, other; *metron*, measure.] Study of relative growth; change of proportions with increase of size; growth rate of a part differing from a standard growth rate or from the growth rate of the whole.

alloparalectotype (ăl′öpărălĕk′tötīp) *n.* [Gk. *allos*, other; *para*, beside; *lektos*, chosen; *typos*, pattern.] Specimen, from the original collection, of the sex opposite to that of the holotype, and described subsequently.

allopatric (ălöpăt′rĭk) *a.* [Gk. *allos*, other; *patra*, native land.] Having separate and mutually exclusive areas of geographical distribution. *Opp.* sympatric.

allopelagic (ăl′öpĕlăj′ĭk) *a.* [Gk. *allos*, other; *pelagos*, sea.] *Pert.* organisms found at any depth of the sea.

allophore (ăl′öfōr) *n.* [Gk. *allos*, other; *pherein*, to bear.] A cell or chromatophore containing red pigment, in skin of fishes, amphibians, and reptiles.

allophytoid (ălŏf′ĭtoid) *n.* [Gk. *allos*, other; *phytos*, growing; *eidos*, form.] A propagative bud, differing from a vegetative bud; a bulbil, as in some lilies.

alloplasm (ăl′öplăzm) *n.* [Gk. *allos*, other; *plasma*, mould.] The differentiated portion of cell-substance not forming independent organelles.

alloplasmatic (ăl′öplăzmăt′ĭk) *a.* [Gk. *allos*, other; *plasma*, mould.] *Appl.* differentiated portion of cell protoplasm; alloplasmic.

alloplast (ăl′öplăst) *n.* [Gk. *allos*, other; *plastos*, formed.] A morphological cell-unit of more than one kind of tissue. *Opp.* homoplast.

allopolyploid (ăl′öpŏl′ĭploid) *n.* [Gk. *allos*, other; *polys*, many; *aploos*, onefold; *eidos*, form.] An organism with more than two sets of chromosomes derived from different species by hybridisation.

allorhizal (ăl′örī′zăl) *a.* [Gk. *allos*, other; *rhiza*, root.] Having opposed root and shoot poles. *Opp.* homorhizal.

all-or-none,—principle that response to a stimulus is either completely effected or is absent, first observed in heart muscle (Bowditch's law).

alloscutum (ăl′öskū′tŭm) *n.* [Gk. *allos*, another; L. *scutum*, shield.] Dorsal area or sclerite behind scutum in larval ticks; *cf.* conscutum.

allosematic (ăl′ösēmăt′ĭk) *a.* [Gk. *allos*, other; *sema*, sign.] Having markings or coloration imitating warning signs in other, usually dangerous, species.

allosomal (ăl′ösō′măl) *a.* [Gk. *allos*, other; *soma*, body.] *Pert.* allosome; *appl.* inheritance of characters controlled by genes located in an allosome.

allosome (ăl′ösōm) *n.* [Gk. *allos*, other; *soma*, body.] A chromosome other than an ordinary or typical one; heterochromosome, *opp.* autosome.

allostoses (ăl′ŏstō′sēs) *n. plu.* [Gk. *allos*, other; *osteon*, bone.] Bones formed in membrane; *cf.* autostoses.

allosynapsis,—allosyndesis, *q.v.*

allosyndesis (ăl′ösĭn′dēsis) *n.* [Gk. *allos*, other; *syndesis*, a binding together.] Pairing of homologous chromosomes from opposite parents, in a polyploid; *cf.* autosyndesis.

allotetraploid,—amphidiploid, *q.v.*

allotherm (ăl'ŏthĕrm) *n.* [Gk. *allos*, other; *therme*, heat.] An organism with body temperature dependent on environmental temperature.

allotrophic (ăl'ötrŏf'ĭk) *a.* [Gk. *allos*, other; *trophe*, nourishment.] Obtaining nourishment from other organisms; saprophytic, or saprozoic; heterotrophic.

allotropic (ălötrŏp'ĭk) *a.* [Gk. *allos*, other; *tropikos*, turning.] Exhibiting mutual tropism, as between gametes.

allotropous (ălŏt'röpŭs) *a.* [Gk. *allos*, any other; *tropos*, direction.] Not limited to, or adapted to, visiting special kinds of flowers, as certain insects. *Opp.* eutropous.

allotype (ăl'ötīp) *n.* [Gk. *allos*, other; *typos*, pattern.] Paratype of the sex opposite to that of the holotype.

allozygote (ăl'özī'gōt) *n.* [Gk. *allos*, other; *zygon*, yoke.] A homozygote having recessive characters, *opp.* protozygote.

alluvial (ălū'vĭăl, ăloo-) *a.* [L. *alluere*, to wash to.] *Pert.* deposits formed by finely divided material laid down by running water.

alpha (α) **cells,**—oxyphilic cells in pars glandularis of pituitary gland; cells with granules insoluble in alcohol, in islets of Langerhans; A-cells.

alpha (α) **granules,**—metachromatic granules in central region of protoplast, as in blue-green algae.

alpha (α) **tocopherol,**—vitamin E.

alphitomorphous (ăl'fĭtömôr'fŭs) *a.* [Gk. *alphiton*, pearl-barley; *morphe*, form.] Having the appearance of peeled barley; *appl.* certain fungi.

alsinaceous (ălsĭnā'shŭs) *a.* [Gk. *alsine*, chickweed.] *Appl.* polypetalous corolla where intervals occur between petals, as in chickweed.

alteration theory,—explains electromotive forces of nerve and muscle by alterations in chemical composition of tissue at cross-section.

alternate (ôltĕr'nāt, ăl-) *a.* [L. *alternus*, one after another.] Not opposite; *appl.* leaves, branches, etc., occurring at different levels successively on opposite sides of stem; every other; taking turns.

alternating cleavage,—spiral cleavage, *q.v.*

alternation of generations,—the occurrence in one life-history of two or more different forms differently produced, usually an alternation of a sexual with an asexual form; alloiogenesis; metagenesis; digenesis; heterogamy; heterogenesis; heterogony.

alternation of parts,—general rule that leaves of different whorls alternate in position with each other, sepals with petals, stamens with petals.

alternative inheritance,—allelism, allelomorphism.

alterne (ăltĕrn', ôl-) *n.* [L. *alternus*, one after another.] Vegetation exhibiting disturbed zonation due to abrupt change in environment, or to interference with normal plant succession.

alternipinnate (ăltĕr'nĭpĭn'āt, ôl-) *a.* [L. *alternus*, one after another; *pinna*, wing.] *Appl.* leaflets or pinnae arising alternately on each side of mid-rib.

altrices (ăltrī'sēz) *n. plu.* [L. *altrix*, nourisher.] Birds whose young are hatched in a very immature condition; *cf.* praecoces.

altricial (ăltrĭs'ĭăl) *a.* [L. *altrix*, nourisher.] Requiring care or nursing after hatching or birth.

alula (ăl'ūlă) *n.* [L. *alula*, *dim.* of *ala*, wing.] A small lobe separated off from wing-base on its posterior edge in certain insects; lower tegula or squama thoracicalis of Diptera; spurious or bastard wing of birds.

alutaceous (ălūtā'shŭs) *a.* [L. *aluta*, alum-dressed leather.] Tan-coloured; leathery; having appearance of minute cracks, *appl.* markings on elytra of certain beetles.

alveola (ăl'vēölă) *n.* [L. *alveolus*, small cavity.] A pit on the surface of an organ; alveolus, *q.v.*

alveolar (ăl′vëölăr) *a.* [L. *alveolus*, small pit.] *Pert.* an alveolus; *pert.* tooth socket; *appl.* artery, nerve, process, canal, in connection with the jaw-bone; *appl.* small cavities in lungs, glands, etc.; *appl.* pores connecting adjacent to air-cells or pulmonary alveoli; *appl.* a theory of structure of protoplasm.

alveolate (ăl′vëölāt, ălvē′ölāt) *a.* [L. *alveolatus*, pitted.] Deeply pitted or honey-combed.

alveolation (ăl′vëölā′shŭn) *n.* [L. *alveolatus*, pitted.] The formation of alveoli; alveolate appearance.

alveolus (ălvē′ölŭs) *n.* [L. *alveolus*, small pit.] A small pit or depression; tooth socket; pyramidal ossicle, supporting tooth in sea-urchin; air-cell of lung; a cavity in glands; cavity in tarsus of spiders, receptacle for haematodocha; pit for articulation of macrotrichia.

alveus (ăl′vëŭs) *n.* [L. *alveus*, cavity.] A white layer of fibres on ventricular surface of hippocampus; utricle of ear; dilatation of thoracic duct.

amacrine (ăm′ăkrĭn) *a.* [Gk. *a*, not; *makros*, long; *is*, fibre.] Having no conspicuous axon; *appl.* cells in inner nuclear layer of retina, with dendrites in inner plexiform layer.

amb (ămb) *n.* [L. *ambulare*, to walk.] Ambulacral area.

ambiens (ăm′bĭĕnz) *n.* [L. *ambire*, to go round.] A thigh muscle in certain birds, the action of which causes the toes to maintain grasp on perch.

ambient (ăm′bĭĕnt) *a.* [L. *ambire*, to go round.] Surrounding; *appl.* vein, the costal nervure when encircling insect wing.

ambilateral (ăm′bĭlăt′ërăl) *a.* [L. *ambo*, both; *latus*, side.] *Pert.* both sides.

ambiparous (ămbĭp′ărŭs) *a.* [L. *ambo*, both; *parere*, to produce.] Containing the beginnings of both flowers and leaves; *appl.* buds.

ambisexual (ăm′bĭsĕk′sūăl) *a.* [L. *ambo*, both; *sexus*, sex.] *Pert.* both sexes; ambosexual; monoecious, *q.v.*

ambisporangiate (ăm′bĭspörăn′jĭāt) *a.* [L. *ambo*, both; Gk. *sporos*, seed; *anggeion*, vessel.] Amphisporangiate, *q.v.*

ambital (ăm′bĭtăl) *a.* [L. *ambire*, to go round.] *Appl.* interambulacral and antambulacral plates of asteroids; outer skeleton of ophiuroid arm.

ambitus (ăm′bĭtŭs) *n.* [L. *ambitus*, going around.] The outer edge or margin; outline of echinoid shell viewed from apical pole.

amblychromatic (ăm′blĭkrōmăt′ĭk) *a.* [Gk. *amblys*, dull; *chroma*, colour.] Staining or stained slightly. *Opp.* trachychromatic.

amboceptor (ăm′bösĕp′tŏr) *n.* [L. *ambo*, both; *capere*, to take.] A specific antibody or immune body necessary for ferment-like action of complement on a toxin or a red blood corpuscle; a lysin.

ambon (ăm′bŏn) *n.* [Gk. *ambon*, raised platform.] Fibrocartilaginous ring surrounding an articular socket, as around acetabulum; circumferential fibrocartilage; labrum.

ambosexual (ăm′bösĕk′sūăl) *a.* [L. *ambo*, both; *sexus*, sex.] Common to, or *pert.*, both sexes; activated by both male and female hormones.

ambulacra (ăm′būlā′kră) *n. plu.* [L. *ambulare*, to walk.] Locomotor tube-feet of echinoderms.

ambulacral,—*pert.* or used for walking; *appl.* limbs of arthropods; *pert.* ambulacra.

ambulacralia (ăm′būlăkrā′lĭă) *n. plu.* [L. *ambulare*, to walk.] Ambulacral plates, *i.e.* plates through which tube-feet protrude.

ambulacriform (ămbūlăk′rĭfôrm) *a.* [L. *ambulare*, to walk; *forma*, shape.] Having the form or appearance of ambulacra.

ameba,—amoeba.

ameiosis (ămīō′sĭs) *n.* [Gk. *a*, without; *meiosis*, diminution.] Occurrence of only one division in meiosis instead of two.

ameiotic (ămīŏt′ĭk) *a.* [Gk. *a*, without; *meion*, smaller.] *Appl.* parthenogenesis in which meiosis is suppressed.

amelification (ămĕl′ĭfĭkā′shŭn) *n.* [M.E. *amell*, enamel; L. *facere*, to make.] Formation of tooth-enamel.

ameloblast (ămĕl′öblăst) *n.* [M.E. *amell*, enamel; Gk. *blastos*, bud.] A columnar or hexagonal cell of internal epithelium of enamel organ; enamel cell, adamantoblast, ganoblast.

amentaceous (ămĕntā′shŭs), **amentiferous** (ămĕntĭf′ërŭs) *a.* [L. *amentum*, thong; *ferre*, to carry.] *Appl.* plants bearing amenta or catkins.

amentum (ămĕn′tŭm) *n.* [L. *amentum*, thong.] A catkin, consisting of bracted axis bearing unisexual flowers, as in poplar and willow; ament.

ameristic (ămĕrĭs′tĭk) *a.* [Gk. *a*, without; *meristos*, divided.] Not divided into parts; unsegmented.

ametabolic (ămĕt′ăbŏl′ĭk) *a.* [Gk. *a*, without; *metabole*, change.] Not changing form; *appl.* ciliates; *appl.* insects that do not pass through marked metamorphosis.

ametoecious (ămĕtē′sĭŭs) *a.* [Gk. *a*, without; *meta*, after; *oikos*, house.] Parasitic on one host during one life cycle, *opp.* metoecious; autoecious, autoxenous.

amicron (ămī′krŏn) *n.* [Gk. *a*, without; *mikros*, small.] An element so small that even the ultramicroscope can only indicate it as a diffuse illumination in the track of the beam; *cf.* submicron.

amicronucleate (ămī′krönū′klëāt) *a.* [Gk. *a*, without; *mikros*, small; L. *nucleus*, kernel.] *Appl.* fragments of certain Protozoa in which there is no micronucleus.

amine (ăm′ĭn) *n.* [Gk. *ammoniakon*, resinous gum.] A nitrogen compound formed in plants, also produced by bacterial action on amino acids, a derivative from ammonia by hydrogen replacement.

amino acids,—compounds containing amino (NH_2) and carboxyl (COOH) groups, and produced from proteins by hydrolysis.

amitosis (ămĭtō′sĭs) *n.* [Gk. *a*, without; *mitos*, thread.] Direct cell-division and cleavage of nucleus without thread-like formation of nuclear material. *Opp.* mitosis.

ammochaeta (ămökē′tă) *n.* [Gk. *ammos*, sand; *chaite*, hair.] Bristle on head of desert ants, arranged in groups and used for removal of sand from forelegs.

ammonitiferous (ăm′ŏnĭtĭf′ërŭs) *a.* [Gk. *Ammon*, Jupiter; L. *ferre*, to carry.] Containing fossil remains of ammonites.

amnion (ăm′nĭŏn) *n.* [Gk. *amnion*, foetal membrane.] A foetal membrane of reptiles, birds, and mammals; inner embryonic membrane of insects; viscous envelope of certain ovules.

amnionic,—amniotic.

amniote (ăm′nĭōt) *n.* [Gk. *amnion*, foetal membrane.] An animal characterised by possession of amnion in foetal life.

amniotic (ămnĭŏt′ĭk) *a.* [Gk. *amnion*, foetal membrane.] *Pert.* amnion; *appl.* folds, sac, cavity, fluid; amnionic.

amoeba (ămē′bă) *n.* [Gk. *amoibe*, change.] A protozoon in which the shape is subject to constant alterations due to formation and retraction of pseudopodia; generally used to typify most primitive animal commonly known.

amoebadiastase (ămē′bădī′ăstās) *n.* [Gk. *amoibe*, change; *dia*, through; *histanai*, to set.] The digestive ferment secreted by amoebae.

amoebiform (ămē′bĭfôrm) *a.* [Gk. *amoibe*, change; L. *forma*, shape.] Shaped like or resembling an amoeba.

amoebism (ămē′bĭzm) *n.* [Gk. *amoibe*, change.] Amoeboid form or behaviour, as of leucocytes.

amoebocyte (ămē′bösīt) *n.* [Gk. *amoibe*, change; *kytos*, hollow.] Any cell having the shape or properties of an amoeba ; one of certain cells in coelom of echinoderms ; a leucocyte, *q.v.*

amoeboid (ămē′boid) *a.* [Gk. *amoibe*, change ; *eidos*, shape.] Resembling an amoeba in shape, in properties, or in locomotion.

amoebula (ămē′būlă) *n.* [Gk. *amoibe*, change.] The swarm-spore of a protist when furnished with pseudopodia ; pseudopodiospore.

amorphous (ămôr′fŭs) *a.* [Gk. *a*, without ; *morphe*, shape.] Of indeterminate or irregular form ; with no visible differentiation in structure.

ampheclexis (ăm′fĕklĕk′sĭs) *n.* [Gk. *amphi*, both ; *eklexis*, choice.] Sexual selection.

ampherotoky,—amphitoky, *q.v.*

amphiapomict (ăm′fĭăp′ŏmĭkt) *n.* [Gk. *amphi*, both ; *apo*, away ; *miktos*, mixed.] A biotype reproduced from facultative sexual forms.

amphiarthrosis (ăm′fĭârthrō′sĭs) *n.* [Gk. *amphi*, both ; *arthron*, joint.] A slightly movable articulation, as a symphysis or a syndesmosis.

amphiaster (ăm′fĭăs′tër) *n.* [Gk. *amphi*, both ; *aster*, star.] The two asters connected by the achromatic spindle formed in mitotic cell division ; a sponge spicule star-shaped at both ends.

amphiastral (ăm′fĭăs′trăl) *a.* [Gk. *amphi*, both ; *aster*, star.] *Appl.* a type of mitosis in which true asters are present at the spindle-poles.

amphibian (ămfĭb′ĭăn) *a.* [Gk. *amphi*, both ; *bios*, life.] Adapted for life either on land or in water ; emersed, *q.v.*

amphibiotic (ăm′fĭbĭŏt′ĭk) *a.* [Gk. *amphi*, both ; *biotikos*, *pert.* life.] Living in water as a larva, on land in the adult stage.

amphibious,—amphibian, amphibiotic.

amphiblastic (ăm′fĭblăs′tĭk) *a.* [Gk. *amphi*, both ; *blastos*, bud.] *Appl.* telolecithal ova with complete but unequal segmentation.

amphiblastula (ăm′fĭblăs′tūlă) *n.* [Gk. *amphi*, both ; *blastos*, bud.] Stage in development of certain sponges, in which posterior end of embryo is composed of granular archaeocytes, and anterior end of flagellate cells.

amphibolic (ăm′fĭbŏl′ĭk) *a.* [Gk. *amphi*, both ; *bole*, throw.] Capable of turning backwards or forwards, as outer toe of certain birds.

amphicarpous (ăm′fĭkâr′pŭs) *a.* [Gk. *amphi*, both ; *karpos*, fruit.] Producing fruit of two kinds, amphicarpic.

amphicoelous (ăm′fĭsē′lŭs) *a.* [Gk. *amphi*, both ; *koilos*, hollow.] Concave on both surfaces ; *appl.* biconcave vertebral centra ; amphicelous.

amphicondylous (ăm′fĭkŏn′dĭlŭs) *a.* [Gk. *amphi*, both; *kondylos*, knuckle.] Having two occipital condyles.

amphicone (ăm′fĭkōn) *n.* [Gk. *amphi*, both ; *konos*, cone.] Cusp of molar of extinct mammals, believed to have evolved into metacone and paracone.

amphicribral,—amphiphloic.

amphicytes (ăm′fĭsīts) *n. plu.* [Gk. *amphi*, both ; *kytos*, hollow.] Endothelial cells surrounding, or forming, capsules of cells of a dorsal root ganglion ; capsule cells.

amphidelphic (ăm′fĭdĕl′fĭk) *a.* [Gk. *amphi*, both ; *delphys*, womb.] Having a paired uterus, as in certain nematodes ; didelphic.

amphidetic (ăm′fĭdĕt′ĭk) *a.* [Gk. *amphi*, both ; *detos*, bound.] Extending behind and in front of umbo ; *appl.* hinge ligaments of some bivalve shells ; *cf.* opisthodetic.

amphidial (ămfĭd′ĭăl) *a.* [Gk. *amphi*, both.] *Pert.* amphids ; *appl.* a unicellular gland in nematodes.

amphidiploid (ăm′fĭdĭp′loid) *a.* [Gk. *amphi*, both ; *diploos*, double.] Double diploid ; allotetraploid. *n.* A hybrid having diploid genomes of both parental species.

amphidisc (ăm′fĭdĭsk) *n.* [Gk. *amphi*, both ; *diskos*, round plate.] A grapnel-shaped spicule of some freshwater sponges.

amphids (ăm'fĭdz) *n. plu.* [Gk. *amphi*, both.] Two anterior lateral chemoreceptive organs in nematodes.

amphigastria (ăm'fĭgăs'trĭă) *n. plu.* [Gk. *amphi*, both ; *gaster*, stomach.] Rudimentary leaves, or scales, on under surface of foliose liverworts.

amphigenesis (ăm'fĭjĕn'ēsĭs) *n.* [Gk. *amphi*, both ; *genesis*, descent.] Amphigony ; sexual reproduction.

amphigenous (ămfĭj'ēnŭs) *a.* [Gk. *amphi*, both ; *-genes*, producing.] Borne or growing on both sides of a structure, as of a leaf ; perigenous, *q.v.*

amphigonic (ăm'fĭgŏn'ĭk) *a.* [Gk. *amphi*, both ; *gone*, seed.] Producing male and female gametes in separate gones in different individuals ; bisexual ; *pert.* amphigony ; *cf.* digonic, syngonic.

amphigony (ămfĭg'ōnĭ) *n.* [Gk. *amphi*, both ; *gonos*, offspring.] Reproduction involving two individuals ; amphigenesis.

amphigynous (ămfĭj'ĭnŭs) *a.* [Gk. *amphi*, both ; *gyne*, female.] *Appl.* antheridium surrounding the base of the oogonium, as in some Peronosporales.

amphikaryon (ăm'fĭkăr'ĭŏn) *n.* [Gk. *amphi*, both ; *karyon*, nut.] An amphinucleus or nucleus with large karyosome (in reference to supposed encapsuling of kinetic nucleus by trophic nucleus) ; nucleus with two haploid sets of chromosomes.

amphimict (ăm'fĭmĭkt) *n.* [Gk. *amphi*, both ; *miktos*, mixed.] A biotype resulting from sexual reproduction ; an obligate sexual organism.

amphimixis (ăm'fĭmĭk'sĭs) *n.* [Gk. *amphi*, both ; *mixis*, mingling.] The mingling of paternal and maternal characteristics by union of male and female pronuclei in fertilisation. *Opp.* apomixis.

amphinucleolus (ăm'fĭnūklē'ōlŭs) *n.* [Gk. *amphi*, both ; L. *nucleolus*, a small kernel.] A double nucleolus comprising basiphil and oxyphil components.

amphinucleus,—amphikaryon, *q.v.*

amphiodont (ăm'fĭōdŏnt) *a.* [Gk. *amphi*, both ; *odous*, tooth.] *Appl.* an intermediate state of mandible development in stag-beetles.

amphiont (ăm'fĭŏnt) *n.* [Gk. *amphi*, both ; *on*, being.] Zygote or sporont formed by coming together of two individuals.

amphiphloic,—periphloic, *q.v.*

amphiplatyan (ăm'fĭplătĭăn) *a.* [Gk. *amphi*, both ; *platys*, flat.] Flat on both ends ; *appl.* vertebral centra.

amphipneustic (ăm'fĭnū'stĭk, -pn-) *a.* [Gk. *amphi*, both ; *pnein*, to breathe.] Having both gills and lungs throughout life-history ; with only anterior and posterior pairs of spiracles functioning, as in most dipterous larvae ; amphipneustous.

amphipodous (ămfĭp'ōdŭs) *a.* [Gk. *amphi*, both ; *pous*, foot.] Having feet for walking and feet for swimming.

amphipyrenin (ăm'fĭpīrē'nĭn) *n.* [Gk. *amphi*, both ; *pyren*, fruit-stone.] Substance of which nuclear membrane is composed.

amphirhinal (ăm'fĭrī'năl) *a.* [Gk. *amphi*, both ; *rhis*, nose.] Having, or *pert.*, two nostrils.

amphisarca (ăm'fĭsâr'kă) *n.* [Gk. *amphi*, both ; *sarx*, flesh.] A superior indehiscent many-seeded fruit with pulpy interior and woody exterior.

amphispermous (ăm'fĭspĕr'mŭs) *a.* [Gk. *amphi*, both ; *sperma*, seed.] Having seed closely surrounded by pericarp.

amphisporangiate (ăm'fĭspōrăn'jĭăt) *a.* [Gk. *amphi*, both ; *sporos*, seed ; *anggeion*, vessel.] Having sporophylls bearing both megasporangia and microsporangia ; hermaphrodite, *appl.* flowers.

amphispore (ăm'fĭspōr') *n.* [Gk. *amphi*, both ; *sporos*, seed.] A reproductive spore which functions as a resting spore in certain algae ; mesospore ; a uredospore modified to withstand dry environment.

amphisternous (ăm′fĭstĕr′nŭs) *a.* [Gk. *amphi*, both ; *sternon*, breastbone.] *Appl.* type of sternum structure in Atelostomata.

amphistomatic (ăm′fĭstŏmăt′ĭk) *a.* [Gk. *amphi*, both ; *stoma*, mouth.] Having stomata on both surfaces, *appl.* certain types of leaves.

amphistomous (ămfĭs′tŏmŭs) *a.* [Gk. *amphi*, both ; *stoma*, mouth.] Having a sucker at each end of body, as certain worms.

amphistylic (ăm′fĭstĭl′ĭk) *a.* [Gk. *amphi*, both ; *stylos*, pillar.] Having jaw arch connected with skull by both hyoid and quadrate, or by both hyoid and palato-quadrate ; exhibiting condition of amphistyly.

amphitene (ăm′fĭtēn) *a.* [Gk. *amphi*, both ; *tainia*, band.] Stage of meiosis in which spireme threads are uniting in pairs ; zygotene.

amphithecium (ămfĭthē′sĭŭm) *n.* [Gk. *amphi*, both ; *thekion*, box.] Peripheral layer of cells in sporangia of liverworts and mosses.

amphitoky (ămfĭt′ŏkĭ) *n.* [Gk. *amphi*, both ; *tokos*, birth.] Parthenogenetic reproduction of both males and females.

amphitriaene (ăm′fĭtrī′ēn) *n.* [Gk. *amphi*, both ; *triaina*, trident.] A double trident-shaped spicule.

amphitrichous (ămfĭt′rĭkŭs) *a.* [Gk. *amphi*, both ; *thrix*, hair.] With a flagellum at each pole ; *appl.* bacteria ; amphitrichate, amphitrichic.

amphitrocha (ămfĭt′rŏkă) *n.* [Gk. *amphi*, both ; *trochos*, wheel.] A free-swimming annelid larva with two rings of cilia.

amphitropous (ămfĭt′rŏpŭs) *a.* [Gk. *amphi*, both ; *trope*, turning.] Having the ovule inverted, with hilum in middle of one side.

amphivasal (ăm′fĭvā′săl, -zăl) *a.* [Gk. *amphi*, both ; L. *vas*, vessel.] With primary xylem surrounding, or on two sides of centric phloem, *appl.* vascular bundle ; amphixylic, perixylic. *Opp.* amphicribral, amphiphloic, periphloic.

amphixylic,—perixylic, *q.v.*

amphocyte (ăm′fŏsīt) *n.* [Gk. *ampho*, both of two ; *kytos*, hollow.] An amphophil cell.

amphogenic (ăm′fŏjĕn′ĭk) *a.* [Gk. *ampho*, both of two ; *-genes*, producing.] Producing offspring consisting of both males and females.

amphophil (ăm′fŏfĭl) *a.* [Gk. *ampho*, both of two ; *philein*, to love.] *Appl.* cells staining with basic and acid dyes ; amphochromatophil ; neutrophil. *n.* Amphocyte.

amphoteric (am′fŏtĕr′ĭk) *a.* [Gk. *amphotere*, in both ways.] With opposite characters ; acidic and also basic.

amplectant (ămplĕk′tănt) *a.* [L. *amplecti*, to embrace.] Clasping or winding tightly round some support, as tendrils.

amplexicaul (ămplĕk′sĭkôl) *a.* [L. *amplecti*, to embrace ; *caulis*, stem.] Clasping or surrounding the stem, as base of leaf.

amplexus (ămplĕk′sŭs) *n.* [L. *amplexus*, embrace.] Sexual embrace, in batrachians.

ampliate (ăm′plĭāt) *a.* [L. *ampliatus*, made wider.] Having outer edge of wing prominent, as in certain insects.

amplification (ăm′plĭfĭkā′shŭn) *n.* [L. *amplificatio*, enlargement.] Changes towards increased structural or functional complexity in ontogeny or phylogeny. *Opp.* reduction.

ampulla (ămpool′ă, -pŭl′-) *n.* [L. *ampulla*, flask.] A membranous vesicle ; dilatation of a lactiferous tubule beneath areola ; dilated portion at one end of each semicircular canal of ear ; dilatation of united common bile-duct and pancreatic duct ; part of oviduct between infundibulum and isthmus ; dilated portion of vas deferens at fundus of urinary bladder ; terminal dilatation of rectum ; pit in skeleton of Hydrocorallina, for medusa ; internal reservoir on ring canal of water-vascular system in echinoderms ; terminal vesicle of sensory canals of elasmobranchs ; submerged bladder of Utricularia.

ampullaceal (ămpŭlā'sēăl) *a.* [L. *ampulla,* flask.] Flask-shaped, *appl.* arachnid spinning glands which furnish silk for foundations, lines, and radii ; *appl.* sensillae.

ampullaceous (ămpŭlā'sēŭs) *a.* [L. *ampulla,* flask.] Flask-shaped ; *appl.* sensillae.

ampullary (ămpool'ărĭ, -pŭl'-) *a.* [L. *ampulla,* flask.] *Pert.* or resembling an ampulla.

ampullula (ămpool'ūlă, -pŭl-) *n.* [*Dim.* of L. *ampulla,* flask.] A small ampulla, as of some lymphatic vessels.

ampyx (ăm'pĭks) *n.* [Gk. *ampyx,* fillet.] A transverse bar connecting the rostralia of Palaeospondylus.

amyelinic (āmīĕlĭn'ĭk) *a.* [Gk. *a,* without ; *myelos,* marrow.] Without myelin ; *appl.* non-medullated or grey nerve-fibres ; amyelinate.

amygdala (ămĭg'dălă) *n.* [L. from Gk. *amygdale,* almond.] Almond ; one of palatal tonsils ; rounded lobe at side of vallecula of cerebellum.

amygdalin (ămĭg'dălĭn) *n.* [Gk. *amygdale,* almond.] A compound occurring in fruit kernels of bitter almonds and other Rosaceae, and producing hydrocyanic acid, glucose and benzaldehyde upon hydrolysis ; $C_{20}H_{27}O_{11}N$.

amylase (ăm'ĭlās) *n.* [L. *amylum,* starch.] An enzyme which converts (α) starch into dextrin, or (β) dextrin into maltose ; amylolytic enzyme.

amyliferous (ăm'ĭlĭf'erŭs) *a.* [L. *amylum,* starch ; *ferre,* to carry.] Containing or producing starch.

amyloclastic,—amylolytic, *q.v.*

amyloid (ăm'ĭloid) *a.* [Gk. *amylon,* starch ; *eidos,* form.] Starch-like. *n.* Starch-like substance.

amyloid bodies,—concretions found in alveoli of adult prostate gland.

amylolytic (ăm'ĭlōlĭt'ĭk) *a.* [Gk. *amylon,* starch ; *lysis,* loosing.] Starch-digesting, *appl.* enzymes.

amylome (ăm'ĭlōm) *n.* [Gk. *amylon,* starch.] Starch-containing wood-parenchyma ; layer of starch-containing cells between central cylinder and leptoids of certain moss rhizomes.

amyloplast (ăm'ĭlōplăst') *n.* [Gk. *amylon,* starch ; *plastos,* formed.] A leucoplast or colourless starch-forming granule in plants; amyloplastid.

amylopsin (ăm'ĭlŏp'sĭn) *n.* [Gk. *amylon,* starch ; *opson,* seasoning.] Pancreatic amylase.

amylose (ăm'ĭlōs) *n.* [L. *amylum,* starch.] The substance forming starch.

amylostatolith (ăm'ĭlōstăt'ōlĭth) *n.* [Gk. *amylon,* starch ; *statos,* stationary ; *lithos,* stone.] A starch grain which moves under the influence of gravity in a statocyte ; *cf.* statolith.

amylum (ăm'ĭlŭm) *n.* [L. *amylum,* starch.] Vegetable starch ; $(C_6H_{10}O_5)_x$.

anabiosis (ăn'ăbīō'sĭs) *n.* [Gk. *ana,* up ; *bios,* life.] Resuscitation after apparent death ; power of revivification, as seen in certain Tardigrada.

anabolism (ănăb'ŏlĭzm) *n.* [Gk. *ana,* up ; *bole,* throw.] The constructive chemical processes in living organisms, *opp.* katabolism.

anabolite (ănăb'ōlīt) *n.* [Gk. *ana,* up ; *bole,* throw.] A substance participating in anabolism.

anacanthous (ăn'ăkăn'thŭs) *a.* [Gk. *an,* not ; *akantha,* prickle.] Without spines or thorns.

anacrogynous (ănăkrŏj'ĭnŭs) *a.* [Gk. *an,* not ; *akros,* apex ; *gyne,* female.] *Appl.* certain liverworts in which female reproductive bodies do not arise at or near apex of shoot. *Opp.* acrogynous.

anacromyoidian (ănăk'rōmīoid'ĭăn) *a.* [Gk. *ana,* up ; *akros,* apex ; *mys,* muscle ; *eidos,* form.] With syringeal muscles attached at dorsal ends of bronchial semi-rings.

anadromous (ănăd'rōmŭs) *a.* [Gk. *ana,* up ; *dramein,* to run.] *Appl.* fishes which migrate from salt to fresh water annually. *Opp.* catadromous.

anaerobe (ănā′ërōb) *n.* [Gk. *an*, without; *aer*, air; *bios*, life.] An anaerobic organism, capable of living in absence of free oxygen. *Opp.* aerobe. *a.* Anaerobic.

anaerobiosis (ănā′ëröbīō′sĭs) *n.* [Gk. *an*, without; *aer*, air; *biosis*, manner of life.] Existence in absence of free oxygen.

anaesthesia (ănĕsthē′sĭă) *n.* [Gk. *an*, without; *aisthesis*, feeling.] Local or general insensibility.

anagenesis (ăn′ăjĕn′ësĭs) *n.* [Gk. *ana*, again; *genesis*, origin.] Regeneration of tissues; progressive evolution.

anahaemin (ăn′ăhē′mĭn) *n.* [Gk. *ana*, again; *haima*, blood.] A proteid substance of liver, acting in regeneration of erythrocytes; haemopoietic principle.

anakinetic (ăn′ăkĭnĕt′ĭk) *a.* [Gk. *ana*, up; *kinein*, to move.] *Appl.* process which restores energy; *cf.* katakinetic.

anakinetomeres (ăn′ăkĭnē′tömērz) *n. plu.* [Gk. *ana*, up; *kinein*, to move; *meros*, part.] Energy-rich reactive atoms or molecules.

anal (ā′năl) *a.* [L. *anus*, anus.] *Pert.*, or situated at or near, the anus; *appl.* posterior median ventral fin of fishes, margin and vein of insect wing, posterior ventral scute of reptiles, etc.

analogues (ăn′ălŏgz) *n. plu.* [Gk. *analogia*, proportion.] Organs of different plants or animals with like function but of unlike origin.

analogy (ănăl′öjĭ) *n.* [G. *analogia*, proportion.] Resemblance in function though not in structure or development.

anamestic (ănămĕs′tĭk) *a.* [Gk. *ana*, up; *mestos*, filled.] *Appl.* small variable bones filling spaces between larger bones of more fixed position, as in fish skulls.

anamniote (ănăm′nĭōt) *n.* [Gk. *a*, not; *amnion*, foetal membrane.] An animal which has no amnion in embryonic life.

anamorpha (ănămôr′fă) *n. plu.* [Gk. *ana*, backwards; *morphe*, form.] Larvae hatched with incomplete number of segments; *cf.* epimorpha.

anamorphosis (ăn′ămôr′fōsĭs) *n.* [Gk. *ana*, throughout; *morphosis*, shaping.] Evolution from one type to another through a series of gradual changes; excessive or abnormal formation of a plant organ.

anandrous (ănăn′drŭs) *a.* [Gk. *a*, without; *aner*, male.] Without stamens.

anangian (ănăn′jĭăn) *a.* [Gk. *a*, without; *anggeion*, vessel.] *Appl.* worms without a vascular system.

anantherous (ăn′ănthërŭs) *a.* [Gk. *a*, without; *antheros*, flowering.] Without anthers.

ananthous (ănăn′thŭs) *a.* [Gk. *a*, without; *anthos*, flower.] Not flowering; without inflorescence.

anaphase (ăn′ăfāz) *n.* [Gk. *ana*, up; *phasis*, appearance.] A stage in mitosis during divergence of daughter chromosomes; the stages of mitosis up to division of chromatin into chromosomes; *cf.* kataphase.

anaphylaxis (ăn′ăfĭlăk′sĭs) *n.* [Gk. *ana*, up; *phylax*, guard.] Condition of being hypersensitive to a serum or foreign protein, caused by first or sensitising dose.

anaphysis (ănăf′ĭsĭs) *n.* [Gk. *ana*, up; *phyein*, to grow.] An out-growth; a sterigma-like filament in apothecium of certain lichens.

anaphyte (ăn′ăfīt) *n.* [Gk. *ana*, up; *phyton*, plant.] Transverse segment of a shoot; an internode.

anaplasia (ănăplā′zĭă) *n.* [Gk. *ana*, again; *plassein*, to form.] Undifferentiation; reversion to a less differentiated structure.

anaplast (ăn′ăplăst) *n.* [Gk. *ana*, up; *plastos*, formed.] A leucoplastid; anaplastid.

anapleurite (ăn′ăploor′īt) *a.* [Gk. *ana*, up; *pleura*, side.] Upper thoracic pleurite, as in certain Thysanura.

anapophysis (ăn′ăpŏf′ĭsĭs) *n.* [Gk. *ana*, up; *apo*, from; *physis*, origin.] A small dorsal projection rising near transverse process in lumbar vertebrae.

anapsid (ănăp′sĭd) *a.* [Gk. *ana*, up; *apsis*, arch.] With skull wholly imperforate or completely roofed over; stegocrotaphic.

anaptychus (ănăp′tĭkŭs) *n.* [Gk. *ana*, throughout; *ptyche*, plate.] Aptychus or operculum consisting of a single plate, as in certain ammonites; *cf.* synaptychus.

anarthrous (ănâr′thrŭs) *a.* [Gk. *a*, without; *arthron*, joint.] Having no distinct joints.

anaschistic (ăn′ăskĭs′tĭk) *a.* [Gk. *ana*, up to; *schistos*, split.] *Appl.* type of tetrads which divide twice longitudinally in meiosis; *cf.* diaschistic.

anastates (ăn′ăstāts) *n.plu.* [Gk. *ana*, up to; *statos*, standing.] Various materials that arise owing to metabolism in a cell, in formation of complex from simple substances. *Opp.* katastates.

anastomosis (ănăs′tŏmō′sĭs) *n.* [Gk. *ana*, up to; *stoma*, mouth.] Union of ramifications of leaf-veins; union of blood-vessels arising from a common trunk; union of nerves; fine threads joining chromonemata in resting nucleus; formation of a network or anastomotic meshwork.

anastral (ănăs′trăl) *a.* [Gk. *an*, not; *aster*, star.] *Appl.* type of mitosis without aster-formation.

anatomy (ănăt′ŏmĭ) *n.* [Gk. *ana*, up; *tome*, cutting.] The science which treats of the structure of plants and of animals, as determined by dissection; usually, human anatomy.

anatoxin,—toxoid, *q.v.*

anatrepsis (ănătrĕp′sĭs) *n.* [Gk. *anatrepein*, to turn over.] Stage of increasing movement in blastokinesis.

anatriaene (ăn′ătrī′ēn) *n.* [Gk. *ana*, up; *triaina*, trident.] Triaene with backwardly directed branches.

anatropous (ănăt′rŏpŭs) *a.* [Gk. *anatrope*, overturning.] Inverted, *appl.* ovules with hilum and micropyle close together and chalaza at other end; anatropal.

anaxial (ănăk′sĭăl) *a.* [Gk. *a*, without; *axis*, axle.] Having no distinct axis; asymmetrical.

anaxon (ănăk′sŏn) *n.* [Gk. *a*, without; *axon*, axis.] A nerve cell having no evident axon; anaxone.

ancestrula (ănsĕs′troolă) *n.* [L. *antecedere*, to go before.] First zooecium of polyzoan colony.

anchor (ăng′kŏr) *n.* [L. *ancora*, anchor.] Anchor-shaped spicule found in skin of Holothuria.

anchylosis (ăng′kĭlō′sĭs) *n.* [Gk. *angchein*, to press tight.] Union of two or more bones or hard parts to form one part, *e.g.* of bone to bone, or tooth to bone; ankylosis.

ancipital (ănsĭp′ĭtăl) *a.* [L. *anceps*, double.] Flattened and having two edges.

ancistroid,—ankistroid.

anconeal (ăngkō′nēal) *a.* [Gk. *angkon*, elbow.] *Pert.* the elbow.

anconeus (ăngkō′nēŭs) *n.* [Gk. *angkon*, elbow.] Small extensor muscle situated over elbow; anconaeus.

andrase (ăn′drās) *n.* [Gk. *aner*, male.] A male-determining factor in form of an enzyme or hormone.

andric (ăn′drĭk) *a.* [Gk. *andrikos*, masculine.] Male, *opp.* gynic.

andrin (ăn′drĭn) *n.* [Gk. *aner*, male.] The testicular androgens.

androclinium,—clinandrium.

androconia (ăn′drŏkō′nĭă) *n. plu.* [Gk. *aner*, male; *konia*, dust.] Modified wing-scales producing a sexually attractive scent in certain male butterflies.

androcyte (ăn′drŏsīt) *n.* [Gk. *aner*, male; *kytos*, hollow.] A cell arising by growth from an androgonium and giving rise to antherozoid.

androdioecious (ăn′drŏdīē′sĭŭs) *a.* [Gk. *aner*, male; *dis*, two; *oikos*, house.] Having male and hermaphrodite flowers on different plants.

androecium (ăndrē'sĭŭm) *n.* [Gk. *aner*, male; *oikos*, house.] Male reproductive organs of a plant; stamens taken collectively.

androgametangium (ăn'drōgăm'-ētăn'jĭŭm) *n.* [Gk. *aner*, male; *gametes*, spouse; *anggeion*, vessel.] A structure producing male sexual cells; antheridium.

androgen (ăn'drōjĕn) *n.* [Gk. *aner*, male; *genos*, descent.] A male hormone; a masculinising substance.

androgenesis (ăn'drōjĕn'ĕsĭs) *n.* [Gk. *aner*, male; *genesis*, descent.] Development of egg furnished with paternal chromosomes only; male parthenogenesis.

androgenetic (ăn'drōjĕnĕt'ĭk) *a.* [Gk. *aner*, male; *genesis*, descent.] Having paternal chromosomes only.

androgenic (ăn'drōjĕn'ĭk) *a.* [Gk. *aner*, male; *gennaein*, to produce.] Stimulating male characters; masculinising; *appl.* hormones; *appl.* tissue capable of elaborating an androgenic hormone; androgenous, *q.v.*

androgenous (ăndrŏj'ĕnŭs) *a.* [Gk. *aner*, male; *genos*, descent.] Producing only male offspring.

androgonidia (ăn'drōgŏnĭd'ĭă) *n.plu.* [Gk. *aner*, male; *gonos*, offspring; *idion*, *dim.*] Male sexual elements formed after repeated divisions of parthenogonidia of Volvox.

androgonium (ăn'drōgō'nĭŭm) *n.* [Gk. *aner*, male; *gonos*, offspring.] An early stage in formation of sperm-cells of plants.

androgynal (ăndrŏj'ĭnăl) *a.* [Gk. *aner*, male; *gyne*, female.] Hermaphrodite; bearing both staminate and pistillate flowers in the same infloresence; with antheridium and oogonium on the same hypha; androgynous.

androgynary (ăndrŏj'ĭnărĭ) *a.* [Gk. *aner*, male; *gyne*, female.] Having flowers with stamens and pistils developed into petals.

androgyne (ăn'drōjīn, ăn'drōjĭn'ē) *a.*, *n.* Hermaphrodite.

androgynism (ăndrŏj'ĭnĭzm) *n.* [Gk. *aner*, male; *gyne*, female.] The condition of bearing both stamens and pistils; hermaphroditism.

andromerogony (ăn'drōmĕrŏg'ōnĭ) *n.* [Gk. *aner*, male; *meros*, part; *gone*, generation.] The development of an egg fragment with only paternal chromosomes.

andromonoecious (ăn'drōmŏnē'sĭŭs) *a.* [Gk. *aner*, male; *monos*, alone; *oikos*, house.] Having male and hermaphrodite flowers on the same plant.

andropetalous (ăn'drōpĕt'ălŭs) *a.* [Gk. *aner*, male; *petalon*, leaf.] Having petaloid stamens.

androphore (ăn'drōfōr) *n.* [Gk. *aner*, male; *phora*, carrying.] Stalk supporting androecium or stamens; stalk carrying male gonophores in Siphonophora.

androphyll (ăn'drōfĭl) *n.* [Gk. *aner*, male; *phyllon*, leaf.] The leaf bearing microspores; the microsporophyll.

androsome (ăn'drōsōm) *n.* [Gk. *aner*, male; *soma*, body.] A male-limited chromosome.

androsporangium (ăn'drōspōrăn'-jĭŭm) *n.* [Gk. *aner*, male; *sporos*, seed; *anggeion*, vessel.] A sporangium containing androspores.

androspore (ăn'drōspōr) *n.* [Gk. *aner*, male; *sporos*, seed.] An asexual zoospore which gives rise to a male dwarf plant; male spore; microspore; pollen grain.

androsterone (ăn'drōstē'rōn) *n.* [Gk. *aner*, male; *stear*, suet.] Male hormone, present in adrenal cortex, obtained from urine; $C_{19}H_{30}O_2$.

androtype (ăn'drōtīp) *n.* [Gk. *aner*, male; *typos*, pattern.] Type specimen of the male of a species.

anebous (ăn'ēbŭs, anē'bŭs) *a.* [Gk. *anebos*, before manhood.] Immature; before puberty; prepubertal.

anelectrotonus (ăn'ēlĕktrōtō'nŭs, ăn'ēlĕktrŏt'ōnŭs) *n.* [Gk. *ana*, up; *elektron*, amber; *tonos*, tension.] Decrease in irritability of a nerve under influence of a non-polarising electric current.

anellus (ănĕl′ŭs) *n.* [L. *anellus*, little ring.] A small ring-shaped or triangular plate supported by valves and vinculum, in Lepidoptera.

anemochorous (ănĕmökō′rŭs) *a.* [Gk. *anemos*, wind; *chorein*, to spread.] Dispersed by wind; with seeds so dispersed; anemochoric.

anemophilous (ănĕmŏf′ĭlŭs) *a.* [Gk. *anemos*, wind; *philein*, to love.] Wind-pollinated.

anemophily (ănĕmŏf′ĭlĭ) *n.* [Gk. *anemos*, wind; *philein*, to love.] Plant-fertilisation by agency of wind.

anemoplankton (ănĕm′öplăngk′tŏn) *n.* [Gk. *anemos*, wind; *plangktos*, wandering.] Wind-borne organisms and living particles; aeroplankton, *q.v.*

anemosporic (ănĕm′öspŏr′ĭk) *a.* [Gk. *anemos*, wind; *sporos*, seed.] Having spores or seeds disseminated by air currents.

anemotaxis (ănĕm′ötăk′sĭs) *n.* [Gk. *anemos*, wind; *taxis*, arrangement.] Directed movement in response to air currents.

anemotropism (ănĕmŏt′röpĭzm) *n.* [Gk. *anemos*, wind; *trope*, turn.] Orientation of body, or plant curvature, in response to air currents.

anencephaly (ănĕnkĕf′ălĭ, -sĕf′-) *n.* [Gk. *an*, not; *engkephalon*, brain.] Condition of having no brain.

anenterous (ănĕn′tërŭs) *a.* [Gk. *an*, without; *enteron*, gut.] Having no alimentary tract; anenteric.

aner (ān′ër, ănār) *n.* [Gk. *aner*, male.] The male of insects, especially of ants.

anestrum,—anoestrus, *q.v.*

aneucentric (ănūsĕn′trĭk) *a.* [Gk. *a*, without; *eu*, well; *kentron*, centre.] Acentric and dicentric, resulting from translocation involving centromere of a chromosome.

aneuploid (ăn′ūploid) *a.* [Gk. *a*, without; *eu*, well; *aploos*, onefold.] Having fewer or more chromosomes than an exact multiple of the haploid number, *opp.* euploid.

aneurine (ănū′rĭn) *n.* [Gk. *a*, without; *neuron*, nerve.] Vitamin B_1, the anti-beri-beri factor in yeast, legumes, cereals, and other foods; aneurin; thiamine (U.S.A.); $C_{12}H_{18}ON_4SCl_2$.

aneuronic (ănūrŏn′ĭk) *a.* [Gk. *a*, without; *neuron*, nerve.] Without innervation; *appl.* chromatophores controlled by hormones.

anfractuose (ănfrăk′tūōs) *a.* [L. *anfractus*, bending.] Wavy, sinuous.

angienchyma (ăn′jĭĕng′kĭmă) *n.* [Gk. *anggeion*, vessel; *engchein*, to pour.] Vascular tissue.

angioblast (ăn′jĭöblăst) *n.* [Gk. *anggeion*, vessel; *blastos*, bud.] One of cells from which lining of blood-vessels is derived; vasoformative cell.

angiocarpic (ăn′jĭökâr′pĭk) *a.* [Gk. *anggeion*, vessel; *karpos*, fruit.] Having fruit enclosed; angiocarpous; *appl.* fungi. *Opp.* gymnocarpic.

angiology (ăn′jĭŏl′öjĭ) *n.* [Gk. *anggeion*, vessel; *logos*, discourse.] Anatomy of blood and lymph vascular systems.

angiospermous (ănjĭöspër′mŭs) *a.* [Gk. *anggeion*, vessel; *sperma*, seed.] Having seeds in a closed case, the ovary.

angiosporous (ănjĭŏs′pörŭs) *a.* [Gk. *anggeion*, vessel; *sporos*, seed.] Having spores contained in a theca or spore capsule.

angiostomatous (ăn′jĭöstŏm′ătŭs) *a.* [Gk. *anggeion*, vessel; *stoma*, mouth.] Narrow-mouthed, *appl.* an order of molluscs, and to a sub-order of snakes, with non-distensible mouth.

angiotonin (ănjĭŏt′ŏnĭn) *n.* [Gk. *anggeion*, vessel; *tonos*, tension.] Substance in circulating blood, formed by reaction between hypertensinogen elaborated in the liver, and renin, causing constriction of arterioles; hypertensin.

ångström (ông′strëm) *n.* [*A. J. Ångström*, Swedish physicist.] One ten millionth part of a millimetre, symbol Å.

angular (ăng'gūlăr) *n.* [L. *angulus*, corner.] A membrane bone of lower jaw in most vertebrates. *a.* Having, or *pert.*, an angle; *appl.* leaf originating at forking of stem, as in many ferns; *appl.* collenchyma with cell-walls thickened in the angles of the cells; *appl.* line of junction, or collarette, between pupillary and ciliary zones of iris.

angulosplenial (ăng'gūlösplē'nĭăl) *n.* [L. *angulus*, corner; *splenium*, patch.] Bone forming most of lower and inner part of mandible in Amphibia.

angulus (ăng'gūlŭs) *n.* [L. *angulus*, angle.] An angle, as that formed by junction of manubrium and body of sternum (angle of Louis).

angustifoliate (ănggŭs'tĭfō'lĭăt) *a.* [L. *angustus*, narrow; *folium*, leaf.] With narrow leaves.

angustirostrate (ănggŭs'tĭrŏs'trāt) *a.* [L. *angustus*, narrow; *rostrum*, beak.] With narrow beak or snout.

anholocyclic (ăn'hŏlösĭk'lĭk) *a.* [Gk. *an*, not; *holos*, whole; *kyklos*, circle.] *Pert.* alternation of generations with suppression of sexual part of cycle; permanently parthenogenetic.

anidian (ănĭd'ĭăn) *a.* [Gk. *an*, not; *eidos*, form.] Formless; *appl.* blastoderm without apparent embryonic axis.

animal pole,—the upper, more rapidly segmenting, portion of a telolecithal egg. *Opp.* vegetal pole.

animal starch,—glycogen.

anion (ăn'īŏn, ăn'ĭŏn) *n.* [Gk. *ana*, up; *ienai*, to go.] A negatively-charged particle or ion which moves up towards the anode or positive pole.

anisocarpous (ănĭsökâr'pŭs) *a.* [Gk. *anisos*, unequal; *karpos*, fruit.] Having number of carpels less than that of other floral whorls.

anisocercal (ănĭsösĕr'kăl) *a.* [Gk. *anisos*, unequal; *kerkos*, tail.] With lobes of tail-fin unequal.

anisochela (ănĭsökē'lă) *n.* [Gk. *anisos*, unequal; *chele*, claw.] A chela with the two parts unequally developed.

anisodactylous (ănĭsödăk'tĭlŭs) *a.* [Gk. *anisos*, unequal; *daktylos*, finger.] Having unequal toes, three toes forward, one backward.

anisodont (ăn'īsödŏnt) *a.* [Gk. *anisos*, unequal; *odous*, tooth.] Having differentiated teeth; heterodont. *Opp.* isodont.

anisogamete (ăn'īsögămēt) *n.* [Gk. *anisos*, unequal; *gametes*, spouse.] One of two conjugating gametes differing in form or size.

anisogametism,—the production of anisogametes, as of macrogametes and microgametes; anisogamety.

anisogamous (ănĭsŏg'ămŭs) *a.* [Gk. *anisos*, unequal; *gamos*, marriage.] *Appl.* differentiated gametes or conjugating bodies.

anisogamy (ănĭsŏg'ămĭ) *n.* [Gk. *anisos*, unequal; *gametes*, spouse.] Conjugation between sharply differentiated gametes; heterogamy.

anisognathous (ăn'īsŏg'năthŭs) *a.* [Gk. *anisos*, unequal; *gnathos*, jaw.] With jaws of unequal width; having teeth in upper and lower jaws unlike.

anisomeres (ăn'īsömērz) *n. plu.* [Gk. *anisos*, unequal; *meros*, part.] Homologous parts or polyisomeres when differing amongst themselves; *cf.* polyanisomere.

anisomerogamy,—anisogamy.

anisomerous (ănĭsŏm'ërŭs) *a.* [Gk. *anisos*, unequal; *meros*, part.] Having unequal numbers of parts in floral whorls.

anisomorphic (ăn'īsömôr'fĭk) *a.* [Gk. *anisos*, unequal; *morphe*, form.] Differing in shape, size, or structure.

anisophylly (ăn'īsöfĭl'ĭ) *n.* [Gk. *anisos*, unequal; *phyllon*, leaf.] Condition of having leaves of two or more sizes or shapes, as in some conifers and aquatic plants.

anisopleural (ănĭsöploo'răl) *a.* [Gk. *anisos*, unequal; *pleura*, side.] Asymmetrical bilaterally.

anisoploid (ăn′īsöploid) *a.* [Gk. *anisos*, unequal; *aploos*, onefold; *eidos*, form.] With an odd number of chromosome sets in somatic cells. *n.* An anisoploid individual.

anisopogonous (ănīsöpōg′önŭs) *a.* [Gk. *anisos*, unequal; *pogon*, beard.] Unequally webbed, with reference to feathers.

anisopterus (ănīsŏp′tërŭs) *a.* [Gk. *anisos*, unequal; *pteron*, wing.] Unequally winged; *appl.* seeds.

anisospore (ănīsöspōr′) *n.* [Gk. *anisos*, unequal; *sporos*, seed.] A dimorphic spore, the sexes differing in size.

anisostemonous (ănīsöstĕm′önŭs) *a.* [Gk. *anisos*, unequal; *stemon*, spun thread.] Having the number of stamens unequal to the number of parts in other floral whorls; having stamens of unequal size.

anisotropic (ănīsötrŏp′ĭk) *a.* [Gk. *anisos*, unequal; *trope*, turn.] *Appl.* eggs with predetermined axis or axes; exhibiting anisotropy; doubly refracting, *appl.* dark bands of voluntary muscle fibre. *Opp.* isotropic.

ankistroid (ăng′kĭstroĭd) *a.* [Gk. *agkistron*, fish-hook; *eidos*, form.] Like a barb; barbed.

ankylosis,—anchylosis, *q.v.*

ankyroid (ăng′kĭroid) *a.* [Gk. *agkyra*, hook; *eidos*, form.] Hook-shaped.

anlage (ân′lâgë) *n.* [Ger. *Anlage*, predisposition.] The first structure or cell group indicating development of a part or organ; inception, primordium, ébauche.

annectent (ănĕk′tënt) *a.* [L. *annectere*, to bind together.] Linking, *appl.* intermediate species or genera.

annelid (ăn′ëlĭd) *a.* [L. *annulus*, ring; Gk. *eidos*, form.] Constructed of ring-like segments, as ringed worms; *pert.* Annelida.

annotinous (ănnō′tĭnŭs) *a.* [L. *annus*, year.] A year old; *appl.* growth during the previous year.

annual (ăn′ūăl) *a.* [L. *annus*, year.] *Appl.* structures or features that are marked off or completed yearly; living for a year only.

annual ring,—one of the rings, seen in transverse sections of dicotyledons, indicating the secondary growth during a year; growth ring of bivalve shells.

annular (ăn′ūlăr) *a.* [L. *annulus*, ring.] Ring-like; *appl.* certain ligaments of wrist and ankle; *appl.* (orbicular) ligament encircling head of radius and attached to radial notch of ulna; *appl.* certain lamina or sternal plates in ants; *appl.* certain vessels in xylem, owing to ring-like thickenings in their interior; *appl.* bands formed on inner surface of cell-wall.

annulate (ăn′ūlāt) *a.* [L. *annulus*, ring.] Ring-shaped; composed of ring-like segments; having colour arranged in ring-like bands or annuli.

annulus (ăn′ūlŭs) *n.* [L. *annulus*, ring.] Any ring-like structure; special ring in fern sporangium, by action of which sporangium bursts; remains of veil in mushrooms; ring of cells in moss capsule whose rupture causes opening; circular groove for transverse flagellum in Dinoflagellata; ring of annelid; growth ring of fish scale; fourth digit of hand.

anococcygeal (ā′nökŏksĭj′ëăl) *a.* [L. *anus*, anus; *coccyx*; Gk. *kokkyx*, cuckoo.] *Pert.* region between coccyx and anus; *appl.* body of fibrous and muscular tissue, nerves, etc.

anoestrus (ănē′strŭs) *n.* [Gk. *an*, not; *oistros*, gad-fly.] The non-breeding period; period of absence of sexual urge; anoestrum; *cf.* dioestrus.

anomaly (ănŏm′ălĭ) *n.* [Gk. *anomalos*, uneven.] Any departure from type characteristics.

anomophyllous (ăn′ŏmöfĭl′ŭs) *a.* [Gk. *anomos*, lawless; *phyllon*, leaf.] With irregularly placed leaves.

anorganology (ăn′ôrgănŏl′öjĭ) *n.* [Gk. *a*, not; *organon*, instrument; *logos*, discourse.] Study of non-living things; abiology.

anorthogenesis (ăn′ôrthöjĕn′ësĭs) *n.* [Gk. *an*, not; *orthos*, straight; *genesis*, descent.] Evolution manifesting changes in direction of adaptations, owing to preadaptation; 'zigzag' evolution.

anorthospiral (ăn′ôrthöspī′răl) *a.* [Gk. *an*, not; *orthos*, straight; *speira*, coil.] Relationally coiled, spirals not interlocking; paranemic. *Opp.* orthospiral, plectonemic.

anosmatic (ănŏsmăt′ĭk) *a.* [Gk. *a*, without; *osme*, smell.] Having no sense of smell; anosmic.

anosmia (ănŏs′mĭă) *n.* [Gk. *a*, without; *osme*, smell.] Absence or loss of sense of smell.

anoxybiotic (ănŏk′sĭbīŏt′ĭk) *a.* [Gk. *a*, not; *oxys*, sharp; *biotos*, means of life.] Capable of living in absence of oxygen; anaerobic.

ansa (ăn′să) *n.* [L. *ansa*, handle.] Loop, as of certain nerves.

anserine (ăn′sërĭn) *n.* [L. *anser*, goose.] A constituent of muscle of fishes, reptiles, and birds; $C_{10}H_{16}O_3N_4$.

ansiform (ăn′sĭfôrm) *a.* [L. *ansa*, handle; *forma*, shape.] Loop-shaped; looped; *appl.* outer cytoplasm in cerebro-spinal ganglia.

antagonist (ăntăg′önĭst) *n.* [Gk. *antagonistes*, adversary.] A muscle acting in opposition to the action produced by a prime mover or agonist; an antihormone, *q.v.*

antambulacral (ănt′ămbūlā′krăl) *a.* [Gk. *anti*, against; L. *ambulare*, to walk.] Not situated on the ambulacral area; abactinal, *q.v.*

antapex (ăntăp′ĕks) *n.* [Gk. *anti*, opposite; L. *apex*, tip.] Tip of hypocone in Dinoflagellata.

antapical (ăntăp′ĭkăl) *a.* [Gk. *anti*, opposite; L. *apex*, tip.] At or *pert.* antapex; *pert.* region opposite apex.

antebrachium (ăn′tëbrā′kĭŭm) *n.* [L. *ante*, before; *brachium*, arm.] The fore-arm, or corresponding portion of a fore-limb.

anteclypeus (ăn′tëklĭp′ëŭs) *n.* [L. *ante*, before; *clypeus*, shield.] Anterior portion of clypeus when differentiated by suture; *cf.* post-clypeus.

antecosta (ăntëkŏs′tă) *n.* [L. *ante*, before; *costa*, rib.] Internal ridge of tergum, for attachment of intersegmental muscles in insects, extended to phragma in alar segments.

antecubital (ăn′tëkū′bĭtăl) *a.* [L. *ante*, before; *cubitus*, elbow.] Anterior to the elbow.

antedorsal (ăn′tëdôr′săl) *a.* [L. *ante*, before; *dorsum*, back.] Situated in front of dorsal fin in fishes.

antefrons (ăn′tëfrŏnz) *n.* [L. *ante*, before; *frons*, forehead.] The portion of frons anterior to antennary base line in certain insects.

antefurca (ăn′tëfŭr′kă) *n.* [L. *ante*, in front; *furca*, fork.] Forked process or sternal apodeme of anterior thoracic segment in insects.

antelabrum (ăntëlā′brŭm) *n.* [L. *ante*, before; *labrum*, lip.] The anterior portion of insect labrum when differentiated.

antemarginal (ăn′tëmâr′jĭnăl) *a.* [L. *ante*, before; *margo*, edge.] *Appl.* sori of ferns when they lie within margin of frond.

antenna (ăntĕn′ă) *n.* [L. *antenna*, sail-yard.] A jointed feeler on head of various Arthropoda.

antennary (ăntĕn′ărĭ) *a.* [L. *antenna*, sail-yard.] Like, or *pert.*, or situated near an antenna; antennal.

antennifer (ăntĕn′ĭfër) *n.* [L. *antenna*, sail-yard; *ferre*, to carry.] Socket of antenna in arthropods; projection on rim of antennal socket, acting as a pivot, in myriopods.

antennule (ăntĕn′ūl) *n.* [L. *dim.* from *antenna*.] A small antenna or feeler, specifically the first pair of antennae in Crustacea.

anteposition (ăn′tëpözĭsh′ŭn) *n.* [L. *ante*, before; *ponere*, to place.] Superposition of whorls in a flower typically alternating.

anterior (ăntē′rĭŏr) *a.* [L. *anterior*, former.] Nearer head end; ventral in human anatomy; facing outwards from axis; previous.

anterolateral,—ventrolateral.

antesternite (ăn′tĕstĕr′nīt) *n.* [L. *ante*, before; *sternum*, breast-bone.] Anterior sternal sclerite of insects; basisternum, eusternum.

anthela (ănthē′lă) *n.* [Gk. *anthein*, to bloom.] The cymose inflorescence of the rush family.

anthelix,—antihelix.

anther (ăn′thĕr) *n.* [Gk. *antheros*, flowering.] The part of a stamen which produces pollen.

antherid,—antheridium.

antheridia,—*plu.* of antheridium.

antheridial cell,—the larger of two cells derived from a microspore and giving rise to an antheridium, or to a cell representing an antheridium.

antheridiophore (ănthĕrĭd′ĭöfōr) *n.* [Gk. *anthos*, flower; *idion*, *dim.*; *pherein*, to bear.] A gametophore bearing antheridia.

antheridium (ănthĕrĭd′ĭŭm) *n.* [Gk. *anthos*, flower; *idion*, *dim.*] An organ or receptacle in which male sexual cells are produced in many cryptogams; male gametangium; cluster of microgametes, as in certain Flagellata.

antherophore (ăn′thĕröfōr) *n.* [Gk. *antheros*, flowering; *pherein*, to bear.] The stalk of a stamen bearing several anthers, in male cone of certain gymnosperms.

antherozoids (ăn′thĕrözō′ĭdz), **antherozooids** (ăn′thĕrözō′oidz) *n. plu.* [Gk. *anthos*, flower; *zoon*, animal; *eidos*, form.] Male sexual cells in antheridia.

anthesis (ănthē′sĭs) *n.* [Gk. *anthos*, flower.] Stage or period at which flower-bud opens; flowering; period of flowering.

anthoblast (ăn′thöblăst) *n.* [Gk. *anthos*, flower; *blastos*, bud.] In Madreporaria, a young sessile polyp producing anthocyathus.

anthocarpous (ăn′thökâr′pŭs) *a.* [Gk. *anthos*, flower; *karpos*, fruit.] *Appl.* aggregated fruits, products of fusion of several flowers, as sorosis and syconus.

anthocaulis (ăn′thökôl′ĭs) *n.* [Gk. *anthos*, flower; L. *caulis*, stem.] The pedicle of a late trophozooid stage of madrepore development.

anthochlore (ăn′thöklōr) *n.* [Gk. *anthos*, flower; *chloros*, yellow.] A yellow pigment dissolved in cell-sap of corolla, as of primrose.

anthocodia (ăn′thökō′dĭă) *n.* [Gk. *anthos*, flower; *kodeia*, head.] The distal portion of a zooid bearing mouth and tentacles, in Alcyonaria.

anthocyanin (ăn′thösī′ănĭn) *n.* [Gk. *anthos*, flower; *kyanos*, dark blue.] One of the blue or violet pigments of flowers, leaves, and stems.

anthocyathus (ăn′thösī′ăthŭs) *n.* [Gk. *anthos*, flower; *kyathos*, cup.] The discoid crown of trophozooid stage in madrepore development.

anthodium (ănthō′dĭŭm) *n.* [Gk. *anthos*, flower; *eidos*, form.] Capitulum or head of Compositae.

anthogenesis (ăn′thöjĕn′ësĭs) *n.* [Gk. *anthos*, flower; *genesis*, descent.] In certain aphids, production of both males and females by asexual forms.

anthophilous (ănthŏf′ĭlŭs) *a.* [Gk. *anthos*, flower; *philein*, to love.] Attracted by flowers; feeding on flowers.

anthophore (ăn′thöfōr) *n.* [Gk. *anthos*, flower; *pherein*, to bear.] Elongation of thalamus between calyx and corolla.

anthophyte (ăn′thöfīt) *n.* [Gk. *anthos*, flower; *phyton*, plant.] A flowering plant; phaenogam, phanerogam, spermatophyte.

anthostrobilus (ăn′thöstrŏb′ĭlŭs) *n.* [Gk. *anthos*, flower; *strobilos*, fir-cone.] Fructification or flower of certain cycads.

anthotaxis (ăn′thötăk′sĭs) *n.* [Gk. *anthos*, flower; *taxis*, arrangement.] Arrangement of flowers on an axis.

anthoxanthin (ăn′thözăn′thĭn) *n.* [Gk. *anthos*, flower; *xanthos*, yellow.] A yellow pigment of flowers.

anthracobiontic (ăn′thrăköbīŏn′tĭk) *a.* [Gk. *anthrax*, charcoal; *bionai*, to live.] Growing on burned-over soil or scorched material; *appl.* fungi.

anthropeic (ănthrōpē'ĭk) *a.* [Gk. *anthropeios*, by human means.] Due to influence of man.

anthropogenesis (ăn'thrōpöjĕn'ësĭs) *n.* [Gk. *anthropos*, man ; *genesis*, descent.] The ontogenesis and phylogenesis of man ; descent of man.

anthropogenetic (ăn'thrōpöjĕnĕt'ĭk) *a.* [Gk. *anthropos*, man ; *genesis*, descent.] *Pert.* anthropogenesis.

anthropogenic (ăn'thrōpöjĕn'ĭk) *a.* [Gk. *anthropos*, man ; *genes*, produced.] Produced or caused by man.

anthropoid (ăn'thröpoid) *a.* [Gk. *anthropos*, man ; *eidos*, form.] Resembling man ; *appl.* tailless apes.

anthropology (ăn'thröpŏl'öjĭ) *n.* [Gk. *anthropos*, man ; *logos*, discourse.] The natural history of man.

anthropometry (ăn'thröpŏm'ëtrĭ) *n.* [Gk. *anthropos*, man ; *metron*, measure.] That part of biology dealing with proportional measurements of parts of the human body.

anthropomorphous (ăn'thröpömôr'-fŭs) *a.* [Gk. *anthropos*, man ; *morphe*, shape.] Resembling man.

anthropotomy (ăn'thröpŏt'ömĭ) *n.* [Gk. *anthropos*, man ; *temnein*, to cut.] Human anatomy.

Anthropozoic,—Psychozoic, *q.v.*

antiae (ăn'tĭē) *n. plu.* [L. *antiae*, forelock.] Feathers at base of bill-ridge of some birds.

anti-ambulacral, — antambulacral, abactinal, *q.v.*

anti-apex,—lower end of axis, as in rootless plants.

antiauxin (ăn'tĭôks'ĭn) *n.* [Gk. *anti*, against ; *auxein*, to grow.] Any organic compound which regulates or inhibits growth stimulation by auxins.

antibiosis (ăn'tĭbīō'sĭs) *n.* [Gk. *anti*, against ; *biosis*, way of life.] Antagonistic association of organisms, as by production of harmful compounds.

antiblastic (ăntĭblăs'tĭk) *a.* [Gk. *anti*, against ; *blastos*, bud.] *Appl.* immunity due to forces which inhibit growth of invading organism.

antibody (ăn'tĭbŏd'ĭ) *n.* [Gk. *anti*, against ; A.S. *bodig*, body.] Any substance formed in blood which reacts with a specific antigen, or inactivates or destroys toxins.

antibrachial (ăn'tĭbrā'kĭăl) *a.* [Gk. *anti*, against ; L. *brachium*, arm.] *Pert.* forearm ; *appl.* fascia, muscles, vein, nerves ; also antebrachial.

antibrachium,—antebrachium, *q.v.*

anticipation (ăn'tĭsĭpā'shŭn) *n.* [L. *ante*, before ; *capere*, to take.] The manifestation of a condition or disease at a progressively earlier age in successive generations.

anticlinal (ăn'tĭklī'năl) *a.* [Gk. *anti*, against ; *klinein*, to slope.] *Appl.* line of division of cells at right angles to surface of apex of a growing point ; in quadrupeds, *appl.* one of lower thoracic vertebrae with upright spine towards which those on either side incline.

anticoagulin (ăn'tĭkōăg'ūlĭn) *n.* [Gk. *anti*, against ; L. *coagulum*, rennet.] A substance which prevents coagulation of drawn blood, as hirudin.

anticryptic (ăn'tĭkrĭp'tĭk) *a.* [Gk. *anti*, against ; *kryptos*, hidden.] *Appl.* protective coloration facilitating attack.

anticubital,—antecubital, *q.v.*

antidiuretic (ăn'tĭdīūrĕt'ĭk) *a.* [Gk. *anti*, against ; *dia*, through ; *ouron*, urine.] Reducing the volume of urine ; *appl.* a hormone of posterior lobe of pituitary gland.

antidromic (ăntĭdrŏm'ĭk) *a.* [Gk. *anti*, opposite ; *dromos*, running.] Contrary to normal direction ; *appl.* conduction of impulse along axon towards body of nerve cell ; antidromous ; *appl.* stipules with fused outer margins.

antidromy (ăntĭd'römĭ) *n.* [Gk. *anti*, against ; *dromos*, running.] Condition of spiral phyllotaxis with genetic spiral changing direction after each cycle.

anti-enzyme (ăn'tĭĕn'zīm) *n.* [Gk. *anti*, against; *en*, within; *zyme*, leaven.] A substance which retards or stops enzyme activity.

antigen (ăn'tĭjĕn) *n.* [Gk. *anti*, against; *genos*, birth.] Substance which causes a series of physiologico-chemical changes resulting in formation of antibodies.

antigeny,—sexual dimorphism.

antihelix (ăn'tĭhē'lĭks) *n.* [Gk. *anti*, opposite; *helix*, a convolution.] The curved prominence in front of helix of ear.

antihormones (ăn'tĭhôr'mōnz) *n. plu.* [Gk. *anti*, against; *hormaein*, to excite.] Substances which prevent the effect of hormones; chalones.

antilobium,—tragus, *q.v.*

antilysin (ăn'tĭlī'sĭn) *n.* [Gk. *anti*, against; *lyein*, to dissolve.] A substance which counteracts a lysin or lysis.

antimeres (ăn'tĭmērz) *n. plu.* [Gk. *anti*, opposite; *meros*, part.] Corresponding parts, as left and right limbs, of a bilaterally symmetrical animal; a series of equal radial parts or actinomeres of a radially symmetrical animal.

antineuritic (ăn'tĭnūrĭt'ĭk) *a.* [Gk. *anti*, against; *neuron*, nerve.] *Appl.* vitamin B_1, lack of which causes polyneuritis.

antipepsin (ăn'tĭpĕp'sĭn) *n.* [Gk. *anti*, against; *pepsis*, digestion.] A stomach secretion which prevents action of pepsin on tissue proteins.

antiperistalsis (ăn'tĭpĕristăl'sĭs) *n.* [Gk. *anti*, against; *peri*, around; *stalsis*, contraction.] Reversed peristalsis; peristaltic action in postero-anterior direction.

anti-pernicious anaemia factor,—vitamin B_{12} or cobalamin, *q.v.*

antipetalous (ăn'tĭpĕt'ălŭs) *a.* [Gk. *anti*, opposite; *petalon*, petal.] With stamens opposite petals.

antiphyte (ăn'tĭfīt) *n.* [Gk. *anti*, opposite; *phyton*, plant.] The sporophyte in the antithetic alternation of generations, *opp.* protophyte.

antipodal (ăntĭp'ŏdăl) *a.* [Gk. *anti*, against; *pous*, foot.] *Appl.* group of three cells at chalazal end of embryo-sac; *appl.* cone of astral rays opposite spindle fibres.

antiprostate (ăn'tĭprŏs'tāt) *n.* [Gk. *anti*, opposite; *prostates*, one who stands before.] Bulbo-urethral or Cowper's gland.

antipygidial (ăn'tĭpījĭd'ĭăl) *a.* [Gk. *anti*, against; *pygidion*, narrow rump.] *Appl.* bristles of seventh abdominal segment which extend to pygidium, in fleas.

antirachitic (ăn'tĭrăkĭt'ĭk) *a.* [Gk. *anti*, against; *rhachis*, spine.] *Appl.* vitamin D, lack of which causes rickets.

antiscorbutic (ăn'tĭskôrbū'tĭk) *a.* [Gk. *anti*, against; L.L. *scorbutus*, scurvy.] *Appl.* vitamin C, lack of which causes scurvy.

antisepalous (ăn'tĭsĕp'ălŭs) *a.* [Gk. *anti*, opposite; F. *sépale*, from L. *separare*, to separate.] With stamens opposite sepals.

antiseptic (ăn'tĭsĕp'tĭk) *a.* [Gk. *anti*, against; *sepsis*, putrefaction.] Preventing putrefaction. *n.* A substance which destroys harmful micro-organisms.

antispadix (ăn'tĭspā'dĭks) *n.* [Gk. *anti*, against; *spadix*, palm branch.] A group of four modified tentacles in internal lateral lobes of Nautilus.

antisquama (ăn'tĭskwā'mă) *n.* [Gk. *anti*, against; L. *squama*, scale.] Basal lobe next squama of insect wing; squama alaris or antitegula.

antisterility factor,—vitamin E.

antistyle (ăn'tĭstīl) *n.* [Gk. *anti*, against; *stylos*, pillar.] Basal projection of stylifer in certain insects.

antitegula (ăn'tĭtĕg'ŭlă) *n* [Gk. *anti*, against; L. *tegula*, tile.] Upper tegula or antisquama, *q.v.*

antithetic (ăn'tĭthĕt'ĭk) *a.* [Gk. *antithesis*, opposition.] *Appl.* alternation of diploid and haploid generations, or of sporophyte and gametophyte generations.

antithrombin (ăn′tĭthrŏm′bĭn) *n.* [Gk. *anti*, against; *thrombos*, clot.] A substance, as formed in liver, which prevents clotting of blood.

antitoxin (ăn′tĭtŏk′sĭn) *n.* [Gk. *anti*, against; *toxikon*, poison.] A substance or antibody which neutralises or binds a toxin.

antitragus (ăn′tĭtrā′gŭs) *n.* [Gk. *anti*, opposite; *tragos*, goat.] Prominence opposite tragus of external ear.

antitrochanter (ăn′tĭtrŏkăn′tĕr) *n.* [Gk. *anti*, against; *trochanter*, a runner.] In birds, an articular surface on ilium against which trochanter of femur plays.

antitrope (ăn′tĭtrōp) *n.* [Gk. *anti*, opposite; *trope*, turn.] Any structure which forms a bilaterally symmetrical pair with another; antibody, *q.v.*

antitropic (ăn′tĭtrŏp′ĭk) *a.* [Gk. *anti*, against; *trope*, turn.] Turned or arranged in opposite directions; arranged to form bilaterally symmetric pairs, as ribs of opposite sides; *cf.* syntropic.

antitropin,—antibody.

antitropous (ăntĭt′rŏpŭs) *a.* [Gk. *anti*, against; *trope*, turn.] Inverted; *appl.* embryos with radicle directed away from hilum; antitropal.

antitype (ăn′tĭtīp) *n.* [Gk. *anti*, equal to; *typos*, pattern.] A specimen of the same type as that chosen for designation of a species, and gathered at the same time and place.

antlia (ănt′lĭă) *n.* [L. *antlia*, pump.] The spiral suctorial proboscis of Lepidoptera.

antorbital (ăntôr′bĭtăl) *a.* [L. *ante*, before; *orbis*, circle.] Situated in front of orbit; *appl.* bone, cartilage, process.

antrorse (ăntrôrs′) *a.*, *adv.* [L. *ante*, before; *vertere*, to turn.] Directed forwards or upwards.

antrum (ăn′trŭm) *n.* [L. *antrum*, cavity.] A cavity or sinus; *e.g.*, maxillary sinus, cavity of pylorus.

anurous (ănū′rŭs) *a.* [Gk. *a*, without; *oura*, tail.] Tailless.

anus (ā′nŭs) *n.* [L. *anus*, anus.] Posterior opening of the alimentary canal.

aorta (āôr′tă) *n.* [Gk. *aorte*, the great artery.] The great trunk artery which carries pure blood to the body through arteries and their branches.

aortic (āôr′tĭk) *a.* [Gk. *aorte*, the great artery.] *Pert.* aorta; *appl.* arch, hiatus, isthmus, lymph glands, semilunar valves, etc.

aortic bodies,—two small masses of chromaffin cells in a capillary plexus, one on each side of foetal abdominal aorta, being part of system for controlling oxygen content and acidity of blood; Zuckerkandl's bodies.

apandrous (ăpăn′drŭs) *a.* [Gk. *apo*, away; *aner*, male.] Without antheridia; parthenogenetic, as oospores in certain Oomycetes.

apandry,—absence or non-function of male organs in plants; apandrous condition.

apatetic (ăp′ătē′tĭk) *a.* [Gk. *apatetikos*, fallacious.] *Appl.* misleading coloration.

aperispermic (ăpĕr′ĭspĕr′mĭk) *a.* [Gk. *a*, without; *peri*, around; *sperma*, seed.] *Appl.* seeds without nutritive tissue.

apertura piriformis,—anterior nasal aperture of skull.

apetalous (ăpĕt′ălŭs) *a.* [Gk. *a*, without; *petalon*, petal.] Without petals; monochlamydeous.

apex (ā′pĕks) *n.* [L. *apex*, summit.] Tip or summit, as of lungs, heart, nose; styloid process of fibula; tip of epicone in Dinoflagellata; wing tip in insects.

aphanipterous (ăf′ănĭp′tĕrŭs) *a.* [Gk. *aphanes*, unseen; *pteron*, wing.] Apparently without wings.

aphantobiont (ăfăn′tōbī′ŏnt) *n.* [Gk. *aphantos*, invisible; *bionai*, to live.] An ultramicroscopic organism; a filtrable virus.

apheliotropism (ăfē′lĭŏt′rŏpĭzm) *n.* [Gk. *apo*, away; *helios*, sun; *trope*, turn.] Tendency to turn away from light; aphototropism.

aphlebia (ăflĕb'yă) *n.* [Gk. *a*, without; *phleps*, vein.] Lateral outgrowth from base of frond-stalk in certain ferns.

aphodal (ăf'ödăl) *a.* [Gk. *apo*, away; *hodos*, path.] *Appl.* type of canal system in sponges.

aphodus (ăf'ödŭs) *n.* [Gk. *aphodos*, departure.] The short tube leading from flagellate chamber to excurrent canal in a type of canal system in sponges.

aphotic (ăfō'tĭk) *a.* [Gk. *a*, without; *phos*, light.] *Pert.* absence of light; *appl.* zone of deep sea where daylight fails to penetrate. *Opp.* photic.

aphyllous (ăfĭl'ŭs) *a.* [Gk. *a*, without; *phyllon*, leaf.] Without foliage leaves.

aphylly (ăfĭl'ĭ) *n.* [Gk. *a*, without; *phyllon*, leaf.] Suppression or absence of leaves.

apical (ăp'ĭkăl) *a.* [L. *apex*, summit.] At tip or summit; *pert.* distal end; *appl.* cell at tip of growing point; *appl.* meristem; *appl.* style arising from summit of ovary; *appl.* dominance, of terminal bud; *appl.* aboral plates of echinoderms; *appl.* neural plate of trochophore and tornaria.

apicotransverse (ăp'ĭkötrănsvĕrs') *adv.* [L. *apex*, summit; *transversus*, crosswise.] Situated across at or near the tip; *appl.* mitotic spindle.

apiculate (ăpĭk'ūlāt) *a.* [*Dim.* of L. *apex*, summit.] Forming abruptly to a small tip, as leaf.

apiculus (ăpĭk'ūlŭs) *n.* [*Dim.* of L. *apex*, summit.] A small apical termination, as in some protozoa, or of certain spores; reflexed portion of antennal club, in some Lepidoptera.

apilary (ăpĭl'ărĭ) *a.* [Gk. *a*, not; *pilos*, felt cap.] Having upper lip wanting or suppressed in corolla.

apileate (ăpĭl'ëāt) *a.* [L. *a*, away; *pileatus*, wearing a cap.] Without a pileus.

apitoxin (āpĭtŏk'sĭn) *n.* [L. *apis*, bee; Gk. *toxikon*, poison.] Main toxic fraction of bee venom.

apituitarism (ăp'ĭtū'ĭtărĭzm) *n.* [L. *a*, away; *pituita*, phlegm.] Absence or deficiency of pituitary gland secretion; hypohypophysism.

aplacental (ăp'lăsĕn'tăl) *a.* [L. *a*, away; *placenta*, flat cake.] Having no placenta, as monotremes.

aplanetic (ăplănĕt'ĭk) *a.* [Gk. *a*, not; *planetes*, wanderer.] Not motile; *appl.* spores.

aplanetism (ăplăn'ĕtĭzm, ăplănē'tĭzm) *n.* [Gk. *a*, not; *planetes*, wanderer.] Absence of motile spores.

aplanogametangium (ăplăn'ögămētăn'jĭŭm) *n.* [Gk. *a*, not; *planos*, wandering; *gametes*, spouse; *anggeion*, vessel.] Cell in which aplanogametes are formed.

aplanogamete (ăplăn'ögămēt') *n.* [Gk. *a*, not; *planos*, wandering; *gametes*, spouse.] A non-motile conjugating germ-cell of various plants and animals.

aplanosporangium (ăplăn'öspörăn'jĭŭm) *n.* [Gk. *a*, not; *planos*, wandering; *sporos*, seed; *anggeion*, vessel.] A sporangium producing aplanospores.

aplanospore (ăplăn'öspōr) *n.* [Gk. *a*, not; *planos*, wandering; *sporos*, seed.] A non-motile resting spore of algae; an encysted spore of fungi; aplanoplastid. *Opp.* planospore.

aplasia (ăplā'zĭă) *n.* [Gk. *a*, without; *plassein*, to mould.] Arrested development; non-development.

aplerotic (ăplērō'tĭk) *a.* [Gk. *a*, not; *pleroun*, to fill.] Not entirely filling a space; *appl.* oospore not extended to oogonial wall. *Opp.* plerotic.

aploperistomatous (ăp'löpĕr'ĭstŏm'ătŭs) *a.* [Gk. *aploos*, single; *peri*, around; *stoma*, mouth.] Having a peristome with one row of teeth, as mosses.

aplostemonous (ăp'löstĕm'önŭs) *a.* [Gk. *aploos*, single; *stemon*, spun thread.] With a single row of stamens.

apneustic (ăpnū′stĭk) *a.* [Gk. *a*, without; *pneustos*, breath.] With spiracles closed or absent; *appl.* aquatic larvae of certain insects.

apobasidium (ăp′öbăsĭd′ĭŭm) *n.* [Gk. *apo*, sprung from; *basis*, base; *idion*, *dim.*] Protobasidium, *q.v.*; a basidium having sterigmata with terminal spores, *opp.* autobasidium.

apobiotic (ăp′öbīŏt′ĭk) *a.* [Gk. *apo*, away; *bios*, life.] Causing or *pert.* decrease in vital energy of cells or tissue; *pert.* apobiosis or physiological death, *opp.* death of entire body.

apocarpous (ăp′ökâr′pŭs) *a.* [Gk. *apo*, away; *karpos*, fruit.] Having separate or partially united carpels. *Opp.* syncarpous.

apocarpy,—apocarpous condition.

apocentric (ăp′ösĕn′trĭk) *a.* [Gk. *apo*, away; *kentron*, centre.] Diverging or differing from the original type, *opp.* archecentric.

apochlorosis (ăp′öklörō′sĭs) *n.* [Gk. *apo*, away; *chloros*, grass green.] The absence of chlorophyll, in Flagellata.

apocrine (ăp′ökrĭn) *a.* [Gk. *apo*, away; *krinein*, to separate.] *Appl.* glands secreting only part of cell contents; *cf.* holocrine, merocrine.

apocyte (ăp′ösīt) *n.* [Gk. *apo*, away; *kytos*, hollow.] A multinucleate cell; a plurinucleate mass of protoplasm.

apodal (ăp′ödăl), *a.* [Gk. *a*, without; *pous*, foot.] Having no feet; without ventral fin; stemless; apodous.

apodema (ăp′ödē′mă) *n.* [Gk. *apo*, away; *demas*, body.] An internal skeletal projection in Arthropoda; apodeme.

apoderma (ăp′ödĕr′mă) *n.* [Gk. *apo*, later; *derma*, skin.] Enveloping membrane secreted during resting stage between instars by certain Acarina.

apodous,—apodal.

apo-enzyme (ăp′öĕn′zīm) *n.* [Gk. *apo*, away; *en*, in; *zyme*, leaven.] Specific protein part of an enzyme, requiring co-enzyme for action.

apogamy (ăpŏg′ămĭ) *n.* [Gk. *apo*, away; *gamos*, marriage.] Reproduction without intervention of sexual organs.

apogeotropic (ăp′öjē′ötrŏp′ĭk) *a.* [Gk. *apo*, away; *gaia*, earth; *trope*, turn.] Turning away from the earth; ageotropic.

apogeotropism (ăp′öjēŏt′röpĭzm) *n.* [Gk. *apo*, away; *gaia*, earth; *trope*, turn.] Tendency to act contrarily to law of gravity; negative geotropism.

apolegamic (ăp′ölēgăm′ĭk) *a.* [Gk. *apolegein*, to choose; *gamos*, marriage.] *Appl.* mating associated with sexual selection.

apomeiosis (ăp′ömīō′sĭs) *n.* [Gk. *apo*, away; *meion*, smaller.] Sporogenesis without haplosis.

apomict (ăp′ömĭkt) *n.* [Gk. *apo*, away; *miktos*, mixed.] A biotype resulting from apogamy and vegetative propagation.

apomixis (ăp′ömĭk′sĭs) *n.* [Gk. *apo*, away; *mixis*, a mixing.] A reproductive anomaly in plants akin to parthenogenesis, but including development from cells other than ovules. *Opp.* amphimixis.

aponeurosis (ăp′önūrō′sĭs) *n.* [Gk. *apo*, from; *neuron*, sinew.] The flattened tendon for insertion of, or membrane investing, certain muscles.

aponeurosis epicranialis,—galea aponeurotica.

apopetalous (ăp′öpĕt′ălŭs) *a.* [Gk. *apo*, away; *petalon*, leaf.] With free petals; *cf.* apetalous.

apophyllous (ăp′öfĭl′ŭs) *a.* [Gk. *apo*, away; *phyllon*, leaf.] *Appl.* the parts of a single perianth whorl when they are free leaves.

apophysis (ăpŏf′ĭsĭs) *n.* [Gk. *apo*, away; *phyein*, to grow.] Process from a bone, usually for muscle attachment; endosternite or sternal apodeme; swelling beneath reproductive structure on fungal hypha; photosynthetic region forming swelling at base of capsule in some mosses; small protuberance at apex of ovuliferous scale in pine.

apoplasmodial (ăp′ŏplăsmō′dĭăl) *a.* [Gk. *apo*, away ; *plasma*, something moulded.] Not forming a typical plasmodium.

apoplastid (ăpŏplăs′tĭd) *n.* [Gk. *apo*, away ; *plastos*, formed ; *idion*, *dim.*] A plastid having no chromatophores.

apopyle (ăp′ŏpīl) *n.* [Gk. *apo*, away ; *pyle*, gate.] Exhalent pore of sponge.

aporogamy (ăpŏrŏg′ămĭ) *n.* [Gk. *a*, without ; *poros*, channel ; *gamos*, marriage.] Fertilisation without entry of pollen-tube through micropyle of ovule, *opp.* porogamy.

aporrhysa (ăpŏr′ĭsă) *n. plu.* [Gk. *aporrhein*, to flow away.] Exhalent canals in sponges ; *opp.* epirrhysa.

aposematic (ăp′ŏsēmăt′ĭk) *a.* [Gk. *apo*, away ; *sema*, signal.] *Appl.* warning colours which serve to frighten away enemies.

aposporogony (ăp′ŏspŏrŏg′ŏnĭ) *n.* [Gk. *apo*, away ; *sporos*, seed ; *gonos*, birth.] Absence of sporogony.

apospory (ăpŏs′pŏrĭ) *n.* [Gk. *apo*, away ; *sporos*, seed.] Production of a gametophyte from a sporophyte without intervention of spore-formation.

apostasis (ăpŏs′tăsĭs) *n.* [Gk. *apo*, away ; *stasis*, standing.] Condition of abnormal growth of axis which thereby causes separation of perianth whorls from one another.

apostaxis (ăp′ŏstăk′sĭs) *n.* [Gk. *apostaxis*, a dribbling.] Excessive or abnormal exudation.

apostrophe (ăpŏs′trŏfē) *n.* [Gk. *apo*, away ; *strophe*, turn.] Arrangement of chloroplasts along lateral walls of leaf cells.

apothecium (ăp′ŏthē′sĭŭm, -shĭŭm) *n.* [Gk. *apo*, away ; *theke*, cup.] A cup-shaped ascocarp ; ascocarp of lichens.

apothelium (ăp′ŏthē′lĭŭm) *n.* [Gk. *apo*, away ; *thele*, nipple.] A secondary tissue derived from a primary epithelium.

apotome (ăp′ŏtōm) *n.* [Gk. *apo*, away ; *tome*, a cutting.] A part appearing as if cut off, as from episternum, trochanter, etc., in Arthropoda.

apotracheal (ăpŏtrā′kēal) *a.* [Gk. *apo*, away ; L. *trachea*, windpipe.] With xylem parenchyma independent of vessels, or dispersed ; *appl.* wood.

apotropous (ăpŏt′rŏpŭs) *a.* [Gk. *apo*, away ; *trope*, turn.] Anatropal and with ventrally - situated raphe.

apotype,—hypotype, *q.v.*

apotypic (ăp′ŏtĭp′ĭk) *a.* [Gk. *apo*, away ; *typos*, pattern.] Diverging from a type.

apparato reticolare,—*see* Golgi complex.

appendage (ăpĕn′dĕj) *n.* [L. *ad*, to ; *pendere*, to hang.] An organ or part attached to a trunk, as a limb, branch, etc. ; a hyphal or rigid structure for attachment or detachment of perithecium to or from mycelium, varying in structure and function in different Ascomycetes.

appendices,—*plu.* of appendix.

appendices colli (ăpĕn′dĭsēz kŏl′ī) *n. plu.* [L. *ad*, to ; *pendere*, to hang ; *collum*, neck.] Exterior throat appendages or tassels, of goat, sheep, pig, etc.

appendicular (ăp′ĕndĭk′ūlăr) *a.* [L. *ad*, to ; *pendere*, to hang.] *Pert.* appendages ; *appl.* skeleton of limbs, *opp.* axial skeleton ; *pert.* vermiform appendix ; *appl.* artery.

appendiculate (ăp′ĕndĭk′ūlāt) *a.* [L. *ad*, to ; *pendere*, to hang.] Having a small appendage, as a stamen or filament.

appendiculum (ăp′ĕndĭk′ūlŭm) *n.* [L. *appendicula*, small appendage.] Remains of the partial veil on rim of pileus.

appendix (ăpĕn′dĭks) *n.* [L. *ad*, to ; *pendere*, to hang.] An outgrowth, especially the vermiform appendix.

applanate (ăpl′ănāt) *a.* [L. *ad*, to ; *planatus*, flattened.] Flattened.

apposition (ăp′özĭsh′ŭn) *n.* [L. *ad*, to; *ponere*, to place.] The formation of successive layers in growth of a cell wall; *cf.* intussusception.

appressorium (ăp′rĕsō′rĭŭm) *n.* [L. *ad*, to; *pressare*, to press.] Adhesive disc, as of haustorium or sucker; modified hyphal tip which may form haustorium or penetrate substrate, as of parasitic fungi.

aproterodont (ăprŏt′ërödŏnt) *a.* [Gk. *a*, without; *proteros*, first; *odous*, tooth.] Having no premaxillary teeth.

apteria (ăptē′rĭă) *n. plu.* [Gk. *a*, without; *pteron*, wing.] Naked or down-covered surfaces between pterylae or feather-tracts.

apterous (ăp′tërŭs) *a.* [Gk. *a*, without; *pteron*, wing.] Wingless; having no wing-like expansions on stems or petioles; exalate.

apterygial (ăp′tërĭj′ĭăl) *a.* [Gk. *a*, without; *pterygion*, *dim.* of *pteron*, wing.] Wingless; without fins.

apterygotous (ăptërĭgō′tŭs) *a.* [Gk. *a*, without; *pterygotos*, winged.] Resembling or *pert.* primitive wingless insects.

aptychus (ăpt′ĭkŭs) *n.* [Gk. *a*, without; *ptyche*, fold.] A horny or calcareous structure, possibly an operculum, of ammonites.

apyrene (ăpī′rēn) *a.* [Gk. *a*, not; *pyren*, fruit-stone.] *Appl.* spermatozoa lacking nucleus; *cf.* eupyrene, oligopyrene; seedless, *appl.* certain cultivated fruits.

aquatic (ăkwăt′ĭk) *a.* [L. *aqua*, water.] *Pert.* water; living in or frequenting water. *n.* An aquatic plant.

aqueduct (ăk′wēdŭkt) *n.* [L. *aqua*, water; *ducere*, to lead.] A channel or passage, as that of cochlea, and of vestibule of ear; aquaeductus.

aqueduct of Sylvius [*F. de Boë* or *Sylvius*, Flemish anatomist],—cerebral aqueduct, aqueduct of the midbrain, or iter, connecting third and fourth ventricle; mesocoele.

aqueous (ā′kwëŭs) *a.* [L. *aqua*, water.] Watery, *appl.* humour, fluid occupying space between lens and cornea; *appl.* tissue consisting of thin-walled watery parenchymatous cells.

arachnactis (ărăknăk′tĭs) *n.* [Gk. *arachne*, spider; *aktis*, ray.] Larval stage of cerianthid Zoantharia.

arachnid (ărăk′nĭd) *a.* [Gk. *arachne*, spider.] Spider-like; *pert.* spiders.

arachnidium (ărăknĭd′ĭŭm) *n.* [Gk. *arachne*, spider; *idion*, *dim.*] The spinning apparatus of a spider, including spinning-glands and spinnerets.

arachnoid (ărăk′noid) *a.* [Gk. *arachne*, spider, cobweb; *eidos*, form.] *Pert.* or resembling a spider; like a cobweb; consisting of fine entangled hairs; *appl.* the thin membrane between dura and pia mater. *n.* The arachnoid membrane.

arachnoideal (ărăknoid′ëăl) *a.* [Gk. *arachne*, cobweb; *eidos*, form.] *Pert.* the arachnoid; *appl.* granulations: Pacchionian bodies, *q.v.*

arbacioid,—*see* diadematoid.

arborescent (âr′börĕs′ënt) *a.* [L. *arborescens*, growing like a tree.] Branched like a tree.

arborisation (âr′börĭzā′shŭn) *n.* [L. *arbor*, tree.] Tree-like branching, as of nerve cell processes; arborescence.

arboroid (âr′böroid) *a.* [L. *arbor*, tree; Gk. *eidos*, like.] Tree-like, designating general structure of a protozoan colony; dendritic.

arbor vitae (ârbŏr vī′tē) *n.* [L. *arbor*, tree; *vita*, life.] The tree of life, *appl.* arborescent appearance of cerebellum in section.

arbuscle (âr′bŭsl) *n.* [L. *arbuscula*, shrub.] A tree-like small shrub, or a dwarf tree; a branched haustorium, as in certain fungi; arbuscula.

arbuscular (ârbŭs′kūlăr) *a.* [L. *arbuscula*, shrub.] Resembling a tree-like small shrub.

arcade (ârkād′) *n.* [L. *arcus*, arch.] An arched channel or passage; a bony arch, as supra- and infra-temporal arches in skull; transverse canal connecting lateral canals, in Ascaris.

Archaean (ârkē′ăn) *a.* [Gk. *archaios*, ancient.] *Appl.* geological era before Palaeozoic; Pre-Cambrian.

archaeocytes (âr′kēōsīts) *n. plu.* [Gk. *archaios*, primitive; *kytos*, hollow.] Cells arising from undifferentiated blastomeres and ultimately giving rise to germ-cells and gametes.

archaeostomatous (âr′kēōstŏm′ătŭs) *a.* [Gk. *archaios*, primitive; *stoma*, mouth.] Having the blastopore persistent and forming mouth.

Archaeozoic (âr′kēōzō′ĭk) *a.* [Gk. *archaios*, ancient; *zoe*, life.] *Pert.* earliest geological era, age of unicellular life.

arch-centra (ârch′sĕn′tră) *n. plu.* [L. *arcus*, bow; *centrum*, centre.] Centra formed by fusion of basal growths of primary arcualia external to chordal sheath; *cf.* chordacentra.

archebiosis (âr′kēbīō′sĭs) *n.* [Gk. *arche*, beginning; *biosis*, living.] The origin of life; archegenesis.

archecentric (âr′kēsĕn′trĭk) *a.* [Gk. *arche*, beginning; *kentron*, centre.] Conforming more or less with the original type, *opp.* apocentric.

archedictyon (âr′kēdĭk′tĭŏn) *n.* [Gk. *arche*, beginning; *diktyon*, net.] An intervein network in wings of some primitive insects.

archegoniophore (âr′kēgō′nĭōfōr) *n.* [Gk. *arche*, beginning; *gonos*, offspring; *pherein*, to bear.] Branches of bryophytes, or parts of fern prothalli, bearing archegonia.

archegonium (âr′kēgō′nĭŭm) *n.* [Gk. *arche*, beginning; *gonos*, offspring.] A female gametangium in which oospheres are formed, and in which the young plant begins development.

archencephalon (ârk′ĕnkĕf′ălŏn, -sĕf-) *n.* [Gk. *arche*, beginning; *engkephalos*, brain.] The primitive forebrain or cerebrum.

archenteron (ârkĕn′tĕrŏn) *n.* [Gk. *arche*, beginning; *enteron*, gut.] The cavity of gastrula which forms primitive gut of embryo.

archeo-,—archaeo-.

archespore (âr′kēspōr) *n.* [Gk. *arche*, beginning; *sporos*, seed.] The tetrahedral or meristematic cell of a sporangium; cell of an archesporium.

archesporium (âr′kēspō′rĭŭm) *n.* [Gk. *arche*, beginning; *sporos*, seed.] A cell or mass of cells, dividing to form spore mother-cells; in liverworts, spore mother-cells and elater-forming cells.

archetype,—architype, *q.v.*

archiamphiaster (âr′kĭăm′fĭăs′tĕr) *n.* [Gk. *archi*, first; *amphi*, on both sides; *aster*, star.] The amphiaster forming first or second polar body in maturation of ovum.

archibenthic (âr′kĭbĕn′thĭk) *a.* [Gk. *archi*, first; *benthos*, depths of sea.] *Pert.* bottom of sea from edge of continental shelf to upper limit of abyssobenthic zone, at depths of *ca.* 200 to 1000 metres.

archiblast (âr′kĭblăst) *n.* [Gk. *archi*, first; *blastos*, bud.] Egg protoplasm.

archiblastic (âr′kĭblăs′tĭk) *a.* [Gk. *archi*, first; *blastos*, bud.] Having total and equal segmentation.

archiblastula (âr′kĭblăs′tūlă) *n.* [Gk. *archi*, first; *blastos*, bud.] Typical hollow ball of cells derived from an egg with total and equal segmentation.

archicarp (âr′kĭkârp) *n.* [Gk. *archi*, first; *karpos*, fruit.] Spirally coiled region of thallus, or stalk bearing oogonium, of certain fungi.

archicerebrum (âr′kĭsĕr′ēbrŭm) *n.* [Gk. *archi*, first; L. *cerebrum*, brain.] The primitive brain, as the supra-oesophageal ganglia of higher invertebrates; primary brain of arthropods.

archichlamydeous (âr′kĭklămĭd′ēŭs) *a.* [Gk. *archi*, first; *chlamys*, cloak.] Having no petals, or having petals entirely separate from one another.

archicoel (âr'kĭsēl) *n.* [Gk. *archi*, first; *koilos*, hollow.] The primary body-cavity or space between alimentary canal and ectoderm in development of various animals.

archidictyon,—*see* archedictyon.

archigenesis (âr'kĭjĕn'ĕsĭs) *n.* [Gk. *archi*, first; *genesis*, descent.] Abiogenesis, *q.v.*

archigony (ârkĭg'ŏnĭ) *n.* [Gk. *archi*, first; *gonos*, begetting.] The first origin of life.

archinephric (âr'kĭnĕf'rĭk) *a.* [Gk. *archi*, first; *nephros*, kidney.] *Appl.* duct into which pronephric tubules open; *pert.* archinephros.

archinephridium (âr'kĭnĕfrĭd'ĭŭm) *n.* [Gk. *archi*, first; *nephros*, kidney; *idion*, *dim.*] Excretory organ of certain larval invertebrates; solenocyte, *q.v.*

archinephros ((âr'kĭnĕf'rŏs) *n.* [Gk. *archi*, first; *nephros*, kidney.] The primitive kidney; Wolffian body.

archipallium (âr'kĭpăl'ĭŭm) *n.* [Gk. *archi*, first; L. *pallium*, mantle.] The olfactory region of cerebral hemispheres, comprising olfactory bulbs and tubercles, pyriform lobes, hippocampus, and fornix. *Opp.* neopallium.

archiplasm (âr'kĭplăzm) *n.* [Gk. *archi*, first; *plasma*, mould.] The substance of attraction-sphere, astral rays, and spindle-fibres; also archoplasm; kinoplasm; idiosome, *q.v.*

archipterygium (âr'kĭtĕrĭj'ĭŭm) *n.* [Gk. *archi*, first; *pterygion*, little wing.] Type of fin in which skeleton consists of elongated segmented central axis and two rows of jointed rays.

architomy (ârkĭt'ŏmĭ) *n.* [Gk. *archi*, first; *tome*, cutting.] Reproduction by fission with subsequent regeneration, in certain annelids; *opp.* paratomy.

architype (âr'kĭtīp) *n.* [Gk. *archi*, first; *typos*, type.] An original type from which others may be derived.

archoplasm,—archiplasm, *q.v.*

arcicentrous (âr'sĭsĕn'trŭs) *a.* [L. *arcus*, bow; *centrum*, centre.] *Appl.* vertebral column in which centra are mainly derived from arch tissue; arcocentrous.

arciferous (ârsĭf'ĕrŭs) *a.* [L. *arcus*, bow; *ferre*, to carry.] *Appl.* pectoral arch of toads, etc., where precoracoid and coracoid are separated and connected by arched epicoracoid.

arciform (âr'sĭfôrm) *a.* [L. *arcus*, bow; *forma*, shape.] Shaped like an arch or bow; arcuate.

arcocentrous (âr'kŏsĕn'trŭs) *a.* [L. *arcus*, bow; *centrum*, centre.] *Appl.* vertebral column with inconspicuous chordal sheath and centra derived from arch tissue.

arcocentrum (âr'kŏsĕn'trŭm) *n.* [L. *arcus*, bow; *centrum*, centre.] A centrum formed from parts of neural and haemal arches.

Arctogaea (ârk'tŏjē'ă, -gâ'yă) *n.* [Gk. *Arktos*, Great Bear; *gaia*, earth.] Zoogeographical area comprising Holarctic, Ethiopian, and Oriental regions.

arcualia (âr'kūā'lĭă) *n. plu.* [L. *arcus*, bow.] Small cartilaginous pieces, dorsal and ventral, fused or free, on vertebral column of fishes.

arcuate (âr'kūāt) *a.* [L. *arcuatus*, curved.] Curved or shaped like a bow.

arculus (âr'kūlŭs) *n.* [*Dim.* of L. *arcus*, bow.] Arc formed by two wing veins of certain insects.

ardellae (ârdĕl'ē) *n. plu.* [Gk. *ardein*, to sprinkle.] Small apothecia of certain lichens, having appearance of dust.

area (ā'rēă) *n.* [L. *area*, ground-space.] A surface, as area opaca, area pellucida, area vasculosa, etc.; part enclosed by a raised ridge, as in Polyzoa; a region.

arenaceous (ărĕnā'shŭs) *a.* [L. *arena*, sand.] Having properties or appearance of sand; sandy; growing in sand.

arenicolous (ărĕnĭk'ŏlŭs) *a.* [L. *arena*, sand; *colere*, to inhabit.] Living in sand; psammophilous.

areola (ărē′ölă) *n.* [L. *areola*, *dim.* of *area*, space.] A small coloured circle round a nipple ; part of iris bordering pupil of eye ; one of small spaces or interstices of a special kind of tissue ; area defined by cracks on surface of lichens ; poroids when surrounded by thickened margins ; scrobicula, *q.v.*

areolar (ărē′ölăr) *a.* [L. *areola*, small space.] Of or like an areola ; *pert.* an areola.

areolate (ărē′ölāt) *a.* [L. *areola*, small space.] Divided into small areas defined by cracks or other margins.

areolation (ărēölā′shŭn) *n.* [L. *areola*, small space.] Areolar pattern or network appearance, as of cell margins in tissue.

areole (ăr′ēōl) *n.* [L. *areola*, small space.] Areola, *q.v.* ; space occupied by a group of hairs or spines, as in Cactus.

argentaffin (ârjĕn′tăfin) *a.* [L. *argentum*, silver ; *affinis*, related.] Staining with silver salts, *appl.* cells ; argyrophil.

argenteal (ârjĕn′tēăl) *a.* [L. *argenteus*, silvern.] *Appl.* layer of eye containing calcic crystals.

argenteous (ârjĕn′tēŭs) *a.* [L. *argenteus*, silvern.] Like silver.

argenteum (ârjĕn′tēŭm) *n.* [L. *argenteus*, silvern.] A dermal reflecting tissue layer of iridocytes, without chromatophores, in fishes.

arginase (âr′jĭnās) *n.*—a liver enzyme acting on the amino-acid arginine ($C_6H_{14}O_2N_4$), urea and ornithine being separated by hydrolysis.

argyrophil (âr′jĭröfĭl) *a.* [Gk. *argyros*, silver ; *philos*, loving.] Staining with silver salts, *appl.* fibres of reticular tissue ; argentaffin ; argentophil, *appl.* basal bodies or blepharoplasts.

aril (ăr′ĭl) *n.* [F. *arille*, Sp. *arillo*, a small hoop.] An additional integument formed on some seeds after fertilisation.

arillode (ăr′ĭlōd) *n.* [F. *arille*, hoop ; Gk. *eidos*, like.] A false arillus arising from region of micropyle as an expansion of exostome.

arillus (ărĭl′ŭs) *n.* [L.L. *arillus*, aril.] An aril, *q.v.*

arista (ărĭs′tă) *n.* [L. *arista*, awn.] Awn ; long-pointed process as in many grasses ; a bristle borne by antenna of many brachycerous Diptera.

aristate (ărĭs′tāt) *a.* [L. *arista*, awn.] Provided with awns, or with a well-developed bristle ; *appl.* insect antenna.

aristogenesis (ăr′ĭstöjĕn′ĕsĭs) *n.* [Gk. *aristos*, best ; *genesis*, descent.] Process of evolving new biomechanism from the germ plasm ; creative principle or potentiality in origin of species.

aristogenic,—eugenic, *q.v.*

Aristotle's lantern,—masticating apparatus of sea-urchin.

aristulate (ărĭs′tūlāt) *a.* [*Dim.* of L. *arista*, awn.] Having a short awn or bristle.

arkyochrome (âr′kĭökrōm) *a.* [Gk. *arkys*, net ; *chroma*, colour.] With Nissl granules arranged like network ; *appl.* certain neurones.

armature (âr′mătūr) *n.* [L. *armatura*, armour.] Anything which serves to defend, as hairs, prickles, thorns, spines, stings, etc.

armilla (ârmĭl′ă) *n.* [L. *armilla*, armlet.] A bracelet-like fringe ; superior annulus or manchette of certain fungi.

armillate,—fringed around ; having an armilla.

arm-palisade,—palisade tissue in which the chloroplast-bearing surface is enlarged by infolding of cell-walls beneath the epidermis.

arolium (ărō′lĭŭm) *n.* [Gk. *arole*, protection.] Median lobe or pad on praetarsus of many insects.

aromorph (ā′römôrf) *n.* [Gk. *airein*, to raise ; *morphe*, form.] A character or structure resulting from aromorphosis.

aromorphosis (ā′römôr′fōsĭs) *n.* [Gk. *airein*, to raise ; *morphosis*, shaping.] Evolutionary change towards an increase in life energy, *e.g.* evolution of a biting mouth skeleton from gill arches ; *opp.* evolution of a merely adaptational character.

array (ărā′) *n.* [O.F. *arroi*, order.] Arrangement in order of magnitude.

arrect (ărĕkt′) *a.* [L. *arrectus*, set upright.] Upright; erect.

arrectores pilorum,—bundles of non-striped muscular fibres associated with hair follicles,—contraction causing hair to stand on end. *Sing.* arrector pili.

arrhenogenic (ărĕn′öjĕn′ĭk) *a.* [Gk. *arrhen*, male; *genos*, offspring.] Producing offspring preponderantly or entirely male.

arrhenoid (ărĕn′oid) *a.* [Gk. *arrhen*, male; *eidos*, form.] Exhibiting male characteristics, as genetically female animals undergoing sex-reversal. *n.* Sperm-aster during fertilisation of ovum.

arrhenoplasm (ărĕn′öplăzm) *n.* [Gk. *arrhen*, male; *plasma*, mould.] Male plasm, in reference to theory that all protoplasm consists of arrhenoplasm and thelyplasm.

arrhenotoky (ărĕnŏt′ökĭ) *n.* [Gk. *arrhen*, male; *tokos*, birth.] Parthenogenetic production of males.

arrhizal (ăr′ĭzăl) *a.* [Gk. *arrhizos*, not rooted.] Without true roots, as some parasitic plants; arrhizous.

arrhostia (ărōstī′ă) *n.* [Gk. *arrhostia*, ill health.] A normal condition or trend in development or evolution. which resembles a diseased condition, *e.g.*, extreme size in certain extinct vertebrates resembling over-action of pituitary gland.

artefact (âr′tēfăkt) *n.* [L. *ars*, art; *factus*, made.] An appearance, or apparent structure, due to preparation and not natural.

artenkreis (âr′tĕnkrīs) *n.* [Ger. *Art*, species; *Kreis*, circle.] Complex of species which replace one another geographically; super-species.

arterial (ârtē′rĭăl) *a.* [L. *arteria*, artery.] *Pert.* an artery, or system of channels by which blood issues to body from heart.

arterial circle,—*see* circulus arteriosus.

arteriolar-venular,—*pert.* arterioles and venules; *appl.* anastomosis.

arteriole (ârtē′rĭōl) *n.* [L. *arteriola*, small artery.] A small artery.

artery (âr′tërĭ) *n.* [L. *arteria*, artery.] A vessel which conveys blood from heart to body.

arthritic (ârthrĭt′ĭk) *a.* [Gk. *arthron*, joint.] *Pert.* or at joints; arthral.

arthrobranchiae (âr′thröbrăng′kĭē) *n. plu.* [Gk. *arthron*, joint; *brangchia*, gills.] Joint-gills, arising at junction of thoracic appendage with trunk, of Arthropoda.

arthrodia (ârthrō′dĭă) *n.* [Gk. *arthron*, joint.] A joint admitting of only gliding movements.

arthrodial (ârthrō′dĭăl) *a.* [Gk. *arthron*, joint.] *Appl.* articular membranes connecting thoracic appendages with trunk, as in arthropods.

arthrogenous (ârthrŏj′ënŭs) *a.* [Gk. *arthron*, joint; *genos*, descent.] Formed as a separate joint, as spores; developed from separated portions of a plant.

arthromere (âr′thrömēr) *n.* [Gk. *arthron*, joint; *meros*, part.] An arthropod body-segment or somite.

arthropod (âr′thröpŏd) *a.* [Gk. *arthron*, joint; *pous*, foot.] With jointed legs; *pert.* phylum including Crustacea, Myriopoda, Insecta, Arachnoidea.

arthropterous (ârthrŏp′tërŭs) *a.* [Gk. *arthron*, joint; *pteron*, wing.] Having jointed fin-rays, as fishes.

arthrospore (ârth′röspōr) *n.* [Gk. *arthron*, joint; *sporos*, seed.] A resting moniliform bacterial cell; a cell formed by segmentation of a hypha.

arthrosterigmata (âr′thröstērĭg′mătă) *n. plu.* [Gk. *arthron*, joint; *sterigma*, support.] Jointed sterigmata.

arthrostracous (ârthrŏs′trăkŭs) *a.* [Gk. *arthron*, joint; *ostrakon*, shell.] Having a segmented shell.

arthrotergal (âr′thrötĕr′găl) *a.* [Gk. *arthron*, joint; L. *tergum*, back.] *Appl.* median dorsal flexor of opisthosoma in Limulus.

arthrous (âr′thrŭs) *a.* [Gk. *arthron*, joint.] Jointed; articulate.

articular (ârtĭk'ūlăr) *a.* [L. *articulus*, joint.] *Pert.* or situated at a joint; *appl.* cartilage, lamellae, surface, capsule, etc.

articularis genus, — subcrureal muscle.

articulated (ârtĭk'ūlātĕd) *a.* [L. *articulus*, joint.] Jointed; articulate; separating easily at certain points.

articulation (âr'tĭkūlā'shŭn) *n.* [L. *articulus*, joint.] A joint between bones or segments, or between segments of a stem.

artifact,—artefact, *q.v.*

artiodactyl (âr'tĭödăk'tĭl) *a.* [Gk. *artios*, even; *daktylos*, finger.] Having an even number of digits.

arytaenoid (ăr'ĭtē'noid) *a.* [Gk. *arytaina*, ladle; *eidos*, form.] Pitcher-like; *appl.* two cartilages at back of larynx, also glands, muscles, etc.

asc,—ascus.

asci,—*plu.* of ascus.

ascidial (ăsĭd'ĭăl) *a.* [Gk. *askidion*, *dim.* of *askos*, bag.] Sac-like; *appl.* certain specialised, or abnormal, floral and foliage leaves; *pert.* ascidium.

ascidian (ăsĭd'ĭăn) *a.* [Gk. *askidion*, little bag.] Like an ascidian or sea-squirt.

ascidium (ăsĭd'ĭŭm) *n.* [Gk. *askidion*, little bag.] A pitcher-leaf, as in Nepenthes.

ascigerous (ăsĭj'ërŭs) *a.* [Gk. *askos*, bag; L. *gerere*, to bear.] Bearing asci, as certain hyphae in fungi; asciferous.

ascocarp (ăs'kökârp) *n.* [Gk. *askos*, bag; *karpos*, fruit.] Asci with their protective covering; sporocarp of Ascomycetes.

ascogenous (ăskŏj'ënŭs) *n.* [Gk. *askos*, bag; *-genes*, producing.] Producing asci; *appl.* hyphae, cells.

ascogonium (ăs'kögō'nĭŭm) *n.* [Gk. *askos*, bag; *gonos*, offspring.] A specialised hyphal branch which gives rise to ascogenous hyphae or an ascus; oogonium of Ascomycetes.

ascoma (ăs'kōmă) *n.* [Gk. *askoma*, leather padding.] Disc-shaped ascocarp in certain fungi.

ascophore (ăs'köfōr) *n.* [Gk. *askos*, bag; *pherein*, to bear.] Ascocarp.

ascoplasm (ăs'köplăzm) *n.* [Gk. *askos*, bag; *plasma*, mould.] Cytoplasm of an ascus involved in spore formation, *opp.* epiplasm.

ascorbic acid,—pure vitamin C, deficiency of which in diet causes dental disorders and scurvy; hexuronic acid, $C_6H_8O_6$.

ascospore (ăs'köspōr) *n.* [Gk. *askos*, bag; *sporos*, seed.] One of the spores produced in an ascus.

ascostome (ăs'köstōm) *n.* [Gk. *askos*, bag; *stoma*, mouth.] Apical pore of an ascus.

ascus (ăs'kŭs) *n.* [Gk. *askos*, bag.] A membranous spore-sac, as of Ascomycetes.

ascuspore,—ascostome.

ascyphous (ăsī'fŭs) *a.* [Gk. *a*, without; *skyphos*, cup.] Without a cup-shaped expansion of the podetium, as some lichens.

-ase [diast*ase*.],—suffix denoting an enzyme, and joined to a root naming the substance acted on or the type of reaction.

asemic (ăsē'mĭk) *a.* [Gk. *asemos*, without sign.] Without markings.

aseptate (ăsĕp'tāt) *a.* [L. *a*, not; *septum*, partition.] Without any septum.

asexual (ăsĕk'sūăl) *a.* [Gk. *a*, without; L. *sexus*, sex.] Having no apparent sexual organs; parthenogenetic or vegetative, as *appl.* reproduction.

asiphonate (ăsī'fönāt) *a.* [L. *a*, not; *sipho*, tube.] *Appl.* larvae whose respiratory tubes open directly to exterior.

asparagine (ăspăr'ăjēn, -gĭn) *n.* [Gk. *asparagos*, asparagus.] A compound, first detected in asparagus, formed from amino-acids in leguminous and other seeds, of importance in nitrogen metabolism of plants; $C_4H_8O_3N_2$.

aspect (ăs'pĕkt) *n.* [L. *aspicere*, to look toward.] Direction facing part of a surface; appearance or look; seasonal appearance.

aspection (ăspĕk'shŭn) *n.* [L. *aspicere*, to look toward.] Seasonal succession of phytological and zoological phenomena.

asperate (ăs'pĕrāt) *a.* [L. *asperare*, to roughen.] Having a rough surface.

asperity (ăspĕr'ĭtĭ) *n.* [L. *asperitas*, roughness.] Roughness, as on a leaf.

asperulate (ăspĕr'ūlāt) *a.* [*Dim.* of L. *asperare*, to roughen.] Minutely rough.

asplanchnic (ăsplăngk'nĭk) *a.* [Gk. *a*, without; *splangchna*, viscera.] Without alimentary canal.

asporocystid (ăspŏr'ŏsĭs'tĭd) *a.* [Gk. *a*, not; *sporos*, seed; *kystis*, bladder; *idion*, *dim.*] *Appl.* oocyst of Sporozoa when zygote divides into sporozoites without sporocyst formation.

asporogenic (ăs'pŏröjĕn'ĭk) *a.* [Gk. *a*, without; *sporos*, seed; *gennaein*, to produce.] Not originating from spores.

asporogenous, — not producing spores.

asporous (ăspō'rŭs) *a.* [Gk. *a*, without; *sporos*, seed.] Having no spores.

assimilation (ăsĭm'ĭlā'shŭn) *n.* [L. *ad*, to; *similis*, like.] Conversion into protoplasm of ingested and digested nutrient material; anabolism.

association (ăsō'sĭā'shŭn) *n.* [L. *ad*, to; *socius*, fellow.] A plant community forming a division of a formation or larger unit of vegetation, as of tundra, grassland, forest, and characterised by dominant species; adherence of gregarines without fusion of nuclei; *appl.* fibres connecting white matter of interior of brain with cortex; *appl.* neurons with intersegmental axons.

associes (ăsō'sĭēz) *n.* [L. *ad*, to; *socius*, fellow.] An association representing a stage in the process of succession.

astacene (ăs'tăsēn) *n.* [L. *astacus*, crayfish.] Carotenoid pigment of certain crustaceans, echinoderms, and fishes; astacin; $C_{40}H_{48}O_4$.

astaxanthin (ăs'tăzăn'thĭn) *n.* [L. *astacus*, crayfish; Gk. *xanthos*, yellow.] An animal carotenoid derived from ingested plant carotenoids, in chromoplasts of certain flagellates, also combining with proteins to form pigments, as of crustaceans; $C_{40}H_{52}O_4$.

astelic (ăstē'lĭk) *a.* [Gk. *a*, without; *stele*, pillar.] Not possessing a stele.

astely (ăstē'lĭ) *n.* [Gk. *a*, without; *stele*, pillar.] Absence of a central cylinder, axis, or stele.

aster (ăs'tĕr) *n.* [Gk. *aster*, star.] The star-shaped achromatinic structure surrounding centrosome during mitosis; star-shaped arrangement of chromosomes during mitosis.

asterigmate (ăstērĭg'māt) *a.* [Gk. *a*, without; *sterigma*, support.] Not borne on sterigmata; *appl.* spores.

asterion (ăstē'rĭŏn) *n.* [Gk. *aster*, star.] The region of posterolateral fontanelle where lambdoid, parieto-mastoid, and occipitomastoid sutures meet.

asteriscus (ăs'tĕrĭs'kŭs) *n.* [Gk. *asteriskos*, *dim.* of *aster*, star.] A small otolith in rudimentary cochlea of teleosts.

asternal (ăstĕr'năl) *a.* [L. *a*, from; *sternum*, breastplate.] *Appl.* ribs whose ventral ends do not join the sternum directly.

asteroid (ăs'tĕroid) *a.* [Gk. *aster*, star; *eidos*, form.] Star-shaped; *pert.* star-fish.

asterospondylous (ăs'tĕröspŏn'dĭlŭs) *a.* [Gk. *aster*, star; *sphondylos*, vertebra.] Having centrum with radiating calcified cartilage; also asterospondylic.

asthenic (ăsthĕn'ĭk) *a.* [Gk. *asthenes*, feeble.] Weak; tall and slender; leptosome.

asthenobiosis (ăs'thĕnöbĭō'sĭs) *n.* [Gk. *asthenes*, feeble; *biosis* manner of life.] Life during a phase of lessened metabolic activity.

astichous (ăs'tĭkŭs) *a.* [Gk. *a*, without; *stichos*, row.] Not set in a row or in rows.

astigmatous (ăstĭg'mătŭs) *a.* [Gk. *a*, without; *stigma*, mark.] Without stigmata or spiracles.

astipulate,—exstipulate, *q.v.*

astogeny (ăstŏj'ĕnĭ) *n.* [Gk. *astos*, citizen; *genos*, descent.] The development of a colony by budding.

astomatous (ăstŏm'ătŭs) *a.* [Gk. *a*, without; *stoma*, mouth.] Not having a mouth; without epidermic pores or stomata.

astomous (ăs'tŏmŭs) *a.* [Gk. *a*, without; *stoma*, mouth.] Without a stomium or line of dehiscence; bursting irregularly.

astragalus (ăstrăg'ălŭs) *n.* [Gk. *astragalos*, ankle-bone.] The talus, second largest tarsal bone in man; a tarsal bone in vertebrates.

astroblast (ăs'trŏblăst) *n.* [Gk. *aster*, star; *blastos*, bud.] A cell giving rise to protoplasmic or to fibrillar astrocytes.

astrocentre (ăs'trŏsĕn'tĕr) *n.* [L. *aster*, star; *centrum*, centre.] Centrosome.

astrocyte (ăs'trŏsīt) *n.* [Gk. *aster*, star; *kytos*, hollow.] A common neuroglia cell; astroglia; macroglia; Deiters' cell; a neuroglial cell with branching protoplasmic processes in grey matter; a fibrillar or spider cell in white matter.

astropodia (ăs'trŏpō'dĭă) *n. plu.* [Gk. *aster*, star; *pous*, foot.] Fine unbranched radiating pseudopodia, as in Heliozoa and some Radiolaria.

astropyle (ăs'trŏpīl, -ŏp'ĭlē) *n.* [Gk. *aster*, star; *pyle*, gate.] Chief aperture of central capsule, in certain Radiolaria.

astrosclereid (ăs'trŏsklē'rēĭd) *n.* [Gk. *aster*, star; *skleros*, hard; *eidos*, form.] A multiradiate sclereid or stone cell; a spiculate or ophiuroid cell.

astrosphere (ăs'trŏsfēr) *n.* [Gk. *aster*, star; *sphaira*, ball.] Central mass of aster without rays; aster exclusive of centrosome; astral sphere.

asymmetrical (ăsĭmĕt'rĭkăl) *a.* [Gk. *asymmetros*, disproportionate.] *Pert.* want of symmetry; having two sides unlike or disproportionate; *appl.* structures or organs which cannot be divided into similar halves by any plane; asymmetric.

asynapsis (ăsĭnăp'sĭs) *n.* [Gk. *a*, not; *synapsis*, union.] Absence of pairing of chromosomes in meiosis; asyndesis.

asynethogametism (ăs'ĭnē'thŏgămē'tĭzm) *n.* [Gk. *a*, not; *synethes*, well suited; *gametes*, spouse.] Incapability of two apparently suitable gametes to unite, owing to presence of an inhibiting factor; gametal incompatability; aëthogametism. *Opp.* synethogametism.

atactostele (ătăk'tŏstē'lē) *n.* [Gk. *ataktos*, irregular; *stele*, post.] A complex stele having bundles scattered in the ground tissue, as in monocotyledons.

atavism (ăt'ăvĭzm) *n.* [L. *atavus*, ancestor.] Reversion, occurrence of an ancestral characteristic not observed in more immediate progenitors.

atavistic (ăt'ăvĭs'tĭk) *a.* [L. *atavus*, ancestor.] *Pert.*, marked by, or tending to atavism.

ateleosis (ătĕlĕō'sĭs) *n.* [Gk. *ateles*, imperfect.] Dwarfism where individual is a miniature adult; *cf.* achondroplasia.

atelia (ătĕl'ĭă) *n.* [Gk. *ateles*, ineffectual.] The apparent uselessness of a character of unknown biological significance; incomplete development.

atelomitic (ătĕlŏmĭt'ĭk) *a.* [Gk. *a*, not; *telos*, end; *mitos*, thread.] *Appl.* other than terminal attachment of chromosome to spindle.

athalamous (ăthăl'ămŭs) *a.* [Gk. *a*, without; *thalamos*, inner room.] Lacking a thalamus.

athrocyte (ăth'rŏsīt) *n.* [Gk. *athroos*, collective; *kytos*, hollow.] A large resorptive cell or paranephrocyte of nephridium in Bryozoa.

athrocytosis (ăth'rŏsītō'sĭs) *n.* [Gk. *athroos*, collected; *kytos*, hollow.] The capacity of cells to selectively absorb and retain solid particles in suspension, as dyes.

atlanto-occipital,—occipito-atlantal, *q.v.*

atlas (ăt'lăs) *n.* [Gk. *Atlas*, a Titan.] The first cervical vertebra.

atokous (ăt'ökŭs) *a.* [Gk. *atokos*, childless.] Without offspring.

atoll (ăt'ôl, ătŏl') *n.* [Mal. *atoll.*] A coral reef surrounding a central lagoon.

atopy (ăt'öpĭ) *n.* [Gk. *atopia*, unusual nature.] Idiosyncrasy, genetic sensitivity to poisonous effects of particular antigens or atopens, as of certain proteins, pollen, etc.

atractoid (ăt'răktoid) *a.* [Gk. *atraktos*, spindle; *eidos*, form.] Spindle-shaped; fusiform.

atretic (ătrē'tĭk) *a.* [Gk. *a*, not; *tretos*, perforated.] Having no opening; imperforate; *appl.* vesicles resulting from degeneration of Graafian follicles, spurious corpora lutea.

atrial (ā'trĭăl) *a.* [L. *atrium*, central room.] *Pert.* atrium; *appl.* cavity, pore, canal, siphon, lobes.

atrichic (ătrĭk'ĭk) *a.* [Gk. *a*, not, *thrix*, hair.] Having no flagella; atrichous, aflagellar.

atriocoelomic (ā'trĭösēlŏm'ĭk) *a.* [L. *atrium*, central room; Gk. *koiloma*, a hollow.] Connecting atrium and coelom; *appl.* funnels, of uncertain function, in Cephalochorda.

atriopore (ā'trĭöpōr) *n.* [L. *atrium*, central room; *porus*, channel.] The opening from atrial cavity to exterior in Cephalochorda; spiracle in tadpole.

atrioventricular (ā'trĭövĕntrĭk'ūlăr) *a.* [L. *atrium*, chamber; *ventriculus*, small cavity.] *Pert.* atrium and ventricle of heart; *appl.* bundle, groove, node, openings.

atrium (ā'trĭŭm) *n.* [L. *atrium*, chamber.] Anterior cavity of heart; tympanic cavity; a division of the vestibule at end of bronchiole; chamber surrounding pharynx in Tunicata and Cephalochorda.

atrochal (ăt'rökăl) *a.* [Gk. *a*, without; *trochos*, wheel.] Without preoral circlet of cilia; *appl.* trochophore when preoral circlet is absent and surface is uniformly ciliated.

atropal,—atropous.

atrophy (ăt'röfĭ) *n.* [Gk. *a*, without; *trophe*, nourishment.] Emaciation; diminution in size and function.

atropous (ât'röpŭs) *a.* [Gk. *a*, without; *trope*, turn.] *Appl.* ovule in proper position, *i.e.* not inverted.

attachment, the spindle attachment; a lasting fusion of two chromosomes.

attenuated (ătĕn'ūātĕd) *a.* [L. *attenuare*, to thin.] Thinned; reduced in density, strength, or pathogenic activity.

atterminal (ăttĕr'mĭnăl) *a.* [L. *ad*, to; *terminus*, end.] Towards a terminal; *appl.* current directed toward thermal cross-section.

attic (ăt'ĭk) *n.* [Gk. *attikos*, Athenian.] The epitympanic recess.

attraction-particle,—centriole.

attraction - sphere, — centrosphere.

auditory (ôd'ĭtörĭ) *a.* [L. *audire*, to hear.] *Pert.* hearing apparatus, *appl.* organ, nucleus, ossicle, capsule, canal, meatus, nerve, vesicle, etc.; *pert.* sense of hearing.

auditory teeth,—of Huschke, projections on upper part of limbus of osseous spiral lamina of cochlea.

Auerbach's plexus [*L. Auerbach*, German anatomist]. A gangliated plexus of non-medullated nerve-fibres, found between the circular and longitudinal layers of muscular coat of small intestine; plexus myentericus.

augmentation (ôgmĕntā'shŭn) *n.* [L. *augere*, to increase.] Increase in number of whorls; *cf.* chorisis.

augmentor (ôgmĕn'tŏr) *a.* [L. *augere*, to increase.] *Appl.* nerves rising from sympathetic system and acting on heart, with antagonistic relation to vagi; accelerator.

aulophyte (ôl'öfīt) *n.* [Gk. *aulon*, hollow way; *phyton*, plant.] A non-parasitic plant growing in hollow of another.

aulostomatous (ôl'östŏm'ătŭs) *a.* [Gk. *aulos*, tube; *stoma*, mouth.] Having a tubular mouth or snout.

aural (ôr'ăl) *a.* [L. *auris*, ear.] *Pert.* ear or hearing.

auricle (ôr'ĭkl) *n.* [L. *auricula*, small ear.] Any ear-like lobed appendage; the external ear; atrium or anterior chamber of heart; lateral chemical receptor in Turbellaria; lateral outgrowth on second abdominal tergum in Anisoptera.

auricula (ôrĭk'ūlă) *n.* [L. *auricula*, small ear.] An auricle.

auricular (ôrĭk'ūlăr) *n.* [L. *auricula*, small ear.] Ear covert of birds. *a. Pert.* an auricle; *appl.* artery, nerve, tubercle, vein.

auricularia (ôrĭk'ūlā'rĭă) *n.* [L. *auricula*, small ear.] A type of larva found among Holothuria.

auricularis (ôrĭkūlā'rĭs) *n.* [L. *auricula*, small ear.] Superior, anterior, posterior, extrinsic muscles of the external ear.

auriculate (ôrĭk'ūlāt) *a.* [L. *auricula*, small ear.] Eared; *appl.* leaf with expanded bases surrounding stem; *appl.* leaf with lobes separate from rest of blade; hastate-auricled.

auriculo-ventricular,—*pert.* or connecting auricle and ventricle of heart; *appl.* bundle, valve.

auriform (ô'rĭfôrm) *a.* [L. *auris*, ear; *forma*, shape.] Resembling the external ear in shape, as shell of Haliotis.

aurophore (ôr'öfōr) *n.* [L. *auris*, ear; Gk. *pherein*, to bear.] An organ projecting from base of pneumatophore of certain Siphonophora.

austral (ôs'trăl) *a.* [L. *australis*, southern.] *Appl.* or *pert.* southern biogeographical region, or restricted to North America between transitional and tropical zones.

Australian (ôstrā'lĭăn) *a.* [L. *australis*, southern.] *Appl.* or *pert.* a zoogeographical region including Papua, Australia, New Zealand, and Pacific islands.

Austro-Columbian, — Neotropical, *q.v.*

autacoid (ôt'ăkoid) *n.* [Gk. *autos*, self; *akos*, remedy; *eidos*, form.] Internal secretion, a hormone or a chalone.

autarticular (ôt'ârtĭk'ūlăr) *n.* [Gk. *autos*, self; L. *articulus*, joint.] Goniale, *q.v.*

autecology (ôt'ēkŏl'öjĭ) *n.* [Gk. *autos*, self; *oikos*, household; *logos*, discourse.] The biological relations between a single species and its environment; ecology of an individual organism; auto-ecology.

autoantibiosis (ôt'öăn'tĭbīō'sĭs) *n.* [Gk. *autos*, self; *anti*, against; *biosis*, a living.] Retardation or inhibition of growth in a medium made stale by the same organism.

autobasidium (ôt'öbăsĭd'ĭŭm) *n.* [Gk. *autos*, self; *basis*, base; *idion*, *dim.*] A basidium having sterigmata bearing spores laterally, *opp.* apobasidium; a non-septate basidium or holobasidium.

autobiology,—idiobiology, *q.v.*

autoblast (ôt'öblăst) *n.* [Gk. *autos*, self; *blastos*, bud.] An independent micro-organism or cell.

autocarp (ôt'ökârp) *n.* [Gk. *autos*, self; *karpos*, fruit.] Fruit resulting from self-fertilisation.

autocatalysis (ôt'ökătăl'ĭsĭs) *n.* [Gk. *autos*, self; *kata*, down; *lysis*, loosing.] Dissolution or reaction of a cell or substance due to influence of a product or secretion of its own.

autochthon (ôtŏk'thŏn) *n.* [Gk. *autochthon*, aborigine.] An indigenous species.

autochthonous (ôtŏk'thönŭs) *a.* [Gk. *autos*, self; *chthon*, ground.] Aboriginal; indigenous; inherited or hereditary, native, *appl.* characteristics; originating within an organ, as pulsation of excised heart; formed where found. *Opp.* allochthonous.

autocoid,—autacoid, *q.v.*

autocyst (ôt'ösĭst) *n.* [Gk. *autos*, self; *kystis*, bladder.] A thick membrane formed by Neosporidia separating them from host tissues.

autodermalia (ôt'ödĕrmā'lĭă) *n. plu.* [Gk. *autos*, self; *derma*, skin.] Dermal spicules with axial cross, within dermal membrane.

autodont (ôt′ödŏnt) *a.* [Gk. *autos*, self; *odous*, tooth.] Designating or *pert.* teeth not directly attached to jaws, as in cartilaginous fishes.

autoecious (ôtē′sĭŭs) *a.* [Gk. *autos*, self; *oikos*, house.] Passing different stages of life-history in the same host; *appl.* parasitic fungi; autoxenous.

autogamous (ôtŏg′ămŭs) *a.* [Gk. *autos*, self; *gamos*, marriage.] Self-fertilising, *opp.* allogamous.

autogamy (ôtŏg′ămĭ) *n.* [Gk. *autos*, self; *gamos*, marriage.] Self-fertilisation, *opp.* allogamy; conjugation of nuclei within a single cell; conjugation of two protozoa originating from division of the same individual.

autogenesis (ôt′öjĕn′ĕsĭs) *n.* [Gk. *autos*, self; *genesis*, birth.] Spontaneous generation; autogeny, autogony.

autogenetic (ôt′öjĕnĕt′ĭk) *a.* [Gk. *autos*, self; *genesis*, birth.] Reproducing spontaneously, as body-cells.

autogenic (ôtöjĕn′ĭk) *a.* [Gk. *autos*, self; *gennaein*, to produce.] Caused by reactions of organisms themselves; *appl.* plant successions, *opp.* allogenic; autonomic or spontaneous, *appl.* movements.

autogenous (ôtŏj′ĕnŭs) *a.* [Gk. *autos*, self; *-genes*, produced.] Produced in the same organism; *appl.* enzymes; *appl.* graft reimplanted in same animal; *appl.* vaccine injected into same animal; *appl.* variations due to changes within chromosomes.

autogony (ôtŏg′ŏnĭ) *n.* [Gk. *autos*, self; *gonos*, offspring.] Autogenesis, *q.v.*

autoheteroploid (ô′töhĕt′ĕröploid) *n.* [Gk. *autos*, self; *heteros*, other; *aploos*, onefold; *eidos*, form.] Heteroploid derived from a single genome or multiplication of some of its chromosomes.

autoinfection (ôt′öĭnfĕk′shŭn) *n.* [Gk. *autos*, self; L. *inficere*, to taint.] Reinfection from host's own parasites.

D

autointoxication (ôt′öĭntŏk′sĭkā′-shŭn) *n.* [Gk. *autos*, self; L. *in*, in; Gk, *toxikon*, poison.] Reabsorption of toxic substances produced by the body.

autolysis (ôtŏl′ĭsĭs) *n.* [Gk. *autos*, self; *lysis*, loosing.] Self-digestion; cell or tissue disintegration by action of autogenous enzymes.

autolytic (ôt′ölĭt′ĭk) *a.* [Gk. *autos*, self; *lysis*, loosing.] Causing or *pert.* autolysis; *appl.* enzymes.

automixis (ôt′ömĭk′sĭs) *n.* [Gk. *autos*, self; *mixis*, mingling.] The union, in a cell, of chromatin derived from common parentage; self-fertilisation.

autonarcosis (ôt′önârkō′sĭs) *n.* [Gk. *autos*, self; *narke*, numbness.] State of being poisoned, rendered dormant, or arrested in growth, owing to self-produced carbon dioxide.

autonomic (ôt′önŏm′ĭk) *a.* [Gk. *autos*, self; *nomos*, law.] Autonomous; self-governing, spontaneous; *appl.* the involuntary nervous system as a whole, comprising parasympathetic and sympathetic systems; induced by internal stimuli, as movements of development, growth, unfolding, etc., *opp.* paratonic; internal, *appl.* environment, *opp.* choronomic.

autopalatine (ôt′öpăl′ătĭn) *n.* [Gk. *autos*, self; L. *palatum*, palate.] In a few teleosts, an ossification at anterior end of pterygoquadrate.

autoparasite (ô′töpăr′ăsīt) *n.* [Gk. *autos*, self; *parasitos*, one who subsists on another.] A parasite growing on another parasite.

autoparthenogenesis (ôt′öpâr′-thĕnöjĕn′ĕsĭs) *n.* [Gk. *autos*, self; *parthenos*, virgin; *genesis*, descent.] Development from unfertilised eggs activated by a chemical or physical stimulus.

autophagous (ôtŏf′ăgŭs) *a.* [Gk. *autos*, self; *phagein*, to eat.] *Appl.* birds capable of running about and securing food for themselves when newly hatched.

autophagy (ôtŏf'ăjĭ) *n.* [Gk. *autos*, self; *phagein*, to eat.] Subsistence by self-absorption of products of metabolism, as consumption of their own glycogen by yeasts.

autophilous (ôtŏf'ĭlŭs) *a.* [Gk. *autos*, self; *philein*, to love.] Self-pollinating; autogamous.

autophya (ôt'ŏfĭ'ă) *n. plu.* [Gk. *autos*, self; *phyein*, to produce.] Elements in formation of shell secreted by animal itself; *cf.* xenophya.

autophyllogeny (ôt'ŏfĭlŏj'ënĭ) *n.* [Gk. *autos*, self; *phyllon*, leaf; *genos*, birth.] Growth of one leaf upon or out of another.

autophyte (ôt'ŏfīt) *n.* [Gk. *autos*, self; *phyton*, plant.] A self-nourished plant; plant nourished directly by inorganic matter; *cf.* saprophyte.

autophytic (ôtŏfĭt'ĭk) *a.* [Gk. *autos*, self; *phyton*, plant.] Autotrophic, *q.v.*; *pert.* autophytes.

autoplasma (ôt'ŏplăz'mă) *n.* [Gk. *autos*, self; *plasma*, mould.] Plasma from same animal used as medium for tissue culture; *cf.* homoplasma, heteroplasma.

autoplast,—chloroplast.

autoplastic (ôt'ŏplăs'tĭk) *a.* [Gk. *autos*, self; *plastos*, formed.] *Appl.* graft to another position in the same individual.

autopodium (ôt'ŏpō'dĭŭm) *n.* [Gk. *autos*, self; *pous*, foot.] The hand or foot.

autopolyploid (ô'tŏpŏl'ĭploid) *n.* [Gk. *autos*, self; *polys*, many; *aploos*, onefold; *eidos*, form.] An organism having more than two sets of homologous chromosomes.

autopotamic (ô'tŏpŏtăm'ĭk) *a.* [Gk. *autos*, self; *potamos*, river.] Thriving in a stream, not in its backwaters; *appl.* potamoplankton.

autoradiography (ô'tŏrādĭŏg'răfĭ) *n.* [Gk. *autos*, self; L. *radius*, ray; Gk. *graphein*, to write.] Method of demonstrating the presence of specific chemical substances by first making them radioactive, then recording on a photographic film their distribution in the body, organs, or tissues.

autoskeleton (ôt'ŏskĕl'ëtŏn) *n.* [Gk. *autos*, self; *skeletos*, dried.] A true skeleton formed within the animal.

autosome (ôt'ŏsōm) *n.* [Gk. *autos*, self; *soma*, body.] A typical chromosome, or euchromosome, *opp.* sex-chromosome; *cf.* allosome.

autospasy (ôtŏs'păsĭ) *n.* [Gk. *autos*, self; *spao*, to pluck off.] Self-amputation; autotilly, autotomy.

autospore (ô'tŏspōr) *n.* [Gk. *autos*, self; *sporos*, seed.] An aplanospore which resembles the parent cell.

autostoses (ôt'ŏstō'sēz) *n. plu.* [Gk. *autos*, self; *osteon*, bone.] Bones formed in cartilage; *cf.* allostoses.

autostylic (ôt'ŏstīl'ĭk) *a.* [Gk. *autos*, self; *stylos*, pillar.] With mandibular arch self-supporting, articulating directly with skull; *cf.* hyostylic.

autosynapsis (ô'tŏsĭnăp'sĭs) *n.* [Gk. *autos*, self; *synapsis*, union.] Autosyndesis.

autosyndesis (ô'tŏsĭn'dësĭs) *n.* [Gk. *autos*, self; *syndesis*, a binding together.] Pairing of chromosomes from the same parent, in a polyploid or allopolyploid; pairing of homogenetic chromosomes; *cf.* allosyndesis.

autotheca (ôt'ŏthē'kă) *n.* [Gk. *autos*, self; *theke*, case.] A theca budded from a stolotheca, and surrounding the female polyp in graptolites.

autotilly (ô'tŏtĭl'ĭ) *n.* [Gk. *autos*, self; *tillesthai*, to pluck.] Autotomy, as in certain spiders.

autotomy (ôtŏt'ŏmĭ) *n.* [Gk. *autos*, self; *tome*, cutting.] Self-amputation of a part, as in certain worms, arthropods, and lizards.

autotransplantation, — transplantation of tissue or organ to another part of same organism; *cf.* homoiotransplantation.

autotrophic (ôt'ötrŏf'ĭk) *a.* [Gk. *autos*, self; *trephein*, to nourish.] Procuring food independently; *appl.* plants which form carbohydrates and proteins from carbon dioxide and inorganic compounds; neither saprophytic nor parasitic; autophytic. *Opp.* heterotrophic.

autotropism (ôtŏt'röpĭzm) *n.* [Gk. *autos*, self; *trope*, turn.] Tendency to grow in a straight line; *appl.* plants unaffected by external influence; tendency of organs to resume original form, after bending or straightening due to external factors; rectipetality.

autoxenous (ôtŏk'sēnŭs, ôt'özĕn'ŭs) *a.* [Gk. *autos*, self; *xenos*, host.] Parasitic on the same host at different stages in life-history; autoecious.

autozooid (ôt'özō'oid) *n.* [Gk. *autos*, self; *zoon*, animal; *eidos*, form.] An independent alcyonarian zooid or individual.

auxenolonic acid,—auxin B, *q.v.*

auxentriolic acid,—auxin A, *q.v.*

auxesis (ôksē'sĭs) *n.* [Gk. *auxesis*, growth.] Growth; increase in size owing to increase in cell size; induction of cell division; *cf.* merisis.

auxetic (ôksĕt'ĭk) *n.* [Gk. *auxein*, to increase.] Any agent which induces cell-division. *a.* Stimulating cell proliferation.

auxilia (ôgzĭl'yă) *n. plu.* [L. *auxilium*, assistance.] Two small sclerites between unguitractor and claws, in insects.

auxiliary cells,—two or more cells adjoining guard cells, or surrounding stomata; accessory or subsidiary cells.

auximone (ôk'sĭmōn) *n.* [Gk. *auximos*, promoting growth.] An accessory growth-stimulating factor in food of plants.

auxins (ôk'sĭnz) *n. plu.* [Gk. *auxein*, to increase.] Growth-regulating hormones of plants; auxin A isolated from growing tips of oat seedlings and human urine, $C_{18}H_{32}O_5$; auxin B, from vegetable sources and urine, accelerates mycelium growth, $C_{18}H_{30}O_4$; heteroauxin (*q.v.*), and a number of other substances.

auxocyte (ôks'ösīt) *n.* [Gk. *auxein*, to increase; *kytos*, hollow.] Androcyte, sporocyte, oocyte, or spermatocyte at growth period.

auxospireme (ôks'ōspī'rēm) *n.* [Gk. *auxein*, to increase; *speirema*, coil.] Spireme formed after syndesis.

auxospore (ôk'söspōr) *n.* [Gk. *auxein*, to increase; *sporos*, seed.] Zygote of diatoms, formed by union of two individuals at limit of decrease in size.

auxotonic (ôk'sötŏn'ĭk) *a.* [Gk. *auxein*, to increase; *tonos*, strain.] Induced by growth; *appl.* movements of immature plants; *opp.* allassotonic; *appl.* contraction against an increasing resistance.

auxotroph (ôk'sötrŏf) *n.* [Gk. *auxein*, to increase; *trophe*, nourishment.] A mutant lacking the capacity of forming an enzyme present in the parental strain, and therefore requiring a supplementary substance for growth.

avicularium (ăvĭkūlā'rĭŭm) *n.* [L. *avicula*, *dim.* of *avis*, bird.] In Polyzoa, a modified zooecium with muscular movable attachments resembling a bird's beak.

avifauna (ăv'ĭfô'nă) *n.* [L. *avis*, bird; *Faunus*, rural deity.] All the bird species or birds of a region or period; ornis.

avitaminosis (ăvī'tămĭnō'sĭs) *n.* [L. *a*, from; *vita*, life; *ammoniacum*, resinous gum.] A condition or disease resulting from vitamin-deficiency.

awn (ôn) *n.* [Icel. *ögn*, chaff.] The 'beard' of grasses; point of leaf, in certain Lycopsida.

axenic (ăksĕn'ĭk) *a.* [Gk. *axenos*, inhospitable.] Without, or deprived of, any commensals, symbionts, or parasites; not contaminated, *appl.* cultures.

axial (ăk'sĭăl) *a.* [L. *axis*, axle.] *Pert.* axis or stem.

axial filament,—central filament, as of a stiff radiating pseudopodium or of a flagellum.

axial sinus,—a nearly vertical canal in echinoderms, opening into internal division of oral ring sinus, and communicating with stone canal.

axial skeleton,—skeleton of head and trunk, *opp.* appendicular skeleton.

axiate pattern,—arrangement of parts with reference to a definite axis.

axil (ăk′sĭl) *n.* [L. *axilla*, arm-pit.] The angle between leaf or branch and axis from which it springs.

axile [ăk′sĭl) *a.* [L. *axis*, axle.] *Pert.*, situated in, or belonging to the axis; *appl.* placentation, free central, *q.v.*

axilemma (ăk′sĭlĕm′ă) *n.* [L. *axis*, axle; Gk. *lemma*, husk.] In medullated nerve fibres, the sheath surrounding axial cylinder.

axilla (ăksĭl′ă, ăk′sĭlă) *n.* [L. *axilla*, arm-pit.] The arm-pit; an axil.

axillary (ăk′sĭlărĭ, ăksĭl′ărĭ) *a.* [L. *axilla*, arm-pit.] *Pert.* axil; growing in axil, as buds; *pert.* arm-pit; *appl.* seventh longitudinal or anal vein of insect wing. *n.* One of the pteralia, *q.v.*

axinost,—axonost, *q.v.*

axipetal (ăksĭp′ëtăl) *a.* [L. *axis*, axle; *petere*, to seek.] Passing towards attachment of axon, *appl.* nerve impulses.

axis (ăk′sĭs) *n.* [L. *axis*, axle.] The main stem or central cylinder; the fundamentally central line of a structure; rachis of trilobites; structure at base of insect wing; the second cervical vertebra.

axis cylinder,—the central tract of a nerve fibre, the impulse transmitter; axon and its myelin sheath.

axodendritic (ăk′södĕndrĭt′ĭk) *a.* [Gk. *axon*, axle; *dendron*, tree.] *Appl.* synapse in which end-brush of axon is in contact with dendritic processes.

axon (ăk′sŏn) *n.* [Gk. *axon*, axle.] The axis-cylinder process of a nerve-cell normally transmitting excitations from its cell body; axone, neuraxon, neurite.

axon hill or **hillock,**—the area of a nerve cell from which the axon arises; cone of origin.

axoneme (ăk′sönēm) *n.* [Gk. *axon*, axle; *nema*, thread.] A thread of strand forming infusorian stalk; an axostyle; the axial filament of a flagellum; axial thread or genoneme of a chromosome.

axonost (ăk′sönŏst) *n.* [Gk. *axon*, axle; *osteon*, bone.] The basal portion of rods supporting dermotrichia of fin-rays; axinost; interspinal.

axoplasm (ăk′söplăzm) *n.* [Gk. *axon*, axle; *plasma*, form.] Plasma surrounding the neurofibrils within the axis cylinder; perifibrillar substance.

axoplast (ăk′söplăst) *n.* [Gk. *axon*, axle; *plastos*, formed.] A filament extending from kinetoplast to end of body in some trypanosomes.

axopodium (ăk′söpō′dĭŭm) *n.* [Gk. *axon*, axle; *pous*, foot.] A pseudopodium with axial filament.

axosomatic (ăk′sösōmăt′ĭk) *a.* [Gk. *axon*, axle; *soma*, body.] *Appl.* synapse in which end-brush of axon terminates about nerve-cell body.

axospermous (ăk′söspĕr′mŭs) *a.* [Gk. *axon*, axle; *sperma*, seed.] With axile placentation.

axostyle (ăk′söstīl) *n.* [Gk. *axon*, axle; *stylos*, pillar.] A slender flexible rod of organic substance forming a supporting axis for the body of many Flagellata.

azoic (ăzō′ĭk) *a.* [Gk. *a*, without; *zoikos*, *pert.* life.] Uninhabited; without remains of organisms or of their products; *appl.* Pre-Cambrian era or rocks.

azonal (ăzō′nal) *a.* [Gk. *a*, without; *zone*, girdle.] Not zoned; *appl.* soils without definite horizons.

azonic,—not restricted to a zone.

azurophil (ăzū′röfĭl, ăzh′ūröfĭl) *a.* [F. *azur*, from Ar. *al azurd*, lapis lazuli; Gk. *philein*, to love.] Staining readily with blue aniline dyes.

azygobranchiate (ăz′ĭgöbrăng′kĭăt) *a.* [Gk. *a*, without; *zygon*, yoke; *brangchia*, gills.] Having gills or ctenidia not developed on one side.

azygoid (ăz′ĭgoid) *a.* [Gk. *a*, without; *zygon*, yoke; *eidos*, form.] Not zygoid; haploid; *appl.* parthenogenesis.

azygomatous (ăzĭgŏm′ătŭs) *a.* [Gk. *a*, without; *zygoma*, a bar.] Without a zygoma or cheek-bone arch.

azygomelous (ăz′ĭgömĕl′ŭs, *a.* [Gk. *a*, without; *zygon*, yoke; *melos*, limb.] Having unpaired appendages; *appl.* fin of Acrania and Cyclostomata.

azygos (ăz′ĭgŏs) *n.* [Gk. *a*, without; *zygon*, yoke.] An unpaired muscle, artery, vein, process.

azygosperm,—azygospore.

azygospore (ăz′ĭgöspōr) *n.* [Gk. *a*, without; *zygon*, yoke; *sporos*, seed.] A spore developed directly from a gamete without conjugation; parthenospore.

azygote (ăz′ĭgōt) *n.* [Gk. *a*, without; *zygon*, yoke.] An organism resulting from haploid parthenogenesis.

azygous (ăz′ĭgŭs) *a.* [Gk. *a*, without; *zygon*, yoke.] Unpaired.

azymic (ăzī′mĭk) *a.* [Gk. *a*, without; *zyme*, leaven.] Not fermented; devoid of enzymes; not resulting from fermentation.

B

Babes-Ernst bodies [*V. Babes*, Romanian bacteriologist; *H. C. Ernst*, American bacteriologist]. Metachromatic or volutin granules, in bacteria.

bacca (băk′ă) *n.* [L. *bacca*, berry.] A pulpy fruit; berry.

baccate (băk′āt) *a.* [L. *bacca*, berry.] Pulpy, fleshy; berried.

bacciferous (băksĭf′ërŭs) *a.* [L. *bacca*, berry; *ferre*, to bear.] Berry-producing, or -bearing.

bacciform (băk′sĭfôrm) *a.* [L. *bacca*, berry; *forma*, shape.] Berry-shaped.

bacillary (băsĭl′ărĭ) *a.* [L. *bacillum*, small staff.] Rod-like; *appl.* layer of rods and cones of retina; *pert.* bacilli.

bacillus (băsĭl′ŭs) *n.* [L. *bacillum*, small staff.] A rod-like bacterium; a single-celled fungus.

back-cross,—to mate a cross or hybrid to a member of one of the parental stocks; a resulting hybrid.

back mutation,—reversion of a mutant gene to its original state; reverse mutation.

bactericidin (băk′tërĭsī′dĭn) *n.* [Gk. *bakterion*, small rod; L. *caedere*, to kill.] A substance that kills bacteria without causing lysis.

bacteriochlorin (băktē′rĭöklō′rĭn) *n.* [Gk. *bakterion*, small rod; *chloros*, green.] Green pigment, related to chlorophyll, in sulphur bacteria.

bacteriochlorophyll (băktē′rĭöklō′röfĭl) *n.* [Gk. *bakterion*, small rod; *chloros*, green; *phyllon*, leaf.] A photosynthetic pigment of bacteria, from which chlorophyll-*a* may be derived; bacteriochlorin.

bacteriology (băk′tērĭŏl′öjĭ) *n.* [Gk. *bakterion*, small rod; *logos*, discourse.] The science dealing with bacteria.

bacteriolysin (băktē′rĭölī′sĭn) *n.* [Gk. *bakterion*, small rod; *lysis*, loosing.] A substance which causes dissolution of bacteria.

bacteriolysis (băk′tērĭŏl′ĭsĭs) *n.* [Gk. *bakterion*, small rod; *lysis*, loosing.] The disintegration and dissolution of bacteria.

bacteriophage (băktē′rĭöfāj′) *n.* [Gk. *bakterion*, small rod; *phagein*, to devour.] A destroyer of bacteria; a bacteriolytic agent; phage.

bacteriopurpurin (băktē′rĭöpŭr′pūrĭn) *n.* [Gk. *bakterion*, small rod; L. *purpura*, purple.] A complex of photosynthetic pigments causing the red, purple, or violet appearance of certain bacteria.

bacteriostatic (băktē′rĭöstăt′ĭk) *a.* [Gk. *bakterion*, small rod; *statikos*, causing to stand.] Inhibiting development of bacteria.

bacteriotropin (băk'tērĭŏ'trŏpĭn) *n.* [Gk. *bakterion*, small rod; *trope*, turn.] An ingredient of blood serum which renders bacteria more readily phagocytable; opsonin.

bacteroid (băk'tĕroid) *n.* [Gk. *bakterion*, small rod; *eidos*, form.] An irregular form of certain bacteria.

baculiform (băk'ūlĭfôrm) *a.* [L. *baculum*, rod; *forma*, shape.] Rod-shaped; *appl.* chromosomes; *appl.* ascospores.

baculum (băk'ūlŭm) *n.* [L. *baculum*, rod.] The penis bone; os priapi.

bailer,—scaphognathite.

Baillarger's line [*J. F. G. Baillarger*, French neurologist]. Outer and inner layer of white fibres parallel to surface of cerebral cortex.

balanced lethals,—heterozygotes in which different lethal genes are in such close proximity on a pair of homologous chromosomes that there is usually no crossing-over.

balancers (băl'ănsĕrz) *n. plu.* [L. *bilanx*, having two scales.] Halteres or poisers of Diptera; paired larval head appendages functioning as props until forelegs are developed in certain salamanders.

balanic (bălăn'ĭk) *a.* [Gk. *balanos*, acorn.] *Pert.* glans penis; *pert.* glans clitoridis.

balanoid (băl'ănoid) *a.* [Gk. *balanos*, acorn; *eidos*, like.] Acorn-shaped; *pert.* barnacles.

balanus (băl'ănŭs) *n.* [L. *balanus*, acorn.] Glans penis; a genus of barnacles.

balausta (bălôs'tă) *n.* [Gk. *balaustion*, blossom.] A many-celled, many-seeded, indehiscent fruit with tough pericarp; fruit of pomegranate.

baleen (bălēn') *n.* [L. *balaena*, whale.] Horny plates attached to upper jaw of true whales; whalebone.

baler,—scaphognathite.

ballast (băl'ăst) *n.* [Sw. *barlast.*] *Appl.* elements present in plants and which are not apparently essential for growth, *e.g.*, Al, Si.

ballistic (bălĭs'tĭk) *a.* [Gk. *ballein*, to throw.] *Appl.* fruits with explosive dehiscence and discharge of seeds.

ballistospores (bălĭs'tŏspōrz) *n. plu.* [Gk. *ballein*, to throw; *sporos*, seed.] Asexual spores, formed on sterigmata and suddenly discharged with excretion of droplet, as in Sporobolomycetes; ballospores.

balsamiferous (băl'sămĭf'ĕrŭs) *a.* [L. *balsamum*, balsam; *ferre*, to bear.] Producing balsam.

banner,—the vexillum or upper petal in Papilionaceae; a muscle banner, *q.v.*, of Anthozoa.

bar of Sanio,—crassula, *q.v.*

baraesthesia (băr'ēsthē'zĭă) *n.* [Gk. *baros*, weight; *aisthesis*, sensation.] The sensation of pressure.

barb (bârb) *n.* [L. *barba*, beard.] One of delicate thread-like structures extending obliquely from a feather rachis, and forming the vane; a hooked hair-like bristle.

barbate (bâr'bāt) *a.* [L. *barbatus*, bearded.] Bearded; having hair tufts.

barbel (bâr'bĕl) *n.* [L.L. *barbellus*, barbel.] A tactile process arising from the head of various fishes.

barbellate (bârbĕl'āt, bâr'bĕlāt) *a.* [L. *barba*, beard.] With stiff hooked hair-like bristles; *appl.* pappus.

barbicel (bâr'bĭsĕl) *n.* [L. *barba*, beard.] Small process on a feather barbule.

barbula (bâr'būlă) *n.* [L. *barbula*, *dim.* of *barba*, beard.] Row of teeth in peristome of certain mosses.

barbule (bâr'būl) *n.* [L. *barbula*, *dim.* of *barba*, beard.] One of small hooked processes fringing barbs of feather; appendage of lower jaw in some teleosts.

baresthesia,—baraesthesia.

bark (bârk) *n.* [Dan. *bark.*] The tissues external to the vascular cambium, collectively; phloem, cortex, and periderm; outer dead tissues and cork.

baroceptor (băr'ŏsĕp'tŏr) *n.*. [Gk *baros*, pressure; L. *capere*, to take.] A receptor in wall of blood-vessels and reacting to changes in blood pressure; baroreceptor.

barotaxis (băröt ăk'sĭs) *n.* [Gk. *baros*, weight ; *taxis*, arrangement.] The reaction to a pressure stimulus.

barrage (bărâzh) *n.* [F. *barrage*, dam.] Zone of inhibition between certain bacterial or fungal colonies, not between others ; aversion zone.

Bartholin's duct [*C. Bartholin, jr.*, Danish anatomist]. The larger duct of the sublingual gland.

Bartholin's glands,—the greater vestibular glands on each side of vagina, homologues of male bulbo-urethral glands.

baryaesthesia,—baraesthesia.

basad (bā'săd) *a.* [L. *basis*, base ; *ad*, to.] Towards the base.

basal (bā'săl) *a.* [L. *basis*, base.] *Pert.*, at, or near the base.

basal bone,—os basale, basale, *q.v.*

basal cell,—uninucleate cell which supports the dome and tip cells of a hyphal crosier ; stalk cell.

basal ganglia,—ganglia connecting cerebrum with other centres.

basal granule,—a thickening, or body, at base of a flagellum in certain protozoa.

basal knobs,—swellings or granules at points of emergence of cilia in ciliated epithelial cells.

basal leaf,—one of the leaves produced near base of stem ; a radical leaf.

basal metabolic rate,—rate of metabolism of a resting organism, expressed as percentage of normal heat production per hour per square metre surface area.

basal metabolism,—standard metabolism, tissue activity or physicochemical changes of a resting organism.

basal placenta,—arises from proximal end of ovary.

basal plates,—certain plates in echinoderms, situated at or near top of stalk in crinoids, in echinoids forming part of apical disc ; fused parachordal plates in skull development ; of placentae, outer wall of intervillous space.

basal wall,—the first plane of division of oospores of ferns and mosses.

basalar (bāsā'lăr) *a.* [L. *basis*, base ; *ala*, wing.] *Appl.* sclerites below wing base in insects.

basale (băsā'lē) *n.* [L. *basis*, base.] A bone of variable structure arising from fusion of pterygiophores and supporting fish fins ; os basale, the fused basioccipital and parasphenoid in Gymnophiona.

basement membrane,—a membrane of modified connective tissue beneath epithelial tissue, as of a gland containing acini or special secreting portions.

baseost (bā'sëöst) *n.* [Gk. *basis*, base ; *osteon*, bone.] Distal element of pterygiophore of teleosts.

basialveolar (bā'sĭăl'vēölăr) *a.* [L. *basis*, base ; *alveolus*, small pit.] Extending from basion to centre of alveolar arch.

basibranchial (bā'sĭbrăng'kĭăl) *n.* [Gk. *basis*, base ; *brangchia*, gills.] Median ventral or basal skeletal portion of branchial arch.

basic (bā'sĭk) *a.* [Gk. *basis*, base.] *Appl.* stains which act in general on nuclear contents of cell ; *cf.* acidic ; *appl.* number, the minimum haploid chromosome number occurring in a series of euploid species of a genus ; chromosome number in gametes of diploid ancestor of a polyploid organism.

basichromatin (bā'sĭkrō'mătĭn) *n.* [Gk. *basis*, base ; *chroma*, colour.] The deeply staining substance of nuclear network ; chromatin.

basiconic (bā'sĭkŏn'ĭk) *a.* [Gk. *basis*, base; *konos*, cone.] Having, or consisting of, a conical process above general surface ; *appl.* sensillae.

basicoxite (bā'sĭkŏks'īt) *n.* [L. *basis*, base ; *coxa*, hip.] Basal ring of coxa.

basicranial (bā'sĭkrā'nĭăl) *a.* [Gk. *basis*, base ; *kranion*, skull.] Situated at or relating to base of skull.

basidia,—*plu.* of basidium.

basidial (băsĭd'ĭăl) *a.* [Gk. *basis*, base ; *idion*, *dim.*] *Pert.* basidia or a basidium.

basidiocarp (băsĭd'ĭōkârp) *n.* [Gk. *basis*, base; *idion*, *dim.*; *karpos*, fruit.] The fruit-body of Basidiomycetes.

basidiolum (băsĭd'ĭōlŭm) *n.* [L.L. *dim.* of Gk. *basidion*, small pedestal.] An undeveloped basidium; a pseudoparaphysis; formerly: paraphysis.

basidiophore (băsĭd'ĭōfōr) *n.* [Gk. *basis*, base; *idion*, *dim.*; *pherein*, to bear.] A sporophore which carries basidia.

basidiospore (băsĭd'ĭōspōr) *n.* [Gk. *basis*, base; *idion*, *dim.*; *sporos*, seed.] A spore or gonidium abstricted from a basidium; a secondary conidium; a basidiogonidium.

basidium (băsĭd'ĭŭm) *n.* [Gk. *basis*, base; *idion*, *dim.*] A special cell or row of cells, of certain fungi, forming spores by abstriction.

basidorsal (bā'sĭdôr'săl) *a.* [L. *basis*, base; *dorsum*, back.] *Appl.* small cartilaginous neural plate.

basifemur (bā'sĭfē'mŭr) *n.* [L. *basis*, base; *femur*, thigh.] Proximal segment of femur, between trochanter and telofemur, in certain Acarina.

basifixed (bā'sĭfĭksd) *a.* [L. *basis*, base; *figere*, to make fast.] Attached by base; innate, having filament attached to anther base.

basifugal (bāsĭf'ūgăl) *a.* [L. *basis*, base; *fugere*, to flee.] Growing away from base.

basifuge (bā'sĭfūj) *n.* [L. *basis*, base; *fugere*, to flee.] A plant unable to tolerate basic soils; calcifuge. *a.* Oxyphilous.

basigamous (bāsĭg'ămŭs) *a.* [Gk. *basis*, base; *gamos*, marriage.] Having oosphere reversed in embryo-sac.

basigynium,—podogynium, *q.v.*

basihyal (bā'sĭhī'ăl) *n.* [Gk. *basis*, base; *hyoeides*, *Y*-shaped.] Broad median plate, the basal or median ventral portion of hyoid arch.

basilabium (bā'sĭlā'bĭŭm) *n.* [L. *basis*, base; *labium*, lip.] Sclerite formed by fusion of labiostipites in insects.

basilar (băz'ĭlăr) *a.* [L. *basis*, base.] *Pert.* near or growing from base; as artery, crest, membrane, plexus, plate, process, style.

basilemma (bā'sĭlĕm'ă) *n.* [Gk. *basis*, base; *lemma*, skin.] Basement membrane.

basilic (băzĭl'ĭk) *a.* [Gk. *basilikos*, royal.] *Appl.* a large vein on inner side of biceps of arm.

basilingual (bā'sĭlĭng'gwăl) *a.* [L. *basis*, base; *lingua*, tongue.] *Appl.* a broad cartilaginous plate, the body of the hyoid, in crocodiles, turtles, and amphibians.

basimandibula (bā'sĭmăndĭb'ūlă) *n.* [L. *basis*, base; *mandibulum*, lower jaw.] A small sclerite, on insect head, at base of mandible.

basimaxilla (bā'sĭmăksĭl'ă) *n.* [L. *basis*, base; *maxilla*, upper jaw.] A sclerite at base of maxilla in insects.

basinym (bā'sĭnĭm) *n.* [Gk. *basis*, base; *onyma*, name.] The name upon which new names of species, etc. have been based; *cf.* isonym.

basioccipital (bā'sĭŏksĭp'ĭtăl) *n.* [L. *basis*, base; *occiput*, back of head.] The median basilar bone or element in occipital region of skull.

basion (bā'sĭŏn) *n.* [Gk. *basis*, base.] The middle of anterior margin of foramen magnum.

basiophthalmite (bā'sĭŏfthăl'mīt) *n.* [Gk. *basis*, base; *ophthalmos*, eye.] The proximal joint of eye-stalk in crustaceans.

basiotic (bā'sĭŏt'ĭk) *a.* [Gk. *basis*, base; *ous*, ear.] Mesotic, *q.v.*

basipetal (bāsĭp'ĕtăl) *a.* [L. *basis*, base; *petere* to seek.] Developing from apex to base; *appl.* leaves and inflorescences. *Opp.* acropetal.

basipharynx (bā'sĭfăr'ĭngks) *n.* [Gk. *basis*, base; *pharyngx*, gullet.] In insects, epipharynx and hypopharynx united.

basiphil (bā'sĭfĭl) *a.* [Gk. *basis*, base; *philein*, to love.] Basophil, *q.v.* *n.* A basiphil cell; a mast cell, *q.v.*

basipodite (bāsĭp'ŏdīt) *n.* [Gk. *basis*, base; *pous*, foot.] The second or distal joint of the protopodite of certain limbs of Crustacea; trochanter of spiders.

basipodium (bā'sĭpō'dĭŭm) *n.* [Gk. *basis*, base; *pous*, foot.] Wrist or ankle.

basiproboscis (bā'sĭprŏbŏs'ĭs) *n.* [Gk. *basis*, base; *proboskis*, trunk.] Membranous portion of proboscis of some insects, consisting of mentum, submentum, and maxillary cardines and stipites.

basipterygium (bā'sĭtĕrĭj'ĭŭm) *n.* [Gk. *basis*, base; *pterygion*, little wing.] A large flat triangular bone in pelvic fin of teleosts, and a bone or cartilage in other fishes.

basipterygoid (bā'sĭtĕr'ĭgoid) *n.* [Gk. *basis*, base; *pteryx*, wing; *eidos*, form.] A process of the basisphenoid in some birds.

basiscopic (bā'sĭskŏp'ĭk) *a.* [Gk. *basis*, base; *skopein*, to view.] Facing towards the base, *opp.* acroscopic.

basisphenoid (bā'sĭsfē'noid) *n.* [Gk. *basis*, base; *sphen*, wedge; *eidos*, form.] Cranial bone between basioccipital and presphenoid.

basisternum (bā'sĭstĕr'nŭm) *n.* [L. *basis*, base; *sternum*, breastbone.] The principal sclerite of insect sternum; antesternite, eusternum.

basistyle (bā'sĭstīl) *n.* [Gk. *basis*, base; *stylos*, pillar.] Proximal part or coxite of gonostyle in mosquitoes; *cf.* dististyle.

basitarsus (bā'sĭtâr'sŭs) *n.* [Gk. *basis*, base; *tarsos*, sole of foot.] Proximal tarsomere or 'metatarsus' of spiders. *Cf.* telotarsus.

basitemporal (bā'sĭtĕm'pŏrăl) *n.* [L. *basis*, base; *tempora*, temples.] A broad membrane bone covering basisphenoidal region of skull.

basitonic (bā'sĭtŏn'ĭk) *a.* [Gk. *basis*, base; *tonos*, brace.] Having anther united at its base with rostellum; basitonous. *Opp.* acrotonic.

basivertebral (bā'sĭvĕr'tĕbrăl) *a.* [L. *basis*, base; *vertebra*, vertebra.] *Appl.* veins within bodies of vertebrae and communicating with vertebral plexuses.

basket cells,—myo-epithelial cells surrounding glandular cells; cerebellar cortical cells with axon branches surrounding Purkinje cells.

basocyte (bā'sŏsīt) *n.* [Gk. *basis*, base; *kytos*, hollow.] A basophil cell; a basophil leucocyte.

basophil (bā'sŏfĭl) *a.* [Gk. *basis*, base; *philein*, to love.] Having a strong affinity for basic stains; also basiphil, basiphilic, basophile, basophilic, basophilous. *n.* A cell which stains with basic dyes.

basoplasm (bā'sŏplăzm) *n.* [Gk. *basis*, base; *plasma*, anything moulded.] Cytoplasm which stains readily with basic dyes.

basopodite,—basipodite.

bast (băst) *n.* [A.S. *baest*, bast.] The inner fibrous bark of certain trees; liber.

bastard merogony,—activation of an enucleated egg fragment by spermatozoon of a different species.

bastard wing,—the alula or ala spuria, consisting of three quill feathers borne on first digit of bird's wing.

bathmotropic (băth'mŏtrŏp'ĭk) *a.* [Gk. *bathmos*, degree; *tropikos*, turning.] Affecting the excitability of tissue, as of muscular tissue. *n.* Bathmotropism.

bathyaesthesia (băth'ĭēsthē'zĭă) *n.* [Gk. *bathys*, deep; *aisthesis*, perception.] Sensation of stimuli within the body; deep sensibility.

bathyal (băth'yăl) *a.* [Gk. *bathys*, deep.] *Appl.* or *pert.* zone of continental slope.

bathylimnetic (băth'ĭlĭmnĕt'ik) *a.* [Gk. *bathys*, deep; *limnetes*, living in marshes.] Living or growing in the depths of lakes or marshes.

bathymetric (băth'imĕt'rĭk) *a.* [Gk. *bathys*, deep; *metron*, measure.] *Pert.* vertical distribution of organisms in space.

bathypelagic (băth'ĭpĕlăj'ĭk) *a.* [Gk. *bathys*, deep; *pelagos*, sea.] *Pert.*, or inhabiting, the deep sea.

bathysmal (băthĭz′măl) *a.* [Gk. *bathys*, deep.] *Pert.* deepest depths of the sea.

batonette (bătŏnĕt) *n.* [F. *bâtonnet*, small stick.] An element of the Golgi apparatus, *q.v.*

batrachian (bătrā′kĭăn) *a.* [Gk. *batrachos*, frog.] Relating to frogs and toads.

B-cells,—beta cells of islets of Langerhans.

B-chromosome, — supernumerary chromosome in maize.

B-complex,—a group of accessory food factors comprising thiamine or vitamin B_1, riboflavin (B_2), pantothenic acid (B_3), niacin or P-P factor, pyridoxin (B_6), biotin (H), inositol, choline, para-amino benzoic acid, and folic acid (M), and B_{12} anti-pernicious-anaemia factor.

bdelloid (dĕl′oid) *a.* [Gk. *bdella*, leech; *eidos*, form.] Having the appearance of a leech.

beard (bērd) *n.* [A. S. *beard*, beard.] Any of the arrangements of hairs which resemble a man's beard, on heads of animals; barbed or bristly hair-like outgrowths on grain; awn.

bedeguar (bĕd′ēgăr) *n.* [From Persian through F. *bédeguar*.] A mossy gall produced on rose-bushes by Cynipides.

behaviorism (bēhā′vĭörĭzm) *n.* [A.S. *behabban*, to hold in.] Theory that the manner in which animals act may be explained in terms of conditioned neuromotor and glandular reactions.

belemnoid (bĕl′ĕmnoid, bĕlĕm′noid) *a.* [Gk. *belemnon*, dart; *eidos*, form.] Shaped like a dart; *appl.* styloid process.

Bellini's ducts [*L. Bellini*, Italian anatomist]. Tubes opening at apex of kidney papilla, and formed by union of smaller straight or collecting tubules.

bell-nucleus,—a solid mass of cells, derived from ectoderm and lying between ordinary ectoderm and mesogloea at apex of medusoid bud.

belonoid (bĕl′önoid) *a.* [Gk. *belone*, needle; *eidos*, form.] Shaped like a needle; aciform, styloid.

benthic (bĕn′thĭk) *a.* [Gk. *benthos*, depths of sea.] *Pert.*, or living on, sea-bottom; benthal.

benthopotamous (bĕn′thöpŏt′ămŭs) *a.* [Gk. *benthos*, depths; *potamos*, river.] *Pert.*, growing, or living, on bed of a river or stream.

benthos (bĕn′thŏs) *n.* [Gk. *benthos*. depths of sea.] The fauna and flora of the sea-bottom.

Berlese's organ [*A. Berlese*, Italian zoologist]. A glandular organ in haemocoel on right side of female abdomen in Cimex, secreting during passage of spermatozoa to spermatheca.

berry (bĕr′ĭ) *n.* [A.S. *berie*, berry.] Superior or inferior, indehiscent, many-seeded fruit, usually with fleshy pericarp; egg of lobster, or crayfish; dark knob-like structure on bill of swan.

Bertini's columns,—renal columns.

beta (β) **cells,**—basophil cells in pars glandularis of pituitary gland; cells elaborating insulin, in islets of Langerhans, B cells.

beta (β) **granules,**—granules in peripheral region of protoplast, a protein reserve in blue-green algae; cyanophycin.

betaine (bē′tăēn) *n.* [L. *beta*, beet.] A basic decomposition product of lecithin, occurring in beet and other plants, and in animals; $C_5H_{11}O_2N$.

between-brain,—diencephalon.

Betz cells [*V. A. Bets*, Russian histologist]. Giant pyramidal cells in motor area of cerebral cortex.

B-horizon,—the lower, illuvial soil layers.

biacuminate (bĭ′ăkū′mĭnāt) *a.* [L. *bis*, twice; *acumen*, point.] Having two tapering points.

biarticulate (bĭ′ârtĭk′ūlāt) *a.* [L. *bis*, twice; *articulus*, joint.] Two-jointed.

bicapsular (bĭkăp′sūlăr) *a.* [L. *bis*, twice; *capsula*, little box.] Having two capsules or vessels; having a biloculate capsule.

bicarinate (bīkăr'ĭnāt) *a.* [L. *bis*, twice; *carina*, keel.] With two keel-like processes.

bicarpellate (bīkâr'pĕlāt) *a.* [L. *bis*, twice; Gk. *karpos*, fruit.] With two carpels; bicarpellary.

bicaudate (bīkô'dāt) *a.* [L. *bis*, twice; *cauda*, tail.] Possessing two tail-like processes; bicaudal.

bicellular (bīsĕl'ūlăr) *a.* [L. *bis*, twice; *cellula*, little cell.] Composed of two cells.

bicentric (bī'sĕntrĭk) *a.* [L. *bis*, twice; *centrum*, centre.] *Pert.* two centres; *appl.* distribution of species, etc., discontinuous owing to alteration in the intervening area.

biceps (bī'sĕps) *n.* [L. *bis*, twice; *caput*, head.] A muscle with two heads or origins, as biceps brachii and femoris.

biciliate (bīsĭl'ĭāt) *a.* [L. *bis*, twice; *cilium*, eyelash.] Furnished with two cilia.

bicipital (bīsĭp'ĭtăl) *a.* [L. *bis*, twice; *caput*, head.] *Pert.* biceps; *appl.* fascia, or lacertus fibrosus, an aponeurosis of distal tendon of the biceps brachii; a groove, the intertubercular sulcus, on upper part of humerus; ridges, the crests of the greater and lesser tubercles of the humerus; *appl.* a rib with dorsal tuberculum and ventral capitulum; divided into two parts at one end.

bicollateral (bīkŏlăt'ĕrăl) *a.* [L. *bis*, twice; *con*, together; *latus*, side.] Having the two sides similar; *appl.* a vascular bundle with phloem on both sides of xylem, as in Cucurbitaceae and Solanaceae.

bicolligate (bīkŏl'ĭgāt) *a.* [L. *bis*, twice; *cum*, together; *ligare*, to bind.] With two stretches of webbing on the foot.

biconjugate (bīkŏn'joogāt) *a.* [L. *bis*, twice; *cum*, with; *jugum*, yoke.] With two similar sets of pairs.

bicornute (bīkôrnūt') *a.* [L. *bis*, twice; *cornutus*, horned.] With two horn-like processes.

bicostate (bīkŏs'tāt) *a.* [L. *bis*, twice, *costa*, rib.] Having two longitudinal ridges or ribs, as a leaf.

bicrenate (bīkrē'nāt) *a.* [L. *bis*, twice; *crena*, notch.] Doubly crenate, as crenate leaves with notched toothed margins.

bicuspid (bīkŭs'pĭd) *a.* [L. *bis*, twice; *cuspis*, point.] Having two cusps or points; *appl.* valve consisting of anterior and posterior cusps attached to circumference of left atrioventricular orifice, mitral valve; *appl.* teeth: premolar.

bicyclic (bīsĭk'lĭk) *a.* [L. *bis*, twice; Gk. *kyklos*, circle.] Arranged in two whorls.

Bidder's ganglia [*F. H. Bidder*, Estonian anatomist]. A collection of nerve-cells in region of the auriculo-ventricular groove.

Bidder's organ,—a rudimentary ovary attached to anterior end of generative organs in the toad.

bidental (bīdĕn'tăl) *a.* [L. *bis*, twice; *dens*, tooth.] Having two teeth, or tooth-like processes; bidentate.

bidenticulate (bī'dĕntĭk'ūlāt) *a.* [L. *bis*, twice; *dim.* of *dens*, tooth.] With two small teeth or tooth-like processes, as some scales.

biennial (bīĕn'ĭăl) *a.* [L. *bis*, twice; *annus*, year.] Lasting for two years. *n.* A biennial plant.

bifacial (bīfā'sĭăl, bīfā'shăl) *a.* [L. *bis*, twice; *facies*, face.] *Appl.* leaves with distinct upper and lower surfaces; dorsiventral.

bifarious (bīfā'rĭŭs) *a.* [L. *bis*, twice; *fariam*, in rows.] Arranged in two rows, one on each side of axis.

bifid (bĭf'ĭd) *a.* [L. *bis*, twice; *findere*, to split.] Forked, opening with a median cleft; divided nearly to middle line.

biflabellate (bī'flăbĕl'āt) *a.* [L. *bis*, twice; *flabellum*, fan.] Doubly flabellate, each side of antennal joints sending out flabellate processes.

biflagellate (bīflăj'ĕlāt) *a.* [L. *bis*, twice; *flagellum*, whip.] Having two flagella.

biflex (bī'flĕks) *a.* [L. *bis*, twice; *flectere*, to bend.] Twice curved.

biflorate (bīflō'rāt) *a.* [L. *bis*, twice; *flos*, flower.] Bearing two flowers; biflorous.

bifoliar (bīfō'lĭăr) *a.* [L. *bis*, twice; *folium*, leaf.] Having two leaves.

bifoliate (bīfō'lĭāt) *a.* [L. *bis*, twice; *folium*, leaf.] *Appl.* palmate compound leaf with two leaflets.

biforate (bĭf'örāt) *a.* [L. *biforis*, having double doors.] Having two foramina or pores; biforous.

biforin (bĭf'örĭn) *n.* [L. *bis*, twice; *foris*, door.] An oblong raphidian cell opening at each end.

biforous (bĭf'örŭs) *a.* [L. *biforis*, with two openings.] *Appl.* spiracles in larvae of certain beetles; biforate.

bifurcate (bīfŭr'kāt) *a.* [L. *bis*, twice; *furca*, fork.] Forked; having two prongs; having two joints, the distal V-shaped and attached by its middle to the proximal.

bigeminal (bījĕm'ĭnăl) *a.* [L. *bis*, twice; *geminus*, double.] With structures arranged in double pairs; *appl.* arrangement of pore-pairs in two rows, in ambulacra of some echinoids; *pert.* corpora bigemina.

bigeminate (bījĕm'ĭnāt) *a.* [L. *bis*, twice; *geminus*, double.] Doubly-paired; twin-forked.

bigeminum,—one of the corpora bigemina.

bigener (bījē'nĕr) *n.* [L. *bis*, twice; *genus*, race.] A bigeneric hybrid.

bigeneric (bī'jĕnĕr'ĭk) *a.* [L. *bis*, twice; *genus*, race.] *Appl.* hybrids between two distinct genera.

bijugate (bījoo'gāt) *a.* [L. *bis*, twice; *jugare*, to join.] With two pairs of leaflets.

bilabiate (bīlā'bĭāt) *a.* [L. *bis*, twice; *labium*, lip.] Two-lipped; *appl.* calyx, corolla, dehiscence.

bilamellar (bīlămĕl'ăr) *a.* [L. *bis*, twice; *lamella*, plate.] Formed of two plates; having two lamellae.

bilaminar (bīlăm'ĭnăr) *a.* [L. *bis*, twice; *lamina*, thin plate.] Having two plate-like layers; diploblastic; bilaminate.

bilateral (bīlăt'ĕrăl) *a.* [L. *bis*, twice; *latus*, side.] Having two sides symmetrical about an axis.

bile (bīl) *n.* [L. *bilis*, bile.] The secretion of the liver, passing to duodenum and assisting digestion.

biliary (bĭl'ĭărĭ) *a.* [L. *bilis*, bile.] Conveying or *pert.* bile.

biliation,—the secretion of bile.

bilicyanin (bĭl'ĭsī'ănĭn) *n.* [L. *bilis*, bile; Gk. *kyanos*, dark blue.] A blue pigment resulting from oxidation of biliverdin; cholecyanin.

bilifulvin,—bilirubin.

bilineurine,—choline.

bilipurpurin (bĭl'ĭpŭr'pūrĭn) *n.* [L. *bilis*, bile; *purpura*, purple.] Phylloerythrin.

bilirubin (bĭl'ĭroo'bĭn) *n.* [L. *bilis*, bile; *ruber*, red.] A reddish-yellow pigment of bile and blood, end-product of hæmoglobin metabolism; also bilifulvin, biliphaein; $C_{32}H_{36}N_4O_6$.

biliverdin (bĭl'ĭvĕr'dĭn) *n.* [L. *bilis*, bile; F. *vert*, green.] A green bile pigment formed by oxidation of bilirubin; $(C_{16}H_{18}N_2O_4)_n$.

bilobate (bīlō'bāt) *a.* [L. *bis*, twice; L.L. *lobus*, from Gk. *lobos*, rounded flap.] Having two lobes.

bilobular (bīlŏb'ūlăr) *a.* [L. *bis*, twice; L. *lobulus*, *dim.* of *lobus*, lobe.] Having two lobules.

bilocellate (bī'lŏsĕl'āt) *a.* [L. *bis*, twice; *locellus*, *dim.* of *locus*, place.] Divided into two compartments; having two locelli.

bilocular (bīlŏk'ūlăr), **biloculine** (bīlŏk'ūlĭn) *a.* [L. *bis*, twice; *locus*, place.] Containing two cavities or chambers; *cf.* loculus.

bilophodont (bīlŏf'ödŏnt) *a.* [L. *bis*, twice; Gk. *lophos*, ridge; *odous*, tooth.] *Appl.* molar teeth of tapir, which have ridges joining the two anterior and two posterior cusps.

bimaculate (bīmăk'ūlāt) *a.* [L. *bis*, twice; *macula*, spot.] Marked with two spots or stains.

bimanous (bĭm'ănŭs) *a.* [L. *bis*, twice; *manus*, hand.] Having two hands; *appl.* certain Primates.

bimastism (bīmăs'tĭzm) *n.* [L. *bis*, twice; Gk. *mastos*, breast.] Condition of having two mammae.

bimuscular (bīmŭs'kūlăr) *a.* [L. *bis*, twice; *musculus*, muscle.] Having two muscles.

binary (bī'nărĭ) *a.* [L. *binarius*, from *bini*, pair.] Composed of two units; *appl.*, *e.g.*, acids composed of hydrogen and one other element.

binary fission,—division of a cell into two by an apparently simple division of nucleus and cytoplasm.

binary nomenclature, — binomial nomenclature, *q.v.*

binate (bī'nāt) *a.* [L. *bini*, two by two.] Growing in pairs; *appl.* leaf composed of two leaflets.

binaural (bīnô'răl) *a.* [L. *bini*, pair; *auris*, ear.] *Pert.* both ears; binotic.

binocular (bĭnŏk'ūlăr) *a.* [L. *bini*, pair; *oculus*, eye.] Having or *pert.* two eyes; stereoscopic, *appl.* vision.

binodal (bīnō'dăl) *a.* [L. *bis*, twice; *nodus*, knob.] Having two nodes, as stem of plant.

binomial (bīnō'mĭăl) *a.* [L. *bis*, twice; *nomen*, name.] Consisting of two names; *appl.* nomenclature, the system of double names given to plants and animals,—first generic name, then specific, as *Felis* (genus) *tigris* (species).

binomialism (bīnō'mĭălĭzm) *n.* [L. *bis*, twice; *nomen*, name.] The system of binomial nomenclature.

binominal,—binomial.

binovular (bĭnôv'ūlăr) *a.* [L. *bini*, pair; *ovum*, egg.] *Pert.* two ova; dizygotic; *appl.* twinning.

binuclear (bīnū'klēăr), **binucleate** (bīnū'klēăt) *a.* [L. *bis*, twice; *nucleus*, small nut.] Having two nuclei.

bioblast (bī'öblăst) *n.* [Gk. *bios*, life; *blastos*, bud.] A hypothetical unit, *q.v.*

biocatalyst (bī'ökăt'ălĭst) *n.* [Gk. *bios*, life; *katalysis*, dissolving.] An enzyme; a ferment.

biocellate (bīŏs'ĕlāt) *a.* [L. *bis*, twice; *ocellus*, *dim.* of *oculus*, eye.] Having two ocelli.

biocenosis,—biocoenosis, *q.v.*

biochemistry (bī'ökĕm'ĭstrĭ) *n.* [Gk. *bios*, life; *chemeia*, transmutation.] The chemistry of living organisms.

biochore (bī'ökōr) *n.* [Gk. *bios*, life; *choris*, separate.] Boundary of a floral or faunal region; climatic boundary of a floral region; a group of similar biotopes.

biochrome (bī'ökrōm) *n.* [Gk. *bios*, life; *chroma*, colour.] Any natural colouring matter of plants and animals; biological pigment.

biocoenosis (bī'ösēnō'sĭs) *n.* [Gk. *bios*, life; *koinos*, common.] A community of organisms inhabiting a biotope; biocenosis.

biocycle (bī'ösīkl) *n.* [Gk. *bios*, life; *kyklos*, place of assembly.] One of the three main divisions of the biosphere: marine, or fresh-water, or terrestrial habitat.

biodemography (bīödĕmŏg'răfĭ) *n.* [Gk. *bios*, life; *demos*, people; *graphein*, to write.] Science dealing with the integration of ecology and genetics of populations.

biodynamics (bī'ödĭnăm'ĭks) *n.* [Gk. *bios*, life; *dynamis*, power.] The science of the active vital phenomena of organisms.

bioecology (bī'öēkŏl'öji) *n.* [Gk. *bios*, life; *oikos*, household; *logos*, discourse.] Ecology of plants and animals.

bioelectric (bī'öēlĕk'trĭk) *a.* [Gk. *bios*, life; *elektron*, amber.] *Appl.* currents produced in living organisms.

bioenergetics (bī'öĕnërjĕt'ĭks) *n.* [Gk. *bios*, life; *energeia*, action.] Study of energy transformations in living organisms.

bioflavonoids (bī'öflā'vönoidz) *n.plu.* [Gk. *bios*, life; L. *flavus*, yellow; Gk. *eidos*, form.] Compounds, occurring in citrus and other fruits, which interact with various metabolic products and enzymes in animals, and maintain normal permeability of capillaries; vitamin P.

biogen (bī'öjĕn), **biogene** (bīöjēn) *n.* [Gk. *bios*, life; *genos*, descent.] A hypothetical unit, *q.v.*; a large living molecule; precursor of bios, *q.v.*

biogenesis (bī'öjĕn'ĕsĭs) *n.* [Gk. *bios*, life; *genesis*, descent.] The theory of the descent of living matter from living matter—*omne vivum e vivo.* *Opp.* abiogenesis.

biogenetic law, — recapitulation theory, *q.v.*

biogenous (bīŏj'ĕnŭs) *a.* [Gk. *bios*, life; *genos*, offspring.] Inhabiting living organisms, as parasites.

biogeny (bīŏj'ĕnĭ) *n.* [Gk. *bios*, life; *genesis*, descent.] The science of the evolution of organisms, comprising ontogeny and phylogeny.

biogeochemistry (bī'öjē'ökĕm'ĭstrĭ) *n.* [Gk. *bios*, life; *ge*, earth; *chemeia*, transmutation.] The study of the distribution and migration of chemical elements present in living organisms and in interaction with their geographical environment.

biogeography (bī'öjēŏg'răfĭ) *n.* [Gk. *bios*, life; *ge*, earth; *graphein*, to write.] The part of biology dealing with the geographical distribution of plants (phytogeography) and animals (zoogeography); chorology.

biological (bīölŏj'ĭkăl) *a.* [Gk. *bios*, life; *logos*, discourse.] Relating to the science of life.

biology (bīŏl'öjĭ) *n.* [Gk. *bios*, life; *logos*, discourse.] The science of life and living.

bioluminescence (bī'ölūmĭnĕs'ĕns, -loo-) *n.* [Gk. *bios*, life; L. *luminescere*, to grow light.] Light-production, as in many groups of animals, and in bacteria and fungi.

biolysis (bīŏl'ĭsĭs) *n.* [Gk. *bios*, life; *lysis*, loosing.] The decomposition of organic matter resulting from activity of living organisms; disintegration of life.

biolytic (bīölĭt'ĭk) *a.* [Gk. *bios*, life; *lyein*, to break up.] *Pert.* biolysis; destroying life.

biomass (bī'ömăs) *n.* [Gk. *bios*, life; *massein*, to squeeze.] Total weight of organisms per unit area.

biome (bīōm) *n.* [Gk. *bios*, life.] A major community of living organisms; a complex of climax communities of plants and animals in a major region, as tundra, forest, grassland, desert, mountain; major life zone.

biometeorology (bī'ömĕtēörŏl'öji) *n.* [Gk. *bios*, life; *meteorologia*, treatise on the heavenly bodies.] The study of the effects of atmospheric conditions upon plants and animals.

biometrics (bīömĕt'rĭks) *n.* [Gk. *bios*, life; *metron*, measure.] The statistical study of living organisms and their variations; biometry.

bion (bī'ŏn), **biont** (bī'ŏnt) *n.* [Gk. *bion*, living.] An independent living organism; an individual organism.

bionergy (bī'ŏnĕrjĭ) *n.* [Gk. *bios*, life; *energeia*, action.] Vital force.

bionomics (bīönŏm'ĭks) *n.* [Gk. *bios*, life; *nomos*, law.] The study of organisms in relation to their environment; bionomy; ecology.

biophore (bī'öfōr) *n.* [Gk. *bios*, life; *pherein*, to carry.] A hypothetical unit, *q.v.*

biophotogenesis (bī'öfōtöjĕn'ĕsĭs) *n.* [Gk. *bios*, life; *phos*, light; *genesis*, origin.] The production and emission of light by plants or by animals; bioluminescence.

biophysics (bīöfĭz'ĭks) *n.* [Gk. *bios*, life; *physis*, nature.] Study of biological phenomena interpreted in terms of physical principles; physics as applicable to biology.

biophyte (bī'öfīt) *n.* [Gk. *bios*, life; *phyton*, plant.] A plant which gets sustenance from living organisms.

bioplasm (bī'öplăzm) *n.* [Gk. *bios*, life; *plasma*, mould.] Living matter; protoplasm.

bioplast (bī'öplăst) *n.* [Gk. *bios*, life; *plastos*, formed.] A minute quantity of living protoplasm capable of reproducing itself.

biopsy (bī'ŏpsĭ) *n.* [Gk. *bios*, life; *opsis*, sight.] Examination of living organisms, organs, or tissues.

biorgan (bī'ôrgăn) *n.* [Gk. *bios*, life; *organon*, instrument.] An organ in the physiological sense, not necessarily a morphological unit.

bios (bī′ŏs) *n.* [Gk. *bios*, life.] Organic life, plant or animal; a complex mixture of vitamins or growth factors; B complex, *q.v.*

bioseries (bi′ösērĭēz) *n.* [Gk. *bios*, life; L. *series*, row.] A succession of changes of any single heritable character.

biosis (bīō′sĭs) *n.* [Gk. *biosis*, a living.] Mode of living; vitality.

biosomes (bī′ösōmz) *n. plu.* [Gk. *bios*, life; *soma*, body.] Structural and functional units in cytoplasm, as chondriosomes, chromidia and plastids.

biosphere (bī′ösfēr) *n.* [Gk. *bios*, life; *sphaira*, globe.] The part of the globe containing living organisms.

biostatics (bī′östăt′ĭks) *n.* [Gk. *bios*, life; *statos*, stationary.] The science of structure in relation to function of organisms.

biosystem,—ecosystem.

biosystematics,—genonomy; taxonomy.

biota (bīō′tă) *n.* [Gk. *bios*, life.] The fauna and flora of a region.

biotic (bīŏt′ĭk) *a.* [Gk. *biotikos*, *pert.* life.] *Pert.* life; vital.

biotic community,—a community of plants and animals as a whole.

biotic formation,—biome.

biotic potential,—highest possible rate of population increase, resulting from maximum natality and minimum mortality.

biotin (bī′ötĭn) *n.* [Gk. *bios*, life.] Vitamin H, a growth substance of yeast, also obtained from liver; or coenzyme R, required by nitrogen-fixing bacteria; antiperosis factor; antiavidin; $C_{10}H_{16}O_3N_2S$.

biotomy (bīŏt′ömĭ) *n.* [Gk. *bios*, life; *tome*, cutting.] The dissection of living organisms; vivisection.

biotonus (bīŏt′ŏnŭs) *n.* [Gk. *bios*, life; *tonos*, tension.] The ratio between assimilation and dissimilation of biogens.

biotope (bī′ötōp) *n.* [Gk. *bios*, life; *topos*, place.] An area in which the main environmental conditions and biotypes adapted to them are uniform; a place where organisms can survive; also, microhabitat.

biotype (bī′ötīp) *n.* [Gk. *bios*, life; L. *typus*, image.] Type of plant or animal; all the individuals of equal genotype.

biovular,—binovular.

biovulate (bīōv′ūlăt) *a.* [L. *bis*, twice; *ovum*, egg.] Containing two ovules.

bipaleolate (bīpā′lëölăt) *a.* [L. *bis*, twice; *palea*, chaff.] Furnished with two small paleae.

bipalmate (bīpăl′māt) *a.* [L. *bis*, twice; *palma*, palm of hand.] Lobed with the lobes again lobed.

biparietal (bī′părī′ētăl) *a.* [L. *bis*, twice; *paries*, wall.] Connected with the two parietal eminences.

biparous (bĭp′ărŭs) *a.* [L. *bis*, twice; *parere*, to bear.] Having two young at a time; dichotomous, *appl.* branching.

bipectinate (bīpĕk′tĭnāt) *a.* [L. *bis*, twice; *pecten*, comb.] Having the two margins furnished with teeth like a comb.

biped (bī′pĕd) *n.* [L. *bis*, twice; *pes*, foot.] A two-footed animal.

bipennate (bīpĕn′āt) *a.* [L. *bis*, twice; *penna*, feather.] Bipenniform; *appl.* muscles in which the tendon of insertion extends through the middle.

bipenniform (bīpĕn′ĭfôrm) *a.* [L. *bis*, twice; *penna*, feather; *forma*, shape.] Feather-shaped, with sides of vane of equal size; bipennate.

bipetalous (bīpĕt′ălŭs) *a.* [L. *bis*, twice; Gk. *petalon*, leaf.] With two petals.

bipinnaria (bīpĭnā′rĭă) *n.* [L. *bis*, twice; *pinna*, feather.] An asteroid larva with two bands of cilia.

bipinnate (bīpĭn′āt) *a.* [L. *bis*, twice; *pinna*, feather.] Having leaflets growing in pairs on paired stems.

bipinnatifid (bī′pĭnăt′ĭfĭd) *a.* [L. *bis*, twice; *pinna*, feather; *findere*, to cleave.] With leaves segmented and these segments again divided.

bipinnatipartite (bī'pĭnăt'ĭpârtīt) *a.* [L. *bis*, twice; *pinna*, feather; *partiri*, to divide.] Bipinnatifid, but with divisions extending nearly to midrib.

bipinnatisect (bī'pĭnăt'ĭsĕkt) *a.* [L. *bis*, twice; *pinna*, feather; *secare*, to cut.] Bipinnatifid, but with divisions extending to midrib.

biplicate (bĭp'lĭkāt) *a.* [L. *bis*, twice; *plicare*, to fold.] Having two folds.

bipocillus (bī'pōsĭl'ŭs) *n.* [L. *bis*, twice; *pocillum*, little cup.] A microsclere with curved shaft and cup-shaped expansion at each end.

bipolar (bīpō'lăr) *a.* [L. *bis*, twice; *polus*, pole.] Having, located at, or *pert.* two ends or poles; *appl.* nerve cells having a process at each end; *appl.* allied species occurring towards Arctic and Antarctic regions.

bipolarity (bī'pölăr'ĭtĭ) *n.* [L. *bis*, twice; *polus*, pole.] The condition of having two polar processes; condition of having two distinct poles, as vegetative and animal poles in an egg; bipolar distribution, as of species.

biradial (bĭrā'dĭăl) *a.* [L. *bis*, twice; *radius*, ray.] Symmetrical both radially and bilaterally, as some coelenterates; disymmetrical.

biramous (bĭrā'mŭs) *a.* [L. *bis*, twice; *ramus*, branch.] Divided into two branches; biramose.

birostrate (bīrŏs'trāt) *a.* [L. *bis*, twice; *rostrum*, beak.] Furnished with two beak-like processes.

birth pore,—uterine pore of trematodes and cestodes; birth-opening of redia of trematodes.

biscoctiform (bĭskŏk'tĭfôrm) *a.* [L. *bis*, twice; *coctus*, baked; *forma*, shape.] Biscuit-shaped; *appl.* spores.

biseptate (bīsĕp'tāt) *a.* [L. *bis*, twice; *septum*, fence.] With two partitions.

biserial (bīsē'rĭăl) *a.* [L. *bis*, twice; *series*, row.] Arranged in two rows or series; biseriate.

biserrate (bīsĕr'āt) *a.* [L. *bis*, twice; *serra*, saw.] Having marginal teeth which are themselves notched.

bisexual (bīsĕk'sūăl, *a.* [L. *bis*, twice; *sexus*, sex.] Having both male and female reproductive organs; hermaphrodite; amphisporangiate, *q.v.*

bisporangiate (bī'spörăn'jĭāt) *a.* [L. *bis*, twice; Gk. *sporos*, seed; *anggeion*, vessel.] Having both micro- and megasporangia; *appl.* strobilus consisting of both micro- and megasporophylls.

bisporic (bīspŏr'ĭk) *a.* [L. *bis*, twice; Gk. *sporos*, seed.] With two spores; *appl.* basidia; disporous.

bistephanic (bī'stĕfăn'ĭk) *a.* [L. *bis*, twice; Gk. *stephanos*, crown.] Joining two points where coronal suture crosses superior temporal ridges.

bistipulate (bīstĭp'ūlāt) *a.* [L. *bis*, twice; *stipula*, stem.] Provided with two stipules.

bistrate (bī'strāt) *a.* [L. *bis*, twice; *stratum*, layer.] Having two layers; *appl. e.g.* indumentum.

bistratose (bīstrā'tōs) *a.* [L. *bis*, twice; *stratum*, layer.] With cells arranged in two layers.

bisulcate (bīsŭl'kāt) *a.* [L. *bis*, twice; *sulcus*, groove.] Having two grooves.

bitemporal (bītĕm'pörăl) *a.* [L. *bis*, twice; *tempora*, temples.] *Appl.* two temporal bones; a line joining posterior ends of two zygomatic processes.

biternate (bītĕr'nāt) *a.* [L. *bis*, twice; *terni*, three by three.] Ternate with each division itself again ternate.

bitheca (bīthē'kă) *n.* [L. *bis*, twice; *theca*, case.] A theca budded from a stolotheca, and surrounding the male polyp in graptolites.

bivalent (bīvā'lĕnt, bĭv'ălĕnt) *a.* [L. *bis*, twice; *valere*, to be strong.] *Appl.* paired homologous chromosomes.

bivalve (bī'vălv) *a.* [L. *bis*, twice; *valvae*, folding-doors.] Consisting of two plates or valves, as a mussel shell; or *appl.* a seed-capsule of similar structure.

biventer cervicis (bīvĕn'tĕr sĕrvī'sĭs) *n.* [L. *bis*, twice ; *venter*, belly ; *cervix*, neck.] The spinalis capitis, or medial part of semispinalis, a muscle of neck, consisting of two fleshy ends with narrow tendinous portion in middle.

biventral (bīvĕn'trăl) *a.* [L. *bis*, twice ; *venter*, belly.] *Appl.* muscles of the biventer type ; digastric ; *appl.* a lobule of the cerebellum.

biverticillate (bī'vĕrtĭs'ĭlāt) *a.* [L. *bis*, twice ; *verticillus*, small whorl.] Having two verticils or whorls.

bivittate (bīvĭt'āt) *a.* [L. *bis*, twice ; *vitta*, band.] With two oil receptacles ; with two stripes.

bivium (bĭv'ĭŭm) *n.* [L. *bis*, twice ; *via*, way.] Generally the posterior pair of ambulacral areas in certain Echinoidea ; the two rays between which the madreporite lies.

bivoltine (bĭvŏl'tĭn) *a.* [L. *bis*, twice ; It. *volta*, time.] Having two broods in a year ; *appl.* silk-worms.

bladder (blăd'ĕr) *n.* [A.S. *blaedre*, bag.] A membranous sac filled with air or fluid ; a cyst ; vesica.

bladder-cell,—a globular modified hyphal cell in integument of carpophore ; volva bladder.

bladderworm stage, — cysticercus stage in tape-worms.

blade (blād) *n.* [A.S. *blaed*, leaf.] The flat part of leaf of grasses ; lamina.

Blandin's glands [*P.-F. Blandin*, French surgeon]. Anterior lingual glands ; glands of Nuhn.

blastaea (blăstē'ă) *n.* [Gk. *blastos*, bud.] A planaea or ciliated planula, a hypothetical stage in evolution.

blastelasma (blăst'ĕlăs'mă) *n.* [Gk. *blastos*, bud ; *elasma*, plate.] Any germ layer formed after formation of epiblast and hypoblast.

blastema (blăst'ēmă) *n.* [Gk. *blastema*, bud.] Formative substance in an egg ; primordium of an organ ; thallus of a lichen.

blastic (blăs'tĭk) *a.* [Gk. *blastos*, bud.] *Pert.* or stimulating enlargement by cell-division ; *opp.* trophic.

blastocarpous (blăs'tōkâr'pŭs) *a.* [Gk. *blastos*, bud ; *karpos*, fruit.] Developing while still surrounded by pericarp.

blastocheme (blăs'tōkēm) *n.* [Gk. *blastos*, bud ; *ochema*, vessel.] A reproductive individual in some Medusae.

blastocholines (blăs'tōkō'lēnz) *n.plu.* [Gk. *blastos*, bud ; *cholos*, halting.] Various substances, present in sporangia, seeds, and fruits, which prevent premature germination ; germination inhibitors.

blastochyle (blăs'tōkīl) *n.* [Gk. *blastos*, bud ; *chylos*, juice.] The fluid in a blastocoel or segmentation-cavity.

blastocoel (blăs'tōsēl) *n.* [Gk. *blastos*, bud ; *koilos*, hollow.] The segmentation-cavity, cavity of a blastula.

blastocolla (blăs'tōkŏl'ă) *n.* [Gk. *blastos*, bud ; *kolla*, glue.] A gummy substance coating certain buds.

blastocone (blăs'tōkōn) *n.* [Gk. *blastos*, bud ; *konos*, cone.] An outer larger cell of first circumferential division, in segmentation of certain eggs.

blastocyst (blăs'tōsĭst) *n.* [Gk. *blastos*, bud ; *kystis*, bladder.] The germinal vesicle.

blastocyte (blăs'tōsīt) *n.* [Gk. *blastos*, bud ; *kytos*, hollow.] Any undifferentiated embryonic cell.

blastoderm (blăs'tōdĕrm) *n.* [Gk. *blastos*, bud ; *derma*, skin.] The germinal disc.

blastodermic vesicle, — hollow sphere of cells, an early stage in development of a fertilised ovum.

blastodisc (blăs'tōdĭsk) *n.* [Gk. *blastos*, bud ; *diskos*, disk.] The germinal area of a developing ovum ; blastodisk, blastoderm, germinal disc.

blastogene,—plasmagene, *q.v.*

blastogenesis (blăs'tōjĕn'ĕsĭs) *n.* [Gk. *blastos*, bud ; *genesis*, descent.] Gemmation or reproduction by budding ; transmission of inherited characters by means of germ-plasm only.

blastogenic (blăs'töjĕn'ĭk) *a.* [Gk. *blastos*, bud; *genos*, offspring.] *Appl.* inactive idioplasm unalterable till time and place of activity are reached; arising from changes in germ cells; *appl.* characteristics of germinal constitution; *appl.* reproduction by budding.

blastokinesis (blăs'tökĭnē'sĭs) *n.* [Gk. *blastos*, bud; *kinesis*, movement.] Movement of embryo in the egg, as in certain insects and cephalopods.

blastomere (blăs'tömēr) *n.* [Gk. *blastos*, bud; *meros*, part.] One of the cells formed during primary divisions of an egg; cleavage cell.

blastoneuropore (blăs'tönū'röpōr) *n.* [Gk. *blastos*, bud; *neuron*, nerve; *poros*, passage.] A temporary passage connecting blastopore and neuropore.

blastophore (blăs'töfōr) *n.* [Gk. *blastos*, bud; *pherein*, to bear.] Embryonic origin of plumule; the reproductive body in Alcyonaria; central part of spermocyte mass which remains unchanged through spermatogenesis in Annelida.

blastophthoria (blăs'töfthō'rĭă) *n.* [Gk. *blastos*, bud; *phthora*, corruption.] Any injurious effect on germ cells or on germ plasm.

blastopore (blăs'töpōr) *n.* [Gk. *blastos*, bud; *poros*, passage.] Channel leading into archenteron of gastrula.

blastosphere (blăs'tösfēr) *n.* [Gk. *blastos*, bud; *sphaira*, globe.] The blastula; blastodermic vesicle; a hollow ball of cells.

blastospore (blăs'töspōr) *n.* [Gk. *blastos*, bud; *sporos*, seed.] An attached thallospore developed by budding and itself capable of budding, as of yeast cells.

blastostyle (blăs'töstīl) *n.* [Gk. *blastos*, bud; *stylos*, pillar.] In Hydrozoa, a columniform zooid with or without mouth and tentacles, bearing gonophores.

blastozoite (blăs'tözō'īt) *n.* [Gk. *blastos*, bud; *zoe*, life.] An individual organism produced by budding.

blastozooid (blăs'tözō'oid) *n.* [Gk. *blastos*, bud; *zoon*, animal; *eidos*, form.] A larval bud in precocious budding in ascidians.

blastula (blăs'tūlă) *n.* [L. *dim.* of Gk. *blastos*, bud.] A hollow ball of cells, with wall usually one layer thick; blastosphere.

blastulation (blăs'tūlā'shŭn) *n.* [L. *blastula*, little bud.] Formation of blastulae.

bleeder,—an individual subject to haemophilia, *q.v.*

bleeding, of plants, exudation of watery sap from vessels at a cut surface, due to root-pressure.

blematogen (blēmăt'öjĕn) *n.* [Gk. *blema*, coverlet; *gennaein*, to produce.] Primordial covering of a carpophore; undeveloped universal veil in agarics; primordial cuticle.

blended inheritance,—mixed race or descent; mingling or non-segregation of parental characteristics.

blendling (blĕn'dlĭng) *n.* [A.S. *blandan*, to mix.] A racial hybrid.

blennoid (blĕn'oid) *a.* [Gk. *blennos*, mucus; *eidos*, form.] Resembling mucus.

blephara (blĕf'ără) *n.* [Gk. *blepharis*, eyelash.] Peristome tooth in mosses.

blepharal (blĕf'ărăl) *a.* [Gk. *blepharon*, eyelid.] *Pert.* eyelids.

blepharoplast (blĕf'äröplăst) *n.* [Gk. *blepharis*, eyelash; *plastos*, formed.] A basal granule in relation with a motor cell organ, as the flagellum of Flagellata; blepharoblast.

blight (blīt) *n.* [A.S. *blaecan*, to grow pale.] An insect or fungus producing a plant disease; the disease itself.

blind pit,—a cell-wall pit which is not backed by a complementary pit.

blind spot,—region of retina devoid of rods and cones and where optic nerve enters; optic disc.

blister (blĭs'tër) *n.* [A.S. *blowan*, to blow.] A subcutaneous bubble or bladder filled with fluid; a certain plant disease.

blood (blŭd) *n.* [A.S. *blód*, blood.] The fluid circulating in the vascular system of animals, distributing food-material and oxygen and collecting waste products.

blood cells,—cells derived by mitosis from ordinary mesoderm cells; primitive haematoblasts.

blood crystals,—crystals of haemoglobin, haemin, or haematoidin, which form when blood is shaken up with chloroform or ether.

blood dust,—fine droplets of neutral fats present in the blood stream; haemokonia.

blood gills,—delicate blood-filled sacs functioning in uptake of salts, in certain insects.

blood groups,—types of blood depending on presence or absence of two agglutinogens (A and B) in the red corpuscles and two agglutinins (α or anti-A, and β or anti-B) in serum or plasma: A cells agglutinate with B type serum, B with A type, AB with A and B type, and O cells not agglutinating with A and B types; *cf.* universal donor, universal recipient.

blood islands, — isolated reddish patches in mesoderm, in which primitive erythroblasts are found enclosed in a mesodermal syncytium; blood anlage, haemangioblast.

blood platelets,—colourless bodies about one-third the size of red corpuscles, and formed from megakaryocytes, and agglutinating in shed blood; thrombocytes; thromboplastids.

blood plates,—minute amoeboid protoplasmic bodies found in blood.

blood serum,—fluid or plasma left after removal of corpuscles and fibrin.

blood shadow,—the colourless stroma of red blood corpuscles.

blood sugar,—$\alpha\beta$-*D*-glucose.

blood vessel,—any vessel or space in which blood circulates; strictly used only in regard to special vessels with well-defined walls.

bloom (bloom) *n.* [A.S. *blówan*, to bloom.] A layer of wax particles on external surface of certain fruits, as grapes, peaches; blossom or flower; seasonal dense phytoplankton.

blubber (blŭb'ër) *n.* [M.E. *blober*, a bubble.] Fat of whales, seals, etc., lying between outer skin and muscle layer.

blue timber,—a wood disease produced by fungus, causing a bluish discoloration.

body blight,—fungal disease of trees.

body cavity,—coelom or space in which viscera lie, mesodermal in origin, and schizocoelic or enterocoelic in development; considered primarily, the generative cavity.

body cell,—a somatic cell as distinct from a germ cell; an antheridial cell.

body stalk,—a band of mesoderm connecting caudal end of embryo with chorion.

Boettcher's cells,—granular cells between Claudius' cells and basilar membrane in organ of Corti.

Bojanus, organ of [*L. H. Bojanus*, Alsatian zoologist]. Excretory organ in lamellibranchs.

boletiform (bōlē'tĭfôrm) *a.* [L. *boletus*, a mushroom; *forma*, shape.] Shaped like a somewhat elliptic spindle, *appl.* spores of some Boletaceae; subfusiform.

bolus (bō'lŭs) *n.* [L. *bolus*, from Gk. *bolos*, lump.] A rounded mass; lump of chewed food.

bone (bōn) *n.* [A.S. *ban*, bone.] Connective tissue in which the ground-substance contains salts of lime.

bone-beds,—deposits formed largely by remains of bones of fishes and reptiles, as Liassic bone-beds.

bones of Bertin [*E. J. Bertin*, French anatomist]. Thin anterior coverings of sphenoidal sinuses.

bonitation (bŏnĭtā'shŭn) *n.* [L. *bonitas*, goodness.] The evaluation of the numerical distribution of a species in a particular locality or season, in relation to agricultural, veterinary, or medical implications.

book gill,—a gill composed of delicate leaf-like lamellae placed one over the other like leaves of a book, as seen in Limulus.

book lung,—a gill similar to a book gill, but modified for air-breathing, and open to exterior only by a small slit, as in scorpions.

booted (boot′ĕd) *a.* [O.F. *boute,* boot.] Equipped with raised horny plates of skin, as feet of some birds; caligate, *q.v.*

bordered pit,—a form of pit, developed on walls of tracheids and wood-vessels, with overarching border of secondary cell-wall.

boreal (bō′rēăl) *a.* [L. *boreas,* north wind.] *Appl.* or *pert.* northern biogeographical region; holarctic except Sonoran, or restricted to nearctic; *pert.* post-glacial age with continental type of climate.

bossed,—bosselated, umbonate.

bosselated (bŏs′ēlātĕd) *a.* [M.E. *bosse,* knob.] Covered with knobs.

bosset (bŏs′ĕt) *n.* [M.E. *bosse,* knob.] The beginning of horn formation in deer in the first year.

bostryx (bŏs′trĭks) *n.* [Gk. *bostrychos,* curl.] A helicoid cyme, cymose inflorescence with blooms on only one side of axis.

Botallo's duct [*L. Botallo,* Italian surgeon]. Ductus arteriosus, a small blood vessel representing sixth gill arch and connecting pulmonary with systemic arch.

botany (bŏt′ănĭ) *n.* [Gk. *botane,* pasture.] The branch of biology dealing with plants; phytology.

bothrenchyma (bŏthrĕng′kĭmă) *n.* Gk. *bothros,* pit; *engchyma,* infusion.] A plant tissue formed of pitted ducts.

bothridium (bŏthrĭd′ĭŭm) *n.* [Gk. *bothros,* trench; *idion, dim.*] A muscular cup-shaped outgrowth from scolex of tape-worms; a phyllidium.

bothrionic (bŏth′rĭŏn′ĭk) *a.* [Gk. *bothros,* pit.] *Appl.* seta arising from the bottom of a pit in the integument.

bothrium (bŏth′rĭŭm) *n.* [Gk. *bothros,* trench.] A sucker; a sucking groove in scolex of tapeworms.

botryoidal (bŏtrĭoid′ăl) *a.* [Gk. *botrys,* bunch of grapes; *eidos,* form.] In the form of a bunch of grapes; *appl.* tissue of branched canals surrounding enteric canal in leeches; botryoid.

botryose (bŏt′rĭōs) *a.* [Gk. *botrys,* bunch of grapes.] Racemose; botryoidal.

botuliform (bŏt′ūlĭfôrm) *a.* [L. *botulus,* sausage; *forma,* form.] Sausage-shaped; allantoid.

bouillon (booyŏng) *n.* [F. *bouillon,* broth.] An infusion or broth, containing watery extract of meat, also peptone, for the cultivation of bacteria.

bouquet (bookā′, book′ā) *n.* [F. *bouquet,* nosegay.] Arrangement of chromosomes in loops with their ends near one side of nuclear wall during zygotene and pachytene in some organisms; bunch of muscles and ligaments connected with the styloid process of the temporal bone.

bourrelet (boor′ĕlā) *n.* [F. *bourrelet,* circular pad.] Poison gland associated with sting in ants.

bouton (bootông) *n.* [F. *bouton,* bud.] Terminal bulb of arborisation of an axon; labellum, in Hymenoptera.

Bowman's capsule [*Sir W. Bowman,* English histologist]. The vesicle of a renal tubule; capsula glomeruli.

Bowman's glands,—serous glands in corium of olfactory mucous membrane.

Bowman's membrane,—anterior elastic membrane of cornea.

braccate (brăk′āt) *a.* [L. *braccae,* breeches.] Having additional feathers on legs or feet, *appl.* birds.

brachelytrous (brăkĕl′ĭtrŭs) *a.* [Gk. *brachys,* short; *elytron,* sheath.] Having short wing-covers.

brachia (brăk'ĭă) *n. plu.* [L. *brachium*, arm.] The arms; two spirally coiled structures, one at each side of mouth, in Brachiopoda; cerebellar peduncles; white lateral bands of colliculi of corpora quadrigemina. *Sing.* brachium.

brachial (brăk'ĭăl) *a.* [L. *brachium*, arm.] *Pert.* arm; arm-like.

brachialis (brăkĭā'lĭs) *n.* [L. *brachialis*, *pert.* arm.] A flexor muscle of the forearm, from lower half of front of humerus to coronoid process of ulna; brachialis anticus.

brachiate (brā̆'kĭāt) *a.* [L. *brachium*, arm.] Branched; having opposite paired branches on alternate sides.

brachidia (brăkĭd'ĭă) *n. plu.* [Gk. *brachion*, arm; *idion*, *dim.*] Calcareous skeleton supporting brachia in certain Brachiopoda.

brachiferous (brăkĭf'ërŭs), **brachigerous** (brăkĭj'ërŭs) *a.* [L. *brachium*, arm; *ferre*, *gerere*, to carry.] Branched.

brachiocephalic (brăk'ĭökĕfăl'ĭk, -sĕf-) *a.* [Gk. *brachion*, arm; *kephale*, head.] *Pert.* arm and head; *appl.* artery, veins.

brachiocubital (brăk'ĭökū'bĭtăl) *a.* [L. *brachium*, arm; *cubitum*, forearm.] *Pert.* arm and forearm.

brachiolaria (brăkĭölā'rĭă) *n.* [L. *brachiolum*, small arm.] A larval stage in metamorphosis of some starfishes.

brachiole (brā̆'kĭōl) *n.* [L. *brachiolum*, small arm.] A pinnule-like structure on ambulacral margin in Blastoidea.

brachiorachidian (brăk'ĭörăkĭd'ĭăn) *a.* [Gk. *brachion*, arm; *rhachis*, spine.] *Pert.* arm and spine.

brachioradialis (brăk'ĭörādĭā'lĭs) *n.* [L. *brachium*, arm; *radius*, ray.] The supinator longus muscle of forearm.

brachium (brăk'ĭŭm) *n.* [L. *brachium*, arm.] Arm or branching structure; upper limb of vertebrates; a bundle of fibres connecting cerebellum to cerebrum or to pons. *Plu.* brachia.

brachyblast,—brachyplast, *q.v.*

brachycephalic (brăk'ĭkĕfăl'ĭk, -sĕf-) *a.* [Gk. *brachys*, short; *kephale*, head.] Short-headed; with cephalic index of over eighty; *cf.* dolichocephalic.

brachycerous (brăkĭs'ërŭs) *a.* [Gk. *brachys*, short; *keras*, horn.] Short-horned; with short antennae.

brachycnemic (brăk'ĭknē'mĭk) *a.* [Gk. *brachys*, short; *kneme*, tibia.] *Appl.* arrangement of mesenteries of Zoantharia where the sixth protocneme is imperfect.

brachydactyly (brăk'ĭdăk'tĭlĭ) *n.* [Gk. *brachys*, short; *daktylos*, digit.] Brachydactylous condition, viz. having digits abnormally short.

brachydont (brăk'ĭdŏnt) *a.* [Gk. *brachys*, short; *odous*, tooth.] *Appl.* molar teeth with low crowns.

brachymeiosis (brăk'ĭmīō'sĭs) *n.* [Gk. *brachys*, short; *meion*, smaller.] A third karyokinetic or second reduction division, as in asci; meiosis involving only one division.

brachyodont,—brachydont, *q.v.*

brachyourous,—brachyural, *q.v.*

brachyplast (brăk'ĭplăst) *n.* [Gk. *brachys*, short; *plastos*, formed.] A short branch or spur bearing leaf tufts, occurring with normal branches on the same plant.

brachypleural (brăk'ĭploo'răl) *a.* [Gk. *brachys*, short; *pleuron*, side.] With short pleura or side plates.

brachypodous (brăkĭp'ödŭs) *a.* [Gk. *brachys*, short; *pous*, foot.] With short legs, or stalk.

brachypterous (brăkĭp'tërŭs) *a.* [Gk. *brachys*, short; *pteron*, wing.] With short wings.

brachysclereid (brăk'ĭsklē'rëĭd) *n.* [Gk. *brachys*, short; *skleros*, hard; *eidos*, form.] A stone cell.

brachysm (brăk'ĭsm) *n.* [Gk. *brachys*, short.] Dwarfism in plants caused by shortening of internodes.

brachystomatous (brăk'ĭstŏm'ătŭs) *a.* [Gk. *brachys*, short; *stoma*, mouth.] With short proboscis; *appl.* certain insects.

brachytic (brăkĭt'ĭk) *a.* [Gk. *brachytes*, shortness.] Dwarfish, *appl.* plants; exhibiting or *pert.* brachysm.

brachytmema (brăk'ĭtmē'mă) *n.* [Gk. *brachys*, short; *tmema*, segment, from *tmegein*, to cut.] Truncated condition or appearance; a cell which ruptures, releasing a gemma, as in bryophytes.

brachyural (brăk'ĭū'răl) *a.* [Gk. *brachys*, short; *oura*, tail.] Having short abdomen usually tucked in below thorax, *appl.* certain crabs.

brachyuric (brăk'ĭū'rĭk) *a.* [Gk. *brachys*, short; *oura*, tail.] Short-tailed.

bract (brăkt) *n.* [L. *bractea*, thin plate of metal.] A floral leaf; a modified leaf in whose axil a flower arises; a hydrophyllium in Siphonophora; distal exite of sixth appendage of Apus.

bract scales,—small scales developed directly on axis of cones; *cf.* ovuliferous scales.

bracteal (brăk'tēăl) *a.* [L. *bractea*, thin metal plate.] *Pert.* a bract.

bracteate (brăk'tēăt) *a.* [L. *bractea*, thin metal plate.] Having bracts.

bracteiform (brăk'tēĭfôrm) *a.* [L. *bractea*, thin metal plate; *forma*, form.] Like a bract.

bracteolate (brăk'tēōlāt) *a.* [L. *bractea*, thin metal plate.] *Appl.* flowers with bracteoles.

bracteole (brăk'tēōl) *n.* [L. *bractea*, thin metal plate.] Secondary bract at base of flower; bractlet.

bracteose (brăk'tēōs) *a.* [L. *bractea*, thin metal plate.] With many bracts.

bractlet,—bracteole.

bradyauxesis (brăd'ĭôksē'sĭs) *n.* [Gk. *bradys*, slow; *auxesis*, growth.] Relatively slow growth; growth of a part at a slower rate than that of the whole, *opp.* tachyauxesis.

bradygenesis (brăd'ĭjĕn'ēsĭs) *n.* [Gk. *bradys*, slow; *genesis*, descent.] Retarded development, in phylogeny, *opp.* tachygenesis.

bradytelic (brădĭtĕl'ĭk) *a.* [Gk. *bradys*, slow; *telos*, fulfilment.] Evolving at a rate slower than the standard rate, *opp.* tachytelic; *cf.* horotelic.

brain (brān) *n.* [A.S. *braegen*, brain.] Centre of nervous system; mass of nervous matter in vertebrates at anterior end of spinal cord, lying in cranium; in invertebrates, supra-oesophageal or suprapharyngeal ganglia.

brain sand,—granular bodies of calcium and ammonium and magnesium phosphates, occurring in pineal gland and pia mater; corpora arenacea; acervulus cerebri.

brain stem,—the mid-brain, pons, and medulla oblongata.

branch gaps,—gaps in the vascular cylinder of a main stem, subtending branch-traces.

branch traces,—the vascular bundles connecting those of a main stem to those of a branch.

branchia (brăng'kĭă) *n.*, **branchiae** (brăng'kĭē) *plu.* [L. *branchiae*, gills.] Gill, gills.

branchiac (brăng'kĭăk), **branchial** (brăng'kĭăl) *a.* [Gk. *brangchia*, gills.] *Pert.* gills.

branchial arch,—one of the bony or cartilaginous arches on side of the pharynx posterior to hyoid arch, and supporting gill bars.

branchial grooves,—outer pharyngeal grooves or visceral clefts, *q.v.*

branchiate (brăng'kĭāt) *a.* [Gk. *brangchia*, gills.] Having gills.

branchicolous (brăngkĭk'ōlŭs) *a.* [L. *branchiae*, gills; L. *colere*, to inhabit.] Parasitic on fish gills; *appl.* certain crustaceans.

branchiferous,—branchiate.

branchiform (brăng'kĭfôrm) *a.* [L. *branchiae*, gills; L. *forma*, shape.] Gill-like.

branchihyal (brăng'kĭhī'ăl) *n.* [Gk. *brangchia*, gills; *hyoeides*, Υ-shaped.] An element of a branchial arch.

branchiocardiac (brăng'kĭōkâr'dĭăk) *a.* [Gk. *brangchia*, gills; *kardia*, heart.] *Pert.* gills and heart; *appl.*

vessel given off ventrally from ascidian heart; *appl.* vessels conveying blood from gills to pericardial sinus in certain crustaceans.

branchiomere (brăng'kĭömēr) *n.* [Gk. *brangchia*, gills; *meros*, part.] A branchial segment.

branchiomeric, — *pert.* branchiomeres; *appl.* muscles derived from gill arches.

branchiopallial (brăng'kĭöpăl'ĭăl) *a.* [Gk. *brangchia*, gills; L. *pallium*, mantle.] *Pert.* gill and mantle of molluscs.

branchiostegal (brăng'kĭŏs'tëgăl) *a.* [Gk. *brangchia*, gills; *stege*, roof.] With or *pert.* a gill cover; *appl.* membrane, rays.

branchiostege (brăng'kĭöstēj') *n.* [Gk. *brangchia*, gills; *stege*, roof.] The branchiostegal membrane.

branchiostegite (brăng'kĭŏs'tëjīt) *n.* [Gk. *brangchia*, gills; *stege*, roof.] Expanded lateral portion of carapace forming gill cover in certain Crustacea.

branchireme (brăng'kĭrēm) *n.* [L. *branchiae*, gills; *remus*, oar.] A branchiate limb; locomotory and respiratory limb of Branchiopoda.

brand (brănd) *n.* [A.S. *beornan*, to burn.] A burnt appearance on leaves, caused by rust and smut fungi.

brand spore,—a thick-walled spore of Ustilaginales; uredospore of Uredinales.

bregma (brĕg'mă) *n.* [Gk. *bregma*, fore-part of head.] That part of skull where frontals and parietals meet; intersection of sagittal and coronal sutures.

brephic (brĕf'ĭk) *a.* [Gk. *brephikos*, childish.] *Appl.* a larval phase preceding that of adult form; neanic.

brevicaudate (brĕv'ĭkô'dāt) *a.* [L. *brevis*, short; *cauda*, tail.] With a short tail.

brevifoliate (brĕv'ĭfō'lĭāt) *a.* [L. *brevis*, short; *folium*, leaf.] Having short leaves.

brevilingual (brĕv'ĭlĭng'gwăl) *a.* [L. *brevis*, short; *lingua*, tongue.] With short tongue.

breviped (brĕv'ĭpĕd) *a.* [L. *brevis*, short; *pes*, foot.] Having short legs; *appl.* certain birds.

brevipennate (brĕv'ĭpĕn'āt) *a.* [L. *brevis*, short; *penna*, feather.] With short wings.

brevirostrate (brĕv'ĭrŏs'trāt) *a.* [L. *brevis*, short; *rostrum*, beak.] With short beak or rostrum.

brevissimus oculi, — obliquus inferior, shortest muscle of eye.

bridge corpuscle,—desmosome, *q.v.*

Broca's area [*P. Broca*, French surgeon]. Parolfactory area of brain.

Broca's gyrus,—left inferior frontal gyrus, speech centre in cerebral cortex.

brochidodrome (brŏkĭd'ödrōm) *a.* [Gk. *brochos*, loop; *dromein*, to run.] *Appl.* veins in leaves when they form loops within the blade.

brochonema (brŏkönē'mă) *n.* [Gk. *brochos*, loop; *nema*, thread.] The spireme in loops to the number of chromosome pairs to be formed.

bromatium (brömā'shĭŭm) *n.* [Gk. *broma*, food.] A swelling on a fungus cultivated by ants, and serving as food.

bronchi (brŏng'kī) *n. plu.* [Gk. *brongchos*, windpipe.] Tubes connecting trachea with lungs. *Sing.* bronchus.

bronchia (brŏng'kĭă) *n. plu.* [Gk. *brongchos*, windpipe.] The subdivisions or branches of each bronchus.

bronchial (brŏng'kĭăl) *a.* [Gk. *brongchos*, windpipe.] *Pert.* bronchi.

bronchiole (brŏng'kĭōl) *n.* [Gk. *brongchos*, windpipe.] A small terminal branch of bronchi.

bronchopulmonary (brŏng'köpŭl'mönărĭ) *a.* [Gk. *brongchos*, windpipe; L. *pulmo*, lung.] *Pert.* bronchi and lungs.

bronchotracheal (brŏng'kötrā'kēal) *a.* [Gk. *brongchos*, windpipe; L. *trachea*, trachea.] *Pert.* bronchi and trachea.

bronchovesicular (brŏng'kövĕsĭk'ūlăr) *a.* [Gk. *brongchos*, windpipe; L. *vesicula*, little sac.] *Pert.* bronchial tubes and lung cells.

bronchus,—*sing.* of bronchi.

brood bud,—a spore of certain types of sporangia; a soredium; a bulbil.

brood cells,—gonidia, *q.v.*

brood pouch,—a sac-like cavity in which eggs or embryos are placed; a space formed by overlapping plates attached to bases of thoracic limbs in certain Crustacea.

brown body,—a brown, rounded mass of compacted degenerate organs in some polyzoa; nephrocyte in ascidians.

brown funnels,—a single pair of organs on dorsal aspect of posterior end of pharynx, in Amphioxus; atrio-coelomic funnels; brown canals.

Brownian movements [*R. Brown*, Scottish botanist]. The passive vibratory movements of fine granules when suspended in a fluid.

Bruch's membrane [*C. W. L. Bruch*, German anatomist]. The basal membrane, inner layer of choroid; lamina basalis.

Brunner's glands [*J. C. Brunner*, Swiss anatomist]. Small tubuloracemose glands containing a proteolytic enzyme, in submucous coat of small intestine; duodenal glands.

brush cell,—echinidium.

bryology (brīŏl'öjĭ) *n.* [Gk. *bryon*, moss; *logos*, discourse.] The science dealing with mosses, also with liverworts; muscology.

bryophyte (brī'öfīt) *n.* [Gk. *bryon*, moss; *phyton*, plant.] Any of the mosses, or liverworts.

bryozoon (brī'özō'ŏn) *n.* [Gk. *bryon*, moss; *zoon*, animal.] A polyzoon, so named from moss-like appearance.

B-substance,—intermedin, *q.v.*

buccae (bŭk'ē) *n. plu.* [L. *bucca*, cheek.] The cheeks.

buccal (bŭk'ăl) *a.* [L. *bucca*, cheek.] *Pert.* the cheek or mouth.

buccinator (bŭk'sĭnā'tŏr) *n.* [L. *buccinator*, trumpeter.] A broad thin muscle of the cheek.

buccolabial (bŭk'ölā'bĭăl) *a.* [L. *bucca*, cheek; *labium*, lip.] *Pert.* mouth cavity and lips.

buccolingual (bŭk'ölĭng'gwăl) *a.* [L. *bucca*, cheek; *lingua*, tongue.] *Pert.* cheeks and tongue.

bucconasal (bŭk'önā'zăl) *a.* [L. *bucca*, cheek; *nasus*, nose.] *Pert.* cheek and nose; *appl.* membrane closing posterior end of olfactory pit.

buccopharyngeal (bŭk'öfărĭn'jëăl) *a.* [L. *bucca*, cheek; Gk. *pharyngx*, throat.] *Pert.* cheeks and pharynx; *appl.* membrane and fascia.

bud (bŭd) *n.* [M.E. *budde*, bud.] A rudimentary shoot, or flower; a gemma, *q.v.*

budding (bŭd'ĭng) *n.* [M.E. *budde*, bud.] The production of buds; reproduction by development of one or more outgrowths or buds which may or may not be set free, in plants and many primitive animals; artificial propagation by insertion of a bud within the bark of another plant.

buffer (bŭf'ër) *n.* [O.F. *buffe*, blow.] *Appl.* salt solution which minimises changes in *p*H when an acid or alkali is added; *appl.* genes controlling the action of an allelomorph, *i.e.* polygenes; *appl.* cells, conidia formed in a chain, as in certain Phycomycetes.

bufotoxins (bū'fötŏk'sĭnz) *n. plu.* [L. *bufo*, toad; Gk. *toxikon*, poison.] Toad venom, as bufotoxin, $C_{34}H_{46}O_{10}$, and bufonin, $C_{34}H_{54}O_2$.

bulb (bŭlb) *n.* [L. *bulbus*, globular root.] A specialised underground bud with thick fleshy leaves; a part resembling a bulb; a bulb-like dilatation; basal part of intromittent organ in spiders; the medulla oblongata.

bulbar (bŭl'băr) *a.* [L. *bulbus*, globular root.] *Pert.* a bulb or bulb-like part; *pert.* medulla oblongata.

bulbiferous (bŭlbĭf'ërŭs) *a.* [L. *bulbus*, bulb; *ferre*, to carry.] Bulb-bearing.

bulbil (bŭl'bĭl) *n.* [L. *bulbus*, bulb.] A fleshy axillary bud which may fall and produce a new plant, as in some lilies; aerial bulb; any small bulb-shaped structure or dilatation.

bulbocavernosus (bŭl'bökăvërnō'sŭs) *n.* [L. *bulbus*, bulb; *cavernosus*, cavernous.] A muscle of perinaeum, ejaculator urinae in the male; sphincter of vagina.

bulbonuclear (bŭl'bönū'klëăr) *a.* [L. *bulbus*, bulb; *nucleus*, kernel.] *Pert.* medulla oblongata and nuclei of cranial nerves.

bulbo-urethral (bŭl'böūrē'thrăl) *a.* [L. *bulbus*, bulb; Gk. *ourethra*, urethra.] *Appl.* two racemose glands, Cowper's or Méry's glands, opening into bulb of male urethra; also *appl.* the greater vestibular glands, Bartholin's glands, in the female.

bulbous (bŭl'bŭs) *a.* [L. *bulbus*, bulb.] Like a bulb; developing from a bulb; having bulbs.

bulbus (bŭl'bŭs) *n.* [L. *bulbus*, bulb.] A bulb; swollen base of stipe in agarics; the knob-like part found in connection with various nerves; a dilatation of base of aorta.

bulla (bool'ă) *n.* [L. *bulla*, bubble.] *Appl.* rounded prominence formed by bones of ear, tympanic bulla; *appl.* prominence of middle ethmoidal air cells; *appl.* structure in head of certain parasitic copepods, becoming extruded and attached to gill-filament of fish.

bullate (bool'āt) *a.* [L. *bulla*, bubble.] Blistered-like; puckered like a savoy-cabbage leaf.

bulliform (bool'ĭfôrm) *a.* [L. *bulla*, bubble; *forma*, shape.] Bubble-shaped; *appl.* thin-walled cells which cause rolling, folding, or opening of leaves by turgor changes.

bundle-sheath,—a layer of large parenchymatous cells surrounding vascular tissue of leaf-vein.

bunodont (bū'nödŏnt) *a.* [Gk. *bounos*, mound; *odous*, tooth.] Having molar teeth with low conical cusps.

bunoid (bū'noid) *a.* [Gk. *bounos*, mound; *eidos*, form.] *Appl.* cusps of cheek-teeth, low and conical.

bunolophodont (bū'nölŏf'ödŏnt) *a.* [Gk. *bounos*, mound; *lophos*, crest; *odous*, tooth.] Between bunodont and lophodont in structure, *appl.* cheek-teeth.

bunoselenodont (bū'nösēlē'nödŏnt) *a.* [Gk. *bounos*, mound; *selene*, moon; *odous*, tooth.] Having internal cusps bunoid, external selenoid; *appl.* cheek-teeth.

bursa (bŭr'să) *n.* [L. *bursa*, purse.] A sac-like cavity; a sac with viscid fluid to prevent friction at joints.

bursa copulatrix,—a genital pouch of various animals.

bursa entiana,—the short duodenum in Chondropterygii.

bursa Fabricii,—a sac opening into dorsal part of posterior region of cloaca in birds, and usually degenerating during adolescence.

bursicule (bŭr'sĭkūl) *n.* [L. *dim.* of *bursa*, purse.] A small sac.

buttress-roots,—branch roots given off above ground, arching away from stem before entering soil, forming additional props.

butyrinase (bū'tĭrĭnās) *n.* [L. *butyrum*, butter.] An enzyme occurring in blood serum.

byssal (bĭs'ăl) *a.* [Gk. *byssos*, fine flax.] *Pert.* the byssus.

byssogenous (bĭsŏj'ënŭs) *a.* [Gk. *byssos*, fine flax; *genos*, birth.] Byssus-forming; *appl.* glands.

byssoid (bĭs'oid) *a.* [Gk. *byssos*, fine flax; *eidos*, shape.] Resembling a byssus; formed of fine threads; byssaceous.

byssus (bĭs'ŭs) *n.* [Gk. *byssos*, fine flax.] The tuft of strong filaments secreted by a gland of certain bivalve molluscs, by which they become attached; the stalk of certain fungi.

C

cacogenesis (kăk'öjĕn'ësĭs) *n.* [Gk. *kakos*, bad; *genesis*, descent.] Inability to hybridise; kakogenesis.

cacogenic (kăk'öjĕn'ĭk) *a.* [Gk. *kakos*, bad; *genos*, birth.] Dysgenic, *q.v.*

cacuminous (kăkū'mĭnŭs) *a.* [L. *cacumen*, peak.] With a pointed top; *appl.* trees.

cadophore (kăd'öfōr) *n.* [Gk. *kados*, cask; *pherein*, to bear.] A dorsal bud-bearing outgrowth in certain tunicates.

caducibranchiate (kădū'sĭbrăng'-kĭāt) *a.* [L. *caducus*, falling; *branchiae*, gills.] With temporary gills.

caducous (kădū'kŭs) *a.* [L. *caducus*, falling.] *Pert.* parts that fall off early, *e.g.* calyx, stipules; fugacious; *cf.* deciduous.

caeca,—*plu.* of caecum.

caecal (sē'kăl) *a.* [L. *caecus*, blind.] Ending without outlet; *appl.* stomach with cardiac part prolonged into blind sac; *pert.* caecum.

caecum (sē'kŭm) *n.* [L. *caecus*, blind.] A blind diverticulum or pouch from some part of alimentary canal.

caecum cupulare,—the closed apical end of the cochlear canal.

caecum vestibulare,—The closed lower end of the cochlear duct.

Caenogaea (sē'nöjē'ă) *n.* [Gk. *kainos*, recent; *gaia*, earth.] A zoogeographical region which includes the Nearctic, Palearctic, and Oriental regions; *cf.* Eogaea; also Cainogea, Kainogaea.

caenogenesis (sē'nöjĕn'ĕsĭs) *n.* [Gk. *kainos*, recent; *genesis*, origin.] The non-phylogenetic processes in development of an individual; development of transitory adaptations in early stages of an individual.

caenogenetic (sē'nöjĕnĕt'ĭk) *a.* [Gk. *kainos*, recent; *genesis*, origin.] Of recent origin.

Caenozoic (sēnözō'ĭk) *a.* [Gk. *kainos*, recent; *zoe*, life.] *Pert.* age of mammals, geological era from Mesozoic to recent times; Tertiary and Quaternary periods; also Cainozoic, Cenozoic, Kainozoic.

caespitose (sĕs'pĭtōs) *a.* [L. *caespes*, turf.] *Pert.* turf; having low, closely matted stems; growing densely in tufts; caespitulose, cespitose.

caisson (kā'sŏn) *n.* [F. *caisson*, coffer.] Box-like arrangement of longitudinal muscle fibres in Lumbricidae.

calamistrum (kăl'ămĭs'trŭm) *n.* [L. *calamistrum*, curling-iron.] A comb-like structure on metatarsus of certain spiders.

calamus (kăl'ămŭs) *n.* [L. *calamus*, reed.] A hollow reed-like stem without nodes; the quill of a feather; calamus scriptorius, the tip of posterior part of floor of fourth ventricle.

calcaneus (kălkā'nēŭs) *n.* [L. *calx*, heel.] The heel; large bone or os calcis of tarsus which forms heel; calcaneum; process on metatarsus of birds.

calcar (kăl'kâr) *n.* [L. *calcar*, spur.] A hollow prolongation or tube at base of sepal or petal; spur-like process on leg or wing of birds; tibial spine in insects; process of calcaneus which supports web between leg and tail in bats; prehallux of frog; internal bony plate strengthening neck of femur; calcar avis, eminence in posterior part of lateral ventricle.

calcarate (kăl'kărāt) *a.* [L. *calcar*, spur.] Spurred; *appl.* petal, corolla.

calcareous (kălkā'rēŭs) *a.* [L. *calcarius*, limy.] Limy; growing on soil derived from decomposition of calcareous rocks; *pert.* limestone.

calcariform (kălkăr'ĭfôrm) *a.* [L. *calcar*, spur; *forma*, shape.] Spurlike.

calcarine (kăl'kărĭn) *a.* [L. *calcar*, spur.] *Pert.* calcar avis; *appl.* fissure extending to hippocampal gyrus, on medial surface of cerebral hemisphere.

calceiform,—calceolate.

calceolate (kăl'sëölāt) *a.* [L. *calceolus*, small shoe.] Slipper-shaped; *appl.* flowers.

calcicole (kăl'sĭkōl) *n.* [L. *calx*, lime; *colere*, to dwell.] A plant which thrives in soils rich in calcium salts; calcipete, calciphile, calciphyte, gypsophyte. *a.* Calcicolous.

calciferol,—vitamin D_2, occurring in fish liver oils, egg yolk, milk, etc., and conserving body calcium and phosphorus ; antirhachitic vitamin ; isomeric with ergosterol from which it is formed by a series of photochemical reactions ; $C_{28}H_{44}O$.

calciferous (kălsĭf'ĕrŭs) *a.* [L. *calx*, lime ; *ferre*, to carry.] Containing or producing lime salts.

calcific (kălsĭf'ĭk) *a.* [L. *calx*, lime ; *facere*, to make.] Producing lime salts ; *appl.* part of oviduct forming egg-shell in reptiles and birds.

calcification (kălsĭfĭkā'shŭn) *n.* [L. *calx*, lime ; *facere*, to make.] The deposition of lime salts in tissue ; the process of accumulation of lime salts in soil development.

calcifuge (kăl'sĭfūj) *n.* [L. *calx*, lime ; *fugere*, to flee.] A plant which thrives only in soils poor in calcium carbonate ; calciphobe.

calcigerous,—calciferous.

calcipete (kăl'sĭpēt) *n.* [L. *calx*, lime ; *petere*, to go towards.] A calcicole, *q.v.* ; a calciphil plant.

calciphile,—calciphyte.

calciphobe,—calcifuge.

calciphyte (kăl'sĭfīt) *n.* [L. *calx*, lime ; Gk. *phyton*, plant.] A plant which thrives only on calcareous soils ; calcicole, calcipete, calciphile, gypsophyte.

calcivorous (kălsĭv'ŏrŭs) *a.* [L. *calx*, lime ; *vorare*, to devour.] *Appl.* plants which live on limestone.

calcospherites (kăl'kŏsfē'rīts) *n. plu.* [L. *calx*, lime ; *sphaera*, globe.] Concentrically laminated granules of calcium carbonate in Malpighian tubes of some insects, in cells associated with fat-body in certain larval Diptera.

calicle,—calycle, calyculus, *q.v.*

caligate (kăl'ĭgāt) *a.* [L. *caliga*, boot.] Sheathed ; veiled ; peronate, *q.v.* ; laminiplantar, *q.v.*

calines (kălēnz) *n. plu.* [Gk. *kalein*, to summon.] Plant hormones influencing growth of specific parts, as of root, stem, or leaf.

callosal (kălō'săl) *a.* [L. *callosus*, hard.] *Pert.* corpus callosum.

callose (kăl'ōs) *n.* [L. *callum*, hard skin.] An occasional carbohydrate or periodic component of plant cell walls, as on sieve-plates. *a.* Having callosities.

callosity (kălŏs'ĭtĭ) *n.* [L. *callositas*, hardness.] Hardened and thickened area on skin, or on bark.

callosum,—corpus callosum, *q.v.*

callow (kăl'ō) *n.* [A.S. *calu*, bald.] A newly hatched worker ant. *a.* Unfledged.

callus (kăl'ŭs) *n.* [L. *callum*, hard skin.] Tissue that forms over cut or damaged plant surface ; deposit of callose on sieve-plates ; small hard outgrowth at base of spikelet or of floret, in some grasses ; a growth of shell-like material within umbilicus of shell ; a mesonotal swelling in some insects ; callosity.

caloricity (kălŏrĭs'ĭtĭ) *n.* [L. *calere*, to be warm.] In animals, the power of developing and maintaining a certain degree of heat.

calorie (kăl'ŏrĭ) *n.* [L. *calere*, to be warm.] Amount of heat required to raise temperature of one gramme of water one degree centigrade (small calorie) ; one large calorie equals one thousand small calories.

calorigenic (kăl'ŏrĭjĕn'ĭk) *a.* [L. *calor*, heat ; *genere*, to beget.] Promoting oxygen consumption and heat production ; calorifacient.

calotte (kălŏt') *n.* [F. *calotte*, skull-cap.] An outer cell group or polar cap in Dicyemidae, for adhesion to kidney of Cephalopoda ; a retractile disc with sensory cilia, in larval Bryozoa ; lid of an ascus.

caltrop (kăl'trŏp) *n.* [A.S. *coltraeppe*, thistle.] A sponge spicule with four rays so disposed that any three being on the ground the fourth projects vertically upwards ; also calthrop.

calvaria (kălvā'rĭă) *n.* [L. *calvaria*, skull.] The dome of the skull.

calx (kălks) *n.* [L. *calx*, lime, heel.] Lime ; calcaneus, *q.v.*

calycanthemy (kăl'ĭkăn'thĕmĭ) *n.* [Gk. *kalyx*, calyx; *anthemon*, flower.] Abnormal development of parts of calyx into petals.

calyces,—*plu.* of calyx.

calyciflorous (kăl'ĭsĭflō'rŭs) *a.* [L. *calyx*, calyx; *flos*, flower.] *Appl.* flowers in which stamens and petals are adnate to the calyx.

calyciform (kălĭs'ĭfôrm) *a.* [L. *calyx*, calyx; *forma*, shape.] Calyx-like in shape.

calycine (kăl'ĭsĭn) *a.* [L. *calyx*, calyx.] *Pert.* a calyx; cup-like.

calycle (kăl'ĭkl) *n.* [L. *calyculus*, little calyx.] An epicalyx; a cup-shaped cavity in a coral; a theca in a hydroid; calyculus; calicle.

calyculus (kălĭk'ūlŭs) *n.* [L. *calyculus*, little calyx.] Cup-shaped or bud-shaped structure; calycle.

calyculus gustatorius,—a taste-bud or taste-bulb, an ovoid buccal sense organ composed of gustatory cells supported and surrounded by sustentacular cells.

calyculus ophthalmicus, — optic cup, formed by invagination of the optic bulb and developing into the retina.

calymma,—kalymma, *q.v.*

calypter (kălĭp'tĕr) *n.* [Gk. *kalyptos*, hidden.] Antitegula or modified alula covering haltere in certain Diptera; calyptron.

calyptoblastic (kălĭp'tōblăs'tĭk) *a.* [Gk. *kalyptos*, hidden; *blastos*, bud.] *Pert.* hydroids in which gonophore is enclosed in a gonotheca.

calyptobranchiate (kălĭp'tōbrăng'kĭăt) *a.* [Gk. *kalyptos*, hidden; *brangchia*, gills.] With gills not visible from exterior.

calyptopsis (kălĭptŏp'sĭs) *n.* [Gk. *kalyptos*, hidden; *opsis*, sight.] A larva with short-stalked eyes, as of some arthropods.

calyptra (kălĭp'tră) *n.* [Gk. *kalyptra*, covering.] Tissue enclosing developing sporogonium in liverworts; remains of archegonium which surround apex of capsule in mosses; neck of archegonium in prothallus of some pteridophytes; root-cap; *cf.* calyptrogen.

calyptrate (kălĭp'trāt) *a.* [Gk. *kalyptra*, covering.] *Appl.* caducous calyx separating from its lower portion or from thalamus; operculate; *appl.* Diptera with halteres hidden by squamae.

calyptrogen (kălĭp'trōjĕn) *n.* [Gk. *kalyptra*, covering; *gennaein*, to produce.] The special layer of cells lying at apex of growing root and giving origin to root-cap.

calyptron (kălĭp'trŏn) *n.* [Gk. *kalyptra*, covering.] The squama of Calypterae; calypter.

calyx (kăl'ĭks) *n.* [Gk. *kalyx*, calyx.] The outer whorl of floral leaves; cup-like portion of pelvis of kidney; theca of certain hydroids; cup-like body of crinoids; cup or head of pedunculate bodies in insects.

cambial (kăm'bĭăl) *a.* [L. *cambium*, change.] *Pert.* cambium.

cambiform (kăm'bĭfôrm) *a.* [L. *cambium*, change; *forma*, shape.] Similar to cambium cells.

cambiogenetic (kăm'bĭōjĕnĕt'ĭk) *a.* [L. *cambium*, change; Gk. *genesis*, origin.] *Appl.* cells which produce cambium.

cambium (kăm'bĭŭm) *n.* [L. *cambium*, change.] The tissue from which secondary growth arises in stems and roots.

Cambrian (kăm'brĭăn) *a.* [L. *Cambria*, Wales.] *Pert.* earliest period, or system of rocks, of Palaeozoic era.

cameration (kămĕrā'shŭn) *n.* [L. *cameratio*, vaulting.] Division into a large number of separate chambers.

camerostome (kăm'ĕrōstōm') *n.* [L. *camera*, chamber; Gk. *stoma*, mouth.] Hollow in anterior part of podosoma, for reception of gnathostoma in Acarina.

campaniform (kămpăn'ĭfôrm) *a.* [L.L. *campana*, bell; *forma*, shape.] Bell- or dome-shaped; *appl.* sensilla.

campanula Halleri [*Dim.* of L.L. *campana*, bell; *A. von Haller*, Swiss anatomist]. Expansion of falciform process at lens in many fishes.

campanulate (kămpăn'ūlāt) *a.* [*Dim.* of L.L. *campana*, bell.] Bell-shaped; *appl.* corolla.

campodeiform (kămpō'dēĭfôrm) *a.* [Gk. *kampe*, caterpillar; *eidos*, form; L. *forma*, shape.] *Appl.* larva resembling a Campodea; thysanuriform.

camptodrome (kămp'tödrōm) *a.* [Gk. *kamptos*, flexible; *dromos*, course.] *Pert.* leaf venation in which secondary veins bend forward and anastomose before reaching margin.

camptotrichia (kămp'tötrĭkyă) *n.plu.* [Gk. *kamptos*, flexible; *thrix*, hair.] Jointed dermal fin-rays in certain primitive fishes.

campylodrome (kăm'pĭlödrōm) *a.* [Gk. *kampylos*, curved; *dromos*, course.] *Appl.* leaf with veins converging at its tip; acrodrome.

campylospermous (kăm'pĭlöspĕr'-mŭs) *a.* [Gk. *kampylos*, curved; *sperma*, seed.] *Appl.* seeds with groove along inner face.

campylotropous (kăm'pĭlŏt'röpŭs) *a.* [Gk. *kampylos*, curved; *trope*, turning.] *Pert.* ovules in which nucellus and embryo-sac are bent so that micropyle points almost back to placenta.

canalicular (kănălĭk'ūlăr) *a.* [L. *canaliculus*, small channel.] *Pert.* canals, or canaliculi.

canalicular apparatus,—the Golgi bodies, regarded as a system of canals.

canaliculus (kănălĭk'ūlŭs) *n.* [L. *canaliculus*, small channel.] One of the small canals containing cell-processes of bone-corpuscles and connecting lacunae in Haversian system; small channel for passage of nerves through various bones.

canaliform (kănăl'ĭfôrm) *a.* [L. *canalis*, canal; *forma*, shape.] Canal-like.

cancellous (kăn'sĕlŭs) *a.* [L. *cancellosus*, latticed.] Consisting of slender fibres and lamellae, which join to form a reticular structure; cancellated; *appl.* inner, more spongy, portion of bony tissue; *appl.* anterior portion of cuttle-bone.

cancrisocial (kăng'krĭsō'shăl) *a.* [L. *cancer*, crab; *socius*, ally.] *Appl.* commensals with crabs.

canine (kănīn', kā'nīn) *n.* [L. *caninus*, *pert.* dog.] The tooth next to incisors. *a. Pert.* canine tooth, or to a fossa and eminence on anterior surface of maxilla.

caninus (kănī'nŭs) *n.* [L. *caninus*, canine.] Muscle from canine fossa to angle of mouth; levator anguli oris.

cannon bone,—bone supporting limb from hock to fetlock, enlarged and fused metacarpals or metatarsals; in birds, the tarsometatarsus.

canopy (kăn'öpĭ) *n.* [Gk. *konopeion*, curtained bed.] Topmost layer of leaves, twigs, and branches of forest trees, or of other woody plants.

canthal (kăn'thăl) *a.* [Gk. *kanthos*, corner of eye.] *Pert.* canthus; *appl.* a scale in certain reptiles.

cantharidin (kănthăr'ĭdĭn) *n.* [*Cantharidae*, blister-beetles, from Gk. *kantharos*.] Poison from accessory glands of genital tract and blood of blister-beetles; $C_{10}H_{12}O_4$.

canthus (kăn'thŭs) *n.* [Gk. *kanthos*, corner of eye.] The angle where upper and lower eyelids meet; commissura palpebrarum.

capillary (kăpĭl'ărĭ) *a.* [L. *capillus*, hair.] Hair-like; *appl.* moisture held between and around particles of soil. *n.* One of minute thin-walled vessels which form networks in various parts of body, *e.g.* blood, lymph, or biliary capillaries.

capillitium (kăp'ĭlĭt'ĭŭm, kăp'ĭlĭsh'-ĭŭm) *n.* [L. *capillus*, hair.] A protoplasmic network of elaters or filaments embedding spores within sporangia of certain fungi.

capitate (kăp'ĭtāt) *a.* [L. *caput*, head.] Enlarged or swollen at tip; gathered into a mass at apex, as compound stigma, some inflorescences; *appl.* a bone, os capitatum.

[redacted]

capitatum (kăpĭtā'tŭm) *n.* [L. *caput*, head.] The third carpale; os magnum.

capitellum (kăp'ĭtĕl'ŭm) *n.* [*Dim.* of L. *caput*, head.] A capitulum or articulatory protuberance at end of a bone.

capitulum (kăpĭt'ūlŭm) *n.* [L. *capitulum*, small head.] A knob-like swelling at end of a bone, *e.g.* on humerus for articulation with radius; part of cirripede body enclosed in mantle, *opp.* peduncle; swollen end of hair or tentacle; enlarged end of insect proboscis, or antenna; exsert part of head in ticks; part of column above parapet in sea-anemones; spherical apothecium containing a powdery mass of spores, in certain lichens; spherical cell at inner end of manubrium in Characeae; head or anthodium, an inflorescence of sessile flowers or florets crowded together on a receptacle and usually surrounded by an involucre.

capreolate (kăprē'ölāt, kăp'rēölāt) *a.* [L. *capreolus*, tendril.] Supplied with tendrils; tendril-shaped.

caprification (kăp'rĭfikā'shŭn) *n.* [L. *caprificus*, wild fig-tree.] Pollination of flowers of fig-tree by Chalcid insects.

capsular (kăp'sūlăr) *a.* [L. *capsula*, little box.] Like or *pert.* a capsule; *appl.* dry, dehiscent, many-seeded fruits, as capsule, follicle, legume, silicula, siliqua.

capsule (kăp'sūl) *n.* [L. *capsula*, little box.] A sac-like membrane enclosing an organ; thickened slime layer surrounding certain bacteria; any closed box-like vessel containing spores, seeds, or fruits; sporogonium, in Bryophyta; a superior, one or more celled, many-seeded, dehiscent fruit; membrane surrounding nerve-cells of sympathetic ganglia.

capsuliferous (kăp'sūlĭf'ërŭs) *a.* [L. *capsula*, little box; *ferre*, to carry.] With, or forming, a capsule; capsuligerous, capsulogenous.

captacula (kăptăk'ūlă) *n. plu.* [L. *captare*, to lie in wait for.] Exsertile filamentous tactile organs near mouth of Scaphopoda.

caput (kăp'ŭt) *n.* [L. *caput*, head.] Head; knob-like swelling at apex; peridium of certain fungi.

caput caecum coli,—former name of caecum.

carapace (kăr'ăpās) *n.* [Sp. *carapacho*, covering.] A chitinous or bony shield covering whole or part of back of certain animals.

carbohydrates (kâr'böhī'drāts) *n. plu.* [L. *carbo*, coal; Gk. *hydor*, water.] Compounds of carbon, hydrogen, and oxygen, aldehydes or ketones constituting sugars, or condensation products thereof.

carbon dioxide (kâr'bŏn dīŏk'sīd) *n.* [L. *carbo*, coal; Gk. *di-*, two; *oxys*, sharp.] Carbonic acid gas, a heavy, colourless gas present in the atmosphere, assimilated by plants and produced by decomposition of organic substances; CO_2.

carbonic anhydrase,—an enzyme, present in erythrocytes, which catalyses the formation of carbonic acid by water and carbon dioxide, and also the decomposition of carbonic acid.

Carboniferous (kâr'bŏnĭf'ërŭs) *a.* [L. *carbo*, coal; *ferre*, to carry.] *Pert.* period of late Palaeozoic era including formation of coal measures.

carcerule,—carcerulus.

carcerulus (kârsĕr'ūlŭs) *n.* [L. *carcer*, prison.] A superior, dry, many-celled fruit, with indehiscent one- or few-seeded carpels cohering by united styles to a central axis.

carcinology (kâr'sĭnŏl'öjĭ) *n.* [Gk. *karkinos*, crab; *logos*, discourse.] The study of Crustacea.

cardia (kâr'dĭă) *n.* [Gk. *kardia*, stomach.] The opening between oesophagus and stomach.

cardiac (kâr'dĭăk) *a.* [Gk. *kardiakos*, *pert.* heart, stomach.] *Pert.*, near, or supplying heart; *appl.* cycle, etc.; *pert.* anterior part of stomach.

cardiac impulse,—motion caused by rapid increase in tension of ventricle.

cardinal (kâr′dĭnăl) *a.* [L. *cardo*, hinge.] *Pert.* that upon which something depends or hinges ; *pert.* hinge of bivalve shell, or to cardo of insects ; *appl.* points for plant growth : minimum, optimum, and maximum temperatures or temperature ranges.

cardinal sinuses and veins,—veins uniting in Cuvier's duct, persistent in most fishes, embryonic in other vertebrates.

cardines,—*plu.* of cardo.

cardioblast (kâr′dĭöblăst) *n.* [Gk. *kardia*, heart ; *blastos*, bud.] One of embryonic cells destined to form walls of heart.

cardiobranchial (kâr′dĭöbrăng′kĭăl) *a.* [Gk. *kardia*, heart ; *brangchia*, gills.] *Appl.* enlarged posterior basibranchial cartilage ventral to heart in elasmobranchs.

cardo (kâr′dō) *n.* [L. *cardo*, hinge.] The hinge of a bivalve shell ; basal sclerite of maxilla in insects, itself divided into eucardo and paracardo.

carina (kărē′nă, kărī′nă) *n.* [L. *carina*, keel.] A keel-like ridge on certain bones, as of breast-bone of birds ; median dorsal plate of a barnacle ; the two coherent anterior petals of a leguminous flower ; ridge on bracts of certain grasses.

carinal (kărī′năl) *a.* [L. *carina*, keel.] Like or *pert.* a keel or ridge ; *appl.* median strand of xylem passing from stem to leaf ; *appl.* canals in protoxylem beneath ridges of stem in Equisetales ; *appl.* dots or puncta on keel of diatom valves ; *appl.* cartilage at the bifurcation of the trachea.

carinate (kăr′ĭnāt) *a.* [L. *carina*, keel.] Having a ridge or keel.

cariniform (kărĭn′ĭfôrm) *a.* [L. *carina*, keel ; *forma*, shape.] Keel-shaped.

carnassial (kârnăs′ĭăl) *a.* [L. *caro*, flesh.] *Pert.* cutting teeth of Carnivora, fourth premolar above and first molar below, — in upper the protocone is reduced, in lower the metaconid.

carnivorous (kârnĭv′örŭs) *a.* [L. *caro*, flesh ; *vorare*, to devour.] Flesh-eating ; *appl.* Carnivora, and to certain plants which feed on entrapped insects.

carotenase (kăr′ŏtēnās) *n.* [L. *carota*, carrot.] A liver enzyme which activates vitamin A formation from carotenes.

carotene (kăr′ötēn) *n.* [L. *carota*, carrot.] A yellow pigment synthesised by plants and present in milk, liver oils, egg yolk, etc. ; provitamin A ; $C_{40}H_{56}$.

carotenoids (kăr′ŏtēnoidz) *n. plu.* [L. *carota*, carrot ; Gk. *eidos*, form.] Pigments occurring in plants and some animal tissues, and including carotene, xanthophylls, and other fat-soluble pigments.

carotid (kărŏt′ĭd) *a.* [Gk. *karos*, heavy sleep.] *Pert.* chief arteries in the neck ; *appl.* arch, ganglion, nerve, etc.

carotid bodies,—two small masses of chromaffin cells associated with carotid sinus, and being part of system for controlling oxygen content and acidity of blood ; glomera carotica.

carotiform (kăr′ötĭfôrm) *a.* [L. *carota*, carrot ; *forma*, shape.] Shaped like a carrot ; *appl.* certain cystidia.

carotin,—carotene, *q.v.*

carotinoids,—carotenoids, *q.v.*

carpal (kâr′păl) *n.* [L. *carpus*, wrist.] A wrist bone. *a. Pert.* wrist.

carpel (kâr′pĕl) *n.* [Gk. *karpos*, fruit.] A division of the seed-vessel ; a simple pistil. *Plu.* Sporophylls which carry megasporangia ; megasporophylls.

carpellary (kâr′pĕlărĭ) *a.* [Gk. *karpos*, fruit.] *Pert.* carpels ; containing a carpel or carpels.

carpellate,—having carpels.

carpocerite (kâr′pösērīt) *n.* [L. *carpus*, wrist ; Gk. *keras*, horn.] Fifth antennal joint in certain Crustacea.

carpogenic (kârpöjĕn′ĭk) *a.* [Gk. *karpos*, fruit ; *gennaein*, to produce.] *Appl.* those cells in red algae which form the carpogonium ; *appl.* cell : oogonium of archicarp ; carpogenous.

carpogonium (kâr'pōgō'nĭŭm) *n.* [Gk. *karpos*, fruit ; *gonos*, birth.] Lower portion of procarp, which contains female nucleus, in some thallophytes ; female gametangium in red algae.

carpolith (kâr'pōlĭth) *n.* [Gk. *karpos*, fruit ; *lithos*, stone.] A fossil fruit.

carpometacarpus (kâr'pōmĕtăkâr'-pŭs) *n.* [Gk. *karpos*, wrist ; *meta*, after.] Portion of wing skeleton formed by fusion of carpal and metacarpal bones, in birds.

carpomycetous (kâr'pōmīsē'tŭs) *a.* [Gk. *karpos*, fruit ; *mykes*, fungus.] Producing fruit-bodies, *appl.* higher fungi.

carpophagous (kârpŏf'ăgŭs) *a.* [Gk. *karpos*, fruit ; *phagein*, to eat.] Feeding on fruit.

carpophore (kâr'pōfōr) *n.* [Gk. *karpos*, fruit ; *pherein*, to bear.] Part of flower axis to which carpels are attached ; stalk of sporocarp.

carpophyll (kâr'pōfĭl) *n.* [Gk. *karpos*, fruit ; *phyllon*, leaf.] A carpel ; a megasporophyll.

carpophyte (kâr'pōfīt) *n.* [Gk. *karpos*, fruit ; *phyton*, plant.] A thallophyte which forms sporocarps.

carpopodite (kâr'pōpōdīt) *n.* [Gk. *karpos*, wrist ; *pous*, foot.] The third joint of endopodite in certain Crustacea ; patella in spiders.

carposoma (kâr'pōsō'mă) *n.* [Gk. *karpos*, fruit ; *soma*, body.] Non-reproductive part of a carpophore ; an immature carpophore.

carposperm (kâr'pōspĕrm) *n.* [Gk. *karpos*, fruit ; *sperma*, seed.] The fertilised oosphere in certain Thallophyta.

carposporangium (kâr'pōspōrăn'-jĭŭm) *n.* [Gk. *karpos*, fruit ; *sporos*, seed ; *anggeion*, vessel.] The terminal cells of filaments developed from fertilised carpogonium in some Thallophyta.

carpospore (kâr'pōspōr) *n.* [Gk. *karpos*, fruit ; *sporos*, seed.] A spore of those formed at end of filaments developed from carpogonium ; one of the spores in the cystocarp of Rhodophyceae.

carposporophyte (kâr'pōspŏ'rōfīt) *n.* [Gk. *karpos*, fruit ; *sporos*, seed ; *phyton*, plant.] The diploid generation of red algae, which consists of filaments forming carpospores at their apices.

carpostome (kâr'pōstōm) *n.* [Gk. *karpos*, fruit ; *stoma*, mouth.] Opening for emission of spores from the cystocarp of red algae.

carpus (kâr'pŭs) *n.* [L. *carpus*, wrist.] The wrist ; region of fore-limb between forearm and metacarpus.

cartilage (kâr'tĭlĕj) *n.* [L. *cartilago*, cartilage.] Gristle, a translucent, bluish-white tissue, firm and elastic, found generally in connection with bones ; cartilaginous structure.

cartilaginous (kâr'tĭlăj'ĭnŭs) *a.* [L. *cartilagineus*, gristly.] Gristly, consisting of or *pert.* cartilage ; resembling consistency of cartilage, as cortex of certain fungi.

caruncle (kărŭng'kl) *n.* [L. *caruncula*, small piece of flesh.] A naked, fleshy excrescence ; small conical body at inner junction of upper and lower eyelids, caruncula lacrimalis ; one of the carunculae hymenales, rounded vestiges of ruptured hymen ; a fleshy outgrowth on head of certain birds, and on certain caterpillars ; a little horny elevation at end of beak of embryo chicks ; piston-like structure within acetabulum of dibranchiate Cephalopoda ; sucking-disc on tarsi of certain mites ; one of outgrowths from various regions of testa of a seed, a strophiole.

caryo-,—also karyo-, *q.v.*

caryolite (kăr'ĭōlīt) *n.* [Gk. *karyon*, nut ; *lytikos*, loosing.] A nucleated muscle fragment undergoing phagocytosis in development of insects.

caryopsis (kăr'ĭŏp'sĭs) *n.* [Gk. *karyon*, nut ; *opsis*, appearance.] A superior, one-celled, one-seeded, indehiscent fruit with a thin dry membranous pericarp inseparably united with the seed ; grain.

casein (kā'sēĭn) *n.* [L. *caseus*, cheese.] A phosphoprotein of milk, formed from caseinogen (casein in U.S.A.) by action of rennin; paracasein (U.S.A.).

Casparian band [*R. Caspary*, German botanist]. A cork- or wood-like strip encircling radial walls of endodermis cells; Casparian strip.

cassideous (kăsĭd'ëŭs) *a.* [L. *cassis*, helmet.] Helmet-like.

caste (kâst) *n.* [L. *castus*, pure.] One of the distinct forms found among certain social insects.

castrate (kăs'trāt) *a.* [L. *castrare*, to castrate.] *Pert.* flowers from which androecium has been removed. *n.* An animal deprived of functional gonads. *v.* To deprive of testes; to gonadectomise; to inhibit development of gonads.

cata-,—*also* kata-, *q.v.*

catacorolla (kăt'ăkörŏl'ă) *n.* [Gk. *kata*, against; L. *corolla*, little wreath.] A secondary corolla.

catadromous (kătăd'römŭs) *a.* [Gk. *kata*, down; *dramein*, to run.] Tending downward; having branches arising from lower side of pinnae, in ferns; having first set of nerves in a frond segment given off on basal side of midrib; *appl.* fishes which migrate from fresh to salt water annually, *opp.* anadromous.

catalase,—an enzyme occurring in plant and animal tissues, which decomposes hydrogen peroxide into water and oxygen.

catalepsis (kătălĕp'sĭs) *n.* [Gk. *katalepsis*, seizure.] A so-called shamming-dead reflex, as in spiders; *cf.* kataplexy.

catallact,—coenobium, homoplast.

catalysis (kătăl'ĭsĭs) *n.* [Gk. *katalysis*, dissolution.] Acceleration or retardation of reaction due to presence of a catalyst.

catalyst (kăt'ălĭst) *n.* [Gk. *katalysis*, dissolving.] An agent, *e.g.* an enzyme, which can accelerate or retard, or initiate, a reaction and apparently remains unchanged; catalysor.

catamenia (kătămē'nĭă) *n.* [Gk. *kata*, according to; *men*, month.] Periodic discharge from uterus; menses.

catapetalous (kăt'ăpĕt'ălŭs) *a.* [Gk. *kata* over; *petalon*, leaf.] Having petals united with the base of monadelphous stamens.

cataphoresis (kăt'ăförē'sĭs) *n.* [Gk. *katapherein*, to carry down.] Migration of particles in suspension, as of living cells, under influence of electric current, the rate depending on voltage; electrophoresis.

cataphyll (kăt'ăfĭl) *n.* [Gk. *kata*, down; *phyllon*, leaf.] Simple form of leaf on lower part of plant, as cotyledon, bud-scale, scale-leaf; cataphyllary leaf. *Opp.* hypsophyll.

cataphyllary (kăt'ăfĭl'ărĭ) *a.* [Gk. *kata*, down; *phyllon*, leaf.] *Appl.* rudimentary or scale-like leaves which act as covering of buds.

cataplasis (kătăp'lăsĭs) *n.* [Gk. *kata*, downward; *plasis*, moulding.] Regression or decline following the mature period or metaplasis.

catapleurite (kăt'aploor'īt) *n.* [Gk. *kata*, down; *pleura*, side.] Thoracic pleurite between anapleurite and trochantin, as in certain Thysanura; coxopleurite.

catelectrotonus (kătēlĕk'trŏt'önŭs, kăt'ēlĕktrŏt'önŭs) *n.* [Gk. *kata*, down; *elektron*, amber; *tonos*, tension.] Increase in irritability of a nerve under influence of non-polarising electric current; katelectrotonus.

catena (kătē'nă) *n.* [L. *catena*, chain.] A sequence of soil types which is repeated in a corresponding sequence of topographical sites, as between ridges and valleys of a region; a bast fibre in Heliocarpus.

catenation (kătēnā'shŭn) *n.* [L. *catenatus*, chained.] End-to-end arrangement of chromosomes; ring formation of alternating paternally and maternally derived chromosomes; a chain, as of diatom frustules.

catenoid (kătē′noid) *a.* [L. *catena*, chain; Gk. *eidos*, form.] Chain-like; *appl.* certain protozoan colonies.

catenular (kătĕn′ūlăr), *a.* [L. *catenula*, little chain.] Chain-like; *appl.* colonies of bacteria, colour-markings on butterfly wings, shells, etc.

catenulate,—forming a chain-like series.

catenuliform,—catenoid, catenular.

caterpillar (kăt′ërpĭl′ăr) *n.* [L.L. *cattus*, cat; L. *pilosus*, hairy.] Young worm-like insect larva, particularly of Lepidoptera; eruca.

cathammal (kăth′ămăl) *a.* [Gk. *kathamma*, anything tied.] *Appl.* plates forming endoderm lamella in some Coelenterata.

catkin (kăt′kĭn) *n.* [A.S. *catkin*, little cat.] A spike with unisexual flowers and pendulous rachis; amentum.

cauda (kô′dă) *n.* [L. *cauda*, tail.] A tail, or tail-like appendage; posterior part of an organ, *e.g.* cauda equina, cauda epididymis; a tube at posterior end of abdomen of certain insects, suggesting presence of a further segment.

caudad (kô′dăd) *adv.* [L. *cauda*, tail; *ad*, toward.] Towards tail region or posterior end.

caudal (kô′dăl) *a.* [L. *cauda*, tail.] Of or *pert.* a tail, *e.g.* caudal fin.

caudate (kô′dāt) *a.* [L. *cauda*, tail.] Having a tail, *e.g.* caudate nucleus; *appl.* a lobe of the liver.

caudatolenticular (kôdā′tölĕntĭk′-ūlăr) *a.* [L. *cauda*, tail; *lens*, lentil.] *Appl.* caudate and lenticular nuclei of corpus striatum.

caudex (kô′dĕks) *n.* [L. *caudex*, tree trunk.] The axis or stem of a woody plant, as of tree-ferns, palms, etc.

caudicle (kô′dĭkl) *n.* [*Dim.* of L. *cauda*, tail.] Stalk of pollinium in orchids.

caudihaemal (kô′dĭhē′măl) *a.* [L. *cauda*, tail; Gk. *haima*, blood.] *Appl.* posterior lower portion of a sclerotome.

caudineural (kôdĭnū′răl) *a.* [L. *cauda*, tail; Gk. *neuron*, nerve.] *Appl.* posterior upper portion of a sclerotome.

caudostyle (kô′döstīl) *n.* [L. *cauda*, tail; Gk. *stylos*, column.] A terminal structure in certain parasitic amoebae.

caudotibialis (kô′dötĭbĭā′lĭs) *n.* [L. *cauda*, tail; *tibia*, shin.] A muscle connecting caudal vertebrae and tibia, as in Phocidae.

caul (kôl) *n.* [M.E. *calle*, covering.] An enclosing membrane; amnion; omentum.

caulescent (kôlĕs′ënt) *a.* [L. *caulis*, stalk.] With leaf-bearing stem above ground.

caulicle (kôl′ĭkl) *n.* [L. *cauliculus*, small stalk.] A small or rudimentary stem; axis of a young seedling.

caulicolous (kôlĭk′ölŭs) *a.* [L. *caulis*, stalk; *colere*, to inhabit.] *Appl.* fungi growing on plant-stems.

cauliflory (kôl′ĭflō′rĭ) *n.* [L. *caulis*, stalk; *flos*, flower.] Condition of having flowers arising from axillary buds on the main stem or older branches; cauliflorous habitus.

cauliform (kôl′ĭfôrm) *a.* [L. *caulis*, stalk; *forma*, shape.] Stem-like.

cauligenous (kôlĭj′ënŭs) *a.* [Gk. *kaulos*, stem; *genos*, birth.] Borne on the stem.

cauline (kô′lĭn) *a.* [L. *caulis*, stalk.] *Pert.* stem; *appl.* leaves growing on upper portion of a stem; *appl.* vascular bundles not passing into leaves.

caulis (kô′lĭs) *n.* [L. *caulis*, stalk.] The stem, in herbaceous plants.

caulocaline (kôl′ökălēn′) *n.* [Gk. *kaulos*, stem; *kalein*, to summon.] A plant hormone, possibly elaborated in roots, which stimulates growth of stem.

caulocarpous (kô′lökâr′pŭs) *a.* [Gk. *kaulos*, stem; *karpos*, fruit.] With fruit-bearing stem.

caulocystidium (kôl′ösĭstĭd′ĭŭm) *n.* [Gk. *kaulos*, stalk; *kystis*, bag; *idion*, *dim.*] One of the cystidium-like structures on stipe of certain Basidiomycetes.

caulome (kô′lōm) *n.* [Gk. *kaulos*,

stem.] The stem structure of a plant as a whole.

caulomer (kôl'ōmĕr) *n.* [Gk. *kaulos*, stem ; *meros*, part.] A secondary axis in a sympodium.

caulotaxis (kôl'ōtăk'sĭs) *n.* [Gk. *kaulos*, stem ; *taxis*, arrangement.] The arrangement of branches on a stem ; caulotaxy.

caulotrichome (kô'lōtrĭk'ōm) *n.* [Gk. *kaulos*, stem ; *trichoma*, growth of hair.] Hair-like or filamentous outgrowths on a stem ; caulocystidia.

cavernicolous (kăvĕrnĭk'ōlŭs) *a.* [L. *caverna*, cavern ; *colere*, to dwell.] Cave-inhabiting.

cavernosus (kăv'ĕrnō'sŭs) *a.* [L. *cavernosus*, chambered.] Full of cavities ; hollow, or resembling a hollow ; *appl.* tissue, nerve, arteries.

cavicorn (kăv'ĭkôrn) *a.* [L. *cavus*, hollow ; *cornu*, horn.] Hollow-horned ; *appl.* certain ruminants.

cavum (kā'vŭm) *n.* [L. *cavus*, hollow.] The lower division of concha caused by origin of helix ; cavity of mouth, larynx, long bones, etc. ; any hollow or chamber.

C-cells,—cells with non-granular cytoplasm in islets of Langerhans, possibly giving rise to A-cells.

cecal,—caecal, *q.v.*

cecidium (sēsĭd'ĭŭm) *n.* [Gk. *kekis*, inky juice, gall.] An excrescence on plants, caused by fungi, mites, or insects ; gall, gall-nut.

cecum,—caecum, *q.v.*

celiac,—coeliac, *q.v.*

cell (sĕl) *n.* [L. *cella*, compartment.] A small cavity or hollow ; a loculus ; a unit mass of protoplasm, usually containing a nucleus or nuclear material ; originally, the cell wall ; space between veins of insect wings.

cellifugal (sĕlĭf'ūgăl) *a.* [L. *cella*, cell ; *fugere*, to flee.] Moving away from a cell.

cellipetal (sĕlĭp'ĕtăl) *a.* [L. *cella*, cell ; *petere*, to seek.] Moving towards a cell.

cell lineage,—the derivation of a tissue or part from a definite blastomere of embryo.

cell organ,—a part of a cell having a special function, as a centrosome ; organoid.

cell plate,—equatorial thickening of spindle fibres from which partition wall arises during division of plant cells.

cell sap,—the more fluid ground substance of the cell.

cellular (sĕl'ūlăr) *a.* [L. *cellula*, small cell.] *Pert.* or consisting of cells.

cellulase (sĕl'ūlās) *n.* [L. *cellula*, small cell.] An enzyme which hydrolyses cellulose, occurring in bacteria and fungi.

cellulin (sĕl'ūlĭn) *n.* [L. *cellula*, little cell.] A carbohydrate found in constrictions of hyphae.

cellulose (sĕl'ūlōs) *n.* [L. *cellula*, small cell.] A carbohydrate forming main part of plant cell walls, also found in tests of tunicates ; $(C_6H_{10}O_5)_x$.

cell-wall,—investing portion of cell.

celo-,—coelo-, *q.v.*

cement (sēmĕnt') *n.* [L. *caementum*, mortar.] A substance chemically and physically allied to bone, investing parts of teeth ; crusta petrosa ; a uniting substance secreted by certain animals.

cementocytes,—cells resembling osteocytes, in lacunae of cement of teeth.

cenanthy,—kenanthy, *q.v.*

cenchrus (sĕng'krŭs) *n.* [Gk. *kengchros*, millet.] A pale-coloured area on mesothorax of saw-flies.

cenenchyma,—coenenchyma.

ceno-,—*see* caeno-, coeno-.

censer mechanism,—method of seed distribution by which seeds are jerked out from fruit by high wind.

centradenia (sĕn'trădē'nĭă) *n.* [Gk. *kentron*, centre ; *aden*, gland.] The type of siphonophore colony in Disconectae.

central (sĕn'trăl) *a.* [L. *centrum*, centre.] Situated in the centre ; *pert.* a vertebral centrum. *n.* A bone in wrist or ankle, situated between proximal and distal rows.

central body,—centrosome, *q.v.*
central cylinder,—stele, *q.v.*
centric (sĕn'trĭk) *a.* [L. *centrum*, centre.] *Appl.* leaves which are cylindrical or terete; having a centromere.
centrifugal (sĕntrĭf'ūgăl) *a.* [L. *centrum*, centre; *fugere*, to flee.] *Appl.* compact cymose inflorescences having youngest flowers towards outside; *appl.* nerves transmitting impressions from nerve centre to parts supplied by nerve.
centriole (sĕn'trĭōl) *n.* [L. *centrum*, centre.] The central particle of the centrosome; the centrosome itself.
centripetal (sĕntrĭp'ĕtăl) *a.* [L. *centrum*, centre; *petere*, to seek.] *Appl.* racemose inflorescences having youngest flowers at apex; *appl.* nerves transmitting impressions from peripheral extremities to nerve centres.
centripetal canals,—blind canals growing from circular canal backwards towards apex of bell in certain Trachomedusae.
centro-acinar (sĕn'tröăs'ĭnăr) *a.* [L. *centrum*, centre; *acinus*, berry.] *Pert.* centre of an alveolus, as in pancreas.
centrodesmus (sĕn'trödĕs'mŭs) *n.* [Gk. *kentron*, centre; *desmos*, bond.] The fibril or system of fibrils temporarily connecting two centrosomes; centrodesm, centrodesmose.
centrodorsal (sĕn'trödôr'săl) *a.* [L. *centrum*, centre; *dorsum*, back.] *Appl.* plate in middle of aboral surface of unstalked crinoids.
centrogenous (sĕntrŏj'ënŭs) *a.* [Gk. *kentron*, centre; *gennaein*, to produce.] *Appl.* a skeleton of spicules which meet in a common centre and grow outwards.
centrolecithal (sĕn'trölĕs'ĭthăl) *a.* [Gk. *kentron*, centre; *lekithos*, yolk.] With yolk aggregated in the centre, *appl.* ovum.
centromere (sĕn'trömēr) *n.* [Gk. *kentron*, centre; *meros*, part.] The part of the chromosome located at the point lying on the equator of the spindle at metaphase and dividing at anaphase, controlling chromosome activity; spindle-attachment region, achromite, kinetochore.
centron (sĕn'trŏn) *n.* [Gk. *kentron*, centre.] Cyton, *q.v.*
centrophormium (sĕn'tröfôr'mĭŭm) *n.* [Gk. *kentron*, centre; *phormis*, small basket.] The Golgi-bodies when in round basket-like form.
centroplasm (sĕn'tröplăzm) *n.* [Gk. *kentron*, centre; *plasma*, mould.] Substance of centrosphere; a more or less definite concentric zone round the aster in mitosis.
centroplast (sĕn'tröplăst) *n.* [Gk. *kentron*, centre; *plastos*, formed.] An extranuclear spherical body forming division centre of mitosis in certain lower organisms.
centrosome (sĕn'trösōm) *n.* [Gk. *kentron*, centre; *soma*, body.] A cell-organ, the centre of dynamic activity in mitosis, consisting of centriole and attraction-sphere.
centrosphere (sĕn'trösfēr) *n.* [Gk. *kentron*, centre; *sphaira*, ball.] The central mass of aster and centrosome; astrosphere; attraction-sphere.
centrotaxis (sĕn'trötăk'sĭs) *n.* [Gk. *kentron*, centre; *taxis*, arrangement.] Orientation of chromatin thread towards cytocentrum during leptotene stage.
centrotheca (sĕn'tröthē'kă) *n.* [Gk. *kentron*, centre; *theke*, case.] Idiozome, *q.v.*
centrum (sĕn'trŭm) *n.* [L. *centrum*, centre.] The main body of a vertebra, from which neural and haemal arches arise; centrosome, centrosphere, *q.v.*
cephal-,—*also* kephal-.
cephalad (kĕf'ălăd, sĕf-) *adv.* [Gk. *kephale*, head; L. *ad*, towards.] Towards head region or anterior end.
cephalanthium (kĕf'ălăn'thĭŭm, sĕf-) *n.* [Gk. *kephale*, head; *anthos*, flower.] The capitulum in composite plants; anthodium.
cephaletron (kĕfălē'trŏn, sĕf-) *n.* [Gk. *kephale*, head; *etron*, belly.] The anterior region of Xiphosura.

cephalic (kĕfăl′ĭk, sĕf-) *a.* [Gk. *kephale*, head.] *Pert.* head; in head region.

cephalic index,—one hundred times maximum breadth divided by maximum length of skull.

cephalin (kĕf′ălĭn, sĕf-) *n.* [Gk. *kephale*, head.] A phospholipide present in nerve fibres and egg-yolk; kephalin; an epimerite bearing trophozoites.

cephalis (kĕf′ălĭs, sĕf-) *n.* [Gk. *kephalis*, little bulb.] The uppermost chamber of monaxonic shells of Radiolaria.

cephalisation (kĕf′ălĭzā′shŭn, sĕf-) *n.* [Gk. *kephale*, head.] Increasing differentiation and importance of anterior end in animal development.

cephalon (kĕf′ălŏn, sĕf-) *n.* [Gk. *kephale*, head.] The head of arthropods; head shield of trilobites.

cephalont (kĕf′ălŏnt, sĕf-) *n.* [Gk. *kephale*, head.] A sporozoan about to proceed to spore-formation.

cephalopod (kĕf′ălŏpŏd, sĕf-) *n.* [Gk. *kephale*, head; *pous*, foot.] Marine mollusc with muscular sucker-bearing arms on head region, *e.g.* cuttle-fish, octopus.

cephalopodium (kĕf′ălŏpō′dĭŭm, sĕf-) *n.* [Gk. *kephale*, head; *pous*, foot.] The head and arms constituting the head-region in cephalopods.

cephalopsin (kĕfălŏp′sĭn, sĕf-) *n.* [Gk. *kephale*, head; *opsis*, sight.] A photopigment resembling visual purple, in eyes of cephalopods and some other invertebrates.

cephalosporium (kĕf′ălŏspō′rĭŭm, sĕf-) *n.* [Gk. *kephale*, head; *sporos*, seed.] A globular mucilaginous mass of spores; spore ball.

cephalostegite (kĕf′ălŏs′tĕjīt, sĕf-) *n.* [Gk. *kephale*, head; *stege*, roof.] Anterior part of cephalothoracic shield.

cephalostyle (kĕf′ălŏstīl, sĕf-) *n.* [Gk. *kephale*, head; *stylos*, pillar.] Anterior end of notochord enclosed in sheath, in Chondrocrania.

cephalotheca (kĕf′ălŏthē′kă, sĕf-) *n.* [Gk. *kephale*, head; *theke*, case.] Head integument in insect pupa.

cephalothorax (kĕf′ălŏthō′răks, sĕf-) *n.* [Gk. *kephale*, head; *thorax*, breast.] The body-region formed by fusion of head and thorax in Arachnida and Crustacea.

cephalotrocha (kĕfălŏt′rŏkă, sĕf-) *n.* [Gk. *kephale*, head; *trochos*, wheel.] A turbellarian larva with eight processes round mouth.

cephalula (kĕfăl′ūlă, sĕf-) *n.* [Gk. *kephale*, head.] Free-swimming embryonic stage in certain brachiopods.

ceptor,—receptor.

cer-,—*also* ker-.

ceraceous (sērā′shŭs) *a.* [L. *cera*, wax.] Waxy; cereous.

ceral (sē′răl) *a.* [L. *cera*, wax.] *Pert.* wax; *pert.* the cere of birds.

cerata (sĕr′ătă, kĕr-) *n. plu.* [Gk. *keras*, horn.] Lobes or leaf-like processes acting as gills on back of nudibranch molluscs.

ceratium (sērā′shĭŭm) *n.* [Gk. *keration*, little horn.] A siliqua without the replum.

ceratobranchial (kĕr′ătŏbrăng′kĭăl, sĕr-). [Gk. *keras*, horn; *brangchia*, gills.] An element of branchial arch.

ceratohyal (kĕr′ătŏhī′ăl, sĕr-) *n.* [Gk. *keras*, horn; *hyoeides*, Υ-shaped.] The component of hyoid arch next below epihyal.

ceratoid (sĕr′ătoid, kĕr′-) *a.* [Gk. *keras*, horn; *eidos*, form.] Like horn; horny; keratoid.

ceratotheca (sĕr′ătŏthē′kă, kĕr-) *n.* [Gk. *keras*, horn; *theke*, case.] The part of the casing of an insect pupa which protects the antennae.

ceratotrichia (kĕr′ătŏtrĭk′ĭă, sĕr-) *n. plu.* [Gk. *keras*, horn; *thrix*, hair.] Horny and non-cellular actinotrichia of elasmobranchs.

cercal (sĕr′kăl) *a.* [Gk. *kerkos*, tail.] *Pert.* the tail; *pert.* cerci, *appl.* hairs, nerve.

cercaria (sĕrkā′rĭă) *n.* [Gk. *kerkos*, tail.] A heart-shaped trematode larva with tail.

cerci,—*plu.* of cercus.

cercid (sĕr′sĭd) *n.* [Gk. *kerkis*, shuttle.] One of minute wandering cells produced by division of archaeocytes in certain sponges.

cercoid (sĕr′koid) *n.* [Gk. *kerkos*, tail; *eidos*, shape.] One of paired appendages on ninth, or tenth, abdominal segment of certain insect larvae.

cercus (sĕr′kŭs) *n.* [Gk. *kerkos*, tail.] A jointed appendage at end of abdomen in many arthropods; appendage bearing acoustic hairs in some insects; cercopod.

cere (sēr) *n.* [L. *cera*, wax.] A swollen fleshy patch at proximal end of bill in birds; ceroma.

cerebellar (sĕr′ĕbĕl′ăr) *a.* [L. *cerebrum*, brain.] *Pert.* the cerebellum or hind-brain.

cerebellum (sĕr′ĕbĕl′ŭm) *n.* [L. *cerebrum*, brain.] The fourth division of brain, arising from differentiation of anterior part of third primary vesicle.

cerebral (sĕr′ĕbrăl) *a.* [L. *cerebrum*, brain.] *Pert.* the brain; *pert.* anterior part of brain or cerebral hemispheres.

cerebral organs,—chemical sense organs, paired ciliated tubes associated with dorsal ganglion and opening to exterior, in nemertines.

cerebrifugal (sĕrĕbrĭf′ūgăl) *a.* [L. *cerebrum*, brain; *fugere*, to flee.] *Appl.* nerve fibres which pass from brain to spinal cord.

cerebroganglion (sĕr′ĕbrŏgăng′glĭŏn) *n.* [L. *cerebrum*, brain; Gk. *ganglion*, swelling.] The supra-oesophageal ganglia of invertebrates.

cerebroid,—cerebrose.

cerebropedal (sĕr′ĕbrŏpĕd′ăl) *a.* [L. *cerebrum*, brain; *pes*, foot.] *Appl.* nerve strands connecting cerebral and pedal ganglia in molluscs.

cerebrose (sĕr′ĕbrōs) *a.* [L. *cerebrum*, brain.] Resembling convolutions of the brain; *appl.* surface of spores, of pileus, etc.

cerebrospinal (sĕr′ĕbrŏspī′năl) *a.* [L. *cerebrum*, brain; *spina*, spine.] *Pert.* brain and spinal cord.

cerebrovisceral (sĕr′ĕbrŏvĭs′ĕrăl) *a.* [L. *cerebrum*, brain; *viscera*, viscera.] *Appl.* connective joining cerebral and visceral ganglia in molluscs.

cerebrum (sĕr′ĕbrŭm) *n.* [L. *cerebrum*, brain.] The fore-brain, arising from differentiation of first primary vesicle.

cereous (sē′rēŭs) *a.* [L. *cereus*, waxen.] Wax-like; waxy.

ceriferous (sērĭf′ĕrŭs) *a.* [L. *cera*, wax; *ferre*, to carry.] Wax-producing; *appl.* organs.

cernuous (sĕr′nūŭs) *a.* [L. *cernuus*, with face turned downwards.] Drooping; pendulous.

ceroma (sē′rōmă) *n* [Gk. *keroma*, waxed surface.] The cere of birds.

cerous (sē′rŭs) *a.* [L. *cera*, wax.] *Appl.* structure resembling a cere.

certation (sĕrtā′shŭn) *n.* [L. *certatio*, contest.] Competition in growth rate of pollen tubes of genetically different types.

cerumen (sĕrū′mĕn) *n.* [L. *cera*, wax.] Wax-like secretion from ceruminous glands of ear; wax secreted by scale insects; wax of nest of certain bees.

cervical (sĕrvī′kăl, sĕr′vĭkăl) *a.* [L. *cervix*, neck.] *Appl.* or *pert.* structures connected with neck, as nerves, bones, blood-vessels, also to cervix or neck of an organ.

cervicum (sĕr′vĭkŭm) *n.* [L. *cervix*, neck.] The neck-region of Arthropoda.

cervix (sĕr′vĭks) *n.* [L. *cervix*, neck.] The neck or narrow mouth of an organ, as cervix uteri.

cespitose,—caespitose, *q.v.*

cetolith (sē′tŏlĭth) *n.* [Gk. *ketos*, whale; *lithos*, stone.] The fused tympanic and petrosal of whales, found in deep-sea dredging.

cevitamic acid,—ascorbic acid or vitamin C.

chaeta (kē′tă) *n.* [Gk. *chaite*, hair.] A seta (*q.v.*), or bristle, as of certain worms.

chaetic (kē′tĭk) *a.* [Gk. *chaite*, hair.] Bristle-like, *appl.* a type of tactile sensilla in insects.

chaetiferous (kētĭf′ĕrŭs) *a.* [Gk. *chaite*, hair; L. *ferre*, to bear.] Bristle-bearing; chaetigerous, setigerous.

chaetophorous (kētŏf'ŏrŭs) *a.* [Gk. *chaite*, hair; *pherein*, to bear.] Bristle-bearing; *appl.* worms and certain insects.

chaetosema (kē'tösē'mă) *n.* [Gk. *chaite*, hair; *sema*, sign.] One of two small sensory organs located on head of certain Lepidoptera, and provided with bristles and sensory cells connected by a sheathed nerve to brain; Jordan's organ.

chaetotaxy (kē'tötăk'sĭ) *n.* [Gk. *chaite*, hair; *taxis*, arrangement.] Bristle pattern or arrangement.

chain behaviour,—a series of actions, each being induced by the antecedent action and being an integral part of a unified performance.

chalaza (kălā'ză) *n.* [Gk. *chalaza*, hail.] One of two spiral bands attaching yolk to membrane of a bird's egg; base of nucellus of ovule, from which integuments arise.

chalaziferous (kălăzĭf'ĕrŭs) *a.* [Gk. *chalaza*, hail; L. *ferre*, to bear.] *Appl.* layer of albumen surrounding yolk and continuous with chalazae.

chalazogamy (kălăzŏg'ămĭ) *n.* [Gk. *chalaza*, hail; *gamos*, marriage.] Fertilisation in which the pollen-tube pierces chalaza of ovule; *cf.* porogamy.

chalice (chăl'ĭs) *n.* [L. *calix*, goblet.] *Appl.* simple gland cells or goblet cells; a modified columnar epithelial gland cell; arms and disc of a crinoid.

chalones (kăl'ōnz) *n. plu.* [Gk. *chalinos*, curb.] Internal secretions which depress activity; *opp.* hormones.

chalonic (kălŏn'ĭk) *a.* [Gk. *chalinos*, curb.] Depressor, inhibitory, or restraining; *appl.* internal secretions; *opp.* hormonic.

chamaephyte (kămĭ'fīt) *n.* [Gk. *chamai*, on the ground; *phyton*, plant.] A plant with shoots that bear dormant buds lying on or near the ground.

chasmatoplasm (kăz'mătöplăzm) *n.* [Gk. *chasma*, expanse; *plasma*, mould.] An expanded form of plasson.

chasmochomophyte (kăz'mökō'möfīt) *n.* [Gk. *chasma*, opening; *choma*, mound; *phyton*, plant.] A plant growing on detritus in rock crevices.

chasmogamy (kăzmŏg'ămĭ) *n.* [Gk. *chasma*, opening; *gamos*, marriage.] Opening of a mature flower to ensure fertilisation, *opp.* cleistogamy.

chasmophyte (kăz'möfīt) *n.* [Gk. *chasma*, opening; *phyton*, plant.] A plant which grows in crevices of rocks; a chasmophilous plant.

cheek (chēk) *n.* [A.S. *céace*, cheek.] The fleshy wall of mouth in mammals; side of face; in invertebrates the lateral portions of head, as fixed and free cheeks of trilobites.

cheilocystidium (kī'lösĭstĭd'ĭŭm) *n.* [Gk. *cheilos*, edge; *kystis*, bag; *idion*, *dim.*] A cystidium in hymenium at edge of lamella; *cf.* pleurocystidium.

cheilotrichome,—cheilocystidium.

cheiropterygium (kīrŏptĕrĭj'ĭŭm) *n.* [Gk. *cheir*, hand; *pteryx*, wing.] The pentadactyl limb typical of higher vertebrates.

chela (kē'lă) *n.* [Gk. *chele*, claw.] The claw borne on certain limbs of Crustacea and Arachnoidea; a short sponge spicule with talon-like projections at one or each end.

chelate (kē'lāt) *a.* [Gk. *chele*, claw.] Claw-like or pincer-like; cheliform; cheliferous, *q.v.*

chelicerae (kēlĭs'ĕrē) *n. plu.* [Gk. *chele*, claw; *keras*, horn.] Anterior chelate or sub-chelate appendages of Arachnoidea; also cheliceres.

cheliferous (kēlĭf'ĕrŭs) *a.* [Gk. *chele*, claw; L. *ferre*, to bear.] Supplied with chelae or claws.

cheliform (kē'lĭfôrm) *a.* [Gk. *chele*, claw; L. *forma*, shape.] Claw-like; *appl.* appendages.

cheliped (kē'lĭpĕd) *n.* [Gk. *chele*, claw; L. *pes*, foot.] A claw-bearing appendage; forceps of decapod crustaceans.

chelophores (kē'lōfōrz) *n. plu.* [Gk. *chele*, claw; *pherein*, to bear.] First pair of appendages in Pycnogonida.

chemiluminescence (kĕm'ĭlūmĭnĕs'ĕns, -loo-) *n.* [Gk. *chemeia*, transmutation; L. *luminescere*, to grow light.] Light production at ordinary temperature during a chemical reaction, as bioluminescence, *q.v.*

chemiotaxis,—chemotaxis.

chemoceptor,—chemoreceptor.

chemokinesis (kĕm'ōkīnē'sĭs) *n.* [Gk. *chemeia*, transmutation; *kinesis*, movement.] Movement, of freely motile organisms, resulting from chemical stimuli.

chemonasty (kĕm'ōnăs'tĭ) *n.* [Gk. *chemeia*, transmutation; *nastos*, close pressed.] Response to diffuse or indirect chemical stimuli.

chemoreceptor (kĕm'ōrēsĕp'tŏr) *n.* [Gk. *chemeia*, transmutation; L. *recipere*, to receive.] A terminal organ receiving chemical stimuli.

chemoreflex (kĕm'ōrē'flĕks) *n.* [Gk. *chemeia*, transmutation; L. *reflectere*, to bend back.] A reflex caused by chemical stimulus.

chemostat (kĕm'ōstăt) *n.* [Gk. *chemeia*, transmutation; *statos*, standing.] Any organ concerned in maintaining constancy of chemical conditions, as of hydrogen ion concentration in blood.

chemosynthesis (kĕm'ōsĭn'thēsĭs) *n.* [Gk. *chemeia*, transmutation; *syn*, with; *tithenai*, to place.] The building up of chemical compounds in organisms.

chemotaxis (kĕm'ōtăk'sĭs) *n.* [Gk. *chemeia*, transmutation; *taxis*, arrangement.] The reaction of cells or freely motile organisms to chemical stimuli; also chemiotaxis.

chemotrophic (kĕmōtrŏf'ĭk) *a.* [Gk. *chemeia*, transmutation; *trophe*, nourishment.] Deriving nourishment from certain inorganic substances, *appl.* certain organisms without chlorophyll, as iron bacteria and sulphur bacteria.

chemotropism (kĕmŏt'rōpĭzm) *n.* [Gk. *chemeia*, transmutation; *trope*, turn.] Curvature of a plant or plant organ in response to chemical stimuli.

chernozem (chĕr'nōzĕm, chĕrnōzyŏm) *n.* [Russ. *chernyi*, black; *zemlya*, soil.] Black soil, characteristic of steppe and grass land and formed under continental climatic conditions; blackearth.

chersophyte (kĕr'sōfīt) *n.* [Gk. *chersa*, waste places; *phyton*, plant.] A plant which grows on waste land.

chestnut soils,—dark-brown soils of semi-arid steppe-lands, fertile under adequate rainfall or when irrigated.

cheta,—chaeta, *q.v.*

chevron (shĕv'rŏn) *a.* [F. *chevron*, rafter, from L. *caper*, goat.] *Appl.* V-shaped bones articulating with ventral surface of spinal column in caudal region of many vertebrates.

chiasma (kĭăz'mă) *n.*, **chiasmata** (kĭaz'mătă) *plu.* [Gk. *chiasma*, cross.] A decussation of fibres, as optic chiasma; in paired chromatids, an exchange of partners in meiosis.

chiasmatypy (kĭăz'mătī'pĭ) *n.* [Gk. *chiasma*, cross; *typos*, character.] A form of recombination of chromosome material in synapsis; chiasmatype, *appl.* theory that chiasmata and crossing-over are causally correlated.

chiastic (kĭăs'tĭk) *a.* [Gk. *chiastos*, diagonally arranged.] Decussating; crossing; obliquely or at right angles to axis; *pert.* chiasmata.

chiastoneural (kĭăs'tōnū'răl) *a.* [Gk. *chiastos*, diagonally arranged; *neuron*, nerve.] *Appl.* certain gastropods in which visceral nerve cords cross and form a figure 8.

chilaria (kīlā'rĭă) *n. plu.* [Gk. *cheilos*, lip.] Pair of processes between sixth pair of appendages in Limulus.

chilidium (kīlĭd'ĭŭm) *n.* [Gk. *cheilos*, lip; *idion*, *dim.*] A shelly plate covering deltidial fissure in dorsal valve of certain Brachiopoda.

chimaera (kĭmē'ră) *n.* [L. *chimaera*, monster.] A single organism developing from two fused rudiments from different individuals, or composed of tissues of two different genotypes ; a mosaic ; chimera.

chimonophilous (kīmōnŏf′ĭlŭs) *a.* [Gk. *cheimon*, winter ; *philein*, to love.] Thriving or growing during winter.

chiropterophilous (kīrŏp′tĕrŏf′ĭlŭs) *a.* [Gk. *cheir*, hand ; *pteron*, wing ; *philos*, loving.] Pollinated by agency of bats.

chiropterygium,—cheiropterygium.

chirotype (kī′rōtīp) *n.* [Gk. *cheir*, hand ; *typos*, pattern.] The specimen of a species designated by a manuscript name or chironym, ratified on publication as being the type specimen.

chitin (kī′tĭn) *n.* [Gk. *chiton*, tunic.] A nitrogenous carbohydrate derivative forming the skeletal substance in arthropods, also constituent of cell-wall in fungi ; isotropic chitin, *opp.* actinochitin.

chitinase (kī′tĭnās) *n.* [Gk. *chiton*, tunic.] An enzyme which hydrolyses chitin, in mould fungi and in digestive juice of snail.

chlamydate (klăm′ĭdāt) *a.* [Gk. *chlamys*, cloak.] Supplied with a mantle.

chlamydeous (klămĭd′ēŭs) *a.* [Gk. *chlamys*, cloak.] *Pert.* flower and envelope.

chlamydospore (klăm′ĭdōspōr) *n.* [Gk. *chlamys*, cloak ; *sporos*, seed.] A thick-walled resting spore of certain fungi and protozoa.

chloragen (klō′răjĕn) *a.* [Gk. *chloros*, sandy yellow ; *genos*, descent.] *Appl.* yellow cells found in connection with alimentary canal of annelids ; also chloragogen.

chloragocyte (klō′răgōsīt) *n.* [Gk. *chloros*, sandy yellow ; *kytos*, hollow.] A chloragogen cell.

chloragogen,—chloragen, *q.v.*

chloragosomes (klō′răgōsōms) *n. plu.* [Gk. *chloros*, sandy yellow ; *soma*, body.] Yellow or brownish globules formed in chloragogen cells.

chloranthy (klōrăn′thĭ, klō′rănthĭ) *n.* [Gk. *chloros*, grass green ; *anthos*, flower.] Reversion of floral leaves to ordinary green leaves.

chlorenchyma (klōrĕng′kĭmă) *n.* [Gk. *chloros*, grass green ; *engchyma*, infusion.] Tissues collectively, or stem tissue, or mesophyll, containing chlorophyll.

chloride cell,—a columnar cell of gill filament, specialised for excretion of chlorides, in certain fishes.

chlorocruorin (klō′rōkroo′ŏrĭn) *n.* [Gk. *chloros*, grass green ; L. *cruor*, blood.] A green respiratory pigment occurring in blood plasma of certain worms.

chlorofucin (klōrōfū′sĭn) *n.* [Gk. *chloros*, green ; L. *fucus*, seaweed.] Chlorophyll *c*, in diatoms and brown algae ; chlorophyll γ.

chloroleucite,—chloroplast.

chlorophane (klō′rōfān) *n.* [Gk. *chloros*, grass green ; *phainein*, to appear.] A green chromophane.

chlorophore (klō′rōfōr) *n.* [Gk. *chloros*, grass green ; *phora*, carrying.] A chlorophyll granule in Protista.

chlorophyll (klō′rōfĭl) *n.* [Gk. *chloros*, grass green ; *phyllon*, leaf.] The green colouring matter found in plants and in some animals ; chlorophyll *a*, $C_{55}H_{72}O_5N_4Mg$; *b*, $C_{55}H_{70}O_6N_4Mg$; *c*, or γ or chlorofucin, *q.v.* ; *c* formerly *appl.* a mixture of chlorophyll *a* and pheophytin *a*.

chloroplast (klō′rōplăst), **chloroplastid** (klō′rōplăs′tĭd) *n.* [Gk. *chloros*, grass green ; *plastos*, moulded.] A minute granule or plastid containing chlorophylls *a* and *b*, found in plant-cells exposed to light.

chloroplast pigments, — chlorophylls, carotene, and xanthophyll.

chlorosis (klōrō′sĭs) *n.* [Gk. *chloros*, pallid.] Abnormal condition characterised by absence of green pigments in plants, owing to lack of light, or to magnesium- or iron-deficiency ; green-sickness in humans.

chlorostatolith (klō'röstăt'ölĭth) *n.* [Gk. *chloros*, grass green; *statos*, stationary; *lithos*, stone.] A chloroplast which moves under the influence of gravity in a statocyte; *cf.* statolith, amylostatolith.

chlorotic (klōrŏt'ĭk) *a.* [Gk. *chloros*, pallid.] *Pert.* or affected by chlorosis.

choana (kō'ănă) *n.* [Gk. *choane*, funnel.] A funnel-shaped opening; posterior naris.

choanocyte (kō'ănösīt) *n.* [Gk. *choane*, funnel; *kytos*, hollow.] A cell with funnel-shaped rim or collar round the base of a flagellum.

choanoid (kō'ănoid) *a.* [Gk. *choane*, funnel; *eidos*, like.] Funnel-shaped; *appl.* eye muscle, retractor bulbi, absent in snakes, birds, and higher primates.

choanosome (kō'ănösōm) *n.* [Gk. *choane*, funnel; *soma*, body.] In sponges, the inner layer with flagellate cells.

cholangioles (kölăn'jĭōlz) *n. plu.* [Gk. *chole*, bile; *anggeion*, vessel.] Terminal or interlobular biliary ducts; bile-capillaries.

cholecyst (kŏl'ësĭst) *n.* [Gk. *chole*, bile; *kystis*, bladder.] Gall-bladder.

cholecystokinin (kŏl'ësĭs'tökī'nĭn) *n.* [Gk. *chole*, bile; *kystis*, bladder; *kinein*, to move.] A duodenal hormone which induces contraction of gall-bladder and relaxation of Oddi's sphincter.

choledoch (kŏl'ëdŏk) *a.* [Gk. *chole*, bile; *dochos*, containing.] *Appl.* common bile duct.

cholehematin,—cholohaematin

choleic (kölē'ĭk) *a.* [Gk. *chole*, bile.] *Pert.* acid contained in ox bile.

cholepyrrhin,—bilirubin.

cholerythrin,—bilirubin.

cholesterol (kölĕs'tërŏl) *n.* [Gk. *chole*, bile; *stereos*, solid.] Cholesterin, a white fatty alcohol found in protoplasm, nerve tissue, bile, yolk, and other animal substances; $C_{27}H_{46}O$.

choline (kŏ'lĭn, -ēn) *n.* [Gk. *chole*, bile.] A crystalline base found in plants and animals, a decomposition product of lecithin; $C_5H_{15}O_2N$.

cholinergic (kŏlĭnĕr'jĭk) *a.* [Gk. *chole*, bile; *ergon*, work.] *Appl.* parasympathetic nerve fibres which liberate acetylcholine from their terminations; *cf.* adrenergic.

cholinesterase,—an enzyme which hydrolyses acetylcholine into choline and acetic acid.

cholochrome (kŏl'ökrōm) *n.* [Gk. *chole*, bile; *chroma*, colour.] A bile pigment; biliphaein.

cholohaematin (kŏl'öhē̆'mătĭn) *n.* [Gk. *chole*, bile; *haima*, blood.] Phylloerythrin; cholehaematin.

cholophaein (kŏl'öfē'ĭn) *n.* [Gk. *chole*, bile; *phaios*, dusky.] Bilirubin.

chomophyte (kō'möfīt) *n.* [Gk. *choma*, mound; *phyton*, plant.] A plant growing in detritus on rocks.

chondral (kôn'drăl) *n.* [Gk. *chondros*, cartilage.] *Pert.* cartilage.

chondric (kôn'drĭk) *a.* [Gk. *chondros*, cartilage.] Gristly, cartilaginous.

chondrification (kôn'drĭfĭkā'shŭn) *n.* [Gk. *chondros*, cartilage; L. *facere*, to make.] Conversion into cartilage.

chondrigen (kôn'drĭjĕn) *n.* [Gk. *chondros*, cartilage; *gennaein*, to produce.] The base matrix of all cartilaginous substance, a collagen.

chondrin (kôn'drĭn) *n.* [Gk. *chondros*, cartilage.] A gelatinous substance obtained from cartilage.

chondriocont (kôn'drĭökŏnt) *n.* [Gk. *chondros*, grain; *kontos*, pole.] A rod-like or fibrillar type of chondriosome.

chondriodieresis (kôn'driödīĕr'ësĭs) *n.* [Gk. *chondros*, grain; *dieressein*, to swing about.] Changes in mitochondria during cell division.

chondriokinesis (kôn'drĭökĭ̄nē'sĭs) *n.* [Gk. *chondros*, grain; *kinesis*, movement.] Division of chondriosomes in mitosis and meiosis.

chondrioma (kôndrĭō'mă) *n.* [Gk. *chondros*, grain.] The chondriosome content of a cell; chondriome.

chondriomere (kôn′drĭömēr) *n*. [Gk. *chondros*, grain; *meros*, part.] Plastomere, *q.v.*; cytomere, *q.v.*

chondriomite (kôn′drĭömīt) *n*. [Gk. *chondros*, grain; *mitos*, thread.] A linear type of chondriosome.

chondrioplast (kôn′drĭöplăst) *n*. [Gk. *chondros*, grain; *plastos*, formed.] A rod-like formation of reticular material; Golgi rod.

chondriosomes (kôn′drĭösōmz) *n. plu.* [Gk. *chondros*, grain; *soma*, body.] Mitochondria, *q.v.*; numerous synonyms: *e.g.* chondriomites, chondrioconts, chondriospheres, chondrioplasts.

chondriosphere (kôn′drĭösfēr) *n*. [Gk. *chondros*, grain; *sphaira*, globe.] A spherical type of chondriosome; mitochondria which have coalesced.

chondroblast (kôn′dröblăst) *n*. [Gk. *chondros*, cartilage; *blastos*, bud.] A cartilage-producing cell.

chondroclast (kôn′dröklăst) *n*. [Gk. *chondros*, cartilage; *klastos*, broken down.] A large multinucleate cell which destroys cartilage matrix; also chondrioclast.

chondrocranium (kôn′drökrā′nĭŭm) *n*. [Gk. *chondros*, cartilage; *kranion*, skull.] The skull when in a cartilaginous condition, either temporarily as in embryos, or permanently as in some fishes.

chondrocyte (kôn′drösīt) *n*. [Gk. *chondros*, cartilage; *kytos*, hollow.] A cartilage cell.

chondrogen,—chondrigen.

chondrogenesis (kôn′dröjĕn′ësĭs) *n*. [Gk. *chondros*, cartilage; *genesis*, descent.] The production or formation of cartilage.

chondroglossus (kôn′dröglŏs′ŭs) *n*. [Gk. *chondros*, cartilage; *glossa*, tongue.] An extrinsic muscle of the tongue, arising from hyoid bone, between genioglossus and hyoglossus.

chondroid (kôn′droid) *a*. [Gk. *chondros*, cartilage; *eidos*, shape.] Cartilage-like; *appl.* tissue, undeveloped cartilage or pseudocartilage serving as support in certain invertebrates and lower vertebrates; *appl.* vesicular supporting tissue of notochord; fibrohyaline.

chondromucoid (kôn′drömū′koid) *n*. [Gk. *chondros*, cartilage; L. *mucus*, mucus; Gk. *eidos*, form.] A basophil protein which with collagen forms ground-substance of cartilage; chondromucin.

chondrophore (kôn′dröfōr) *n*. [Gk. *chondros*, cartilage; *pherein*, to bear.] A structure which supports the inner hinge cartilage in a bivalve shell.

chondroseptum (kôn′drösĕp′tŭm) *n*. [Gk. *chondros*, cartilage; L. *septum*, partition.] The cartilaginous part of the septum of the nose.

chondroskeleton (kôn′dröskĕl′ëtŏn) *n*. [Gk. *chondros*, cartilage; *skeleton*, dried body.] A cartilaginous skeleton.

chondrosteous (kôndrŏs′tëus) *a*. [Gk. *chondros*, cartilage; *osteon*, bone.] Having a cartilaginous skeleton.

chondrosternal (kôn′dröstĕr′năl) *a*. [Gk. *chondros*, cartilage; *sternon*, breast.] *Pert.* rib cartilages and sternum.

chone (kō′nē) *n*. [Gk. *chone*, funnel.] A passage through cortex of sponges, with one or more external openings, and one internal opening.

chorda (kôr′dă) *n*. [Gk. *chorde*, string.] Any cord-like structure; chorda dorsalis or notochord; chorda tympani, a branch of the facial nerve; chorda umbilicalis; chorda vocalis. *Plu.* chordae.

chordacentra (kôr′dăsĕn′tră) *n. plu.* [Gk. *chorde*, string; L. *centrum*, centre.] Centra formed by conversion of chordal sheath into a number of rings; *cf.* archcentra.

chordae tendineae,—tendinous cords connecting papillary muscles with valves of heart.

chordae willisii,—fibrous bands crossing superior sagittal sinus of dura mater.

chordate (kôr'dāt) *a.* [Gk. *chorde,* string.] Having a notochord.

chordotonal (kôr'dötō'năl) *a.* [Gk. *chorde,* string; *tonos,* tone.] *Appl.* rod-like or bristle-like receptors for mechanical and sound vibrations, in various parts of body of insects.

chore (kō'rē) *n.* [Gk. *chore,* place.] An area manifesting a unity of geographical or environmental conditions; *cf.* biochore, biotope.

choreiathetose (kŏrĭăth'ĕtōs) *a.* [Gk. *choreia,* dance; *athetos,* lawless.] Arhythmic and uncoordinated; *appl.* foetal movements.

choriocapillaris (kŏr'ĭökăpĭl'ărĭs, -kăp'ĭlā'rĭs) *n.* [Gk. *chorion,* skin; L. *capillaris,* capillary.] The innermost vascular layer of choroid.

chorioid,—choroid, *q.v.*

chorion (kŏ̄'rĭŏn) *n.* [Gk. *chorion,* skin.] An embryonic membrane external to and enclosing the amnion; allantochorion, *q.v.*; a hardened shell covering egg of insects; outer membrane of seed.

chorion frondosum,—villous placental part of chorion.

chorion laeve, — smooth non-placental part of chorion.

chorionic (kŏrĭŏn'ĭk) *a.* [Gk. *chorion,* skin.] *Pert.* the chorion; *appl.* gonadotrophic hormone or prolan.

chorioretinal (kŏ̄r'ĭörĕt'ĭnăl) *a.* [Gk. *chorion,* skin; L. *retina,* retina.] *Pert.* choroid and retina.

choripetalous (kō'rĭpĕt'ălŭs) *a.* [Gk. *choris,* separate; *petalon,* leaf.] Having separate petals.

choriphyllous (kō'rĭfĭl'ŭs) *a.* [Gk. *choris,* separate; *phyllon,* leaf.] Having perianth parts distinct.

chorisepalous (kō'rĭsĕp'ălŭs) *a.* [Gk. *choris,* separate; F. *sépale,* sepal.] Having the sepals separate.

chorisis (kō'rĭsĭs) *n.* [Gk. *choris,* separate.] Increase in parts of floral whorl due to division of its primary members; deduplication.

choroid (kōr'oid) *a.* [Gk. *chorion,* skin; *eidos,* form.] *Appl.* delicate and highly vascular membranes. *n.* Layer of eye between retina and sclera.

choroidal (köroid'ăl) *a.* [Gk. *chorion,* skin; *eidos,* form.] *Pert.* choroid.

chorology (kōrŏl'öjĭ) *n.* [Gk. *choros,* place; *logos,* discourse.] Biogeography; geographical distribution; biotopography; science of the distribution of organisms or of organs.

choronomic (kōrönŏm'ĭk) *a.* [Gk. *choros,* place; *nomos,* law.] External, *appl.* influences of geographical or regional environment, *opp.* autonomic.

chorotypes (kō'rötīps) *n. plu.* [Gk. *choros,* place; *typos,* pattern.] Local types.

chresard (krēsârd') *n.* [Gk. *chresis,* use; *ardo,* I water.] Soil water available for plant growth; *cf.* echard, holard.

chroma (krō'mă) *n.* [Gk. *chroma,* colour.] The hue and saturation of a colour.

chromaffin (krō'măfĭn) *a.* [Gk. *chroma,* colour: L. *affinis,* related.] Chromaphil.

chromaphil (krō'măfĭl) *a.* [Gk. *chroma,* colour; *philein,* to love.] Stained by chromic acid or its salts when adrenaline is present; *appl.* cells forming medullary parts of suprarenal bodies; *appl.* bodies or paraganglia; chromophil, chromaffin.

chromaphobe (krō'măfōb) *a.* [Gk. *chroma,* colour; *phobos,* fear.] *Appl.* non-stainable cells or tissues; chromophobe.

chromasie (krō'măsĭ) *n.* [Gk. *chroma,* colour.] Increase of chromatin in nucleus and formation of nucleolus; *cf.* achromasie.

chromatic (krōmăt'ĭk) *a.* [Gk. *chroma,* colour.] Colourable by means of staining reagents; *pert.*

colour; having hue and saturation; having chromatophores.

chromatic sphere,—the sphere formed by coalescence of chromosomes after anaphase in mitosis.

chromatic threshold,—the minimal stimulus, varying with wave length of light, which induces a colour sensation.

chromaticity (krōmătĭs'ĭtĭ) *n.* [Gk. *chroma*, colour.] Unlikeness to grey, or saturation of a colour.

chromatid (krō'mătĭd) *n.* [Gk. *chroma*, colour.] A component of a tetrad in meiosis; a half-chromosome between early prophase and metaphase in mitosis, or between diplotene and second metaphase in meiosis.

chromatid bridge,—a chromatid joining two centromeres during anaphase, in paracentric inversions.

chromatin (krō'mătĭn) *n.* [Gk. *chroma*, colour.] A substance in the nucleus which contains nucleic acid proteids, and stains with basic dyes.

chromatocyte (krō'mătösīt) *n.* [Gk. *chroma*, colour; *kytos*, hollow.] Any cell containing a pigment.

chromatogen organ,—a brownish lobed body, the axial organ of certain echinoderms.

chromatoid grains,—grains in cell-protoplasm, which stain similarly to chromatin.

chromatolysis (krō'mătŏl'ĭsĭs) *n.* [Gk. *chroma*, colour; *lysis*, loosing.] Disintegration of Nissl granules, as in fatigued nerve-cells; tigrolysis.

chromatophil (krō'mătöfĭl) *a.* [Gk. *chroma*, colour; *philein*, to love.] Staining easily; chromophilous.

chromatophore (krō'mătöfōr) *n.* [Gk. *chroma*, colour; *pherein*, to bear.] A coloured plastid of plants and animals; a colourless body in cytoplasm and developing into a leucoplast, chloroplast, or chromoplast; a pigment cell, or group of cells, which under control of the sympathetic nervous system can be altered in shape to produce a colour change.

chromatophoric (krō'mătöfŏr'ĭk) *a.* [Gk. *chroma*, colour; *pherein*, to bear.] Containing pigment; *pert.* chromatophores.

chromatophorotropic (krō'mătöfō'rötrŏp'ĭk) *a.* [Gk. *chroma*, colour; *pherein*, to bear; *trope*, turn.] *Appl.* a hormone, intermedin, secreted by pars intermedia of pituitary and causing expansion of chromatophores; *appl.* hormone of crustacean eye-stalk.

chromatophyll (krō'mătöfĭl) *n.* [Gk. *chroma*, colour; *phyllon*, leaf.] The colouring matter of plant-like flagellates; also chromophyll.

chromatoplasm (krō'mătöplăzm) *n.* [Gk. *chroma*, colour; *plasma*, mould.] The colour or pigment matter in cells.

chromatosome,—chromosome.

chromatospherite (krō'mătösfēr'īt) *n.* [Gk. *chroma*, colour; *sphaira*, globe.] A nucleolus, *q.v.*

chromidia (krōmĭd'ĭă) *n. plu.* [Gk. *chroma*, colour; *idion*, *dim.*] Extra-nuclear particles of chromatin, which may replace or be re-formed into nuclei; gonidia, *q.v.*

chromidial substance,—minute basophil granules containing iron, occurring in cytoplasm as chromophil or tigroid bodies.

chromidiogamy (krōmĭd'ĭŏg'ămĭ) *n.* [Gk. *chroma*, colour; *idion*, *dim.*; *gamos*, marriage.] The union of chromidia from two conjugants.

chromidiosomes (krōmĭd'ĭösömz) *n. plu.* [Gk. *chroma*, colour; *idion*, *dim.*; *soma*, body.] The smallest chromatin particles of which the chromidial mass is composed.

chromiole (krō'mĭōl) *n.* [Gk. *chroma*, colour.] One of the minute granules of which a chromomere is composed.

chromo-argentaffin (krō'möârjĕn'-tăfĭn) *a.* [Gk. *chroma*, colour; L. *argentum*, silver; *affinis*, related.] Staining with bichromates and silver nitrate; *appl.* flask-shaped cells in epithelium of crypts of Lieberkühn.

chromoblast (krō'möblăst) *n.* [Gk. *chroma*, colour; *blastos*, bud.] An embryonic cell giving rise to a pigment cell.

chromocentre (krōmösĕn′tër) *n.* [Gk. *chroma*, colour; *kentron*, centre.] The fused heterochromatic region around centromeres; fused prochromosomes.

chromocyte (krō′mösīt) *n.* [Gk. *chroma*, colour; *kytos*, hollow.] Any pigmented cell.

chromogen (krō′möjĕn) *n.* [Gk. *chroma*, colour; *genos*, birth.] The substance which is converted into a pigment, *e.g.* by oxidation; a chromogenic organism.

chromogenesis (krō′möjĕn′ësĭs) *n.* [Gk. *chroma*, colour; *genesis*, origin.] The production of colour or pigment.

chromogenic (krō′möjĕn′ĭk) *a.* [Gk. *chroma*, colour; *genos*, birth.] Colour-producing; *appl.* organisms, as bacteria.

chromoleucite,—chromoplast.

chromolipides (krō′mölĭp′īdz) *n. plu.* [Gk. *chroma*, colour; *lipos*, fat.] The carotenoids and related pigments.

chromomere (krō′mömēr) *n.* [Gk. *chroma*, colour; *meros*, part.] One of the chromatin granules of which a chromosome is formed, and which corresponds to an id or a gene; granular part of blood platelet, *opp.* hyalomere.

chromonema (krō′mönē′mă) *n.* [Gk. *chroma*, colour; *nema*, thread.] A coiled or convoluted thread in prophase of mitosis; central thread in chromosome. *Plu.* chromonemata.

chromoparous (krōmŏp′ărŭs) *a.* [Gk. *chroma* colour; L. *parere*, to bring forth.] Having coloured excreta, *appl.* bacteria.

chromophanes (krō′möfānz) *n. plu.* [Gk. *chroma*, colour; *phainein*, to show.] Red, yellow, and green oil globules found in retina of birds, reptiles, fishes, marsupials; any retinal pigments.

chromophil (krō′möfĭl) *a.* [Gk. *chroma*, colour; *philein*, to love.] Chromaphil, chromaffin, *q.v.*; chromophilic.

chromophilous (krōmŏf′ĭlŭs) *a.* [Gk. *chroma*, colour; *philos*, loving.] Staining readily; chromatophil.

chromophobe (krō′möfōb) *a.* [Gk. *chroma*, colour; *phobos*, fear.] Non-stainable or staining slightly; *appl.* certain cells of pituitary gland; chromaphobe.

chromophore (krō′möfōr) *n.* [Gk. *chroma*, colour; *pherein*, to bear.] Any substance to whose presence colour in a compound is due.

chromophyll,—chromatophyll, *q.v.*

chromoplast (krō′möplăst) *n.* [Gk. *chroma*, colour; *plastos*, moulded.] A coloured plastid or pigment body; coloured plastid other than a chloroplast; chromoplastid.

chromoproteins (krō′möprō′tëĭnz) *n. plu.* [Gk. *chroma*, colour; *protos*, first.] Substances formed by combination of a protein with a pigment or chromophore.

chromosomal vesicle,—karyomere, *q.v.*

chromosome (krō′mösōm) *n.* [Gk. *chroma*, colour; *soma*, body.] One of deeply staining bodies, the number of which is constant for the cells of a species, into which the chromatin resolves itself during karyokinesis and meiosis.

chromosome-races,—races differing in number of chromosomes or of chromosome sets.

chromosomin (krōmösō′mĭn) *n.* [Gk. *chroma*, colour; *soma*, body.] One of the protein constituents of chromosomes.

chromospire (krō′möspīr) *n.* [Gk. *chroma*, colour; *speira*, coil.] A spireme-like thread formed from nuclear granules in haplomitosis.

chronaxie, chronaxy (krō′năksĭ) *n.* [Gk. *chronos*, time; *axia*, value.] Latent period between electrical stimulus and muscular response; minimal excitation time required with a current of an intensity twice the threshold necessary for excitation when the duration of the stimulus is prolonged; chronaxia.

chronotropic (krŏn′ötrŏpĭk) *a.* [Gk. *chronos*, time; *trope*, turning.] Affecting the rate of action, as accelerator and inhibitory cardiac nerves.

chrysalis (krĭs′ălĭs) *n.* [Gk. *chrysallis*, gold, golden thing.] Pupa stage of certain insects.

chrysocarpous (krĭs′ökâr′pŭs) *a.* [Gk. *chrysos*, gold ; *karpos*, fruit.] With golden-yellow fruit.

chrysophanic (krĭsöfăn′ĭk) *a.* [Gk. *chrysos*, gold ; *phainein*, to show.] Having a golden or bright orange colour, *appl.* an acid formed in certain lichens and in leaves.

chrysophyll (krĭs′öfĭl) *n.* [Gk. *chrysos*, gold ; *phyllon*, leaf.] A yellow colouring matter in plants, a decomposition product of chlorophyll.

chylaceous (kīlā′sëus) *a.* [Gk. *chylos*, juice.] Of the nature of chyle.

chyle (kīl) *n.* [Gk. *chylos*, juice.] Lymph containing globules of emulsified fat, found in the lacteals during digestion.

chylifaction (kī′lĭfăk′shŭn) *n.* [Gk. *chylos*, juice ; L. *facere*, to make.] Formation of chyle ; also chylification ; chylopoiesis.

chyliferous (kīlĭf′ërŭs) *a.* [Gk. *chylos*, juice ; L. *ferre*, to carry.] Chyle-conducting ; *appl.* tubes or vessels ; chylophoric.

chylific (kīlĭf′ĭk) *a.* [Gk. *chylos*, juice ; L. *facere*, to make.] Chyle-producing ; *appl.* ventricle or true stomach of insects.

chylification,—chylifaction.

chylocaulous (kīlöcôl′ŭs) *a.* [Gk. *chylos*, juice ; *kaulos*, stem.] With fleshy stems.

chylocyst (kī′lösĭst) *n.* [Gk. *chylos*, juice ; *kystis*, bladder.] The chyle receptacle ; cisterna chyli.

chylomicrons (kīlömī′krŏnz) *n. plu.* [Gk. *chylos*, juice ; *mikros*, small.] Minute fatty particles in plasma, plentiful during fat digestion.

chylophoric,—chyliferous.

chylophyllous (kī′löfĭl′ŭs) *a.* [Gk. *chylos*, juice ; *phyllon*, leaf.] With fleshy leaves ; *appl.* certain desert plants.

chylopoiesis (kī′löpoiē′sĭs) *n.* [Gk. *chylos*, juice ; *poiesis*, a making.] The production of chyle.

chyme (kīm) *n.* [Gk. *chymos*, juice.] The partially digested food after leaving the stomach.

chymification (kī′mĭfĭkā′shŭn) *n.* [Gk. *chymos*, juice ; L. *facere*, to make.] The process of converting food into chyme.

chymosin,—rennin, *q.v.*

chymotrypsin (kī′mötrĭp′sĭn) *n.* [Gk. *chymos*, juice ; *tryein*, to rub down ; *pepsis*, digestion.] An enzyme which, in the small intestine, splits the various protein products of the action of pepsin and trypsin.

chymotrypsinogen (kī′mötrĭpsĭn′öjĕn) *n.* [Gk. *chymos*, juice ; *tryein*, to rub down ; *pepsis*, digestion ; *-genes*, producing.] A pancreatic enzyme which is converted into chymotrypsin.

chytridium (kĭtrĭd′ĭŭm) *n.* [Gk. *chytridion*, little pot.] The spore vessel of certain fungi.

cibarium (sĭbā′rĭŭm) *n.* [L. *cibaria*, victuals.] The part of the buccal cavity anterior to pharynx, in insects.

cicatricial tissue, — newly - formed fibrillar connective tissue which closes and draws together wounds.

cicatricle (sĭkăt′rĭkl), **cicatricula** (sĭk′ătrĭk′ūlă), **cicatrix** (sĭkā′trĭks) *n.* [L. *cicatrix*, scar.] The blastoderm in bird and reptile eggs ; a small scar in place of previous attachment of an organ ; a scar ; the mark left after healing of a wound in plants.

cicinnal (sĭs′ĭnăl) *a.* [Gk. *kikinnos*, curled lock.] *Appl.* uniparous cymose branching in which daughter axes are developed right and left alternately ; cincinnal.

cilia (sĭl′ĭă) *n. plu.* [L. *cilium*, eyelid.] Hairlike vibratile outgrowths of ectoderm, or processes, of many cells ; barbicels of a feather ; eyelashes.

ciliaris (sĭlĭā′rĭs) *n.* [L. *cilium*, eyelid.] Unstriped muscle forming a ring outside anterior part of choroid and, attached to ciliary processes, acting on convexity of lens.

ciliary (sĭl′ĭărĭ) *a.* [L. *cilium*, eyelid.] *Pert.* cilia ; *pert.* eyelashes ; *appl.* sudoriferous glands ; *appl.* certain structures in the eyeball, as arteries, body, processes, muscle; *appl.* branches of nasociliary nerve and to ganglion.

ciliate (sĭl'ĭāt) *a.* [L. *cilium*, eyelid.] Provided with cilia; ciliated.

ciliated epithelium,—an epithelium found lining various passages, usually with columnar cells provided with cilia on the free surface.

ciliograde (sĭl'ĭögrād) *a.* [L. *cilium*, eyelid; *gradus*, step.] Progressing by movement of cilia.

ciliolum (sĭlī'ölŭm) *n.* [*Dim.* of L. *cilium*, eyelid.] A minute cilium.

ciliospore (sĭl'ĭöspōr) *n.* [L. *cilium*, eyelid; Gk. *sporos*, seed.] A ciliated protozoan swarm-spore.

cilium (sĭl'ĭŭm) *n.* [L. *cilium*, eyelid.] *Sing.* of cilia, *q.v.*

cinchonine (sĭn'könĭn) *n.* [After Countess *de Chinchón*.] Alkaloid found in various Rubiaceae; $C_{19}H_{22}ON_2$.

cincinnus (sĭnsĭn'ŭs) *n.* [L. *cincinnus*, curl.] A scorpioid cyme.

cinclides (sĭng'klĭdēz) *n. plu.* [Gk. *kingklis*, latticed gate.] Perforations, in body wall of certain Anthozoa, for extrusion of acontia. *Sing.* cinclis.

cinerea (sĭnē'rēa) *n.* [L. *cinereus*, ashen.] The grey matter of the nervous system.

cinereous, — ashy-grey; tephrous.

cingula,—*plu.* of cingulum. *n. sing.* Ring formed by hyphal proliferation around upper part of stipe, uniting with incurved edge of pileus; *plu.* cingulae.

cingulate (sĭng'gūlāt) *a.* [L. *cingulum*, girdle.] Having a girdle or cingulum; shaped like a girdle; *appl.* a gyrus and sulcus above corpus callosum.

cingulum (sĭng'gūlŭm) *n.* [L. *cingulum*, girdle.] Any structure which is like a girdle; part of plant between root and stem; part of diatom frustule uniting valves; a ridge round base of crown of a tooth; a tract of fibres connecting callosal and hippocampal convolutions of brain; outer ciliary zone on disc of rotifers; clitellum, *q.v.*

cion,—scion, *q.v.*

circinate (sĭr'sĭnāt) *a.* [L. *circinatus*, made round.] Rolled on the axis, so that apex is centre.

circulation (sĕr'kūlā'shŭn) *n.* [L. *circulatio*, act of circulating.] The regular movement of any fluid within definite channels in the body; streaming movement of protoplasm of plant cells.

circulus (sĭr'kūlŭs) *n.* [L. *circulus*, circle.] Any ringlike arrangement, as of blood-vessels caused by branching or connection with one another, as circulus major of iris, or as of markings of fish scales.

circulus arteriosus,—a vascular ring at base of brain; circle of Willis.

circumduction (sĕr'kŭmdŭk'shŭn) *n.* [L. *circum*, around; *ductus*, led.] The form of motion exhibited by a bone describing a conical space with the articular cavity as apex.

circumferential (sĕr'kŭmfĕrĕn'shăl) *a.* [L. *circum*, around; *ferre*, to bear.] *Appl.* cartilages which surround certain articulatory fossae; *appl.* primary lamellae parallel to circumference of bone.

circumfila (sĕr'kŭmfī'lă) *n. plu.* [L. *circum*, around; *filum*, thread.] Looped or wreathed filaments on antennal segments, as in gall-midges.

circumflex (sĕr'kŭmflĕks) *a.* [L. *circum*, around; *flectere*, to bend.] Bending round; *appl.* certain arteries, veins; *appl.* nerve, the axillary nerve.

circumfluence (sĕrkŭm'flooĕns) *n.* [L *circum*, around; *fluens*, flowing.] In Protozoa, ingestion by protoplasm flowing towards food and surrounding it after contact; *cf.* circumvallation.

circumgenital (sĕr'kŭmjĕn'ĭtăl) *a.* [L. *circum*, around; *gignere*, to beget.] Surrounding the genital pore; *appl.* glands secreting waxy powder in oviparous species of Coccidae.

circumnutation (sĕr'kŭmnūtā'shŭn) *n.* [L. *circum*, around; *nutare*, to nod.] The irregular elliptical or spiral movement exhibited by apex of a growing stem, shoot or tendril.

circumoesophageal (sĕr'kŭmēsŏfăj'ēăl) *a.* [L. *circum*, around; Gk. *oisophagos*, gullet.] *Appl.* structures or organs surrounding or passing along the gullet.

circumpolar (sĕr'kŭmpō'lăr) *a.* [L. *circum*, around; *polus*, end of axle.] *Appl.* flora and fauna of Polar regions.

circumpulpar (sĕr'kŭmpŭl'păr) *a.* [L. *circum*, around; *pulpa*, fruit-pulp.] *Appl.* dentine forming layer around pulp cavity of teeth, as in fishes.

circumscissile (sĕr'kŭmsĭs'ĭl) *a.* [L. *circum*, around; *scindere*, to cut.] Splitting along a circular line; *appl.* dehiscence exhibited by a pyxidium.

circumscript (sĕr'kŭmskrĭpt) *a.* [L. *circumscribere*, to draw line around.] *Appl.* marginal sphincter when sharply defined, in sea-anemones.

circumvallate (sĕr'kŭmvăl'āt) *a.* [L. *circum*, around; *vallum*, rampart.] Encircled by a wall, as of tissue; vallate, *appl.* certain tongue papillae.

circumvallation (sĕr'kŭmvălā'shŭn) *n.* [L. *circum*, around; *vallare*, to wall.] Ingestion of food by extruded pseudopodia, as in protozoa or in phagocytes.

circumvascular (sĕr'kŭmvăs'kūlăr) *a.* [L. *circum*, around; *vasculum*, small vessel.] *Appl.* dentine lining vascular canals in pulp cavity of teeth, as in fishes.

cirral (sĭr'ăl) *a.* [L. *cirrus*, curl.] *Pert.* cirri or a cirrus. *n.* Any of the hollow ossicles in cirri of crinoids.

cirrate (sĭr'āt) *a.* [L. *cirratus*, having curls.] Having cirri.

cirrhi, cirrhus,—cirri, cirrus.

cirri (sĭr'ī) *n. plu.* [L. *cirrus*, curl.] Tendrils; appendages of barnacles; jointed filaments of axis or of aboral surface of crinoids; barbels of fishes; respiratory and tactile appendages of worms; organs of copulation in some molluscs and trematodes; hairlike structures on appendages of insects.

cirrose (sĭr'ōs, sĭrōs') *a.* [L. *cirrus*, curl.] With cirri or tendrils.

cirrus (sĭr'ŭs) *n.* [L. *cirrus*, curl.] Tendril; a tendril-like structure; coherent spores discharged through an ostiole. *Plu.* cirri, *q.v.*

cisterna (sĭstĕr'nă) *n.* [L. *cisterna*, cistern.] Closed space containing fluid, as any of the subarachnoid spaces; cisterna chyli, the dilated beginning of the thoracic duct, receiving lymph and chyle from vessels of hind limbs and abdomen; a minute tubule of endoplasmic network.

cistron,—the portion of a chromosome within which a number of mutational entities or loci is integrated for one function.

citrin (sĭt'rĭn) *n.* [L.L. *citrus*, lemon.] A factor in lemon juice which regulates capillary permeability; vitamin P.

citrulline (sĭtrŭl'ĭn) *n.* [L. *citrullus*, water-melon.] An amino acid first obtained from water-melon, also occurring as intermediate product in formation of urea from ornithine; $C_6H_{13}O_3N_3$.

cladanthous (klădăn'thŭs) *a.* [Gk. *klados*, sprout; *anthos*, flower.] Having terminal archegonia on short lateral branches; cladocarpous.

cladautoicous (klăd'ôtoik'ŭs) *a.* [Gk. *klados*, sprout; *autos*, self; *oikos*, house.] With antheridia on a special stalk, as in mosses.

cladocarpous,—cladanthous, *q.v.*

cladode (klăd'ōd) *n.* [Gk. *klados*, sprout.] Branch arising from axil of leaf, or green flattened stem, resembling a foliage leaf; cladophyll, cladophyllum, phylloclade.

cladodont (klăd'ōdŏnt) *a.* [Gk. *klados*, sprout; *odous*, tooth.] Having or *appl.* teeth with prominent central and small lateral cusps.

cladogenesis (klădōjĕn'ĕsĭs) *n.* [Gk. *klados*, sprout; *genesis*, descent.] Branching of evolutionary lineages so as to produce new types.

cladogenous (klădŏj'ënŭs) *a.* [Gk. *klados*, sprout; *gennaein*, to produce.] Stem-borne; *appl.* certain roots; cladanthous, *q.v.*

cladome (klădōm') *n.* [Gk. *klados*, sprout.] The group of superficially situated rays in a triaene.

cladophyll (klăd'ŏfĭl) *n.* [Gk. *klados*, sprout; *phyllon*, leaf.] Cladode.

cladoptosis (klăd'ŏptō'sĭs) *n.* [Gk. *klados*, sprout; *ptosis*, falling.] Annual or other shedding of twigs.

cladose (klăd'ōs) *a.* [Gk. *klados*, sprout.] Branched.

cladosiphonic (klăd'ŏsīfŏn'ĭk) *a.* [Gk. *klados*, sprout; *siphon*, tube.] With insertion of leaf-trace on periphery of the axial stele; *opp.* phyllosiphonic.

cladotyle (klăd'ŏtīl) *n.* [Gk. *klados*, sprout; *tylos*, knob.] A rhabdus with one actine branched, the other tylote.

cladus (klā'dŭs) *n.* [Gk. *klados*, branch.] A branch, as of a branched spicule.

clamp-connections, — swellings on certain dikaryotic hyphae, for passage of daughter nuclei to cell below, with subsequent septum formation; also occurring in whorls, for distribution of nuclei to hyphal branches.

clandestine (klăndĕs'tĭn) *a.* [L. *clandestinus*, from *clam*, secretly.] *Appl.* evolution which is not apparent in adult forms; or of adult characters from ancestral embryonic characters.

clasmatoblast (klăz'mătŏblăst, klăs-) *n.* [Gk. *klasma*, fragment; *blastos*, bud.] A mast cell.

clasmatocyte (klăz'măt'ŏsīt, klăsmăt'-ŏsīt) *n.* [Gk. *klasma*, fragment; *kytos*, hollow.] A variable basiphil phagocyte or macrophage in areolar tissue; a histiocyte.

claspers (klâs'përz) *n. plu.* [M.E. *claspen*, to hold.] Rod-like processes on pelvic fins of certain male elasmobranchs; outer gonapophyses of insects; valves or harpes of male Lepidoptera; any modification of an organ or part to enable the two sexes to clasp one another; tendrils or climbing shoots.

claspettes,—harpagones, *q.v.*

class (klâs) *n.* [L. *classis*, division.] A division of a phylum and divided into orders, in classification of plants or animals.

clathrate (klăth'rāt) *a.* [Gk. *klethra*, lattice.] Lattice-like; clathroid.

Claudius' cells,—outer columnar or cuboid cells adjoining Hensen's cells in organ of Corti.

claustrum (klôs'trŭm) *n.* [L. *claustrum*, bar.] In cerebral hemispheres, a thin layer of grey substance lateral to external capsule; one of the Weberian ossicles in Cyprinidae and Characinidae.

clava (klā'vă) *n.* [L. *clava*, club.] A club-shaped spore-bearing structure of certain fungi; the knob-like end of antenna of certain insects; swelling at end of fasciculus gracilis of medulla oblongata.

clavate (klā'vāt) *a.* [L. *clava*, club.] Club-shaped; thickened at one end.

clavicle (klăv'ĭkl) *n.* [L. *clavicula*, small key.] Collar-bone, forming anterior or ventral portion of the shoulder-girdle.

clavicular (klăvĭk'ūlăr) *a.* [L. *clavicula*, small key.] *Pert.* clavicle.

clavicularium (klăvĭk'ūlā'rĭŭm) *n.* [L. *clavicula*, small key.] The epiplastron of Chelonia, probably corresponding to clavicles of other forms.

claviform (klăv'ĭfôrm) *n.* [L. *clava*, club; *forma*, form.] Club-shaped; clavate.

clavola (klăvō'lă) *n.* [L. *clava*, club.] The flagellar portion, or terminal joints, of insect antenna.

clavula (klăv'ūlă) *n.* [L. *clava*, club.] A monactinal modification of triaxon spicule; a minute ciliated spine on fasciole of Spatangidae; a clavate sporophore of certain fungi.

clavus (klā'vŭs) *n.* [L. *clavus*, nail.] The part of an hemelytron lying next scutellum in Hemiptera; a projection or crotchet from scape of spiders; ergot disease in grasses.

claw (klô) *n.* [A.S. *clawu,* claw.] The unguis or stalk of a petal; a sharp curved nail on finger or toe; forceps of certain crustaceans; curved process on limb of insect.

clearing foot,—filamentous process of exopodite of second maxilla in Phyllocarida.

cleavage (klē'vĕj) *n.* [A.S. *cleofan,* to cut.] The series of karyokinetic divisions which change the egg into a multicellular embryo.

cleavage cell,—blastomere, *q.v.*

cleavage nucleus,—nucleus of fertilised egg or zygote produced by union of male and female pronuclei; the egg-nucleus of parthenogenetic eggs.

cleidoic (klīdō'ĭk) *a.* [Gk. *kleis,* bar; *oon,* egg.] Having or *pert.* eggs enclosed within a shell or membrane.

cleistocarp (klī'stökârp) *n.* [Gk. *kleistos,* closed; *karpos,* fruit.] Cleistothecium, *q.v.*

cleistocarpous (klī'stökâr'pŭs) *a.* [Gk. *kleistos,* closed; *karpos,* fruit.] Having closed ascocarps; with non-operculate capsules, *appl.* mosses; cleistocarpic.

cleistogamic (klīstögăm'ĭk) *a.* [Gk. *kleistos,* closed; *gamos,* marriage.] *Pert.* or possessed of characteristics of cleistogamy; cleistogamous.

cleistogamy (klīstŏg'ămĭ) *n.* [Gk. *kleistos,* closed; *gamos,* marriage.] State of having small inconspicuous self-fertilising flowers; fertilisation without opening of florets, *opp.* chasmogamy.

cleistogene (klī'stöjēn) *n.* [Gk. *kleistos,* closed; *genos,* descent.] A plant with cleistogamous flowers.

cleistothecium (klīstöthē'sĭŭm) *n.* [Gk. *kleistos,* closed; *theke,* box.] An ascocarp which remains closed and produces its spores internally.

cleithrum (klī'thrŭm) *n.* [Gk. *kleithron,* bar.] The pair of additional clavicles in Stegocephalia; clavicular element of some fishes.

climacteric (klīmăktĕr'ĭk) *n.* [Gk. *klimakter,* step of staircase.] A critical phase, or period of change, in living organisms; *appl.* change associated with menopause, or with male function; *appl.* phase of increased respiratory activity at ripening of fruit.

climatype (klī'mătīp) *n.* [Gk. *klima,* climate; *typos,* image.] A biotype resulting from selection in a particular climate; climatic ecotype.

climax (klī'măks) *n.* [Gk. *klimax,* ladder.] The mature or stabilised stage in a successional series of communities, when dominant species are completely adapted to environmental conditions; completion of development, *appl.* leaves.

clinandrium (klīnăn'drĭŭm) *n.* [Gk. *kline,* bed; *aner,* man.] A cavity in the column between anthers in orchids.

clinanthium (klīnăn'thĭŭm) *n.* [Gk. *kline,* bed; *anthos,* flower.] A dilated floral receptacle, as in capitulum of Compositae.

cline (klīn) *n.* [Gk. *klinein,* to slant.] A series of form changes; gradient of biotypes; character-gradient.

clinging fibres,—tendril fibres, *q.v.*

clinidium (klīnĭd'ĭŭm) *n.* [Gk. *klinidion,* small couch.] A filament in a pycnidium, which produces spores.

clinoid (klī'noid) *a.* [Gk. *kline,* couch; *eidos,* form.] *Appl.* processes of sella turcica.

clinology (klĭnŏl'öjĭ) *n.* [Gk. *klinein,* to decline; *logos,* discourse.] The study of the decline of organisms after maturity, or after their prime in groups or in phylogeny.

clinosporangium (klī'nöspörăn'jĭŭm) *n.* [Gk. *kline,* bed; *spora,* seed; *anggeion,* vessel.] Pycnidium, *q.v.*

clinospore (klī'nöspōr) *n.* [Gk. *kline,* bed; *spora,* seed.] A spore abjointed from a clinidium; a conidium, *q.v.*

clisere (klī'sēr) *n.* [*cli*mate; *sere.*] Succession of communites which results from a changing climate.

clitellum (klītĕl'ŭm) *n.* [L. *clitellae,* pack-saddle.] The saddle or swollen glandular portion of skin of certain annelid worms.

clitoris (klī'tōrĭs) *n.* [Gk. *kleiein*, to enclose.] An erectile organ, homologous with penis, at upper part of vulva.

clivus (klī'vŭs) *n.* [L. *clivus*, slope.] A shallow depression in sphenoid, behind dorsum sellae; posterior sloped part of the monticulus.

cloaca (klöā'kă) *n.* [L. *cloaca*, sewer.] The common chamber into which intestinal, genital, and urinary canals open, in vertebrates except most mammals.

clone (klōn) *n.* [Gk. *klon*, twig.] An individual produced asexually; group of individuals propagated by mitosis from a single ancestor; an apomict strain.

clonus (klōn'ŭs) *n.* [Gk. *klonos*, violent motion.] A series of muscular contractions when individual contractions are discernible; incomplete tetanus.

club hair,—a hair forming a keratinised club-shaped bulb, becoming detached from papilla, and eventually shed.

clunes (kloon'ēz) *n. plu.* [L. *clunes*, buttocks.] Buttocks; nates.

cluster-crystals, — globular aggregates of calcium oxalate crystals in plant cells; sphaeraphides.

cluster-cup,—aecidium, *q.v.*

clypeal (klĭp'ëăl) *a.* [L. *clypeus*, shield.] *Pert.* clypeus of insects.

clypeate (klĭp'ëāt) *a.* [L. *clypeus*, shield.] Round or buckler-like; clypeiform; having a clypeus.

clypeola (klĭpē'ölă), **clypeole** (klĭp'-ëōl) *n.* [L. *clypeus*, shield.] A sporophyll in the spike of an Equisetum.

clypeo-labral (klĭp'ëölăb'răl) *a.* [L. *clypeus*, shield; *labrum*, lip.] *Appl.* suture between clypeus and labrum.

clypeus (klĭp'ëŭs) *n.* [L. *clypeus*, shield.] A sclerite on anteromedian part of insect head; a band of tissue round mouth of perithecium of certain fungi.

cnemial (knē'mĭăl, nē'mĭăl) *a.* [Gk. *kneme*, tibia.] *Pert.* tibia; *appl.* ridge along dorsal margin of tibia.

cnemidium (knēmĭd'ĭŭm, nēmĭd'-ĭŭm) *n.* [Gk. *knemis*, legging; *idion*, *dim.*] Lower part of bird's leg devoid of feathers, generally scaly.

cnemis (knē'mĭs, nē'mĭs) *n.* [Gk. *knemis*, legging.] Shin or tibia.

cnida (knī'dă, nī'dă) *n.* [Gk. *knide*, nettle.] A cnidoblast; a nematocyst.

cnidoblast (knī'döblăst, nī'döblăst) *n.* [Gk. *knide*, nettle; *blastos*, bud.] Stinging cell of Coelentera.

cnidocil (knī'dösĭl, nī'dösĭl) *n.* [Gk. *knide*, nettle; L. *cilium*, eyelid.] A minute process projecting externally from a cnidoblast.

cnidophore (knī'döfōr, nī'döfōr) *n.* [Gk. *knide*, nettle; *pherein*, to bear.] A modified zooid which bears nematocysts.

cnidopod (knī'döpŏd, nī'döpŏd) *n.* [Gk. *knide*, nettle; *pous*, foot.] Drawn-out basal part of a nematocyst, embedded in mesogloea.

cnidosac (knī'dösăk, nī'dösăk) *n.* [Gk. *knide*, nettle; *sakkos*, bag.] A kidney-shaped swelling or battery, often protected by a hood, found on dactylozooids of Siphonophora.

coactate (köăk'tāt) *a.* [L. *coacta*, felt.] Closely matted but smooth, *appl.* surface.

coaction (kōăk'shŭn) *n.* [L. *cum*, with; *actio*, action.] The reciprocal activity of organisms within a community.

coadaptation (kō'ădăptā'shŭn) *n.* [L. *cum*, with; *ad*, to; *aptare*, to fit.] The correlated variation in two mutually dependent organs.

coagulation (kōăgūlā'shŭn) *n.* [L. *cum*, together; *agere*, to drive.] Curdling or clotting; the changing from a liquid to a viscous or solid state by chemical reaction; *appl.* vitamin K, the antihaemorrhagic accessory food factor.

coagulin (kōăg'ūlĭn) *n.* [L. *coagulum*, rennet.] Any agent capable of coagulating albuminous substances.

coagulocyte (kōăg'ūlösīt) *n.* [L. *cum*, together; *agere*, to drive; Gk. *kytos*, hollow.] A granular haemocyte or cystocyte, in insects.

coagulum (kōăg'ūlŭm) *n.* [L. *coagulum*, rennet.] Any coagulated mass; clot; curd.

coaptation (kōăptā'shŭn) *n.* [L. *cum*, together; *aptare*, to fit.] Mutual adjustment of parts; dependence of function upon the presence of an organic structure or character.

coarctate (kōârk'tāt) *a.* [L. *coarctare*, to press together.] Compressed; closely connected; with abdomen separated from thorax by a constriction.

coarctate larva or **pupa,**—semipupa; pseudopupa; a larval stage of certain Diptera.

cobalamin,—an organic compound containing cobalt, $C_{63}H_{90}N_{14}O_{44}PCo$, present in liver and animal foods; vitamin B_{12}, anti-pernicious anaemia factor and promoting growth; B_{12a} cyanocobalamin; B_{12b} hydroxocobalamin; B_{12c} nitrocobalamin.

cocci (kŏk'sī) *n. plu.* [Gk. *kokkos*, berry.] Septicidal carpels; spore mother cells of certain hepatics; rounded cells, as certain bacteria.

coccogone (kŏk'ögōn) *n.* [Gk. *kokkos*, berry; *gonos*, birth.] A reproductive cell in certain algae.

coccoid (kŏk'oid) *a.* [Gk. *kokkos*, berry; *eidos*, form.] Like or *pert.* a coccus; spherical or globose.

coccolith (kŏk'ölĭth) *n.* [Gk. *kokkos*, berry; *lithos*, stone.] A calcareous spicule in certain Flagellata.

coccospheres (kŏk'ösfērz) *n. plu.* [Gk. *kokkos*, berry; *sphaira*, globe.] Remains of hard parts of certain algae and radiolarians.

coccus (kŏk'ŭs) *n.* [Gk. *kokkos*, berry.] *Sing.* of cocci, *q.v.*

coccygeal (kŏksĭj'ëăl) *a.* [Gk. *kokkyx*, cuckoo.] *Pert.* or in region of coccyx.

coccyx (kŏk'sĭks) *n.* [Gk. *kokkyx*, cuckoo.] The terminal part of the vertebral column beyond the sacrum.

cochlea (kŏk'lëă) *n.* [Gk. *kochlias*, snail.] Anterior part of labyrinth of the ear, spirally coiled like a snail's shell; a coiled legume.

cochlear (kŏk'lëăr) *a.* [Gk. *kochlias*, snail.] *Appl.* aestivation when wholly internal leaf is next but one to wholly external leaf; *pert.* the cochlea.

cochleariform (kŏk'lëăr'ĭfôrm) *a.* [Gk. *kochlias*, snail; L. *forma*, shape.] Screw- or spoon-shaped; *pert.* thin plate or process of bone separating tensor tympani canal from Eustachian tube.

cochleate (kŏk'lëāt) *a.* [Gk. *kochlias*, snail.] Screw-like; spiral.

cocoon (kökoon') *n.* [F. *cocon*, cocoon.] The protective case of many larval forms before they become pupae; silky or other covering formed by many animals for their eggs.

coelarium,—coelomic epithelium; mesothelium.

coelenteron (sēlĕn'tërŏn) *n.* [Gk. *koilos*, hollow; *enteron*, intestine.] Cavity in body of Coelenterata.

coeliac (sē'lĭăk) *a.* [Gk. *koilia*, belly.] *Pert.* the abdominal cavity; *appl.* arteries, veins, nerves, plexus.

coeloblast (sē'löblăst) *n.* [Gk. *koilos*, hollow; *blastos*, bud.] A division of the embryonic hypoblast.

coeloconic (sē'lökŏn'ĭk) *a.* [Gk. *koilos*, hollow; *konos*, cone.] Having, or consisting of, a conical process situated in a pit; *appl.* sensillae.

coelogastrula (sē'lögăs'troolă) *n.* [Gk. *koilos*, hollow; *gaster*, stomach.] A gastrula developed from a blastula with a segmentation cavity.

coelom (sē'löm) *n.* [Gk. *koiloma*, hollow.] Body cavity, *q.v.*

coelomate (sē'lömāt sēlō'māt,) *a.* [Gk. *koiloma*, hollow.] Having a coelom.

coelomesoblast (sēlömĕs'öblăst) *n.* [Gk. *koilos*, hollow; *mesos*, middle; *blastos*, bud.] In segmentation, the mesoblastic bands destined to form wall of coelom and outgrowths.

coelomic (sēlōm'ĭk) *a.* [Gk. *koiloma*, hollow.] *Pert.* a coelom.

coelomocytes (sēlō′mösīts) *n. plu.* [Gk. *koiloma*, hollow; *kytos*, hollow vessel.] Coelomic corpuscles, including amoebocytes and eleocytes, in annelids; mesenchymatous cells in body cavity of nematodes; cells in coelomic fluid and in water-vascular and haemal systems, including morula-shaped cells, spindle-shaped cells, phagocytes, and crystal cells, in echinoderms.

coelomoduct (sēlō′mödŭkt) *n.* [Gk. *koiloma*, hollow; L. *ducere*, to lead.] A channel leading from body cavity to exterior.

coelomopores (sēlō′möpōrz) *n. plu.* [Gk. *koiloma*, hollow; *poros*, passage.] Ducts leading directly from pericardial cavity to exterior, peculiar to Nautilus.

coelomostome (sēlō′möstōm) *n.* [Gk. *koiloma*, hollow; *stoma*, mouth.] The external opening of a coelomoduct.

coelosperm (sē′löspĕrm) *n.* [Gk. *koilos*, hollow; *sperma*, seed] A carpel, hollow on its inner surface.

coelozoic (sē′lözō′ĭk) *a.* [Gk. *koilos*, hollow; *zoon*, animal.] *Appl.* a trophozoite when situated in some cavity of the body.

coenangium (sēnăn′jĭŭm) *n.* [Gk. *koinos*, common; *anggeion*, vessel.] A coenocytic sporangium.

coenanthium (sēnăn′thĭŭm) *n.* [Gk. *koinos*, common; *anthos*, flower.] Inflorescence with a nearly flat receptacle having upcurved margins.

coenenchyma (sēnĕng′kĭmă) *n.* [Gk. *koinos*, common; *engchyma*, infusion.] Common tissue which connects the polyps or zooids of a compound coral; coenenchyme.

coenobium (sēnō′bĭŭm) *n.* [Gk. *koinos*, common; *bios*, life.] A unicellular colony with no marked distinction between vegetative and reproductive units; colony or unit of undifferentiated cells.

coenoblast (sē′nöblăst) *n.* [Gk. *koinos*, common; *blastos*, bud.] A germ-layer which gives origin to endoderm and mesoderm.

coenocentre (sē′nösĕn′tĕr) *n.* [Gk. *koinos*, common; *kentron*, centre.] A deeply-staining body accompanying the ovum in certain fungi.

coenocyte (sē′nösīt) *n.* [Gk. *koinos*, common; *kytos*, hollow.] A plant body in which constituent protoplasts are not separated by cell walls. *a.* Coenocytic.

coenoecium (sēnē′sĭŭm) *n.* [Gk. *koinos*, common; *oikos*, house.] The common groundwork of a polyzoan colony.

coenogametangium (sē′nögămētăn′-jĭŭm) *n.* [Gk. *koinos*, common; *gametes*, spouse; *anggeion*, vessel.] A coenocytic gametangium, as in Zygomycetes.

coenogamete (sē′nögămēt′) *n.* [Gk. *koinos*, common; *gametes*, spouse.] A multinucleate gamete.

coenogamy (sēnŏg′ămĭ) *n.* [Gk. *koinos*, common; *gamos*, marriage.] The union of coenogametangia.

coenogenesis (sē′nöjĕn′ësĭs) *n.* [Gk. *koinos*, common; *genesis*, descent.] Common descent from the same ancestry; blood relationship.

coenogony (sēnŏg′önĭ) *n.* [Gk. *koinos*, common; *gone*, generation.] Reproduction by means of coenocytes.

coenosarc (sē′nösârk) *n.* [Gk. *koinos*, common; *sarx*, flesh.] The common tissue uniting the polyps in a compound colony.

coenosite (sē′nösīt) *n.* [Gk. *koinos*, common; *sitos*, food.] An organism habitually sharing food with another; a commensal.

coenosteum (sēnŏs′tëŭm) *n.* [Gk. *koinos*, common; *osteon*, bone.] The common colonial skeleton in corals.

coenotrope (sē′nötrōp) *n.* [Gk. *koinos*, common; *trope*, turning.] Behaviour common to a group of organisms or to a species.

coenozygote (sē′nözī′gōt) *n.* [Gk. *koinos*, common; *zygon*, yoke.] A zygote formed by coenogametes.

coenurus (sēnū′rŭs) *n.* [Gk. *koinos*, common; *oura*, tail.] A metacestode with large bladder, from whose walls many daughter-cysts arise, each with one scolex.

co-enzyme (kō′ĕn′zīm) *n.* [L. *cum*, with; Gk. *en*, in; *zyme*, leaven.] A substance which activates an enzyme or accelerates its action; co-ferment.

cog-tooth,—spur or projection of incudal facet of malleus.

coherent (kōhē′rĕnt) *a.* [L. *cohaerere*, to stick together.] With similar parts united; adherent.

cohesion (kōhē′zhŭn) *n.* [L. *cohaerere*, to stick together.] Condition of union of separate parts of floral whorl; *cf.* adhesion.

cohort (kō′hôrt) *n.* [L. *cohors*, enclosure.] A group of related families; in earlier classifications a somewhat indefinitely limited group.

coino-,—coeno-.

coition (kōĭsh′ŭn) *n.* [L. *coire*, to go together.] Sexual intercourse; coitus; copulation.

colchicine (kŏl′kĭsĭn) *n.* [L. *colchicum*, meadow saffron, from *Colchis*, ancient Mingrelia.] An alkaloid obtained from meadow saffron, influencing mitosis and tissue metabolism; $C_{22}H_{25}O_6N$.

coleogen (kŏl′ëōjĕn) *n.* [Gk. *koleos*, sheath; *gennaein*, to produce.] Meristematic layer giving rise to endodermis.

coleopterous (kŏl′ëŏp′tĕrŭs) *a.* [Gk. *koleos*, sheath; *pteron*, wing.] Having the anterior wings hard and used as elytra; *pert.* beetles.

coleoptile (kŏl′ëŏptĭl) *n.* [Gk. *koleos*, sheath; *ptilon*, feather.] The first leaf in seedling of monocotyledons.

coleorhiza (kŏl′ëōrī′ză) *n.* [Gk. *koleos*, sheath; *rhiza*, root.] The layer surrounding the radicle.

colic (kŏl′ĭk) *a.* [Gk. *kolon*, colon.] *Pert.* the colon.

coliform (kō′lĭfôrm) *a.* [L. *colum*, strainer; *forma*, shape.] Sieve-like; cribriform. [Gk. *kolon*, colon.] Resembling colon bacilli.

collagen (kŏl′ăjĕn) *n.* [Gk. *kolla*, glue; *genos*, descent.] A scleroprotein, occurring as chief constituent of white connective tissue fibres and organic part of bone, also of some fish scales.

collar (kŏl′ăr) *n.* [M.E. *coler*, collar.] The choana of a collared cell; a prominent fold behind the proboscis in Hemichorda; the fleshy rim projecting beyond the edge of a snail shell; any structure comparable with a collar; collum, *q.v.*; junction between root and stem; collet, *q.v.*

collar cell,—choanocyte.

collarette,—line of junction between pupillary and ciliary zones of anterior surface of iris; iris frill, angular line.

collateral (kŏlăt′ĕrăl) *a.* [L. *cum*, with; *latera*, sides.] Side by side; *appl.* ovules; *appl.* bundles with xylem and phloem in the same radius; *appl.* fine lateral branches from the axon of a nerve cell; *appl.* prevertebral ganglia of sympathetic system; *appl.* inheritance of character from a common ancestor in individuals not lineally related; *appl.* circulation established through anastomosis with other parts when the chief vein is obstructed.

collective fruit,—fruit formed from complete inflorescences, as mulberry and pine-apple.

collector (kŏlĕk′tŏr) *n.* [L. *colligere*, to collect.] One of the pollen-retaining hairs on stigma or style of certain flowers; collecting hair.

collenchyma (kŏlĕng′kĭmă) *n.* [Gk. *kolla*, glue; *engcyhma*, infusion.] Parenchymatous peripheral supporting tissue with cells more or less elongated and thickened, either at the angles (angular c.), or on walls adjoining intercellular spaces (lacunar c.), or tangentially (lamellar c.); the middle layer of sponges; collenchyme.

collencyte (kŏl′ĕnsīt) *n.* [Gk. *kolla*, glue; *en*, in; *kytos*, hollow.] A clear cell with thread-like pseudopodia found in sponges.

collet (kŏl′ĕt) *n.* [F. *collet*, collar.] Root zone, of hypocotyl, where cuticle is absent.

colleterium (kŏl′ĕtē′rĭŭm) *n.* [Gk. *kolla*, glue.] A colleterial or mucus-secreting gland in female reproductive system of insects.

colleters (kŏlē′tĕrz) *n. plu.* [Gk. *kolletos*, glued.] The hairs, usually secreting a gluey substance, which cover many resting buds; multicellular glandular trichomes.

colletocystophore (kŏlē′tösĭst′öfōr) *n.* [Gk. *kolletos*, glued; *kystis*, bladder; *pherein*, to bear.] The statorhabd of Haliclystus.

colliculate (kŏlĭk′ūlāt) *a.* [L. *dim.* of *collis*, hill.] Having small elevations.

colliculus (kŏlĭk′ūlŭs) *n.* [L. *colliculus*, little hill.] A prominence of corpora quadrigemina; a rounded elevation near apex of antero-lateral surface of arytaenoid cartilages; slight elevation formed by optic nerve at entrance to retina; elevation of urethral crest, with openings of ejaculatory ducts and prostatic utricle.

colloblast (kŏl′öblăst) *n.* [Gk. *kolla*, glue; *blastos*, bud.] A cell on tentacles and pinnae of ctenophores, which carries little globules of adhesive substance; lasso-cell.

colloid (kŏl′oid) *n.* [Gk. *kolla*, glue; *eidos*, form.] A gelatinous substance which does not readily diffuse through an animal or vegetable membrane; *opp.* crystalloid; a substance composed of two homogeneous parts or phases, one of which is dispersed in the other.

collophore (kŏl′öfōr) *n.* [Gk. *kolla*, glue; *pherein*, to bear.] The ventral tube of Collembola.

collum (kŏl′ŭm) *n.* [L. *collum*, neck.] Neck; collar, *q.v.*; any collar-like structure; dorsal plate of first body-segment in Diplopoda; basal portion of sporogonium in mosses.

colon (kō′lŏn) *n.* [Gk. *kolon*, colon.] The second portion of intestine of insects; part of the large intestine of vertebrates.

colony (kŏl′ŏnĭ) *n.* [L. *colonia*, farm.] Any collection of organisms living together, *appl.* ants, bees; a group of animals or plants living together and somewhat isolated, or established in a new area; a coenobium; a group of bacteria or of other micro-organisms in a culture.

colostrum (kŏlŏs′trŭm) *n.* [L. *colostrum*.] Milk secreted at end of pregnancy and differing from that secreted later.

colulus (kŏl′ūlŭs) *n.* [*Dim.* of L. *colus*, distaff.] A small conical structure between anterior spinnerets of spiders.

columella (kŏl′ūmĕl′ă) *n.* [L *columella*, small column.] A prolongation of stalk into sporangium; central core in root-cap; central pillar in skeleton of some corals; the central pillar in gasteropod shells; epipterygoid; the rod, partly bony, partly cartilaginous, connecting tympanum with inner ear in birds, reptiles, and amphibians; the axis of cochlea; lower part of nasal septum.

columellar (kŏl′ūmĕl′ăr) *a.* [L. *columella*, small column.] *Pert.* columella.

column (kŏl′ŭm), **columna** (kŏlŭm′nă) *n.* [L. *columna*, pillar.] Any structure like a column, as spinal column; actinian body; stalk of a crinoid; longitudinal bundle of nerve fibres in white matter of spinal cord; nasal septum edge; thick muscular strands found in ventricle; stamens in mallows; united stamens and style in orchids.

columnals (kŏlŭm′nălz) *n. plu.* [L. *columna*, pillar.] Stem ossicles in crinoids.

columnar (kŏlŭm′năr) *a.* [L. *columna*, pillar.] *Pert.*, or like, a column or columna; *appl.* cells longer than broad; *appl.* epithelium of columnar cells.

colyone,—*see* kolyone.

coma (kō′mă) *n.* [Gk. *kome*, hair.] A terminal cluster of bracts, as in pine-apple; hair-tufts on certain seeds. [Gk. *koma*, deep sleep.] Stupor.

Comanchean (kömăn′chēan) *a.* [*Comanche* County, Texas.] Lower Cretaceous in North America.

comb (kōm) *n.* [A. S. *camb.*] A comb-like structure, as swimming-plate, ctenidium, pecten, strigilis, honeycomb, fleshy crest, mushroom gill.

comb-ribs, — meridional rows of swimming-plates of ctenophora.

comes (kō′mēz) *n.* [L. *comes*, companion.] A blood-vessel that runs alongside a nerve.

comitalia (kŏmĭtā′lĭă) *n. plu.* [L. *comitari*, to accompany.] Small di- or tri-actine spicules in sponges.

comma (kŏm′ă) *n.* [Gk. *komma*, short clause.] A sarcomere; inocomma; *appl.* tract, certain nerve fibres in dorsal or posterior column of spinal cord; *appl.* bacillus, the spirillum causing cholera.

commensal (kŏmĕn′săl) *n.* [L. *cum*, with; *mensa*, table.] An organism living with another and sharing the food, both species as a rule benefiting by the association.

comminator (kŏm′ĭnātŏr) *a.* [L. *cum*, with; *minari*, to threaten.] *Appl.* muscles which connect adjacent jaws in Aristotle's lantern.

commissure (kŏm′ĭsūr) *n.* [L. *commissura*, seam.] The union-line between two parts; inner side of mericarp; carpellary cohesion plane; a connecting band of nerve tissue.

comose (kō′mōs) *a.* [L. *comosus*, hairy.] Hairy; having a tuft of hairs.

companion cell,—a narrow cell, retaining its nucleus, derived from a cell giving rise also to a sieve-tube element, in phloem of angiosperms.

compass (kŭm′păs) *n.* [L. *cum*, together; *passus*, pace.] A curved bifid ossicle, part of Aristotle's lantern.

compass plants,—certain plants with permanent north and south direction of their leaf edges.

compensation point,—incidence of balance between respiration and photosynthesis, as determined by intensity of light at a given temperature: compensation intensity; limit of sea or lake depth below which plants lose more by respiration than they gain by photosynthesis: compensation depth or level.

competence (kŏm′pĕtĕns) *n.* [L. *competere*, to suit.] Reactive state permitting directional development and differentiation in response to a stimulus, as of part of an embryo in response to an evocator or organiser stimulus.

complement (kŏm′plĕmĕnt) *n.* [L. *complere*, to fill up.] The substance in the blood-serum which when destroyed by heat acts with an amboceptor to produce lysis; alexin; a group composed of one, two, or more genomes or chromosome sets derived from a single nucleus.

complemental air,—volume of air which can be taken in addition to that drawn in during normal breathing.

complemental male,—a purely male form, usually small, found living in close proximity to the ordinary hermaphrodite form in certain animals, as barnacles.

complementary (kŏm′plĕmĕn′tărĭ) *n.* [L. *complere*, to fill up.] The coronoid bone. *a. Appl.* non-suberised cells loosely arranged in cork tissue and forming air passages; *appl.* genes producing a similar effect when inherited separately but a different effect together.

complexus (kŏmplĕk′sŭs) *n.* [L. *complexus*, embrace.] An aggregate; *appl.* muscle, the semi-spinalis capitis.

complicant (kŏm′plĭkănt) *a.* [L. *cum*, together; *plicare*, to fold.] Folding over one another; *appl.* elytra of certain insects.

complicate (kŏm′plĭkāt) *a.* [L. *cum*, together; *plicare*, to fold.] Folded; conduplicate; *appl.* leaves folded longitudinally so that right and left halves are in contact; *appl.* insect wings; compound, *appl.* fruit-body composed of pileoli with stipes joining to form a somewhat central stipe, as in some Hymenomycetes.

composite (kŏm'pŏsĭt) *a.* [L. *cum*, together; *ponere*, to place.] Closely-packed, as a capitulum; *appl.* fruits, as sorosis, syconus, strobilus.

compound (kŏm'pownd) *a.* [L. *cum*, together; *ponere*, to place.] Made up of several elements; *appl.* flowers, pistils, leaves, medullary rays, eyes, etc.; *appl.* starch grains with two or more hila.

compound spore,—sporidesm, *q.v.*

compressor (kŏmprĕs'ŏr) *n.* [L. *cum*, together; *premere*, to press.] Something that serves to compress; *appl.* muscles, as compressor naris.

conarium (kōnā'rĭŭm) *n.* [Gk. *konarion*, little cone.] Transparent deep-sea larva of Velella; the pineal gland or epiphysis cerebri.

concatenate (kŏnkăt'ĕnāt) *a.* [L. *cum*, together; *catenatus*, chained.] Forming a chain, as spores.

concentric (kŏnsĕn'trĭk) *a.* [L. *cum*, together; *centrum*, centre.] Having a common centre; *appl.* vascular bundles with one kind of tissue surrounding another; *appl.* corpuscles of Hassall.

conceptacle (kŏnsĕp'tăkl) *n.* [L. *concipere*, to conceive.] A depression in thallus of certain algae in which gametangia are borne.

conceptive (kŏnsĕp'tĭv) *a.* [L. *concipere*, to conceive.] Capable of being fertilised and producing an embryo.

concha (kŏng'kă) *n.* [Gk. *kongche*, shell.] The cavity of the external ear, which opens into the external acoustic meatus; a superior, middle, and inferior projection from lateral wall of nasal cavity; turbinal body; one of two curved plates of sphenoidal bone; a marine shell.

conchiform (kŏng'kĭfôrm) *a.* [L. *concha*, shell; *forma*, shape.] Shaped like a concha; shell-shaped; conchoid.

conchiolin (kŏngkī'ŏlĭn) *n.* [Gk. *kongche*, shell.] The organic substance that forms the basis of shells of molluscs.

conchology (kŏngkŏl'ŏjĭ) *n.* [Gk. *kongche*, shell; *logos*, discourse.] The branch of zoology dealing with molluscs or their shells.

conchula (kŏng'kūlă) *n.* [L. *concha*, shell.] The conspicuous protuberant lip of the modified sulcus in Peachia.

concolorate (kŏnkŭl'ŏrāt) *a.* [L. *concolor*, of the same colour.] Similarly coloured on both sides.

concrescence (kŏnkrĕs'ĕns) *n.* [L. *concrescere*, to grow together.] The growing together of parts.

concrete (kŏnkrēt) *a.* [L. *concretus*, grown together.] Grown together to form a single structure.

condensation (kŏndĕnsā'shŭn) *n.* [L. *condensatio*; from *cum*, together, *densare*, to make thick.] Process of making or becoming thick; contraction, thickening and spiralisation of chromatids during prophase.

condensed (kŏndĕn'sd) *a.* [L. *condensare*, to press close together.] *Appl.* inflorescence with short-stalked or sessile flowers closely crowded.

conditional,—*appl.* dominance owing to influence of modifying genes.

conditioned,—*appl.* reflex depending on new functional connections in central nervous system; *appl.* stimulus inducing a conditioned reflex.

conducting (kŏndŭk'tĭng) *a.* [L. *conducere*, to lead together.] Conveying; *appl.* tissues, bundles.

conduction (kŏndŭk'shŭn) *n.* [L. *conducere*, to lead together.] The transference of soluble matter from one part of a plant to another; the transmission of an excitation, function of nervous system.

conductivity (kŏn'dŭktĭv'ĭtĭ) *n.* [L. *conducere*, to lead together.] Power of transmitting an impulse.

conductor (kŏndŭk'tŏr) *n.* [L. *conducere*, to lead together.] That which can transmit; a projection at base of embolus in spiders.

conduplicate (kŏndū'plĭkāt) *a.* [L. *conduplicare*, to fold together.] *Appl.* cotyledons folded to embrace the radicle; *appl.* vernation when one half of the leaf is folded upon the other.

condylar (kŏn'dĭlăr) *a.* [Gk. *kondylos*, knuckle.] *Pert.* a condyle.

condyle (kŏn'dĭl) *n.* [Gk. *kondylos*, knuckle.] The antheridium of stoneworts; a process on a bone for purposes of articulation; a rounded structure adapted to fit into a socket.

condyloid (kŏn'dĭloid) *n.* [Gk. *kondylos*, knuckle; *eidos*, form.] Shaped like, or situated near a condyle.

cone (kōn) *n.* [Gk. *konos*, cone.] The female flower of Coniferae, with woody axis and spirally-arranged carpels; strobile; terminal spike or fructification in clubmosses and horsetails; a conical elevation on an egg just before fertilisation; a conical or flask-shaped cell of the retina.

cone of origin,—small clear area of nerve cell at the point of exit of the axon; implantation cone; axon hill.

cone of Wulzen [*R. Wulzen*, American physiologist]. A structure projecting forwards from pars intermedia into hypophysial cavity in pituitary region of ox and pig.

cone-bipolars, — bipolar cells whose inner ends ramify in contact with dendrites of ganglionic cells.

conferted (kŏnfĕr'tĕd) *a.* [L. *confertus*, crowded.] Closely assembled or packed.

confluence (kŏn'flooëns) *n.* [L. *confluere*, to flow together.] Angle of union of superior sagittal and transverse sinuses at occipital bone; confluens sinuum, torcular Herophili.

congeneric (kŏn'jënĕr'ĭk) *a.* [L. *congener*, of same race.] Belonging to the same genus.

congenetic (kŏnjĕnĕt'ĭk) *a.* [L. *cum*, with; Gk. *genesis*, descent.] Having the same origin; alike in descent.

congenital (kŏnjĕn'ĭtăl) *a.* [L. *cum*, with; *gignere*, to beget.] Present at birth; born with.

congestin (kŏnjĕs'tĭn) *n.* [L. *congestus*, heaped up.] A toxin of sea-anemone tentacles.

conglobate (kŏn-glō'bāt) *a.* [L. *conglobatus*, formed into a ball.] Ball-shaped; *appl.* gland on lower side of ductus ejaculatorius in insects.

conglomerate (kŏn-glŏm'ërāt) *a.* [L. *cum*, together; *glomerare*, to wind.] Bunched or crowded together.

congression (kŏngrĕsh'ŭn) *n.* [L. *congressio*, meeting.] Chromosome movement to equatorial plane of spindle at metaphase.

coni (kō'nī) *n. plu.* [L. *conus*, cone.] Cones; coni vasculosi; lobules forming head of epididymis.

conidia,—*plu.* of conidium.

conidial (könĭd'ĭăl) *a.* [Gk. *konis*, dust; *idion*, *dim.*] *Pert.* a conidium.

conidiiferous (könĭd'ĭĭf'ërŭs) *a.* [Gk. *konis*, dust; *idion*, *dim.*; L. *ferre*, to bear.] Bearing conidia.

conidiocarp (könĭd'ĭökârp) *n.* [Gk. *konis*, dust; *idion*, *dim.*; *karpos*, fruit.] A collection of conidiophores enclosed in a covering; a pycnidium.

conidiole (könĭd'ĭōl) *n.* [*Dim.* of *conidium.*] A small or a secondary conidium.

conidiophore (könĭd'ĭöfōr) *n.* [Gk. *konis*, dust; *idion*, *dim.*; *pherein*, to bear.] A hypha with sterigmata which bear conidia.

conidiospore (könĭd'ĭöspōr) *n.* [Gk. *konis*, dust; *idion*, *dim.*; *sporos*, seed.] Spore or conidium produced when dry conditions inhibit reproduction by zoospores, in Phycomycetes.

conidium (könĭd'ĭŭm) *n.* [Gk. *konis*, dust; *idion*, *dim.*] A fungal spore asexually produced by constriction of sterigma or of part of a hypha; gonidium.

coniferous (könĭf'ërŭs) *a.* [L. *conus*, cone; *ferre*, to bear.] Cone-bearing.

conjugate (kŏn'joogāt) *v.* [L. *conjugare*, to join together.] To unite, as protozoa; to undergo conjugation. *a.* United in pairs; *appl.* pores united by a groove; *appl.* division in pairs of monoploid nuclei.

conjugated (kŏn'joogātĕd) *a.* [L. *conjugare*, to join together.] United; *appl.* protein, when molecule united to non-protein molecule.

conjugation (kŏn'joogā'shŭn) *n.* [L. *cum*, together; *jugare*, to yoke.] The temporary union or complete fusion of two gametes or unicellular organisms; the pairing of chromosomes.

conjunctiva (kŏn'jŭngktī'vă) *n.* [L. *cum*, together; *jungere*, to join.] Mucous membrane of eye, lining eyelids and reflected over fore part of sclera and constituting corneal epithelium.

conjunctive (kŏnjŭngk'tĭv) *a.* [L. *cum*, together; *jungere*, to join.] *Appl.* parenchyma cells in interspaces of stelar elements.

connate (kŏn'nāt, kŏnāt') *a.* [L. *cum*, together; *gnatus*, born.] Firmly joined together from birth; connate-perfoliate, joined together at base so as to surround stem, *appl.* opposite sessile leaves.

connective (kŏnĕk'tĭv) *n.* [L. *connectere*, to bind together.] A connecting band of nerve tissue between two ganglia; tissue separating two lobes of anther; the structure and zone between successive conidia.

connective tissue,—a mesoblastic tissue with a large amount of intercellular substance, and usually connecting and supporting other tissues.

connexivum (kŏnĕk'sĭvŭm) *n.* [L. *connectere*, to fasten together.] Flattened lateral margin of abdomen in bugs.

connivent (kŏnī'vĕnt) *a.* [L. *connivere*, to close the eyes.] Converging; arching over so as to meet.

conoid (kō'noid) *a.* [Gk. *konos*, cone; *eidos*, form.] Cone-like, but not quite conical.

conoid ligament,—one of the fasciculi of the coraco-clavicular ligament.

conoid tubercle,—coracoid tuberosity, a small rough eminence on posterior border of clavicle, serving for attachment of conoid ligament.

conopodium (kōnŏpō'dĭŭm) *n.* [Gk. *konos*, cone; *pous*, foot.] A conical receptacle or thalamus of a flower.

conotheca (kōnŏthē'kă) *n.* [Gk. *konos*, cone; *theke*, case.] Thin integument of phragmocone.

conscutum (kŏn'skūtŭm) *n.* [L. *cum*, together with; *scutum*, shield.] Dorsal shield formed by united scutum and alloscutum in certain ticks.

consensual (kŏnsĕn'sūăl) *a.* [L. *consensus*, agreement.] *Appl.* involuntary action correlated with voluntary action; reacting to excitation of a corresponding organ; *appl.* contraction of both pupils when only one retina is directly stimulated.

consimilar (kŏnsĭm'ĭlăr) *a.* [L. *consimilis*, entirely similar.] Similar in all respects; with both sides alike, as some diatoms.

consociation (kŏn'sōsĭā'shŭn) *n.* [L. *consociatio*, partnership.] A unit of a plant association, characterised by a single dominant species.

consocies (kŏnsō'sĭēz) *n.* [L. *cum*, together; *socius*, fellow.] A consociation representing a stage in the process of succession.

consortes (kŏnsôr'tēz) *n. plu.* [L. *consortes*, partners.] Associate organisms other than symbionts, commensals, or hosts and parasites. *Sing.* consors.

consortium (kŏnsôr'tĭŭm) *n.* [L. *consortium*, partnership.] The compound thallus of lichens.

consperse (kŏnspĕrs') *a.* [L. *conspersus*, besprinkled.] Densely scattered; *appl.* dot-like markings, pores, etc.

constitutive (kŏn'stĭtūtĭv) *a.* [L. *constituere*, to establish.] Naturally present in an organism; *appl.* enzymes, *opp.* adaptive or inducible enzymes.

constricted (kŏnstrĭk'tĕd) *a.* [L. *constrictus*, drawn together.] Narrowed; compressed at regular intervals.

constriction (kŏnstrĭk'shŭn) *n.* [L. *constrictus*, drawn together.] A constricted part or place, as a node of Ranvier; non-spiralising chromosome segment at metaphase, either associated with the centromere, or acentric, or controlled by the nucleolus.

constrictor (kŏnstrĭk'tŏr) *n.* [L. *constrictus*, drawn together.] A muscle which compresses or constricts, *e.g.*, constrictor pharyngis, c. urethrae.

consute (kŏn'sūt, kŏnsūt') *a.* [L. *consuere*, to sew together.] With stitch-like markings; *appl.* elytra of certain beetles.

contabescence (kŏn'tăbĕs'ĕns) *n.* [L. *contabescere*, to waste away.] Abortion or atrophy of stamens.

contact receptor,—a receptor in epidermis or in dermis.

context (kŏn'tĕkst) *n.* [L. *cum*, together; *texere*, to weave.] The layers developed between hymenium and true mycelium in certain fungi.

continuity (kŏntĭnū'ĭtĭ) *n.* [L. *continuus*, continuous.] Succession without a break, especially continuity of germ plasm.

contorted (kŏntôr'tĕd) *a.* [L. *contortus*, twisted together.] Twisted; *appl.* aestivation in which one leaf overlaps the next with one margin, and is overlapped by the previous on the other.

contortuplicate (kŏntŏr'tūplĭkāt *a.* [L. *cum*, with; *torquere*, to twist; *plicare*, to fold.] *Appl.* bud with contorted and plicate leaves.

contour (kŏn'toor) *n.* [F. *contour*, circuit.] Outline of a figure or body; *appl.* outermost feathers that cover the body of a bird.

contractile (kŏntrăk'tĭl) *a.* [L. *cum*, together; *trahere*, to draw.] Capable of contracting.

contractile cell,—any cell in a sporangium or an anther wall which by hygroscopic contraction helps to open the organ.

contractile fibre-cells, — elongated, spindle-shaped, more or less polyhedral, nucleated muscle-cells, containing a central bundle of fibrillae.

contractile vacuole,—a small spherical vesicle, found in cytoplasm of many Protista, with excretory or hydrostatic function.

contractility (kŏn'trăktĭl'ĭtĭ) *n.* [L. *cum*, together, *trahere*, to draw.] The power by which muscle-fibres are enabled to contract.

contractin,—presumable neurohumor inducing contraction of chromatophores in crustaceans. *Opp.* expantin.

contracture (kŏntrăk'tūr) *n.* [L. *contractus*, drawn together.] Contraction of muscles persisting after stimulus has been removed.

contra-deciduate (kŏn'trădēsĭd'ūāt) *a.* [L. *contra*, opposite to; *decidere*, to fall off.] *Appl.* foetal placenta and distal part of allantois.

contralateral (kŏn'trălăt'ĕrăl) *a.* [L. *contra*, opposite to; *latus*, side.] *Pert.* or situated on the opposite side, *opp.* ipsilateral.

contranatant (kŏn'trănā'tănt) *a.* [L. *contra*, against; *natare*, to swim.] Swimming or migrating against the current, *opp.* denatant.

conuli (kŏ̄'nūlī) *n. plu.* [*Dim.* of L. *conus*, cone.] Tent-like projections on surface of certain sponges caused by principal skeletal elements.

conus (kō'nŭs) *n.* [L. *conus*, cone.] Any cone-shaped structure, as conus arteriosus, a structure between ventricle and aorta in fishes and amphibians; diverticulum of right ventricle from which pulmonary artery arises; conus medullaris, the tapering end of spinal cord.

convergence (kŏnvĕr'jĕns) *n.* [L. *convergere*, to incline together.] The development of similar characters in organisms belonging to different groups; heterogenetic homoeomorphosis; homoplasty; coordinated movement of eyes when focusing a near point.

convolute (kŏn'vŏlūt) *a.* [L. *cum*, together; *volvere*, to wind.] Rolled together; *appl.* leaves and cotyledons; *appl.* shells in which outer whorls overlap inner; coiled; convoluted, *appl.* parts of renal tubule.

convolution (kŏn′vōlū′shŭn) *n.* [L. *cum*, together; *volvere*, to wind.] A coiling or twisting, as of brain, intestine.

coprobiont (kŏp′röbīŏnt) *n.* [Gk. *kopros*, dung; *bionai*, to live.] Any coprophytic or coprozoic organism; coprophage.

coprodaeum (kŏp′rödē′ŭm) *n.* [Gk. *kopros*, dung; *odos*, way.] The division of cloaca which receives rectum.

coprolite (kŏp′rölīt) *n.* [Gk. *kopros*, dung; *lithos*, stone.] Petrified faeces.

coprophage,—coprobiont.

coprophagous (kŏprŏf′ăgŭs) *a.* [Gk. *kopros*, dung; *phagein*, to eat.] Feeding on dung; *appl.* insects.

coprophil (kŏp′röfĭl) *a.* [Gk. *kopros*, dung; *philos*, loving.] *Appl.* dung bacteria and flagellates; coprophytic.

coprophyte (kŏp′röfīt) *n.* [Gk. *kopros*, dung; *phyton*, plant.] A dung-inhabiting plant. *a.* Coprophytic.

coprozoic (kŏp′rözō′ĭk) *a.* [Gk. *kopros*, dung; *zoon*, animal.] Inhabiting faeces, as some protozoa.

coprozoite (kŏp′rözō′īt) *n.* [Gk. *kopros*, dung; *zoon*, animal.] A dung-inhabiting or coprozoic animal.

copula (kŏp′ūlă) *n.* [L. *copula*, bond.] A ridge in development of the tongue, formed by union of ventral ends of second and third arches; basihyal or os interglossum in certain reptiles; any bridging or connecting structure.

copulant (kŏp′ūlănt) *n.* [L. *copulare*, to couple.] A unit in conjugation with another, as nuclei, cells, hyphae, thalli, etc.

copularium (kŏpūlā′rĭŭm) *n.* [L. *copula*, bond.] A cyst formed around two associated gametocytes, in gregarines.

copulation (kŏpūlā′shŭn) *n.* [L. *copula*, bond.] Sexual union; coition; in protozoa, complete fusion of two individuals; conjugation, as in yeasts.

coracoid (kŏr′ăkoid) *a.* [Gk. *korax*, crow; *eidos*, form.] *Appl.* or *pert.* bone or part of the pectoral girdle between scapula and sternum; *appl.* ligament which stretches over the suprascapular notch.

coracoid process, — the rudimentary coracoid element fused to the scapula in most mammals.

coralliferous (kŏrălĭf′ërŭs) *a.* [Gk. *korallion*, coral; L. *ferre*, to bear.] Coral-forming; containing coral.

coralliform,—coralloid.

coralligenous (kŏrălĭj′ënŭs) *a.* [Gk. *korallion*, coral; *gennaein*, to produce.] Coral-forming.

coralline (kŏr′ălīn) *a.* [Gk. *korallion*, coral.] Resembling a coral; *appl.* Hydrozoa and Polyzoa; composed of coral; *appl.* certain Algae; *appl.* a Pliocene crag or deposit containing fossil Polyzoa and Mollusca.

corallite (kŏr′ălīt) *n.* [Gk. *korallion*, coral.] Cup of a single polyp of coral.

coralloid (kŏr′ăloid) *a.* [Gk. *korallion*, coral; *eidos*, form.] Resembling, or branching like a coral; *appl.* gleba, roots, etc.

corallum (kŏrăl′ŭm) *n.* [Gk. *korallion*, coral.] Skeleton of compound coral.

corbicula (kôrbĭk′ūla) *n.* [*Dim.* of L. *corbis*, basket.] Basket-like arrangement of a teleutosorus or telium; *plu.* of corbiculum. *Plu.* corbiculae.

corbiculum (kôrbĭk′ūlŭm) *n.* [L. *dim.* of *corbis*, basket.] Fringe of hair on insect tibia; the pollen-collecting apparatus of a bee. *Plu.* corbicula.

corbula (kôr′būlă) *n.* [L. *corbula*, little basket.] The phylactocarp of Aglaeophenia, etc., a stem with alternate branches rising upwards and forming a pod-like structure.

cord (kôrd) *n.* [Gk. *chorde*, cord.] Any cord-like structure, as spinal cord, spermatic cord.

cordate (kôr′dāt) *a.* [L. *cor*, heart.] Heart-shaped; cordiform.

cordiform tendon,—the central aponeurosis of the diaphragm.

cordylus (kôrdī'lus) *n.* [Gk. *kordyle*, swelling.] An intertentacular exumbral structure with core of vacuolated cells and flattened ectoderm.

coremata (kŏrē'mătă) *n. plu.* [Gk. *korema*, broom.] Paired sacs bearing hairs, on membrane between seventh and eighth abdominal segments, accessory copulatory organ in moths.

coremiform (kŏrē'mĭfôrm) *a.* [Gk. *korema*, broom ; L. *forma*, shape.] Formed like a broom or sheaf.

coremiospore (kŏrē'mĭöspōr) *n.* [Gk. *korema*, broom ; *sporos*, seed.] One of a series of spores in the top of a coremium.

coremium (kŏrē'mĭŭm) *n.* [Gk. *korema*, broom.] A sheaf-like aggregation of conidiophores, or of hyphae.

coriaceous (kōrĭā'shŭs) *a.* [L. *corium*, leather.] Leathery ; *appl.* leaves.

corium (kō'rĭŭm) *n.* [L. *corium*, leather.] The middle division of an elytron ; deeper-seated layer of the skin, consisting of a vascular connective tissue ; cutis vera ; derma.

cork (kôrk) *n.* [Sp. *alcorque*, cork.] A tissue derived usually from outer layer of cortex in woody plants.

cork-cambium,—phellogen, *q.v.*

corm (kôrm) *n.* [Gk. *kormos*, trunk.] An enlarged solid subterranean stem, rounded in shape, composed of two or more internodes and covered externally by a few thin membranous scales or cataphyllary leaves ; cormus, *q.v.*

cormel (kôr'mĕl) *n.* [Gk. *kormos*, trunk.] A secondary corm produced by an old corm.

cormidium (kôrmĭd'ĭŭm) *n.* [Gk. *kormos*, trunk ; *idion*, *dim.*] An aggregation of individuals in a siphonophore, borne on the coenosarc and capable of liberation therefrom.

cormoid (kôr'moid) *a.* [Gk. *kormos*, trunk ; *eidos*, form.] Like a corm.

cormophylogeny (kôr'möfīlŏj'ĕnĭ) *n.* [Gk. *kormos*, trunk ; *phyle*, tribe ; *genos*, offspring.] Development of families or races.

cormophyte (kôr'möfīt) *n.* [Gk. *kormos*, trunk ; *phyton*, plant.] A plant which possesses stem and root. *Opp.* thallophyte.

cormous (kôr'mŭs) *a.* [Gk. *kormos*, trunk.] Corm-producing.

cormus (kôr'mŭs) *n.* [Gk. *kormos*, tree-trunk.] A corm ; body of a seed-plant, *opp.* thallus ; body or colony of a compound animal.

cornea (kôr'nëă) *n.* [L. *corneus*, horny.] The transparent covering on anterior surface of eyeball ; outer transparent part of each element of a compound eye.

corneagen (kôr'nëăjĕn) *a.* [L. *cornu*, horn ; Gk. *-genes*, producing.] Cornea-producing ; *appl.* cells immediately below cuticle, which secrete cuticular lens and are renewed on ecdysis.

corneal (kôr'nëăl) *a.* [L. *corneus*, horny.] *Pert.* the cornea.

corneoscute (kôr'nëöskūt) *n.* [L. *corneus*, horny ; *scutum*, shield.] An epidermal scale.

corneous (kôr'nëŭs) *a.* [L. *corneus*, horny.] Horny ; *appl.* sheath covering bill of birds.

cornicle (kôr'nĭkl) *n.* [L. *corniculum*, little horn.] A wax-secreting organ of aphids ; corniculum, *q.v.*

corniculate (kôrnĭk'ūlāt) *a.* [L. *corniculum*, little horn.] Having small horns.

corniculate cartilages,—two small, conical, elastic cartilages articulating with apices of arytaenoids ; Santorini's cartilages, cornicula laryngis.

corniculum (kôrnĭk'ūlŭm) *n.* [L. *dim.* of *cornu*, horn.] A small horn or horn-like process.

cornification (kôr'nĭfĭkā'shŭn) *n.* [L. *cornu*, horn ; *facere*, to make.] Formation of outer horny layer of epidermis.

cornua (kôr'nūă) *n. plu.* [L. *cornu*, horn.] Horns ; horn-like prolongations, as of bones, nerve tissues, cavities, etc. ; the dorsal, lateral, and ventral columns of grey substance in spinal cord. *Sing.* cornu.

cornucopia (kôr′nūkō′pĭă) *n.* [L. *cornu*, horn; *copia*, plenty.] Part of taeniae of fourth ventricle, covering chorioid plexus.

cornule (kôr′nūl) *n.* [L. *cornulum*, *dim.* of *cornu*, horn.] A small horn-like process; one of the horny jaw-plates of Ornithorhynchus.

cornute (kôrnūt′) *a.* [L. *cornutus*, horned.] With horn-like processes.

corolla (körŏl′ă) *n.* [L. *corolla*, small crown.] The petals of a flower.

corollaceous (kŏr′ŏlā′shŭs) *a.* [L. *corolla*, crown.] *Pert.* a corolla.

corolliferous (kŏr′ŏlĭf′ërŭs) *a.* [L. *corolla*, small crown; *ferre*, to bear.] Having a corolla.

corona (körō′nă) *n.* [L. *corona*, crown.] A cup-shaped body formed by union of scales on perianth leaves, as in daffodil; theca and arms of a crinoid; echinoid test excepting apical and antapical plates; ciliated disc or circular band of certain animals; head or upper portion of any structure.

corona radiata,—layer of cells surrounding mammalian egg; fibres of internal capsule of brain.

coronal (kŏrō′năl) *a.* [L. *corona*, crown.] *Pert.* corona; *appl.* suture between frontal and parietal bones; situated in the coronal sutural plane; *appl.* later roots of grasses, *opp.* seminal.

coronary (kŏr′ŏnărĭ) *a.* [L. *corona*, crown.] Crown-shaped or crown-like; encircling; *appl.* arteries, bones, sinus, ligaments, plexus, vein.

coronary arteries,—arteries supplying tissue of heart; labial arteries.

coronary bone,—a small conical bone in mandible of reptiles; small pastern bone of horse.

coronary sinus,—channel receiving most cardiac veins and opening into right auricle.

coronate (kŏr′ŏnāt) *a.* [L. *corona*, crown.] Having a corona; having a row of tubercles encircling a structure, or mounted on whorls of spiral shells.

coronet (kŏr′ŏnĕt) *n.* [L. *corona*, crown.] The burr of an antler.

coronoid (kŏr′ŏnoid) *a.* [Gk. *koronis*, crook-beaked; *eidos*, form.] Shaped like a beak; *appl.* processes. [L. *corona*, crown.] *n.* Coronary bone of reptiles.

coronula (kŏrŏ̆n′ūlă) *n.* [*Dim.* of L. *corona*, crown.] A group of cells forming a crown on the oosphere, as in Charophyta.

corpora (kôr′pöra) *n. plu.* [L. *corpus*, body.] Bodies. *See* corpus.

corpora adiposa,—fat-bodies, *q.v.*

corpora albicantia,—white bodies or scars formed in ovarian follicle after disintegration of luteal cells; corpora mamillaria, ganglia below posterior part of third ventricle.

corpora allata,—paired ovoid whitish endocrine glands in insects.

corpora amylacea,—spherical bodies of nucleic acid and protein, more numerous with age, in alveoli of prostate gland; amyloid bodies.

corpora arenacea,—brain sand.

corpora bigemina,—the optic lobes of vertebrate brain, corresponding to the superior colliculi of corpora quadrigemina of mammals.

corpora cardiaca,—neuroglandular bodies between cerebral ganglia and corpora allata, in some insects.

corpora cavernosa,—erectile masses of tissue, forming anterior part of body of penis; erectile tissue of clitoris.

corpora mamillaria, — two white bodies enclosing grey matter in hypothalamus, beneath floor of third ventricle; corpora albicantia.

corpora pedunculata,—mushroom bodies, groups of association cells with axons forming bundles in protocerebrum of insects.

corpora quadrigemina, — four rounded eminences or colliculi which form dorsal part of mesencephalon.

corpus (kôr′pŭs) *n.* [L. *corpus*, body.] Body; any fairly homogeneous structure which forms part of an organ; core of apical meristem within the tunica. *Plu.* corpora.

corpus albicans,—white tissue replacing corpus luteum in non-pregnancy; mamillary body.

corpus callosum,—the broad transverse band of white substance connecting the cerebral hemispheres.

corpus fibrosum,—fibrous tissue remaining after disintegration of corpus luteum.

corpus geniculatum, — geniculate body, *q.v.*

corpus haemorrhagicum, — body developed from ruptured Graafian follicle around blood clot, and later developing into corpus luteum.

corpus highmoreanum,—mediastinum testis, *q.v.*

corpus luteum,—the glandular body developed from a Graafian follicle after extrusion of ovum; yellow body.

corpus spongiosum, — a mass of erectile tissue forming posterior wall of penis; corpus cavernosum urethrae.

corpus sterni,—sternebrae fused into a single mesosternal bone: mesosternum or gladiolus.

corpus striatum,—a mass of grey matter containing white nerve fibres and consisting of the caudate nucleus which projects into the lateral ventricle, and of the lenticular nucleus.

corpuscle (kôr'pŭsl, kôrpŭs'l) *n.* [L. *corpusculum*, small body.] A protoplasmic cell, floating freely in a fluid, or embedded in a matrix; any minute particle, as in a cell; any of various small multicellular structures, as Malpighian corpuscle, tactile corpuscle, etc.

correlation (kŏr'ĕlā'shŭn) *n.* [L.L. *correlatio*, relationship.] Mutual relationship; proportional growth; interdependence of characters, particularly of quantitative characters, measured by correlation coefficient which is plus or minus one if characters are exactly inter-related, and zero if entirely unrelated; combination of nervous impulses in sensory centres, resulting in adaptive reactions; determination of the relation of homotaxis to geologic time.

correlator (kŏr'ĕlātŏr) *n.* [L.L. *correlatio*, relationship.] A diffusible substance correlating activities of coleoptile tip and hypocotyl; auxin, *q.v.*

corrugator (kŏr'oogātŏr) *a.* [L. *corrugare*, to wrinkle.] Wrinkled or wrinkling; *appl.* muscles.

cortex (kôr'tĕks) *n.* [L. *cortex*, bark.] The extrastelar fundamental tissue of the sporophyte; outer or more superficial part of an organ.

cortical (kôr'tĭkăl) *a.* [L. *cortex*, bark.] *Pert.* the cortex.

corticate (kôr'tĭkāt) *a.* [L. *cortex*, bark.] Having a special outer covering.

corticiferous (kôr'tĭsĭf'ĕrŭs) *a.* [L. *cortex*, bark; *ferre*, to carry.] Forming or having a bark-like cortex.

corticolous (kôrtĭk'ölŭs) *a.* [L. *cortex*, bark; *colere*, to inhabit.] Inhabiting, or growing on, bark.

corticospinal (kôr'tĭköspī'năl) *a.* [L. *cortex*, bark; *spina*, spine.] *Pert.* or connecting cerebral cortex and spinal cord; *appl.* tracts.

corticosterone,—the active constituent of adrenal cortical hormone; $C_{21}H_{30}O_4$.

corticostriate (kôr'tĭköstrī'āt) *a.* [L. *cortex*, bark; *stria*, channel.] *Appl.* fibres which join corpus striatum to cerebral cortex.

corticotrophic, corticotropic, — adrenocorticotrophic, *q.v.*

cortin (kôr'tĭn) *n.* [L. *cortex*, bark.] Adrenal cortex extract, containing cortical hormones.

cortina (kôrtē'nă) *n.* [L. *cortina*, vault.] The velum in some agarics.

cortinate (kôr'tĭnāt) *a.* [L. *cortina*, vault.] Having a velum; of a cobweb-like texture.

Corti's membrane. [*A. Corti*, Italian histologist]. Tectorial membrane covering spiral organ of Corti.

Corti's organ, the organon spirale, on inner portion of membrana basilaris of ear.

Corti's rods,—double row of arching rods based on basilar membrane and forming the spiral tunnel of Corti.

coruscation (kŏrŭskā'shŭn) *n.* [L. *coruscatio*, flash.] Twinkle, rapid fluctuation in a flash or oscillation in light emission, as of fire-flies.

corymb (kôr'ĭmb) *n.* [Gk. *korymbos*, cluster of flowers.] A raceme with lower pedicels elongated so that the top is nearly flat.

corymbose (kŏrĭm'bōs) *a.* [Gk. *korymbos*, cluster of flowers.] *Pert.* or like a corymb; arranged in a corymb; corymbous.

coscinoid (kŏs'sĭnoid) *a.* [Gk. *koskinon*, sieve; *eidos*, form.] Sieve-like.

cosmine (kŏs'mĭn) *n.* [Gk. *kosmios*, regular.] The outer layer of dentine-like material in cosmoid and ganoid scales.

cosmoid (kŏs'moid) *a.* [Gk. *kosmios*, regular; *eidos*, form.] Having an outer periodically resorbed layer of cosmine, *appl.* dermal bones, scales, and lepidotrichia in Crossopterygii.

cosmopolitan (kŏzmöpŏl'ĭtăn), **cosmopolite** (kŏzmŏp'ölīt) *a.* [Gk. *kosmos*, world; *polites*, citizen.] World-wide in distribution.

costa (kŏs'tă) *n.* [L. *costa*, rib.] A rib; anything rib-like in shape, as a ridge on shell, coral, etc.; anterior vein, or margin, of insect wing; comb-rib or swimming-plate of Ctenophora; structure at base of undulating membrane in Trichomonadidae. *Plu.* costae.

costaeform (kŏs'tēfôrm) *a.* [L. *costa*, rib; *forma*, shape.] Rib-like; *appl.* unbranched parallel leaf-veins.

costal (kŏs'tăl) *a.* [L. *costa*, rib.] *Pert.* ribs or rib-like structures; *appl.* bony shields of Chelonia; *pert.* costa of insect wing; *pert.* primary brachial series in Crinoids; *pert.* a main rib.

costalia (kŏstā'lĭă) *n. plu.* [L. *costa*, rib.] The supporting plates in theca of Cladoidea.

costate (kŏs'tāt) *a.* [L. *costa*, rib.] With one or more longitudinal ribs; with ridges or costae.

coterminous (kōtĕr'mĭnŭs) *a.* [L. *cum*, with; *terminus*, end.] Of similar distribution; bordering on.

cotyle (kŏt'ĭlē) *n.* [Gk. *kotyle*, cup.] A cup-like cavity; acetabulum.

cotyledon (kŏtĭlē'dŏn) *n.* [Gk. *kotyle*, cup.] The seed-leaf, primary or first leaf of an embryonic sporophyte; a patch of villi on mammalian placenta.

cotyledonary (kŏtĭlē'dönărĭ) *a.* [Gk. *kotyle*, cup.] *Pert.* cotyledons; with villi grouped in cotyledons, *appl.* placenta.

cotyliform,—cotyloid.

cotyloid (kŏt'ĭloid) *a.* [Gk. *kotyle*, cup; *eidos*, form.] Cup-shaped; *pert.* the acetabular cavity.

cotylophorous (kŏtĭlŏf'örŭs) *a.* [Gk. *kotyle*, cup; *pherein*, to bear.] With a cotyledonary placenta.

cotype (kō'tīp) *n.* [L. *cum*, with; *typus*, image.] An additional type specimen, frequently collected in same place at same time, or a specimen from a description of which, along with others, the type is defined; syntype.

covariation (kō'vārĭā'shŭn) *n.* [L. *con*, with; *varius*, diverse.] Correlation, *q.v.*

cover scales,—small scales arranged spirally and developed directly on the axis of a cone of Coniferae; bract scales.

covert (kŭv'ërt) *n.* [F. *couvrir*, to cover.] *Appl.* feathers covering bases of quills in birds.

cowled (kowld) *a.* [L. *cucullus*, hood.] Furnished with or shaped like a hood; cucullate.

Cowper's glands [*W. Cowper*, English surgeon]. Bulbo-urethral glands, *q.v.*

coxa (kŏk'să) *n.* [L. *coxa*, hip.] Proximal joint of leg of an insect or arachnid; the hip.

coxal (kŏk'săl) *a.* [L. *coxa*, hip.] *Pert.* the coxa; *appl.* glands; *pert.* the hip.

coxite (kŏk'sīt) *n.* [L. *coxa*, hip.] One of paired lateral plates in contiguity with insect sternum; limb base bearing stylus in Thysanura.

coxocerite (kôk'sösërīt) *n.* [L. *coxa*, hip; Gk. *keras*, horn.] The proximal or basal joint of insect antenna.

coxopleurite,—catapleurite, *q.v.*

coxopodite (kŏks'öpödīt) *n.* [L. *coxa*, hip; Gk. *pous*, foot.] The proximal part of protopodite of crustacean limb; coxa of spiders.

coxosternum (kŏk'söstĕr'nŭm) *n.* [L. *coxa*, hip; *sternum*, breast-bone.] Plate formed by fusion of coxites and sternum; vinculum, in Lepidoptera.

crampon (krăm'pŏn) *n.* [F. *crampon*, adventive root.] An aerial root, as in ivy.

cranial (krā'nĭăl) *a.* [Gk. *kranion*, skull.] *Pert.* skull, or that part which encloses the brain; *appl.* bones, fossae, nerves, muscles, blood-vessels, etc.

craniate (krā'nĭāt) *a.* [Gk. *kranion*, skull.] Having a skull.

cranidium (krănĭd'ĭŭm) *n.* [Gk. *kranion*, skull; *idion*, *dim.*] Glabella together with fixed genae, in trilobites.

cranihaemal (krā'nĭhē'măl) *a.* [Gk. *kranion*, skull; *haima*, blood.] *Appl.* anterior lower portion of a sclerotome.

cranineural (krā'nĭnū'răl) *a.* [Gk. *kranion*, skull; *neuron*, nerve.] *Appl.* anterior upper portion of a sclerotome.

craniology (krā'nĭŏl'öjĭ) *n.* [Gk. *kranion*, skull; *logos*, discourse.] The study of the skull.

craniometry (krā'nĭŏm'ëtrĭ) *n.* [Gk. *kranion*, skull; *metron*, measure.] The science of the measurement of skulls.

craniosacral (krā'nĭösā'krăl) *a.* [Gk. *kranion*, skull; L. *sacer*, sacred.] *Pert.* skull and sacrum; *appl.* nerves, the parasympathetic system.

cranium (krā'nĭŭm) *n.* [Gk. *kranion*; L. *cranium*, skull.] The skull of any craniate, or more particularly, that part enclosing the brain.

craspedodromous (krăs'pëdŏd'römŭs) *a.* [Gk. *kraspedon*, edge; *dramein*, to run.] With nerves running directly from mid-rib to margin.

craspedote (krăs'pëdōt) *a.* [Gk. *kraspedon*, edge.] Having a velum.

craspedum (krăs'pëdŭm) *n.* [Gk. *kraspedon*, edge.] A mesenteric filament of sea-anemones.

crassula (krăs'ūlă) *n.* [L. *crassus*, thick.] Thickened bar on middle lamella between two bordered pits in tracheids of wood of conifers; bar of Sanio. *Plu.* crassulae.

crateriform (krātĕr'ĭfôrm) *a.* [L. *crater*, bowl; *forma*, shape.] Bowl-shaped; *appl.* receptacle.

craticular (krătĭk'ūlăr) *a.* [L. *craticula*, gridiron.] Crate-like; *appl.* stage in life-history of a diatom where new valves are formed before the old are lost.

creatine (krē'ătĭn) *n.* [Gk. *kreas*, flesh.] A nitrogenous substance found in muscles, brain, and blood of vertebrates; $C_4H_9O_2N_3$.

creatinine (krē'ătĭnĭn) *n.* [Gk. *kreas*, flesh.] A katabolic product in muscle and other tissues, excreted in urine; $C_4H_7ON_3$.

cremaster (krëmăs'tĕr) *n.* [Gk. *kremastos*, hung.] A thin muscle along the spermatic cord; a stout terminal abdominal spine in subterranean insect pupae; the anal hooks for suspension of pupae.

cremocarp (krĕm'ökârp) *n.* [Gk. *kremamai*, to hang down; *karpos*, fruit.] An inferior, dry, indehiscent, bilocular, two-seeded fruit.

crena (krē'nă) *n.* [L. *crena*, notch.] Notch in a crenate margin, as of leaf; cleft, as anal cleft; deep groove, as longitudinal sulcus of heart.

crenate (krē'nāt) *a.* [L. *crena*, notch.] With scalloped margin.

crenation (krĕnā'shŭn) *n.* [L. *crenatus*, notched.] A scalloped margin, or rounded tooth, as of leaf; crenature; notched or wrinkled appearance, as of erythrocytes exposed to hypertonic solutions.

crenulate (krĕn'ūlāt) *a.* [*Dim.* of L. *crena*, notch.] With margins minutely crenate; crenellated, crenulated.

crepis (krē'pĭs) *n.* [Gk. *krepis*, foundation.] The fundamental spicule by deposition of silica upon which a desma is formed.

crepitation (krĕpĭtā'shŭn) *n.* [L. *crepitare*, to crackle.] In insects, the discharge of a fluid with an explosive sound.

crepuscular (krĕpŭs'kūlăr) *a.* [L. *crepusculum*, dusk.] *Pert.* dusk; flying before sunrise or in twilight.

crescent (krĕs'ënt) *n.* [L. *crescere*, to grow.] A crescentic structure.

crescentiform (krĕsĕn'tĭfôrm) *a.* [L. *crescere*, to grow; *forma*, shape.] Crescent-shaped; crescentic; *appl.* mouth of Sipunculoidea.

crescents of Gianuzzi, — small crescent-shaped bodies in mucous alveoli of the salivary glands; demilunes of Heidenhain.

crest (krĕst) *n.* [L. *crista*, crest.] A ridge on a bone; a fleshy longitudinal ridge, as in newts; crown or feather tuft on head of birds; a ridge in certain seeds.

Cretaceous (krētā'shŭs) *a.* [L. *creta*, chalk.] *Appl.*, and *pert.*, the last period of the Mesozoic era; Upper Cretaceous in North America.

cribellum (krĭbĕl'ŭm) *n.* [L. *dim.* of *cribrum*, sieve.] A plate perforated by openings of silk ducts in certain spiders; a perforated chitinous plate in some insects.

cribriform (krĭb'rĭfôrm) *a.* [L. *cribrum*, sieve; *forma*, shape.] Sieve-like.

cribriform organ, — folded membrane carrying papillae in inter-radial angles of certain starfishes.

cribriform plate, — the portion of ethmoid, or of mesethmoid, perforated by many foramina for exit of olfactory nerves; lamina cribrosa.

cribrose (krĭb'rōs) *a.* [L. *cribrum*, sieve.] Having sieve-like pitted markings.

cricoid (krī'koid) *a.* [Gk. *krikos*, ring; *eidos*, form.] Ring-like; *appl.* cartilage in larynx, articulating with thyroid and arytaenoid cartilages; *appl.* placenta lacking villi on central part of disc, as in certain Edentata.

crinome (krīn'ōm) *n.* [L. *crinis*, hair.] Network formed in cytoplasm by basophil substances reacting to vital staining.

criocone (krī'ökōn) *a.* [Gk. *krios*, ram; *konos*, cone.] With uncoiled spiral shaped like ram's horn; *appl.* shell of certain ammonites.

crissal (krĭs'ăl) *a.* [L. *crissare*, to move haunches.] *Pert.* the crissum.

criss-cross,—*appl.* inheritance when offspring resemble the parent of the opposite sex.

crissum (krĭs'ŭm) *n.* [L. *crissare*, to move haunches.] The circum-cloacal region of a bird; vent-feathers or lower tail-coverts.

crista (krĭs'tă) *n.* [L. *crista*, crest.] A crest or ridge; projection from ectoloph into median valley in lophodont molars; a fine membrane attached to body of certain spirochaetes; ligule of palm-leaves.

crista acustica,—thickening, covered with neuroepithelium, of membrane lining ampullae of semicircular canals; a chordotonal structure in Orthoptera.

crista galli,—anterior median process of cribriform plate.

crista urethralis,—verumontanum, *q.v.*

cristate (krĭs'tāt) *a.* [L. *cristatus*, crested.] Crested; cristiform, shaped like a crest.

crochet (krŏshā') *n.* [F. *crochet*, small hook.] The projection of the protoloph in lophodont molars; a balancer in larval salamanders; a larval locomotory hook in insects.

crop (krŏp) *n.* [M.E. *croppe*, craw.] Sac-like dilatation of gullet of a bird; a similar structure in alimentary canal of insect or worm; ingluvies.

crosier (krō'zhyër) *n.* [M.E. *croce*, crook.] Circinate young frond of fern; hook formed by terminal cells of ascogenous hyphae; flat spiral shell, as of Spirula.

cross (krŏs) *n.* [M.E. *crois*, cross.] An organism produced by mating parents of different breeds. *v.* To hybridise.

crossing-over, — interchange of corresponding chromosome segments by homologous pairs of chromosomes during maturation.

crossover,—a chromatid formed as a result of crossing-over.

crotaphite (krŏt'ăfīt) *n.* [Gk. *krotaphos*, side of forehead.] The temporal fossa.

crotchet (krŏch'ĕt) *n.* [F. *crochet*, small hook.] A curved chaeta, notched at the end; uncinus; clavus, in spiders; crochet of larval insects.

crown (krown) *n.* [L. *corona*, crown.] The exposed part of a tooth, especially the grinding surface; distal part of antler; crest; head; cup and arms of a crinoid; corona, *q.v.*; leafy upper part of a tree.

crozier,—crosier, *q.v.*

cruciate (kroo'shĭăt, kroo'sĭăt) *a.* [L. *crux*, cross.] Cruciform; with leaves or petals in form of a cross; X-shaped or +-shaped, *appl.* muscles, ligaments; crucial.

cruciform (kroos'ĭfôrm) *a.* [L. *crux*, cross; *forma*, shape.] Arranged like the points of a cross; *appl.* division, promitosis in Plasmodiophorales.

crumena (krŭmē'nă) *n.* [L. *crumena*, purse.] A sheath for retracted stylets, as in Hemiptera.

cruor (kroo'ŏr) *n.* [L. *cruor*, blood.] The clots in coagulated blood.

cruorin (kroo'ŏrĭn) *n.* [L. *cruor*, blood.] Haemoglobin.

crura (kroo'ră) *n. plu.* [L. *crura*, legs.] The shanks; leg-like or columnar structures; lumbar part of diaphragm muscle fibres; proximal processes of corpora cavernosa penis; branches of incus and stapes; pillars of subcutaneous inguinal ring; posterior pillars of fornix; crura cerebri, *q.v.*

crura cerebri,—the cerebral peduncles, two cylindrical masses forming the ventrolateral portion of midbrain.

crural (kroo'răl) *a.* [L. *crus*, leg.] *Pert.* the thigh.

crureus (kroorē'ŭs) *n.* [L. *crus*, leg.] Vastus intermedius muscle of thigh.

crus (krŭs) *n.* [L. *crus*, leg.] The shank; any leg-like organ; common duct of superior and posterior semicircular canals; anterior end of helix of external ear. *Plu.* crura.

crusta (krŭs'tă) *n.* [L. *crusta*, shell.] Ventral part or base or pes of cerebral peduncles; cement layer of teeth, crusta petrosa.

crustaceous (krŭstā'shŭs) *a.* [L. *crusta*, shell.] With crustacean characteristics; crustose, *q.v.*

crustose (krŭs'tōs) *a.* [L. *crusta*, shell.] Forming crusts on substratum, *appl.* lichens.

crymophil (krī'mŏfĭl) *a.* [Gk. *krymos*, frost; *philein*, to love.] Cryophil, psychrophil.

cryophil (krī'ŏfĭl) *a.* [Gk. *kryos*, chill; *philein*, to love.] Thriving at a low temperature; cryophilic.

cryophylactic (krī'ŏfĭlăk'tĭk) *a.* [Gk. *kryos*, frost; *phylaktikos*, preservative.] Resistant to low temperatures; *appl.* bacteria.

cryoplankton (krī'ŏplăngk'tŏn) *n.* [Gk. *kryos*, frost; *plangktos*, wandering.] Glacial and polar plankton; algal communities thriving on snow.

cryoscopic (krī'ŏskŏp'ĭk) *a.* [Gk. *kryos*, frost; *skopein*, to view.] *Appl.* method of determining osmotic pressure, using a freezing-point depression.

crypt (krĭpt) *n.* [Gk. *kryptos*, hidden.] A simple glandular tube or cavity; pit of stoma; depression in uterine mucous membrane.

cryptic (krĭp'tĭk) *a.* [Gk. *kryptos*, hidden.] *Appl.* protective coloration facilitating concealment; *appl.* polymorphism due to presence of recessive genes; *appl.* species extremely similar as to external appearance but which do not normally interbreed.

cryptocarp (krĭp'tökârp) *n.* [Gk. *kryptos*, hidden; *karpos*, fruit.] A fruit-like structure, the sporophyte phase in red algae; cystocarp.

cryptogam (krĭp'tögăm) *n.* [Gk. *kryptos*, hidden; *gamos*, union.] A plant without apparent reproductive organs: a spore-plant. *Cf.* phanerogam.

cryptogene (krĭp'töjēn) *a.* [Gk. *kryptos*, hidden; *genos*, origin.] Of unknown descent; having an indeterminate phylogeny.

cryptohaplomitosis (krĭp'tŏhăp'lömĭtō'sĭs) *n.* [Gk. *kryptos*, hidden; *haploos*, simple; *mitos*, thread.] Type of cell-division in some flagellates where chromatin divides into two masses which pass to opposite poles without spireme-formation.

cryptomere (krĭp'tömēr) *n.* [Gk. *kryptos*, hidden; *meros*, part.] A hidden recessive hereditary factor.

cryptomitosis (krĭp'tömĭtō'sĭs) *n.* [Gk. *kryptos*, hidden; *mitos*, thread.] Division of unicellular organisms, in which chromatin assembles in the equatorial region without apparent chromosome formation.

cryptonema (krĭp'tönē'mă) *n.* [Gk. *kryptos*, hidden; *nema*, thread.] A filamentous outgrowth or paraphysis in a cryptostoma.

cryptoneurous (krĭp'tönū'rŭs) *a.* [Gk. *kryptos*, hidden; *neuron*, nerve.] With no definite or distinct nervous system.

cryptophyte (krĭp'töfīt) *n.* [Gk. *kryptos*, hidden; *phyton*, plant.] A plant perennating by means of rhizomes, corms, or bulbs under ground, or of under water buds.

cryptoplasm (krĭp'töplăzm) *n.* [Gk. *kryptos*, hidden; *plasma*, form.] The non-granular portion of cytoplasm.

cryptoptile (krĭp'tötīl, -ptīl) *n.* [Gk. *kryptos*, hidden; *ptilon*, feather.] A feather filament, developed from papilla.

cryptorchid (krĭptôr'kĭd) *a.* [Gk. *kryptos*, hidden; *orchis*, testis.] Having testes abdominal in position.

cryptorhetic (krĭp'törĕt'ĭk) *a.* [Gk. *kryptos*, hidden; *rhein*. to flow.] Secreting internally; endocrine.

cryptosolenial (krĭp'tösōlē'nĭăl) *a.* [Gk. *kryptos*, hidden; *solen*, channel.] *Appl.* region of attachment of Malpighian vessels to hind-gut in certain Coleoptera.

cryptostomata (krĭp'töstŏm'ătă) *n. plu.* [Gk. *kryptos*, hidden; *stoma*, mouth.] Non-sexual conceptacles in Fucaceae. *Sing.* cryptostoma.

cryptozoic (krĭp'tözō'ĭk) *a.* [Gk. *kryptos*, hidden; *zoon*, animal.] *Appl.* fauna dwelling in darkness, or under stones, bark, etc.

cryptozoite (krĭp'tözō'īt) *n.* [Gk. *kryptos*, hidden; *zoon*, animal.] Stage of sporozoite when living in tissues before entering blood.

crypts of Lieberkühn,—*see* Lieberkühn's crypts.

crystallin (krĭs'tălĭn) *n.* [Gk. *krystallos*, ice.] A globulin which is the principal constituent of lens of eye.

crystalline (krĭs'tălīn) *a.* [Gk. *krystallinos*, crystalline.] Transparent; *appl.* various structures.

crystalline style,—a proteid hyaline rod with amylolytic function, in alimentary canal of some molluscs.

crystalloid (krĭs'tăloid) *n.* [Gk. *krystallos*, ice; *eidos*, form.] A substance which in solution readily diffuses through an animal membrane; *opp.* colloid; a protein crystal found in certain plant cells.

crystal-sand,—a deposit of minute crystals of calcium oxalate, as in Solanaceae.

crystal-spore,—an isospore containing a crystal, of Radiolaria.

cteinophyte (tīn'öfīt, ktīn'öfīt) *n.* [Gk. *kteinein*, to kill; *phyton*, plant.] A parasitic plant, *e.g.* fungus, which destroys its host.

cteinotrophic (tī'nötrŏf'ĭk, ktī-) *a.* [Gk. *kteinein*, to kill; *trophe*, nourishment.] Parasitic and destroying the host, as cteinophytes.

ctene (tēn, ktēn) *n.* [Gk. *kteis*, comb.] The swimming-plates of ctenophores.

ctenidium (těnĭd'ĭŭm, ktěnĭd'ĭŭm) *n.* [Gk. *kteis*, comb; *idion*, *dim.*] The respiratory apparatus in molluscs, feather-like or comb-like in appearance; a row of spines forming a comb in some insects.

ctenocyst (těn'ösĭst, ktěn'ösĭst) *n.* [Gk. *kteis*, comb; *kystis*, bladder.] Aboral sense organ of Ctenophora.

ctenoid (těn'oid, ktěn'oid) *a.* [Gk. *kteis*, comb; *eidos*, form.] With comb-like margin, as scales.

ctenophoral (těnŏf'örăl, ktěnŏf'örăl) *a.* [Gk. *kteis*, comb; *pherein*, to bear.] Supplied with swimming-plates.

ctenose (těn'ōs, ktěn'ōs) *a.* [Gk. *kteis*, comb.] Comb-like; *appl.* type of seta.

ctetology (tētŏl'öjĭ, ktē-) *n.* [Gk. *ktetos*, acquired; *logos*, discourse.] Aspect of biology concerned with acquired characters.

ctetosome (tē'tösōm, ktē') *n.* [Gk. *ktetos*, acquired; *soma*, body.] A supernumerary chromosome associated with a sex chromosome during meiosis.

cubical (kū'bĭkăl) *a.* [L. *cubus*, cube.] *Appl.* cells as long as broad.

cubital (kū'bĭtăl) *a.* [L. *cubitalis*, of elbow.] *Pert.* the elbow; *appl.* joint including the humero-ulnar, humeroradial, and proximal radio-ulnar articulations; *pert.* the ulna or cubitus. *n.* A secondary wing-quill, connected with the ulna.

cubitus (kū'bĭtŭs) *n.* [L. *cubitum*, elbow.] The ulna, forearm; primary vein in an insect wing.

cuboid (kū'boid) *a.* [Gk. *kyboeides*, cube-like.] Nearly cubic in shape. *n.* Outermost of distal tarsal bones.

cuboidal (kūboid'ăl) *a.* [Gk. *kyboeides*, cube-like.] *Pert.* the cuboid.

cucullate (kū'kŭlāt, kūkŭl'āt) *a.* [L. *cucullus*, hood.] With hood-like sepals or petals; with prothorax hood-shaped.

cucullus (kūkŭl'ŭs) *n.* [L. *cucullus*, hood.] A hood-shaped structure; upper part of harpe, in Lepidoptera.

cuiller (kwē'yā) *n.* [F. *cuiller*, spoon.] Spoon-like terminal portion of male insect clasper.

cuirass (kwĭrăs') *n.* [F. *cuirasse*, leathern jacket.] Bony plates or scales arranged like a cuirass; a lorica, *q.v.*

culm (kŭlm) *n.* [L. *culmus*, stalk.] The stem of grasses and sedges.

culmen (kŭl'měn) *n.* [L. *culmen*, summit.] Median longitudinal ridge of a bird's beak; part of superior vemis, continuous laterally with quadrangular lobules of anterior lobe of cerebellum.

cultellus (kŭltěl'ŭs) *n.* [L. *cultellus*, little knife.] A sharp knife-like organ, one of mouth-parts of certain blood-sucking flies.

culture (kŭl'tūr) *n.* [L. *cultura*; *colere*, to till.] The cultivation of micro-organisms or tissues in prepared media.

cumulose (kū'mūlōs) *a.* [L. *cumulus*, heap.] *Appl.* deposits consisting chiefly of plant remains, *e.g.* peat.

cumulus (kū'mūlŭs) *n.* [L. *cumulus*, heap.] The mass of epithelial cells bulging into cavity of an ovarian follicle and in which ovum is embedded; cumulus oophorus, discus proligerus.

cuneate (kū'nëāt) *a.* [L. *cuneatus*, wedge-shaped.] Wedge-shaped; *appl.* leaves with broad abruptly-pointed apex and tapering to the base; *appl.* a fasciculus and tubercle formed by a grey nucleus at posterior end of rhomboid fossa of medulla oblongata.

cuneiform (kūnē'ĭfôrm) *a.* [L. *cuneus*, wedge; *forma*, shape.] Wedge-shaped; *appl.* distal tarsal bones; *appl.* a carpal bone, os triquetrum; *appl.* two small cartilages of larynx.

cuneus (kū'nëŭs) *n.* [L. *cuneus*, wedge.] A division of elytron of certain insects; a wedge-shaped area of the occipital lobe between calcarine fissure and medial part of parieto-occipital fissure.

cup (kŭp) *n.* [A.S. *cuppe*, cup.] Any structure resembling a cup.

cupula (kū′pūlă) *n.* [L. *cupula*, little tub.] The bony apex of cochlea; the part of pleura over the apex of lung; cupule, *q.v.*

cupulate (kū′pūlāt) *a.* [L. *cupula*, little tub.] Cup-shaped; *appl.* certain aecidia; having a cup-shaped structure or a cupule.

cupule (kūp′ūl) *n.* [L. *cupula*, little tub.] The involucre of female flower of oak, etc.; the gemmae-bearing cup of Marchantia; a small sucker of various animals.

curviserial (kŭr′vĭsē′rĭăl) *a.* [L. *curvus*, curve; *series*, row.] *Appl.* phyllotaxis in which divergence is such that orthostichies themselves are slightly twisted spirally.

cushion (koosh′ŭn) *n.* [M.E. *cuis-chen*, cushion.] The central thick region in prothallus of fern; *appl.* habitus of many plants, as in certain alpine species; torus tubarius, prominence behind pharyngeal opening of Eustachian tube; tubercle or elevation of laryngeal surface of epiglottis; embryonic endocardial thickening of wall of atrial canal; pulvillus, *q.v.*

cusp (kŭsp) *n.* [L. *cuspis*, point.] A prominence, as on teeth; a sharp point.

cuspidate (kŭs′pĭdāt) *a.* [L. *cuspi-dare*, to make pointed.] Terminating in a point; *appl.* leaves, teeth.

cutaneous (kūtā′nëŭs) *a.* [L. *cutis*, skin.] *Pert.* the skin.

cuticle (kū′tĭkl) *n.* [L. *cuticula*, thin skin.] An outer skin or pellicle; the epidermis; cuticula.

cuticular (kūtĭk′ūlăr) *a.* [L. *cuticula*, thin skin.] *Pert.* the cuticle or external integument; *appl.* transpiration through the cuticle.

cuticularisation (kūtĭk′ūlărīzā′shŭn) *n.* [L. *cuticula*, thin skin.] Cutinisation in external layers of epidermal cells.

cutin (kū′tĭn) *n.* [L. *cutis*, skin.] A substance allied to cellulose found in external layers of thickened epidermal cells.

cutinisation (kū′tĭnīzā′shŭn) *n.* [L. *cutis*, skin.] The deposition of cutin in cell-wall, thereby forming a cuticle.

cutis (kū′tĭs) *n.* [L. *cutis*, skin.] The corium, or deeper layer of the skin; layer investing pileus and stipe.

cutocellulose (kū′tösĕl′ūlōs) *n.* [L. *cutis*, skin; *cellula*, small cell.] Cellulose with cutin, as in plant epidermis.

cutose (kū′tōs) *n.* [L. *cutis*, skin.] Cutin, *q.v.*

Cuvier, ducts of [*G.L.C.F.D. Cuvier*, French comparative anatomist]. Short veins opening into sinus venosus, and formed by union of anterior and posterior cardinal veins.

Cuvierian organs,—glandular tubes extending from cloaca of holothurians.

cyanic (sīăn′ĭk) *a.* [Gk. *kyanos*, dark blue.] Blue, bluish; *appl.* flowers, birds' eggs.

cyanin (sī′ănĭn) *n.* [Gk. *kyanos*, cornflower.] The blue pigment or anthocyanin of the cornflower; $C_{27}H_{30}O_{16}$.

cyanocobalamin,—vitamin B_{12a}.

cyanogenesis (sī′ănöjĕn′ësĭs) *n.* [Gk. *kyanos*, blue; *genesis*, origin.] The elaboration of hydrocyanic acid, prussic acid, as in certain plants.

cyanophil (sīăn′öfĭl) *a.* [Gk. *kyanos*, blue; *philein*, to love.] With special affinity for blue or green stains; *appl.* cell structure.

cyanophycin (sī′ănöfī′sĭn) *n.* [Gk. *kyanos*, blue; *phykos*, seaweed.] Protein reserve forming granules in peripheral region of cells in blue-green algae; β granules.

cyanophyll (sīăn′öfĭl) *n.* [Gk. *kyanos*, blue; *phyllon*, leaf.] A bluish-green colouring matter in plants.

cyathium (sī′ăthĭŭm) *n.* [Gk. *kyathos*, cup.] The peculiar inflorescence in Euphorbia, a cup-shaped involucre with stamens and stalked gynoecium, each stamen and the gynoecium being a separate flower.

cyathozooid (sī′ăthözō′oid) *n.* [Gk. *kyathos*, cup; *zoon*, animal; *eidos*, shape.] The primary zooid in certain tunicates.

cyathus (sī'ăthŭs) *n.* [L. *cyathus*, cup.] A small cup-shaped organ; the gemma-cup of Marchantia.

cybernetics (sībĕrnĕt'ĭks) *n.* [Gk. *kybernētikos*, skilled in governing.] Science of communication and control, as by nervous system and brain.

cycle (sīkl) *n.* [Gk. *kyklos*, circle.] The circulation of a fluid through a definite series of vessels; recurrent series of phenomena, as life-cycle, ovarian cycle, etc.

cyclic (sī'klĭk) *a.* [Gk. *kyklos*, circle.] Having parts of flower arranged in whorls; cyclical; periodic.

cyclocoelic (sī'klōsē'lĭk) *a.* [Gk. *kyklos*, circle; *koilia*, intestines.] With the intestine coiled in one or more distinct spirals.

cyclogenous (sīklŏj'ënŭs) *a.* [Gk. *kyklos*, circle; *gennaein*, to produce.] Exogenous; *appl.* a stem growing in concentric circles.

cyclogeny (sīklŏj'ënĭ) *n.* [Gk. *kyklos*, circle; *genos*, generation.] Production of a succession of different morphological types in a life-cycle.

cycloid (sī'kloid) *a.* [Gk. *kyklos*, circle; *eidos*, shape.] *Appl.* scales with evenly curved free border.

cyclomorial (sī'klōmŏr'ĭăl) *a.* [Gk. *kyklos*, circle; *morion*, constituent part.] *Appl.* scales, growing in area by apposition of marginal zones, as in Palaeozoic elasmobranchs.

cyclomorphosis (sī'klōmôr'fōsĭs) *n.* [Gk. *kyklos*, circle; *morphosis*, form.] A cycle of changes in form, as seasonal changes in daphnids.

cyclopean (sīklōpē'ăn), **cyclopic** (sīklŏp'ĭk) *a.* [Gk. *kyklos*, circle; *ops*, eye.] *Appl.* single median eye developed under certain artificial conditions instead of the normal pair.

cyclosis (sīklō'sĭs) *n.* [Gk. *kyklosis*, whirling round.] Circulation, as of protoplasm within a cell.

cyclospermous (sī'klōspĕr'mŭs) *a.* [Gk. *kyklos*, circle; *sperma*, seed.] With embryo coiled in a circle or spiral.

cyclospondylic (sī'klōspŏndĭl'ĭk) *a.* [Gk. *kyklos*, circle; *sphondylos*, vertebra.] *Appl.* centra in which the internal calcareous matter is confined to the middle zone.

cyclospondylous (sī'klōspŏn'dĭlŭs) *a.* [Gk. *kyklos*, circle; *sphondylos*, vertebra.] *Appl.* vertebra formed of successive concentric layers of cartilage; also cyclospondylic.

cyesis (sīē'sĭs) *n.* [Gk. *kyesis*, conception.] Pregnancy.

cylindrical (sĭlĭn'drĭkăl) *a.* [Gk. *kylindros*, cylinder.] *Appl.* leaves rolled on themselves, or to solid cylinder-like leaves; *appl.* a type of silk gland in spiders; tubuliform.

cymba (sĭm'bă) *n.* [L. *cymba*, boat.] Upper part of concha of ear; a boat-shaped sponge spicule.

cymbiform (sĭm'bĭfôrm) *a.* [L. *cymba*, boat; *forma*, shape.] Boat-shaped; navicular, scaphoid.

cymbium (sĭmbī'ŭm) *n.* [Gk. *kymbion*, small boat.] Boat-shaped tarsus of pedipalpus in certain spiders.

cyme (sīm) *n.* [L. *cyma*, young sprout.] Any determinate inflorescence.

cymose (sī'mōs) *a.* [L. *cyma*, young sprout.] Sympodially branched, *appl.* inflorescence.

cymotrichous (kīmŏt'rĭkŭs, sī-) *a.* [Gk. *kyma*, wave; *thrix*, hair.] Having wavy hair.

cynarrhodium (sĭnărō'dĭŭm), **cynarrhodon** (sĭnărōd'ŏn) *n.* [Gk. *kyon*, dog; *rhodon*, rose.] An etaerio with achenes placed on concave thalamus.

cynopodous (sĭnŏp'ōdŭs) *a.* [Gk. *kyon*, dog; *pous*, foot.] With non-retractile claws.

cyphella (sĭfĕl'ă) *n.* [Gk. *kyphella*, hollow of ear.] Small cavity on thallus of certain lichens.

cyphonautes (sī'fōnôt'ēz) *n.* [Gk. *kyphos*, bent; *nautes*, sailor.] Young free-swimming larva of certain Polyzoa.

cypsela (sĭpsĕl'ă) *n.* [Gk. *kypsele*, hollow vessel.] An inferior bicarpellary achene, as in Compositae.

cyst (sĭst) *n.* [Gk. *kystis*, bladder.] The enclosing membrane round a resting cell or apocyte; a bladder or air vesicle in certain seaweeds; abnormal sac containing fluid.

cysteine (sĭs'tēĭn) *n.* [Gk. *kystis*, bladder.] A reduction product of cystine, occurring in urinary bladder concretions; $C_3H_7O_2NS$.

cystenchyma (sĭstĕng'kĭmă) *n.* [Gk. *kystis*, bladder; *engchyma*, infusion.] A parenchyma in sponges with large vesicular cell-structure.

cystencytes (sĭs'tĕnsīts) *n. plu.* [Gk. *kystis*, bladder; *en*, in; *kytos*, hollow.] In sponges, collencytes which have acquired a vesicular structure.

cystic (sĭs'tĭk) *a.* [Gk. *kystis*, bladder.] *Pert.* a cyst; *pert.* gall-bladder or to urinary bladder.

cysticercoid (sĭs'tĭsĕr'koid) *a.* [Gk. *kystis*, bladder; *kerkos*, tail; *eidos*, form.] *Appl.* the bladderworm stage of tapeworms.

cysticercus (sĭs'tĭsĕr'kŭs) *n.* [Gk. *kystis*, bladder; *kerkos*, tail.] The larval form or bladderworm stage of certain tapeworms.

cysticolous (sĭstĭk'ŏlŭs) *a.* [Gk. *kystis*, bladder; L. *colere*, to inhabit.] Living in a cyst.

cystid (sĭs'tĭd) *n.* [Gk. *kystis*, bladder; *idion*, *dim.*] A fossil Cystoid; a cystidium, *q.v.*

cystidiform (sĭstĭd'ĭfôrm) *a.* [Gk. *kystis*, bladder; *idion*, *dim.*; L. *forma*, form.] *Appl.* clavate cells on gill margins in agarics.

cystidium (sĭstĭd'ĭŭm) *n.* [Gk. *kystis*, bladder; *idion*, *dim.*] A hair-like inflated cell in the hymenial layer of some fungi.

cystine (sĭs'tēn) *n.* [Gk. *kystis*, bladder.] Amino acid found in plants, egg albumin and keratin; dicysteine, $C_6H_{12}O_4N_2S_2$.

cystoarian (sĭstōă'rĭăn) *a.* [Gk. *kystis*, bladder; *oarion*, small egg.] *Appl.* gonads when enclosed in coelomic sacs, as in most teleosts. *Opp.* gymnoarian.

cystocarp (sĭs'tŏkârp) *n.* [Gk. *kystis*, bladder; *karpos*, fruit.] A cyst arising from carpogonial branch and containing spores, in certain Rhodophyceae; cryptocarp.

cystocyte (sĭs'tŏsīt) *n.* [Gk. *kystis*, bladder; *kytos*, hollow.] Cystencyte, *q.v.*; a granular blood-cell in insects; coagulocyte.

cystogenous (sĭstŏj'ēnŭs) *a.* [Gk. *kystis*, bladder; *-genes*, producing.] Cyst-forming; *appl.* large nucleated cells which secrete the cyst, in cercaria.

cystolith (sĭs'tŏlĭth) *n.* [Gk. *kystis*, bladder; *lithos*, stone.] A mass of calcium carbonate, occasionally of silica, formed on ingrowths of epidermal cell walls in some plants; a vesical calculus.

cyston (sĭs'tŏn) *n.* [Gk. *kystis*, bladder.] A dactylozooid modified for excretory purposes, in Siphonophora.

cystospore (sĭs'tŏspōr) *n.* [Gk. *kystis*, bladder; *sporos*, seed.] A carpospore; a cyst containing a zoospore.

cystozooid (sĭs'tŏzō'oid) *n.* [Gk. *kystis*, bladder; *zoon*, animal; *eidos*, form.] The body portion of a metacestode, *opp.* acanthozooid.

cytase (sī'tās) *n.* [Gk. *kytos*, hollow.] A cellulose digesting or hydrolysing enzyme; protopectinase.

cytaster (sītăs'tĕr) *n.* [Gk. *kytos*, hollow; *aster*, star.] A star-shaped achromatinic figure consisting of attraction-sphere and aster rays; aster, *opp.* karyaster.

cytes (sīts) *n. plu.* [Gk. *kytos*, hollow.] Spermatocyte and oocyte stages of germ-cell formation; auxocytes.

cytobiotaxis,—cytoclesis, *q.v.*; cytotaxis, *q.v.*

cytoblast (sī'tŏblăst) *n.* [Gk. *kytos*, hollow; *blastos*, bud.] The cell nucleus; a hypothetical unit, *q.v.*

cytoblastema (sī'tŏblăs'tēmă) *n.* [Gk. *kytos*, hollow; *blastema*, growth.] The formative material from which cells were supposed to arise.

cytocentrum (sī'tŏsĕn'trŭm) *n.* [Gk. *kytos*, hollow; *kentron*, centre.] Centrosome; idiozome.

cytochroic (sī'tökrō'ĭk) *a.* [Gk. *kytos*, hollow; *chros*, complexion.] With pigmented cytoplasm.

cytochrome (sī'tökrōm) *n.* [Gk. *kytos*, hollow; *chroma*, colour.] A chromoprotein essential for oxidation-reduction processes in plant and animal cells; histohaematin; myohaematin.

cytochylema (sī'tökīlē'mă) *n.* [Gk. *kytos*, hollow; *chylos*, juice.] Cytolymph, *q.v.*

cytoclesis (sī'töklē'sĭs) *n.* [Gk. *kytos*, hollow; *klesis*, summons.] The influence of a cell group or placode upon development or differentiation of neighbouring cells; *cf.* organiser.

cytococcus (sī'tökŏk'ŭs) *n.* [Gk. *kytos*, hollow; *kokkos*, kernel.] The nucleus of a fertilised egg.

cytocyst (sī'tösĭst) *n.* [Gk. *kytos*, hollow; *kystis*, bladder.] The envelope formed by remains of host-cell within which a protozoan parasite multiplies.

cytode (sī'tōd) *n.* [Gk. *kytos*, hollow; *eidos*, form.] A non-nucleated protoplasmic mass.

cytoderm (sī'töděrm) *n.* [Gk. *kytos*, hollow; *derma*, skin.] A cell-wall.

cytodiaeresis (sī'tödīē'rēsĭs) *n.* [Gk. *kytos*, hollow; *diairesis*, division.] Mitosis; karyokinesis.

cytogamy (sītŏg'ămĭ) *n.* [Gk. *kytos*, hollow; *gamos*, marriage.] Cell-conjugation.

cytogene,—plasmagene, *q.v.*

cytogenesis (sī'töjĕn'ēsĭs) *n.* [Gk. *kytos*, hollow; *genesis*, descent.] Development or formation of cells.

cytogenetic (sī'töjĕnĕt'ĭk) *a.* [Gk. *kytos*, hollow; *genesis*, descent.] *Pert.* cytogenesis; *pert.* cytogenetics; *appl.* map showing location of genes within a chromosome.

cytogenetics (sī'töjĕnĕt'ĭks) *n.* [Gk. *kytos*, hollow; *genesis*, descent.] Genetics in relation to cytology; the cytological aspect of genetics.

cytogenous (sītŏj'ënŭs) *a.* [Gk. *kytos*, hollow; *genos*, offspring.] Producing cells; *appl.* lymphatic tissue.

cytoglobin (sī'töglō'bĭn) *n.* [Gk. *kytos*, hollow; L. *globus*, globe.] A protein which retards coagulation of blood.

cytohyaloplasma (sī'töhī'ălöplăz'mă) *n.* [Gk. *kytos*, hollow; *hyalos*, glass; *plasma*, mould.] The substance of the cytomitome; hyaloplasm.

cytokinesis (sī'tökĭnē'sĭs) *n.* [Gk. *kytos*, hollow; *kinesis*, movement.] Changes attending general cytoplasm during karyokinesis; the separation of daughter-cells following division of parent cell.

cytology (sītŏl'öjĭ) *n.* [Gk. *kytos*, hollow vessel; *logos*, discourse.] The science dealing with structure, functions, and life-history of cells.

cytolymph (sī'tölĭmf) *n.* [Gk. *kytos*, hollow; L. *lympha*, water.] Cell-sap; the fluid part of cytoplasm.

cytolysin (sī'tölī'sĭn) *n.* [Gk. *kytos*, hollow; *lysis*, loosing.] A substance inducing cytolysis.

cytolysis (sītŏl'ĭsĭs) *n.* [Gk. *kytos*, hollow; *lysis*, loosing.] Cell-dissolution; cell-degeneration.

cytome (sī'tōm) *n.* [Gk. *kytos*, hollow.] The microsome or cytosome system of a cell.

cytomeres (sī'tömērz) *n. plu.* [Gk. *kytos*, hollow; *meros*, part.] Cells in Caryotropha formed by division of schizont and giving rise to merozoites; agametoblasts; non-nuclear portions of sperms.

cytometry (sītŏm'ētrĭ) *n.* [Gk. *kytos*, hollow; *metreo*, to compute.] Count of cells; blood count.

cytomicrosome (sī'tömī'krösōm) *n.* [Gk. *kytos*, hollow; *mikros*, small; *soma*, body.] A microsome of cytoplasm, *opp.* karyomicrosome.

cytomitome (sī'tömĭtōm) *n.* [Gk. *kytos*, hollow; *mitos*, thread.] The cytoplasmic thread-work.

cytomorphosis (sī'tömôr'fōsĭs) *n.* [Gk. *kytos*, hollow; *morphosis*, shaping.] The life-history of cells; the series of structural modifications of cells or successive generations of cells; cellular change, as in senescence.

cytoidon (sī'tŏn) *n.* [Gk. *kytos*, hollow.] The body of a nerve cell; neurocyton.

cytophan (sī'tŏfăn) *n.* [Gk. *kytos*, hollow; *phaneros*, visible.] Ovoid matrix surrounding karyophans in spironeme and axoneme fibres in infusorian stalk.

cytopharynx (sī'tŏfăr'ĭngks) *n.* [Gk. *kytos*, hollow; *pharyngx*, gullet.] A tube-like structure leading from mouth into endoplasm in certain protozoa.

cytophil (sī'tŏfĭl) *a.* [Gk. *kytos*, hollow; *philein*, to love.] *Pert.* haptophorous groups; having an affinity for cells.

cytophore (sī'tŏfōr) *n.* [Gk. *kytos*, hollow; *phora*, burden.] A cell regarded as bearer of parasitic Sporozoa; central non-nucleated protoplasm in sperm morula; blastophore.

cytoplasm (sī'tŏplăzm) *n.* [Gk. *kytos*, hollow; *plasma*, mould.] Substance of cell-body exclusive of nucleus; *cf.* karyoplasm.

cytoproct (sī'tŏprŏkt), **cytopyge** (sī'tŏpīj') *n.* [Gk. *kytos*, hollow; *proktos*, anus; *pyge*, rump.] A cell-anus.

cytoreticulum (sī'tŏrĕtĭk'ūlŭm) *n.* [Gk. *kytos*, hollow; L. *reticulum*, little net.] The cytoplasmic thread-work; cytomitome; spongioplasm.

cytosine (sī'tŏsĭn) *n.* [Gk. *kytos*, hollow.] A cleavage product of nucleic acid; $C_4H_6N_3O$.

cytosome (sī'tŏsōm) *n.* [Gk. *kytos*, hollow; *soma*, body.] The cytoplasmic part of a cell; a microsome, *q.v.*

cytostome (sī'tŏstōm) *n.* [Gk. *kytos*, hollow; *stoma*, mouth.] A cell-mouth.

cytotaxis (sī'tŏtăk'sĭs) *n.* [Gk. *kytos*, hollow; *taxis*, arrangement.] Rearrangement of cells on stimulation.

cytothesis (sĭtŏth'ĕsĭs) *n.* [Gk. *kytos*, hollow; *thesis*, arranging.] Regenerative tendency of a cell.

cytotoxin (sī'tŏtŏk'sĭn) *n.* [Gk. *kytos*, hollow; *toxikon*, poison.] A cell-poisoning substance formed in blood serum; cytolysin; enzymoid.

cytotrophoblast (sī'tŏtrŏf'ŏblăst) *n.* [Gk. *kytos*, hollow; *trophe*, nourishment; *blastos*, bud.] Inner layer of trophoblast, layer of Langhans.

cytotropism (sĭtŏt'rŏpĭzm) *n.* [Gk. *kytos*, hollow; *trope*, turning.] The mutual attraction of two or more cells.

cytozoic (sī'tŏzō'ĭk) *a.* [Gk. *kytos*, hollow; *zoon*, animal.] Living within a cell; *appl.* sporozoan trophozoite.

cytozyme (sī'tŏzīm) *a.* [Gk. *kytos*, hollow; *zyme*, leaven.] Thrombokinase, *q.v.*

cytula (sĭt'ūlă) *n.* [Gk. *kytos*, hollow.] The fertilised ovum or parent cell.

D

dacryocyst (dăk'rĭŏsĭst) *n.* [Gk. *dakryon*, tear; *kystis*, bladder.] Lacrimal sac; saccus lacrimalis.

dacryoid (dăk'rĭoid) *a.* [Gk. *dakryon*, tear; *eidos*, shape.] Tear-shaped; lacrimiform; *appl.* spores.

dacryon (dăk'rĭŏn) *n.* [Gk. *dakryon*, tear.] Point of junction of anterior border of lacrimal with frontal bone and frontal process of maxilla.

dactyl (dăk'tĭl) *n.* [Gk. *daktylos*, finger.] A digit; finger, or toe; terminal ventral projection of praetarsus in scorpions; dactylus.

dactylar (dăk'tĭlăr) *a.* [Gk. *daktylos*, finger.] *Pert.* finger or digit.

dactyline,—dactyloid.

dactylognathite (dăk'tĭlŏg'năthīt) *n.* [Gk. *daktylos*, finger; *gnathos*, jaw.] Terminal segment of a maxillipede.

dactyloid (dăk'tĭloid) *a.* [Gk. *daktylos*, finger; *eidos*, form.] Like a finger or fingers.

dactylopatagium (dăk'tĭlŏpătā'jĭŭm) *n.* [Gk. *daktylos*, finger; L. *patagium*, border.] Ectopatagium, *q.v.*

dactylopodite (dăk'tĭlŏp'ŏdīt) *n.* [Gk. *daktylos*, finger; *pous*, foot.] Distal joint in certain limbs of Crustacea; metatarsus and tarsus, of spiders.

dactylopore (dăk'tĭlōpōr') *n.* [Gk. *daktylos*, finger; *poros*, channel.] Opening in skeleton of Milleporina, for protrusion of a dactylozooid.

dactylopterous (dăk'tĭlŏp'tërŭs) *a.* [Gk. *daktylos*, finger; *pteron*, wing.] With anterior rays of pectoral fins more or less free.

dactylozooid (dăk'tĭlözō'oid) *n.* [Gk. *daktylos*, finger; *zoon*, animal; *eidos*, form.] A hydroid modified for catching prey, long, with tentacles or short knobs, with or without a mouth.

dactylus (dăk'tĭlŭs) *n.* [Gk. *daktylos*, finger.] Part of tarsus of an insect; dactyl of scorpions.

dart (dârt) *n.* [O.F. *dart*, dagger.] Any structure resembling a dart; *appl.* a crystalline structure in molluscs.

dart sac,—a small sac, containing a limy dart, attached to vagina near its orifice in some gastropods.

dartoid (dâr'toid) *a.* [Gk. *dartos*, flayed.] *Pert.* the dartos.

dartos (dâr'tŏs) *n.* [Gk. *dartos*, flayed.] Tunica dartos, a thin layer of non-striped muscle united to skin of scrotum or of labia majora.

Darwinian tubercle,—the slight prominence on helix, of external ear, near the point where it bends downwards.

Darwinism (dâr'wĭnĭzm) *n.* [*C. Darwin*]. The theory of origin of species by natural selection working on slight variations that occur, thereby selecting those best adapted to survive.

dasypaedes (dăs'ĭpē'dēz) *n. plu.* [Gk. *dasys*, hairy; *pais*, child.] Birds whose young are downy at hatching.

dasyphyllous (dăs'ĭfĭl'ŭs) *a.* [Gk. *dasys*, hairy; *phyllon*, leaf.] With thickly haired leaves.

dauermodification (dow'ërmŏdĭfĭkā'shŭn) *n.* [Ger. *Dauer*, duration; L. *modificatio*, modification.] A change induced by environmental factors and persisting for several generations but not permanently, the organism eventually reverting to type.

daughter (dô'tër) *n.* [A.S. *dohtor*, daughter.] Offspring of first generation with no reference to sex, as daughter-cell, daughter-nucleus, etc.; daughter-chromosome: a chromatid during anaphase.

day-neutral,—*appl.* plants in which flowering can be induced by either a long or a short photoperiod. *Cf.* long-day, short-day.

dealation (dēălā'shŭn) *n.* [L. *de*, away; *alatus*, winged.] The removal of wings, as by female ants after fertilisation, or by termites.

deamination (dēăm'ĭnāshŭn) *n.* [L. *de*, down; Gk. *ammoniakon*, resinous gum.] Removal of the amino (NH_2) radical from an amino acid; the conversion of ammonium salts into urea, partly accomplished in the liver.

death (dĕth) *n.* [A.S. *deáth*, death.] Complete and permanent cessation of vital functions in an organism.

death-point,—temperature above or below which organisms cannot exist.

Débove's membrane [*M. G. Débove*, French histologist]. Layer between tunica propria and epithelium of tracheal, bronchial, and intestinal mucous membranes; subepithelial endothelium.

decalcify (dēkăl'sĭfī) *v.* [L. *de*, away; *calx*, lime; *facere*, to make.] To deprive of lime salts; to treat with acids for removal of calcareous part.

decamerous (dĕkăm'ërŭs) *a.* [Gk. *deka*, ten; *meros*, part.] With the various parts arranged in tens.

decandrous (dĕkăn'drŭs) *a.* [Gk. *deka*, ten; *aner*, male.] Having ten stamens.

decaploid (dĕk'ăploid) *a.* [Gk. *deka*, ten; *aploos*, onefold; *eidos*, form.] Having ten times the haploid number of chromosomes.

decapod (dĕk'ăpŏd) *a.* [Gk. *deka*, ten; *pous*, foot.] Of Crustacea, with five pairs of legs on thorax; of Cephalopoda, with ten arms.

decapodiform (dĕk′ăpŏd′ĭfôrm) *a.* [Gk. *deka*, ten; *pous*, foot; L. *forma*, shape.] Resembling a decapod, *appl.* certain insect larvae.

decemfid (dĕsĕm′fĭd) *a.* [L. *decem*, ten; *findere*, to cleave.] Cut into ten segments.

decemfoliate (dĕs′ĕmfō′lĭāt) *a.* [L. *decem*, ten; *folium*, leaf.] Ten-leaved.

decemjugate (dĕsĕm′joogāt) *a.* [L. *decem*, ten; *jugare*, to join.] With ten pairs of leaflets.

decempartite (dĕs′ĕmpâr′tīt) *a.* [L. *decem*, ten; *partiri*, to divide.] Ten-lobed; divided into ten lobes.

decidua (dēsĭd′ūă) *n.* [L. *decidere*, to fall off.] The mucous membrane lining the pregnant uterus, cast off after parturition.

decidua capsularis,—portion of the decidua over the ovum.

decidua parietalis,—the decidua vera lining the body of the uterus.

decidua placentalis,—portion of the decidua between myometrium and ovum; decidua basalis.

decidual (dēsĭd′ūăl) *a.* [L. *decidere*, to fall off.] *Pert.* decidua.

deciduate (dēsĭd′ūāt) *a.* [L. *decidere*, to fall off.] Characterised by having a decidua; partly formed by the decidua.

deciduous (dēsĭd′ūŭs) *a.* [L. *decidere*, to fall down.] Falling at end of growth period or at maturity.

declinate (dĕk′lĭnāt) *a.* [L. *de*, away; *clinare*, to bend.] Bending aside in a curve, as anther filament in horse-chestnut.

declivis (dēklī′vis) *n.* [L. *declivis*, sloping.] Part of superior vermis, continuous laterally with lobulus simplex of cerebellar hemispheres.

decollated (dēkŏl′ātĕd) *a.* [L. *de*, away from; *collum*, neck.] With apex of spire wanting.

decomposed (dē′kŏmpōzd′) *a.* [L. *de*, away; *cum*, with; *pausare*, to rest.] Not in contact; not adhering, said of barbs of feather when separate; decayed.

decomposite,—decompound.

decompound (dē′kŏmpound′) *a.* [L. *de*, away; *cum*, with; *ponere*, to place.] With monopodial branching very complete, and ultimate wings little developed; *appl.* leaf.

deconjugation (dē′kŏnjoogā′shŭn) *n.* [L. *de*, away from; *conjugare*, to join together.] Separation of paired chromosomes, as before end of meiotic prophase.

decorticate (dēkôr′tĭkāt) *v.* [L. *decorticare*, to peel.] To remove bark or cortex. *a.* With cortex ablated.

decticous (dēk′tĭkŭs) *n.* [Gk. *dektikos*, biting.] Having functional mandibles for opening puparium or cocoon; *appl.* pupa of some insects. *Opp.* adecticous.

decumbent (dēkŭm′bĕnt) *a.* [L. *decumbere*, to lie down.] *Appl.* stems which trail on ground, but rise at apex.

decurrent (dēkŭr′ĕnt) *a.* [L. *decurrere*, to run downwards.] Having leaf base prolonged down stem as a winged expansion or rib; prolonged down stipe, as gills of agaric.

decussate (dĕkŭs′āt) *a.* [L. *decussare*, to cross.] Crossed; having paired leaves, succeeding pairs crossing at right angles.

decussation (dĕk′ŭsā′shŭn) *n.* [L. *decussare*, to cross.] Decussate condition of leaves; crossing of nerves with interchange of fibres, as in optic and pyramidal tracts.

dedifferentiation (dēdĭf′ĕrĕnshĭā′-shŭn) *n.* [L. *de*, away from; *differentia*, difference.] The losing of characteristics of specialised cells and regression to a more simple state.

dédoublement (dā′dooblĕmông′) *n.* [F. *dédoublement*, dividing into two.] Chorisis; deduplication.

deduplication (dēdū′plĭkā′shŭn) *n.* [L. *de*, by reason of; *duplicare*, to double.] Chorisis, *q.v.*

defaecation (dē′fēkā′shŭn) *n.* [L. *defaecatio*, voiding of excrement.] The expulsion of faeces; defecation.

defensive (dĕfĕn′sĭv) *a.* [L. *defendere*, to defend.] Protective; *appl.* proteid substances which destroy toxic substances of bacteria; *appl.* numerous organs or parts of organs in various animals or plants.

deferent (dĕf′ĕrĕnt) *a.* [L. *deferre*, to carry away.] Conveying away; *appl.* ducts, vasa deferentia, *q.v.*

deferred (dēfĕrd′) *a.* [L. *deferre*, to carry off.] *Appl.* shoots arising from dormant buds.

deficiency,—inactivation or absence of a chromosomal segment or gene.

deficiency diseases, — pathological conditions in plants and animals, due to lack of certain necessary nutritive substances; *e.g.* crown rot in sugar beet due to boron deficiency; diseases in mammals due to vitamin deficiency, absence of vitamin A causing poor growth and xerophthalmia,—of B_1, beriberi,—of B_2, retardation of growth, —of C, scurvy,—of D, rickets,—of E, infertility and paralysis,—of K, bleeding,—etc.

definite (dĕf′ĭnĭt) *a.* [L. *definire*, to limit.] Fixed, constant; cymose, *appl.* inflorescences with primary axis terminating early in a flower; *appl.* stamens limited to twenty in number.

definitive (dēfĭn′ĭtĭv) *a.* [L. *definire*, to limit.] Defining or limiting; complete, fully developed; final, *appl.* host of adult parasite.

deflorate (dēflō′rāt) *a.* [L. *deflorere*, to shed blossoms.] After the flowering stage.

defoliate (dēfō′lĭāt) *a.* [L. *defoliare*, to strip of leaves.] Bared at the annual fall. *v.* To deprive of leaves.

degeneration (dējĕnĕrā′shŭn) *n.* [L. *degenerare*, to degenerate.] Change to a less specialised or functionally less active form; retrogressive evolution.

deglutition (dēglootĭsh′ŭn) *n.* [L. *de*, down; *glutire*, to swallow.] The process of swallowing.

ehiscence (dēhĭs′ēns) *n.* [L. *dehiscere*, to gape.] The spontaneous opening of an organ or structure along certain lines or in a definite direction.

deinopore (dī′nōpōr) *n.* [Gk. *deinos*, urn; *poros*, channel.] A cell bridge.

deirids (dī′rĭdz) *n. plu.* [Gk. *deiras*, chain of hills.] Cervical papillae in Nematoda.

Deiters' cells [*O. F. C. Deiters*, German anatomist]. Supporting cells between rows of outer hair-cells in organ of Corti; outer phalangeal cells.

delamination (dēlăm′ĭnā′shŭn) *n.* [L. *de*, down; *lamina*, layer.] The dividing off of cells to form new layers.

deletion (dēlē′shŭn) *n.* [L. *delere*, to efface.] A deficiency of an acentric part of chromosome; absence of a chromosome segment and of the genes involved.

deliquescent (dĕl′ĭkwĕs′ĕnt] *a.* [L. *deliquescere*, to become fluid.] Having lateral buds the more vigorously developed, so that the main stem seems to divide into a number of irregular branches; becoming fluid.

delitescence (dēlĭtĕs′ēns) *n.* [L. *delitescere*, to lie hidden.] The latent period of a poison; incubation period of a pathogenic organism.

delomorphic (dē′lōmôr′fĭk) *a.* [Gk. *delos*, visible; *morphe*, shape.] With definite form, *appl.* oxyntic cells of the gastric glands; delomorphous.

delthyrium (dĕlthī′rĭŭm) *n.* [Gk. *delos*, visible; *thyrion*, little door.] The opening, between hinge and beak, for peduncle exit in many Brachiopoda.

deltidium (dĕltĭd′ĭŭm) *n.* [Gk. Δ, delta; *idion*, *dim.*] A plate covering the delthyrium.

deltoid (dĕl′toid) *a.* [Gk. Δ, delta; *eidos*, form.] More or less triangular in shape, *appl.* muscle, etc.; *appl.* oral plates on calyx of Blastoidea.

demanian (dĕmăn'ĭăn) *a.* [*J. G. de Man*, French zoologist]. *Appl.* a complex system of paired efferent tubes connecting with intestine and uteri in Nematoda, and associated with gelatinous secretion for protection of eggs.

deme (dēm) *n.* [Gk. *demos*, people.] Assemblage of taxonomically closely related individuals; aggregate of single cells.

demersal (dēmĕr'săl) *a.* [L. *demergere*, to plunge into.] Living on or near bottom of sea or lake; sunk.

demersed (dēmĕr'sd) *a.* [L. *demergere*, to plunge into.] Growing under water; *appl.* parts of plants.

demibranch,—hemibranch, *q.v.*

demifacet (dĕmĭfăs'ĕt) *n.* [L. *dimidius*, half; *facies*, face.] Part of parapophysis facet when divided between centra of two adjacent vertebrae.

demilunes,—crescentic cells; crescentic bodies of cells of some salivary gland alveoli, crescents of Gianuzzi or demilunes of Heidenhain.

demiplate (dĕm'ĭplāt) *n.* [L. *dimidius*, half; F. *plate*, flat.] Plate cut off by fusion of adjoining plates behind it from central suture line of ambulacral area in echinoderms.

demisheath (dĕm'ĭshēth) *n.* [L. *dimidius*, half; A.S. *sceath*, sheath.] One of paired protecting covers of insect ovipositor.

demoid (dē'moid) *a.* [Gk. *demos*, the commons.] Abundant.

denatant (dēnā'tănt) *a.* [L. *de*, down from; *natare*, to swim.] Swimming, drifting, or migrating with the current, *opp.* contranatant.

dendriform (dĕn'drĭfôrm) *a.* [Gk. *dendron*, tree; L. *forma*, shape.] Dendroid; tree-like.

dendrite (dĕn'drīt) *n.* [Gk. *dendron*, tree.] A fine branch of a dendron; a dendron.

dendritic (dĕndrĭt'ĭk) *a.* [Gk. *dendron*, tree.] Dendroid; *appl.* tree-like structures or markings; like, *pert.*, or having, dendrites or dendrons.

dendrochronology (dĕn'drökrönŏl'öjĭ) *n.* [Gk. *dendron*, tree; *chronos*, time; *logos*, discourse.] Determination of age of trees or timber; dating by comparative study of tree rings; science of tree-ring analysis and its implications.

Dendrogaea (dĕn'dröjē'ă) *n.* [Gk. *dendron*, tree; *gaia*, earth.] A biogeographical region including all the neotropical region except temperate South America.

dendroid (dĕn'droid) *a.* [Gk. *dendron*, tree; *eidos*, form.] Tree-like; much branched.

dendrology (dĕndrŏl'öjĭ) *n.* [Gk. *dendron*, tree; *logos*, discourse.] The study of trees.

dendron (dĕn'drŏn) *n.* [Gk. *dendron*, tree.] A protoplasmic process of the nerve cell, which conducts impulses towards the cell-body.

denitrification (dē'nītrĭfĭkā'shŭn) *n.* [L. *de*, away; Gk. *nitron*, soda; L. *facere*, to make.] Reduction of nitrates, to nitrites and ammonia, as in plant tissues, or to molecular nitrogen, as by certain soil bacteria.

dens (dĕnz) *n.* [L. *dens*, tooth.] Tooth, or tooth-like process; odontoid process of axis or epistropheus.

dens serotinus,—the third molar or wisdom-tooth.

dental (dĕn'tăl) *a.* [L. *dens*, tooth.] *Pert.* teeth; *appl.* nerves, blood-vessels, canals, furrows, papillae, sac, tissue, etc.

dentary (dĕn'tărĭ) *a.* [L. *dens*, tooth.] *Pert.* dentaries, membrane bones in lower jaw of many vertebrates. *n.* Dentary bone or os dentale.

dentate (dĕn'tāt) *a.* [L. *dens*, tooth.] Toothed; with sharp saw-like teeth on the margin.

dentate-ciliate,—with teeth and hairs on the margins; *appl.* leaves.

dentate-crenate,—with marginal teeth somewhat rounded.

denticles (dĕn'tĭklz) *n. plu.* [L. *denticulus*, little tooth.] Small tooth-like processes; the paragnaths of certain Polychaeta; the teeth within the secondary orifice in Polyzoa; the scales of certain Elasmobranchii.

denticulate (dĕntĭk′ūlāt) *a.* [L. *denticulus*, little tooth.] Having denticles; with minute marginal teeth.

dentin,—dentine, *q.v.*

dentinal (dĕn′tĭnăl) *a.* [L. *dens*, tooth.] *Pert.* dentine; *appl.* tubules, *i.e.* canaliculi dentales.

dentine (dĕn′tĭn) *n.* [L. *dens*, tooth.] A hard, elastic substance, chemically resembling bone, composing the greater part of teeth and denticles; dentin.

dentition (dĕntĭsh′ŭn) *n.* [L. *dens*, tooth.] The number, arrangement, and kind of teeth; teething.

deperulation (dē′pērūlā′shŭn) *n.* [L. *de*, away; *dim.* of *pera*, wallet.] The pushing apart or throwing off, of bud scales.

depigmentation (dēpĭg′mĕntā′shŭn) *n.* [L. *de*, away; *pingere*, to paint.] The destruction of colour in a cell, by natural or experimental physiological processes.

depilation (dĕp′ĭlā′shŭn) *n.* [L. *de*, away; *pilus*, hair.] Loss of hairy covering, as of plants when maturing; removal of hair.

deplanate (dĕp′lănāt) *a.* [L. *deplanare*, to level.] Levelled, flattened.

depressant (dēprĕs′ănt) *n.* [L. *deprimere*, to keep down.] Anything that lowers vital activity.

depressomotor (dēprĕs′ōmō′tŏr) *n.* [L. *deprimere*, to keep down; *movere*, to move.] Any nerve which lowers muscular activity.

depressor (dēprĕs′ŏr) *n.* [L. *deprimere*, to keep down.] Any muscle which lowers or depresses any structure; *appl.* a nerve which lowers the activity of an organ.

depula (dĕp′ūlă) *n.* [Gk. *depas*, goblet.] Invaginated blastula preceding gastrula stage in development of embryo.

deric (dĕr′ĭk) *a.* [Gk. *deros*, skin.] Dermic; *appl.* epithelium, synonym of epidermis.

derm,—derma, dermis.

derma (dĕr′mă) *n.* [Gk. *derma*, skin.] The layers of integument below the epidermis; dermis.

dermal (dĕr′măl) *a.* [Gk. *derma*, skin.] *Pert.* derma, or skin.

dermalia (dĕrmā′lĭă) *n. plu.* [Gk. *derma*, skin.] Microscleres in the dermal membrane of sponges.

dermarticulare (dĕr′mârtĭk′ūlā′rē) *n.* [Gk. *derma*, skin; L. *articulus*, joint.] The goniale, *q.v.*

dermatic,—dermal.

dermatogen (dĕr′mătōjĕn) *n.* [Gk. *derma*, skin; *genos*, birth.] The young or embryonic epidermis in plants; antigen of skin disease.

dermatoglyphics (dĕr′mătōglĭf′ĭks) *n.* [Gk. *derma*, skin; *glyphein*, to carve.] Skin, palm, finger, sole, toe prints; print formulae.

dermatoid (dĕr′mătoid) *a.* [Gk. *derma*, skin; *eidos*, form.] Resembling a skin; functioning as a skin.

dermatomes (dĕr′mătōmz) *n. plu.* [Gk. *derma*, skin; *tome*, cutting.] Lateral parts of segmental mesoderm, which develop into connective tissue of corium or dermis; dermatomeres; skin areas supplied by individual spinal nerves.

dermatophyte (dĕr′mătōfīt) *n.* [Gk. *derma*, skin; *phyton*, plant.] Any fungous parasite of skin; dermatophyton, dermophyte, epidermophyte.

dermatoplasm (dĕr′mătōplăzm) *n.* [Gk. *derma*, skin; *plasma*, mould.] Cell-wall protoplasm.

dermatoplast (dĕr′mătōplăst′) *n.* [Gk. *derma*, skin; *plastos*, moulded.] A protoplast with a cell wall.

dermatopsy (dĕr′mătŏp′sĭ′) *n.* [Gk. *derma*, skin; *opsis*, sight.] Condition of seeing with the skin, *i.e.* with a skin sensitive to light.

dermatoskeleton,—exoskeleton.

dermatosome (dĕr′mătōsōm′) *n.* [Gk. *derma*, skin; *soma*, body.] One of vital units forming a cell-membrane.

dermatozoon (dĕr′mătōzō′ŏn) *n.* [Gk. *derma*, skin; *zoon*, animal.] Any animal parasite of the skin; ectozoon.

dermentoglossum (dĕrm′ĕntöglŏs′-ŭm) *n.* [Gk. *derma*, skin ; *entos*, within ; *glossa*, tongue.] A bone arising by fusion of dentinal bases, covering entoglossum, in some fishes.

dermethmoid (dĕrmĕth′moid) *n.* [Gk. *derma*, skin ; *ethmos*, sieve ; *eidos*, form.] Supra-ethmoid, *q.v.*

dermic (dĕr′mĭk) *a.* [Gk. *derma*, skin.] *Pert.*, or derived from, skin.

dermis (dĕr′mĭs) *n.* [Gk. *derma*, skin.] Derma, *q.v.* ; corium.

dermoblast (dĕr′möblăst′) *n.* [Gk. *derma*, skin ; *blastos*, bud.] The layer of mesoblast which gives rise to the derma.

dermoccipitals (dĕrm′ŏksĭp′ĭtălz) *n. plu.* [Gk. *derma*, skin ; L. *occiput*, back of head.] Two bones taking the place of interparietal in some lower forms and in development of higher.

dermomyotome (dĕr′mömī′ötōm) *n.* [Gk. *derma*, skin ; *mys*, muscle ; *tome*, cutting.] The dorsilateral part of mesodermal somites.

dermo-ossification (dĕr′möŏs′ĭfĭkā′-shŭn) *n.* [Gk. *derma*, skin ; L. *os*, bone ; *fieri*, to become.] A bone formed in the skin.

dermopharyngeal (dĕr′möfărĭn′jëăl) *n.* [Gk. *derma*, skin ; *pharyngx*, gullet.] Superior or inferior plate of membrane bone supporting pharyngeal teeth in some fishes.

dermophyte,—dermatophyte, *q.v.*

dermosclerites (dĕr′mösklēr′īts) *n. plu.* [Gk. *derma*, skin ; *skleros*, hard.] Masses of spicules found in tissues of Alcyonidae.

dermoskeleton (dĕr′möskĕl′ĕtŏn) *n.* [Gk. *derma*, skin ; *skeletos*, dried.] Exoskeleton, *q.v.*

dermotrichia (dĕr′mötrĭk′ĭă) *n. plu.* [Gk. *derma*, skin ; *thrix*, hair.] Dermal fin-rays.

dermozoon,—dermatozoon, *q.v.*

derotreme (dĕr′ötrēm) *n.* [Gk. *deros*, skin ; *trema*, aperture.] Skin forming an operculum, as in Megalobatrachus.

dertrotheca (dĕr′tröthē′ka) *n.* [Gk. *dertron*, beak ; *theke*, box.] The horny casing of bird maxilla.

dertrum (dĕr′trŭm) *n.* [Gk. *dertron*, beak.] Any modification of the casing of maxilla in birds.

Descemet's membrane [*J. Descemet*, French anatomist]. The posterior elastic lamina of cornea ; Demour's membrane.

descending (dēsĕn′dĭng) *a.* [L. *de*, down ; *scandere*, to climb.] Directed downwards, or towards caudal region ; *appl.* blood-vessels, nerves, etc.

desegmentation (dēsĕg′mĕntā′shŭn) *n.* [L. *de*, from ; *segmentum*, piece cut off.] Fusion of segments originally separate.

deserticolous (dĕz′ërtĭk′ölŭs) *a.* [L. *desertus*, waste ; *colere*, to inhabit.] Desert-inhabiting.

desma (dĕs′mă, dĕz-) *n.* [Gk. *desma*, bond.] Megasclere which forms characteristic skeletal network of Lithistida.

desmactinic (dĕs′măktĭn′ĭk,) *a.* [Gk. *desma*, bond ; *aktis*, ray.] With podia continued upwards to apical plate, *appl.* Stelleroidea ; *cf.* lysactinic.

desmergate (dĕs′mĕrgāt) *n.* [Gk. *desma*, bond ; *ergates*, worker.] A type of ant intermediate between worker and soldier.

desmocyte (dĕs′mösīt) *n.* [Gk. *desmos*, bond ; *kytos*, hollow.] A connective tissue cell ; fibroblast.

desmogen (dĕs′möjĕn,) *n.* [Gk. *desmos*, bond ; *genos*, descent.] Merismatic or growing tissue.

desmognathous (dĕsmŏg′năthŭs) *a.* [Gk. *desmos*, bond ; *gnathos*, jaw.] Having maxillopalatines fused in middle line owing to other peculiarities in skull ; *appl.* certain birds.

desmology (dĕsmŏl′öjĭ) *n.* [Gk. *desmos*, bond ; *logos*, discourse.] The anatomy of ligaments ; *cf.* syndesmology.

desmones (dĕs′mōnz) *n. plu.* [Gk. *desmos*, bond.] Chemical substances exchanged by way of protoplasmic bridges between cells ; amboceptors, *q.v.*

desmose (dĕs′mōs) *n.* [Gk. *desmos*, bond.] A strand connecting blepharoplasts at mitosis.

desmosome (dĕs′mösōm) *n.* [Gk. *desmos*, bond; *soma*, body.] A thickening of intercellular connections in epithelium; bridge corpuscle.

desquamation (dĕs′kwămā′shŭn) *n.* [L. *de*, away; *squama*, scale.] Shedding of cuticle or epidermis in flakes.

desynapsis (dē′sĭnăp′sĭs) *n.* [L. *de*, away from; Gk. *synapsis*, union.] Failure of synapsis, caused by disjunction of homologous chromosomes.

determinant (dētĕr′mĭnănt) *n.* [L. *determinare*, to limit.] A hypothetical unit, being an aggregation of biophores determining the development of a cell or of an independently variable group of cells; hereditary factor.

determinate (dētĕr′mĭnāt) *a.* [L. *determinare*, to limit.] With certain limits; *appl.* inflorescence with primary axis terminated early with a flower-bud; *appl.* cleavage; *appl.* evolution: orthogenesis.

determination (dētĕr′mĭnā′shŭn) *n.* [L. *determinatio*, boundary.] The process adjusting regional development according to relative location of region and organisation centre.

determinator (dētĕr′mĭnātŏr) *n.* [L. *determinare*, to determine.] A gene that controls the male or female character of haploid mycelium at the site of formation of a fruit-body.

detorsion (dētôr′shŭn) *n.* [L. *de*, away; *torquere*, to twist.] Torsion in an opposite direction to that of original, resulting in a more or less posterior position of anus and circumanal complex.

detoxication (dē′tŏksĭkā′shŭn) *n.* [L. *de*, away; Gk. *toxikon*, poison.] The inhibition of effects of toxins in the body, either by a protective synthesis of comparatively harmless substances, or by means of antibodies.

detrusor (dētroo′sŏr) *n.* [L. *detrudere*, to thrust from.] The outer of three layers of the muscular coat of the urinary bladder; physiologically, all three layers; detrusor urinae, detrusor vesicae.

deuter cell,—eurycyst, *q.v.*

deutero-,—*also see* deuto-.

deuterocerebrum(dū′tërösĕr′ēbrŭm) *n.* [Gk. *deuteros*, second; L. *cerebrum*, brain.] That portion of crustacean brain from which antennular nerves arise. *Cf.* deutocerebrum.

deuterocoele (dū′tërösēl) *n.* [Gk. *deuteros*, second; *koilos*, hollow.] The coelom.

deuterocone (dū′tërökōn′) *n.* [Gk. *deuteros*, second; *konos*, cone.] Mammalian premolar cusp corresponding to molar protocone.

deuteroconidium (dū′tërökŏnĭd′-ĭŭm) *n.* [Gk. *deuteros*, second; *konis*, dust; *idion*, *dim.*] One of the conidia produced by division of a hemispore or protoconidium, in dermatophytes.

deuterogamy (dū′tërŏg′ămĭ) *n.* Gk. *deuteros*, second; *gamos*, marriage.] Secondary fertilisation; pairing substituting for the union of gametes as in fungi.

deuterogenesis (dū′tëröjĕn′ĕsĭs) *n.* [Gk. *deuteros*, second; *genesis*, origin.] Second phase of embryonic development, involving growth in length and consequent bilateral symmetry; *cf.* protogenesis.

deuteroplasm,—deutoplasm, *q.v.*

deuteropolydesmic (dū′tëröpŏlĭdĕs′mĭk) *a.* [Gk. *deuteros*, second; *desmos*, bond.] *Appl.* cyclomorial scales composed mainly of synpolydesmic scales.

deuteroproteose (dū′tëröprō′tēōs) *n*, [Gk. *deuteros*, second; *protos*, first.] A secondary product from digestion of proteids.

deuterostoma (dū′tërŏs′tömă) *n.* [Gk. *deuteros*, second; *stoma*, mouth.] A mouth formed secondarily, as distinct from gastrula mouth.

deuterotoky (dū'tĕrŏt'ŏkĭ) *n.* [Gk. *deuteros*, second; *tokos*, birth.] Reproduction of both sexes from parthenogenetic eggs; *cf.* arrhenotoky and thelyotoky.

deuterotype (dū'tĕrötīp) *n.* [Gk. *deuteros*, second; *typos*, pattern.] The specimen chosen to replace the original type specimen for designation of a species.

Deuterozoic (dū'tĕrözō'ĭk) *a.* [Gk. *deuteros*, second; *zoe*, life.] *Appl.* and *pert.* the newer Palaeozoic faunal epoch, the age of fishes, also of pteridosperms.

deuterozooid (dū'tĕrözō'oid) *n.* [Gk. *deuteros*, second; *zoon*, animal; *eidos*, form.] A zooid produced by budding from a primary zooid.

deuthyalosome (dūthī'ălösōm) *n.* [Gk. *deuteros*, second; *hyalos*, glass; *soma*, body.] The nucleus remaining in ovum after formation of first polar body.

deuto-,—*also see* deutero-.

deutoblasts (dū'töblăsts) *n. plu.* [Gk. *deuteros*, second; *blastos*, bud.] The amoeba-like bodies formed from protoblasts in zygote of Microclossia, and liberated to multiply in the blood.

deutobroch (dū'töbrŏk) *a.* [Gk. *deuteros*, second; *brochos*, mesh.] *Appl.* nuclei of gonia preparing for leptotene stage; *cf.* protobroch.

deutocerebrum (dū'tösĕr'ĕbrŭm) *n.* [Gk. *deuteros*, second; L. *cerebrum*, brain.] Portion of insect brain derived from fused ganglia of antennary segment of head; deutocerebron. *Cf.* deuterocerebrum.

deutomalae (dū'tömā'lē) *n. plu.* [Gk. *deuteros*, second; *malon*, cheek.] The broad plate in Chaetognatha, formed by fusion of second pair of mouth appendages; second pair of mouth appendages in certain Myriopoda.

deutomerite (dūtŏm'ĕrīt) *n.* [Gk. *deuteros*, second; *meros*, part.] The posterior division of certain gregarines; *cf.* primite.

deutonephros (dū'tönĕf'rŏs) *n.* [Gk. *deuteros*, second; *nephros*, kidney.] Mesonephros.

deutonymph (dū'tönĭmf) *n.* [Gk. *deuteros*, second; *nymphe*, chrysalis.] Second nymphal stage or instar, either chrysalis-like or motile, in development of Acaridae; hypopus stage.

deutoplasm (dū'töplăzm) *n.* [Gk. *deuteros*, second; *plasma*, mould.] Yolk or food material in cytoplasm of ovum or other cell.

deutoscolex (dū'töskō'lĕks) *n.* [Gk. *deuteros*, second; *skolex*, worm.] A secondary scolex produced by budding, in bladderworm stage of certain tape-worms.

deutosomes (dū'tösōmz) *n. plu.* [Gk. *deuteros*, second; *soma*, body.] Granules of nucleolus cast out into cytoplasm, from which yolk is said to arise.

deutosternum (dū'töstĕr'nŭm) *n.* [Gk. *deuteros*, second; *sternon*, chest.] Sternite of segment bearing pedipalpi in Acarina.

deutovum (dūtō'vŭm) *n.* [Gk. *deuteros*, second; L. *ovum*, egg.] A stage in the metamorphosis of certain mites, a secondary or deutovarial membrane surrounding the embryo until the larval stage.

development (dēvĕl'ŏpmënt) *n.* [F. *développer*, to unfold.] The changes undergone by an organism from its beginning to maturity.

deviation (dēvĭā'shŭn) *n.* [L. *de*, away from; *via*, way.] Divergence from corresponding developmental stages.

Devonian (dĕvō'nĭăn) *a.* [*Devon*, where strata were first studied.] *Pert.* or *appl.* Palaeozoic geological period preceding Carboniferous.

dexiotropic (dĕk'sĭötrŏp'ĭk) *a.* [Gk. *dexios*, right; *trope*, turn.] Turning from left to right, as whorls; *appl.* shells; *appl.* spiral cleavage of cells; *appl.* movement of Volvox.

dextral (dĕk'străl) *a.* [L. *dexter*, right-hand.] Dexiotropic, *q.v.*

dextrin (dĕk′strĭn) *n.* [L. *dexter*, right-hand.] A soluble substance derived from starch by exposure to high temperature for a short time.

dextrorse (dĕkstrôrs′) *a.* [L. *dexter*, right; *vertere*, to turn.] Growing in a spiral which twines from left to right; clockwise. *Opp.* sinistrorse.

dextrose (dĕk′strōs) *n.* [L. *dexter*, right.] Grape sugar or glucose, the end product of starch digestion, $C_6H_{12}O_6$.

diabetogenic (dīăbē′töjĕn′ĭk) *a.* [Gk. *diabainein*, to cross over; *gignesthai*, to beget.] Causing diabetes; *appl.* a prepituitary hormone antagonistic to insulin, affecting carbohydrate metabolism; *appl.* a hormone of sinus gland of eye stalk in crustaceans.

diachaenium (dī′ăkē′nĭŭm) *n.* [Gk. *dis*, twice; *a*, not; *chainein*, to gape.] Each part of a cremocarp.

diachronous (dīăk′rönŭs) *a.* [Gk. *dia*, asunder; *chronos*, time.] Dating from different periods; *appl.* fossils occurring in the same geological formation, though in different areas, due, *e.g.*, to changes in sea-level.

diachyma (dīăk′ĭmă) *n.* [Gk. *dia*, throughout; *chymos*, juice.] Leaf parenchyma.

diacoel (dī′ăsēl) *n.* [Gk. *dia*, through; *koilos*, hollow.] Third ventricle of brain.

diacranteric (dī′ăkrăntĕr′ĭk) *a.* [Gk. *dia*, asunder; *kranteres*, wisdom teeth.] With diastema between front and back teeth, as in snakes.

diactinal (dīăk′tĭnăl) *a.* [Gk. *dis*, twice; *aktis*, ray.] With two rays pointed at ends.

diadelphous (dī′ădĕl′fŭs) *a.* [Gk. *dis*, twice; *adelphos*, brother.] Having stamens in two bundles owing to fusion of filaments.

diadematoid (dī′ădĕm′ătoid) *a.* [Gk. *diadema*, crown; *eidos*, shape.] Of Echinoidea, having three primary pore plates with occasionally a secondary between aboral and middle primary; as *opp.* arbacioid, one primary, with secondary on each side, and triplechinoid, two primaries, with one or more secondaries between.

diadromous (dīăd′römŭs) *a.* [Gk. *diadromos*, wandering.] Having nerves or veins radiating in fan-like manner; *appl.* leaves.

diaene (dī′ēn) *n.* [Gk. *dis*, twice; an analogy of triaene, from Gk. *triaina*, trident.] A form of triaene, with one of the cladi reduced or absent.

diageotropism (dī′ăjēŏt′röpĭzm) *n.* [Gk. *dia*, through; *ge*, earth; *trope*, turn.] Tendency in certain parts of plants to assume position at right angles to direction of gravity.

diagnosis (dī′ăgnō′sĭs) *n.* [Gk. *diagnosis*, discrimination.] A concise description of an organism with full distinctive characters; discrimination of a physiological or pathological condition by its distinctive signs.

diagnostic (dī′ăgnŏs′tĭk) *a.* [Gk. *diagnosis*, discrimination.] Distinguishing; differentiating the species or genus, etc., from others similar.

diaheliotropism (dī′ăhēlĭŏt′röpĭzm) *n.* [Gk. *dia*, through; *helios*, sun; *trope*, turn.] Diaphototropism.

diakinesis (dī′ăkĭnē′sĭs) *n.* [Gk. *dia*, through; *kinesis*, movement.] The later prophase stage of meiosis, between diplotene and prometaphase; movement of chromosomes between metaphase and telophase.

dialyneury (dī′ălĭnū′rĭ) *n.* [Gk. *dialyein*, to reconcile; *neuron*, nerve.] In certain gastropods, condition of having pleural ganglia united to opposite visceral nerve by anastomosis with pallial nerve.

dialypetalous (dī′ălĭpĕt′ălŭs) *a.* [Gk. *dia*, asunder; *lyein*, to loose; *petalon*, leaf.] Polypetalous.

dialyphyllous (dī′ălĭfĭl′ŭs) *a.* [Gk. *dia*, asunder; *lyein*, to loose; *phyllon*, leaf.] With separate leaves.

dialysepalous (dī′ălĭsĕp′ălŭs) *a.* [Gk. *dia*, asunder; *lyein*, to loose; F. *sépale*, sepal.] Polysepalous.

dialysate (dīăl′ĭsāt) *n.* [Gk. *dialysis*, parting.] Any substance which passes through a semipermeable membrane during dialysis; diffusate. *Opp.* retentate.

dialysis (dīăl′ĭsĭs) *n.* [Gk. *dia*, asunder; *lysis*, loosing.] Separation of dissolved crystalloids and colloids through semipermeable membrane, crystalloids passing more readily; permeation.

dialystely (dī′ălĭstē′lĭ) *n.* [Gk. *dia*, asunder; *lyein*, to loose; *stele*, post.] A condition in which the steles in the stem remain more or less separate.

diamesogamous (dī′ămĕsŏg′ămŭs) *a.* [Gk. *dia*. through; *mesos*, medium; *gamos*, marriage.] Fertilised through external agency, as by means of wind, insects, etc.

diancistron (dī′ănsĭs′tron) *n.* [Gk. *dis*, twice; *angkistron*, hook.] A spicule resembling a stout sigma, but the inner margin of both hook and shaft thins out to a knife edge and is notched. *Plu.* diancistra.

diandrous (dīăn′drŭs) *a.* [Gk. *dis*, twice; *aner*, man.] Having two free stamens.

diapause (dī′ăpôz) *n.* [Gk. *diapauein*, to make to cease.] A spontaneous state of dormancy during development, as of insects; resting stage between anatrepsis and katatrepsis in blastokinesis; sexual rest period, *appl.* annelids; *cf.* quiescence.

diapedesis (dī′ăpēdē′sĭs) *n.* [Gk. *diapedesis*, leaping through.] Emigration of white blood corpuscles through walls of capillaries into surrounding tissue; migration of cells to exterior, in certain larval sponges.

diaphototropism (dī′ăfōtŏt′rŏpĭzm) *n.* [Gk. *dia*, through; *phos*, light; *trope*, turn.] Tendency of plant organs to assume a position at right angles to rays of light; diaheliotropism.

diaphragm (dī′ăfrăm), **diaphragma** (dī′ăfrăg′mă) *n.* [Gk. *diaphragma*, midriff.] The wall which separates the small cell, the prothallus, from rest of macrospore in Hydropterideae; a septum at nodes in Equisetum; a sheet of muscular tissue attached to introvert in worms; single strongly developed septum in Terebelliformia; perforated tissue that subdivides tentacle cavity in Polyzoa; a fibro-muscular abdominal septum enclosing perineural sinus in certain insects; the transverse septum separating cephalothorax from abdomen in certain Arachnida; a special fan-shaped muscle spreading from anterior end of ilia to oesophagus and base of lungs in Anura; a partition partly muscular, partly tendinous, separating cavity of chest from abdominal cavity in mammals; fold of dura mater on sella turcica.

diaphysis (dīăf′ĭsĭs) *n.* [Gk. *dia*, through; *phyein*, to bring forth.] Shaft of limb bone, *opp.* epiphysis; abnormal growth of an axis or shoot.

diaplexus (dī′aplĕk′sŭs) *n.* [Gk. *dia*, through; L. *plexus*, interwoven.] Chorioid plexus of the third ventricle of the brain.

diapophysis (dī′ăpŏf′ĭsĭs) *n.* [Gk. *dia*, through; *apo*, from; *phyein*, to produce.] Lateral or transverse process of neural arch.

diapsid (dīăp′sĭd) *a.* [Gk. *dis*, twice; *apsis*, arch.] *Appl.* skulls with supra- and infra-temporal fossae distinct; *cf.* synapsid.

diarch (dī′ârk) *a.* [Gk. *dis*, twice; *arche*, origin.] With two xylem and two phloem bundles; *appl.* root in which protoxylem bundles meet and form a plate of tissue across cylinder with phloem bundle on each side; *appl.* a bipolar type of spindle.

diarthric (dīâr′thrĭk) *a.* [Gk. *dis*, twice; *arthron*, joint.] *Pert.* two joints; biarticulate.

diarthrosis (dī′ârthrō′sĭs) *n.* [Gk. *dis*, twice; *arthron*, joint.] An articulation allowing considerable movement.

diaschistic (dī'ăskĭs'tĭk) *a.* [Gk. *dia*, through; *schistos*, split.] *Appl.* type of tetrads which divide once transversely and once longitudinally in meiosis; *cf.* anaschistic.

diaspore (dī'ăspōr) *n.* [Gk. *diaspora*, dispersion (*dia*, asunder; *spora*, seed).] Any spore, seed, fruit, or other portion of a plant when being dispersed and able to produce a new plant; disseminule, propagule.

diastase (dī'ăstās) *n.* [Gk. *diastanai*, to separate.] An enzyme which acts principally in converting starch into sugar.

diastasis (dīăs'tăsĭs) *n.* [Gk. *diastasis*, interval.] Rest period preceding systole.

diastatic (dī'ăstăt'ĭk) *a.* [Gk. *dia*, through; *histanai*, to set.] *Pert.* diastase, or having similar properties; *pert.* diastasis.

diastem (dī'ăstĕm), **diastema** (dīăs'tēmă) *n.* [Gk. *diastema*, interval.] A toothless space usually between two types of teeth; an equatorial modification of protoplasm preceding cell division.

diaster (dīăs'tĕr) *n.* [Gk. *dis*, twice; *aster*, star.] The stage in mitosis where daughter chromosomes are grouped near spindle poles ready to form a new nucleus.

diastole (dīăs'tŏlē) *n.* [Gk. *diastole*, difference.] Rhythmical relaxation of heart; rhythmical expansion of a contractile vacuole. *Opp.* systole.

diastomatic (dī'ăstŏmăt'ĭk) *a.* [Gk. *dia*, through; *stoma*, mouth.] Through stomata or pores; giving off gases from spongy parenchyma through stomata.

diathesis (dīăth'ĕsĭs) *n.* [Gk. *diathesis*, disposition.] A constitutional predisposition to a type of reaction, disease, or development.

diatom (dī'ătŏm) *n.* [Gk. *dia*, through; *temnein*, to cut.] A unicellular form of alga with walls impregnated with silica.

diatomin (dīăt'ŏmĭn) *n.* [Gk. *diatemnein*, to cut through.] A yellow pigment resembling fucoxanthin, in plastids of diatoms.

diatropism (dīăt'rŏpĭzm) *n.* [Gk. *dia*, through; *trope*, turn.] The tendency of organs or organisms to place themselves at right angles to line of action of stimulus.

diaxon (dīăk'sŏn) *a.* [Gk. *dis*, twice; *axon*, axis.] With two axes, as certain sponge spicules.

diaxone (dīăk'sōn) *n.* [Gk. *dis*, twice; *axon*, axis.] A nerve-cell with two axis-cylinder processes.

diblastula (dīblăs'tūlă) *n.* [Gk. *dis*, twice; *blastos*, bud.] A coelenterate embryo consisting of two layers arranged round a central cavity.

dibranchiate (dībrăng'kĭāt) *a.* [Gk. *dis*, twice; *brangchia*, gills.] With two gills.

dicaryo-,—dikaryo-.

dicellate (dī'sĕlāt) *a.* [Gk. *dikella*, two-pronged hoe.] With two prongs; *appl.* sponge spicules.

dicentral (dīsĕn'trăl) *a.* [Gk. *dia*, through; *kentron*, centre.] *Appl.* canal in fish vertebral centrum.

dicentric (dīsĕn'trĭk) *a.* [Gk. *dis*, twice; *kentron*, centre.] Having two centromeres; *appl.* chromatids, chromosomes.

dicerous (dĭs'ĕrŭs) *a.* [Gk. *dikeros*, two-horned.] Having two horns; with two antennae.

dichasium (dĭkā'zĭŭm) *n.* [Gk. *dichazein*, to divide in two.] A cymose inflorescence in which two lateral branches occur about same level.

dichlamydeous (dī'klămĭd'ĕŭs) *a.* [Gk. *dis*, twice; *chlamys*, cloak.] Having both calyx and corolla.

dichocarpous (dĭkŏkâr'pŭs) *a.* [Gk. *dichos*, in two ways; *karpos*, fruit.] With two forms of fructification, *appl.* certain fungi.

dichogamy (dĭkŏg'ămĭ) *n.* [Gk. *dicha*, in two; *gamos*, marriage.] Maturing of sexual elements at different times, ensuring cross-fertilisation; *cf.* protandry, protogyny.

dichophysis (dĭkŏf'ĭsĭs) *n.* [Gk. *dicha*, in two; *physis*, constitution.] A rigid dichotomous hypha, as in hymenium and trama.

dichoptic (dĭkŏp′tĭk) *a.* [Gk. *dicha*, in two; *opsis*, sight.] With eyes quite separate.

dichorhinic (dĭk′ŏrī′nĭk) *a.* [Gk. *dicha*, differently; *rhines*, nostrils.] *Pert.* the nostrils separately; *appl.* different olfactory stimuli.

dichotomous (dĭkŏt′ömŭs) *a.* [Gk. *dicha*, in two; *temnein*, to cut.] *Pert.*, characterised by dichotomy.

dichotomy (dĭkŏt′ömĭ) *n.* [Gk. *dicha*, in two; *temnein*, to cut.] Branching which results from division of growing point into two equal parts; repeated forking.

dichroic (dīkrō′ĭk) *a.* [Gk. *dis*, twice; *chros*, colour.] Exhibiting dichroism, as chlorophyll solution; *cf.* dichromatic.

dichroism (dī′krōĭzm) *n.* [Gk. *dis*, twice; *chros*, colour.] Property of showing two colours, as one colour by transmitted and the other by reflected light.

dichromatic (dī′krōmăt′ĭk) *a.* [Gk. *di-*, two; *chroma*, colour.] With two colour varieties; seeing only two colours.

dichromic,—dichroic, *q.v.*; dichromatic, *q.v.*

dichromophil (dĭkrōm′öfĭl) *a.* [Gk. *di-*, two; *chroma*, colour; *philein*, to love.] Staining with both acid and basic dyes.

dichthadiigyne (dĭkthădiī′jīnē) *n.* [Gk. *dichthadios*, double; *gyne*, female.] A gynaecoid ant with voluminous ovaries, and without eyes and wings; a dichthadiiform female.

diclinous (dī′klĭnŭs, dīklī′nŭs) *a.* [Gk. *di-*, asunder; *kline*, bed.] With stamens and pistils on separate flowers; with staminate and pistillate flowers on same plant.

dicoccous (dīkŏk′ŭs) *a.* [Gk. *di-*, two; *kokkos*, kernel.] Having two one-seeded coherent capsules.

dicoelous (dīsē′lŭs) *a.* [Gk. *di-*, two; *koilos*, hollow.] Having two cavities.

dicont,—dikont.

dicostalia (dī′kŏstā′lĭă) *n.* [Gk. *di-*, two; L. *costa*, rib.] The secundibrachs or second brachial series in a crinoid.

dicotyledon (dīkŏtĭlē′dŏn) *n.* [Gk. *di-*, two; *kotyledon*, cup-shaped hollow.] A plant with two seed-leaves.

dicratic (dīkrăt′ĭk) *a.* [Gk. *di-*, two; *kratos*, power.] With two spores of a tetrad being of one sex, and the other two of the opposite sex; *appl.* basidium. *Opp.* monocratic.

dictyodromous (dĭk′tĭŏd′römŭs) *a.* [Gk. *diktyon*, net; *dramein*, to run.] Net-veined, when the smaller veins branch and anastomose freely.

dictyogen (dĭk′tĭöjĕn) *n.* [Gk. *diktyon*, net; *-genes*, producing.] A net-leaved plant.

dictyokinesis (dĭk′tĭökīnē′sĭs) *n.* [Gk. *diktyon*, net; *kinesis*, movement.] The breaking-up of the Golgi-apparatus at mitosis and segregation of dictyosomes to daughter-cells.

dictyonalia (dĭk′tĭŏnā′lĭă) *n.* [Gk. *diktyon*, net.] The principal parenchyma spicules of Dictyonina and of many Lyssacina.

dictyosome (dĭk′tĭösōm) *n.* [Gk. *diktyon*, net; *soma*, body.] An element of the Golgi-apparatus, *q.v.*

dictyospore (dĭk′tĭöspōr) *n.* [Gk. *diktyon*, net; *sporos*, seed.] A spore, with transverse and longitudinal septa, of reticular appearance; muriform spore.

dictyostele (dĭk′tĭöstē′lē] *n.* [Gk. *diktyon*, net; *stele*, post.] A network formed by meristeles.

dictyotic (dĭk′tĭŏt′ĭk) *a.* [Gk. *diktyon*, net.] *Appl.* moment of shell or skeleton formation, or lorication moment, as of siliceous skeleton of radiolarians; *appl.* stage in cell growth where chromosomes are lost to view in nuclear reticulum.

dicyclic (dīsĭk′lĭk) *a.* [Gk. *di-*, two; *kyklos*, circle.] Having a row of perradial infrabasals, *appl.* theca of Crinoidea; with two whorls; biennial, *appl.* herbs.

dicystic (dīsĭs′tĭk) *a.* [Gk. *di-*, two; *kystis*, bag.] With two encysted stages.

didactyl (dīdăk′tĭl) *a.* [Gk. *di-*, two; *daktylos*, digit.] Having two fingers, toes or claws.

didelphic (dīdĕl′fĭk) *a.* [Gk. *di-*, double; *delphys*, womb.] Having two uteri, as marsupials; amphidelphic.

didymospore (dĭd′ĭmōspōr) *n.* [Gk. *didymos*, twin; *sporos*, seed.] A two-celled spore.

didymous (dĭd′ĭmŭs) *a.* [Gk. *didymos*, twin.] Growing in pairs.

didynamous (dīdĭn′ămŭs) *a.* [Gk. *di-*, two; *dynamis*, power.] With four stamens, two long, two short.

diecious,—dioecious, *q.v.*

diel (dī′ĕl) *a.* [L. *dies*, day.] During or *pert.* 24 hours; at 24-hour intervals; *appl.* life rhythms; *cf.* crepuscular, diurnal, nocturnal.

diencephalon (dĭ′ĕnkĕf′ălŏn, -sĕf′-) *n.* [Gk. *dia*, between; *engkephalos*, brain.] Part of the fore-brain, comprising thalamencephalon, pars mamillaris hypothalami, and posterior part of third ventricle; between-brain, ’tween-brain, interbrain.

diestrum,— dioestrus, *q.v.*

differentiation (dĭf′ĕrĕn′shĭā′shŭn) *n.* [L. *differre*, to differ.] Modification in structure and function of the parts of an organism, owing to division of labour.

diffluence (dĭf′looĕns) *n.* [L. *dis*, away; *fluere*, to flow.] Disintegration by vacuolisation.

diffusate (dĭfū′sāt) *n.* [L. *diffusus*, poured forth.] Any substance which passes through a semipermeable membrane during dialysis; dialysate. *Opp.* retentate.

diffuse (dĭfūs′) *a.* [L. *diffundere*, to pour.] Widely spread; not localised; not sharply defined at margin; *appl.* placenta with villi on all parts except poles.

diffuse-porous, — *appl.* wood in which vessels of approximately the same diameter tend to be evenly distributed in a growth ring; *cf.* ring-porous.

digametic (dīgămĕt′ĭk) *a.* [Gk. *dis*, twice; *gametes*, spouse.] Exhibiting digamety; having two types of gametes, one producing males, the other females; heterogametic.

digastric (dīgăs′trĭk) *a.* [Gk. *di-*, two; *gaster*, belly.] Two-bellied, *appl.* muscles fleshy at ends, tendinous in middle; biventral; *appl.* one of the suprahyoid muscles; *appl.* a branch of facial nerve.

digenesis (dījĕn′ĕsĭs) *n.* [Gk. *dis*, twice; *genesis*, descent.] Alternation of generations, *q.v.*

digenetic (dī′jĕnĕt′ĭk) *a.* [Gk. *dis*, twice; *genesis*, descent.] *Pert.* digenesis; requiring an alternation of hosts, *appl.* certain parasites.

digenic (dījĕn′ĭk) *a.* [Gk. *dis*, twice; *genos*, descent.] *Pert.* or controlled by two genes.

digenoporous (dī′jĕnŏp′ŏrŭs) *a.* [Gk. *dis*, twice; *genos*, birth; *poros*, pore.] With two genital pores, *appl.* many Turbellaria.

digestion (dĭjĕs′chŭn) *n.* [L. *digestio*, digestion.] The process by which nutrient materials are rendered absorbable by action of various juices.

digestive (dĭjĕs′tĭv) *a.* [L. *digestio*, digestion.] *Pert.* digestion, or having power of aiding in digestion.

digit (dĭj′ĭt) *n.* [L. *digitus*, finger.] Terminal division of limb in any vertebrate above fishes; toe or finger; distal part of chelae and chelicerae.

digital (dĭj′ĭtăl) *a.* [L. *digitus*, finger.] *Pert.* finger or digit; also *appl.* structures resembling a digit. *n.* Distal joint of spider's pedipalp.

digitaliform (dĭj′ĭtăl′ĭfôrm) *a.* [L. *digitus*, finger; *forma*, shape.] Finger-shaped, *appl.* corollae which are like the finger of a glove.

digitate (dĭj′ĭtāt) *a.* [L. *digitus*, finger.] Having parts arranged like the fingers in a hand; with fingers.

digitiform (dĭj′ĭtĭfôrm) *a.* [L. *digitus*, finger; *forma*, shape.] Finger-shaped; *appl.* roots.

digitigrade (dĭj′ĭtĭgrād′) *a.* [L. *digitus*, finger; *gradus*, step.] Walking with only the digits touching the ground.

digitinervate (dĭj'ĭtĭnĕr'vāt) *a.* [L. *digitus*, finger; *nervus*, sinew.] Having veins radiating out from base like fingers of a hand, with usually five or seven veins; *appl.* leaves.

digitipartite (dĭj'ĭtĭpâr'tīt) *a.* [L. *digitus*, finger; *partire*, to divide.] Having leaves divided up in a hand-like pattern.

digitipinnate (dĭj'ĭtĭpĭn'āt) *a.* [L. *digitus*, finger; *pinna*, feather.] Having digitate leaves of which the leaflets are pinnate.

digitule (dĭj'ĭtūl) *n.* [L. *digitulus*, little finger.] Any small finger-like process; small process on insect tarsi.

digitus,—*see* digit.

diglyphic (dīglĭf'ĭk) *a.* [Gk. *dis*, twice; *glyphein*, to engrave.] Having two siphonoglyphs.

digoneutic (dī'gŏnū'tĭk) *a.* [Gk. *dis*, twice; *goneuein*, to produce.] Breeding twice a year.

digonic (dīgŏn'ĭk) *a.* [Gk. *dis*, twice; *gone*, seed.] Producing male and female gametes in separate gones in the same individual; *cf.* amphigonic.

digonoporous (dī'gŏnŏp'ŏrŭs) *a.* [Gk. *dis*, twice; *gone*, seed; *poros*, pore.] With two distinct genital apertures, male and female.

digynous (dĭj'ĭnŭs) *a.* [Gk. *di-*, two; *gyne*, woman.] Having two carpels.

diheliotropism, — diaheliotropism, *q.v.*

diheterozygote (dī'hĕtĕrŏzī'gōt) *n.* [Gk. *dis*, twice; *heteros*, other; *zygotos*, yoked together.] A dihybrid.

dihybrid (dīhī'brĭd) *n.* [Gk. *dis*, twice; L. *hibrida*, mixed offspring.] A cross whose parents differ in two distinct characters; an organism heterozygous regarding two pairs of alleles.

dihydrotachysterol,—vitamin D_4, irradiation product of dihydro derivative of ergosterol, which counteracts impaired parathyroid function; $C_{28}H_{46}O$.

dikaryon (dīkā'rĭŏn) *n.* [Gk. *dis*, twice; *karyon*, nucleus.] A pair of nuclei, as in cells of ascogenous hyphae.

dikaryospore (dīkăr'ĭŏspōr) *n.* [Gk. *dis*, double; *karyon*, kernel; *sporos*, seed.] A spore with two nuclei.

dikaryotic,—*pert.* dikaryon; diploid.

dikont (dī'kŏnt) *a.* [Gk. *dis*, twice; *kontos*, punting-pole.] Having two flagella; biflagellate, dimastigote.

dilatator,—dilator, *q.v.*

dilated (dīlā'tĕd) *a.* [L. *dilatare*, to enlarge.] Expanded, or flattened; *appl.* parts of insects, etc., with a wide margin.

dilator (dīlā'tŏr) *n.* [L. *dilatare*, to expand.] Name *appl.* any muscle that expands or dilates an organ.

dilemma (dīlĕm'ă) *n.* [Gk. *dis*, double; *lemma*, assumption.] Distinction of alternative stimuli, retarding the reaction.

dilophous (dīlŏf'ŭs) *a.* [Gk. *di-*, two; *lophos*, crest.] *Appl.* a tetractinal spicule with two rays forked like a crest.

diluvial (dĭlū'vĭăl) *a.* [L. *diluvium*, deluge.] *Pert.* the present, in geological reckoning.

dimastigote (dīmăs'tĭgōt) *a.* [Gk. *dis*, twice; *mastix*, whip.] Having two flagella; biflagellate, dikont.

dimegaly (dīmĕg'ălĭ) *n.* [Gk. *dis*, twice; *megalos*, great.] Condition of having two sizes or a bimodal size frequency; *appl.* spermatozoa, ova.

dimerous (dĭm'ĕrŭs) *a.* [Gk. *dis*, twice; *meros*, part.] In two parts; having each whorl of two parts; with a two-jointed tarsus.

dimidiate (dĭmĭd'ĭāt) *a.* [L. *dimidius*, half.] Having only one-half developed; having capsule split on one side.

dimitic (dīmĭt'ĭk) *a.* [Gk. *dis*, twice; *mitos*, thread.] Having both supporting and generative hyphae. *cf.* trimitic.

dimorphic (dīmôr'fĭk) *a.* [Gk. *dis*, twice; *morphe*, shape.] Having, or *pert.*, two different forms.

dimorphism (dīmôr'fĭzm) *n.* [Gk. *dis*, twice; *morphe*, shape.] Condition of having stamens of two different lengths, of having two different kinds of leaves, flowers, etc.; state of having two different forms according to sex, or of one sex, two different kinds of zooids, or of offspring; of broods which, owing to differing conditions, differ in size or colouring; state of having reciprocally transformable unicellular and filamentous types, as in some bacteria and fungi.

dimyaric (dĭmĭăr'ĭk) *a.* [Gk. *dis*, twice; *mys*, muscle.] Having two adductor muscles; dimyarian.

dinergate (dĭnĕr'gāt) *n.* [Gk. *dinein*, to roam; *ergates*, worker.] A soldier ant.

dineuronic (dīnūrŏn'ĭk) *a.* [Gk. *dis*, twice; *neuron*, nerve.] With double innervation; *appl.* chromatophores with concentrating and dispersing nerve fibres.

dinomic (dīnŏm'ĭk) *a.* [Gk. *dis*, twice; *nomos*, district.] *Appl.* an organism restricted to two of the biogeographical divisions of the globe.

dioecious (dīē'sĭŭs) *a.* [Gk. *dis*, twice; *oikos*, house.] Having sexes separate; having male and female flowers on different individuals; gonochoristic; exhibiting dioecism or gonochorism.

dioestrus (dīē'strŭs) *n.* [Gk. *dia*, between; *oistros*, gadfly.] The quiescent period between heat periods in polyoestrous animals; dioestrum.

dioicous,—dioecious.

dionychous (dīŏn'ĭkŭs) *a.* [Gk. *di-*, two; *onyx*, nail.] Having two claws, as on tarsi of certain spiders.

dioptrate (dīŏp'trāt) *a.* [Gk. *dis*, twice; *ops*, eye.] Having eyes or ocelli separated by a narrow line.

dioptric (dīŏp'trĭk) *a.* [Gk. *dioptron*, spying-glass.] *Pert.* transmission and refraction of light; *appl.* structures, as cornea, lens, aqueous and vitreous humors.

diorchic (dīôr'kĭk) *a.* [Gk. *dis*, twice; *orchis*, testis.] Having two testes.

dipetalous (dīpĕt'ălŭs) *a.* [Gk. *dis*, twice; *petalon*, leaf.] Having two petals.

diphasic (dīfā'zĭk) *a.* [Gk. *dis*, twice; *phainein*, to appear.] *Appl.* extended life cycle of some protozoa, including the active stage; *cf.* monophasic; periodically changing two states or appearances, as of winter and summer pelage or plumage.

diphycercal (dĭf'ĭsĕr'kăl) *a.* [Gk. *diphyes*, twofold; *kerkos*, tail.] With a tail in which vertebral column runs straight to tip, thereby dividing the fin symmetrically.

diphygenetic (dĭf'ĭjĕnĕt'ĭk) *a.* [Gk. *diphyes*, twofold; *genetes*, begotten.] Producing embryos of two different types, as Dicyemida.

diphygenic (dĭf'ĭjĕn'ĭk) *a.* [Gk. *diphyes*, twofold; *genos*, descent.] With two types of development.

diphyletic (dī'fīlĕt'ĭk) *a.* [Gk. *dis*, twice; *phylon*, race.] *Pert.* or having origin in two lines of descent.

diphyllous (dīfĭl'ŭs) *a.* [Gk. *dis*, twice; *phyllon*, leaf.] Two-leaved.

diphyodont (dĭf'ĭōdŏnt') *a.* [Gk. *diphyes*, twofold; *odous*, tooth.] With deciduous and permanent sets of teeth.

diplanetary (dīplăn'ĕtărĭ), **diplanetic** (dī'plănĕt'ĭk) *a.* [Gk. *dis*, twice; *planetikos*, wandering.] With two distinct types of zoospores.

diplanetism (dīplăn'ĕtĭzm) *n.* [Gk. *dis*, twice; *planetikos*, wandering.] Condition of having two periods of motility in one life history, as of zoospores in some fungi.

diplarthrous (dĭplâr'thrŭs) *a.* [Gk. *diploos*, double; *arthron*, joint.] With tarsal or carpal bones of one row articulating with two bones in the other.

dipleurula (dīploor'ūlă) *n.* [Gk. *dis*, twice; *pleuron*, side.] A bilaterally symmetrical larva of echinoderms; an echinopaedium.

diplobiont (dĭp′lōbī′ŏnt) *n.* [Gk. *diploos*, double; *bion*, living.] An organism characterised by two kinds of individuals, asexual and sexual.

diploblastic (dĭp′lōblăs′tĭk) *a.* [Gk. *diploos*, double; *blastos*, bud.] Having two distinct germ layers.

diplocardiac (dĭp′lōkâr′dĭăk) *a.* [Gk. *diploos*, double; *kardia*, heart.] With the two sides of the heart quite distinct.

diplocaulescent (dĭp′lōkôlĕs′ĕnt) *a.* [Gk. *diploos*, double; *kaulos*, stem.] With secondary stems.

diplochlamydeous (dĭp′lōklămĭd′ëŭs) *a.* [Gk. *diploos*, double; *chlamys*, cloak.] Having a double perianth.

diplochromosome (dĭp′lōkrō′mōsōm) *n.* [Gk. *diploos*, double; *chroma*, colour; *soma*, body.] Anomalous chromosome having four chromatids, instead of two, attached to centromere.

diplocyte (dĭp′lōsīt) *n.* [Gk. *diploos*, double; *kytos*, hollow.] A cell having conjugate nuclei; synkaryocyte.

diplodal (dĭp′lōdăl) *a.* [Gk. *diploos*, double; *hodos*, way.] Having both prosodus and aphodus; *appl.* Porifera.

diploe (dĭp′lōē) *n.* [Gk. *diploe*, double.] The cancellous tissue between outer and inner lamellae of certain skull bones; tail of scorpion; mesophyll.

diplogangliate (dĭp′lōgăng′glĭāt) *a.* [Gk. *diploos*, double; *ganglion*, ganglion.] With ganglia in pairs.

diplogenesis (dĭp′lōjĕn′ĕsĭs) *n.* [Gk. *diploos*, double; *genesis*, descent.] Supposed change in germ plasm that accompanies 'use and disuse' changes occurring in body tissues; development of two parts instead of usual single part.

diploic (dĭplō′ĭk) *a.* [Gk. *diploos*, double.] Occupying channels in cancellous tissue of bones; *pert.* diploe.

diploid (dĭp′loid) *a.* [Gk. *diploos*, double; *eidos*, form.] Having a double set of chromosomes; *appl.* typical or zygotic somatic number of chromosomes of a species. *n.* A diploid organism; *cf.* haploid.

diploidisation,—doubling of number of chromosomes in haploid cells or hyphae.

diplokaryon (dĭp′lōkăr′ĭŏn) *n.* [Gk. *diploos*, double; *karyon*, nut.] A nucleus with two diploid sets of chromosomes, *opp.* amphikaryon.

diplonema (dĭp′lōnē′mă) *n.* [Gk. *diploos*, double; *nema*, thread.] Double thread of diplotene stage in meiosis.

diplonephridia (dĭp′lōnĕfrĭd′ĭă) *n. plu.* [Gk. *diploos*, double; *nephros*, kidney; *idion*, *dim.*] Nephridia derived partly from ectoderm, partly from mesoderm.

diploneural (dĭp′lōnū′răl) *a.* [Gk. *diploos*, double; *neuron*, nerve.] Supplied with two nerves.

diplont (dĭp′lŏnt) *n.* [Gk. *diploos*, double; *on*, being.] An organism having diploid somatic nuclei, *opp.* haplont.

diploperistomous(dĭp′lōpĕrĭs′tōmŭs) *a.* [Gk. *diploos*, double; *peri*, around; *stoma*, mouth.] Having a double projection or peristome.

diplophase (dĭp′lōfāz) *n.* [Gk. *diploos*, double; *phasis*, aspect.] Stage in life history of an organism when nuclei are diploid; sporophyte phase; diplotene stage in meiosis.

diplophyll (dĭp′lōfĭl) *n.* [Gk. *diploos*, double; *phyllon*, leaf.] A leaf having palisade tissue on upper and lower side with intermedial spongy parenchyma.

diplophyte (dĭp′lōfīt) *n.* [Gk. *diploos*, double; *phyton*, plant.] A diploid plant or sporophyte. *Opp.* haplophyte or gametophyte.

diploplacula (dĭp′lōplăk′ūlă) *n.* [Gk. *diploos*, double; *plakoeis*, flat cake.] A flattened blastula consisting of two layers of cells.

diplopore (dĭp′lōpōr) *n.* [Gk. *diploos*, double; *poros* passage.] Respiratory organ in Cystoidea.

diploptile (dĭp′lötīl, -ptīl) *a.* [Gk. *diploos*, double; *ptilon*, feather.] Double neossoptile, without rachis, formed by precocious development of the barbs of the teleoptile.

diplosis (dĭplō′sĭs) *n.* [Gk. *diploos*, double.] Doubling of the chromosome number, in syngamy.

diplosome (dĭp′lösōm) *n.* [Gk. *diploos*, double; *soma*, body.] A double centrosome lying outside the nuclear membrane; a paired heterochromosome.

diplosomite (dĭplösō′mīt) *n.* [Gk. *diploos*, double; *soma*, body.] Body segment consisting of two annular parts, prozonite and metazonite, in Diplopoda.

diplosphene (dĭp′lösfēn) *n.* [Gk. *diploos*, double; *sphen*, wedge.] Wedge-shaped process on neural arch of certain fossil reptiles.

diplospondylic (dĭp′löspŏndĭl′ĭk) *a.* [Gk. *diploos*, double; *sphondylos*, vertebra.] With two centra to each myotome, or with one centrum and well-developed intercentrum; exhibiting diplospondyly.

diplostemonous (dĭp′löstĕm′önŭs) *a.* [Gk. *diploos*, double; *stemon*, warp.] With two whorls of stamens in regular alternation with perianth leaves; with stamens double the number of petals.

diplostichous (dĭplŏs′tĭkŭs) *a.* [Gk. *diploos*, double; *stichos*, row.] Arranged in two rows or series.

diplostromatic (dĭp′löstrōmăt′ĭk) *a.* [Gk. *diploos*, double; *stroma*, bedding.] *Appl.* fungi having both entostroma and ectostroma. *Opp.* haplostromatic.

diplotegia (dĭp′lötē′jĭă) *n.* [Gk. *diploos*, double; *tegos*, roof.] An inferior fruit with dry dehiscent pericarp.

diplotene (dĭp′lötēn) *a.* [Gk. *diploos*, double; *tainia*, band.] *Appl.* stage in meiosis at which bivalent chromosomes split longitudinally.

diploxylic (dĭp′lözīl′ĭk) *a.* [Gk. *diploos*, double; *xylon*, wood.] *Appl.* leaf-trace bundles with inner and outer strands of wood, in certain extinct plants.

diplozoic (dĭp′lözō′ĭk) *a.* [Gk. *diploos*, double; *zoon*, animal.] Bilaterally symmetrical.

dipnoan (dĭp′nōăn) *a.* [Gk. *dis*, twice; *pnein*, to breathe.] Breathing by gills and lungs.

dipolar,—bipolar.

diporpa (dīpôr′pă) *n.* [Gk. *dis*, double; *porpe*, buckle.] Embryo of the trematode Diplozoon, which permanently unites with another.

diprotodont (dīprō′tödŏnt) *a.* [Gk. *dis*, twice; *protos*, first; *odous*, tooth.] Having two anterior incisors large and prominent, the rest of incisors and canines being smaller or absent.

dipterocecidium (dĭp′tërösēsĭd′ĭŭm) *n.* [Gk. *dis*, twice; *pteron*, wing; *kekis*, gall nut; *idion*, *dim.*] Gall caused by a dipterous insect.

dipterous (dĭp′tërŭs) *a.* [Gk. *dis*, twice; *pteron*, wing.] With two wings or wing-like expansions; *pert.* Diptera.

directive bodies,—polar bodies.

directive mesenteries,—in Zoantharia, the dorsal and ventral pairs of mesenteries.

directive sphere,—centrosphere.

dirhinic (dī′rīnĭk) *a.* [Gk. *di-*, two; *rhines*, nostrils.] Having two nostrils; *pert.* both nostrils. *Cf.* dichorhinic.

disaccharides (dīsăk′ărīdz) *n. plu.* [Gk. *dis*, twice; L. *saccharum*, sugar.] Sugars composed of two simple sugars, *e.g.*, lactose, maltose, sucrose.

disarticulate (dĭs′ârtĭk′ūlāt) *v.* [L. *dis*, asunder; *articulatus*, jointed.] To separate at a joint. *a.* Separated at a joint or joints.

disc (dĭsk) *n.* [L. *discus*, disc.] Any flattened portion like a disc in shape; middle part of capitulum in Compositae; adhesive tip of tendril; base of sea-weed thallus; circumoral area in many animals; circular areas at opposite poles of many animals; any modification of thalamus; area marking entrance of optic nerve into eye; cup-shaped tactile structures in skin; mass of cells of membrana granulosa which projects into cavity of egg follicle; anisotropic and isotropic parts of contractile fibrils of muscular tissue; disk.

disc-florets,—inner florets borne on abbreviated and reduced peduncle in many inflorescences.

discal (dĭs'kăl) *a.* [L. *discus*, disc.] *Pert.* any disc-like structure; *appl.* cross-vein between third and fourth longitudinal veins of insect wing. *n.* A large cell at base of wing of Lepidoptera completely enclosed by wing-nervures, also in some Diptera.

disciflorous (dĭs'kĭflō'rŭs, dĭs'ĭflō'rŭs) *a.* [L. *discus*, disc; *flos*, flower.] With flowers in which receptacle is large and disc-like.

disciform (dĭs'kĭfôrm, dĭs'ĭfôrm) *a.* [L. *discus*, disc; *forma*, shape.] Flat and circular; disc-shaped, discoid.

disclimax (dĭs'klī'măks) *n.* [Gk. *dis*, double; *klimax*, ladder.] Disturbance climax, stage in plant succession replacing or modifying true climax, usually due to animal and human agency; *e.g.* cultivated crops.

discoblastic (dĭs'köblăs'tĭk) *a.* [Gk. *diskos*, disc; *blastos*, bud.] *Pert.* meroblastic eggs in which area of segmentation is disc-shaped.

discoblastula (dĭs'köblăs'tūlă) *n.* [Gk. *diskos*, disc; *blastos*, bud.] A blastula formed from a meroblastic egg with disc-like blastoderm.

discocarp (dĭs'kökârp) *n.* [Gk. *diskos*, disc; *karpos*, fruit.] Special enlargement of thalamus below calyx; apothecium; a disc-shaped ascocarp.

discocellular vein,—discal vein.

discoctasters (dĭsk'ŏktăs'tërz) *n. plu.* [Gk. *diskos*, disc; *okto*, eight; *aster*, star.] Sponge spicules with eight rays terminating in discs, each disc corresponding in position to corners of a cube; modified hexactines.

discodactylous (dĭs'ködăk'tĭlŭs) *a.* [Gk. *diskos*, disc; *daktylos*, finger.] With sucker at end of digit.

discohexactine (dĭs'köhĕksăk'tĭn) *n.* [Gk. *diskos*, disc; *hex*, six; *aktis*, ray.] A sponge spicule with six equal rays meeting at right angles.

discohexaster (dĭs'köhĕksăs'tër) *n.* [Gk. *diskos*, disc; *hex*, six; *aster*, star.] A hexactine with rays ending in discs.

discoid (dĭs'koid) *a.* [Gk. *diskos*, disc; *eidos*, form.] Flat and circular; disc-shaped, disciform.

discoidal (dĭskoi'dăl) *a.* [Gk. *diskos*, disc; *eidos*, form.] Disc-like; *appl.* segmentation in which blastoderm forms a one-layered disc or cap which spreads over yolk; *appl.* placenta.

discontinuity (dĭs'kŏntĭnū'ĭtĭ) *n.* [O.F. *discontinuer*; from L. *dis-*, asunder; *continuare*, to continue.] Occurrence in two or more separate areas or geographical regions; disjunction; *appl.* layer: thermocline.

discontinuous variation, — mutation, *q.v.*

disconula (dĭskŏn'ūlă) *n.* [Gk. *diskos*, disc.] Eight-rayed stage in larval development of certain Coelentera.

discooctaster,—discoctaster, *q.v.*

discoplacenta (dĭs'köplăsĕn'tă) *n.* [L. *discus*, disc; *placenta*, placenta.] A placenta with villi on a circular cake-like disc.

discoplasm (dĭs'köplăzm) *n.* [Gk. *diskos*, disc; *plasma*, form.] Colourless framework or stroma of a red blood corpuscle.

discorhabd (dĭs'körăbd) *n.* [Gk. *diskos*, disc; *rhabdos*, rod.] A linear sponge spicule with disc-like outgrowths or whorls of spines.

discous,—disciform, discoid.

discus (dĭs'kŭs) *n.* [L. *discus*, Gk. *diskos*, quoit.] Disc; a flat and circular structure or part.

discus proligerus,—in a Graafian follicle, the mass of cells of membrana granulosa in which the ovum is embedded.

disjunct (dĭsjŭngkt′) *a.* [L. *disiunctus*, separated.] With body regions separated by deep constrictions.

disjunction (dĭsjŭngk′shŭn) *n.* [L. *disiunctus*, separated.] Divergence of paired chromosomes at anaphase; geographical distribution in discontinuous areas.

disjunctive symbiosis,—a mutually helpful condition of symbiosis although there is no direct connection between the partners.

disjunctor (dĭsjŭngk′tŏr) *n.* [L. *disiunctus*, separated.] Weak connective structure, or an intercalary cell, and zone of separation between successive conidia; 'bridge', connective.

disk (dĭsk) *n.* [Gk. *diskos*, disc.] *See* disc.

disomic (dī′sōmĭk) *a.* [Gk. *dis*, twice; *soma*, body.] *Pert.* or having two homologous chromosomes, or genes.

disoperation (dĭs′ŏpĕrā′shŭn) *n.* [L. *dis-*, asunder; *operatio*, work.] Coactions resulting in disadvantage to individual or to group; indirectly harmful influence of organisms upon each other.

dispermic (dīspĕr′mĭk) *a.* [Gk. *dis*, twice; *sperma*, seed.] *Pert.*, or by, two spermatozoa; *appl.* fertilisation of an ovum.

dispermous (dīspĕr′mŭs) *a.* [Gk. *dis*, twice; *sperma*, seed.] Having two seeds.

dispermy (dīspĕr′mĭ) *n.* [Gk. *dis*, twice; *sperma*, seed.] The entrance of two spermatozoa into an ovum.

dispersal (dĭspĕr′săl) *n.* [L. *dispergere*, to disperse.] The actual scattering or distributing of organisms on earth's surface; transport of diaspores.

disphotic,—dysphotic.

dispireme (dīspī′rēm) *n.* [Gk. *dis*, twice; *speirema*, skein.] The stage of karyokinesis in which each daughter nucleus has given rise to a spireme.

displacement (dĭsplās′mĕnt) *n.* [O.F. *desplacier*, to displace.] An abnormal position of any part of a plant due to its shifting from its normal place of insertion.

dispore (dī′spōr) *n.* [Gk. *dis*, twice; *sporos*, seed.] One of a pair of basidial spores.

disporocystid (dī′spōrŏsĭs′tĭd) *a.* [Gk. *dis*, twice; *sporos*, seed; *kystis*, bladder.] *Appl.* oocyst of Sporozoa when two sporocysts are present.

disporous (dīspō′rŭs) *a.* [Gk. *dis*, twice; *sporos*, seed.] With two spores.

dissected (dĭsĕk′tĕd) *a.* [L. *dissecare*, to cut open.] Having lamina cut into lobes, incisions reaching nearly to midrib; with parts displayed.

disseminule (dĭs-sĕm′ĭnūl) *n.* [L. *disseminare*, to scatter seed.] Any spore, seed, fruit, or bud when being dispersed and able to produce a new plant; diaspore.

dissepiment (dĭs′sĕp′ĭmĕnt) *n.* [L. *dissaepire*, to separate.] The partition found in some compound ovaries; in corals, one of oblique calcareous partitions stretching from septum to septum and closing interseptal loculi below.

dissilient (dĭsĭl′ĭĕnt) *a.* [L. *dissilire*, to burst asunder.] Springing open; *appl.* capsules of various plants which dehisce explosively.

dissimilation (dĭs′sĭmĭlā′shŭn) *n.* [L. *dissimilis*, different.] Katabolism, *q.v.*

dissoconch (dĭs′ŏkŏngk′) *n.* [Gk. *dissos*, double; *kongche*, shell.] The shell of a veliger larva.

dissogeny (dĭsŏj′ĕnĭ) *n.* [Gk. *dissos*, double; *genos*, descent.] Condition of having two sexually mature periods in the same animal—one in larva, one in adult; also dissogony.

distad (dĭs′tăd) *adv.* [L. *distare*, to stand apart; *ad*, to.] Towards or at a position away from centre or from point of attachment; in a distal direction.

distal (dĭs'tăl) *a.* [L. *distare*, to stand apart.] Standing far apart, distant, *appl.* bristles, etc.; *pert.* end of any structure farthest from middle line of organism or from point of attachment. *Opp.* proximal.

distalia (dĭstā'lĭă) *n. plu.* [L. *distare*, to stand apart.] The distal or third row of carpal or of tarsal bones.

distance receptor,—a sense-organ which reacts to stimuli emanating from distant objects; an olfactory, visual, or auditory receptor; disticeptor, distoceptor, teleceptor.

distemonous (dīstĕm'ŏnŭs) *a.* [Gk. *dis*, twice; *stemon*, spun thread.] Having two stamens; diandrous.

distichalia (dĭstĭkā'lĭă) *n. plu.* [Gk. *distichos*, with two rows.] In Crinoidea, the secondary brachialia.

distichate,—distichous.

distichous (dĭs'tĭkŭs) *a.* [Gk. *distichos*, with two rows.] Two-ranked; *appl.* alternate leaves, so arranged that first is directly below third.

distichy,—distichous condition; arrangement in two rows.

distipharynx (dĭs'tĭfăr'ĭngks) *n.* [L. *distans*, standing apart; Gk. *pharyngx*, gullet.] A short tube formed by union of epi- and hypopharynx in some insects.

distiproboscis (dĭs'tĭprōbŏs'ĭs) *n.* [L. *distans*, standing apart; Gk. *proboskis*, trunk.] Distal portion of insect proboscis, part of ligula.

dististyle (dĭs'tĭstīl) *n.* [L. *distans*, standing apart; Gk. *stylos*, pillar.] Distal part or style borne on basistyle, *q.v.*, of gonostyle in mosquitoes.

distoceptor (dĭs'tösĕp'tŏr) *n.* [L. *distare*, to stand apart; *recipere*, to receive.] A distance receptor, *q.v.*; teleceptor.

distractile (dĭstrăk'tīl) *a.* [L. *distractus*, pulled asunder.] Widely separate; *appl.* usually to long-stalked anthers.

distribution (dĭs'trĭbū'shŭn) *n.* [L. *distributus*, divided.] Range of an organism or group in biogeographical divisions of globe.

disymmetrical (dīsĭmĕt'rĭkăl) *a.* [Gk. *dis*, twice; *syn*, with; *metron*, measure.] Biradial, *q.v.*

dithecal (dīthē'kăl) *a.* [Gk. *dis*, twice; *theke*, box.] Two-celled, as anthers.

ditokous (dĭt'ökŭs) *a.* [Gk. *dis*, twice; *tokos*, birth.] Producing two at a time, either eggs or young.

ditrematous (dītrē'mătŭs) *a.* [Gk. *dis*, twice; *trema*, opening.] With separate genital openings; with anus and genital openings separate.

ditrochous (dĭt'rökŭs) *a.* [Gk. *dis*. twice; *trochos*, runner.] With a divided trochanter.

ditypism (dītī'pĭzm) *n.* [Gk. *dis*, twice; *typos*, type.] Occurrence or possession of two types; sex differentiation, represented by + and —, of two apparently similar haplonts.

diuresis (dīūrē'sĭs) *n.* [Gk. *dia*, through; *ouron*, urine.] Increased or excessive secretion of urine.

diurnal (dīŭr'năl) *a.* [L. *diurnus*, *pert.* day.] Opening during the day only; active in the day-time.

divaricate (dīvăr'ĭkāt) *a.* [L. *divaricatus*, stretched apart.] Widely divergent; bifid; forked.

divaricators (dīvăr'ĭkātŏrz) *n. plu.* [L. *divaricatus*, stretched apart.] Muscles stretching from ventral valve to cardinal process, in brachiopods; muscles in avicularia.

divergency (dīvĕr'jĕnsĭ) *n.* [L. *divergere*, to bend away.] The fraction of a stem circumference, usually constant for a species, which separates two consecutive leaves in a spiral.

divergent (dīvĕr'jĕnt) *a.* [L. *divergere*, to bend away.] Separated from one another; *appl.* leaves.

diversity index,—of a community, the ratio between number of species and number of individuals.

diverticillate,—biverticillate.

diverticulate (dī'vĕrtĭk'ūlāt) *a.* [L. *divertere*, to turn aside.] Having a diverticulum; having short offshoots approximately at right angles to axis, *appl.* certain hyphae;

having a projection where attached to sterigma, *appl.* certain spores.

diverticulum (dī'vĕrtĭk'ūlŭm) *n.* [L. *divertere*, to turn away.] A tube or sac, blind at distal end, branching off from a canal or cavity; filament of carpogonium, giving rise to carpospore in red algae.

divided (dĭvī'dĕd) *a.* [L. *dividere*, to divide.] With lamina cut by incisions reaching midrib; *appl.* leaves.

division centre,—centriole.

dizoic (dīzō'ĭk) *a.* [Gk. *dis*, twice; *zoon*, animal.] *Pert.* spore containing two sporozoites.

dizygotic (dī'zīgŏt'ĭk) *a.* [Gk. *dis*, twice; *zygotes*, yoked.] Originating from two fertilised ova; *appl.* twins; dizygous; binovular.

Dobie's line,—Z-disc or telophragma.

docoglossate (dŏk'ŏglŏs'āt) *a.* [Gk. *dokos*, shaft; *glossa*, tongue.] Having an elongated radula with few marginal teeth, as limpets.

dodecagynous (dōdĕkăj'ĭnŭs) *a.* [Gk. *dodeka*, twelve; *gyne*, woman.] Having twelve pistils.

dodecamerous (dōdĕkăm'ĕrŭs) *a.* [Gk. *dodeka*, twelve; *meros*, part.] Having each whorl composed of twelve parts.

dodecandrous (dōdĕkăn'drŭs) *a.* [Gk. *dodeka*, twelve; *aner*, man.] Having at least twelve stamens.

Dogiel's cells [*G. S. Dogiel*, Russian neurologist]. Nerve-cells within spinal ganglia, with axons branching close to cell-bodies.

dolabriform (dŏlā'brĭfôrm) *a.* [L. *dolabra*, mattock; *forma*, shape.] Axe-shaped; dolabrate.

dolichocephalic (dŏl'ĭkŏkĕfăl'ĭk,-sĕf-) *a.* [Gk. *dolichos*, long; *kephale*, head.] Long-headed; with cephalic index of under 75; *cf.* brachycephalic.

dolichohieric (dŏl'ĭkŏhī'ĕrĭk) *a.* [Gk. *dolichos*, long; *hieros*, sacred.] With sacral index below 100; *cf.* platyhieric.

dolichostylous (dŏl'ĭkŏstī'lŭs) *a.* [Gk. *dolichos*, long; *stylos*, pillar.] *Pert.* long-styled anthers in dimorphic flowers.

dolioform (dō'lĭŏfôrm) *a.* [L. *dolium*, wine-cask; *forma*, shape.] Barrel-shaped.

Dollo's law [*L. Dollo*, Belgian palaeontologist]. The principle that evolution is not reversible.

dome cell,—the penultimate cell of a crosier, containing two nuclei which fuse, being the first stage in development of an ascus; loop cell.

dominant (dŏm'ĭnănt) *a.* [L. *dominans*, ruling.] *Appl.* plants which by their extent determine biotic conditions in a given area; *appl.* species prevalent in a particular community, or at a given period; *appl.* character possessed by one parent which in a hybrid masks the corresponding alternative character derived from the other parent; *appl.* the parental allele manifested in the F_1 heterozygote; *opp.* recessive; *appl.* stimulated part of brain when excitation is increased by stimuli usually inducing other reflexes; *appl.* parts of body controlling less active parts.

dominator (dŏm'ĭnātŏr) *n.* [L. *dominator*, ruler.] A broad band of the spectrum which evokes sensation of luminosity in light-adapted eye; *cf.* modulator.

dopa (dō'pă) *n.* [*D*ihydr*o*xy*p*henyl*a*lanine.] An amino-acid formed from tyrosine by action of ultraviolet rays, and oxidised by dopa-oxidase or dopase to a red precursor of melanin, as in basal layers of epidermis; $C_9H_{11}O_4N$.

dormancy (dôr'mănsĭ) *n.* [F. *dormir*, from L. *dormire*, to sleep.] A resting or quiescent condition; reduction in protoplasmic activity due to carbon dioxide concentration, *appl.* seeds; hibernation and aestivation.

dormancy callus,—callose deposited on sieve areas at the onset of winter.

dorsad (dôr'săd) *adv.* [L. *dorsum*, back; *ad*, to.] Towards back or dorsal surface, *opp.* ventrad.

dorsal (dôr′săl) *a.* [L. *dorsum*, back.] *Pert.* or lying near back, *opp.* ventral surface; *pert.* surface farthest from axis; upper surface of thallus or prothallus of ferns, etc.

dorsalis (dôrsā′lĭs) *n.* [L. *dorsum*, back.] The artery which supplies the back of any organ.

dorsiferous (dôrsĭf′ërŭs) *a.* [L. *dorsum*, back; *ferre*, to carry.] With sori on back of leaf; carrying the young on the back.

dorsifixed (dôr′sĭfĭk′st) *a.* [L. *dorsum*, back; *fingere*, to fix.] Having filament attached to back of anther.

dorsigerous,—dorsiferous.

dorsigrade (dôr′sĭgrād) *a.* [L. *dorsum*, back; *gradus*, step.] Having back of digit on the ground when walking.

dorsilateral (dôr′sĭlăt′ërăl) *a.* [L. *dorsum*, back; *latus*, side.] Of or *pert.* the back and sides; dorsal and lateral.

dorsispinal (dôr′sĭspī′năl) *a.* [L. *dorsum*, back; *spina*, spine.] *Pert.* or referring to back and spine.

dorsiventral (dôr′sĭvĕn′trăl) *a.* [L. *dorsum*, back; *venter*, belly.] With upper and lower surfaces distinct; bifacial; *cf.* dorsoventral.

dorsocentral (dôr′sösĕn′trăl) *a.* [L. *dorsum*, back; *centrum*, centre.] *Pert.* mid-dorsal surface; *pert.* aboral surface of echinoderms.

dorsolumbar (dôr′sölŭm′băr) *a.* [L. *dorsum*, back; *lumbus*, loin.] *Pert.* lumbar region of back.

dorsoumbonal (dôr′söŭm′bōnăl) *a.* [L. *dorsum*, back; *umbo*, shieldboss.] Lying on the back near the umbo.

dorsoventral (dôr′sövĕn′trăl) *a.* [L. *dorsum*, back; *venter*, belly.] *Pert.* structures which stretch from dorsal to ventral surface; *cf.* dorsiventral.

dorsulum (dôr′sūlŭm) *n.* [*Dim.* of L. *dorsum*, back.] Upper surface lying between collar and scutellum; mesonotum.

dorsum (dôr′sŭm) *n.* [L. *dorsum*, back.] The sulcular surface of Anthozoa; tergum or notum of insects and crustaceans; inner margin of insect wing; the back of higher animals; upper surface, as of tongue.

dorylaner (dŏr′ĭlānër) *n.* [Gk. *dory*, spear; *aner*, male.] An exceptionally large male ant of driver-ant group.

double fertilisation,—fusion of one of two gametes derived from division of the generative nucleus of the microspore with the oosphere nucleus, and of the other with the primary endosperm nucleus, in angiosperms.

doublure (dooblūr′) *n.* [F. *doublure*, lining.] The reflected margin of carapace in Trilobita and Xiphosura.

Doyère's cone ([*L. Doyère*, French physiologist]. End-plate or eminence where nerve fibre branches and enters sarcolemma.

drepaniform,—drepanoid.

drepanium (drĕpā′nĭŭm) *n.* [Gk. *drepane*, sickle.] A helicoid cyme with secondary axes developed in a plane parallel to that of main peduncle and its first branch.

drepanoid (drĕp′ănoid) *a.* [Gk. *drepanoeides*, sickle-shaped.] Sickle-shaped; falcate, falciform.

drift (drĭft) *n.* [A.S. *drifan*, to drive.] Transported, *opp.* bed-rock, soils; process of change in gene frequencies in a population of breeding individuals; Sewall Wright effect; genetico-automatic process.

dromaeognathous (drŏm′ēŏg′năthŭs) *a.* [Gk. *dramein*, to run; *gnathos*, jaw.] Having a palate in which palatines and pterygoids do not articulate, owing to intervention of vomer.

dromotropic (drŏm′ötrŏp′ĭk) *a.* [Gk. *dromos*, course; *trope*, turn.] Bent in a spiral; influencing nerve conductivity.

drone (drōn) *n.* [A.S. *dran*.] The male bee.

dropper (drŏp′ër) *n.* [A.S. *dreópan*, to drop.] Rhizomatous downward outgrowth of a bulb, which may form a new bulb.

drop-roots,—buttress-roots.

drupaceous (droopā'shŭs) *a.* [Gk. *dryppa*, olive.] *Pert.* drupe ; bearing drupes ; drupe-like.

drupe (droop) *n.* [Gk. *dryppa*, olive.] A superior, one-celled fruit with one or two seeds and the pericarp differentiated into a thin epicarp, a fleshy sarcocarp, and a hard endocarp, as of plum.

drupel (droop'ĕl) *n.* [Gk. *dryppa*, olive.] An individual component of aggregate fruit, as of raspberry ; drupelet, drupeole.

dry (drī) *a.* [A.S. *dryge*, dry.] *Appl.* achenial, capsular, and schizocarpic fruits. *Opp.* succulent.

drymophytes (drī'möfīts) *n. plu.* [Gk. *drymos*, coppice ; *phyton*, plant.] Small trees, bushes, and shrubs.

duct (dŭkt) *n.* [L. *ducere*, to lead.] Any tube which conveys fluid or other substance ; a tube formed by a series of cells which have lost their walls at the points of contact; ductus.

ductless glands,—glands which do not communicate with any organ directly by means of a duct ; endocrine organs.

ductule (dŭk'tūl) *n.* [L. *ducere*, to lead.] A minute duct ; fine thread-like terminal portion of a duct.

ductus (dŭk'tŭs) *n.* [L. *ducere*, to lead.] Duct, *q.v.*

ductus deferens,—vas deferens.

ductus ejaculatorius,—a narrow muscular tube at end of vas deferens in various invertebrates.

Dufour's gland [*L. Dufour*, French entomologist]. An alkaline gland with duct leading to terebra or sting of certain Hymenoptera.

dulosis (dū'lōsĭs) *n.* [Gk. *doulosis*, subjugation.] Slavery, among ants.

dumb-bell bone,—prevomer, *q.v.*

dumose (dū'mōs) *a.* [L. *dumosus*, bushy.] Shrub-like in appearance.

duodenal (dū'ödē'năl) *a.* [L. *duodeni*, twelve each.] *Pert.* duodenum.

duodenum (dū'ödē'nŭm) *n.* [L. *duodeni*, twelve each.] That portion of small intestine next to pyloric end of stomach.

duplex (dū'plĕks) *a.* [L. *duplex*, two-fold.] Double ; compound, *appl.* flowers ; diploid ; having two dominant genes, in polyploidy ; consisting of two distinct structures ; having two distinct parts.

duplication (dū'plĭkā'shŭn) *n.* [L. *duplex*, double.] Chorisis, *q.v.* ; a translocated chromosome fragment attached to one of normal set.

duplicature (dū'plĭkătūr) *n.* [L *duplex*, double.] A circular fold near base of protrusible portion of a polyzoan polypide.

duplicident (dūplĭs'ĭdĕnt) *a.* (L. *duplex*, double ; *dens*, tooth.] With two pairs of incisors in upper jaw, one behind the other.

duplicity (dūplĭs'ĭtĭ) *n.* [L. *dupliciter*, doubly.] Condition of being two-fold ; *appl.* theory that cones are the photopic, or colour, receptors, and rods the scotopic, or brightness, receptors.

duplicodentate (dū'plĭködĕn'tāt) *a.* [L. *duplex*, double ; *dens*, tooth.] With marginal teeth on leaf bearing smaller teeth-like structures.

dura mater (dū'ră mā'tĕr) *n.* [L. *dura*, hard ; *mater*, mother.] The tough membrane lining the whole cerebro-spinal cavity.

dura spinalis,—the tough membrane lining the spinal canal.

dural (dū'răl) *a.* [L. *dura*, hard.] *Pert.* dura mater ; *appl.* sheath of optic nerve.

duramen (dūrā'mĕn) *n.* [L. *duramen*, hardness.] The hard, darker central region of a tree-stem; the heart-wood.

duvet (dūvā') *n.* [F. *duvet*, down.] Downy coating, as soft matted coating by certain fungi.

dwarf male,—small three- or four-celled plant formed from androspore of Oedogonium ; a small, usually simply formed, individual in many classes of animals, either free or carried by the female.

dyad (dī'ăd) *n.* [Gk. *dyas*, two.] The half of a tetrad group ; a bivalent chromosome.

dynamic (dīnăm'ĭk) *a*. [Gk. *dynamis*, power.] Producing or manifesting activity, *opp*. static; *appl*. specific dynamic action, the calorigenic action of food, increasing metabolism above basal rate.

dynamoneure (dīnăm'önūr) *n*. [Gk. *dynamai*, to be able to do; *neuron*, nerve.] A motor neurone.

dynamoplastic (dī'nămöplăs'tĭk) *a*. [Gk. *dynamis*, power; *plastos*, formed.] *Appl*. active type of energid-product; *opp*. paraplastic.

dysgenic (dĭsjĕn'ĭk) *a*. [Gk. *dysgeneia*, low birth.] *Pert*. tending towards, or productive of, racial degeneration; kakogenic, *opp*. eugenic.

dysharmonic (dĭs'hârmŏn'ĭk) *a*. [Gk. *dys-*, mis-; *harmonia*, a fitting together.] Changing relative size of parts with increase in body size; heterogonic.

dysmerism (dĭs'mërĭzm) *n*. [Gk. *dys-*, mis-; *meros*, part.] An aggregate of unlike parts.

dysmerogenesis (dĭs'mĕröjĕn'ësĭs) *n*. [Gk. *dys-*, mis-; *meros*, part; *genesis*, descent.] Segmentation resulting in unlike parts.

dysphotic (dĭs'fōtĭk) *a*. [Gk. *dys-*, mis-; *phos*, light.] Dim; *appl*. zone, waters at depths between 80 and 600 metres, between euphotic and aphotic zones, *q.v.*; lower layer of photic zone.

dysploid,—aneuploid, *q.v.*

dyspnoea (dĭspnē'ă) *n*. [Gk. *dyspnoos*, breathless.] Difficulty in breathing.

dysteleology (dĭs'tĕlëŏl'öjĭ) *n*. [Gk. *dys-*, mis-; *teleos*, ended; *logos*, discourse.] Haeckel's doctrine of purposelessness in Nature; appearance of uselessness, as of certain organs or other structures; frustration of function.

dystrophic (dĭstrŏf'ĭk) *a*. [Gk. *dys-*, mis-; *trephein*, to nourish.] Wrongly or inadequately nourished; inhibiting adequate nutrition; *pert*. faulty nutrition.

Dzierzon theory [*J. Dzierzon*, Silesian apiculturist]. Belief that males of honey-bee are always produced from unfertilised eggs.

E

ear (ēr) *n*. [A.S. *éare*.] The auditory organ; among invertebrates, the various structures supposed to have an auditory function; the specialised tufts of hair or feathers which are close to, or similar to an external ear or pinna; an ear-shaped structure; the spike of grasses, usually of cereals.

eared (ērd) *a*. [A.S. *éare*.] Having external ears or pinnae; with tufts of feathers resembling ears; having long bristles or processes, as in grains of corn; auriculate.

ebracteate (ēbrăk'tëāt), **ebracteolate** (ēbrăk'tëölāt) *a*. [L. *ex*, out of; *bractea*, thin plate.] Without bracts; without bracteoles.

ecad,—oecad, *q.v.*

ecalcarate (ēkăl'kărāt) *a*. [L. *ex*, out of; *calcar*, spur.] Having no spur or spur-like process.

ecardinal (ēkâr'dĭnăl) *a*. [L. *ex*, out of; *cardo*, hinge.] Having no hinge; also ecardinate.

ecarinate (ēkăr'ĭnāt) *a*. [L. *ex*, out of; *carina*, keel.] Not furnished with a keel or keel-like ridge.

ecaudate (ēkô'dāt) *a*. [L. *ex*, out of; *cauda*, tail.] Without a tail.

ecblastesis (ĕk'blăstē'sĭs) *n*. [Gk. *ek*, out of; *blastos*, bud.] Proliferation of main axis of inflorescence.

eccritic (ĕkrĭt'ĭk) *a*. [Gk. *ekkrinein*, to expel, to select.] Causing or *pert*. excretion; preferred, *appl*. temperature, etc. *n*. A substance or other agent which promotes excretion.

ecdemic (ĕkdĕm'ĭk) *a*. [Gk. *ek*, out of; *demos*, people.] Not native.

ecderon (ĕk'dërŏn) *n*. [Gk. *ek*, out; *deros*, skin.] The outer or epidermal layer of skin.

ecderonic (ĕkdërŏn'ĭk) *a*. [Gk. *ek*, out; *deros*, skin.] Ectodermic; epiblastic.

ecdysial (ĕkdĭs'ĭăl) *a*. [Gk. *ekdysai*, to strip.] *Pert*. ecdysis; *appl*. fluid between old and new cuticle which aids in disintegration of old cuticle.

moulting fluid; *appl.* line along which cuticle splits in moulting; *appl.* glands, Verson's glands, secreting moulting fluid.

ecdysis (ĕk'dĭsĭs) *n.* [Gk. *ekdysai*, to strip.] The act of moulting a cuticular layer or structure; *cf.* endysis.

ecdysone (ĕk'dĭsōn) *n.* [Gk. *ekdysai*, to strip.] The moulting hormone or growth and differentiation hormone of Arthropoda.

ece,—oike, *q.v.*

ecesis,—oikesis, *q.v.*

echard (ĕkârd') *n.* [Gk. *echein*, to keep; *ardo*, I water.] Soil water not available for plant growth; *cf.* chresard, holard.

echinate (ĕk'ĭnāt) *a.* [Gk. *echinos*, hedgehog.] Furnished with spines or bristles.

echinenone (ĕkĭn'ēnōn) *n.* [Gk. *echinos*, sea-urchin.] A carotenoid pigment of sea-urchin gonads, a provitamin A.

echinidium (ĕkĭnĭd'ĭŭm) *n.* [Gk. *echinos*, spine; *idion*, *dim.*] Marginal hair, with small pointed or branched outgrowths, of pileus of fungi; brush cell.

echinochrome (ĕkī'nōkrōm) *n.* [Gk. *echinos*, sea-urchin; *chroma*, colour.] A red-brown respiratory pigment of echinoderms; $C_{12}H_{11}O_7$.

echinococcus (ĕkī'nōkŏk'ŭs) *n.* [Gk. *echinos*, spine; *kokkos*, berry.] A vesicular metacestode developing a number of daughter cysts, each with many heads.

echinoid (ĕkī'noid) *a.* [Gk. *echinos*, sea-urchin; *eidos*, form.] *Pert.* or like sea-urchins.

echinopaedium (ĕkī'nōpē'dĭŭm) *n.* [Gk. *echinos*, sea-urchin; *paidion*, young child.] Dipleurula, *q.v.*

echinopluteus (ĕkī'nōploo'tēŭs) *n.* [L. *echinus*, sea-urchin; *pluteus*, shed.] Larva or pluteus of echinoids, from supposed resemblance to an upturned easel.

echinulate (ĕkĭn'ūlāt) *a.* [Gk. *echinos*, spine.] Having small spines; having pointed outgrowths, *appl.* bacterial cultures.

echolocation (ĕk'ōlōkā'shŭn) *n.* [L. *echo*, echo; *locare*, to place.] Location of objects by means of echos, as of supersonic sounds emitted by animals, *e.g.* by bats.

eclipse (ĕklĭps') *n.* [Gk. *ekleipein*, to leave incomplete.] Plumage assumed after spring moult, as in drake; period of multiplication of a bacterial virus during which it fails to be noticed in an infected cell.

eclosion (ĕklō'zhŭn) *n.* [L. *e*, out; *clausus*, shut.] Hatching from an egg, or of an imago.

eco-,—*see also* oeco-, oiko-.

ecobiotic (ē'kōbīŏt'ĭk) *a.* [Gk. *oikos*, household; *biosis*, manner of life.] *Appl.* adaptation to particular mode of life within a habitat.

ecodeme (ē'kōdēm) *n.* [Gk. *oikos*, household; *demos*, people.] A deme occupying a particular ecological habitat.

ecoid,—oecoid, *q.v.*

ecology (ēkŏl'ōjĭ) *n.* [Gk. *oikos*, household; *logos*, discourse.] That part of biology which deals with relationship between organisms and their surroundings; bionomics.

economic density,—of a population, the number of individuals per unit of the inhabited area, *opp.* population density in an area only partly inhabited.

ecorticate (ēkôr'tĭkāt) *a.* [L. *e*, out of; *cortex*, rind.] Without a cortex; *appl.* certain lichens.

ecostate (ēkŏs'tāt) *a.* [L. *e*, out; *costa*, rib.] Without costae; not costate.

ecosystem (ē'kōsĭs'tēm) *n.* [Gk. *oikos*, household; *systema*, composite whole.] Ecological system formed by the interaction of coacting organisms and their environment.

ecotone (ē'kōtōn) *n.* [Gk. *oikos*, household; *tonos*, brace.] A transitional species in intermediate area between two associations; the boundary line or transitional area between two communities.

ecotope (ē'kötōp) *n.* [Gk. *oikos*, household; *topos*, place.] A particular kind of habitat within a region.

ecotype (ē'kötīp) *n.* [Gk. *oikos*, household; *typos*, pattern.] A biotype resulting from selection in a particular habitat; habitat type.

ecphoria (ĕkfō'rĭă) *n.* [Gk. *ekphorion*, produce.] The revival of a latent memory pattern or engram.

ecsoma (ĕksō'mă) *n.* [Gk. *ek*, from out of; *soma*, body.] Retractile posterior part of body in certain trematodes.

ectad (ĕk'tăd) *adv.* [Gk. *ektos*, outside; L. *ad*, towards.] Towards the exterior; outwards externally. *Opp.* entad.

ectadenia (ĕk'tădē'nĭă) *n. plu.* [Gk. *ektos*, outside; *aden*, gland.] Ectodermal accessory genital glands in insects; *cf.* mesadenia.

ectal (ĕk'tăl) *a.* [Gk. *ektos*, outside.] Outer; external; *appl.* layer or membrane on margin of exciple. *Opp.* ental.

ectamnion (ĕktăm'nĭŏn) *n.* [Gk. *ektos*, outside; *amnion*, foetal membrane]. Ectodermal thickening in proamnion, beginning of head-fold.

ectangial (ĕk'tănjĭăl) *a.* [Gk. *ektos*, outside; *anggeion*, vessel.] Outside a vessel; produced outside a primary sporangium; ectoangial. *Opp.* entangial.

ectendotrophic (ĕk'tĕndötrŏf'ĭk) *a.* [Gk. *ectos*, without; *endon*, within; *trophe*, nourishment.] Partly ectotrophic and partly endotrophic, *appl.* mycorhizic fungus.

ectental line,—the line where ectoderm and endoderm meet at blastopore of a gastrula.

ectepicondylar (ĕkt'ĕpĭkŏn'dĭlăr) *a.* [Gk. *ektos*, outside; *epi*, upon; *kondylos*, knob.] *Appl.* radial foramen of humerus.

ectethmoid (ĕktĕth'moid) *n.* [Gk. *ektos*, outside; *ethmos*, sieve; *eidos*, form.] Lateral ethmoid bone.

ecthoraeum (ĕk'thŏrē'ŭm) *n.* [Gk. *ekthroskein*, to leap out.] The thread of a nematocyst.

ectoangial,—ectangial.

ectoascus (ĕk'töăs'kŭs) *n.* [Gk. *ektos*, outside; *askos*, bag.] Outer membrane of an ascus in certain Ascomycetes; *cf.* endoascus.

ectobatic (ĕk'töbăt'ĭk) *a.* [Gk. *ektos*, outside; *bainein*, to go.] Efferent; exodic, centrifugal. *Opp.* endobatic.

ectoblast (ĕk'töblăst) *n.* [Gk. *ektos*, outside; *blastos*, bud.] Epiblast, *q.v.*

ectobronchus (ĕk'töbrŏng'kŭs) *n.* [Gk. *ektos*, outside; *brongchos*, windpipe.] Lateral branch of main bronchus in birds; also ectobronchium.

ectocarpous (ĕk'tökâr'pŭs) *a.* [Gk. *ektos*, outside; *karpos*, fruit.] Having gonads of ectodermal origin.

ectochondrostosis (ĕk'tökôndrŏstō'sĭs) *n.* [Gk. *ektos*, outside; *chondros*, cartilage; *osteon*, bone.] Deposition of lime-salts beginning in perichondrium and gradually invading cartilage

ectochone (ĕk'tökōnē) *n.* [Gk. *ektos*, outside; *choane*, funnel.] A funnel-shaped chamber into which lead the ostia in certain sponges.

ectochroic (ĕk'tökrō'ĭk] *a.* [Gk. *ektos*, outside; *chros*, complexion.] Having pigment on the surface of a cell. *Opp.* endochroic.

ectocoelic (ĕk'tösē'lĭk)*a.* [Gk. *ektos*, outside; *koilos*, hollow.] *Pert.* structures situated outside the enteron of coelenterates.

ectocondyle (ĕk'tökŏn'dĭl) *n.* [Gk. *ektos*, outside; *kondylos*, knob.] The outer condyle of a bone.

ectocranial (ĕk'tökrā'nĭăl) *a.* [Gk. *ektos*, outside; *kranion*, skull.] *Pert.* outside of skull.

ectocrine (ĕk'tökrīn) *a.* [Gk. *ektos*, outside; *krinein*, to separate.] *Appl.* and *pert.* organic substances or decomposition products in the external medium which inhibit or stimulate plant life. *n.* An ectocrine compound; environmental hormone, external diffusion hormone.

ectocuneiform (ĕk'tökūnē'ĭfôrm) *n.* [Gk. *ektos*, outside; L. *cuneus*, wedge; *forma*, shape.] A bone in distal row of tarsus; third cuneiform.

ectocyst (ĕk'tösĭst) *n.* [Gk. *ektos*, outside; *kystis*, bladder.] Outer layer of zooecium in Polyzoa; outer covering of encysted Protozoa; epicyst.

ectoderm (ĕk'tödĕrm) *n.* [Gk. *ektos*, outside; *derma*, skin.] The outer layer of a multicellular animal; the epidermis in higher mammals.

ectoentad (ĕk'töĕn'tăd) *a.* [Gk. *ektos*, without; *entos*, within; L. *ad*, towards.] From without inwards, *opp.* entoectad.

ectoenzyme (ĕk'töĕn'zīm) *n.* [Gk. *ektos*, outside; *en*, in; *zyme*, leaven.] Any extracellular enzyme; exoenzyme.

ecto-ethmoid,—ectethmoid, *q.v.*

ectogenesis (ĕk'töjĕn'ĕsĭs) *n.* [Gk. *ektos*, outside; *genesis*, descent.] Embryonic development outside the maternal organism; development in an artificial environment.

ectogenous (ĕktŏj'ĕnŭs) *a.* [Gk. *ektos*, outside; *genos*, birth.] Able to live an independent life; originating outside the organism.

ectoglia (ĕktŏglī'ă) *n.* [Gk. *ektos*, outside; *glia*, glue.] An outer layer in central nervous system.

ectolecithal (ĕk'tölĕs'ĭthăl) *a.* [Gk. *ektos*, outside; *lekithos*, yolk of egg.] Having yolk surrounding formative protoplasm.

ectoloph (ĕk'tölŏf) *n.* [Gk. *ektos*, outside; *lophos*, crest.] The ridge stretching from paracone to metacone in a lophodont molar.

ectomere (ĕk'tömēr) *n.* [Gk. *ektos*, outside; *meros*, part.] An epiblast cell which gives rise to ectoderm.

ectomesogloeal (ĕk'tömĕsöglē'ăl, -mēz-) *a.* [Gk. *ektos*, outside; *mesos*, middle; *gloia*, glue.] *Pert.* ectoderm and mesogloea; *appl.* muscle fibres of disc of sea-anemones.

-ectomy (ĕk'tömĭ). [Gk. *ek*, out; *temnein*, to cut.] Suffix signifying an excision, *e.g.* thyroidectomy, gonadectomy, etc.

ectoneural (ĕk'tönū'ral) *a.* [Gk. *ektos*, outside; *neuron*, nerve.] *Appl.* system of oral ring, radial, and subepidermal nerves in echinoderms.

ectoparasite (ĕk'töpăr'ăsīt) *n.* [Gk. *ektos*, outside; *para*, beside; *sitos*, food.] A parasite that lives on the exterior of an organism.

ectopatagium (ĕk'töpătāj'ĭŭm) *n.* [Gk. *ektos*, outside; L. *patagium*, border.] The part of the wing-like membrane of bats which is carried on metacarpals and phalanges.

ectophloeodic (ĕk'töflēŏd'ĭk) *a.* [Gk. *ektos*, outside; *phloios*, bark.] Growing on bark or other outer surface of plants, *appl.* lichens; ectophloeodal, epiphloeodal.

ectophyte (ĕk'töfīt) *n.* [Gk. *ektos*, outside; *phyton*, plant.] An external plant parasite.

ectophytic (ĕk'töfĭt'ĭk) *a.* [Gk. *ektos*, outside; *phyton*, plant.] *Pert.* ectophytes; ectotrophic, *q.v.*

ectopic (ĕktŏp'ĭk) *a.* [Gk. *ek*, out of; *topos*, place.] Not in normal position; *appl.* organs, gestation, etc. *Opp*. entopic.

ectopic pairing,—pairing between bands located in different regions of a chromosome.

ectoplasm (ĕk'töplăzm) *n.* [Gk. *ektos*, outside; *plasma*, mould.] The external layer of protoplasm in a cell, usually modified; ectosarc of protozoan cell; layer next cell-wall.

ectoplast (ĕk'töplăst) *n.* [Gk. *ektos*, outside; *plastos*, formed.] The protoplasmic film or plasma-membrane just within the true wall of a cell.

ectopterygoid (ĕk'tötĕr'ĭgoid,-ptĕr-) *n.* [Gk. *ektos*, outside; *pteryx*, wing; *eidos*, form.] A ventral membrane bone behind palatine and extending to quadrate; mesopterygoid; os transversum between pterygoid and maxilla in many reptiles and in some fishes; *cf.* entopterygoid.

ectoretina (ĕk'törĕt'ĭnă) *n.* [Gk. *ektos*, outside; L. *rete*, net.] Outer pigmented layer of retina.

ectosarc (ĕk'tösârk) *n.* [Gk. *ektos*, outside; *sarx*, flesh.] The external layer of protoplasm in a protozoon.

ectosite (ĕk'tösīt) *n.* [Gk. *ektos*, outside; *sitos*, food.] External parasite; ectoparasite.

ectosome (ĕk'tösōm) *n.* [Gk. *ektos*, outside; *soma*, body.] The enveloping portion of a sponge containing no flagellated chambers; a type of cell granule.

ectosphere (ĕk'tösfēr) *n.* [Gk. *ektos*, outside; *sphaira*, globe.] The outer zone of attraction-sphere.

ectospore (ĕk'töspōr) *n.* [Gk. *ektos*, outside; *sporos*, seed.] The spore formed at end of each sterigma in Basidiomycetes.

ectostosis (ĕk'tŏstō'sĭs) *n.* [Gk. *ektos*, outside; *osteon*, bone.] Formation of bone in which ossification begins under the perichondrium and either surrounds or replaces the cartilage.

ectostracum (ĕktŏs'trăkŭm) *n.* [Gk. *ektos*, outside; *ostrakon*, shell.] Outer primary layer or exocuticle of exoskeleton in Acarina.

ectostroma (ĕk'töstrō'mă) *n.* [Gk. *ektos*, outside; *stroma*, bedding.] Fungal tissue penetrating cortical tissue of host and bearing conidia; epistroma. *Cf.* entostroma.

ectotheca (ĕk'töthē'kă) *n.* [Gk. *ektos*, outside; *theke*, cup.] Outer coating of gonotheca in certain hydroids.

ectothecal,—*pert.*, ectotheca; not enclosed by a theca.

ectotrachea (ĕk'töträkē'ă) *n.* [Gk. *ektos*, outside; L. *trachea*, windpipe.] An epithelial layer on outer side of insect tracheae.

ectotrophic (ĕk'tötrŏf'ĭk) *a.* [Gk. *ektos*, outside; *trephein*, to nourish.] Finding nourishment from outside; *appl.* fungi which surround roots of host with hyphae. *Opp.* endotrophic.

ectotropic (ĕk'tötrŏp'ĭk) *a.* [Gk. *ektos*, outside; *trepein*, to turn.] Tending to curve or curving outwards.

ectoturbinal (ĕk'tötŭr'bĭnăl) *n.* [Gk. *ektos*, outside; L. *turbo*, whirl.] A division of the ethmoturbinal.

ectozoon (ĕk'tözō'ŏn) *n.* [Gk. *ektos*, outside; *zoon*, animal.] An external animal parasite; epizoon.

ecumene (ĕk'ūmĕn'ē) *n.* [Gk. *oikoumene*, habitable world.] Any inhabited region; the biosphere.

edaphic (ĕdăf'ĭk) *a.* [Gk. *edaphos*, ground.] *Pert.* or influenced by conditions of soil or substratum.

edaphology (ĕdăfŏl'öjĭ) *n.* [Gk. *edaphos*, ground; *logos*, discourse.] Soil science; particularly the study of the influence of soil on living organisms; *cf.* pedology.

edaphon (ĕd'ăfŏn) *n.* [Gk. *edaphos*, ground.] The organisms living within the soil; soil flora and fauna.

edeagus,—aedeagus, *q.v.*

edentate (ēdĕn'tāt) *a.* [L. *ex*, without; *dens*, tooth.] Without teeth or tooth-like projections.

edestin (ĕdĕs'tĭn) *n.* [Gk. *edestos*, eatable.] A plant globulin, main protein of sunflower and certain other seeds.

edge effect,—tendency to have greater variety and density of organisms in the boundary zone between communities or in an ecotone.

edge hair,—a cystidiform cell on gill margin in agarics.

edge species,—species living primarily or most frequently or numerously at junctions of communities; *cf.* ecotone, hybrid swarms.

edriophthalmic (ĕd'rĭŏfthăl'mĭk) *a.* [Gk. *edra*, seat; *ophthalmos*, eye.] Having sessile eyes; *appl.* certain Crustacea.

effector (ĕfĕk'tŏr) *n.* [L. *efficere*, to carry out.] An organ which reacts to stimulus by producing work or substance, as muscle, electric and luminous organs, glands; a motor end-organ in muscle.

efferent (ĕf'ĕrĕnt) *a.* [L. *ex*, out; *ferre*, to carry.] Conveying from, *appl.* vessels, lymphatics, etc.; carrying outwards, *appl.* impulses carried outwards by motor nerves.

effigurate (ĕfĭg'ūrāt) *a*. [L. *ex*, out ; *figurare*, to shape.] Having a definite shape or outline. *Opp*. effuse.

efflorescence (ĕflörĕs'ĕns) *n*. [L. *efflorescere*, to blossom.] Blossoming ; time of flowering ; bloom.

effoliation (ĕffölĭā'shŭn) *n*. [L. *ex*, out of ; *folium*, leaf.] Shedding or removal of leaves.

effuse (ĕfūs') *a*. [L. *effusus*, poured out.] Spreading loosely, *appl*. inflorescence ; spreading thinly, *appl*. bacterial cultures.

egest (ējĕst') *v*. [L. *egerere*, to discharge.] To throw out ; to void ; to excrete.

egesta (ējĕs'tă) *n. plu*. [L. *egestus*, discharged.] The sum-total of substances and fluids discharged from body.

egg (ĕg) *n*. [A.S. *æg*, Icel. *egg*.] The matured female germ-cell ; ovule.

egg-albumin,—the chief constituent of white of egg, a mixture of glucoproteins.

egg-apparatus,—the two synergids and ovum proper, near micropyle in embryo-sac of seed plants.

egg-calyx,—dilatation of oviduct at base of ovarioles in insects.

egg-case,—a protective covering for eggs.

egg-cell,—the ovum proper apart from any layer of cells derived from it or from other cells.

egg-membrane,—the layer of tough tissue lining an egg shell.

egg-nucleus, — the female pronucleus.

egg-tooth,—a small structure on tip of upper jaw, or of beak, by which the embryo breaks its shell.

eiloid (ī'loid) *a*. [Gk. *eilein*, to roll up ; *eidos*, form.] Shaped like a coil.

ejaculate (ējăk'ūlāt) *n*. [L. *ejaculatus*, thrown out.] The emitted seminal fluid.

ejaculatory (ējăk'ūlătörĭ) *a*. [L. *ejaculare*, to throw out.] Throwing out ; *appl*. certain ducts.

ejaculatory sac,—organ pumping ejaculate from vas deferens through ejaculatory duct to penis, in certain insects.

ekto-,—*see* ecto-

elaborate (ēlăb'örāt) *v*. [L. *elaborare*, to work out.] To change from a crude state to a state capable of assimilation ; to form complex organic substances from simple materials.

elaeoblast (ĕlē'öblăst) *n*. [Gk. *elaion*, oil ; *blastos*, bud.] A mass of nutrient material at posterior end of body in certain tunicates.

elaeocyte (ĕlē'ösīt) *n*. [Gk. *elaion*, oil ; *kytos*, hollow.] A cell containing fatty droplets, found in coelomic fluid of annelids.

elaeodochon (ĕl'ēŏd'ökŏn) *n*. [Gk. *elaiodochos*, oil-containing.] The preen-gland or oil-gland in birds.

elaioplast (ĕlī'öplăst') *n*. [Gk. *elaion*, oil ; *plastos*, moulded.] A plastid in a plant cell which forms or helps to form oil globules.

elaiosome,—elaioplast.

elaiosphere (ĕlī'ösfēr) *n*. [Gk. *elaion*, oil ; *sphaira*, globe.] An oil globule in a plant cell.

elastic fibro-cartilage,—consists of cartilage cells and a matrix pervaded by a network of yellow elastic fibres which branch and anastomose in all directions.

elastica externa,—external layer of notochordal sheath.

elastica interna, — the epitheliomorph layer of notochordal cells.

elastin (ēlăs'tĭn) *n*. [Gk. *elaunein*, to draw.] The scleroprotein of which elastic fibres are composed.

elater (ĕl'ătĕr) *n*. [Gk. *elater*, driver.] One of the filaments in the capillitium of slime fungi ; one of cells with a spiral thickening which assist in dispersing spores from capsule in liverworts ; one of the spore appendages formed from epispore in horsetails ; furcula or springing organ in Collembola.

elaterophore (ĕlăt'ĕröfōr) *n*. [Gk. *elater*, driver ; *pherein*, to bear.] Tissue bearing the elaters, in some liverworts.

electosome (ēlĕk′tŏsōm) *n.* [Gk. *eklektikos*, chosen; *soma*, body.] A chondriosome regarded as a centre for elaborating and fixing chemical constituents of protoplasm.

electric organ,—modifications of muscles or groups of muscles which discharge electric energy, found in certain fishes.

electroblast (ĕlĕk′trŏblăst) *n.* [Gk. *elektron*, amber; *blastos*, bud.] A modified muscle fibre which gives rise to an electroplax.

electroendosmotic layer,—a hypothetical 'membrane' present between two neurons or between neuron and muscle cell.

electrolemma (ēlĕk′trŏlĕm′ă) *n.* [Gk. *elektron*, amber; *lemma*, skin.] Membrane surrounding an electroplax.

electrophoresis (ĕlĕk′trŏfŏrē′sĭs) *n.* [Gk. *elektron*, amber; *pherein*, to bear.] Transport of substances, as of colloidal particles, resulting from differences in electrical potential.

electropism,—electrotropism, *q.v.*

electroplax (ēlĕk′trŏplăks) *n.* [Gk. *elektron*, amber; *plax*, plate.] One of the constituent plates of an electric organ.

electrotaxis (ēlĕk′trŏtăk′sĭs) *n.* [Gk. *elektron*, amber; *taxis*, arrangement.] Orientation of movement within an electric field.

electrotonic (ēlĕk′trŏtŏn′ĭk) *a.* [Gk. *elektron*, amber; *tonos*, tension.] *Pert.* a state of electric tension.

electrotonus (ēlĕktrŏt′ŏnŭs, ēlĕktrŏtŏn′ŭs) *n.* [Gk. *elektron*, amber; *tonos*, tension.] The modified condition of a nerve when subjected to a constant current of electricity.

electrotropism (ĕlĕktrŏt′rŏpĭzm) *n.* [Gk. *elektron*, amber; *trope*, turn.] Reaction of an organism to electric stimuli; plant curvature in an electric field.

eleidin (ĕlē′ĭdĭn) *n.* [Gk. *elaia*, olive.] Substance found as small granules or droplets in stratum granulosum of epidermis.

eleo,—*see* elaeo-, elaio-.

eleutherodactyl (ĕlū′thĕrŏdăk′tĭl) *a.* [Gk. *eleutheros*, free; *daktylos*, finger.] Having hind toe free.

eleutheropetalous (ĕlū′thĕrŏpĕt′ălŭs) *a.* [Gk. *eleutheros*, free; *petalon*, leaf.] Having petals or components of whorl free or separate.

eleutherophyllous (ĕlū′thĕrŏfĭl′ŭs) *a.* [Gk. *eleutheros*, free; *phyllon*, leaf.] Having components of perianth whorls free.

eleutherosepalous (ĕlū′thĕrŏsĕp′ălŭs) *a.* [Gk. *eleutheros*, free; F. *sépale*, sepal.] Having sepals free or separate.

elevator (ĕl′ĕvātŏr) *n.* [L. *elevare*, to lift up.] Any muscle which raises a part.

eligulate (ēlĭg′ūlāt) *a.* [L. *ex*, out; *ligula*, little tongue.] Having no ligule; *appl.* certain club-mosses.

elimination bodies,—nucleic acid material expelled from each chromosome during meiosis, remaining in middle of spindle and disintegrating during telophase.

ellipsoid (ĕlĭp′soid) *a.* [Gk. *elleipsis*, a falling short; *eidos*, shape.] Oval. *n.* Localised thickening of coat of arterioles in spleen; Malpighian body of the spleen; filbillar outer end of inner segment of retinal rods and cones.

elliptical (ĕlĭp′tĭkăl) *a.* [Gk. *elleipsis*, a falling short.] Oval-shaped; *appl.* leaves of about same breadth at equal distances from base and apex, which are slightly acute.

eluvial (ēlū′vĭăl) *a.* [L. *ex*, out; *luere*, to wash.] *Appl.* leached upper layers or A horizon of soil.

elytriform (ĕlĭt′rĭfôrm) *a.* [Gk. *elytron*, sheath; L. *forma*, shape.] Shaped like an elytrum.

elytroid (ĕl′ĭtroid) *a.* [Gk. *elytron*, sheath; *eidos*, resemblance.] Resembling an elytrum.

elytrophore (ĕl′ĭtrŏfōr) *n.* [Gk. *elytron*, covering; *pherein*, to carry.] Structure on prostomium of certain polychaetes, bearing an elytron.

elytrum (ĕl′ĭtrŭm) *n.* [Gk. *elytron*, sheath.] The anterior wing of certain insects, hard and case-like; one of scales or shield-like plates found on dorsal surface of some polychaetes; also elytron.

emarginate (ēmâr′jĭnāt) *a.* [L. *ex*, out; *marginare*, to delimit.] Having a notch at apex; having a notched margin.

embole (ĕm′bŏlē) *n.* [Gk. *embole*, a throwing in.] Invagination; also emboly.

embolic (ĕmbŏl′ĭk) *a.* [Gk. *embole*, a throwing in.] Pushing or growing in.

embolium (ĕmbō′lĭŭm) *n.* [Gk. *embolos*, wedge.] Outer or costal part of wing, or basal part of hemelytron, in certain insects.

embolomerous (ĕm′bŏlŏm′ērŭs) *a.* [Gk. *embolos*, wedge; *meros*, part.] Having two vertebral rings in each segment, due to union of hypocentra with neural arch, and union of two pleurocentra below notochord.

embolus (ĕm′bŏlŭs) *n.* [Gk. *embolos*, wedge.] A projection closing the foramen of an ovule, as in Armeria; apical division of the palpus in certain spiders; a clot blocking a blood-vessel; horn core or os cornu of ruminants.

embryo (ĕm′brĭŏ) *n.* [Gk. *embryon*, embryo.] A young organism in early stages of development.

embryo cell,—one of two cells formed from first division of fertilised egg in certain plants, developing later into embryo, the other developing into suspensor.

embryogenesis (ĕm′brĭŏjĕn′ēsĭs) *n.* [Gk. *embryon*, embryo; *genesis*, descent.] Origin of the embryo; embryogeny, *q.v.*

embryogeny (ĕmbrĭŏj′ēnĭ) *n.* [Gk. *embryon*, embryo; *gennaein*, to produce.] The processes by which the embryo is formed; origin, cellular pattern, and functions of the embryo.

embryology (ĕmbrĭŏl′ŏjĭ) *n.* [Gk. *embryon*, embryo; *logos*, discourse.] That part of biology dealing with formation and development of the embryo.

embryonal knot,—inner cell mass of blastodermic vesicle.

embryonic (ĕmbrĭŏn′ĭk) *a.* [Gk. *embryon*, embryo.] *Pert.* embryo.

embryonomy (ĕmbrĭŏn′ŏmĭ) *n.* [Gk. *embryon*, embryo; *nomos*, law.] The laws of embryonic development; classification of embryos. *a.* Embryonomic.

embryophore (ĕm′brĭŏfōr) *n.* [Gk. *embryon*, embryo; *pherein*, to bear.] Ciliated mantle enclosing embryo in many tape-worms, and formed from superficial blastomeres of embryo.

embryophyta (ĕm′brĭŏfĭ′tă) *n. plu.* [Gk. *embryo*, embryo; *phyton*, plant.] Plants having an enclosed embryo, as those with an archegonium, or bearing seeds.

embryo-sac,—the megaspore; female gametophyte in angiosperms.

embryotectonics (ĕm′brĭŏtĕktŏn′ĭks) *n.* [Gk. *embryon*, embryo; *tekton*, builder.] The structure or cellular pattern of the embryo.

embryotega (ĕm′brĭŏt′ēgă) *n.* [Gk. *embryon*, embryo; *tegos*, roof.] Small hardened portion of testa which marks micropyle in some seeds and separates like a little lid at period of germination.

embryotrophy (ĕm′brĭŏt′rŏfĭ) *n.* [Gk. *embryon*, embryo; *trophe*, nourishment.] Nourishment of embryo, or means adapted therefor.

emergence (ēmĕr′jĕns) *n.* [L. *emergere*, to come up.] An outgrowth from subepidermal tissue; an epidermal appendage.

emersed (ēmĕrs′t) *a.* [L. *emergere*, to come up.] Rising above surface of water; *appl.* leaves.

eminence (ĕm′ĭnĕns) *n.* [L. *eminens*, eminent.] Ridge or projection on surface of bones; eminentia.

emissary (ĕm′ĭsărĭ) *a.* [L. *emittere*, to send out.] Coming out; name *appl.* veins passing through apertures in cranial wall and establishing connection between sinuses inside and veins outside.

emmenine (ĕm′ēnĭn) *n.* [Gk. *emmenos*, monthly.] A placental gonadotrophic hormone.

empennate,—pinnate.

empodium (ĕmpō′dĭŭm) *n.* [Gk. *en*, in ; *pous*, foot.] A small variable median structure between claws of feet in many insects and spiders.

emulsin (ēmŭl′sĭn) *n.* [L. *emulgere*, to milk out.] A hydrolytic enzyme found in certain plants and some invertebrates.

enamel (ĕnăm′ĕl) *n.* [O.F. *esmaillier*, to coat with enamel.] The hard material containing over 90 per cent. calcium and magnesium salts which forms a cap over dentine, or may form a complete coat to tooth or scale.

enamel cells,—cells which form enamel, collectively the enamel organ ; adamantoblasts, ameloblasts.

enantiobiosis (ĕnăn′tĭōbīō′sĭs) *n.* [Gk. *enantios*, opposite ; *bios*, life.] Antagonistic symbiosis.

enantioblastic (ĕnăn′tĭōblăs′tĭk) *a.* [Gk. *enantios*, opposite ; *blastos*, bud.] Formed at end of seed opposite placenta.

enantiomorphic (ĕnăn′tĭōmôr′fĭk) *a.* [Gk. *enantios*, opposite ; *morphe*, form.] Similar but contraposed, as mirror image, right and left hand ; deviating from normal symmetry.

enarthrosis (ĕn′ârthrō′sĭs) *n.* [Gk. *en*, in ; *arthron*, joint.] Ball-and-socket joint.

enation (ēnā′shŭn) *n.* [L. *enatus*, grown from.] A non-reproductive accessory part emerging from surface of telome ; outgrowth from a previously smooth surface.

encephalisation (ĕnkĕf′ălīzā′shŭn, -sĕf′-) *n.* [Gk. *engkephalos*, brain.] Brain formation by the forward-shifting and centralising tendency of co-ordinating neurones.

encephalocoel (ĕnkĕf′ălōsēl, -sĕf-) *n.* [Gk. *engkephalos*, brain ; *koilos*, hollow.] Cavity within the brain ; cerebral ventricle, the anterior dilatation of neurocoel.

encephalomere (ĕnkĕf′ălōmēr, -sĕf-) *n.* [Gk. *engkephalos*, brain ; *meros*, part.] A brain segment.

encephalon (ĕnkĕf′ălŏn, -sĕf-) *n.* [Gk. *engkephalos*, brain.] The brain.

encephalospinal (ĕnkĕf′ălōspī′năl, -sĕf-) *a.* [Gk. *engkephalos*, brain ; L. *spina*, spine.] *Pert.* brain and spinal cord.

enchondral,—endochondral, intracartilaginous, *q.v.*

enchylema (ĕnkīlē′mă) *n.* [Gk. *en*, in ; *chylos*, juice.] The more fluid portion of a cell ; cell sap.

encretion (ĕnkrē′shŭn) *n.* [Gk. *en*, within ; *krinein*, L. *cernere*, to put apart.] Endocrine secretion ; hormone.

encyst (ĕnsĭst′) *v.* [Gk. *en*, in ; *kystis*, bladder.] Of a cell or small organism, to surround itself with an outer coat or capsule.

encystation (ĕnsĭstā′shŭn), **encystment** (ĕnsĭst′mĕnt) *n.* [Gk. *en*, in ; *kystis*, bladder.] Formation of a firm, resistant envelope or capsule.

endarch (ĕnd′ârk) *a.* [Gk. *endon*, within ; *arche*, beginning.] With central protoxylem, or with several surrounding a central pith.

endaspidean (ĕnd′ăspĭd′ēăn) *a.* [Gk. *endon*, within ; *aspis*, shield.] With scutes extending on inner surface of tarsus.

end-brain,—telencephalon, *q.v.*

end-bulbs,—minute cylindrical or oval bodies, consisting of capsule containing a semi-fluid core in which axis cylinder terminates either in a bulbous extremity or in a coiled plexiform mass, being end-organs in mucous and serous membranes, in skin of genitalia, and in synovial layer of certain joints.

end cell —a cell incapable of further differentiation.

end disc, end ring,—*see* ring centriole.

endemic (ĕndĕm′ĭk) *a.* [Gk. *endemos*, native.] Restricted to a certain region or part of a region.

enderon (ĕn′dĕrŏn) *n.* [Gk. *en*, in ; *deros*, skin.] The inner or endodermal layer.

enderonic (ĕn′dĕrŏn′ĭk) *a.* [Gk. *en*, in; *deros*, skin.] Endodermal.

endites (ĕndīts) *n. plu.* [Gk. *endon*, within.] Offshoots on mesial border of certain appendages of arthropods.

endo-,—*see also* ento-.

endoascus (en′döăs′kŭs) *n.* [Gk. *endon*, within; *askos*, bag.] Inner membrane of an ascus, protruding after rupture of the ectoascus, as in certain Ascomycetes.

endobasal (ĕn′döbā′săl) *a.* [Gk. *endon*, within; *basis*, base.] *Appl.* body, the kinetic element of central intranuclear structure; *cf.* endosome.

endobatic (ĕn′döbăt′ĭk) *a.* [Gk. *endon*, within; *bainein*, to go.] Afferent; esodic, centripetal. *Opp.* ectobatic.

endobiotic (ĕn′döbīŏt′ĭk) *a.* [Gk. *endon*, within; *biotikos*, *pert.* life.] Living within a substratum or within another living organism. *Opp.* exobiotic.

endoblast (ĕn′döblăst) *n.* [Gk. *endon*, within; *blastos*, bud.] Hypoblast; coeloblast and myoblast.

endocardiac (ĕn′dökâr′dĭăk) *a.* [Gk. *endon*, within; *kardia*, heart.] Situated within the heart; endocardial.

endocardium (ĕn′dökâr′dĭŭm) *n.* [Gk. *endon*, within; *kardia*, heart.] The membrane which lines inner surface of heart.

endocarp (ĕn′dökârp) *n.* [Gk. *endon*, within; *karpos*, fruit.] The innermost layer of pericarp, usually hard, in drupaceous fruits.

endocarpic (ĕn′dökâr′pĭk) *a.* [Gk. *endon*, within; *karpos*, fruit.] *Pert.* endocarp; angiocarpic, *q.v.*

endocarpoid (ĕn′dökâr′poid) *a.* [Gk. *endon*, within; *karpos*, fruit; *eidos*, form.] Having the disc-like ascocarps embedded in the thallus.

endochiton (ĕndökī′tŏn) *n.* [Gk. *endon*, within; *chiton*, coat.] Innermost layer of oogonial wall, as in Fucales; endochite; *cf.* exochiton, mesochiton.

endochondral (ĕn′dökôn′drăl) *a.* [Gk. *endon*, within; *chondros*, cartilage.] Beginning or forming inside the cartilage, *appl.* ossification; *cf.* perichondral.

endochondrostosis (ĕn′dökôndrŏstō′sĭs) *n.* [Gk. *endon*, within; *chondros*, cartilage; *osteon*, bone.] Ossification in cartilage from within outwards.

endochone (ĕn′dökōnē) *n.* [Gk. *endon*, within; *choane*, funnel.] Spacious sub-cortical crypt in sponge tissue, from which arise incurrent canals.

endochorion (ĕn′dökō′rĭŏn) *n.* [Gk. *endon*, within; *chorion*, chorion.] Inner lamina of chorion of insect eggs.

endochroic (ĕn′dökrō′ĭk) *a.* [Gk. *endon*, within; *chros*, complexion.] Having pigment within a cell or hypha. *Opp.* ectochroic.

endochrome (ĕn′dökrōm) *n.* [Gk. *endon*, within; *chroma*, colour.] Any colouring matter or pigment within a cell.

endochrome plate,—a band of yellowish chromatophores found in protoplasmic portion of certain diatoms.

endochromidia (ĕn′dökrōmĭd′ĭă) *n. plu.* [Gk. *endon*, within; *chroma*, colour; *idion*, *dim.*] Metachromatic corpuscles, formed from colloidal solution of metachromatin.

endochylous (ĕn′dökī′lŭs) *a.* [Gk. *endon*, within; *chylos*, juice.] With water-cells within internal tissue.

endocoelar (ĕn′dösē′lăr) *a.* [Gk. *endon*, within; *koilos*, hollow.] *Pert.* inner wall of coelom, or splanchnopleure.

endocoelic (ĕn′dösē′lĭk) *a.* [Gk. *endon*, within; *koilos*, hollow.] In sea-anemones, *appl.* radial area on disc covering space between two mesenteries of the same pair; *appl.* inner cycle or cycles of tentacles, *opp.* exocoelic.

endocone (ĕn′dökōn) *n.* [Gk. *endon*, within; *konos*, cone.] A conical structure formed in certain cephalopod shells.

endocranium (ĕn′dökrā′nĭŭm) *n.* [Gk. *endon*, within; *kranion*, skull.] Process on inner surface of cranium of certain insects; neurocranium, *q.v.*

endocrine (ĕn′dökrīn) *n.* [Gk. *endon*, within; *krinein*, to separate.] A ductless gland. *a.* *Appl.* or *pert.* organs of internal secretion. *Opp.* exocrine.

endocrinology (ĕn′dökrĭnŏl′öjĭ) *n.* [Gk. *endon*, within; *krinein*, to separate; *logos*, discourse.] Study of endocrine glands and secretions, and of hormonal substances and their effects.

endocuticula (ĕn′dökūtĭk′ūlă) *n.* [Gk. *endon*, within; L. *dim.* of *cutis*, skin.] The elastic inner layer of insect cuticle; inner layer of integument in spiders.

endocycle (ĕn′dösī′kl) *n.* [Gk. *endon*, within; *kyklos*, circle.] A layer of tissue separating internal phloem from endodermis.

endocyclic (ĕn′dösīk′lĭk) *a.* [Gk. *endon*, within; *kyklos*, circle.] With the mouth remaining in axis of coil of gut, *appl.* crinoids; having an apical system with double circle of plates surrounding anus, *appl.* echinoids; *pert.* endocycle.

endocyst (ĕn′dösĭst) *n.* [Gk. *endon*, within; *kystis*, bladder.] The soft body wall in a polyzoan zooid; the membranous inner lining of a protozoan cyst; *cf.* epicyst.

endoderm (ĕn′dödĕrm) *n.* [Gk. *endon*, within; *derma*, skin.] The hypoblast; the epithelium of digestive and respiratory organs, and of glands appended to digestive tract.

endoderm disc,—posterior unpaired thickening on ventral surface of blastoderm of crayfish.

endoderm lamella,—a thin sheet of endoderm stretching between adjacent radial canals, and between circular canal and enteric cavity in certain Coelenterata.

endodermis (ĕn′dödĕr′mĭs) *n.* [Gk. *endon*, within; *derma*, skin.] Innermost layer of cortex in plants; layer surrounding pericycle.

endoenzyme (ĕn′döĕn′zīm) *n.* [Gk. *endon*, within; *en*, in; *zyme*, leaven.] Any intracellular enzyme.

endogamy (ĕndŏg′ămĭ) *n.* [Gk. *endon*, within; *gamos*, marriage.] Zygote formation within the cyst by reciprocal fusion of division products of daughter nuclei; self-pollination; inbreeding.

endogastric (ĕn′dögăs′trĭk) *a.* [Gk. *endon*, within; *gaster*, belly.] Having curvature of body with enclosing shell towards ventral side; within the stomach.

endogenous (ĕndŏj′ĕnŭs) *a.* [Gk. *endon*, within; *-genes*, producing.] Originating within the organism; endogenic, *opp.* exogenous; autogenic, *opp.* allogenic; developing from a deep-seated layer; *appl.* metabolism concerned with tissue waste and growth.

endogenous multiplication,—spore formation, *q.v.*

endogeny (ĕndŏj′ĕnĭ) *n.* [Gk. *endon*, within; *genos*, descent.] Development from a deep-seated layer.

endognath (ĕn′dönăth) *n.* [Gk. *endon*, within; *gnathos*, jaw.] The inner branch of oral appendages of Crustacea.

endognathion (ĕn′dönăth′ĭŏn) *n.* [Gk. *endon*, within; *gnathos*, jaw.] Mesial segment of human premaxilla.

endogonidium (ĕn′dögŏnĭd′ĭŭm) *n.* [Gk. *endon*, within; *dim.* of *gone*, seed.] A gonidium formed in a gonidangium or receptacle; the colony-forming cells in such forms as Volvox.

endolabium (ĕn′dölā′bĭŭm) *n.* [Gk. *endon*, within; L. *labium*, lip.] A membranous lobe in interior of mouth on middle parts of front of labium.

endolaryngeal (ĕn′dölărĭn′jĕăl) *a.* [Gk. *endon*, within; *laryngx*, larynx.] *Pert.* or in the larynx.

endolithic (ĕn′dölĭth′ĭk) *a.* [Gk. *endon*, within; *lithos*, stone.] Burrowing or existing in stony substratum, as algal filaments.

endolymph (ĕn′dölĭmf) *n.* [Gk. *endon*, within; L. *lympha*, water.] The fluid in membranous labyrinth of ear.

endolymphangial (ĕn′dölĭmfăn′jĭăl) *a.* [Gk. *endon*, within; L. *lympha*, water; Gk. *anggeion*, vessel.] Situated in a lymphatic vessel.

endolymphatic (ĕn′dölĭmfăt′ĭk) *a.* [Gk. *endon*, within; L. *lympha*, water.] *Pert.* lymphatics, or to ear labyrinth ducts.

endolysin (ĕndŏlī′sĭn) *n.* [Gk. *endon*, within; *lysis*, loosing.] Intracellular substance of leucocytes which destroys engulfed bacteria.

endolysis (ĕndŏl′ĭsĭs) *n.* [Gk. *endon*, within; *lysis*, loosing.] Intracellular dissolution.

endomere (ĕn′dömēr) *n.* [Gk. *endon*, within; *meros*, part.] A hypoblast cell which gives rise to endoderm.

endometrium (ĕn′dömē′trĭŭm) *n.* [Gk. *endon*, within; *metra*, womb.] Mucous membrane lining the uterus.

endomitosis (ĕn′dömĭtō′sĭs) *n.* [Gk. *endon*, within; *mitos*, thread.] A form of mitosis occurring in endopolyploidy; multiplication of chromonemata or chromosomes without division of nucleus.

endomixis (ĕn′dömĭk′sĭs) *n.* [Gk. *endon*, within; *mixis*, mixing.] A stage comparable with parthenogenesis in the reproductive rhythm of some protozoa; a type of nuclear reorganisation.

endomysium (ĕn′dömĭz′ĭŭm) *n.* [Gk. *endon*, within; *mys*, muscle.] The connective tissue binding muscle fibres.

endoneurium (ĕn′dönū′rĭŭm) *n.* [Gk. *endon*, within; *neuron*, nerve.] The delicate connective tissue holding together and supporting nerve fibres within funiculus.

endoparasite (ĕn′döpăr′ăsīt) *n.* [Gk. *endon*, within; *parasitos*, eating at another's table.] Any organism living parasitically within another.

endoperidium (ĕn′döpērĭd′ĭŭm) *n.* [Gk. *endon*, within; *peridion*, little pouch.] Inner layer of peridium.

endophragm (ĕn′döfrăm) *n.* [Gk. *endon*, within; *phragma*, fence.] A septum formed by cephalic and thoracic apodemes in Crustacea.

endophragmal (ĕn′döfrăg′măl) *a.* [Gk. *endon*, within; *phragma*, fence.] *Pert.* the endophragm.

endophyllous (ĕn′döfĭl′ŭs) *a.* [Gk. *endon*, within; *phyllon*, leaf.] Sheathed by a leaf; living within a leaf, *appl.* parasites.

endophyte (ĕn′döfīt) *n.* [Gk. *endon*, within; *phyton*, plant.] A plant growing within another, either as parasite or otherwise.

endophytic (ĕn′döfĭt′ĭk) *a.* [Gk. *endon*, within; *phyton*, plant.] Living in the tissues of plants.

endoplasm (ĕn′döplăzm) *n.* [Gk. *endon*, within; *plasma*, mould.] The endosarc or inner portion of protoplasm in a cell.

endoplasmic reticulum,—ergastoplasm, kinoplasm, *q.v.*

endoplast (ĕn′döplăst) *n.* [Gk. *endon*, within; *plastos*, moulded.] Cell-nucleus; macronucleus of certain Protista.

endoplastule (ĕn′döplăs′tūl) *n.* [Gk. *endon*, within; *plastos*, moulded.] The micronucleus of certain Protista.

endopleura (ĕn′döploo′ră) *n.* [Gk. *endon*, within; *pleura*, side.] The inner seed-coat or tegmen.

endopleurite (ĕn′döploo′rīt) *n.* [Gk. *endon*, within; *pleura*, side.] The epimeral portion of an apodeme; infolding between pleurites.

endopodite (ĕn′dŏpödīt) *n.* [Gk. *endon*, within; *pous*, foot.] The inner or mesial branch of a biramous crustacean limb, or the only part of biramous limb remaining.

endopolyploidy (ĕn′döpŏl′ĭploidĭ) *n.* [Gk. *endon*, within; *polys*, many; *aploos*, onefold; *eidos*, form.] Polyploidy resulting from repeated doubling of chromosome number without normal mitosis.

endoral (ĕndō′răl) *a.* [Gk. *endon*, within; L. *os*, mouth.] *Pert.* structures situated in the vestibule of certain protozoa.

endorhachis (ĕn′dōrā′kĭs) *n.* [Gk. *endon*, within ; *rhachis*, backbone.] A layer of connective tissue lining canal of vertebral column and cavity of skull.

endosarc (ĕn′dōsârk) *n.* [Gk. *endon*, within; *sarx*, flesh.] Endoplasm, *q.v.*

endosclerite (ĕn′dōsklē′rīt) *n.* [Gk. *endon*, within ; *skleros*, hard.] Any sclerite of the endoskeleton of Arthropoda.

endoscopic (ĕn′dōskŏp′ĭk) *a.* [Gk. *endon*, within ; *skopein*, to look.] With apex directed inwards toward base of archegonium, *appl.* embryo. *Opp.* exoscopic.

endosiphuncle (ĕn′dōsī′fŭngkl) *n.* [Gk. *endon*, within ; L. *siphunculus*, little tube.] The tube leading from protoconch to siphuncle in certain Cephalopoda.

endosite (ĕn′dōsīt) *n.* [Gk. *endon*, within ; *sitos*, food.] Internal parasite ; endoparasite.

endoskeleton (ĕn′dōskĕl′ētŏn) *n.* [Gk. *endon*, within ; *skeletos*, dried up.] Internal skeleton, *opp.* exoskeleton.

endosmosis (ĕn′dŏsmō′sĭs) *n.* [Gk. *endon*, within ; *osmos*, impulse.] The passage inwards through a permeable or semipermeable membrane, of a less concentrated solution. *Opp.* exosmosis.

endosome (ĕn′dōsōm) *n.* [Gk. *endon*, within ; *soma*, body.] Chromatinic mass near centre of a vesicular nucleus ; karyosome.

endosperm (ĕn′dōspĕrm) *n.* [Gk. *endon*, within ; *sperma*, seed.] The nutritive tissue of certain seeds ; nutritive residue of female prothallus surrounding an embryo.

endospore (ĕn′dōspōr), *n.* [Gk. *endon*, within ; *sporos*, seed.] Inner coat of sporocyst in some protozoa ; an asexual spore ; a sporangial or endogenous spore.

endosporium,—inner coat of a spore wall.

endosteal (ĕndŏs′tēăl) *a.* [Gk. *endon*, within ; *osteon*, bone.] *Pert.* endosteum.

endosternite (ĕn′dōstĕr′nīt) *n.* [Gk. *endon*, within ; L. *sternum*, sternum.] Internal skeletal plate for muscle attachment ; median sternal apodeme ; a free skeleton situated in prosoma between alimentary canal and nerve cord in arachnids.

endosteum (ĕndŏs′tēŭm) *n.* [Gk. *endon*, within ; *osteon*, bone.] The internal periosteum lining the cavities of bones.

endostosis (ĕn′dŏstō′sĭs) *n.* [Gk. *endon*, within ; *osteon*, bone.] Ossification which begins in cartilage.

endostracum (ĕndŏs′trăkŭm) *n.* [Gk. *endon*, within ; *ostrakon*, shell.] The inner layer of mollusc shell.

endostyle (ĕn′dōstīl) *n.* [Gk. *endon*, within ; *stylos*, pillar.] A band of thickened epithelium on oesophageal wall of a tornaria ; two ventral longitudinal folds separated by a groove in pharynx of Tunicata ; a longitudinal groove lined by ciliated epithelium on ventral wall of pharynx of Amphioxus ; precursor of thyroid gland.

endotergite (ĕn′dōtĕr′jīt, -gīt) *n.* [Gk. *endon*, within; L. *tergum*, back.] An infolding from a tergite of insects, for muscle attachment ; phragma.

endotheca (ĕn′dōthē′kă) *n.* [Gk. *endon*, within ; *theke*, box.] The system of dissepiments in a coral calyx; the oval surface of Cystidea.

endothecial (ĕn′dōthē′sĭăl) *a.* [Gk. *endon*, within ; *theke*, box.] *Pert.* endothecium ; with asci in an ascocarp.

endothecium (ĕn′dōthē′sĭŭm) *n.* [Gk. *endon*, within ; *theke*, box.] The central region of an epibasal octant of oospore of liverworts and mosses ; inner lining of an anther ; inner dehiscing layer in ginkgo and angiosperms.

endotheliocyte (ĕn′dōthē′lĭōsīt) *n.* [Gk. *endon*, within ; *thele*, nipple ; *kytos*, hollow.] A mononuclear phagocyte derived from endothelium ; endothelial phagocyte or primitive wandering cell ; a histiocyte ; a macrophage.

endothelium (ĕn′dŏthē′lĭŭm) *n.* [Gk. *endon*, within; *thele*, nipple.] A squamous epithelium which lines serous cavities, the heart, blood and lymphatic vessels.

endothermic (ĕn′dŏthĕr′mĭk) *a.* [Gk. *endon*, within; *therme*, heat.] Binding or utilising heat-energy, *opp.* exothermic.

endothorax (ĕn′dŏthō′răks) *n.* [Gk. *endon*, within; *thorax*, chest.] The apodeme system in a crustacean thorax; *cf.* entothorax.

endotoxin (ĕn′dŏtŏk′sĭn) *n.* [Gk. *endon*, within; *toxikon*, poison.] A toxin within bacterial protoplasm, *opp.* exotoxin.

endotrachea (ĕn′dŏtrăkē′ă) *n.* [Gk. *endon*, within; L. *trachia*, windpipe.] The innermost, chitinous coat of tracheal tubes of insects.

endotrophic (ĕn′dŏtrŏf′ĭk) *a.* [Gk. *endon*, within; *trophe*, nourishment.] *Appl.* space within peritrophic membrane of insects; finding nourishment from within; *appl.* fungi inhabiting root cortex of host. *Opp.* ectotrophic.

endozoic (ĕn′dŏzō′ĭk) *a.* [Gk. *endon*, within; *zoon*, animal.] Living within an animal, *opp*, epizoic; *cf.* entozoic.

endozoochore (ĕn′dŏzō′ŏkōr) *n.* [Gk. *endon*, within; *zoon*, animal; *chora*, place.] Any spore, seed, or organism dispersed by being carried within an animal. *Opp.* epizoochore.

end-plates,—motor end-organs, the ramified expansions within the muscular fibre which form the ends of a motor nerve.

end-sac,—the sac-like vestigial portion of coelom in excretory glands of certain Crustacea.

endysis (ĕn′dĭsĭs) *n.* [Gk. *endysis*, putting on.] The development of a new coat; *cf.* ecdysis.

energesis (ĕn′ĕrjē′sĭs) *n.* [Gk. *energein*, to be active.] The process by which energy is liberated through katabolic action.

energid (ĕnĕr′jĭd) *n.* [Gk. *energos*, working; *idion*, *dim.*] Any living uninucleated protoplasmic unit with or without a cell wall.

enervose (ĕnĕr′vōs) *a.* [L. *ex*, without; *nervus*, sinew.] Having no veins, *appl.* certain leaves.

engram (ĕn′grăm) *n.* [Gk. *en*, in; *graphein*, to write.] A character impression in the mnemic theory of heredity; a latent memory image.

engraved (ĕngrāv′d) *a.* (F. *en*, in; A.S. *grafan*, to dig.] With irregular linear grooves on the surface.

enhalid (ĕnhăl′ĭd) *a.* [Gk. *en*, in presence of; *hals*, salt.] Containing salt-water, *appl.* soils; growing in saltings or on loose soil in salt-water, *appl.* plants.

enphytotic (ĕnfĭtŏt′ĭk) *a.* [Gk. *en*, in; *phyton*, plant.] Afflicting plants; *appl.* diseases restricted to a locality; *cf.* epiphytotic.

ensiform (ĕn′sĭfôrm) *a.* [L. *ensis*, sword; *forma*, shape.] Sword-shaped; xiphoid.

entad (ĕn′tăd) *adv.* [Gk. *entos*, within; L. *ad*, towards.] Towards the interior; inwards; internally. *Opp.* ectad.

ental (ĕn′tăl) *a.* [Gk. *entos*, within.] Inner; internal. *Opp.* ectal.

entangial (ĕntăn′jĭal) *a.* [Gk. *entos*, within; *anggeion*, vessel.] Within a vessel; produced inside a sporangium; entoangial. *Opp.* ectangial.

entelechy (ĕntĕl′ĕkĭ) *n.* [Gk. *en*, in; *telos*, end; *echein*, to hold.] Vital principle or influence guiding living organisms in right direction.

entepicondylar (ĕnt′ĕpĭkŏn′dĭlăr) *a.* [Gk. *entos*, within; *epi*, upon; *kondylos*, knob.] *Pert.* lower or condylar end of humerus; *appl.* ulnar foramen.

enteral (ĕn′tĕrăl) *a.* [Gk. *enteron*, gut.] Within intestine; also *appl.* the parasympathetic portion of the autonomic nervous system.

enteric (ĕntĕr′ĭk) *a.* [Gk. *enteron*, gut.] *Pert.* alimentary canal.

enteroblast (ĕn′tĕrŏblăst) *n.* [Gk. *enteron*, gut; *blastos*, bud.] The hypoblast after formation of the mesoblast.

enterocoel (ĕn′tërösēl′) *n.* [Gk. *enteron*, gut; *koilos*, hollow.] A coelom arising as a pouch-like outgrowth of archenteric cavity, or as a series of such outgrowths.

enterocrinin (ĕn′tërökrī′nĭn) *n.* [Gk. *enteron*, gut; *krinein*, to separate.] A hormone of small intestine, which stimulates secretion of intestinal juice.

enteroderm (ĕn′tërödĕrm) *n.* [Gk. *enteron*, gut; *derma*, skin.] Enteroblast.

enterogastrone (ĕn′tërögăs′trōn) *n.* [Gk. *enteron*, gut; *gaster*, stomach.] A duodenal hormone which inhibits secretion and motility of stomach.

enterokinase (en′tërökī′nās) *n.* [Gk. *enteron*, gut; *kinein*, to move.] Incomplete enzyme of intestinal juice which converts trypsinogen into trypsin.

enteron (ĕn′tërŏn) *n.* [Gk. *enteron*, gut.] The alimentary tract.

enteronephric (ĕn′tërönĕf′rĭk) *a.* [Gk. *enteron*, gut; *nephros*, kidney.] With nephridia opening into gut; *opp.* exonephric, *appl.* Oligochaeta.

enteroproct (ĕn′tëröprŏkt) *n.* [Gk. *enteron*, gut; *proktos*, anus.] The opening from endodermal gut into proctodaeum.

enterostome (ĕn′tëröstōm) *n.* [Gk. *enteron*, gut; *stoma*, mouth.] The aboral opening of the actinopharynx, leading to coelenteron; the posterior opening of stomodaeum into endodermal gut.

enterosympathetic (ĕn′tërösĭmpăthĕt′ĭk) *a.* [Gk. *enteron*, gut; *syn*, with; *pathos*, feeling.] *Appl.* that part of the nervous system supplying the intestine.

enterozoon (ĕn′tërözō′ŏn) *n.* [Gk. *enteron*, gut; *zoon*, animal.] Any animal parasite inhabiting the intestines.

enthetic (ĕnthĕt′ĭk) *a.* [Gk. *enthetos*, put in.] Introduced; implanted.

entire (ĕntīr′) *a.* [O.F. *entier*, untouched.] Unimpaired; with continuous margin, *appl.* leaves, bacterial colony, etc.

ento-,—*see also* endo-.

entoangial,—entangial, *q.v.*

entobranchiate (ĕn′töbrăng′kĭăt) *a.* [Gk. *entos*, within; *brangchia*, gills.] Having internal gills.

entobronchus (ĕn′töbrŏng′kŭs) *n.* [Gk. *entos*, within; *brongchos*, windpipe.] The dorsal secondary branch of bronchus in birds; entobronchium.

entochondrite (ĕn′tökôn′drīt) *n.* [Gk. *entos*, within; *chondros*, cartilage.] Plastron or endosternum of Limulus.

entochondrostosis (ĕn′tökŏndrŏstō′sĭs) *n.* [Gk. *entos*, within; *chondros*, cartilage; *osteon*, bone.] Ossification from within outwards.

entocodon (ĕn′tökō′dŏn) *n.* [Gk. *entos*, within; *kodon*, bell.] The lens-shaped mass of cells, in development of medusoid, which sinks below level of superficial ectoderm, and ultimately develops a cavity.

entocoel (ĕn′tösēl) *n.* [Gk. *entos*, within; *koilos*, hollow.] The space enclosed by a pair of mesenteries in Anthozoa.

entocondyle (ĕn′tökŏn′dĭl) *n.* [Gk. *entos*, within; *kondylos*, knob.] Condyle on mesial surface of a bone.

entoconid (ĕn′tökō′nĭd) *n.* [Gk. *entos*, within; *konos*, cone.] The postero-internal cusp of a lower molar.

entocuneiform (ĕn′tökūnē′ĭfôrm) *n.* [Gk. *entos*, within; *kuneos*, wedge; L. *forma*, shape.] The most internal of distal tarsal bones.

entocyemate (ĕn′tösīē′māt) *a.* [Gk. *entos*, within; *kyema*, embryo.] With embryos having amnion and allantois.

entoderm-,—endoderm-, *q.v.*

entoectad (ĕn′töĕk′tăd) *a.* [Gk. *entos*, within; *ektos*, without; L. *ad*, towards.] From within outwards, *opp.* ectoentad.

entogastric (ĕn′tögăs′trĭk) *a.* [Gk. *entos*, within; *gaster*, belly.] *Pert.* interior of stomach; *appl.* gastric budding in medusae.

entoglossal (ĕn′töglŏs′ăl) *a.* [Gk. *entos*, within; *glossa*, tongue.] Lying in substance of tongue.

entoglossum (ĕn′töglŏs′ŭm) *n.* [Gk. *entos*, within; *glossa*, tongue.] Extension of basihyal into tongue in some fishes; also glossohyal.

entomochoric (ĕnt′ŏmökō′rik) *a.* [Gk. *entomon*, insect; *chorein*, to spread.] Dispersed by insects; depending on insects for spreading spores, etc. *n.* Entomochory.

entomogenous (ĕn′tömŏj′ĕnŭs) *a.* [Gk. *entomon*, insect; *genes*, born.] Growing in or on insects, as certain fungi.

entomology (ĕn′tömŏl′öjĭ) *n.* [Gk. *entomon*, insect; *logos*, discourse.] That part of zoology which deals with insects.

entomophagous (ĕn′tömŏf′ăgŭs) *a.* [Gk. *entomon*, insect; *phagein*, to eat.] Insect-eating; insectivorous.

entomophilous (ĕn′tömŏf′ĭlŭs) *a.* [Gk. *entomon*, insect; *philein*, to love.] Pollinated by agency of insects.

entomophyte (ĕn′tömöfīt) *n.* [Gk. *entomon*, insect; *phyton*, plant.] Any fungus growing on or in insects.

entomo-urochrome (ĕn′tŏmöū′rö-krōm) *n.* [Gk. *entomon*, insect; *ouron*, urine; *chroma*, colour.] Greenish or yellowish pigment in urine of insects.

entoneural (ĕn′tönū′ral) *a.* [Gk. *entos*, within; *neuron*, nerve.] *Appl.* system of aboral ring and genital nerves in echinoderms.

entoparasite,—endoparasite, *q.v.*

entophyte,—endophyte, *q.v.*

entopic (ĕntŏp′ĭk) *a.* [Gk. *en*, in; *topos*, place.] In normal position, *opp.* ectopic.

entoplasm,—endoplasm, *q.v.*

entoplastron (ĕn′töplăs′trŏn) *n.* [Gk. *entos*, within; F. *plastron*, breast-plate.] The anterior median plate in chelonian plastra, often called episternum, probably homologous with interclavicle of other reptiles.

entopterygoid (ĕn′töptĕr′ĭgoid) *n.* [Gk. *entos*, within; *pteryx*, wing; *eidos*, form.] A dorsal membrane bone behind the palatine in some fishes; *cf.* ectopterygoid.

entoretina (ĕn′törĕt′ĭnă) *n.* [Gk. *entos*, within; L. *rete*, net.] Inner or neural part of retina, the retina proper.

entosphere (ĕn′tösfēr) *n.* [Gk. *entos*, within; *sphaira*, globe.] The inner portion of attraction-sphere.

entosternite,—endosternite, *q.v.*

entosternum (ĕntöstĕr′nŭm) *n.* [Gk. *entos*, within; L. *sternum*, breast-bone.] Entoplastron, *q.v.*; an internal process of sternum of numerous arthropods.

entostroma (ĕn′töstrō′mă) *n.* [Gk. *entos*, within; *stroma*, bedding.] Stroma producing perithecia in Ascomycetes; hypostroma. *Cf.* ectostroma.

entothorax (ĕn′töthō′răks) *n.* [Gk. *entos*, within; *thorax*, chest.] An insect apophysis or sternite.

entoturbinals (ĕn′tötŭr′bĭnălz) *n.plu.* [Gk. *entos*, within; L. *turbo*, whorl.] A division of ethmoturbinals.

entotympanic (ĕn′tötĭmpăn′ĭk) *n.* [Gk. *entos*, within; *tympanon*, drum.] A separate tympanic element in some genera; also metatympanic.

entovarial (ĕnt′ōvā′rĭăl) *a.* [Gk. *entos*, within; L. *ovum*, egg.] *Pert.* canal formed in ovaries of some fishes by insinking and closure of a groove formed by covering epithelium.

entozoa (ĕn′tözō′ă) *n. plu.* [Gk. *entos*, within; *zoon*, animal.] Internal animal parasites.

entozoic (ĕn′tözō′ĭk) *a.* [Gk. *entos*, within; *zoe*, subsistence.] Living within the body or substance of another animal or plant; *pert.* entozoa.

entrochite (ĕn′trŏkīt) *n.* [Gk. *en*, in; *trochos*, wheel.] The joint of fossil stem of a stalked crinoid.

enucleate (ēnū′klēāt) *v.* [L. *e*, out of; *nucleus*, kernel.] To deprive of a nucleus, as in microdissection of cells. *a.* Lacking a nucleus.

envelope (ĕn′vĕlōp) *n.* [F. *enveloppe*, covering.] An outer covering of an egg; any surrounding structure, *e.g.* floral envelope.

environment (ĕnvī′rŏnmĕnt) *n.* [F. *environ*, about.] The sum-total of external influences acting on an organism or on part of an organism.

enzootic (ĕn′zōōt′ĭk) *a.* [Gk. *en*, in; *zoon*, animal.] Afflicting animals; *appl.* disease restricted to a locality.

enzyme (ĕn′zīm) *n.* [Gk. *en*, in, *zyme*, leaven.] A catalyst produced by living organisms and acting on one or more specific substrates; a ferment; *cf.* apo-enzyme, co-enzyme, holo-enzyme.

Eocene (ē′ösēn) *n.* [Gk. *eos*, dawn; *kainos*, recent.] Early epoch of the Tertiary period, between Palaeocene and Oligocene.

Eogaea (ē′öjē′ă) *n.* [Gk. *eos*, dawn; *gaia*, earth.] A zoogeographical division including Africa, South America, and Australasia; *cf.* Caenogaea.

eosinophil (ē′ösĭn′öfĭl) *a.* [Gk. *eos*. dawn; *philein*, to love.] *Appl.* cells which readily stain red with eosin; oxyphil.

eosinophile,—eosinophil leucocyte.

Eozoic (ē′özō′ĭk) *a.* [Gk. *eos*, dawn; *zoe*, life.] *Appl.* Archaean or Pre-Cambrian period.

epacme (ĕpăk′mē) *n.* [Gk. *epi*, upon; *akme*, prime.] The stage in phylogeny of a group just previous to its highest point of development.

epactal (ĕpăk′tăl) *a.* [Gk. *epaktos*, adventitious.] Supernumerary; intercalary. *n.* A sutural or Wormian bone.

epalpate (ēpăl′pāt) *a.* [L. *ex*, without; *palpus*, palp.] Not furnished with palpi.

epanthous (ĕpăn′thŭs) *a.* [Gk. *epi*, upon; *anthos*, flower.] Living on flowers; *appl.* certain fungi.

epapillate (ēpăp′ĭlāt) *a.* [L. *ex*, without; *papilla*, nipple.] Not having papillae.

epapophysis (ĕp′ăpŏf′ĭsĭs) *n.* [Gk. *epi*, upon; *apophysis*, offshoot.] A median process arising from centre of vertebral neural arch.

eparterial (ĕp′ârtē′rĭăl) *a.* [Gk. *epi*, upon; L. *arteria*, artery.] Situated above an artery; *appl.* branch of right bronchus.

epaulettes (ĕp′ôlĕts) *n. plu.* [F. *épaule*, shoulder.] Branched or knobbed processes projecting from outer side of oral arms of many Scyphozoa; crescentic ridges of cilia in echinopluteus; tegulae of Hymenoptera.

epaxial (ĕpăk′sĭăl) *a.* [Gk. *epi*, upon; L. *axis*, axle.] Above the axis; dorsal; usually *appl.* axis formed by vertebral column.

epedaphic (ĕp′ēdăf′ĭk) *a.* [Gk. *epi*, upon; *edaphos*, soil.] *Pert.*, or depending upon, climatic conditions.

epencephalon (ĕp′ĕnkĕf′ălŏn, -sĕf-) *n.* [Gk. *epi*, upon; *engkephalos*, brain.] The cerebellum.

ependyma (ĕpĕn′dĭmă) *n.* [Gk. *ependyma*, outer garment.] The layer of cells lining cavities of brain and spinal cord; ependyme.

ependymal (ĕpĕn′dĭmăl) *a.* [Gk. *ependyma*, outer garment.] *Pert.* ependyma.

ephapse (ĕfăps′) *n.* [Gk. *ephaptein*, to reach.] Region of contiguity between two axons lying side by side.

ephaptic (ĕfăp′tĭk) *a.* [Gk. *ephaptein*, to reach.] *Pert.* an ephapse; *appl.* delay, the interval between stimulation of one (pre-ephaptic) axon and response of an apposed other (post-ephaptic) axon.

epharmonic (ĕf′ârmŏn′ĭk) *a.* [Gk. *epi*, towards; *harmos*, fitting.] *Pert.* epharmosis; adaptive; adapted to environment; *appl.* convergence: morphological resemblance of different species inhabiting the same environment.

epharmosis (ĕf′ârmō′sĭs) *n.* [Gk. *epi*, towards; *harmos*, fitting.] The process of adaptation of organisms to new environmental conditions; attainment of the state of adaptation or epharmony.

ephebic (ĕfē′bĭk) *a.* [Gk. *ephebos*, adult.] Adult; *pert.* stage in development or phylogeny between childhood and old-age stages.

ephemeral (ĕfĕm'ĕrăl) *n.* [Gk. *ephemeros*, lasting for a day.] A short-lived plant or animal species. *a.* Short-lived; taking place once only, *appl.* plant movements, as expanding of buds; completing life-cycle within a brief period.

ephippial (ĕfĭp'ĭăl) *a.* [Gk. *ephippion*, saddle-cloth.] *Pert.* ephippium; *appl.* winter eggs, as of rotifers and daphnids.

ephippium (ĕfĭp'ĭŭm) *n.* [Gk. *ephippion*, saddle-cloth.] The pituitary fossa, or fossa hypophyseos of sphenoid; a thickened and indurated part of shell separating from the rest at ecdysis; a saddle-shaped modification of cuticle derived, later detached, from carapace and enclosing winter eggs, in Daphniidae.

ephyra (ĕf'ĭră), **ephyrula** (ĕfĭr'ūlă) *n.* [Gk. *Ephyra*, a sea-nymph.] The small free-swimming jelly-fish stage of certain Scyphozoa, produced by strobilation of scyphistoma.

epibasal (ĕp'ĭbā'săl) *n.* [Gk. *epi*, upon; *basis*, base.] Upper segment of an oospore, ultimately giving rise to the shoot. *Opp.* hypobasal.

epibasidium (ĕp'ĭbăsĭd'ĭŭm) *n.* [Gk. *epi*, upon; *basis*, base; *idion*, *dim.*] The part of a heterobasidium which bears sterigmata and is separated by a septum from the hypobasidium; a basidium, *q.v.*

epibenthos (ĕp'ĭbĕn'thŏs) *n.* [Gk. *epi*, upon; *benthos*, depths.] Fauna and flora of sea-bottom between low-water mark and hundred fathom line.

epibiotic (ĕp'ĭbīŏt'ĭk) *a.* [Gk. *epibionai*, to survive.] Surviving, *appl.* endemic species that are relics of a former flora or fauna; growing on the exterior of living organisms.

epiblast (ĕp'ĭblăst) *n.* [Gk. *epi*, upon; *blastos*, bud.] The outer layer of the gastrula; ectoblast; a rudimentary second cotyledon, as in grasses.

epiblema (ĕp'ĭblē'mă) *n.* [Gk. *epiblema*, cover.] The outermost layer of root-tissue; piliferous layer; epiblem.

epibole (ĕpĭb'ölē) *n.* [Gk. *epibole*, putting on.] Growth of one part over another in embryonic stages; also epiboly.

epibolic (ĕp'ĭbŏl'ĭk) *a.* [Gk. *epibole*, putting on.] Growing so as to cover over; *appl.* type of gastrulation.

epibranchial (ĕp'ĭbrăng'kĭăl) *a.* [Gk. *epi*, upon; *brangchia*, gills.] *Pert.* second upper element in branchial arch; efferent branchial, *appl.* vessels.

epicalyx (ĕp'ĭkăl'ĭks) *n.* [Gk. *epi*, upon; *kalyx*, cup.] Stipules, fused in pairs, producing an apparent outer or extra calyx; structure just below calyx produced by aggregation of bracts or bracteoles.

epicanthus (ĕp'ĭkăn'thŭs) *n.* [Gk. *epi*, upon; *kanthos*, corner of eye.] A prolongation of upper eyelid over inner angle of eye; Mongolian fold.

epicardia (ĕp'ĭkâr'dĭă) *n.* [Gk. *epi*, upon; *kardia*, stomach.] Antrum cardiacum or abdominal portion of oesophagus.

epicardium (ĕp'ĭkâr'dĭŭm) *n.* [Gk. *epi*, upon; *kardia*, heart.] The visceral part of pericardium; tubular prolongation of branchial sac in many ascidians, which takes part in budding.

epicarp (ĕp'ĭkârp) *n.* [Gk. *epi*, upon; *karpos*, fruit.] Outer layer of the pericarp; exocarp.

epicentral (ĕp'ĭsĕn'trăl) *a.* [Gk. *epi*, upon; *kentron*, centre.] Attached to or arising from vertebral centra; *appl.* intermuscular bones.

epicerebral (ĕp'ĭsĕr'ĕbrăl) *a.* [Gk. *epi*, upon; L. *cerebrum*, brain.] Situated above the brain.

epichilium (ĕp'ĭkīl'ĭŭm) *n.* [Gk. *epi*, upon; *cheilos*, lip.] Terminal lobe of lower petal of orchid; epichile.

epichondrosis (ĕp′ĭkôndrō′sĭs) *n.* [Gk. *epi*, upon; *chondros*, cartilage.] Formation of cartilage on periosteum, as in production of antlers.

epichordal (ĕp′ĭkôr′dăl) *a.* [Gk. *epi*, upon; *chorde*, cord.] Upon the notochord; *appl.* vertebrae in which ventral cartilaginous portions are almost completely suppressed; *appl.* upper lobe of caudal fin in fishes.

epichroic (ĕp′ĭkrō′ĭk) *a.* [Gk. *epi*, upon; *chros*, colour.] Discolouring, as after injury.

epicoel (ĕp′ĭsēl) *n.* [Gk. *epi*, upon; *koilos*, hollow.] Cavity of mid-brain in lower vertebrates; cerebellar cavity; a perivisceral cavity formed by invagination; also epicoele, epicoelia.

epicondylar (ĕp′ĭkŏn′dĭlăr) *a.* [Gk. *epi*, upon; *kondylos*, knob.] *Pert.* epicondyle.

epicondyle (ĕp′ĭkŏn′dĭl) *n.* [Gk. *epi*, upon; *kondylos*, knob.] A medial and a lateral protuberance at distal end of humerus and femur.

epicone (ĕp′ĭkōn) *n.* [Gk. *epi*, upon; *konos*, cone.] The part anterior to girdle in Dinoflagellata, *opp.* hypocone.

epicoracoid (ĕp′ĭkŏr′ăkoid] *a.* [Gk. *epi*, upon; *korax*, crow; *eidos*, form.] *Pert.* an element, usually cartilaginous, at sternal end of coracoid in amphibians, reptiles, and monotremes.

epicormic (ĕp′ĭkôr′mĭk) *a.* [Gk. *epi*, upon; *kormos*, trunk.] Growing from a dormant bud.

epicotyl (ĕp′ĭkŏt′ĭl) *n.* [Gk. *epi*, upon; *kotyle*, vase.] The axis of a plumule.

epicotyledonary (ĕp′ĭkŏtĭlē′dŏnărĭ) *a.* [Gk. *epi*, upon; *kotyle*, cup.] Above the cotyledons.

epicoxite (ĕp′ĭkŏk′sīt) *n.* [Gk. *epi*, upon; L. *coxa*, hip.] A small process at posterior end of toothed part of coxa of second to fifth pairs of appendages in Eurypterida.

epicranial (ĕp′ĭkrā′nĭăl) *a.* [Gk. *epi*, upon; *kranion*, skull.] *Pert.* cranium; *appl.* aponeurosis, muscles, bones, suture.

epicranium (ĕp′ĭkrā′nĭŭm) *n.* [Gk. *epi*, upon; *kranion*, skull.] The region between and behind eyes in insect head; scalp; the structures covering the cranium.

epicranius (ĕp′ĭkrā′nĭŭs) *n.* [Gk. *epi*, upon; *kranion*, skull.] The scalp muscle, consisting of occipitalis and frontalis, connected by galea aponeurotica; occipitofrontalis.

epicrine (ĕp′ĭkrĭn) *a.* [Gk. *epi*, upon; *krinein*, to separate.] *Appl.* glands in which secretion is voided without disintegration of cells.

epicritic (ĕp′ĭkrĭt′ĭk) *a.* [Gk. *epi*, upon; *krinein*, to judge.] *Appl.* stimuli and nerve systems concerned with delicate touch and other special sensations in skin.

epictesis (ĕpĭk′tēsĭs) *n.* [Gk. *epiktesis*, further gain.] Capacity of a living cell to concentrate salt solutions diffusing into the cell.

epicuticula (ĕp′ĭkū′tĭk′ūlă) *n.* [Gk. *epi*, upon; L. *dim.* of *cutis*, skin.] Lamella or membrane external to exocuticula of insects.

epicutis (ĕp′ĭkū′tĭs) *n.* [Gk. *epi*, upon; L. *cutis*, skin.] Outer layer of cutis of mushrooms, *opp.* subcutis.

epicyemate (ĕp′ĭsīē′māt) *a.* [Gk. *epi*, upon; *kyema*, embryo.] With embryo lying on the yolk-sac.

epicyst (ĕp′ĭsĭst) *n.* [Gk. *epi*, upon; *kystis*, bladder.] The external resistant cyst of an encysted protozoan; *cf.* endocyst.

epicyte (ĕp′ĭsīt) *n.* [Gk. *epi*, upon; *kytos*, hollow.] The external layer of ectoplasm in certain protozoa.

epidemes (ĕp′ĭdēmz) *n. plu.* [Gk. *epi*, upon; *demas*, body.] In certain insects, small pieces closely related with articulation of wings.

epidermatoid (ĕp′ĭdĕr′mătoid) *a.* [Gk. *epi*, upon; *derma*, skin; *eidos*, form.] Resembling epidermis or epiderm; *appl.* fungal cortex made up of a single layer of cells; epidermioid.

epidermis (ĕp′ĭdĕr′mĭs) *n.* [Gk. *epi*, upon; *derma*, skin.] The outermost protective layer of stems, roots and leaves; scarf-skin or external layer of skin, a non-vascular stratified epithelium of ectodermic origin; single layer of ectoderm in invertebrates.

epidermophyte,—dermatophyte.

epididymis (ĕp′ĭdĭd′ĭmĭs) *n.* [Gk. *epi*, upon; *didymos*, testicle.] A mass at back of testicle composed chiefly of vasa efferentia; the coiled anterior end of Wolffian duct.

epidural (ĕp′ĭdū′răl) *a.* [Gk. *epi*, upon; L. *dura*, hard.] *Pert.* dura mater; *appl.* space between dura mater and wall of vertebral canal.

epigaeous,—epigeal.

epigamic (ĕp′ĭgăm′ĭk) *a.* [Gk. *epi*, upon; *gamos*, marriage.] Tending to attract opposite sex, *e.g.* colour displayed in courtship.

epigamous (ĕpĭg′ămŭs) *a.* [Gk. *epi*, upon; *gamos*, marriage.] Designating that stage in polychaetes in which immature forms become heteronereid, while sexual elements are ripening; epigamic, *q.v.*

epigaster (ĕp′ĭgăs′tĕr) *n.* [Gk. *epi*, upon; *gaster*, belly.] That part of embryonic intestine which later develops into colon.

epigastric (ĕp′ĭgăs′trĭk) *a.* [Gk. *epi*, upon; *gaster*, belly.] *Pert.* anterior wall of abdomen; middle region of upper zone of artificial divisions of abdomen.

epigastrium (ĕp′ĭgăs′trĭŭm) *n.* [Gk. *epi*, upon; *gaster*, stomach.] The epigastric region; sternal portions of meso- and metathorax of insects.

epigastroid,—epipubis, *q.v.*

epigeal (ĕp′ĭjē′ăl) *a.* [Gk. *epi*, upon; *ge*, earth.] Living near the ground, *appl.* insects; borne above ground, *appl.* cotyledons when they form first foliage leaves; also epigean, epigeic, epigeous.

epigenesis (ĕp′ĭjĕn′ĕsĭs) *n.* [Gk. *epi*, upon; *genesis*, descent.] Theory of generation, that embryo is an entirely new creation, not a mere unfolding of preformed structures.

epigenetics (ĕp′ĭjĕnĕt′ĭks) *n.* [Gk. *epi*, upon; *genesis*, descent.] Study of the mechanisms causing phenotypic effects to be produced by the genes of a genotype.

epigenotype (ĕp′ĭjĕn′ōtīp) *n.* [Gk. *epi*, upon; *genos*, descent; *typos*, image.] The concatenation of processes linking genotype and phenotype.

epigenous (ĕpĭj′ĕnŭs) *a.* [Gk. *epi*, upon; *genos*, descent.] Developing or growing on a surface.

epigeous,—epigeal.

epiglottis (ĕp′ĭglŏt′ĭs) *n.* [Gk. *epi*, upon; *glotta*, tongue.] A thin lamella of fibro-cartilage between root of tongue and entrance to larynx; epistome in Polyzoa; epipharynx in Insecta.

epignathous (ĕpĭg′năthŭs) *a.* [Gk. *epi*, upon; *gnathos*, jaw.] Having upper jaw longer than lower.

epigone,—epigonium.

epigonial (ĕpĭgō′nĭăl) *a.* [Gk. *epi*, upon; *gone*, seed.] *Appl.* sterile posterior portion of genital ridge.

epigonium (ĕpĭgō′nĭŭm) *n.* [Gk. *epi*, upon; *gone*, seed.] The young sporangial sac in liverworts.

epigynal (ĕpĭj′ĭnăl) *a.* [Gk. *epi*, upon; *gyne*, woman.] *Pert.* epigynum.

epigynous (ĕpĭj′ĭnŭs) *a.* [Gk. *epi*, upon; *gyne*, woman.] Having the various whorls adnate to ovary, thus apparently inserted in ovary.

epigynum (ĕpĭj′ĭnŭm) *n.* [Gk. *epi*, upon; *gyne*, woman.] External female genitalia in Arachnida; also epigyne, epigynium.

epigyny (ĕpĭj′ĭnĭ) *n.* [Gk. *epi*, upon; *gyne*, woman.] Condition of having whorls apparently inserted in ovary.

epihyal (ĕp′ĭhī′ăl) *a.* [Gk. *epi*, upon; *hyoeides*, Υ-shaped.] *Pert.* upper portion of ventral part of hyoid arch. *n.* Upper element of ventral portion, a cartilage or bone in centre of stylohyoid ligament.

epihymenium (ĕp′ĭhīmē′nĭŭm) *n.* [Gk. *epi*, upon; *hymen*, membrane.] A thin tissue of interwoven hyphae covering the hymenium, as of Basidiomycetes.

epilabrum (ĕpĭlā′brŭm) *n.* [Gk. *epi*, upon; L. *labrum*, lip.] A process at side of labrum in Myriapoda.

epilemmal (ĕpĭlĕm′ăl) *a.* [Gk. *epi*, upon; *lemma*, skin.] *Appl.* sensory nerve endings on surface of sarcolemma.

epilimnion (ĕp′ĭlĭm′nyŏn) *n.* [Gk. *epi*, upon; *limne*, lake.] Upper water layer, above thermocline, in lakes. *Opp.* hypolimnion.

epilithic (epĭlĭth′ĭk) *a.* [Gk. *epi*, upon; *lithos*, stone.] Attached on rocks; *appl.* algae, lichens.

epimandibular (ĕp′ĭmăndĭb′ūlăr) *a.* [Gk. *epi*, upon; L. *mandibulum*, jaw.] *Pert.* a bone in lower jaw of vertebrates.

epimeletic (ĕp′ĭmĕlĕtĭk) *a.* [Gk. *epimeles*, careful.] *Appl.* animal behaviour relating to the care of others.

epimembranal (ĕp′ĭmĕm′brănăl) *a.* [Gk. *epi*, upon; *membrana*, skin.] Situated or formed on the surface of a membrane; *appl.* pigmentation.

epimeral (ĕpĭmē′răl) *a.* [Gk. *epi*, upon; *meros*, thigh.] *Pert.* epimeron.

epimere (ĕp′ĭmēr) *n.* [Gk. *epi*, upon; *meros*, part.] The dorsal muscle-plate of mesothelial wall.

epimerite (ĕp′ĭmērīt) *n.* [Gk. *epi*, upon; *meros*, part.] Deciduous portion of protomerite in certain Gregarinina.

epimeron (ĕpĭmē′rŏn) *n.* [Gk. *epi*, upon; *meros*, thigh.] A portion of pleuron in insects which may be posterior or nearly as far forward as episternum; posterior pleurite of subcoxa; portion of arthropod segment between tergum and limb insertions.

epimorpha (ĕp′ĭmôr′fă) *n. plu.* [Gk. *epi*, upon; *morphe*, form.] Larvae hatched with all appendages developed; *cf.* anamorpha.

epimorphic,—maintaining the same form in successive stages of growth.

epimorphosis (ĕp′ĭmôr′fōsĭs) *n.* [Gk. *epi*, upon; *morphosis*, shaping.] That type of regeneration in which proliferation of new material precedes development of new part.

epimysium (ĕp′ĭmĭz′ĭŭm) *n.* [Gk. *epi*, upon; *mys*, muscle.] The sheath of areolar tissue which invests the entire muscle; *cf.* perimysium.

epinasty (ĕp′ĭnăstĭ) *n.* [Gk. *epi*, upon; *nastos*, close-pressed.] The more rapid growth of upper surface of a dorso-ventral organ, *e.g.* a leaf, thus causing unrolling or downward curvature.

epinephrine (ĕp′inĕf′rēn) *n.* [Gk. *epi*, upon; *nephros*, kidney.] Adrenaline; adrenin.

epinephros (ĕp′ĭnĕf′rŏs) *n.* [Gk. *epi*, upon; *nephros*, kidney.] The suprarenal or adrenal body.

epineural (ĕp′ĭnū′răl) *a.* [Gk. *epi*, upon; *neuron*, nerve.] Arising from vertebral neural arch; *pert.* canal external to radial nerve in certain echinoderms; *appl.* sinus between embryo and yolk, beginning of body cavity in insects.

epineurium (ĕp′ĭnū′rĭŭm) *n.* [Gk. *epi*, upon; *neuron*, nerve.] The external sheath of a nerve cord.

epinotum (ĕp′ĭnō′tŭm) *n.* [Gk. *epi*, upon; *noton*, back.] Propodeon, *q.v.*

epiopticon (ĕp′ĭŏp′tĭkŏn) *n.* [Gk. *epi*, upon; *opsis*, sight.] The middle zone of optic lobes of insects.

epiostracum (ĕp′ĭŏs′trăkŭm) *n.* [Gk. *epi*, upon; *ostrakon*, shell.] Thin cuticle or epicuticle covering exocuticle or ectostracum in Acarina.

epiotic (ĕp′ĭōt′ĭk) *a.* [Gk. *epi*, upon; *ous*, the ear.] *Pert.* upper element of bony capsule of ear; *appl.* centre of ossification of mastoid process.

epiparasite (ĕp′ĭpăr′ăsīt) *n.* [Gk. *epi*, upon; *parasitos*, eating at another's table.] Ectoparasite, *q.v.*

epipelagic (ĕp′ĭpĕlăj′ĭk) *a.* [Gk. *epi*, upon; *pelagos*, sea.] *Pert.* deep-sea water between surface and bathypelagic zone.

epiperidium,—exoperidium, *q.v.*

epipetalous (ĕpĭ'pĕtălŭs) *a.* [Gk. *epi*, upon; *petalon*, leaf.] Having stamens inserted on petals.

epipetreous (ĕp'ĭpĕt'rëŭs) *a.* [Gk. *epi*, upon; *petraios*, *pert.* rock.] Growing on rocks.

epipharyngeal (ĕp'ĭfărĭn'jëăl) *a.* [Gk. *epi*, upon; *pharyngx*, throat.] *Pert.* upper or dorsal aspect of pharynx.

epipharynx (ĕp'ĭfăr'ĭngks) *n.* [Gk. *epi*, upon; *pharyngx*, throat.] A projection on roof of mouth cavity of certain insects; membranous lining of labrum and clypeus drawn out with labrum to form a piercing organ, as in Diptera; lingua.

epiphloeodal (ĕpĭflē'ödăl) *a.* [Gk. *epi*, upon; *phloios*, bark.] *Pert.* epiphloem; growing on outer bark; *appl.* lichens; epiphloeodic, ectophloeodic.

epiphloem (ĕpĭflō'ĕm) *n.* [Gk. *epi*, upon; *phloios*, bark.] Outer bark.

epiphragm (ĕp'ĭfrăm) *n.* [Gk. *epiphragma*, covering.] A layer of hardened mucous matter, or a calcareous plate, closing the opening of certain gastropod shells; membrane which closes the capsule in certain mosses; a closing membrane in sporophores of certain fungi.

epiphyll (ĕp'ĭfĭl) *n.* [Gk. *epi*, upon; *phyllon*, leaf.] A plant which grows on leaves, *e.g.* various lichens.

epiphyllous (ĕp'ĭfĭl'ŭs) *a.* [Gk. *epi*, upon; *phyllon*, leaf.] Growing on leaves; united to perianth, *appl.* stamens.

epiphysial (ĕp'ĭfĭz'ĭăl) *a.* [Gk. *epi*, upon; *phyein*, to grow.] *Pert.* or similar to the epiphysis; epiphyseal.

epiphysis (ĕpĭf'ĭsĭs) *n.* [Gk. *epi*, upon; *phyein*, to grow.] Any part or process of a bone which is formed from a separate centre of ossification and later fuses with the bone; pineal body; pineal and parapineal organs; stout bar firmly fused to alveolus of each jaw and articulating with rotulae in sea-urchins; certain processes on tibia of insects; caruncle near hilum of seed.

epiphyte (ĕp'ĭfīt) *n.* [Gk. *epi*, upon; *phyton*, plant.] Plant which lives on surface of other plants.

epiphytic (ĕp'ĭfĭt'ĭk) *a.* [Gk. *epi*, upon; *phyton*, plant.] Living on, or attached to, surface of a plant, *opp.* endophytic; *pert.* or similar to an epiphyte.

epiphytotic (ĕp'ĭfĭtŏt'ĭk) *a.* [Gk. *epi*, upon; *phyton*, plant.] *Pert.* disease epidemic in plants.

epiplankton (ĕp'ĭplăng'ktŏn) *n.* [Gk. *epi*, upon; *plangktos*, wandering.] That portion of plankton from surface to one hundred fathoms.

epiplasm (ĕp'ĭplăzm) *n.* [Gk. *epi*, upon; *plasma*, mould.] Cytoplasm of a brood mother-cell remaining unused in brood formation; cytoplasm of ascus remaining after spore formation.

epiplastron (ĕp'ĭplăs'trŏn) *n.* [Gk. *epi*, upon; F. *plastron*, breastplate.] One of anterior pair of bony plates in plastron of Chelonia.

epiplectotrichoderm (ĕp'ĭplĕk'tötrĭk'ödĕrm) *n.* [Gk. *epi*, upon; *plektos*, plaited; *thrix*, hair; *derma*, skin.] An epitrichoderm, *q.v.*, of interwoven hyphae.

epipleura (ĕp'ĭploo'ră) *n.* [Gk. *epi*, upon; *pleura*, rib.] Epithecal part of cingulum in diatoms; one of rib-like structures in teleosts which are not preformed in cartilage; an uncinate process in birds; the turned down outer margin of elytra of certain beetles.

epiploic (ĕpĭplō'ĭk) *a.* [Gk. *epiploon*, caul of entrails.] *Pert.* omentum.

epiploic foramen,—opening between bursa omentalis and large sac of peritoneum; foramen of Winslow.

epiploon (ĕpĭp'lōŏn) *n.* [Gk. *epiploon*, caul of entrails.] Great omentum; insect adipose tissue.

epipodial (ĕp'ĭpō'dĭăl) *a.* [Gk. *epi*, upon; *pous*, foot.] *Pert.* epipodium.

epipodite (ĕp'ĭpödīt) *n.* [Gk. *epi*, upon; *pous*, foot.] A process arising from basal joint of crustacean limb and usually extending into gill chamber.

epipodium (ĕp′ĭpō′dĭŭm) *n.* [Gk. *epi*, upon; *pous*, foot.] The leaf-blade or lamina; embryonic leaf-lamina; ridge, fold, or lobe along edge of foot of Gastropoda; raised ring on an ambulacral plate in Echinoidea.

epiprecoracoid (ĕp′ĭprēkŏr′ăkoid) *n.* [Gk. *epi*, upon; L. *prae*, before; Gk. *korax*, crow; *eidos*, form.] A small cartilage at ventral end of precoracoid in pectoral girdle in some Chelonia.

epiproct (ĕp′ĭprŏkt) *n.* [Gk. *epi*, upon; *proktos*, anus.] A supra-anal plate representing tergum of tenth or eleventh segment in some insects.

epipteric (ĕp′ĭptĕr′ĭk) *a.* [Gk. *epi*, upon; *pteron*, wing.] Winged at tip, *appl.* certain seeds; epipterous; *pert.* or shaped like, or placed above wing; *appl.* a small skull bone between parietal and sphenoidal ala. *n.* Epipteric bone.

epipterygoid (ĕp′ĭtĕr′ĭgoid) *n.* [Gk. *epi*, upon; *pteryx*, wing.] A small bone extending nearly vertically downwards from prootic to pterygoid; also columella cranii.

epipubic (ĕp′ĭpū′bĭk) *a.* [Gk. *epi*, upon; L. *pubes*, adult.] *Pert.* or borne upon pubis; *appl.* certain cartilages or bones principally in marsupials; *appl.* anterior median process of ischiopubic plate.

epipubis (ĕp′ĭpū′bĭs) *n.* [Gk. *epi*, upon; L. *pubes*, adult.] Unpaired cartilage or bone borne anteriorly on pubis; also epigastroid.

epirhizous (ĕp′ĭrī′zŭs) *a.* [Gk. *epi*, upon; *rhiza*, root.] Growing upon a root.

epirrhysa (ĕpĭrī′să) *n. plu.* [Gk. *epirrhein*, to flow into.] Inhalant canals in sponges, *opp.* aporrhysa.

episclera (ĕp′ĭsklē′ră) *n.* [Gk. *epi*, upon; *skleros*, hard.] Connective tissue between sclera and conjunctiva.

episematic (ĕp′ĭsēmăt′ĭk) *a.* [Gk. *epi*, upon; *sema*, sign.] Aiding in recognition; *appl.* coloration, markings.

episeme (ĕp′isēm) *n.* [Gk. *epi*, upon; *sema*, sign.] A marking or colour aiding in recognition.

episepalous (ĕp′ĭsĕp′ălŭs) *a.* [Gk. *epi*, upon; F. *sépale*, sepal.] Adnate to sepals.

episkeletal (ĕp′ĭskĕl′ĕtăl) *a.* [Gk. *epi*, upon; *skeletos*, hard.] Outside the endoskeleton.

episperm (ĕp′ĭspĕrm) *n.* [Gk. *epi*, upon; *sperma*, seed.] The outer coat of seed; testa of spermoderm.

episporangium (ēp′ĭspŏrăn′jĭŭm) *n.* [Gk. *epi*, upon; *sporos*, seed; *anggeion*, vessel.] An indusium.

epispore (ĕp′ĭspōr) *n.* [Gk. *epi*, upon; *sporos*, seed.] The outer layer of a spore wall; episporium; perispore, *q.v.*; perinium, *q.v.*

epistasis (ĕpĭs′tăsĭs) *n.* [Gk. *epi*, upon; *stasis*, standing.] Dominance of a gene over another, non-allelomorphic gene; epistasy.

epistasy (ĕpĭs′tăsĭ) *n.* [Gk. *epi*, upon; *stasis*, standing.] Greater degree of modification manifested by one of two related types in phylogenesis; masking of one hereditary character by another; epistasis, *q.v.*

epistatic (ĕp′ĭstăt′ĭk) *a.* [Gk. *epistates*, master.] *Appl.* the predominating of two characters whose genes are not allelomorphs; exhibiting or *pert.* the condition of epistasis; *cf.* hypostatic.

epistellar (ĕp′ĭstĕl′ăr) *a.* [Gk. *epi*, upon; L. *stella*, stare.] Above the stellate ganglion; *appl.* neurosecretory body regulating muscular tonicity, as in Cephalopoda.

episternalia (ĕp′ĭstĕrnā′lĭă) *n. plu.* [Gk. *epi*, upon; *sternon*, breast-bone.] Two small elements preformed in cartilage frequently intervening in development between clavicles and sternum, and ultimately fusing with sternum.

episternite (ĕp′ĭstĕr′nīt) *n.* [Gk. *epi*, upon; *sternon*, breast-bone.] One of portions of an ovipositor formed from side portions of a somite.

episternum (ĕp′ĭstĕr′nŭm) *n.* [Gk. *epi*, upon; L. *sternum*, breast-bone.] The interclavicle; also applied to an anterior cartilaginous element of sternum; a lateral division of an arthropod somite, above sternum and in front of epimeron; anterior pleurite of subcoxa.

epistoma,—epistome.

epistome (ĕp'ĭstōm) *n.* [Gk. *epi*, upon; *stoma*, mouth.] A small lobe overhanging mouth in Polyzoa and containing a part of body cavity; the region between antenna and mouth in Crustacea; anterior median plate on reflected margin of carapace of certain trilobites; subcheliceral plate in certain ticks; that portion of insect head immediately behind labrum; portion of rostrum of certain Diptera.

epistroma (ĕp'ĭstrō'mă) *n.* [Gk. *epi*, upon; *stroma*, bedding.] Ectostroma, *q.v.* *Cf.* hypostroma.

epistrophe (ĕpĭs'trŏfĭ) *n.* [Gk. *epistrophe*, moving about.] The position assumed by chloroplasts along outer and inner cell-walls when exposed to diffuse light.

epistropheus (ĕp'ĭstrō'fēŭs) *n.* [Gk. *epistrophe*, turning.] The second cervical or axis vertebra.

epithalamus (ĕp'ĭthăl'ămŭs) *n.* [Gk. *epi*, upon; *thalamos*, chamber.] Part of thalamencephalon, comprising trigonum habenulae, pineal body, and posterior commissure.

epithalline (ĕp'ĭthăl'ĭn) *a.* [Gk. *epi*, upon; *thallos*, branch.] Growing upon the thallus.

epithallus (ĕp'ĭthăl'ŭs) *n.* [Gk. *epi*, upon; *thallos*, branch.] Cortical layer of hyphae covering gonidia of lichens.

epitheca (ĕp'ĭthē'kă) *n.* [Gk. *epi*, upon; *theke*, cup.] An external layer surrounding lower part of theca in many corals; theca covering epicone in Dinoflagellata; older half of frustule in diatoms.

epithecium (ĕp'ĭthē'sĭŭm) *n.* [Gk. *epi*, upon; *theke*, cup.] The surface of spore-cases in lichens and fungi.

epithelial (ĕp'ĭthē'lĭăl) *a.* [Gk. *epi*, upon; *thele*, nipple.] *Pert.* epithelium; epitheliomorph.

epithelial bodies,—the parathyroids.

epitheliofibrillae (ĕpĭthē'lĭŏfībrĭl'ē) *n. plu.* [Gk. *epi*, upon; *thele*, nipple; L. *fibrilla*, small fibre.] Parallel or reticular fibrillae of columnar epithelium analogous to myofibrillae.

epitheliomorph (ĕpĭthē'lĭŏmôrf) *a.* [Gk. *epi*, upon; *thele*, nipple; *morphe*, form.] Resembling epithelium; epithelioid; *appl.* layer of cells, or elastica interna, which secretes notochordal sheath.

epithelium (ĕp'ĭthē'lĭŭm) *n.* [Gk. *epi*, upon; *thele*, nipple.] Any cellular tissue covering a free surface or lining a tube or cavity.

epithem (ĕp'ĭthĕm) *n.* [Gk. *epi*, upon; *tithenai*, to put.] A plant tissue of specialised cells and intercellular spaces forming a hydathode; the secretory layer in nectaries; an excrescence on the beak of birds; also epithema and epitheme.

epitokous (ĕpĭt'ŏkŭs) *a.* [Gk. *epi*, upon; *tokos*, birth.] Designating the heteronereid stage of certain polychaetes.

epitrematic (ĕp'ĭtrēmăt'ĭk) *a.* [Gk. *epi*, upon; *trema*, pore.] *Appl.* upper lateral bar of branchial basket of lamprey.

epitrichial (ĕp'ĭtrĭk'ĭăl) *a.* [Gk. *epi*, upon; *thrix*, hair.] *Pert.* or resembling the epitrichium.

epitrichium (ĕp'ĭtrĭk'ĭŭm) *n.* [Gk. *epi*, upon; *thrix*, hair.] An outer layer of foetal epidermis of many mammals, usually shed before birth.

epitrichoderm (ĕp'ĭtrĭk'ŏdĕrm) *n.* [Gk. *epi*, upon; *thrix*, hair; *derma*, skin.] A trichoderm, *q.v.*, when the coating of a pileus is two-layered. *Cf.* epiplectotrichoderm.

epitrochlea (ĕp'ĭtrŏk'lēă) *n.* [Gk. *epi*, upon; L. *trochlea*, Gk. *trochilia*, pulley.] Inner condyle at distal end of humerus.

epitympanic (ĕp'ĭtĭmpăn'ĭk) *a.* [Gk. *epi*, upon; L. *tympanum*, kettle-drum.] Situated above tympanum.

epityphlon (ĕp'ĭtĭf'lŏn) *n.* [Gk. *epi*, upon; *typhlon*, caecum.] The vermiform appendix.

epivalve (ĕp'ĭvălv) *n.* [Gk. *epi*, upon; L. *valva*, fold.] Valve of epitheca in diatoms; the apical part of envelope in certain Dinoflagellata; epicone.

epixylous (ĕpĭzī'lŭs, ĕpĭk'sĭlŭs) *a.* [Gk. *epi*, upon; *xylon*, wood.] Growing upon wood.

epizoic (ĕp'ĭzō'ĭk) *a.* [Gk. *epi*, upon; *zoon*, animal.] Living on or attached to the body of an animal.

epizoochore (ĕp'ĭzō'ökōr) *n.* [Gk. *epi*. upon; *zoon*, animal; *chora*, place.] Any spore, seed, or organism dispersed by being carried upon the body of an animal. *Opp.* endozoochore.

epizoon (ĕp'ĭzō'ŏn) *n.* [Gk. *epi*, upon; *zoon*, animal.] An animal living on another; an external parasite; ectozoon.

epizootic (ĕp'ĭzōŏt'ĭk) *a.* [Gk. *epi*, upon; *zoon*, animal.] Common among animals. *n.* Disease affecting a large number of animals simultaneously, corresponding to epidemic in man.

epizygal (ĕpĭz'ĭgăl) *n.* [Gk. *epi*, upon; *zygon*, yoke.] The upper ossicle in a syzygial pair of brachials or columnars in crinoids.

eplicate (ē'plĭkāt) *a.* [L. *e*, out of; *plicatus*, folded.] Not folded; not plaited.

eponychium (ĕp'ŏnĭk'ĭŭm) *n.* [Gk. *epi*, upon; *onyx*, nail.] The thin cuticular fold which overlaps lunula of nail; dorsal portion of a neonychium.

eponym (ĕp'ŏnĭm) *n.* [Gk. *epi*, by; *onyma*, name.] Name of a person used in designation of an entity, as of a species, organ, law, disease, etc.

epoophoron (ĕp'ōŏf'örŏn) *n.* [Gk. *epi*, upon; *oon*, egg; *pherein*, to bear.] A rudimentary organ (homologous with epididymis), remains of Wolffian body of embryo, lying in mesosalpinx between ovary and uterine tube; organ of Rosenmüller.

epulosis (ĕpūlō'sis) *n.* [Gk. *epi*, over; *oule*, scar.] Formation of a scar; cicatrisation.

equal (ē'kwăl) *a.* [L. *aequalis*, equal.] Having the portions of the lamina equally developed on the two sides of midrib; *appl.* leaves.

equation division,—homeotypic or second division in meiosis.

equatorial furrow,—division round equator of segmenting egg.

equatorial plate,—group of chromosomes lying at equator of spindle during mitosis; locus of new cell-wall after cell-division.

equibiradiate (ē'kwĭbīrā'dĭăt) *a.* [L. *aequus*, equal; *bis*, twice; *radius*, ray.] With two equal rays.

equicellular (ē'kwĭsĕl'ūlăr) *a.* [L. *aequus*, equal; *cellula*, cell.] Composed of equal cells.

equifacial (ē'kwĭfā'shăl) *a.* [L. *aequus*, equal; *facies*, face.] Having equivalent surfaces or sides, as vertical leaves.

equilateral (ē'kwĭlăt'ĕrăl) *a.* [L. *aequus*, equal; *latus*, side.] Having the sides equal; *appl.* shells symmetrical about a transverse line drawn through umbo.

equilenin (ĕkwĭlē'nĭn) *n.* [L. *equus*, horse.] An oestrogenic hormone present in urine of the pregnant mare; $C_{18}H_{18}O_2$.

equiline (ĕk'wĭlēn) *n.* [L. *equus*, horse.] An oestrogenic hormone, more physiologically active than equilenin, occurring in urine of the pregnant mare; $C_{18}H_{20}O_2$.

equipotent (ēkwĭp'ötĕnt) *a.* [L. *aequus*, equal; *potens*, powerful.] Totipotent, *q.v.*

equitant (ĕk'wĭtănt) *a.* [L. *equitare*, to ride.] Overlapping saddlewise, as leaves in leaf-bud.

equivalve (ē'kwĭvălv') *a.* [L. *aequus*, equal; *valva*, valve.] Having two halves of a shell alike in form and size.

erect (ĕrĕkt') *a.* [L. *erigere*, to raise up.] Directed towards summit of ovary, *appl.* ovule; not decumbent.

erectile (ĕrĕk'tĭl) *a.* [L. *erigere*, to raise up.] Capable of being erected.

erectile tissue,—a tissue capable of being made rigid by distention of blood-vessels within it.

erection (ērĕk'shŭn) *n.* [L. *erigere*, to raise up.] The state of a part which has become swollen and distended through accumulation of blood in erectile tissue.

erector (ērĕk'tŏr) *n.* [L. *erigere*, to raise up.] A muscle which raises up an organ or part.

ereidesm (ĕrēĭ'dĕzm) *n.* [Gk. *ereidein*, to support; *desma*, bond.] An epithelial intracellular fibre.

Eremian (ĕrē'mĭăn) *a.* [Gk. *eremia*, desert.] *Appl.* or *pert.* part of the Palaearctic region including deserts of North Africa and Asia.

eremic (ĕrē'mĭk) *a.* [Gk. *eremos*, desert.] *Pert.*, or living in, deserts.

eremobic (ĕrēmŏ'bĭk) *a.* [Gk. *eremos*, solitude; *bios*, life.] Growing or living in isolation; having a solitary existence.

eremochaetous (ĕr'ēmökē'tŭs) *a.* [Gk. *eremos*, lonely; *chaite*, hair.] Having no regularly arranged system of bristles; *appl.* flies.

eremophyte (ĕr'ēmöfīt') *n.* [Gk. *eremos*, solitude; *phyton*, plant.] A desert plant.

erepsin (ĕrĕp'sĭn) *n.* [L. *eripere*, to set free.] A proteolytic enzyme of intestinal juice and body tissues.

ergaloid (ĕr'găloid) *a.* [Gk. *ergon*, work; *eidos*, form.] Having the adults sexually capable though wingless.

ergastic (ĕrgăs'tĭk) *a.* [Gk. *ergastikos*, fit for working.] *Pert.* metaplasm; *appl.* lifeless cell-inclusions, as fat, starch, etc.

ergastoplasm (ĕrgăs'töplăzm) *n.* [Gk. *ergazesthai*, to work; *plasma*, mould.] Archoplasm; kinoplasm.

ergastoplasmic (ĕrgăs'töplăz'mĭk) *a.* [Gk. *ergazesthai*, to work; *plasma*, mould.] *Appl.* fibrillae of gland cells which may induce production of secretory granules.

ergatandromorph (ĕrgătăn'drömôrf) *n.* [Gk. *ergates*, worker; *aner*, male; *morphe*, form.] An ant or other social insect in which worker and male characters are blended.

ergatandrous (ĕrgătăn'drŭs) *a.* [Gk. *ergates*, worker; *aner*, man.] Having worker-like males.

ergataner (ĕrgăt'ănĕr) *n.* [Gk. *ergates*, worker; *aner*, male.] A male ant resembling a worker; an ergatoid or ergatomorphic male.

ergate (ĕr'gāt) *n.* [Gk. *ergates*, worker.] A worker-ant; ergates.

ergatogyne (ĕrgă'tŏj'ĭnē) *n.* [Gk. *ergates*, worker; *gyne*, female.] A female ant resembling a worker; an ergatoid or ergatomorphic female.

ergatogynous (ĕrgătŏj'ĭnŭs) *a.* [Gk. *ergates*, worker; *gyne*, woman.] Having worker-like females.

ergatoid (ĕrgăt'oid) *a.* [Gk. *ergates*, worker; *eidos*, form.] Resembling a worker, *appl.* ants; ergatomorphic.

ergones (ĕr'gōnz) *n. plu.* [Gk. *ergon*, work.] Organic substances of which small amounts suffice for activation or regulation of a physiological process, as enzymes, hormones, and vitamins; also ergines.

ergonomy (ĕr'gŏn'ömĭ) *n.* [Gk. *ergon*, work; *nomos*, law.] The differentiation of functions; physiological differentiation associated with morphological specialisation.

ergoplasm,—kinoplasm.

ergosterol,—a sterol occurring in plants and animals, with photochemical reaction products leading to formation of its isomer vitamin D_2; $C_{28}H_{44}O$.

ergot (ĕr'gŏt) *n.* [O.F. *argot*, spur.] A small bare patch found on limbs of horse-tribe, representing last remnant of naked palm of hand and sole of foot; condition of ovary of grasses produced by a fungus; rye smut; sclerotium of Claviceps, yielding several alkaloids, *e.g.* ergotoxine and ergometrine, which stimulate uterine muscle.

erichthoidina (ĕrĭk'thoid'ĭnă) *n.* [Gk. *erechthein*, to break; *eidos*, form.] Larval stage of Stomatopoda comparable with zoaea.

erichthus (ĕrĭk'thŭs) *n.* [Gk. *erechthein*, to break.] Larval stage of Stomatopoda, comparable with pseudozoaea.

erineum (ĕrĭn'ēŭm) *n.* [Gk. *erineos*, woollen.] An outgrowth of abnormal hairs produced on leaves by certain gall-mites.

eriocomous (ĕrĭŏk'ömŭs) *a.* [Gk. *erion*, wool; *kome*, hair.] Having woolly hair; fleece-haired.

eriophyllous (ĕr'ĭöfĭl'ŭs) *a.* [Gk. *erion*, wool; *phyllon*, leaf.] Having leaves with a cottony appearance.

erose (ĕrōs') *a.* [L. *erodere*, to wear away.] Having margin irregularly notched; *appl.* leaf, bacterial colony.

erosion (ĕrō'zhŭn) *n.* [L. *erodere*, to wear away.] Decay which usually starts at apex of many gastropod shells.

erostrate (ērŏs'trāt) *a.* [L. *ex*, without; *rostrum*, beak.] Having no beak; *appl.* anthers.

ersaeome (ĕr'sēōm) *n.* [Gk. *erse*, young.] The free monogastric generation of Siphonophora.

eruciform (ēroo'sĭfôrm) *a.* [L. *eruca*, caterpillar; *forma*, shape.] Having the shape of, or resembling a caterpillar; *appl.* insect larvae; *appl.* spores of certain lichens.

erumpent (ērŭm'pĕnt) *a.* [L. *erumpere*, to break out.] Breaking through suddenly; *appl.* fungal hyphae.

erythrin (ĕrĭth'rĭn) *n.* [Gk. *erythros*, red.] A red colouring matter found in certain algae and lichens; $C_{20}H_{22}O_{10}$.

erythrism (ĕrĭth'rĭzm) *n.* [Gk. *erythros*, red.] Abnormal presence, or excessive amount, of red colouring matter, as in petals, feathers, hair, eggs; *cf.* rufinism.

erythroblasts (ĕrĭth'röblăsts) *n. plu.* [Gk. *erythros*, red; *blastos*, bud.] Nucleated cells, derived from mesoderm, which later contain haemoglobin and develop into red blood corpuscles.

erythrochroism,—erythrism.

erythrocruorin (ĕrĭth'rökroo'örĭn) *n.* [Gk. *erythros*, red; L. *cruor*, blood.] Red iron-containing respiratory pigment in some invertebrates.

erythrocyte (ĕrĭth'rösīt) *n.* [Gk. *erythros*, red; *kytos*, hollow.] A red blood corpuscle.

erythrocyte-maturing factor,—formed by action of pyloric gland secretion (intrinsic factor) on extrinsic factor in food, and stored in liver, and necessary for maturation of red blood cells in bone-marrow; symbol: EMF; cyanocobalamin or vitamin D_4.

erythrocytolysis (ĕrĭth'rösītŏl'ĭsĭs) *n.* [Gk. *erythros*, red; *kytos*, cell; *lysis*, loosing.] Destruction of red blood corpuscles; haemolysis.

erythron (ĕrĭth'rŏn) *n.* [Gk. *erythros*, red; *on*, being.] The red cells in bone marrow and circulating blood, collectively.

erythrophilous (ĕr'ĭthrŏf'ĭlŭs) *a.* [Gk. *erythros*, red; *philein*, to love.] Having special affinity for red stains; *appl.* structures in a cell or to a type of cells.

erythrophore (ĕrĭth'röfōr) *n.* [Gk. *erythros*, red; *pherein*, to bear.] A reddish-purple pigment-bearing cell.

erythrophyll (ĕrĭth'röfĭl) *n.* [Gk. *erythros*, red; *phyllon*, leaf.] A red colouring matter of some leaves and of red algae.

erythropoiesis (ĕrĭth'röpoiē'sĭs) *n.* [Gk. *erythros*, red; *poiesis*, making.] The production of red blood corpuscles.

erythropsin (ĕrĭthrŏp'sĭn) *n.* [Gk. *erythros*, red; *opsis*, sight.] Red colouring matter in insect eyes; rhodopsin, *q.v.*

erythrotin (ĕrĭth'rötĭn) *n.* [Gk. *erythros*, red.] Vitamin B_{12}, extracted from liver, anti-pernicious anaemia factor, and growth factor for certain micro-organisms.

erythrozyme (ĕrĭth'rözīm) *n.* [Gk. *erythros*, red; *zyme*, leaven.] An enzyme capable of decomposing ruberythric acid, and acting upon glucosides.

escape (ĕskāp′) *n.* [M.E. *escapen.*] A plant originally cultivated, now found wild.

escutcheon (ĕskŭch′ŭn) *n.* [O.F. *escuchon*, shield.] Area on rump of many quadrupeds which is either variously coloured or has the hair specially arranged; mesoscutellum of certain insects; ligamental area of certain bivalves.

escutellate,—exscutellate, *q.v.*

eseptate (ēsĕp′tāt) *a.* [L. *ex*, without; *septum*, enclosure.] Not supplied with septa.

esodic (ēsŏd′ĭk) *a.* [Gk. *eisodos*, a coming in.] Afferent; centripetal. *Opp.* exodic.

esophageal,—oesophageal.

esophagus,—oesophagus.

esoteric (ĕsōtĕr′ĭk) *a.* [Gk. *esoterikos*, arising within.] Arising within the organism.

espathate (ēspăth′āt) *a.* [L. *ex*, without; *spatha*, broad blade.] Having no spathe.

esquamate (ēskwā′māt) *a.* [L. *ex*, without; *squama*, scale.] Having no scale.

essential oils,—volatile oils, composed of various constituents and contained in plant organs, with characteristic odour.

esth-,—*see* aesth-.

estipulate (ēstĭp′ūlāt) *a.* [L. *ex*, without; *stipula*, stem.] Having no stipules.

estival,—aestival.

estivation,—aestivation.

estr-,—*see* oestr-.

estriate (ēstrī′āt) *a.* [L. *e*, out of; *striatus*, grooved.] Not marked by narrow parallel grooves or lines; not streaked.

estuarine (ĕs′tūărĭn) *a.* [L. *aestuarium*, estuary.] *Pert.* or found in an estuary; *appl.* organisms.

etaerio (ĕtē′rĭō) *n.* [Gk. *etairia*, association.] An aggregate fruit, composed of achenes, berries, drupels, follicles, or samaras; eterio; *cf.* syncarp.

etheogenesis (ē′thēöjĕn′ĕsĭs) *n.* [Gk. *etheos*, youth; *genesis*, descent.] Parthenogenesis producing males; development of a male gamete without fertilisation.

Ethiopian (ē′thĭō′pĭăn) *a.* [Gk. *aithiops*, burned-face.] *Appl.* or *pert.* a zoogeographical region including Africa south of the Sahara and southern Arabia, and divisible into African and Malagasy subregions.

ethmohyostylic (ĕth′möhī′östĭl′ĭk) *a.* [Gk. *ethmos*, sieve; Υ; *stylos*, pillar.] With mandibular suspension from ethmoid region and hyoid bar.

ethmoid (ĕth′moid) *a.* [Gk. *ethmos*, sieve; *eidos*, shape.] *Pert.* bones which form a considerable part of walls of nasal cavity.

ethmoidal (ĕthmoi′dăl) *a.* [Gk. *ethmos*, sieve; *eidos*, shape.] *Pert.* ethmoid bones or region.

ethmoidal notch,—a quadrilateral space separating the two orbital parts of the frontal bone; incisura ethmoidalis.

ethmolysian (ĕth′mölĭs′ĭăn) *a.* [Gk. *ethmos*, sieve; *lyein*, to loosen.] *Pert.* an apical system in which the madreporite extends backwards till it separates the two posterolateral genitals.

ethmopalatine (ĕth′möpăl′ătĭn) *a.* [Gk. *ethmos*, sieve; L. *palatus*, palate.] *Pert.* ethmoid and palatine bones, or their region.

ethmophract (ĕth′möfrăkt) *a.* [Gk. *ethmos*, sieve; *phrassein*, to fence in.] *Pert.* a simple, compact, apical system with pores occurring only in right anterior corner.

ethmoturbinals (ĕth′mötŭr′bĭnălz) *n. plu.* [Gk. *ethmos*, sieve; L. *turbo*, whorl.] Cartilages or bones in nasal cavity which are folded so as to increase olfactory area.

ethmovomerine (ĕth′mövō′mĕrĭn) *a.* [Gk. *ethmos*, sieve; L. *vomer*, ploughshare.] *Pert.* ethmoid and vomer regions; *appl.* the cartilage which forms nasal septum in early embryo.

ethnography (ĕthnŏg′răfĭ) *n.* [Gk. *ethnos*, nation; *graphein*, to write.] The description of the races of mankind.

ethnology (ĕthnŏl′öjĭ) *n.* [Gk. *ethnos*, nation; *logos*, discourse.] Science dealing with the different races of mankind, their distribution, relationship, and activities.

ethology (ēthŏl′öjĭ) *n.* [Gk. *ethos*, custom; *logos*, discourse.] Bionomics; study of habits in relation to habitat; study of behaviour.

ethomerous (ēthŏm′ërŭs) *a.* [Gk. *ethos*, custom; *meros*, part.] Having the normal number of parts or segments; with normal number of chromosomes.

etiolation (ē′tĭölā′shŭn) *n.* [F. *étioler*, to blanch.] Blanched condition produced in plants reared in darkness, or by disease.

etiolin (ē′tĭölĭn) *n.* [F. *étioler*, to blanch.] A yellowish pigment found in chloroplasts of plants grown in darkness; protochlorophyll.

etiology,—aetiology, *q.v.*

euapogamy (ū′ăpŏg′ămĭ) *n.* [Gk. *eu*, well; *apo*, away; *gamos*, marriage.] Diploid apogamy, haploid apogamy being meiotic euapogamy.

euaster (ūăs′tër) *n.* [Gk. *eu*, good; *aster*, star.] An aster in which the rays meet at a common centre.

eucarpic (ū′kârpĭk) *a.* [Gk. *eu*, well; *karpos*, fruit.] Having the fruit-body formed by only a part of the thallus; *appl.* Phycomycetes having rhizoids or haustoria. *Opp.* holocarpic.

eucentric (ūsĕn′trĭk) *a.* [Gk. *eu*, well; *kentron*, centre.] Pericentric, *q.v.*

eucephalous (ūkĕf′ălŭs, -sĕf-) *a.* [Gk. *eu*, good; *kephale*, head.] With well-developed head; *appl.* certain insect larvae.

euchroic (ūkrō′ĭk) *a.* [Gk. *eu*, well; *chros*, colour.] Having normal pigmentation; *opp.* epichroic, *appl.* fungi.

euchromatic (ū′krōmăt′ĭk) *a.* [Gk. *eu*, well; *chroma*, colour.] *Pert.* euchromatin; *appl.* chromosome regions which never become heteropycnotic. *Opp.* heterochromatic.

euchromatin (ūkrō′mătĭn) *n.* [Gk. *eu*, well; *chroma*, colour.] Chromatin making up bulk of chromosome and including active genes.

euchromosome (ūkrō′mösōm) *n.* [Gk. *eu*, well; *chroma*, colour; *soma*, body.] A typical chromosome, or autosome.

eucoen (ūsēn) *n.* [Gk. *eu*, well; *koinos*, common.] Those members of a biocoenosis which are unable to live in a different environment. *Opp.* tychocoen.

eucone (ūkōn) *a.* [Gk. *eu*, good; *konos*, cone.] Having crystalline cones fully developed in single elements of compound eye.

eudipleural (ū′dīploo′răl) *a.* [Gk. *eu*, good; *dis*, double; *pleuron*, side.] Symmetrical about a median plane; bilaterally symmetrical.

eudoxome (ū′dŏksōm) *n.* [Gk. *eudoxos*, glorious.] Monogastric free-swimming stage of a siphonophore without nectocalyx.

eugamic (ūgăm′ĭk) *a.* [Gk. *eu*, well; *gamos*, marriage.] *Appl.* mature period, *opp.* agamic or youthful, and aged or senescent.

eugenic (ūjĕn′ĭk) *a.* [Gk. *eugenes*, well-born.] *Pert.* or tending towards racial improvement.

eugenics (ūjĕn′ĭks) *n.* [Gk. *eu*, well; *genos*, birth.] The science dealing with the factors which tend to improve or impair stock.

euglenoid (ūglē′noid) *a.* [Gk. *eu*, well; *glene*, eyeball, puppet; *eidos*, form.] *Pert.* or like Euglena; *appl.* characteristic movement of Euglena.

eugonic (ūgŏn′ĭk) *a.* [Gk. *eu*, well; *gonos*, produce.] Prolific; growing profusely, *appl.* bacterial colonies.

euhaline (ūhăl′īn) *a.* [Gk. *eu*, well; *halinos*, saline.] Living only in saline inland waters; *cf.* euryhaline.

eumelanin (ū′mĕl′ănĭn) *n.* [Gk. *eu*, well; *melas*, black.] Black melanin; *cf.* phaeomelanin.

eumerism (ū′mërĭzm) *n.* [Gk. *eu*, well; *meros*, part.] An aggregation of like parts.

eumeristem (ū'mĕr'ĭstĕm) *n.* [Gk. *eu*, well; *meristos*, divided.] Meristem composed of isodiametric thin-walled cells.

eumerogenesis (ū'mĕr'öjĕn'ësĭs) *n.* [Gk. *eu*, well; *meros*, part; *genesis*, descent.] Segmentation in which the units are similar at least for a certain time.

eumitosis (ūmĭtō'sĭs) *n.* [Gk. *eu*, well; *mitos*, thread.] Typical mitosis.

eumitotic (ūmĭtŏt'ĭk) *a.* [Gk. *eu*, well; *mitos*, thread.] Anaschistic, *q.v.*; *pert.* eumitosis.

euphotic (ūfō'tĭk) *a.* [Gk. *eu*, well; *phos*, light.] Well illuminated, *appl.* zone, surface waters to depth of about 80 metres; upper layer of photic zone; *cf.* dysphotic.

euphotometric (ū'fōtömĕt'rĭk) *a.* [Gk. *eu*, well; *phos*, light; *metron*, measure.] *Appl.* leaves oriented to receive maximum diffuse light; *cf.* panphotometric.

euplastic (ūplăs'tĭk) *a.* [Gk. *eu*, well; *plastos*, moulded.] Readily organised, easily forming a tissue.

euplectenchyma (ū'plĕktĕng'kĭmă) *n.* [Gk. *eu*, well; *plektos*, plaited; *engchyma*, infusion.] Fungal tissue composed of intertwined hyphae arranged in groups approximately at right angles to each other in three dimensions.

euploid (ū'ploid) *a.* [Gk. *eu*, well; *haploos*, onefold; *eidos*, form.] Polyploid when total chromosome number is an exact multiple of the haploid number. *Opp.* aneuploid.

eupotamic (ūpŏt'ămĭk) *a.* [Gk. *eu*, well; *potamos*, river.] Thriving both in streams and in their backwaters; *appl.* potamoplankton.

eupyrene (ū'pīrēn') *a.* [Gk. *eu*, well; *pyren*, fruit-stone.] *Appl.* sperms of normal type; *cf.* apyrene, oligopyrene.

eurybaric (ū'rĭbăr'ĭk) *a.* [Gk. *eurys*, wide; *baros*, weight.] *Appl.* animals adaptable to great differences in altitude, *opp.* stenobaric.

eurybathic (ū'rĭbăth'ĭk) *a.* [Gk. *eurys*, wide; *bathys*, deep.] Having a large vertical range of distribution, *opp.* stenobathic.

eurybenthic (ū'rĭbĕn'thĭk) *a.* [Gk. *eurys*, wide; *benthos*, depth of the sea.] *Pert.* or living within a wide range of depth of the sea-bottom. *Opp.* stenobenthic.

eurychoric (ū'rĭkō'rĭk) *a.* [Gk. *eurys*, wide; *choros*, place.] Widely distributed, *opp.* stenochoric.

eurycyst (ū'rĭsĭst) *n.* [Gk. *eurys*, wide; *kystis*, bladder.] Large cell of middle vein in mosses; deuter cell; pointer cell.

euryhaline (ū'rĭhăl'īn) *a.* [Gk. *eurys*, wide; *halinos*, saline.] *Appl.* marine organisms adaptable to a wide range of salinity, *opp.* stenohaline.

euryhygric (ū'rĭhī'grĭk) *a.* [Gk. *eurys*, wide; *hygros*, wet.] *Appl.* organisms adaptable to a wide range of atmospheric humidity.

euryoecious (ū'rĭē'sĭŭs) *a.* [Gk. *eurys*, wide; *oikos*, abode.] Having a wide range of habitat selection, *opp.* stenoecious.

euryphagous (ūrĭf'ăgŭs) *a.* [Gk. *eurys*, wide; *phagein*, to eat.] Subsisting on a large variety of foods, *opp.* stenophagous; *cf.* omnivorous.

eurypylous (ū'rĭpī'lŭs) *a.* [Gk. *eurys*, broad; *pyle*, gate.] Wide at the opening; *appl.* canal system of sponges in which the chambers open directly into excurrent canals by wide apopyles, and receive water from incurrent canals through prosopyles.

eurysome (ū'rĭsōm) *a.* [Gk. *eurys*, broad; *soma*, body.] Short and stout, *opp.* leptosome.

eurythermic (ū'rĭthĕr'mĭk) *a.* [Gk. *eurys*, wide; *therme*, heat.] *Appl.* organisms adaptable to a wide range of temperature, *opp.* stenothermic, eurythermal, eurythermous.

eurytopic (ū'rĭtŏp'ĭk) *a.* [Gk. *eurys*, wide; *topos*, place.] Having a wide range of geographical distribution, *opp.* stenotopic.

eusporangiate (ū'spŏrăn'jĭāt) *a.* [Gk. *eu*, well; *sporos*, seed; *anggeion*, vessel.] Having sporogenous tissue derived from inner cell that follows periclinal division of superficial initial; *cf.* leptosporangiate.

Eustachian (ūstā'kĭăn) *a.* [*B. Eustachio*, Italian physician]. *Appl.* tube or canal connecting tympanic cavity with pharynx; *appl.* valve guarding orifice of inferior vena cava in atrium of heart.

eustele (ūstē'lē) *n.* [Gk. *eu*, well; *stele*, pillar.] The arrangement of vascular tissue into collateral or bicollateral bundles with conjunctive tissue between, as in gymnosperms and dicotyledons.

eusternum (ūstĕr'nŭm) *n.* [Gk. *eu*, well; *sternon*, breastplate.] A sternal sclerite of insects; antesternite, basisternum.

eustomatous (ūstŏm'ătŭs) *a.* [Gk. *eu*, well; *stoma*, mouth.] Having a distinct mouth-like opening.

eustroma (ūstrŏ'mă) *n.* [Gk. *eu*, well; *stroma*, bedding.] Stroma formed of fungus cells only.

eutelegenesis (ū'tĕlĕjĕn'ĕsĭs) *n.* [Gk. *eu*, well; *tele*, afar; *genesis*, descent.] Improved breeding by artificial insemination.

euthenics (ūthĕn'ĭks) *n.* [Gk. *euthenein*, to thrive.] The science of betterment of human race on the side of intellect and morals; the study of environmental agencies contributing to racial improvement.

eutherian (ūthē'rĭăn) *a.* [Gk. *eu*, well; *therion*, small animal.] *Appl.* placental mammals with development uterine till full-time.

euthycomous (ūthĭk'ŏmŭs) *a.* [Gk. *euthys*, straight; *kome*, hair.] Straight-haired.

euthyneurous (ū'thĭnū'rŭs) *a.* [Gk. *euthys*, straight; *neuron*, nerve.] Having visceral loop of nervous system untwisted.

eutrophic (ūtrŏf'ĭk) *a.* [Gk. *eu*, well; *trophe*, nourishment.] Providing, or *pert.*, adequate nutrition. *Opp.* dystrophic.

eutropic (ūtrŏp'ĭk) *a.* [Gk. *eu*, well; *tropikos*, turning.] Turning sunward; dextrorse.

eutropous (ū'trŏpŭs) *a.* [Gk. *eu*, well; *tropos*, direction.] Adapted to visiting special kinds of flowers, as certain insects. *Opp.* allotropous.

evaginate (ēvăj'ĭnāt) *v.* [L. *evaginare*, to unsheath.] To evert from a sheathing structure; to protrude by eversion.

evagination (ē'văjĭnā'shŭn) *n.* [L. *e*, out; *vagina*, sheath.] The process of unsheathing, or product of this process; an outgrowth.

evanescent (ĕv'ănĕs'ĕnt) *a.* [L. *evanescere*, to vanish.] Disappearing early; *appl.* flowers which fade quickly.

evection (ēvĕk'shŭn) *n.* [L. *e*, out; *vehere*, to convey.] Displacement of parent cell at septum of a filament, causing dichotomous appearance, as in certain algae.

evelate (ēvē'lāt) *a.* [L. *e*, out of; *velatus*, veiled.] Without a veil or velum; *appl.* fungi.

eviscerate (ĕvĭs'ĕrāt) *v.* [L. *ex*, out; *viscera*, entrails.] To disembowel; to eject the viscera, as do holothurians on capture.

evocation (ĕv'ŏkā'shŭn) *n.* [L. *evocare*, to call forth.] The biochemical process whereby induced differentiation is called forth; induction as such.

evocator (ĕv'ŏkātŏr) *n.* [L. *evocator*, caller forth.] The chemical stimulus furnished by an organiser, *q.v.*

evolute (ĕv'ŏlūt) *a.* [L. *evolvere*, to unroll.] Turned back; unfolded.

evolutility (ĕv'ŏlūtĭl'ĭtĭ) *n.* [L. *evolvere*, to unroll.] Capability to evolve or change in structure; capacity to change in growth and form as a result of nutritional or other environmental factors.

evolution (ĕv'ŏlū'shŭn) *n.* [L. *evolvere*, to unroll.] The gradual development of organisms from preexisting organisms since the dawn of life.

evolvate (ēvŏl'vāt) *a.* [L. *e*, out of; *volva*, wrapper.] Without a volva.

exalate (ĕksā′lāt) *a.* [L. *ex*, without; *ala*, wing.] Not having wing-like appendages; apterous.

exalbuminous (ĕk′sălbū′mĭnŭs) *a.* [L. *ex*, without; *albumen*, white of egg.] Without albumen; *appl.* seeds without endosperm or perisperm; exendospermous.

exannulate (ĕksăn′ūlāt) *a.* [L. *ex*, without; *annulus*, ring.] Having a sporangium not furnished with an annulus; *appl.* certain ferns.

exarate (ĕks′ărāt) *a.* [L. *exaratus*, ploughed up.] *Appl.* a pupa with free wings and legs. *Opp.* obtect.

exarch (ĕks′ârk) *n.* [L. *ex*, without; Gk. *arche*, beginning.] With protoxylem strands outside metaxylem, or in touch with pericycle.

exasperate (ĕgzăs′pĕrāt) *a.* [L. *exasperare*, to roughen.] Furnished with hard, stiff points.

excentric (ĕksĕn′trĭk) *a.* [L. *ex*, out of; *centrum*, centre.] One-sided; having the two portions of lamina unequally developed.

exciple (ĕk′sĭpl) *n.* [L. *excipula*, receptacles.] The marginal wall, or outer covering, of apothecium in certain lichens; excipulum.

excitability,—capacity of a living cell, or tissue, to respond to an environmental change or stimulus.

excitation (ĕk′sĭtā′shŭn) *n.* [L. *excitare*, to rouse.] Act of producing or increasing stimulation; immediate response of protoplasm to a stimulus.

excitatory cells,—motor cells in sympathetic nervous system.

excitonutrient (ĕksī′tönū′trĭënt) *a.* [L. *excitare*, to rouse; *nutriens*, feeding.] Causing or increasing nutrient activities.

exconjugant (ĕkskŏn′jŏogănt) *n.* [L. *ex*, out; *conjugare*, to yoke.] An organism which is leading an independent life after conjugation with another.

excorticate,—decorticate.

excreta (ĕkskrē′tă) *n. plu.* [L. *excretum*, separated.] Waste material eliminated from body or any tissue thereof; deleterious substances formed within a plant.

excrete (ĕkskrēt′) *v.* [L. *ex*, out; *cernere*, to sift.] To eliminate waste material from body; to withdraw useless materials from the place of most active metabolism in plant.

excretion (ĕkskrē′shŭn) *n.* [L. *ex*, out; *cernere*, to sift.] Act of eliminating waste material, or the product of the elimination.

excurrent (ĕkskŭr′ënt) *a.* [L. *ex*, out; *currere*, to run.] *Pert.* ducts, channels, or canals in which there is an outgoing flow; with undivided main stem; having midrib projecting beyond apex.

excurved (ĕkskŭrvd′) *a.* [L. *ex*, out; *curvare*, to curve.] Curved outwards from centre; excurvate.

excystation (ĕks′-sĭstā′shŭn) *n.* [L. *ex*, out of; Gk. *kystis*, bladder.] Emergence from encysted condition.

exendospermous (ĕks′ĕndöspĕr′mŭs) *a.* [L. *ex*, without; Gk. *endon*, within; *sperma*, seed.] Without endosperm; exalbuminous, *q.v.*

exflagellation (ĕksflăj′ëlā′shŭn) *n.* [L. *ex*, out of; *flagellum*, whip.] Process of microgamete formation by microgametocyte in Haemosporidia.

exfoliation (ĕksfō′lĭā′shŭn) *n.* [L. *ex*, out; *folium*, leaf.] The shedding of leaves or scales from a bud.

exhalant (ĕks′hā′lănt) *a.* [L. *ex*, out; *halare*, to breathe.] Capable of carrying from the interior outwards.

exindusiate (ĕk′sĭndū′zĭāt) *a.* [L. *ex*, out; *indusium*, cover.] Having the sporangia uncovered or naked.

exine,—extine, *q.v.*

exinguinal (ĕk′sĭng′gwĭnăl) *a.* [L. *ex*, out; *inguen*, groin.] Occurring outside the groin; *pert.* second joint of arachnid leg.

exites (ĕk′sīts) *n. plu.* [Gk. *exo*, without.] Offshoots on outer lateral border of axis of certain arthropod limbs.

exobiotic (ĕk′söbīöt′ĭk) *a.* [Gk. *exo*, without; *biotikos*, *pert.* life.] Living on the exterior of a substratum. *Opp.* endobiotic.

exocardiac (ĕk'sökâr'dĭăk) *a.* [Gk. *exo*, without; *kardia*, heart.] Situated outside the heart.

exocarp (ĕk'sökârp) *n.* [Gk. *exo*, without; *karpos*, fruit.] Outer layer of the pericarp; epicarp.

exoccipital (ĕk'sŏksĭp'ĭtăl) *a.* [L. *ex*, without; *occiput*, back of head.] *Pert.* a skull bone on each side of the foramen magnum.

exochiton (ĕk'sökī'tŏn) *n.* [Gk. *exo*, without; *chiton*, coat.] Outermost layer of oogonial wall, as in Fucales; exochite; *cf.* endochiton, mesochiton.

exochorion (ĕk'sökō'rĭŏn) *n.* [Gk. *exo*, without; *chorion*, chorion.] Outer layer of membrane secreted by follicular cells surrounding the egg in ovary of insects.

exocoel (ĕk'sösēl) *n.* [Gk. *exo*, without; *koilos*, hollow.] The space between mesenteries of adjacent couples in certain Zoantharia; exocoelom, *q.v.*

exocoelar (ĕk'sösē'lăr) *a.* [Gk. *exo*, without; *koilos*, hollow.] *Pert.* parietal wall of coelom.

exocoelic (ĕk'sösē'lĭk) *a.* [Gk. *exo*, without; *koilos*, hollow.] In Zoantharia, *pert.* space between adjacent couples of mesenteries; *appl.* radial areas on disc; *appl.* outermost cycle of tentacles.

exocoelom (ĕk'sösē'lŏm) *n.* [Gk. *exo*, without; *koilos*, hollow.] Extra-embryonic body cavity of embryo.

exocone (ĕk'sökōn) *a.* [Gk. *exo*, without; *konos*, cone.] *Appl.* insect compound eye with cones of cuticular origin.

exocrine (ĕk'sökrĭn) *a.* [Gk. *exo*, outwards; *krinein*, to separate.] *Appl.* glands whose secretion is drained by ducts; *cf.* endocrine, apocrine.

exocuticula (ĕk'sökūtĭk'ūlă) *n.* [Gk. *exo*, without; L. *dim.* of *cutis*, skin.] Middle layer of insect cuticle, between endocuticula and epicuticula; outer layer of integument in spiders.

exoderm (ĕk'södĕrm) *n.* [Gk. *exo*, without; *derma*, skin.] The dermal layer of sponges.

exodermis (ĕk'södĕr'mĭs) *n.* [Gk. *exo*, without; L. *dermis*, skin.] A specialised layer below the piliferous layer; ectoderm, *q.v.*

exodic (ĕksŏd'ĭk) *a.* [Gk. *exodos*, a going out.] Efferent; centrifugal. *Opp.* esodic.

exoenzyme (ĕk'söĕn'zīm) *n.* [Gk. *exo*, outside; *en*, in; *zyme*, leaven.] Any extracellular enzyme.

exogamete (ĕk'sögămēt') *n.* [Gk. *exo*, without; *gametes*, mate.] A reproductive cell which fuses with one derived from another source.

exogamy (ĕksŏg'ămĭ) *n.* [Gk. *exo*, without; *gamos*, marriage.] Conjugation or fusion of isogametes with others of a different brood; outbreeding.

exogastric (ĕk'sögăs'trĭk) *a.* [Gk. *exo*, outwards; *gaster*, stomach.] Having the shell coiled towards dorsal surface of body.

exogastrula (ĕk'sögăs'troolă) *n.* [Gk. *exo*, without; *gaster*, stomach.] An hour-glass shaped sea-urchin larva induced experimentally.

exogenous (ĕksŏj'ĕnŭs) *a.* [Gk. *exo*, outside; *-genes*, produced.] Originating outside the organism; developed from superficial tissue, the superficial meristem; growing from parts which were previously ossified; *appl.* metabolism concerned with effector activities and temperature.

exognathion (ĕk'sögnăth'ĭŏn) *n.* [Gk. *exo*, without; *gnathos*, jaw.] The maxillary portion of upper jaw; the maxilla with exception of endognathion and mesognathion.

exo-intine (ĕk'söĭn'tĭn) *n.* [Gk. *exo*, without; L. *intus*, within.] Middle layer of a spore-covering, between extine and intine.

exolete (ĕk'sölēt) *a.* [L. *exolescere*, to grow out of use.] Disused; emptied, *appl.* capsules, perithecia, etc.

exomixis (ĕk'sömĭk'sĭs) *n.* [Gk. *exo*, outside; *mixis*, mingling.] Union of sex-elements derived from different sources, *opp.* endomixis.

exonephric (ĕk'sönĕf'rĭk) *a.* [Gk. *exo*, without; *nephros*, kidney.] With nephridia opening to exterior; *opp.* enteronephric, *appl.* Oligochaeta.

exoparasite,—ectoparasite, *q.v.*

exoperidium (ĕk'söpērĭd'ĭŭm) *n.* [Gk. *exo*, without; *peridion*, a small wallet.] The outer layer of spore case in certain fungi; epiperidium.

exophylaxis (ĕk'söfĭlăk'sĭs) *n.* [Gk. *exo*, without; *phylax*, guard.] Protection afforded against pathogenic organisms by skin secretions.

exophytic (ĕk'söfĭt'ĭk) *a.* [Gk. *exo*, outside of; *phyton*, plant.] On, or *pert.*, exterior of plants; *appl.* oviposition. *Opp.* endophytic.

exoplasm (ĕk'söplăzm) *n.* [Gk. *exo*, without; *plasma*, mould.] Ectoplasm, *q.v.*

exopodite (ĕk'söpŏdīt) *n.* [Gk. *exo*, without; *pous*, foot.] The outer branch of a typical biramous crustacean limb.

exoscopic (ĕk'söskŏp'ĭk) *a.* [Gk. *exo*, without; *skopein*, to look.] With apex emerging through archegonium, *appl.* embryo. *Opp.* endoscopic.

exoskeleton (ĕk'söskĕl'ētŏn) *n.* [Gk. *exo*, without; *skeletos*, hard.] A hard supporting structure secreted by ectoderm or by skin.

exosmosis (ĕk'sŏsmō'sĭs) *n.* [Gk. *exo*, outwards; *osmos*, impulse.] The passing out through a membrane of a gas or fluid. *Opp.* endosmosis.

exospore (ĕk'söspōr), **exosporium** (ĕk'söspō'rĭŭm) *n.* [Gk. *exo*, without; *sporos*, seed.] Outer coating of sporangial wall; a conidium.

exosporous (ĕk'söspō'rŭs) *a.* [Gk. *exo*, without; *sporos*, seed.] With spores borne or discharged exteriorly.

exostome (ĕk'söstōm) *n.* [Gk. *exo*, without; *stoma*, mouth.] Outer portion of peristome in mosses. Opening or foramen in outer wall of ovule.

exostosis (ĕk'sŏstō'sĭs) *n.* [Gk. *exo*, without; *osteon*, bone.] Formation of knots on surface of wood; formation of knob-like outgrowths of bone at a damaged portion, or of dental tissue in a similar way.

exoteric (ĕk'sōtĕr'ĭk) *a.* [Gk. *exoteros*, beyond.] Produced or developed outside the organism.

exotheca (ĕk'söthē'kă) *n.* [Gk. *exo*, without; *theke*, box.] The extracapsular tissue of a coral.

exothecal (ĕk'söthē'kăl) *a.* [Gk. *exo*, without; *theke*, box.] *Pert.* tissue outside the theca of a coral.

exothecate (ĕk'söthē'kāt) *a.* [Gk. *exo*, without; *theke*, box.] Having an exotheca.

exothecium (ĕk'söthē'sĭŭm) *n.* [Gk. *exo*, without; *theke*, case.] The outer specialised dehiscing cell layer of the gymnosperm sporangium; *cf.* endothecium.

exothermic (ĕk'söthĕr'mĭk) *a.* [Gk. *exo*, outwards; *therme*, heat.] Releasing heat-energy, *opp.* endothermic.

exotic (ĕgzŏt'ĭk) *a.* [Gk. *exotikos*, foreign.] Introduced or non-endemic. *n.* A foreign plant or animal not acclimatised.

exotospore (ĕksō'töspōr) *n.* [Gk. *exotos*, outward; *sporos*, seed.] A sporozoite.

exotoxin (ĕk'sötŏk'sĭn) *n.* [Gk. *exo*, outwards; *toxikon*, poison.] A soluble toxin excreted by bacteria, *opp.* endotoxin.

exotropism (ĕksŏt'röpĭzm) *n.* [Gk. *exo*, outwards; *trope*, turn.] Curvature away from axis, exhibited by a laterally geotropic organ.

expalpate,—epalpate, *q.v.*

expantin,—presumable neurohumor inducing expansion of chromatophores in crustaceans. *Opp.* contractin.

expiration (ĕk'spĭrā'shŭn) *n.* [L. *exspirare*, to breathe out.] The act of emitting air from lungs; emission of carbon dioxide by plants and animals.

expiratory (ĕkspī'rătörĭ) *a.* [L. *exspirare*, to breathe out.] *Pert.* or used in expiration; *appl.* muscles.

explanate (ĕks'plănāt) *a.* [L. *ex*, out; *planare*, to make plain.] Having a flat extension.

explantation (ĕk′splăntā′shŭn) *n.* [L. *ex*, out of; *plantare*, to plant.] Tissue culture away from organism of its origin.

explosive,—*appl.* flowers in which pollen is suddenly discharged on decompression of stamens by alighting insect, as of Cytisus and Ulex; *appl.* fruits with sudden dehiscence, seeds being discharged to some distance; *appl.* evolution, rapid formation of numerous types; tachytypogenesis; *appl.* speciation, rapid formation of species from a single species in one locality.

expressivity,—the degree to which a gene produces an effect.

exsculptate (ĕks′skŭlp′tāt) *a.* [L. *ex*, out; *sculpere*, to carve.] Having the surface marked with more or less regularly arranged raised lines with grooves between.

exscutellate (ĕkskū′tĕlāt) *a.* [L. *ex*, without; *scutellum*, small shield.] Having no scutellum; *appl.* insects.

exserted (ĕksĕr′tĕd) *a.* [L. *exserere*, to stretch out.] Protruding beyond some including organ or part; *appl.* stamens which project beyond corolla.

exsertile (ĕksĕr′tĭl) *a.* [L. *exserere*, to stretch out.] Capable of extrusion.

exstipulate (ĕkstĭp′ūlāt) *a.* [L. *ex*, without; *stipula*, stem.] Without stipules.

exstrophy (ĕks′strŏfĭ) *n.* [Gk. *exo*, outwards; *strophe*, turning.] Eversion, as normal or anomalous projection of luteal tissue to exterior of ovary.

exsuccate (ĕks-sŭk′āt) *a.* [L. *ex*, out; *succus*, juice.] Sapless; without juice; without latex; exsuccous.

exsufflation (ĕks′sŭflā′shŭn) *n.* [L. *ex*, out; *sufflare*, to blow.] Forced expiration from lungs.

extend (ĕkstĕnd′) *v.* [L. *ex*, out; *tendere*, to stretch.] To straighten out, *opp.* to flex or bend any organ.

extensor (ĕkstĕn′sŏr) *n.* [L. *ex*, out; *tendere*, to stretch.] Any muscle which extends a limb or part. *Opp.* flexor.

exterior (ĕkstē′rĭŏr) *a.* [L. *externus*, on outside.] Situated on side away from axis or definitive plane.

external (ĕkstĕr′năl) *a.* [L. *externus*, outside.] Outside or near the outside; away from the mesial plane.

externum (ĕkstĕr′nŭm) *n.* [L. *externus*, outward.] Outer region or cortex of a mitochondrium or of Golgi apparatus, or of acroblast.

exteroceptor (ĕk′stĕrŏsĕp′tŏr) *n.* [L. *exter*, outside; *capere*, to take.] A receptor which receives stimuli from outside the body; a contact receptor, or a distance receptor.

extine (ĕk′stīn) *n.* [L. *exter*, outside.] Outer coat of spore or pollen grain; exosporium. *Opp.* intine.

extra-axillary (ĕk′strâ-ăks′ĭlărĭ) *a.* [L. *extra*, beyond; *axilla*, armpit.] Arising above axil of leaf, said of branches which develop from upper bud when there are more than one in connection with axil.

extrabranchial (ĕk′străbrăng′kĭăl) *a.* [L. *extra*, beyond; Gk. *brangchia*, gills.] Arising outside the branchial arches.

extracapsular (ĕk′străkăp′sūlăr) *a.* [L. *extra*, outside; *capsula*, small box.] Arising or situated outside a capsule; *appl.* ligaments, etc., in connection with a joint; *appl.* protoplasm lying outside the central capsule in some protozoa; *appl.* dendrites.

extracellular (ĕk′străsĕl′ūlăr) *a.* [L. *extra*, outside; *cellula*, little cell.] Occurring outside the cell; diffused out of the cell.

extracolumella (ĕk′străkŏl′ūmĕl′ă) *n.* [L. *extra*, beyond; *columella*, small column.] Distal element of auditory skeletal structure; also hyostapes.

extraembryonic (ĕk′strâĕm′brĭŏn′ĭk) *a.* [L. *extra*, outside; Gk. *embryon*, foetus.] Situated outside the embryo proper, as portion of blastoderm.

extraenteric (ĕk′strâĕntĕr′ĭk) *a.* [L. *extra*, outside; Gk. *enteron*, gut.] Outside the alimentary tract.

extrafloral (ĕk′străflō′răl) *a.* [L. *extra*, outside; *flos*, flower.] Situated outside the flower; *appl.* nectaries.

extrafoveal (ĕk′străfō′vēăl) *a.* [L. *extra*, beyond; *fovea*, depression.] *Pert.* macula lutea surrounding fovea centralis; *appl.* rod vision. *Opp.* foveal.

extrahepatic (ĕk′străhēpăt′ĭk) *a.* [L. *extra*, outside; Gk. *hepar*, liver.] *Appl.* cystic duct and common bile duct.

extramatrical (ĕk′strămăt′rĭkăl) *a.* [L. *extra*, outside; *mater*, mother.] Located or growing on the surface of a matrix.

extranuclear (ĕk′strănū′klēăr) *a.* [L. *extra*, outside; *nucleus*, kernel.] *Pert.* structures or forces acting outside the nucleus; situated outside the nucleus.

extraocular (ĕk′străŏk′ūlăr) *a.* [L. *extra*, outside; *oculus*, eye.] Exterior to the eye; *appl.* antennae of insects.

extraperitoneal,—subperitoneal.

extraspicular (ĕk′străspĭk′ūlăr) *a.* [L. *extra*, outside; *spicula*, small spike.] With spicules having one end embedded in spongin and the other end free.

extrastapedial (ĕk′străstăpē′dĭăl) *a.* [L. *extra*, beyond; *stapes*, stirrup.] Extending beyond the stapedio-columellar junction.

extrastelar (ĕk′străstē′lăr) *a.* [L. *extra*, outside; Gk. *stele*, column.] *Pert.* ground tissue outside vascular tissue.

extravaginal (ĕk′străvăj′ĭnăl) *a.* [L. *extra*, outside; *vagina*, sheath.] Forcing a way through the sheath, as shoots of many plants.

extravasate (ĕksträv′ăsāt) *v.* [L. *extra*, outside; *vas*, vessel.] To force its way from the proper channel into the surrounding tissue, said of blood, etc.

extraventricular (ĕk′străvĕntrĭk′ūlăr) *a.* [L. *extra*, beyond; *ventriculus*, belly.] Situated or arising beyond the ventricle.

extraxylary (ĕk′străzī′lărĭ) *a.* [L. *extra*, outside; Gk. *xylon*, wood.] On the outside of the xylem; *appl.* fibres.

extremity (ĕkstrĕm′ĭtĭ) *n.* [L. *extremitas*, limit.] The limb, or distal portion of a limb; distal end of any limb-like structure.

extrinsic (ĕkstrĭn′sĭk) *a.* [L. *extrinsecus*, on outside.] Acting from the outside; not wholly within the part, *appl.* muscles; *appl.* cycles in population of a species, due to environmental fluctuation; *appl.* brightness due to objective light intensity. *Opp.* intrinsic.

extrorse (ĕkstrôrs′) *a.* [L. *extrorsus*, outwardly.] Turned away from axis; *appl.* dehiscence of anthers.

exudation (ĕk′sūdā′shŭn) *n.* [L. *exudare*, to sweat.] Any discharge through an incision or pore, *e.g.* gums, resins, moisture, etc.

exumbral (ĕksŭm′brăl) *a.* [L. *ex*, out; *umbra*, shade.] *Pert.* rounded upper surface of a jelly-fish.

exumbrella (ĕks′ŭmbrĕl′ă) *n.* [L. *ex*, out; *umbra*, shade.] Upper, convex surface of jelly-fish.

exuviae (ĕksū′vĭē) *n. plu.* [L. *exuere*, to strip off.] Cast-off skins, shells, etc., of animals.

exuvial (ĕksū′vĭăl) *a.* [L. *exuere*, to strip off.] Ecdysial; *appl.* insect glands whose secretion facilitates ecdysis.

eye (ī) *n.* [A.S. *éage*.] The organ of sight or vision; a pigment spot in various animals and in lower plants; the bud of a tuber.

eye-spots,—certain pigment spots in many lower plants and animals, and also in some vertebrates, which have a visual function; ocelli.

eye-teeth,—upper canine teeth.

F

F_1,—denotes first filial generation, or hybrids arising from a first cross, successive generations arising from this one being denoted by F_2, F_3, etc. P_1 denotes parents of F_1 generation, P_2 the grandparents, etc.

fabella (făbĕl'ă) *n.* [*Dim.* of L. *faba*, bean.] A small fibrocartilage ossified in tendon of the lateral head of the gastrocnemius.

fabiform (făb'ĭfôrm) *a.* [L. *faba*, bean; *forma*, shape.] Bean-shaped.

Fabrician [*J. C. Fabricius*, Danish entomologist]. *Appl.* a classification of the Arthropoda based on the anatomy of the mouth-parts.

facet (făs'ĕt) *n.* [F. *facette*, small face.] A smooth, flat, or rounded surface for articulation; an ocellus; corneal portion of insect eye.

facial (fā'shăl) *a.* [L. *facies*, face.] *Pert.* face; *appl.* artery, bones, veins, etc.; *appl.* seventh cerebral nerve.

faciation (făsĭā'shŭn) *n.* [L. *facies*, face.] Formation or character of facies; a grouping of dominant species within an association; geographical differences in abundance or proportion of dominant species in a community; *cf.* lociation.

facies (fā'shĭēz) *n.* [L. *facies*, face.] The face; a surface, in anatomy; the general aspect of a plant; aspect, as superior and inferior; a particular modification of a biotope; a grouping of dominant plants in the course of a successional series; one of different types of deposit in a geological series or system; the palaeontological and lithological character of a deposit.

facilitation (făsĭlĭtā'shŭn) *n.* [L. *facilitas*, easiness.] Diminution of resistance to a stimulus subsequent to previous stimulation, as of nerves; Ger. Bahnung.

faciolingual (fā'sĭōlĭng'gwăl) *a.* [L. *facies*, face; *lingua*, tongue.] *Pert.* or affecting face and tongue.

factor (făk'tŏr) *n.* [L. *facere*, to make.] Any agent (biotic, climatic, nutritional, etc.) contributing to a result; a Mendelian factor or gene; a determinant.

factorial (făktō'rĭăl) *a.* [L. *facere*, to make.] *Pert.* genetic factors or genes.

facultative (făk'ŭltā'tĭv) *a.* [L. *facultas*, faculty.] Having the power of living under different conditions; conditional; *appl.* organisms which may be normally self-dependent, but which are adaptable to a parasitic or semiparasitic mode of life; *appl.* aerobes, anaerobes; *appl.* parthenogenesis, symbionts, saprophytes, gametes, etc. *Opp.* obligate.

faeces (fē'sēz) *n. plu.* [L. *faeces*, dregs.] Excrement from alimentary canal.

falcate (făl'kāt) *a.* [L. *falx*, sickle.] Sickle-shaped; hooked.

falces (făl'sēz) *n. plu.* [L. *falces*, sickles.] Chelicerae, of arachnids.

falciform (făl'sĭfôrm) *a.* [L. *falx*, sickle; *forma*, shape.] Sickle-shaped or scythe-shaped; *appl.* ligament, a dorso-ventral fold of peritoneum, attached to under surface of diaphragm and anterior and upper surfaces of liver; *appl.* process, processus falciformis, a fold of choroid penetrating retina near optic disc and ending at back of lens, functioning in accommodation in teleosts; *appl.* body, a sporozoite; *appl.* young, sporocysts enclosing several spores in certain sporozoa.

falcula (făl'kūlă) *n.* [L. *falcula*, little hook.] A curved scythe-like claw; the falx cerebelli.

falcular,—sickle-shaped; falculate; *pert.* falcula; *pert.* falx.

falculate,—curved, and sharp at the point.

Fallopian tube [*G. Fallopio*, Italian anatomist]. Uterine tube, upper portion of oviduct in mammals; anterior portion of the Müllerian duct.

false fruits,—fruits formed from the receptacle or other parts of the flower, in addition to the ovary, or from complete inflorescences.

false ribs,—those ribs whose cartilaginous ventral ends do not join the sternum directly; asternal ribs.

false vocal cords,—ventricular folds of larynx, two folds of mucous membrane, each covering a ligament, anterior to true vocal cords.

falx (fălks) *n.* [L. *falx*, sickle.] A sickle-shaped fold of the dura mater; inguinal aponeurosis of transverse and internal oblique muscles of abdomen; a sickle-shaped hypha.

family (făm'ĭlĭ) *n.* [L. *familia*, household.] Term used in classification, signifying a group of related genera, families being grouped into orders.

famulus (făm'ūlŭs) *n.* [L. *famulus*, attendant.] A tarsal sensory seta in certain mites.

fan (făn) *n.* [A.S. *fann*, fan.] A bird's tail feathers; a flabellum, *q.v.*; a rhipidium, *q.v.*; vannus, *q.v.*

fang (făng) *n.* [A.S. *fang*, grip.] A long-pointed tooth, especially the poison tooth of snakes; the root of a tooth.

faradisation (făr'ădĭzā'shŭn) *n.* [*M. Faraday*, English physicist]. Method of stimulation inducing partial or complete tetanus.

farctate (fârk'tāt) *a.* [L. *farctus*, stuffed.] Filled, not hollow.

farina (fărē'nă, fărī'nă) *n.* [L. *farina*, flour.] The pollen of plants; the fine mealy-like powder found on some insects.

farinaceous (făr'ĭnā'shŭs) *a.* [L. *farina*, flour.] Containing flour; starchy; farinose.

farinose (făr'ĭnōs) *a.* [L. *farina*, flour.] Producing, or covered with, fine powder or dust.

fascia (făs'ĭă, făsh'ĭă) *n.* [L. *fascia*, band.] An ensheathing band of connective tissue.

fascial (făs'ĭăl, făsh'ĭăl) *a.* [L. *fascia*, bundle.] *Pert.* a fascia, ensheathing and binding.

fasciated (făs'ĭā'tĕd, făsh'ĭā'tĕd) *a.* [L. *fascia*, bundle.] Banded; arranged in fascicles; *appl.* stems or branches malformed and flattened.

fasciation (făshĭā'shŭn) *n.* [L. *fascia*, bundle.] The formation of fascicles; coalescent development of branches of a shoot-system, as in cauliflower.

fascicle (făs'ĭkl) *n.* [L. *fasciculus*, small bundle.] A small bundle or tuft, as of fibres, or of leaves.

fascicular (făsĭk'ūlăr) *a.* [L. *fasciculus*, small bundle.] *Pert.* a fascicle; arranged in bundles or tufts; *appl.* cambium, tissue.

fasciculus (făsĭk'ūlŭs) *n.* [L. *fasciculus*, small bundle.] A fascicle; a group, bundle, or tract of nerve fibres, as of medulla spinalis.

fasciola (făsī'ōlă) *n.* [L. *fasciola*, small bandage.] A narrow colour band; a delicate lamina continuous with supracallosal gyrus.

fasciole (făs'ĭōl) *n.* [L. *fasciola*, small bandage.] Ciliated band on certain echinoids for sweeping water over surrounding parts.

fastigiate (făstĭj'ĭāt) *a.* [L. *fastigare*, to slope up.] With branches close to stem and erect, *opp.* patent; in pyramidal or conical form.

fastigium (făstĭj'ĭŭm) *n.* [L. *fastigium*, gable.] Angular top of roof of fourth ventricle, formed by contact of anterior and posterior medullary vela of cerebellum.

fat (făt) *n.* [A.S. *faet*, fat.] Adipose tissue; any part of animal tissue which has its cells filled with a greasy or oily reserve material.

fat-body,—one of the vascularised tissue structures filled with fat globules and associated with gonads in Amphibia; one of the subcutaneous organs along ventral sides and enlarged during breeding season in Lacertilia; tissue of indeterminate form distributed throughout body of insects and functioning as nutritive reserve; corpus adiposum; epiploon.

fat soluble,—*appl.* vitamins A, D, E, and K.

fatigue (fătēg') *n.* [L. *fatigare*, to weary.] Effect produced by long stimulation on cells of an organ.

fauces (fôs'ēz) *n. plu.* [L. *fauces*, throat.] Upper or anterior part of throat between palate and pharynx; mouth of a spirally coiled shell; throat of a corolla.

fauna (fôn'ă) *n.* [L. *faunus*, god of woods.] All the animals peculiar to a country, area, or period.

faunal region,—an area characterised by a special group or groups of animals.

faunula (fôn'ūlă) *n.* [*Dim.* of *fauna*.] Animal population of a small unit area, as of intestine, bark, etc.

favella (făvĕl'ă) *n.* [L. *favus*, honeycomb.] A conceptacle of certain red algae.

faveolate (făvē'ölāt) *a.* [L. *faveolus*, *dim.* of *favus*, honey-comb.] Honeycombed or alveolate.

faveolus (făvē'ölŭs) *n.* [L. *faveolus*, small honey-comb.] A small depression or pit; alveola.

favoid (făv'oid) *a.* [L. *favus*, honeycomb; Gk. *eidos*, form.] Resembling a honey-comb.

favose (făvōs') *a.* [L. *favus*, honeycomb.] Honeycombed; alveolate.

feather-epithelium,—epithelium of cells, each having a process with numerous lateral filaments, on inner surface of nictitating membrane of many reptiles and birds, for cleaning the eye surface.

feather-veined,—*appl.* leaf in which veins run out from mid-rib in regular series at an acute angle; pinnately veined.

feces,—faeces.

Fechner's Law [*G. T. Fechner*, German psychophysicist]. The tendency of intensity of sensation to vary as the logarithm of the stimulus.

fecundate (fē'kŭndāt) *v.* [L. *fecundare*, to make fruitful.] To impregnate; to fertilise; to pollinate.

fecundity (fēkŭn'dĭtĭ) *n.* [L. *fecunditas*, fruitfulness.] Power of a species to multiply rapidly; capacity to form reproductive elements.

female (fē'māl) *n.* [L. *femina*, women.] A pistillate flower; an egg-producing or young-producing animal—symbol ♀.

female pronucleus,—the nucleus left in the ovum after maturation.

femoral (fĕm'örăl) *a.* [L. *femur*, thigh.] *Pert.* thigh; *appl.* artery, vein, nerve, etc.; crural. *n.* Paired femoral shield of plastron in Chelonia.

femur (fē'mŭr) *n.* [L. *femur*, thigh.] The thigh-bone, proximal bone of hind limb in vertebrates; third joint in insect and spider leg counting from proximal end.

fenchone (fĕn'chōn) *n.* [Ger. *Fenchel*, fennel.] A ketone, the essential oil in oil of fennel; $C_{10}H_{16}O$.

fenestra (fĕnĕs'tră) *n.* [L. *fenestra*, window.] An opening in a bone, or between two bones, or in a plant membrane; a pit on head of cockroach; fontanelle of termites; a transparent spot on wings of insects.

fenestrate (fĕnĕs'trāt) *a.* [L. *fenestra*, window.] Having small perforations or transparent spots, *appl.* insect wings; having numerous perforations, *appl.* leaves, dissepiments.

fenestrated membrane,—a close network of yellow elastic fibres resembling a membrane with perforations, as in inner tunic of arteries; basal membrane of compound eye, penetrated by ommatidial nerve fibres.

fenestrule (fĕnĕs'trool) *n.* [*Dim.* of L. *fenestra*, window.] Small opening between branches of a polyzoan colony.

feral (fē'răl) *a.* [L. *fera*, wild animal.] Wild, or escaped from cultivation or domestication and reverted to wild state.

ferment (fĕr'mĕnt) *n.* [L. *fermentum*, ferment.] An organised substance, capable of producing fermentation; an enzyme.

fermentation (fĕr'mĕntā'shŭn) *n.* [L. *fermentum*, ferment.] A transformation occurring in organic substance, usually of a carbohydrate, caused by action of a ferment; zymosis.

ferrichrome (fĕr'ĭkrōm) *n.* [L. *ferrum*, iron; Gk. *chroma*, colour.] An iron-containing nitrogenous pigment, precursor of cytochrome, found in smut fungi.

ferrocytes (fĕr'ŏsīts) *n. plu.* [L. *ferrum*, iron; Gk. *kytos*, hollow.] Cells formed from lymphocytes, containing iron compounds and concerned with tunicin production in ascidians.

ferruginous (fĕroo'jĭnŭs) *a.* [L. *ferruginus*, rusty.] Having the appearance of iron rust.

fertile (fĕr'tĭl) *a.* [L. *fertilis*, fertile.] Capable of producing living offspring; of eggs or seeds, capable of developing.

fertilisation (fĕr'tĭlĭzā'shŭn) *n.* [L. *fertilis*, fertile.] The union of male and female pronuclei; pollination.

fertilisation - tube,—process of an antheridium, penetrating oogonial wall, for passage of male gamete in certain fungi.

fertility vitamin,—α-tocopherol or vitamin E; anti-sterility vitamin.

fertilizin (fĕr'tĭlĭ'zĭn) *n.* [L. *fertilis*, fertile.] A soluble colloidal substance produced by certain eggs and causing sperm agglutination, also inducing cleavage; gynogamone II.

festoon (fĕstoon') *n.* [F. *feston*, garland.] The margin, with rectangular divisions, of integument in ticks; rim of gum round neck of tooth.

fetlock (fĕt'lŏk) *n.* [A.S. *fot*, foot; *locc*, tuft of hair.] The tuft of hair behind a horse's pastern joint; the pastern joint itself.

fetus,—*see* foetus.

fibre (fī'bĕr) *n.* [L. *fibra*, band.] A strand of nerve, muscle, connective, or bast tissue; elongated plant-cell for mechanical strength; fiber.

fibre tracheids,—fibres of a nature intermediate between that of libriform fibres and of tracheids.

fibril (fī'brĭl) *n.* [L. *fibrilla*, small fibre.] A small thread-like structure or fibre; a component part of a fibre; a root-hair; a slender filiform outgrowth on some lichens.

fibrillae (fībrĭl'ē) *n. plu.* [L. *fibrilla*, small fibre.] Thread-like branches of roots; minute elastic fibres secreted within spongin cells; minute muscle-like threads found in various infusorians; fibrils.

fibrillate (fĭb'rĭlāt) *a.* [L. *fibrilla*, small fibre.] Having fibrillae or hair-like structures.

fibrilloblast,—odontoblast, *q.v.*

fibrillose (fībrĭl'ōs, fī'brĭlōs) *a.* [L. *fibrilla*, small fibre.] Furnished with fibrils; *appl.* mycelia of certain fungi.

fibrin (fī'brĭn) *n.* [L. *fibra*, band.] An insoluble protein found in blood after coagulation, readily digested in gastric juice.

fibrinogen (fībrĭn'öjĕn) *n.* [L. *fibra*, band; Gk. *-genes*, producing.] A soluble protein of blood, which, by activity of thrombin, yields fibrin and produces coagulation.

fibroblast (fī'bröblăst) *n.* [L. *fibra*, band; Gk. *blastos*, bud.] A connective tissue cell; fibrocyte, desmocyte.

fibrocartilage (fī'brökâr'tĭlēj) *n.* [L. *fibra*, band; *cartilago*, gristle.] A kind of cartilage whose matrix is mainly composed of fibres similar to connective tissue fibres, found at articulations, cavity margins, and osseous grooves.

fibrocyte (fī'brösīt) *n.* [L. *fibra*, band; Gk. *kytos*, hollow.] A connective tissue cell; desmocyte.

fibrous (fī'brŭs) *a.* [L. *fibra*, band.] Composed of fibres; *appl.* tissue, roots, mycelium, etc.

fibula (fĭb'ūlă) *n.* [L. *fibula*, buckle.] Outer and smaller shin bone.

fibulare (fĭb'ūlā'rē) *n.* [L. *fibula*, buckle.] The outer element of proximal row of tarsus.

fidelity (fĭdĕl'ĭtĭ) *n.* [L. *fidelitas*, faithfulness.] The degree of limitation of a species to a particular habitat.

field,—a dynamic system in which all the parts are interrelated and in equilibrium, so that a change in any part affects the whole.

filament (fĭl'ămĕnt) *n.* [L. *filum*, thread.] A thread-like structure; the stalk of anther; a hypha, *q.v.*; stalk of a down-feather; a cryptoptile; slender apical end of egg-tube of insect ovary.

filamentous (fĭlămĕn′tŭs) *a.* [L. *filum*, thread.] Thread-like; having filaments; *appl.* form or margin of certain bacterial colonies; *appl.* thallus of fruticose lichens; *appl.* amino acids, etc.

filator (fĭl′ătŏr) *n.* [L. *filum*, thread.] A structure forming part of the spinning organ of silkworms and which regulates size of the silk fibre.

filial generation,—F_1, etc., *q.v.*

filial regression,—tendency of offspring of outstanding parentage to revert to average for species.

filicauline (fĭl′ĭkôl′ĭn) *a.* [L. *filum*, thread; *caulis*, stalk.] With a thread-like stem.

filiciform (fĭl′ĭsĭfôrm) *a.* [L. *filix*, fern; *forma*, shape.] Shaped like the frond of a fern; fern-like.

filicoid,—filiciform.

filiform (fĭ′lĭfôrm) *a.* [L. *filum*, thread; *forma*, shape.] Thread-like.

filiform papillae,—papillae on the tongue, ending in numerous minute slender processes.

filigerous (fĭlĭj′ĕrŭs) *a.* [L. *filum*, thread; *gerere*, to carry.] With thread-like outgrowths or flagella.

Filippi's glands,—paired glands with ducts conveying viscid secretion into silk ducts.

fillet (fĭl′ĕt) *n.* [L. *filum*, thread.] Band of white matter in mid-brain and medulla oblongata; lemniscus.

filoplume (fĭ′löploom) *n.* [L. *filum*, thread; *pluma*, feather.] A delicate hair-like feather with long axis and a few free barbs at apex.

filopodia (fĭ′löpō′dĭă) *n. plu.* [L. *filum*, thread; Gk. *pous*, foot.] Protozoan thread-like pseudopodia.

filose (fĭ′lōs) *a.* [L. *filum*, thread.] Slender; thread-like; *appl.* pseudopodia of protozoa.

filter-passers,—organisms capable of passing through a filter which arrests bacteria; microhenads; viruses.

filtration (fĭltrā′shŭn) *n.* [F. *filtrer*, to strain.] *Appl.* iridial angle of cornea; straining, as of lymph through capillary walls.

filum terminale, — the terminal thread, a slender grey filament, of the spinal cord.

fimbria (fĭm′brĭă) *n.* [L. *fimbria*, fringe.] Any fringe-like structure; a posterior prolongation of fornix to hippocampus; one of delicate processes fringing the mouth of tube or duct, as of oviduct, or of siphon of molluscs.

fimbriated (fĭm′brĭā′tĕd) *a.* [L. *fimbriatus*, fringed.] Fringed at margin, as petals, tubes, ducts, antennae.

fimicolous (fĭmĭk′ölŭs) *a.* [L. *fimus*, dung; *colere*, to dwell.] Inhabiting or growing on dung.

fin (fĭn) *n.* [A.S. *finn*, fin.] A fold of skin with fin-rays and skeletal supports, in most fishes.

finials (fĭn′ĭălz) *n. plu.* [L. *finis*, end.] The ossicles of the distal rami of crinoids, which do not branch again.

fin-rays,—horny supports of fins.

fissile (fĭs′ĭl) *a.* [L. *fissilis*, cleft.] Tending to split; cleavable.

fissilingual (fĭs′ĭlĭng′gwăl) *a.* [L. *fissus*, cleft; *lingua*, tongue.] With bifid tongue.

fission (fĭsh′ŭn) *n.* [L. *fissus*, cleft.] Cleavage of cells; division of a unicellular organism into two or more parts.

fissiparous (fĭsĭp′ărŭs) *a.* [L. *fissus*, cleft; *parere*, to beget.] Reproducing by fission.

fissiped (fĭs′ĭpĕd) *n.* [L. *fissus*, cleft; *pes*, foot.] With cleft feet, that is, with digits of feet separated.

fissirostral (fĭs′ĭrŏs′trăl) *a.* [L. *fissus*, cleft; *rostrum*, beak.] With deeply-cleft beak.

fissure (fĭsh′ūr) *n.* [L. *fissura*, cleft.] A cleft, deep groove, or furrow dividing an organ into lobes, or subdividing and separating certain areas of the lobes; sulcus.

fistula (fĭs′tūlă) *a.* [L. *fistula*, pipe.] Pathological or artificial pipe-like opening; trachea, water-conducting vessel.

fistular (fĭs'tūlăr) *a.* [L. *fistula*, pipe.] Like a fistula; pipe-like; hollow, as stems of Umbelliferae.

fix (fĭks) *v.* [L. *fixus*, fixed.] To kill, and preserve; to establish; to retain.

fixation muscles, — muscles which prevent disturbance of body equilibrium generally, and fix limbs in case of limb-movements.

flabellate (flăbĕl'āt) *a.* [L. *flabellare*, to fan.] Fan-shaped; *appl.* pectinate antennae with long processes.

flabelliform (flăbĕl'ĭfôrm) *a.* [L. *flabellum*, fan; *forma*, shape.] Fan-shaped.

flabellinerved (flăbĕl'ĭnĕrvd) *a.* [L. *flabellum*, fan; *nervus*, sinew.] *Appl.* leaves with many radiating nerves.

flabellum (flăbĕl'ŭm) *n.* [L. *flabellum*, fan.] Any fan-shaped organ or structure; distal exite of branchiopodan limb; epipodite of certain crustacean limbs; terminal lobe of glossa in certain insects; diverging white fibres in corpus striatum.

flagella,—*plu.* of flagellum.

flagellate (flăj'ĕlāt) *a.* [L. *flagellum*, whip.] Furnished with flagella; like a flagellum.

flagelliform (flăjĕl'ĭfôrm) *a.* [L. *flagellum*, whip; *forma*, shape.] Lash-like; like a flagellum.

flagellula (flăjĕl'ūlă) *n.* [L. *flagellula*, *dim.* of *flagellum*, whip.] A flagellate zoospore or flagellispore.

flagellum (flăjĕl'ŭm) *n.* [L. *flagellum*, whip.] The lash-like process of many Protista and of cells, as in choanocytes and certain male gametes; external structure on basal joint of chelicera of Pseudoscorpiones; distal part of antenna in some arthropods, as in Diptera; a long slender runner or creeping stem.

flame cells,—the terminal cells of branches of excretory system in many worms, with cavity continuous with lumen of duct, and containing a cilium or bunch of cilia, the motions of which give a flickering appearance similar to that of a flame; a pronephridiostome.

flavedo (flăvē'dō) *n.* [L. *flavus*, yellow.] Exocarp of hesperidium; *cf.* albedo.

flavescent (flăvĕs'ĕnt) *a.* [L. *flavescere*, to turn yellow.] Growing yellow.

flavin (flā'vĭn) *n.* [L. *flavus*, yellow.] A water-soluble yellow pigment of cells; lyochrome.

flavonoids,—*see* bioflavonoids.

flavoproteins (flā'vōprō'tēĭnz) *n. plu.* [L. *flavus*, yellow; Gk. *proteios*, first.] Compounds of proteins and flavin, being yellow enzymes which can be alternately reduced and oxidised, essential in cell metabolism.

flavoxanthin (flā'vōzăn'thĭn) *n.* [L. *flavus*, yellow; Gk. *xanthos*, yellow.] A yellow colouring matter in petals, as of Ranunculaceae; $C_{40}H_{56}O_3$.

flex (flĕks) *v.* [L. *flectere*, to bend.] To bend; *appl.* movement of limbs.

flexor (flĕk'sŏr) *n.* [L. *flexus*, bent.] A muscle which bends a limb, or part, by its contraction.

flexor plate,—a median plate supporting praetarsus of insects, for attachment of tendon of claw flexor.

flexuous (flĕk'sūŭs) *a.* [L. *flexus*, bent.] Curving in a zig-zag manner; flexuose.

flexure (flĕk'sūr) *n.* [L. *flexus*, bent.] A curve or bend; *appl.* curve in embryonic brain, curve of intestine.

float (flōt) *n.* [A.S. *fleotan*, to float.] The pneumatophore of siphonophores; one of four tracheal sacs in aquatic larva of Culicidae; a large spongy mass serving as a float in some pteridophytes.

floating ribs,—ribs not uniting at their ventral end with the sternum.

floccose (flŏk'ōs) *a.* [L. *floccus*, a lock of wool.] Covered with wool-like tufts; *appl.* bacterial growth.

floccular (flŏk'ūlăr) *a.* [L. *floccus*, lock of wool.] *Pert.* the flocculus.

flocculence (flŏk'ūlĕns) *n.* [L. *floccus*, lock of wool.] Adhesion in small flakes, as of a precipitate.

flocculent (flŏk'ūlĕnt) *a.* [L. *floccus*, lock of wool.] Covered with a soft waxy substance giving appearance of wool; covered with small woolly tufts.

flocculus (flŏk'ūlŭs) *n.* [L.L. *dim.* of L. *floccus*, lock of wool.] A small accessory lobe on each lateral lobe of the cerebellum; a posterior hairy tuft in some Hymenoptera.

floccus (flŏk'ŭs) *n.* [L. *floccus*, lock of wool.] The tuft of hair terminating a tail; downy plumage of young birds; mass of hyphal filaments in algae and fungi.

flora (flō'ră) *n.* [L. *flos*, flower.] The plants peculiar to a country, area, specified environment, or period.

floral (flō'răl) *n.* [L. *flos*, flower.] *Pert.* the flora of a country or area; *pert.* flowers.

florescence (flōrĕs'ĕns) *n.* [L. *florescere*, to begin to flower.] Bursting into bloom; anthesis.

floret (flō'rĕt) *n.* [L. *flos*, flower.] One of the small individual flowers of a composite flower; flower with lemma and palea, of grasses.

floricome (flō'rĭkōm) *n.* [L. *flos*, flower; *coma*, hair.] A form of branched hexaster spicule.

florigen (flō'rĭjĕn) *n.* [L. *flos*, flower; *gignere*, to produce.] A plant substance which stimulates change in buds to flowering condition; flowering hormone.

florigenic (flō'rĭjĕn'ĭk) *a.* [L. *flos*, flower; *gignere*, to produce.] *Appl.* principle originating in leaves which stimulates flowering.

florula (flō'rūlă) *n.* [*Dim.* of *flora.*] Plant population of a small unit area, as of compost heap, etc.

floscelle (flŏsĕl') *n.* [L. *flosculus*, little flower.] Flower-like structure round the mouth, composed of five bourrelets and five phyllodes, in some echinoids.

flosculus (flŏs'kūlŭs) *n.* [L. *flosculus*, little flower.] A small flower; a floret, *q.v.*; floscule.

floss (flŏs) *n.* [O.F. *flosche*, down.] A downy or silky substance; the loose pieces of silk in a cocoon.

flower (flow'ĕr) *n.* [L. *flos*, flower.] The blossom of a plant, comprising generally sepals, petals, stamens, and pistil; a leafy shoot adapted for reproductive purposes.

flowering glume,—lemma, *q.v.*

fluviatile (floo'vĭătĭl) *a.* [L. *fluviatilis*, *pert.* river.] Growing in or near streams; inhabiting and developing in streams, *appl.* certain insect larvae; caused by rivers, *appl.* deposits.

fluviomarine (floo'vĭōmărēn') *a.* [L. *fluvius*, stream; *mare*, sea.] *Pert.* or inhabiting rivers and sea.

fluvioterrestrial (floo'vĭōtĕrĕs'trĭăl) *a.* [L. *fluvius*, stream; *terra*, land.] Found in streams and in the land beside them.

flux (flŭks) *n.* [L. *fluere*, to flow.] Term *appl.* species that are not yet stable.

foetal (fē'tăl) *a.* [L. *foetus*, offspring.] Embryonic; *pert.* a foetus.

foetid glands,—small sac-like glands which secrete an ill-smelling fluid, in Orthoptera.

foetus (fē'tŭs) *n.* [L. *foetus*, offspring.] An embryo in egg or in uterus.

folacin,—folic acid.

foliaceous (fō'lĭā'shŭs) *a.* [L. *folium*, leaf.] Having the form or texture of a foliage leaf; thin and leaf-like.

Folian process [*C. Folli* or *Folius*, Italian anatomist]. Anterior process of malleus; processus gracilis.

foliar (fō'lĭăr) *a.* [L. *folium*, leaf.] *Pert.* or consisting of leaves; bearing leaves, *appl.* spurs, *cf.* brachyplast.

foliation (fōlĭā'shŭn) *n.* [L. *folium*, leaf.] The production of leaves; leafing.

folic (fō'lĭk) *a.* [L. *folium*, leaf.] *Appl.* acid obtained from spinach, and liver extract, $C_{15}H_{15}O_8N_5$, and existing in various forms, with haematopoietic and other effects; *e.g.* vitamins B_c, B_{12}, M, factors R and S, rhizopterine, etc.

folicaulicolous (fō′lĭkôlĭk′ŏlŭs) *a.* [L. *folium*, leaf; *caulis*, stalk; *colere*, to inhabit.] Growing on leaves and stems; *appl.* certain fungi and lichens; folicaulicole.

foliicolous (fōlĭĭk′ŏlŭs) *a.* [L. *folium*, leaf; *colere*, to dwell.] Growing on leaves; *appl.* certain fungi and lichens.

foliobranchiate (fō′lĭöbrăng′kĭăt) *a.* [L. *folium*, leaf; *branchiae*, gills.] Possessing leaf-like gills.

foliolae (fō′lĭölē) *n. plu.* [L. *folium*, *dim.*, leaf.] Leaf-like appendages of telum.

foliolate (fō′lĭölāt) *a.* [L. *folium*, *dim.*, leaf.] *Pert.*, having, or like, leaflets.

foliole (fō′lĭōl) *n.* [L. *folium*, *dim.*, leaf.] Small leaf-like organ or appendage; a leaflet, as of a compound leaf.

foliose (fō′lĭōs) *a.* [L. *folium*, leaf.] With many leaves; leafy.

folium (fō′lĭŭm) *n.* [L. *folium*, leaf.] A flattened structure in the cerebellum, expanding laterally into superior semilunar lobules.

follicle (fŏl′ĭkl) *n.* [L. *folliculus*, small sac.] A capsular fruit which opens on one side only; cavity or sheath; an ovarian follicle; a hair follicle.

follicles of Langerhans [*P. Langerhans*, German anatomist]. Groups of cells in submucosa at junction of fore-gut and mid-gut of larval cyclostomes, secreting an insulin-like substance and being homologous to islets of Langerhans.

follicle-stimulating hormone, — a gonadotrophic hormone, prolan A, which stimulates ovarian follicles and testis; symbol FSH.

follicular (fŏlĭk′ūlăr), **folliculate** (fŏlĭk′ūlāt) *a.* [L. *folliculus*, small sac.] *Pert.*, like, or consisting of follicles; *appl.* an ovarian hormone.

folliculose (fŏlĭk′ūlōs) *a.* [L. *folliculus*, small sac.] Having follicles.

Fontana's spaces [*F. Fontana*, Italian anatomist]. Spaces in trabecular tissue of angle of iris, communicating with the anterior chamber of the eye and with the sinus venosus sclerae.

fontanelle (fŏn′tănĕl) *n.* [F. *fontanelle*, little fountain.] A gap or space between bones in the cranium, closed only by membrane; depression on head of termites.

fonticulus (fŏntĭk′ūlŭs) *n.* [L. *fonticulus*, *dim.* of *fons*, fountain.] A fontanelle; depression at anterior end of sternum, the jugular notch.

food-chain,—sequence of organisms in which each is food of a later member of the sequence.

food vacuole,—a small vacuole containing fluid and food-particles, in endosarc of many Protista.

food-web, — interconnected food-chains.

foot (foot) *n.* [A.S. *fot*, foot.] An embryonic structure in vascular cryptogams through which nourishment is obtained from prothallus; basal portion of sporophyte in mosses; an organ of locomotion, differing widely in different animals, from tube-foot of echinoderms, muscular foot of gastropods and other molluscs, tarsus of insects, to foot of vertebrates.

foot-jaws,—poison-claws or first pair of legs in centipedes; maxillipedes.

foot-plates,—terminal enlargements of processes of protoplasmic astrocytes in contact with minute blood-vessels; perivascular feet.

foramen (fŏrā′mĕn) *n.* [L. *foramen*, opening.] The opening through coats of ovule; any small perforation; aperture through a bone or membranous structure.

foramen (occipitale) magnum,—the opening in occipital region of skull through which passes the spinal cord.

foramen of Monro [*A. Monro* (primus), Scottish anatomist]. Interventricular foramen, passage between third and lateral ventricles; porta or foramen interventriculare.

foramina,—*plu.* of foramen.

foraminate (fŏrăm′ĭnāt) *a.* [L. *foramen*, opening.] Pitted; having foramina or perforations.

foraminiferous (fŏrăm′ĭnĭf′ërŭs) *a.* [L. *foramen*, opening; *ferre*, to carry.] Having foramina; containing shells of Foraminifera.

forb (fôrb) *n.* [Gk. *phorbe*, pasture.] A pasture herb.

forceps (fôr′sĕps) *n.* [L. *forceps*, tongs.] The clasper-shaped anal cercus of some insects; large fighting or seizing claw of crabs and lobsters; fibres of corpus callosum curving into frontal and occipital lobes.

forcipate (fôr′sĭpāt) *a.* [L. *forceps*, tongs.] Resembling forceps, or forked like forceps.

forcipulate (fôrsĭp′ūlāt) *a.* [*Dim.* of L. *forceps*, tongs.] Shaped like a small forceps; *appl.* asteroid pedicellariae.

fore-brain,—prosencephalon, *q.v.*

foremilk,—colostrum, *q.v.*

forespore,—early stage in endospore formation, in bacteria.

forfex (fôr′fĕks) *n.* [L. *forfex*, shears.] A pair of anal organs which open and shut transversely, occurring in certain insects.

forficate (fôr′fĭkāt) *a.* [L. *forfex*, shears.] Deeply notched.

forficiform (fôrfĭs′ĭfôrm) *a.* [L. *forfex*, shears; *forma*, form.] Scissor-shaped; *appl.* type of forcipulate pedicellariae.

forma (fôr′mă) *n.* [L. *forma*, shape.] Form; taxonomic unit consisting of individuals that differ from those of a larger unit by a single character; smallest category in botanical classification.

formation (fôrmā′shŭn) *n.* [L. *forma*, shape.] Structure arising from an accumulation of deposits; the vegetation proper to a definite type of habitat; production.

formative (fôr′mătĭv) *a.* [L. *forma*, shape.] Plastic; *appl.* matter which is living and developable.

formicarian (fôr′mĭkā′rĭăn) *a.* [L. *formica*, ant.] *Pert.* ants; *appl.* plants which attract ants by means of sweet secretions.

formicarium (fôr′mĭkā′rĭŭm) *n.* [L. *formica*, ant.] Ants' nest, particularly an artificial arrangement for purposes of study; formicary.

fornicated (fôr′nĭkā′tĕd) *a.* [L. *fornicatus*, vaulted.] Concave within, convex without; arched.

fornices,—*plu.* of fornix.

fornix (fôr′nĭks) *n.* [L. *fornix*, vault.] An arched recess, as between eyelid and eye-ball, or between vagina and cervix uteri; an arched sheet of white longitudinal fibres beneath corpus callosum; scutum of Cheilostomata; one of arched scales in the orifice of some flowers.

fossa (fŏs′ă) *n.* [L. *fossa*, ditch.] A pit or trench-like depression.

fosse (fŏs) *n.* [L. *fossa*, ditch.] A fossa; a circular groove formed by upper part of parapet in sea-anemones.

fossette (fŏsĕt′) *n.* [F. *fossette*, small pit, from L. *fossa*, ditch.] A small pit or depression; a socket containing base of antennule in arthropods; groove for resilium in bivalve shells; depression on grinding surface of a tooth.

fossil (fŏs′ĭl) *n.* [L. *fossilis*, dug up.] Petrified animal or plant, or portion thereof, as found in rocks.

fossiliferous (fŏs′ĭlĭf′ërŭs) *a.* [L. *fossilis*, dug up; *ferre*, to carry.] Containing fossils.

fossorial (fŏsō′rĭăl) *n.* [L. *fossor*, digger.] Adapted for digging; *appl.* animals, claws, feet.

fossula (fŏs′ūlă) *n.* [*Dim.* of L. *fossa*, ditch.] A small fossa; small pit with reduced septa on one side of a corallite cup in Rugosa.

fossulate (fŏs′ūlāt) *a.* [*Dim.* of L. *fossa*, ditch.] With slight hollows or grooves.

fossulet (fŏs′ūlĕt) *n.* [*Dim.* of L. *fossa*, ditch.] A long narrow depression.

fourchette (foorshĕt′) *n.* [F. *fourchette*, fork.] Furcula of birds; frog of equine hoof; frenulum of labia minora.

fovea (fō′vëă) *n.* [L. *fovea*, depression.] A small pit, fossa, or depression; a small hollow at leaf base in Isoëtes, containing a sporangium; pollinium base in orchids.

fovea centralis, — central and thinnest part of macula lutea, without rods and with long and slender cones.

fovea dentis,—facet on atlas, for articulation with dens of axis.

foveal (fō'vēăl) *a.* [L. *fovea,* depression.] *Pert.* fovea; *pert.* fovea centralis; *appl.* cone vision. *Opp.* extrafoveal.

foveate (fō'vēăt) *a.* [L. *fovea,* depression.] Pitted.

foveola (fŏvē'ŏlă) *n.* [L. *foveola,* small depression.] A small pit; a shallow cavity in bone; a small depression just above fovea in leaf of Isoëtes.

foveolae opticae,—two pigmented areas in depressions of neural plate of amphibian embryo, the primordia of eyes.

foveolate (fŏv'ēŏlăt) *a.* [L. *foveola,* small depression.] Having regular small depressions.

foveole,—foveola.

fraenulum,—*see* frenulum.

fraenum,—*see* frenum.

fragmentation (frăg'mēntā'shŭn) *n.* [L. *frangere,* to break.] Division into small portions; nuclear division by simple splitting; amitosis.

fraternal,—dizygotic, *appl.* twins.

free (frē) *a.* [A.S. *freo,* acting at pleasure.] Motile; unattached; distinct; separate.

free central placentation,—axile placentation, fixation of ovules to central axis of ovary.

free-martin,—a sterile female twin-born with a male.

frenate (frē'nāt) *a.* [L. *frenare,* to bridle.] Having a frenum or frenulum.

frenulum (frĕn'ūlŭm) *n.* [L. *frenulum, dim.* of *frenum,* bridle.] A fold of membrane, as of tongue, clitoris, etc.; a process on hind-wing of Lepidoptera for attachment to fore-wing; a thickening of sub-umbrella of certain Scyphomedusae.

frenum (frē'nŭm) *n.* [L. *frenum,* bridle.] A frenulum; a fold of integument at junction of mantle and body of Cirripedia, ovigerous in Pedunculata; also fraenum.

frigofuge (frĭg'ŏfūj) *n.* [L. *frigus,* cold; *fugere,* to flee.] An organism which does not tolerate cold.

frond (frônd) *n.* [L. *frons,* leafy branch.] A leaf, especially of fern or palm; thallus of certain sea-weeds; leaf-like thalloid shoot, as of lichen.

frondescence (frŏndĕs'ĕns) *n.* [L. *frondescere,* to put forth leaves.] Development of leaves.

frons (frŏnz) *n.* [L. *frons,* forehead.] Forehead; or comparable structure.

frontal (frŭn'tăl) *a.* [L. *frons,* forehead.] In region of forehead; *appl.* artery, vein, lobe, convolution; *appl.* head-organ of nemertines; a prostomial ridge of polychaetes; palps of certain nereids; specialised feeding surface in certain ciliates; ganglion, gland, and pore in insects; *appl.* plane at right angles to median longitudinal or sagittal plane. *n.* A frontal scale in reptiles; frontal bone.

frontalis (frŏntā'lĭs) *n.* [L. *frons,* forehead.] Frontal part of the scalp muscle or epicranius.

frontocerebellar fibres, — fibres passing from frontal region to cerebellum.

frontoclypeus (frŭn'tŏklĭp'ēŭs) *n.* [L. *frons,* forehead; *clypeus,* shield.] Frons and clypeus fused, in insects.

fronto-ethmoidal,—*pert.* frontal and ethmoidal bones; *appl.* suture.

frontonasal (frŭn'tŏnā'zăl) *a.* [L. *frons,* forehead; *nasus,* nose.] *Pert.* forehead or frontal region and nose; *appl.* ducts and process.

frontoparietal (frŭn'tŏpărī'ĕtăl) *a.* [L. *frons,* forehead; *paries,* wall.] *Pert.* frontal and parietal bones; *appl.* suture: the coronal suture; *cf.* parietofrontal.

frontosphenoidal (frŭn'tŏsfēnoid'ăl) *a.* [L. *frons,* forehead; Gk. *sphen,* wedge; *eidos,* form.] *Pert.* frontal and sphenoid bones; *appl.* a process of zygomatic bone articulating with frontal.

fructification (frŭk'tĭfĭkā'shŭn) *n.* [L. *fructus*, fruit; *facere*, to make.] Fruit formation; fruit-body; any spore-producing structure in cryptogams.

fructose (frŭk'tōs) *n.* [L. *fructus*, fruit.] Fruit-sugar; laevulose; $C_6H_{12}O_6$.

frugivorous (froojĭv'örŭs) *a.* [L. *frux*, fruit; *vorare*, to devour.] Fruit-eating; *appl.* certain animals.

fruit (froot) *n.* [F. *fruit*, from L. *fructus*, fruit.] The fertilised and developed ovary of a plant.

fruit-body,—the spore-bearing structure, as a sporangiocarp, basidiocarp, conidiocarp.

fruit-spot,—sorus, as of ferns.

frustose (frŭs'tōs) *a.* [L. *frustum*, piece.] Cleft into polygonal pieces; covered with markings resembling cracks.

frustule (frŭs'tūl) *n.* [L. *frustulum*, small fragment.] The siliceous two-valved shell and protoplasm of a diatom.

frutescent (frootĕs'ĕnt) *a.* [L. *frutex*, shrub.] Becoming shrub-like; fruticose, *q.v.*

frutex (froo'tĕks) *n.* [L. *frutex*, shrub.] Shrub.

fruticose (froo'tĭkōs) *a.* [L. *fruticosus*, bushy.] Like a shrub; *appl.* thallus of certain lichens.

fruticulose (frootĭk'ūlōs) *a.* [*Dim.* of L. *fruticosus*, bushy.] Like a small shrub.

fucivorous (fūsĭv'örŭs) *a.* [L. *fucus*, seaweed; *vorare*, to devour.] *Appl.* seaweed-eating animals.

fucoid (fū'koid) *a.* [L. *fucus*, seaweed; Gk. *eidos*, form.] *Pert.* or resembling seaweed.

fucosan (fū'kösăn) *n.* [L. *fucus*, seaweed.] Product of carbon-assimilation in brown seaweeds.

fucoxanthin (fū'közăn'thĭn) *n.* [L. *fucus*, seaweed; Gk. *xanthos*, yellow.] The main carotenoid pigment of brown algae; $C_{40}H_{56}O_6$.

fugacious (fūgā'shŭs) *a.* [L. *fugax*, fleeting.] Evanescent; falling off early; caducous; *appl.* petals, etc.

fulcral (fŭl'krăl) *a.* [L. *fulcrum*, support.] *Pert.* or acting as a fulcrum; *appl.* triangular plates aiding in movement of stylets in Hymenoptera.

fulcrate (fŭl'krāt) *a.* [L. *fulcrum*, support.] Having a fulcrum.

fulcrum (fŭl'krŭm) *a.* [L. *fulcrum*, support.] A supporting organ such as a tendril or stipule; sporophore in lichens; plate supporting rami of incus in mastax of rotifers; the lower surface of a ligula; a chitinous structure in base of insect rostrum; hinge-line of brachiopods; spine-like scale on anterior fin-rays of many ganoids.

fulturae (fŭltū'rē) *n.plu.* [L. *fultura*, prop.] A pair of sclerites supporting the hypopharynx in myriopods. *Sing.* fultura.

function (fŭngk'shŭn) *n.* [L. *functio*, performance.] The action proper to any organ or part.

functional (fŭngk'shönăl) *a.* [L. *functio*, performance.] Acting normally; acting or working part of an organ as distinct from remainder.

fundament,—primordium, *q.v.*

fundamentum,—hypocotyl, *q.v.*

fundatrix (fŭndā'trĭks) *n.* [L. *fundare*, to found.] Stem mother, a female founding a new colony by oviposition; *appl.* Aphides.

fundic (fŭn'dĭk) *a.* [L. *fundus*, bottom.] *Pert.* a fundus; *appl.* cells of stomach.

fundiform (fŭn'dĭfôrm) *a.* [L. *funda*, sling; *forma*, shape.] Looped; *appl.* a ligament of penis.

fundus (fŭn'dŭs) *n.* [L. *fundus*, bottom.] The base of an organ, as of stomach, urinary bladder, etc.; boundary between underground and above-ground portions of plant axis.

fungicolous (fŭnjĭk'ölŭs) *a.* [L. *fungus*, mushroom; *colere*, to inhabit.] Living in or on fungi.

fungiform (fŭn′jĭfôrm) *a.* [L. *fungus*, mushroom; *forma*, shape.] Fungoid or shaped like a fungus; *appl.* tongue papillae.

fungine (fŭn′jĭn) *n.* [L. *fungus*, mushroom.] Chitinous substance forming cell-wall of fungi.

fungistatic (fŭn′jĭstăt′ĭk) *a.* [L. *fungus*, mushroom; Gk. *statikos*, causing to stand.] Inhibiting the development of fungi.

fungivorous (fŭnjĭv′ŏrŭs) *a.* [L. *fungus*, mushroom; *vorare*, to devour.] *Appl.* fungus-eating animals and plants.

fungous (fŭng′gŭs) *a.* [L. *fungus*, mushroom.] With character or consistency of fungus; fungoid.

funicle (fū′nĭkl) *n.* [L. *funiculus*, small cord.] An ovule stalk; a slender strand attaching peridiolum to peridium; a small cord or band, as of nerve fibres; a large double strand of cells passing from aboral end of coelom to aboral wall of zooecium of Molluscoidea; also funiculus.

funicular (fūnĭk′ūlăr) *a.* [L. *funiculus*, small cord.] Consisting of a small cord or band; *pert.* a funiculus or funicle.

funiculus (fūnĭk′ūlŭs) *n.* [L. *funiculus*, small cord.] A funicle, *q.v.*; one of the ventral, lateral, and dorsal columns of white matter of the spinal cord.

funiform (fū′nĭfôrm) *a.* [L. *funis*, rope; *forma*, shape.] Like a cord or rope.

funnel (fŭn′ĕl) *n.* [L. *fundere*, to pour.] Siphon of cephalopods.

funnelform (fŭn′ĕlfôrm) *a.* [L. *fundere*, to pour; *forma*, shape.] Widening gradually from a narrow base; infundibuliform.

furca (fŭr′kă) *n.* [L. *furca*, fork.] The apophysis or entothorax of insect metathorax; forked intercoxal plate, as in Copepoda.

furcal (fŭr′kăl) *a.* [L. *furca*, fork.] Forked; *appl.* a branching nerve of lumbar plexus.

furcasternum (fŭr′kăstĕr′nŭm) *n.* [L. *furca*, fork; *sternum*, breast-bone.] Forked poststernite or sternellum in many insects.

furcate (fŭr′kāt) *a.* [L. *furca*, fork.] Branching like prongs of a fork.

furciferous (fŭrsĭf′ĕrŭs) *a.* [L. *furca*, fork; *ferre*, to carry.] Bearing a forked appendage, as some insects.

furcula (fŭr′kūlă) *n.* [L. *furcula*, *dim.* of *furca*, fork.] A forked process or structure; the merrythought bone; a transverse ridge in embryonic pharynx, giving rise to epiglottis; partially fused abdominal appendages forming springing organ in Collembola.

furred (fŭrd) *a.* [O.F. *forre*, sheath.] Having short decumbent hairs thickly covering the surface.

fuscin (fŭs′sĭn) *n.* [L. *fuscus*, dusky.] A brown pigment in retinal epithelium.

fuseau (fūzō) *n.* [F. *fuseau*, from L. *fusus*, spindle.] A spindle-shaped structure; a spindle-shaped, thick-walled spore divided by septa, in certain fungi; a fusiform macroconidium.

fusi (fū′zī) *n. plu.* [L. *fusus*, spindle.] In spiders, organs composed of two retractile processes which issue from mammulae and form threads.

fusiform (fū′zĭfôrm) *a.* [L. *fusus*, spindle; *forma*, shape.] Spindle-shaped; tapering gradually at both ends; *appl.* innermost layer of cerebral cortex; *appl.* a gyrus of temporal lobe.

fusion-nucleus,—central nucleus of embryo-sac formed by fusion of odd nuclei from each end.

fusocellular (fū′zōsĕl′ūlăr) *a.* [L. *fusus*, spindle; *cellula*, small room.] Having, or *pert.*, spindle-shaped cells.

fusulae (fū′zūlē) *n. plu.* [*Dim.* of L. *fusus*, spindle.] Spools, minute tubes of spinneret.

G

galactase (gălăk′tās) *n.* [Gk. *gala*, milk.] An enzyme, trypsin-like in action, found in milk.

galactin (gălăk'tĭn) *n.* [Gk. *gala*, milk.] The prepituitary lactogenic hormone, prolactin ; a polysaccharide occurring in certain plants, *e.g.* in lupin.

galactoblast (gălăk'töblăst) *n.* [Gk. *gala*, milk ; *blastos*, bud.] A fat-containing globule or colostrum corpuscle in mammary acini.

galactophorous (găl'ăktŏf'örŭs) *a.* [Gk. *gala*, milk ; *pherein*, to carry.] Lactiferous ; *appl.* ducts of mammary glands.

galactose (gălăk'tōs) *n.* [Gk. *gala*, milk.] A sugar found as a constituent of various carbohydrates in plants, and of lactose and certain glycolipids and glycoproteins in animals.

galactosis (găl'ăktō'sĭs) *n.* [Gk. *gala*, milk.] Milk secretion.

galactotropic (gălăk'tötrŏp'ĭk) *a.* [Gk. *gala*, milk ; *trope*, turn.] Stimulating milk secretion ; *appl.* hormone : prolactin, *q.v.*

galbulus (găl'būlŭs) *n.* [L. *galbulus*, cypress nut.] A modified cone with fleshy scales, as in cypress.

galea (gāl'ëă) *n.* [L. *galea*, helmet.] A helmet-shaped petal, or other similarly-shaped structure ; epicranial aponeurosis, the galea aponeurotica, of the scalp muscle or occipitofrontalis ; galea capitis, thin sheath covering head of spermatozoon ; outer division of stipes or endopodite of first maxilla of insects, itself divided into basigalea and distigalea ; a prominence of movable digit of chelicerae in Pseudoscorpiones.

galeate (gāl'ëāt) *a.* [L. *galeatus*, helmed.] Helmet-shaped ; hooded.

Galen, veins of [*Galen*, Greek physician]. Internal cerebral veins and great cerebral vein formed by their union.

galeriform (gălē'rĭfôrm) *a.* [L. *galerum*, hide-cap ; *forma*, form.] Shaped like a cap.

gall (gôl) *n* [A.S. *gealla*, gall.] Bile, secretion of liver. [L. *galla*, gall-nut.] An excrescence on plants, caused by fungi, mites, and insects, especially by Cynipidae and Cecidomyidae ; cecidium.

gall - bladder, — pear - shaped or spherical sac which stores bile.

galloxanthin (gălözăn'thĭn) *n.* [L. *gallus*, cock ; Gk. *xanthos*, yellow.] Carotenoid pigment associated with retinal cones in domestic fowl.

galvanotaxis (găl'vănötăk'sĭs), **galvanotropism** (găl'vănŏt'röpĭzm) *n.* [*L. Galvani*, Italian physiologist]. Response or reaction to electrical stimulus.

gametal (gămē'tăl) *a.* [Gk. *gametes*, spouse.] *Pert.* a gamete ; reproductive.

gametangiogamy (gămēt'ănjĭŏg'ămĭ) *n.* [Gk. *gametes*, spouse ; *anggeion*, vessel ; *gamos*, marriage.] The union of gametangia.

gametangium (găm'ētăn'jĭŭm) *n.* [Gk. *gametes*, spouse ; *anggeion*, vessel.] A structure producing sexual cells.

gametes (gămēts') *n. plu.* [Gk. *gametes*, spouse.] Cells derived from gametocytes which conjugate and form zygotes ; sexual cells.

gametic (gămĕt'ĭk) *a.* [Gk. *gametes*, spouse.] *Pert.* gamete ; *appl.* a mutation occurring before maturation of gamete ; *appl.* linkage.

gametids (gămē'tĭdz) *n. plu.* [Gk. *gametes*, spouse.] Primary sporoblasts destined to become gametes.

gametoblast (gămē'töblăst) *n.* [Gk. *gametes*, spouse ; *blastos*, bud.] Plasson ; formulative substance.

gametocyst (gămē'tösĭst) *n.* [Gk. *gametes*, spouse ; *kystis*, bladder.] Cyst surrounding two associated free forms in sexual reproduction of gregarines.

gametocyte (gămē'tösīt) *n.* [Gk. *gametes*, spouse ; *kytos*, hollow.] The mother-cell of a gamete.

gametogamy (gămētŏg'ămĭ) *n.* [Gk. *gametes*, spouse ; *gamos*, marriage.] The union of gametes ; syngamy.

gametogenesis (gămē'töjĕn'ësĭs) *n.* [Gk. *gametes*, spouse ; *genesis*, origin.] Gamete formation ; gametogeny.

gametogenic (gămē′töjĕn′ĭk) *a.* [Gk. *gametes*, spouse; *genos*, descent.] Arising from spontaneous changes in chromosomes of gametes; *appl.* variation.

gametogonium (gămē′tögō′nĭŭm) *n.* [Gk. *gametes*, spouse; *gonos*, offspring.] A cell producing a gamete, a gametocyte.

gametoid (gămē′toid) *n.* [Gk. *gametes*, spouse; *eidos*, form.] A structure behaving like a gamete, as apocytes uniting to form a zygotoid.

gametokinetic (gămē′tökĭnĕt′ĭk) *a.* [Gk. *gametes*, spouse; *kinein*, to move.] Stimulating gamete formation; *appl.* hormones, as follicle-stimulating hormone or prolan A.

gametophore (gămē′töfōr) *n.* [Gk. *gametes*, spouse; *pherein*, to bear.] A special part of a gametophyte on which gametangia are borne; a hyphal outgrowth which fuses with a similar neighbouring outgrowth to form a zygospore.

gametophyll (gămē′töfĭl) *n.* [Gk. *gametes*, spouse; *phyllon*, leaf.] A modified leaf bearing sexual organs; a micro- or macro-sporophyll.

gametophyte (gămē′töfīt) *n.* [Gk. *gametes*, spouse; *phyton*, plant.] The gamete-forming phase in alternation of plant generations; haplophyte; sexual generation of plants; pollen grain and embryo-sac; *cf.* sporophyte.

gametospore (gămē′töspōr) *n.* [Gk. *gametes*, spouse; *sporos*, seed.] A sporidium or spore that unites with another by means of a bridging structure.

gamic (găm′ĭk) *a.* [Gk. *gamos*, marriage.] Fertilised.

gammation (gămā′shŭn) *n.* [Gk. *gammation*, *dim.* of *gamma*.] An angular bar beside the branchial arches of Palaeospondylus.

gamobium (gămō′bĭŭm) *n.* [Gk. *gamos*, marriage; *bios*, life.] The sexual generation in alternation of generations, *opp.* agamobium.

gamocyst (găm′ösĭst) *n.* [Gk. *gamos*, marriage; *kystis*, bladder.] Oocyst, or sporocyst.

gamodeme (găm′ödēm) *n.* [Gk. *gamos*, marriage; *demos*, people.] A deme forming a relatively isolated intrabreeding community.

gamodesmic (găm′ödĕs′mĭk) *a.* [Gk. *gamos*, marriage; *desma*, bond.] Having the vascular bundles fused together instead of separated by connective tissue.

gamogastrous (găm′ögăs′trŭs) *a.* [Gk. *gamos*, marriage; *gaster*, belly.] *Appl.* a pistil formed by union of ovaries, but with styles and stigmata free.

gamogenesis (găm′öjĕn′ësĭs) *n.* [Gk. *gamos*, marriage; *genesis*, descent.] Sexual reproduction.

gamogenetic (găm′öjënĕt′ĭk) *a.* [Gk. *gamos*, marriage; *genesis*, descent.] Sexual; reproduced from union of sex elements.

gamogony (gămŏg′önĭ) *n.* [Gk. *gamos*, marriage; *gone*, descent.] Sporogony in protozoa.

gamones (găm′ōnz) *n. plu.* [Gk. *gamos*, marriage.] Secretions of gametes, which act on gametes of the opposite sex; androgamones and gynogamones.

gamont (gămŏnt′) *n.* [Gk. *gamos*, marriage; *on*, being.] A sporont.

gamopetalous (găm′öpĕt′ălŭs) *a.* [Gk. *gamos*, marriage; *petalon*, leaf.] With coherent petals; sympetalous.

gamophase (găm′öfāz) *n.* [Gk. *gamos*, marriage; *phasis*, aspect.] The haploid phase of a life-cycle; haplophase; *cf.* zygophase.

gamophyllous (găm′öfĭl′ŭs) *a.* [Gk. *gamos*, marriage; *phyllon*, leaf.] With united perianth leaves; monophyllous.

gamosepalous (găm′ösĕp′ălŭs) *a.* [Gk. *gamos*, marriage; F. *sépale*, sepal.] With coherent sepals; monosepalous.

gamostele (găm′östē′lē) *n.* [Gk. *gamos*, marriage; *stele*, pillar.] Stele formed from fusion of several steles.

gamostelic (găm′östē′lĭk) *a.* [Gk. *gamos*, marriage; *stele*, pillar.] *Appl.* condition in which steles of a polystelic stem are fused together.

gamostely (găm'östē'lĭ) *n.* [Gk. *gamos*, marriage; *stele*, pillar.] The arrangement of polystelic stems when the separate steles are fused together surrounded by pericycle and endodermis.

gamotropism (gămŏt'röpĭzm) *n.* [Gk. *gamos*, union; *trope*, turn.] Tendency to mutual attraction, exhibited by movements of gametes.

ganglia,—*plu.* of ganglion.

gangliar (găng'glĭăr) *a.* [Gk. *ganglion*, little tumour.] *Pert.* a ganglion or ganglia.

gangliate (găng'glĭāt) *a.* [Gk. *ganglion*, little tumour.] Having ganglia.

gangliform (găng'glĭfôrm) *a.* [Gk. *gangglion*, little tumour; L. *forma*, shape.] In the form of a ganglion.

ganglioblast (găng'glĭöblăst) *n.* [Gk. *gangglion*, little tumour; *blastos*, bud.] Mother-cell of gangliocyte.

gangliocyte (găng'glĭösīt) *n.* [Gk. *gangglion*, little tumour; *kytos*, hollow.] A ganglion cell outside the central nervous system.

ganglioid (găng'glĭoid) *a.* [Gk. *gangglion*, little tumour; *eidos*, form.] Like a ganglion.

ganglion (găng'glĭŏn) *n.* [Gk. *ganglion*, little tumour.] A mass of nerve cell bodies and giving origin to nerve fibres; a nerve centre.

ganglionated (găng'glĭŏnā'tëd) *a.* [Gk. *gangglion*, little tumour.] Supplied with ganglia; gangliate.

ganglioneural (găng'glĭönū'răl) *a.* [Gk. *gangglion*, little tumour; *neuron*, nerve.] *Appl.* a system of nerves, consisting of a series of ganglia connected by nerve strands.

ganglioneuron (găng'glĭönū'rŏn) *n.* [Gk. *gangglion*, little tumour; *neuron*, nerve.] A nerve cell of a ganglion.

ganglionic (găng'glĭŏn'ĭk) *a.* [Gk. *gangglion*, little tumour.] *Pert.*, consisting of, or in neighbourhood of a ganglion; *appl.* layer of retina, arteries, arterial system of brain.

ganglioplexus (găng'glĭöplĕk'sŭs) *n.* [Gk. *gangglion*, little tumour; L. *plexus*, braided.] A diffuse ganglion.

ganoblast (găn'öblăst) *n.* [Gk. *ganos*, sheen; *blastos*, bud.] An ameloblast.

ganoid (găn'oid) *a.* [Gk. *ganos*, sheen; *eidos*, form.] *Appl.* scales of ganoid fishes, rhomboidal, joined like parquetry and consisting of a layer of bone with superficial enamel.

ganoine (găn'öĭn) *n.* [Gk. *ganos*, sheen.] The outer layer of a ganoid scale, formed by the corium; enamel-like substance in formation of ameloblasts; ganoin.

gape (gāp) *n.* [A.S. *geapan*, to open wide.] The distance between the open jaws of birds, fishes, etc.

garland cells,—a chain of nephrocytes, in Diptera.

garland stage—stage of garland-like arrangement of chromatin at poles of nucleus in prophase of meiosis.

Gärtner's **canal**,—longitudinal duct of epoophoron, representing mesonephric duct, alongside the uterus and in lateral wall of vagina.

gas gland,—glandular portion of air-bladder of fishes.

Gaskell's bridge (*W. H. Gaskell*, English physiologist]. Atrioventricular bundle; bundle of His.

Gasserian ganglion [*A. P. Gasser*, German anatomist]. The semilunar ganglion on sensory root of fifth cranial nerve.

gastero-,—*also* gastro-.

gasteromycetous (găs'tëromīsē'tŭs) *a.* [Gk. *gaster*, stomach; *mykes*, mushroom.] Having the spores developed in a gleba within a peridium.

gasterospore (găs'tërospōr) *n.* [Gk. *gaster*, stomach; *sporos*, seed.] A thick-walled globular spore formed within a fruit-body.

gastraea (găstrē'ă) *n.* [Gk. *gaster*, stomach.] A hypothetical gastrula-like animal; the ancestral metazoan, according to Haeckel.

gastraeum (găstrē'ŭm) *n.* [Gk. *gaster*, stomach.] Ventral side of body.

gastral (găs'trăl) *a.* [Gk. *gaster*, stomach.] *Pert.* stomach, as gastral cavity, cortex, layer, etc.

gastralia (găstrā'lĭă) *n. plu.* [Gk. *gaster*, stomach.] Microscleres in the gastral membranes of Hexactinellida ; abdominal ribs, as in some reptiles.

gastric (găs'trĭk) *a.* [Gk. *gaster*, stomach.] *Pert.* or in region of stomach ; *appl.* arteries, glands, nerves, veins.

gastrin (găs'trĭn) *n.* [Gk. *gaster*, stomach.] A hormone secreted by pyloric mucosa and which stimulates gastric secretion.

gastro-,—*also* gastero-.

gastrocentrous (găs'trösĕn'trŭs) *a.* [Gk. *gaster*, stomach ; *kentron*, centre.] *Appl.* vertebrae with centra formed by pairs of interventralia, while the basiventralia are reduced.

gastrocnemius (găs'trökne̅'mĭŭs) *n.* [Gk. *gaster*, stomach ; *kneme*, tibia.] Large muscle of calf of leg.

gastrocoel (găs'trösēl) *n.* [Gk. *gaster*, stomach ; *koilos*, hollow.] The archenteron of a gastrula.

gastrocolic (găs'trökŏl'ĭk) *a.* [Gk. *gaster*, stomach ; *kolon*, gut.] *Pert.* stomach and colon ; *appl.* ligament, the greater omentum.

gastrocutaneous (găs'trökūtā'nëŭs) *a.* [Gk. *gaster*, stomach ; L. *cutis*, skin.] *Appl.* pores leading from intestine to surface in Hemichorda.

gastrocystis (găs'trösĭs'tĭs) *n.* [Gk. *gaster*, stomach ; *kystis*, bladder.] Blastocyst.

gastrodermis (găs'trödĕr'mĭs) *n.* [Gk. *gaster*, stomach ; *derma*, skin.] Enteroblast.

gastroduodenal (găs'trödūödē'năl) *a.* [Gk. *gaster*, stomach ; L. *duodeni*, twelve each.] *Pert.* stomach and duodenum ; *appl.* an artery.

gastroepiploic (găs'tröĕpĭplō'ĭk) *a.* [Gk. *gaster*, stomach ; *epiploon*, omentum.] *Pert.* stomach and great omentum ; *appl.* arteries, veins.

gastrointestinal (găs'tröĭntĕs'tĭnăl) *a.* [Gk. *gaster*, stomach ; L. *intestinum*, gut.] *Pert.* stomach and intestines.

gastrolienal (găs'trölīē'năl) *a.* [Gk. *gaster*, stomach ; L. *lien*, spleen.] *Pert.* stomach and spleen ; *appl.* ligament ; gastrosplenic.

gastrolith (găs'trölĭth) *n.* [Gk. *gaster*, stomach ; *lithos*, stone.] A mass of calcareous matter found on each side of gizzard of crustaceans before a moult.

gastroparietal (găs'tröpărī'ĕtăl) *a.* [Gk. *gaster*, stomach ; L. *paries*, wall.] *Pert.* stomach and body wall.

gastrophrenic (găs'tröfrĕn'ĭk) *a.* [Gk. *gaster*, stomach ; *phren*, midriff.] *Pert.* stomach and diaphragm ; *appl.* ligament.

gastropod (găs'tröpŏd) *n.* [Gk. *gaster*, stomach ; *pous*, foot.] A mollusc with ventral muscular disc adapted for creeping ; gasteropod.

gastropores (găs'tröpōrz) *n. plu.* [Gk. *gaster*, stomach ; *poros*, channel.] The larger pores, for nutrient persons, of hydroid corals.

gastropulmonary (găs'tröpŭl'mönărĭ) *a.* [Gk. *gaster*, stomach ; L. *pulmo*, lung.] *Pert.* stomach and lungs.

gastrosplenic (găs'trösplĕn'ĭk) *a.* [Gk. *gaster*, stomach ; *splen*, spleen.] *Pert.* stomach and spleen ; gastrolienal.

gastrostege (găs'tröstēj) *n.* [Gk. *gaster*, stomach ; *stege*, roof.] A ventral scale of snakes.

gastrovascular (găs'trövăs'kūlăr) *a.* [Gk. *gaster*, stomach ; L. *vasculum*, small vessel.] Serving both digestive and circulatory purposes, as canals of some Coelentera.

gastrozooid (găs'trözō'oid) *n.* [Gk. *gaster*, stomach ; *zoon*, animal ; *eidos*, form.] In coelenterate colonies, the nutrient person with mouth and tentacles ; trophozooid in some tunicates.

gastrula (găs'troolă) *n.* [Gk. *gaster*, stomach.] The cup- or basin-shaped structure formed by invagination of a blastula.

gastrulation (găs'troolā'shŭn) *n.* [Gk. *gaster*, stomach.] Formation of gastrula from blastula by invagination.

geitonogamy (gī'tŏnŏg'ămĭ) *n.* [Gk. *geiton*, neighbour; *gamos*, marriage.] Fertilisation of a flower by another from the same plant.

gelatigenous (jĕl'ătĭj'ënŭs) *a.* [L. *gelare*, to congeal; Gk. *-genes*, producing.] Gelatine-producing.

gelatine (jĕl'ătĭn) *n.* [L. *gelare*, to congeal.] A jelly-like substance obtained from animal tissue.

gelatinous (jĕlăt'ĭnŭs) *a.* [L. *gelare*, to congeal.] Jelly-like in consistency.

geminate (jĕm'ĭnāt) *a.* [L. *gemini*, twins.] Growing in pairs; binate; paired; *appl.* species or subspecies: corresponding forms in corresponding but separate regions, as reindeer and caribou.

gemini (jĕm'ĭnī) *n. plu.* [L. *gemini*, twins.] Bivalent chromosomes; pairs of paternal and maternal chromosomes at parasyndesis.

geminiflorous (jĕm'ĭnĭflō'rŭs) *a.* [L. *gemini*, twins; *flos*, flower.] *Appl.* a plant whose flowers are arranged in pairs.

gemma (jĕm'ă) *n.* [L. *gemma*, bud.] A bud or outgrowth of a plant or animal which develops into a new organism; a leaf-bud, *opp.* flower-bud; a chlamydospore, *q.v.*; a hypothetical unit, *q.v.*

gemmaceous (jĕmā'shŭs) *a.* [L. *gemma*, bud.] *Pert.* gemmae or buds.

gemma-cup,—cyathus, *q.v.*

gemmate (jĕm'āt) *a.* [L. *gemmare*, to bud.] Having buds.

gemmation (jĕmā'shŭn) *n.* [L. *gemma*, bud.] Budding; bud-formation by means of which new independent individuals are developed in plants and animals; arrangement of buds.

gemmiferous (jĕmĭf'ërŭs) *a.* [L. *gemma*, bud; *ferre*, to bear.] Bud-bearing; gemmate.

gemmiform (jĕm'ĭfôrm) *a.* [L. *gemma*, bud; *forma*, shape.] Shaped like a bud; *appl.* pedicellariae of echinoderms.

gemmiparous (jĕmĭp'ărŭs) *a.* [L. *gemma*, bud; *parere*, to produce.] Reproducing by bud-formation.

gemmulation (jĕm'ūlā'shŭn) *n.* [L. *gemmula*, little bud.] Gemmule-formation.

gemmule (jĕm'ūl) *n.* [L. *gemmula*, little bud.] A pangen; a moss bud; one of the internal buds of Porifera arising asexually and coming into activity on death of parent organism; one of the minute protoplasmic processes on branch of a dendrite, contact point in synapse.

gena (jē'nă) *n.* [L. *gena*, cheek.] The cheek or side part of head; antero-lateral part of prosoma of trilobites, and of insect head.

genal, *pert.* the cheek; *appl.* facial suture and to caeca of stomach of trilobites; *appl.* angle of cheek.

gene (jēn) *n.* [Gk. *genos*, descent.] A unit hereditary factor in the chromosome; also gen; regarded as multiple, composed of genomeres; *cf.* cistron.

gene flow,—the spreading of genes resulting from outcrossing and from subsequent crossing within a group; genorheithrum, *q.v.*

gene mutation,—a heritable variation caused by changes at a particular locus; point-mutation.

genecology (jĕn'ēkŏl'ŏjĭ) *n.* [Gk. *genos*, descent; *oikos*, household; *logos*, discourse.] Ecology in relation to genetics.

Gené's organ [*C. G. Gené*, Italian zoologist]. Subscutal or cephalic gland secreting a viscid substance used in transferring eggs to dorsal surface, in ticks.

geneogenous (jĕnëŏj'ënŭs) *a.* [Gk. *genea*, birth; *gennaein*, to produce.] Congenital.

geneology (jĕn'ëŏl'ŏjĭ) *n.* [Gk. *genos*, descent; *logos*, discourse.] The study of development of individual and race; embryology and palaeontology combined.

genera,—*plu.* of genus.

generalised (jĕn'ĕrălīz'd) *a.* [L. *generalis*, of one kind.] Combining characteristics of two or more groups, as in many fossils.

generation (jĕn'ĕrā'shŭn) *n.* [L. *generatio*, reproduction.] Production; formation; the individuals of a species equally remote from a common ancestor.

generative (jĕn'ĕrătĭv) *a.* [L. *generare*, to beget.] Concerned in reproduction; *appl.* smaller of two cells into which a pollen grain primarily divides.

generative ferment,—a specific substance, present in small quantities in blood, necessary for formation of gonadial internal secretions.

generator cell,—a cell including a dikaryon, which gives rise to aecidiospore mother-cells or to probasidia.

generic (jĕnĕr'ĭk) *a.* (L. *genus*, race.] Common to all species of a genus; *pert.* a genus.

generitype (jĕnĕr'ĭtīp) *n.* [L. *genus*, race; *typus*, image.] The typical species of a genus.

genesiology (jĕn'ĕsĭŏl'ŏjĭ) *n.* [Gk. *genesis*, descent; *logos*, discourse.] Science dealing with reproduction.

genesis (jĕn'ĕsĭs) *n.* [Gk. *genesis*, descent.] Formation, production, or development of a cell, organ, individual, or species.

genetic (jĕnĕ'tĭk) *a.* [Gk. *genesis*, descent.] *Pert.* genesis; *pert.* genetics.

genetic factor,—gene. *q.v.*

genetic spiral,—in spiral phyllotaxis, imaginary spiral line following points of insertion of successive leaves.

genetics (jĕnĕt'ĭks) *n.* [Gk. *genesis*, descent.] That part of biology dealing with heredity and variation.

genetype,—genotype.

genial (jĕn'ĭăl) *a.* [Gk. *geneion*, chin.] *Pert.* the chin; *appl.* chin-plates of reptiles; *appl.* tubercles on inside of mandible, for insertion of genioglossal and geniohyoid muscles.

genic (jēn'ĭk) *a.* [Gk. *genos*, descent.] *Pert.* genes.

genic balance,—harmonious interaction of genes.

genicular (jĕnĭk'ūlăr) *a.* [L. *geniculum*, little knee.] *Pert.* region of the knee; *appl.* arteries, etc., *pert.* geniculum.

geniculate (jĕnĭk'ūlāt) *n.* [L. *geniculum*, little knee.] Bent like a knee-joint; *appl.* antenna; *pert.* geniculum, *appl.* a ganglion of the facial nerve; *appl.* bodies, lateral and medial corpora geniculata, constituting the metathalamus; having upper part of filament forming an angle more or less obtuse with lower.

geniculation (jĕnĭk'ūlā'shŭn) *n.* [L. *geniculum*, little knee.] A knee-like joint or flexure.

geniculum (jĕnĭk'ūlŭm) *a.* [L. *geniculum*, little knee.] Sharp bend in a nerve; part of the facial nerve in temporal bone where it turns abruptly towards stylo-mastoid foramen.

genioglossal (jĕn'īōglŏs'ăl) *a.* [Gk. *geneion*, chin; *glossa*, tongue.] Connecting chin and tongue; *appl.* muscle; geniohyoglossal.

geniohyoid (jĕn'īōhī'oid) *a.* [Gk. *geneion*, chin; *hyoeides*, Υ-shaped.] *Pert.* chin and hyoid; *appl.* muscles.

genital (jĕn'ĭtăl) *a.* [L. *gignere*, to beget.] *Pert.* the region of reproductive organs; *appl.* corpuscles, glands, ridge, tubercle, veins, etc.

genitalia (jĕn'ĭtālĭă) *n. plu.* [L. *gignere*, to beget.] Genitals, the organs of reproduction, especially the external organs.

genito-anal (jĕn'ĭtōā'năl) *a.* [L. *gignere*, to beget; *anus*, vent.] In the region of genitalia and anus.

genitocrural (jĕn'ĭtōkroo'răl) *a.* [L. *gignere*, to beget; *crus*, leg.] In the region of genitalia and thigh; *appl.* a nerve originating from first and second lumbar nerves.

genito-enteric (jĕn'ĭtōĕntĕr'ĭk) *a.* [L. *gignere*, to beget; Gk. *enteron*, gut.] *Pert.* genitalia and intestine.

genitofemoral (jĕn'ĭtōfĕm'ŏrăl) *a.* [L. *gignere*, to beget; *femur*, thigh-bone.] Genitocrural.

genitourinary,—*see* urinogenital.

genitoventral (jĕn′ĭtövĕn′trăl) *a.* [L. *gignere*, to beget; *venter*, belly.] *Appl.* plate formed by fused epigynial and ventral sclerites, in certain Acarina.

Gennari's band [*F. Gennari*, Italian anatomist]. A layer of white fibres in middle cell-lamina of cerebral cortex, especially of occipital lobe; line of Gennari.

genoblast (jĕn′öblăst) *n.* [Gk. *genos*, offspring; *blastos*, bud.] A mature germ-cell exclusively male or female.

genoholotype (jĕn′öhŏl′ötīp) *n.* [Gk. *genos*, race; *holos*, whole; *typos*, image.] A species defined as typical of its genus.

genome (jĕ̄n′ōm) *n.* [Gk. *genos*, offspring.] Minimum group or set of chromosomes derived from a zygote or gamete; genom.

genomere (jĕn′ömēr) *n.* [Gk. *genos*, offspring; *meros*, part.] A unit of a gene, regarded as a multiple.

genonema (jĕn′önē′mă) *n.* [Gk. *genos*, descent; *nema*, thread.] Axial thread on which genes are located in chromosome; axoneme; chromonema; a chromatid in its genetical aspect.

genonomy (jĕnŏn′ömĭ) *n.* [Gk. *genos*, descent; *nomos*, law.] The study of laws of relationships with reference to classification of organisms.

genophenes (jĕ̄n′öfēnz) *n. plu.* [Gk. *genos*, offspring; *phainein*, to appear.] Reaction types of the same genotype.

genorheithrum (jĕn′örē′thrŭm) *n.* [Gk. *genos*, descent; *rheithron*, stream.] The passage or descent of genes in phylogenesis.

genosome (jĕ̄n′ösōm) *n.* [Gk. *genos*, descent; *soma*, body.] The part of the chromosome bearing the locus of a gene.

genospecies (jĕ̄n′öspē′shēz) *n.* [Gk. *genos*, race; L. *species*, particular kind.] A species consisting of individuals having the same genotype.

genosyntype (jĕnösĭn′tīp) *n.* [Gk. *genos*, race; *syn*, with; *typos*, image.] A series of species together defined as typical of their genus.

genotype (jĕn′ötīp) *n.* [Gk. *genos*, race; *typos*, image.] Genetic or factorial constitution of an individual; group of individuals possessing the same genetic constitution; biotype; genoplast; type species of a genus, generitype.

genotypic (jĕn′ötĭp′ĭk) *a.* [Gk. *genos*, race; *typos*, image.] *Pert.* genotype; *appl.* characters arising from hereditary endowment.

genovariation,—point mutation, *q.v.*

genu (jĕn′ū) *n.* [L. *genu*, knee.] Knee; segment between femur and tibia in some Acarina; a knee-like bend in an organ or part; anterior end of corpus callosum.

genus (jē′nŭs) *n.*, **genera** (jĕn′ĕră) *plu.* [L. *genus*, race.] A group of closely related species, in classification of plants or animals.

genys (jĕn′ĭs) *n.* [Gk. *genys*, jaw.] Lower jaw.

geobionts (jē′öbīŏnts) *n. plu.* [Gk. *ge*, earth; *bion*, living.] Organisms permanently inhabiting the soil.

geobios (jē′öbī′ŏs) *n.* [Gk. *ge*, earth; *bios*, life.] Terrestrial life; edaphon, *q.v.*

geoblast (jē′öblăst) *n.* [Gk. *ge*, earth; *blastos*, bud.] A germinating plumule of which the cotyledons remain underground.

geobotany,—plant geography, phytogeography.

geocarpic (jē′ökâr′pĭk) *a.* [Gk. *ge*, earth; *karpos*, fruit.] Having the fruits maturing underground.

geocryptophyte (jē′ökrĭp′töfīt) *n.* [Gk. *ge*, earth; *kryptos*, hidden; *phyton*, plant.] A plant with dormant parts underground; geophyte.

geology (jēŏl′öjĭ) *n.* [Gk. *ge*, earth; *logos*, discourse.] The science dealing with structure, activities, and history of the earth.

geomalism (jēŏm′ălĭzm) *n.* [Gk. *ge*, earth; *omalos*, level.] Response to the influence of gravitation; horizontal habitus.

geonastic (jēŏnăs′tĭk) *a.* [Gk. *ge*, earth; *nastos*, pressed.] Curving towards the ground.

geonemy (jēŏn′ĕmĭ) *n.* [Gk. *ge*, earth; *nemein*, to inhabit.] The geographical distribution of organisms; biogeography; chorology.

geophilous (jēŏf′ĭlŭs) *a.* [Gk. *ge*, earth; *philein*, to love.] Living in or on the earth.

geophyte (jē′ŏfīt) *n.* [Gk. *ge*, earth; *phyton*, plant.] A land plant; a plant with dormant parts (tubers, bulbs, rhizomes) underground.

geosere (jē′ösēr) *n.* [Gk. *ge*, earth; L. *serere*, to put in a row.] A sere originating on a clay substratum.

geotaxis (jē′ötăk′sĭs) *n.* [Gk. *ge*, earth; *taxis*, arrangement.] Locomotor response to gravity.

geotonus (jēŏt′önŭs) *n.* [Gk. *ge*, earth; *tonos*, tension.] Normal position in relation to gravity.

geotropism (jēŏt′röpĭzm) *n.* [Gk. *ge*, earth; *trope*, turn.] Tendency to respond to stimulus of gravity, usually positive, by turning downwards, as in growth of a root.

gephyrocercal (jĕf′īrösĕr′kăl, jĕfī′rösĕr′kăl) *a.* [Gk. *gephyra*, bridge; *kerkos*, tail.] *Appl.* secondary diphycercal caudal fin brought about by reduction of extreme tip of heterocercal or homocercal fin.

geratology (jĕr′ătŏl′öjĭ) *n.* [Gk. *geras*, old age; *logos*, discourse.] Study of the factors of decadence and old age of populations; *cf.* gerontology.

germ (jĕrm) *n.* [L. *germen*, bud.] A unicellular micro-organism; a seed; a bud; a developing egg.

germ band,—primitive streak, of early embryo.

germ-cell,—a reproductive cell, *opp.* somatic cell; a primitive male or female element.

germ-centre,—an area of lymph-corpuscle division in nodules of lymph gland tissue.

germ-disc,—a small green cellular plate of the germ tube of liverworts; *cf.* germinal disc.

germ gland,—gonad.

germ-layer,—an early differentiated layer of cells.

germ nucleus,—an egg or sperm nucleus.

germ plasm,—idioplasm, the physical basis of inheritance.

germ pore,—the exit pore of a germ tube in the spore integument.

germ stock,—stolon of tunicates.

germ theory,—biogenesis; the theory that living organisms can be produced or developed only from living organisms.

germ track,—lineage of zygote in developing organism; continuity of germ cells.

germ tube,—short filamentous tube put forth by a germinating spore.

germ vitellarium, — an organ, of platyhelminths, producing both ova and vitelline material.

germ yolk gland,—in some Rhabdocoelida, an embryonic structure consisting of fertile portion of egg and a sterile portion which functions as a yolk gland feeding the fertile portion.

germarium (jĕrmā′rĭŭm) *n.* [L. *germen*, bud.] An ovary; distal portion of an ovariole.

germen (jĕr′mĕn) *n.* [L. *germen*, bud.] A mass of undifferentiated cells, the primary form of germ cells.

germiduct (jĕr′mĭdŭkt) *n.* [L. *germen*, bud; *ducere*, to lead.] Oviduct, of trematodes.

germigen (jĕr′mĭjĕn) *n.* [L. *germen*, bud; *generare*, to beget.] Ovary, of trematodes.

germinal (jĕr′mĭnăl) *a.* [L. *germen*, bud.] *Pert.* a seed, a germ-cell, or reproduction.

germinal bands,—two sets of rows of cells in early development of annulates.

germinal cells,—the cells concerned in reproduction, set apart early in embryonic life.

germinal centres,—areas of lymph-cell production within nodules of lymphoid tissue, as of lymph nodes, of tonsils, and in splenic corpuscles.

germinal disc,—the disc-like area of an egg yolk on which segmentation first appears; blastodisc.

germinal epithelium,—the layer of columnar epithelial cells covering the stroma of an ovary.

germinal layers,—primary layers of cells in a developing ovum: epiblast, hypoblast, and later, mesoblast; histogens, *q.v.*

germinal lid,—operculum of a pollen-grain.

germinal spot,—the nucleolus of an ovum.

germinal vesicle,—the nucleus of an ovum before formation of polar bodies.

germination (jĕr'mĭnā'shŭn) *n.* [L. *germen*, bud.] Beginning of growth; budding; sprouting; development.

germination hormone, — substance formed in endosperm of Gramineae and which stimulates growth of the coleoptile and inhibits that of the root; blastanin.

germiparity (jĕr'mĭpăr'ĭtĭ) *n.* [L. *germen*, bud; *parere*, to beget.] Reproduction by germ-formation.

germogen (jĕr'möjĕn) *n.* [L. *germen*, bud; Gk. *genos*, offspring.] The central cell of gastrula-like phase, or infusorigen, in development of Rhombozoa; the residual nucleus, or unused portion, after formation of rhombogen by division of primary germogen or primitive central cell.

gerontal (jĕrŏn'tăl) *a.* [Gk. *geron*, old man.] Senile.

gerontic (jĕrŏn'tĭk) *a.* [Gk. *geron*, old man.] *Pert.* old age; gerontal; *appl.* stage in phylogeny.

gerontology (jĕr'ŏntŏl'öjĭ) *n.* [Gk. *geron*, old man; *logos*, discourse.] The study of senescence and senility; geratology, *q.v.*

gestalt (gĕstâlt') *n.* [Ger. *Gestalt*, form.] Organised or unified response to an arrangement of stimuli; co-ordinated movements or configuration of motor reactions; a mental process considered as an organised pattern, involving explanation of parts in terms of the whole; a pattern considered in relation to background or environment; *appl.* morphology irrespective of taxonomic relationships.

gestation (jĕstā'shŭn) *n.* [L. *gestare*, to bear.] The intra-uterine period in development of an embryo.

giant cells,—large nerve-cells in annelids; myeloplaxes; osteoclasts, large multinuclear protoplasmic masses found in marrow, spleen; megakaryocytes, *q.v.*; Langhans' cells, *q.v.*; Betz cells, *q.v.*; gigantocytes.

giant chromosomes,—polytene or large chromosomes, as in salivary gland cells of larval Diptera.

giant fibres,—greatly enlarged and modified nerve-fibres running longitudinally through ventral nerve cord of some invertebrates.

Gianuzzi, crescents of,—*see* crescents.

gibberellins (jĭb'ĕrĕl'ĭnz) *n. plu.* [*Gibberella*, a fungal genus.] Metabolic products of *Gibberella fujikuroi*, and in flowering plants, which stimulate growth in coleoptiles and shoots, gibberellic acid being a growth factor complementary to auxins.

gibbous (gĭb'ŭs) *a.* [L. *gibbus*, hump.] Inflated; saccate or pouched, as the lateral sepals of Cruciferae; gibbose.

gigantocyte (jīgăn'tösīt) *n.* [Gk. *gigas*, giant; *kytos*, hollow.] Giant cell, *q.v.*

gill (gĭl) *n.* [M.E. *gille*, gill.] A plate-like or filamentous outgrowth; respiratory organ of aquatic animals; radial lamella on under side of pileus of agarics.

gill arch,—part of visceral skeleton in region of functional gills; branchial arch.

gill basket,—the branchial skeleton of lampreys, composed of continuous cartilage.

gill book,—the respiratory organ of certain Palaeostraca, consisting of a large number of leaf-like structures between which water circulates.

gill cleft,—a branchial cleft formed on side of pharynx.

gill cover,—an operculum.

gill helix,—a spirally coiled gill-like organ in certain Clupeidae.

gill plume,—the gill or ctenidium of the majority of Gasteropoda.

gill pouch,—an oval pouch containing gills and communicating directly or indirectly with exterior, as in Myxine and Petromyzon.

gill rakers,—small spine-like structures attached in a single or double row to branchial arches, preventing escape of food.

gill remnants, — epithelial, post-branchial, or suprapericardial bodies arising in pharynx of higher vertebrates.

gill rods,—gelatinous rods supporting the pharynx in Cephalochorda; branchial rays in certain fishes.

gill slits,—a series of perforations leading from pharynx to exterior, persistent in lower vertebrates, embryonic in higher.

gill trama,—the structure between the hymenial layers of a gill, as in agarics.

gingival (jĭnjī'văl) *a.* [L. *gingivae*, gums.] *Pert.* the gums.

ginglymoid (gĭng'glĭmoid) *a.* [Gk. *gingglymos*, hinge - joint; *eidos*, form.] Constructed like a hinge-joint.

ginglymus (gĭng'glĭmŭs) *n.* [Gk. *gingglymos*, hinge-joint.] An articulation constructed to allow of motion in one plane only.

Giraldès' organ [*J. A. C. C. Giraldès*, Portuguese surgeon]. The paradidymis.

girdle (gĕr'dl) *n.* [A.S. *gyrdan*, to gird.] In appendicular skeleton, the supporting structure at shoulder and hip, each consisting typically of one dorsal and two ventral elements; spicule-bearing portion of mantle not covered by shell-plates in Polyplacophora; transverse groove in Dinoflagellata, containing transverse flagellum and separating epicone and hypocone; the cingulum of diatoms.

girdle bundles,—leaf-trace bundles which girdle the stem and converge at the leaf insertion, as in Cycadales.

girdle scar,—a series of scale scars on axis of bud.

gito-,—geito-.

gizzard (gĭz'ărd) *n.* [O.F. *gezier*, gizzard.] Muscular grinding chamber of alimentary canal of various animals; proventriculus of insects.

glabella (glăbĕl'ă) *n.* [L. *glaber*, bald.] The space on forehead between superciliary ridges; the elevated median region of cephalic shield of Trilobita.

glabrate (glā'brāt) *a.* [L. *glaber*, smooth.] Becoming hairless; glabrescent; with a nearly smooth surface.

glabrous (glā'brŭs) *a.* [L. *glaber*, smooth.] With a smooth, even surface; without hairs.

glacial (glā'sĭăl) *a.* [L. *glacies*, ice.] *Pert.* or *appl.* the Pleistocene epoch of the Quaternary period, characterised by periodic glaciation.

gladiate (glăd'ĭāt) *a.* [L. *gladius*, sword.] Shaped like a sword; ensiform.

gladiolus (glădī'ōlŭs, glăd'ĭōlŭs) *n.* [L. *gladiolus*, small sword.] The mesosternum or corpus sterni.

gladius (glăd'ĭŭs) *n.* [L. *gladius*, sword.] The pen or chitinous shell in Chondrophora; *cf.* phragmocone, sepion.

glairine (glā'rēn) *n.* [F. *glaire*, white of egg.] Glairy film found or thermal springs and formed by pectic zoogloea.

gland (glănd) *n.* [L. *glans*, acorn.] Single cell or mass of cells specialised for elaboration of secretions either for use in the body or for excretion; glans.

gland cell,—an isolated secreting cell; a cell of glandular epithelium.

glandula (glăn'dūlă) *n.* [L. *glandula*, small acorn.] A gland; one of the bundles of hyphae ending in basidia with a viscous secretion appearing as spots on the surface of the stipe of certain fungi; a glutinous gland subserving cohesion of pollinia; arachnoid granulation on outer surface of dura mater.

glandula vesiculosa,—seminal vesicle.

glandulae Pacchionii,—arachnoideal granulations or Pacchionian bodies, *q.v.*

glandular (glăn'dūlăr) *a.* [L. *glandula*, small acorn.] With or *pert.* glands; with secreting function.

glandular epithelium,—the tissue of glands, composed of polyhedral, columnar, or cubical cells whose protoplasm contains or elaborates the material to be secreted.

glandular tissue,—tissue of single or massed cells, parenchymatous and filled with granular protoplasm, adapted for secretion of aromatic substances in plants.

glandule,—glandula.

glandulose-serrate (glăn'dūlōs-sĕr'āt) *a.* [L. *glandula*, small acorn; *serratus*, sawn.] Having the serrations tipped with glands.

glans (glăns) *n.* [L. *glans*, acorn.] A nut; a hard, dry, indehiscent one-celled fruit, as an acorn; a gland; the glans penis; the glans clitoridis.

glareal (glā'rëăl) *a.* [L. *glarea*, gravel.] *Pert.*, or growing on, dry gravelly ground.

Glaserian fissure [*J. H. Glaser*, Swiss anatomist]. Petrotympanic fissure.

glaucescent (glôsĕs'ënt) *a.* [L. *glaucus*, sea-green.] Somewhat glaucous.

glaucous (glôk'ŭs) *a.* [L. *glaucus*, sea-green.] Bluish green; covered with a pale green bloom.

gleba (glē'bă) *n.* [L. *gleba*, clod.] The central part of the sporophore in certain fungi; the spore-forming apparatus in certain plants.

gleba chamber,—peridiolum, *q.v.*

glebula (glē'būlă) *n.* [L. *glebula*, small clod.] A small prominence on a lichen thallus.

glenohumeral (glē'nōhū'mërăl) *a.* [Gk. *glene*, socket; L. *humerus*, humerus.] *Pert.* glenoid cavity and humerus; *appl.* ligaments.

glenoid (glē'noid) *a.* [Gk. *glene*, socket; *eidos*, form.] Like a socket; *appl.* cavity into which head of humerus fits, the mandibular fossa, and various ligaments.

glenoidal labrum,—a fibro-cartilaginous rim attached round the margin of glenoid cavity and of acetabulum.

glia (glē'ă, glī'ă) *n.* [Gk. *glia*, glue.] Gliacyte; neuroglia cell, a supporting cell of nervous tissue.

gliadin (glī'ădĭn) *n.* [Gk. *glia*, glue.] A substance interacting with glutenin to form gluten in cereals; the prolamine of wheat and rye seeds; formerly, any prolamine.

gliding growth,—*see* sliding growth.

gliosomes (glī'ösōmz) *n. plu.* [Gk. *glia*, glue; *soma*, body.] Granules in protoplasm of neuroglia, possibly in relation with mitochondria.

Glisson's capsule [*F. Glisson*, English physician]. A fibrous capsule within liver, enclosing hepatic artery, portal vein, lymphatic vessels, and bile duct.

globate (glō'bāt) *a.* [L. *globus*, globe.] Globe-shaped; globular.

globigerina ooze,—sea-bottom mud which is largely composed of shells of Foraminifera.

globin (glō'bĭn) *n.* [L. *globus*, globe.] The basic protein constituent of haemoglobin.

globoid (glō'boid) *n.* [L. *globus*, globe; Gk. *eidos*, form.] A spherical body in aleurone grains, a double phosphate of calcium and magnesium.

globose (glōbōs') *a.* [L. *globus*, globe.] Spherical or globe-shaped; globular.

globule (glŏb'ūl) *n.* [L. *globulus*, small globe.] Any minute spherical structure; the antheridium of Characeae; globulus.

globulin (glŏb'ūlĭn) *n.* [L. *globus*, globe.] A protein, insoluble in water, such as fibrinogen, vitellin, crystallin, legumin.

globulose (glŏb'ūlōs) *a.* [L. *globus*, globe.] Spherical; consisting of, or containing globules.

globulus (glŏb'ūlŭs) *n.* [L. *globulus*, small globe.] A globule ; spherical or club-shaped sensory organ at bifurcation of antenna in Pauropoda.

globus major and **minor,**—head and tail of epididymis.

globus pallidus,—part of lentiform nucleus of corpus striatum.

glochidiate (glŏkĭd'ĭāt) *a.* [Gk. *glochis*, arrow-point.] Furnished with barbed hairs.

glochidium (glŏkĭd'ĭŭm) *n.* [Gk. *glochis*, arrow-point ; *idion*, *dim.*] Hairs bearing barbed processes seen on massulae of certain rhizocarps ; the larva of fresh-water mussels such as Unio and Anodon.

gloea (glē'ă) *n.* [Gk. *gloia*, glue.] An adhesive secretion of some protozoa.

gloeocystidium (glē'ŏsĭstĭd'ĭŭm) *n* [Gk. *gloios*, sticky ; *kystis*, bag ; *idion*, *dim.*] A cystidium containing a slimy or oily substance.

glomera,—*plu.* of glomus.

glomera carotica,—carotid bodies, *q.v.*

glomerular (glŏmĕr'ūlăr) *a.* [L. *glomus*, ball.] *Pert.* or like a glomerulus.

glomerulate (glŏmĕr'ūlāt) *a.* [L. *glomus*, ball.] Arranged in clusters.

glomerule (glŏm'ĕrūl) *n.* [L. *glomus*, ball.] A condensed cyme of almost sessile flowers ; a compact cluster.

glomeruliferous (glŏmĕr'ūlĭf'ĕrŭs) *a.* [L. *glomus*, ball ; *ferre*, to carry.] Having the flowers arranged in glomerules.

glomerulus (glŏmĕr'ūlŭs) *n.* [L. *glomus*, ball.] Network of capillary blood-vessels ; inturned portion of a Bowman's capsule ; oval body terminating olfactory fibres in rhinencephalon ; a mass of interlacing intracapsular dendrites, in sympathetic ganglia ; excretory organ of Enteropneusta ; a small mass of spores ; a glomerule.

glomus (glō'mŭs) *n.* [L. *glomus*, ball.] A number of glomeruli run together ; coccygeal and carotid bodies, consisting largely of chromaffin cells.

glossa (glŏs'ă) *n.* [Gk. *glossa*, tongue.] A tongue-like projection in middle of labium of insects.

glossal (glŏs'ăl) *a.* [Gk. *glossa*, tongue.] *Pert.* the tongue.

glossarium (glŏsā'rĭŭm) *n.* [Gk. *glossa*, tongue.] The slender-pointed glossa of certain Diptera.

glossate (glŏs'āt) *a.* [Gk. *glossa*, tongue.] Having a tongue or tongue-like structure.

glosso-epiglottic (glŏs'ŏĕpĭglŏt'ĭk) *a.* [Gk. *glossa*, tongue ; *epi*, upon ; *glotta*, tongue.] *Pert.* tongue and epiglottis ; *appl.* folds of mucous membrane.

glossohyal (glŏs'ŏhī'ăl) *n.* [Gk. *glossa*, tongue ; *hyoeides*, Υ-shaped.] Median basihyal of fishes ; entoglossum.

glosso-kinaesthetic area,—a brain area in Broca's convolution immediately connected with speech.

glossopalatine (glŏs'ŏpăl'ătĭn) *a.* [Gk. *glossa*, tongue ; L. *palatus*, palate.] Connecting tongue and soft palate ; *appl.* arch, muscle.

glossophagine (glŏsŏf'ăjĭn) *a.* [Gk. *glossa*, tongue ; *phagein*, to eat.] Securing food by means of the tongue.

glossopharyngeal (glŏs'ŏfărĭn'jēăl) *a.* [Gk. *glossa*, tongue ; *pharynx*, gullet.] *Pert.* tongue and pharynx ; *appl.* ninth cranial nerve.

glossophorous (glŏsŏf'ŏrŭs) *a.* [Gk. *glossa*, tongue ; *pherein*, to bear.] Having a tongue or a radula.

glossopodium (glŏs'ŏpō'dĭŭm) *n.* [Gk. *glossa*, tongue ; *pous*, foot.] The sheathing leaf-base of Isoëtes.

glossotheca (glŏs'ŏthē'kă) *n.* [Gk. *glossa*, tongue ; *theke*, box.] The proboscis-covering part of pupal integument of insects.

glottis (glŏt'ĭs) *n.* [Gk. *glotta*, tongue.] The opening into the windpipe.

glucagon (glook'ăgŏn) *n.* [Gk. *glykys*, sweet ; *agon*, contest.] A pancreatic hormone which stimulates glycogenolysis in the liver, causing increase in blood-sugar ; hyperglycaemic-glycogenolytic factor.

glucase (glook'ās) *n.* [Gk. *glykys*, sweet.] A plant enzyme which produces grape sugar from maltose.

glucokinin (glook'ökī'nĭn) *n.* [Gk. *glykys*, sweet ; *kinein*, to move.] A plant substance capable of reducing blood-sugar ; 'vegetable insulin'.

glucoproteins,—*see* glycoproteins.

glucose (glook'ōs) *n.* [Gk. *glykys*, sweet.] The grape sugar of plants and animals ; dextrose, $C_6H_{12}O_6$.

gluma (gloom'ă) *n.* [L. *gluma*, husk.] A bract at base of a grass inflorescence or spikelet ; a chaffy or membranous bract ; empty glume, *opp.* flowering glume or lemma.

glumaceous (gloomā'shŭs) *a.* [L. *gluma*, husk.] Dry and scaly like glumes ; formed of glumes.

glume,—gluma, *q.v.* ; lemma, *q.v.*

glumiferous (gloomĭf'ërŭs) *a.* [L. *gluma*, husk ; *ferre*, to bear.] Bearing or producing glumes.

glumiflorous (gloom'ĭflō'rŭs) *a.* [L. *gluma*, husk ; *flos*, flower.] Having flowers with glumes or bracts at their bases.

glutaeal (glootē'ăl) *a.* [Gk. *gloutos*, buttock.] *Pert.* or in region of buttocks ; *appl.* arteries, muscles, nerves, tuberosity, veins.

glutaeus (glootē'ŭs) *n.* [Gk. *gloutos*, buttock.] A muscle of the buttock.

glutathione (gloot'ăthī'ŏn) *n.* [L. *gluten*, glue ; Gk. *theion*, sulphur.] A sulphur-containing tri-peptide found in different tissues and capable of being alternately reduced and oxidised ; $C_{10}H_{17}O_6N_3S$.

gluten (gloot'ĕn) *n.* [L. *gluten*, glue.] A nitrogenous substance obtainable from some cereals, a product of gliadin and glutenin.

glutenin (gloot'ĕnĭn) *n.* [L. *gluten*, glue.] A substance of cereals interacting with gliadin to form gluten.

glutinous (gloot'ĭnŭs) *a.* [L. *gluten*, glue.] Having a sticky or slimy surface.

glycerin (glĭs'ërĭn), **glycerol** (glĭs'ërôl) *n.* [Gk. *glykys*, sweet.] The sweet principle of natural fats and oils ; $C_3H_5(OH)_3$.

glycine (glī'sĭn) *n.* [Gk. *glykys*, sweet.] Amino acetic acid or glycocoll, obtainable from other amino acids, plays part in the formation of creatine and other compounds ; $C_2H_5O_2N$.

glycogen (glī'köjĕn) *n.* [Gk. *glykys*, sweet.] A carbohydrate storage product of plants and animals, $(C_6H_{10}O_5)x$; animal starch.

glycogenase (glī'köjënās') *n.* [Gk. *glykys*, sweet ; *-genes*, producing.] An enzyme which causes synthesis of storage glycogen in liver.

glycogenesis (glī'köjĕn'ësĭs) *n.* [Gk. *glykys*, sweet ; *genesis*, origin.] The transformation of glucose into glycogen, as in liver and muscle.

glycogenolysis (glī'köjĕnŏl'ĭsĭs) *n.* [Gk. *glykys*, sweet ; *-genes*, producing ; *lysis*, loosing.] The disintegration of glycogen and production of glucose phosphate.

glycolysis (glīkŏl'ĭsĭs) *n.* [Gk. *glykys*, sweet ; *lyein*, to loosen.] Decomposition of glucose or of glycogen, by hydrolysis.

glycophyte (glī'köfīt) *n.* [Gk. *glykys*, sweet ; *phyton*, plant.] A plant unable to thrive on substratum containing more than 0.5 per cent. sodium chloride in solution ; *opp.* halophyte.

glycoproteins (glī'köprō'tëĭnz) *n. plu.* [Gk. *glykys*, sweet ; *proteion*, first.] Compounds of protein with a carbohydrate, including mucins and mucoids ; mucoproteins.

glycosecretory (glī'kösēkrē'törĭ) *a.* [Gk. *glykys*, sweet ; L. *secretus*, set apart.] Connected with the secretion of glycogen.

glycotropic (glī'kötrŏp'ĭk) *a.* [Gk. *glykys*, sweet ; *trope*, turn.] *Appl.* factor secreted by prepituitary and which inhibits peripheral action of insulin ; glycotrophic.

gnathic (năth'ĭk) *a.* [Gk. *gnathos*, jaw.] *Pert.* the jaw ; gnathal.

gnathion (năth'ĭŏn) *n.* [Gk. *gnathos*, jaw.] Lowest point of the median line of the lower jaw.

gnathism (năth'ĭzm) *n.* [Gk. *gnathos*, jaw.] Formation of jaw with reference to degree of projection.

gnathites (năth'īts) *n. plu.* [Gk. *gnathos*, jaw.] The buccal appendages of arthropods.

gnathobase (năth'öbās) *n.* [Gk. *gnathos*, jaw; *basis*, base.] An inwardly turned masticatory process on protopodite of appendages near mouth of Crustacea; basal segment of appendages with spines directed toward mouth of Arachnoidea.

gnathochilarium (năth'ökīlā'rĭŭm) *n.* [Gk. *gnathos*, jaw; *cheilos*, lip.] First maxillae and sternal plate in Pauropoda, united in Diplopoda.

gnathopod (năth'öpŏd) *n.* [Gk. *gnathos*, jaw; *pous*, foot.] Any crustacean limb in oral region modified to assist with food.

gnathopodite (năth'ŏpödīt) *n.* [Gk. *gnathos*, jaw; *pous*, foot.] A maxilliped of an arthropod.

gnathos (nă'thŏs) *n.* [Gk. *gnathos*, jaw.] A median sclerite on ventral side of ninth tergum in Lepidoptera.

gnathosoma (năth'ösō'mă) *n.* [Gk. *gnathos*, jaw; *soma*, body.] The mouth region, including oral appendages, of Arachnoidea.

gnathostegites (năthŏs'tĕjīts) *n. plu.* [Gk. *gnathos*, jaw; *stege*, roof.] Pair of covering plates for mouth parts of some crustaceans.

gnathostomatous (năth'östŏm'ătŭs) *a.* [Gk. *gnathos*, jaw; *stoma*, mouth.] With jaws at the mouth.

gnathotheca (năth'öthē'kă) *n.* [Gk. *gnathos*, jaw; *theke*, case.] The horny outer covering of a bird's lower jaw.

gnathothorax (năth'öthō'răks) *n.* [Gk. *gnathos*, jaw; *thorax*, chest.] The part of the cephalothorax posterior to protocephalon, in Malacostraca.

gnesiogamy (nē'sĭŏg'ămĭ) *n.* [Gk. *gnesios*, lawful; *gamos*, marriage.] Fertilisation by an individual of the same species; intraspecific zygosis.

goblet cells,—mucus-secreting cells of columnar epithelia; chalice cells.

Golgi apparatus or **complex** [*C. Golgi*, Italian histologist]. Cell-constituents, localised or diffuse, often consisting of separate elements, the Golgi bodies, batonettes, dictyosomes or pseudochromosomes, containing lipoprotein, and concerned with cellular synthesis and secretion; originally apparato reticolare, canalicular system, internal reticular apparatus, the reticulum being possibly an artefact.

Golgi, organs of,—Golgi-Mazzoni corpuscles.

Golgi-Mazzoni corpuscles [*C. Golgi* and *V. Mazzoni*, Italian histologists]. Cylindrical end-organs or small Pacinian corpuscles at junction of tendon and muscle.

golgiokinesis (gŏl'jĭökīnē'sĭs) *n.* [*C. Golgi*; Gk. *kinesis*, movement.] Division of the Golgi apparatus during mitosis.

golgiosomes (gŏl'jĭösōmz) *n. plu.* [*C. Golgi*; Gk. *soma*, body.] Golgi bodies or material produced by division of the Golgi apparatus during mitosis.

gomphosis (gŏmfō'sĭs) *n.* [Gk. *gomphos*, bolt.] Articulation by insertion of a conical process into a socket, as of roots of teeth into alveoli.

gonad (gŏn'ăd) *n.* [Gk. *gone*, birth.] A sexual gland, either ovary, or testes, or ovotestis.

gonadectomy (gŏn'ădĕk'tömĭ) *n.* [Gk. *gone*, birth; *ek*, out; *tome*, cutting.] Excision of gonad, castration in the male, spaying in female.

gonadin (gŏnā'dĭn) *n.* [Gk. *gone*, birth.] Active principle of sex glands controlling secondary sexual characteristics.

gonadotrophins (gŏnădŏt'rŏfĭnz) *n. plu.* [Gk. *gone*, birth; *trephein*, to nourish.] Two prepituitary hormones: 1. Follicle-stimulating hormone or prolan A; gametogenetic or gametokinetic hormones; thylakentrin. 2. Luteinising or interstitial-cell-stimulating hormone; prolan B; metakentrin. Chorionic gonadotrophin secreted by chorionic cells of placenta and excreted in pregnancy urine, resembling but not identical with luteinising hormone. Serum gonadotrophins:

follicle-stimulating hormone in blood of pregnant mares, luteinising hormone in that of women.

gonadotropic (gŏn′ădötrŏp′ĭk) *a.* [Gk. *gone*, birth; *trope*, turn.] Affecting the gonad; *appl.* prepituitary hormones and certain hormones obtained from urine and other body fluids and tissues, particularly during pregnancy; *appl.* effects; gonadotrophic.

gonadotropin (gŏn′ădŏt′röpĭn) *n.* [Gk. *gone*, birth; *trope*, turn.] Any gonadotropic hormone or substance.

gonaduct,—gonoduct.

gonal (gŏ̄n′ăl) *n.* [Gk. *gone*, birth.] *Appl.* middle portion of genital ridge which alone forms functional gonad; gonidial, *q.v.*

gonangium (gŏnăn′jĭŭm) *n.* [Gk. *gone*, birth; *anggeion*, vessel.] Any enveloping structure in which reproductive elements are produced; a gonotheca; a dilated cup of perisarc protecting the blastostyle of Calyptoblastea.

gonapod,—gonopodium, *q.v.*

gonapophyses (gŏn′ăpŏf′ĭsēz) *n. plu.* [Gk. *gone*, birth; *apo*, from; *phyein*, to grow.] Chitinous outgrowths or valves subserving copulation in insects; the component parts of a sting.

gone (gŏn′ē) *n.* [Gk. *gone*, generation.] One of four daughter cells of an auxocyte; the generative portion of a gonad; an organism possessing a gone. *v.* To produce a gone.

gongylidia (gŏn′jĭlĭd′ĭă) *n. plu.* [Gk. *gongylos*, round; *idion*, *dim.*] Hyphal swellings or modifications in fungi cultivated by certain ants.

gongylus (gŏn′jĭlŭs) *n.* [Gk. *gongylos*, round.] A globular reproductive body, as of certain algae and lichens.

gonia (gŏ̄′nĭă) *n. plu.* [Gk. *gone*, seed.] Primitive sex cells, spermatogonia or oogonia.

goniale (gōnĭâ′lē) *n.* [Gk. *gonia*, angle.] In some vertebrates a bone of lower jaw beside articular.

gonic (gŏn′ĭk) *a.* [Gk. *gone*, generation.] *Pert.* gones; *pert.* semen.

gonid,—gonidium.

gonidangium (gŏn′ĭdăn′jĭŭm) *n.* [Gk. *dim.* of *gone*, seed; *anggeion*, vessel.] A structure producing or containing gonidia.

gonidia (gŏnĭd′ĭă) *n. plu.* [Gk. *dim.* of *gone*, seed.] Minute reproductive bodies of many bacteria; asexual non-motile reproductive cells produced upon gametophytes; algal constituents of lichens. *Sing.* gonidium.

gonidial,—*pert.* gonidia.

gonidiferous (gŏnĭdĭf′ĕrŭs) *a.* [Gk. *dim.* of *gone*, seed; L. *ferre*, to carry.] Bearing or producing gonidia.

gonidimium (gŏn′ĭdĭm′ĭŭm) *n.* [L.L. *dim.* of Gk. *gone*, seed.] A gonidial structure smaller than a gonidium and larger than a gonimium.

gonidiogenous (gŏnĭd′ĭŏj′ĕnŭs) *a.* [Gk. *dim.* of *gone*, seed; *-genes*, producing.] Bearing or producing gonidia; gonidiferous.

gonidioid (gŏnĭd′ĭoid) *a.* [Gk. *dim.* of *gone*, seed; *eidos*, form.] Like a gonidium; *appl.* certain algae.

gonidiophore (gŏnĭd′ĭöfōr) *n.* [Gk. *dim.* of *gone*, seed; *pherein*, to bear.] An aerial hypha supporting a gonidangium.

gonidiophyll (gŏnĭd′ĭöfĭl) *n.* [Gk. *dim.* of *gone*, seed; *phyllon*, leaf.] A gametophyte leaf bearing gonidia.

gonidium,—*sing.* of gonidia.

gonimic,—gonidial.

gonimium (gŏnĭm′ĭŭm) *n.* [Gk. *gonimos*, productive.] One of the bluish-green gonidia of certain lichens.

gonimoblasts (gŏn′ĭmöblăsts) *n. plu.* [Gk. *gonimos*, productive; *blastos*, bud.] Filamentous outgrowths of a fertilised carpogonium of certain algae.

gonimolobe (gŏn′ĭmölōb) *n.* [Gk. *gonimos*, productive; *lobos*, lobe.] A group of carposporangia borne on a gonimoblast.

gonion (gōnī′ŏn) *n.* [Gk. *gonia*, angle.] The angle point on the lower jaw.

gonoblast (gŏn′öblăst) *n.* [Gk. *gonos*, offspring; *blastos*, bud.] A reproductive cell in animals.

gonoblastid (gŏn'öblăs'tĭd) *n.* [Gk. *gonos*, offspring; *blastos*, bud; *idion*, *dim.*] A blastostyle of Hydrozoa; gonoblastidium.

gonocalyx (gŏn'ökā'lĭks) *n.* [Gk. *gonos*, offspring; *kalyx*, cup.] The bell of a medusiform gonophore.

gonocheme (gŏn'ökēm) *n.* [Gk. *gonos*, offspring; *ochema*, support.] A medusoid bearing sex-cells, in Hydrozoa.

gonochorism (gŏn'ökō'rĭzm) *n.* [Gk. *gonos*, offspring; *chorismos*, separation.] The history or development of sex differentiation; sex determination; dioecism.

gonochoristic (gŏn'ökōrĭs'tĭk) *a.* [Gk. *gonos*, offspring; *choristos*, separated.] Having the sexes separate; producing distinct males and females; dioecious.

gonocoel (gŏn'ösēl) *n.* [Gk. *gone*, seed; *koilos*, hollow.] The cavity containing the gonads.

gonocoxa (gŏn'ökŏk'să) *n.* [Gk. *gone*, seed; L. *coxa*, hip.] Base or coxite of a gonopod in insects.

gonocytes (gŏn'ösīts) *n. plu.* [Gk. *gone*, seed; *kytos*, hollow.] Sexual cells of sponges; mother-cells of ova and spermatozoa.

gonodendron (gŏn'ödĕn'drŏn) *n.* [Gk. *gonos*, offspring; *dendron*, tree.] A branching blastostyle in Physalia.

gonoduct (gŏn'ödŭkt) *n.* [Gk. *gonos*, birth; L. *ductus*, led.] A genital duct leading from gonad to exterior.

gonoecium (gŏnē'sĭŭm) *n.* [Gk. *gonos*, begetting; *oikia*, house.] A reproductive individual of a polyzoan colony.

gonogenesis (gŏn'öjĕn'ĕsĭs) *n.* [Gk. *gone*, seed; *genesis*, descent.] Gametogenesis.

gonomery (gŏnŏm'ĕrĭ) *n.* [Gk. *gonos*, descent; *meros*, part.] Theory that paternal and maternal chromosomes remain in separate groups throughout life; separate grouping of paternal and maternal chromosomes during cleavage stages of some organisms.

gononephrotome (gŏn'önĕf'rötōm) *n.* [Gk. *gone*, seed; *nephros*, kidney; *temnein*, to cut.] Embryonic segment containing primordia of the urinogenital system.

gononucleus (gŏn'önū'klëŭs) *n.* [Gk. *gonos*, begetting; L. *nucleus*, kernel.] The generative nucleus or micronucleus of many Protozoa.

gonophore (gŏn'öfōr) *n.* [Gk. *gone*, seed; *pherein*, to bear.] An elongation of thalamus between corolla and stamens; a reproductive zooid in a hydroid colony.

gonoplasm (gŏn'öplăzm) *n.* [Gk. *gone*, seed; *plasma*, mould.] The generative part of protoplasm.

gonopodium (gŏn'öpō'dĭŭm) *n.* [Gk. *gone*, seed; *pous*, foot.] The modified anal fin serving as copulatory organ in male poeciliid fishes; gonopod or clasper of male myriopods and insects.

gonopore (gŏn'öpōr) *n.* [Gk. *gone*, seed; *poros*, channel.] Reproductive aperture.

gonosome (gŏn'ösōm) *n.* [Gk. *gone*, seed; *soma*, body.] The reproductive zooids of a hydrozoan colony collectively.

gonosphaerium (gŏn'ösfē'rĭŭm) *n.* [Gk. *gone*, seed; *sphaira*, globe.] An oosphere.

gonospore (gŏn'öspōr) *n.* [Gk. *gonos*, offspring; *sporos*, seed.] A spore produced as consequence of a reduction division.

gonostyle (gŏn'östīl) *n.* [Gk. *gonos*, birth; *stylos*, pillar.] The blastostyle; sexual palpon or siphon of Siphonophora; gonostylus, bristle-like process on gonocoxa of insects; clasper of Diptera.

gonotheca (gŏn'öthē'kă) *n.* [Gk. *gonos*, birth; *theke*, cup.] A transparent protective expansion of the perisarc round a blastostyle or gonophore.

gonotokont,—an auxocyte, *q.v.*

gonotome (gŏn'ötōm) *n.* [Gk. *gonos*, birth; *temnein*, to cut.] An embryonic segment containing the primordium of the gonad.

gonotrema (gŏnötrē'mă) *n.* [Gk. *gonos*, offspring; *trema*, hole.] Genital aperture, as in Arachnida; gonotreme.

gonotype (gŏn'ötīp) *n.* [Gk. *gonos*, offspring; *typos*, pattern.] Immediate offspring of a type specimen.

gonozooid (gŏn'özō'oid) *n.* [Gk. *gonos*, birth; *zoon*, animal; *eidos*, form.] A gonophore or reproductive individual of a hydrozoan colony; a zooid containing a gonad.

gonydial (gŏnĭd'ĭăl) *a.* [Gk. *genys*, lower jaw.] *Pert.* a gonys.

gonys (gŏn'ĭs) *n.* [Gk. *genys*, lower jaw.] Lower part or keel of bird's bill.

Götte's larva,—larva with four ciliated lobes, of Polycladida.

Graafian follicle [*R. de Graaf*, Dutch anatomist]. A vesicular capsule in ovary and surrounding an ovum; ovisac with developing ova.

Graber's organ,—a complex larval organ, presumably sensory, in Tabanidae.

gracilis (grăs'ĭlĭs) *n.* [L. *gracilis*, slender.] A superficial muscle on medial side of the thigh; a fasciculus of medulla oblongata; nucleus of grey matter ventral to clava.

graduated (grăd'ūātĕd) *a.* [L. *gradus*, step.] Tapering; becoming longer or shorter by steps.

graft-hybrid,—an individual formed from graft and stock, and showing characteristics of both; graft chimaera.

grain (grān) *n.* [L. *granum*, grain.] The caryopsis or seed of cereals; a granular prominence on the back of a sepal.

graminifolious (grăm'ĭnĭfō'lĭŭs) *a.* [L. *gramen*, grass; *folium*, leaf.] With grass-like leaves.

graminivorous (grăm'ĭnĭv'örŭs) *a.* [L. *gramen*, grass; *vorare*, to eat.] Grass-eating.

graminology,—agrostology.

grammate (grăm'āt) *a.* [Gk. *gramme*, line.] Striped; marked with lines or slender ridges.

grana (grā'nă) *n. plu.* [L. *granum*, grain.] Minute particles consisting of a pile of thin double platelets, probably containing chlorophyll, in chloroplasts.

Grandry's corpuscle [— *Grandry*, Belgian anatomist]. An end-organ of touch, in beak and tongue of birds.

granellae (grănĕl'ē) *n. plu.* [L. *dim.* of *granum*, grain.] Oval, refractile granules consisting chiefly of barium sulphate, found in the tubes of certain Sarcodina.

granellarium (grăn'ĕlā'rĭŭm) *n.* [L. *dim.* of *granum*, grain.] The system of granellae-containing tubes of Sarcodina.

granose (grăn'ōs) *a.* [L. *granum*, grain.] In appearance like a chain of grains, like some insect antennae; moniliform.

granular (grăn'ūlăr) *a.* [L. *granum*, grain.] Consisting of grains or granules; appearing as if made up of granules.

granulation (grăn'ūlā'shŭn) *n.* [L. *granum*, grain.] A grain-like formation or eminence; *appl.* arachnoid elevations or Pacchionian glands on outer surface of dura mater.

granule (grăn'ūl) *n.* [L. *granulum*, small grain.] A small particle of matter; a small grain.

granule cells,—ovoid or spheroid cells formed of soft protoplasm containing basiphil granules.

granule glands,—the prostate glands of flatworms; skin glands of amphibians.

granules of Nissl,—*see* Nissl granules.

granulocytes (grăn'ūlösīts) *n. plu.* [L. *granulum*, small grain; Gk. *kytos*, cell.] Granular white blood corpuscles or polymorphs; myeloid cells formed in bone marrow.

granum,—*sing.* of grana.

graphiohexaster (grăf'ĭöhĕksăs'tër) *n.* [Gk. *graphis*, style; *hex*, six; *aster*, star.] A hexaster spicule with long outwardly-directed filamentous processes from four rays.

grater (grā'tër) *n.* [O.F. *grater*, to scrape.] A denticle of Eunice.

graveolent (grăv′ĕōlĕnt) *a.* [L. *graveolens*, strong-smelling.] Having a strong or offensive odour.

gravid (grăv′ĭd) *a.* [L. *gravidus*, loaded.] *Appl.* female with eggs, or pregnant uterus.

graviperception (grăv′ĭpërsĕp′shŭn) *n.* [L. *gravis*, heavy; *percipere*, to feel.] Irritability to gravity; geotropic reaction.

gravitational (grăv′ĭtā′shŏnăl) *a.* [L. *gravis*, heavy.] *Appl.* water in excess of soil requirements, which sinks under action of gravity and drains away.

gravity (grăv′ĭtĭ) *n.* [L. *gravitas*, heaviness.] The force of attraction of all bodies towards each other; the tendency of terrestrial bodies to be drawn towards the earth's centre.

gray,—grey.

green glands,—the excretory antennary glands of certain Crustacea.

gregaloid (grĕg′ăloid) *a.* [L. *grex*, flock; Gk. *eidos*, form.] *Appl.* colony of protozoa of indefinite shape, usually with gelatinous base, formed by incomplete division of individuals or partial union of adults.

gregarious (grĕgā′rĭŭs) *a.* [L. *grex*, flock.] Tending to herd together; colonial; growing in clusters.

grey matter,—tissue abundantly supplied with nerve cells, of greyish colour, internal to white matter in spinal cord, external in cerebrum.

grey nerve-fibres, — semitransparent, grey or yellowish-grey, gelatinous non-medullated nerve-fibres, comprising most of the fibres of the sympathetic system and some of the cerebro-spinal; amyelinate fibres.

groin (groin) *n.* [A.S. *grynde*, depression.] The depressed part of body between abdomen and thigh.

groove (groov) *n.* [Dut. *groef*, channel.] Any channel, furrow, or depression, as carotid, costal, optic, primitive vertebral groove.

ground tissue,—*see* conjunctive parenchyma.

growing point,—a part of plant body at which cell-division is localised, generally terminal and composed of meristematic cells.

growth factor G,—vitamin B_2 or riboflavin, *q.v.*

growth hormones, — in animals, growth-promoting pituitary secretions; in plants, auxins.

grumose (groom′ōs) *a.* [L. *grumus*, hillock.] Clotted; knotted; collected into granule masses; grumous.

grumulus (groo′mūlŭs) *n.* [*Dim.* of L. *grumus*, hillock.] Polar organ or caudal cell cluster in insect embryo.

gryochrome (grī′ŏkrōm) *a.* [Gk. *gry*, morsel; *chroma*, colour.] With Nissl granules irregularly scattered; *appl.* neurones, as in spinal ganglia.

guanase (gwân′ās) *n.* [Peruvian *huanu*, dung.] An enzyme that catalyses the transformation of guanine into xanthine.

guanidine (gwân′ĭdĭn) *n.* [Peruvian *huanu*, dung.] A substance produced by oxidation of guanin, whose metabolism is regulated by parathyroids; CH_5N_3.

guanine (gwân′ĭn) *n.* [Peruvian *huanu*, dung.] A purine base found in some plants, teleosts, mammals, etc.; $C_5H_5ON_5$.

guanophore (gwân′ŏfōr) *n.* [Peruvian *huanu*, dung; Gk. *pherein*, to bear.] A yellow pigment-bearing cell; an iridocyte.

guanylic (gwân′ĭlĭk) *a.* [Peruvian *huanu*, dung.] *Appl.* a nucleic acid, yielding guanin, found in pancreas and liver, also in certain fungi.

guard (gârd) *n.* [O.F. *guarder*, to guard.] Sheath of a phragmocone; rostrum of a belemnite.

guard cells, — cells surrounding stomata of aerial epidermis of plant tissue.

gubernacular (gū′bërnăk′ūlăr) *a.* [L. *gubernaculum*, rudder.] *Pert.* the gubernaculum.

gubernaculum (gū'bërnăk'ūlŭm) *n.* [L. *gubernaculum*, rudder.] A cord stretching from epididymis to scrotal wall ; mesocardial ligament ; tissue between gum and dental sac of permanent teeth ; strands of blastostylar ectoderm between gonophore and gonotheca in Hydromedusae ; a posterior flagellum functioning as a rudder.

Guérin's glands [*A. F. M. Guérin*, French surgeon]. Para-urethral or Skene's glands.

guest insect,—an insect living or breeding in the nest of another.

gula (gū'lă) *n.* [L. *gula*, gullet.] The upper part of throat ; median ventral sclerite of insect head.

gulamentum (gū'lămĕn'tŭm) *n.* [L. *gula*, gullet ; *mentum*, chin.] Plate formed by fusion of gula and submentum in insects.

gular (gū'lăr) *a.* [L. *gula*, gullet.] *Pert.* throat ; *appl.* median and lateral plates between rami of mandible in Crossopterygii and Polypterini. *n.* An anterior unpaired horny shield on plastron of Chelonia.

gullet (gŭl'ët) *n.* [O.F. *goulet*, from L. *gula*, gullet.] The oesophagus, a muscular canal extending from mouth cavity to stomach ; the canal between cytostome and endoplasm of Ciliata.

gum (gŭm) *n.* [L. *gummi*, gum.] An exudation of certain plants and trees ; vegetable mucilage.

gummiferous (gŭmĭf'ërŭs) *a.* [L. *gummi*, gum ; *ferre* to carry.] Gum-producing or exuding.

gummosis (gŭmō'sĭs) *n.* [L. *gummi*, gum.] Condition of plant tissue when cell-walls become gummy.

gums (gŭmz) *n. plu.* [A.S. *goma*, jaws.] Dense fibrous tissues investing jaws ; gingivae.

gustatory (gŭs'tātörĭ) *a.* [L. *gustare*, to taste.] *Pert.* sense of taste ; *appl.* cells, hairs, pores, calyculus, nerves, etc.

gut (gŭt) *n.* [A.S. *gut*, channel.] Intestine or part thereof, according to structure of animal.

gutta (gŭt'ă) *n.* [L. *gutta*, drop.] A small spot of colour on insect wing or elsewhere. [Mal. *gatah*, gum.] Latex of various trees in Malaya ; main constituent of gutta-percha and balata.

guttate (gŭt'āt) *a.* [L. *gutta*, drod.] Having drop-like markings.

guttation (gŭtā'shŭn) *n.* [L. *gutta*, drop.] Formation of drops of water on plants from moisture in air ; exudation of aqueous solutions, as through hydathodes, or by sporangiophores, or by nectaries.

guttiferous (gŭtĭf'ërŭs) *a.* [L. *gutta*, drop ; *ferre*, to carry.] Having or yielding drops ; exuding a resin or gum.

guttiform (gŭt'ĭfôrm) *a.* [L. *gutta*, drop ; *forma*, shape.] Drop-like ; in the form of a drop.

guttula (gŭt'ūlă) *n.* [L. *guttula*, small drop.] Droplet ; a small drop-like spot.

guttulate (gŭt'ūlāt) *a.* [L. *guttula*, small drop.] In the form of a small drop, as markings.

guttulose,—covered with, or containing, droplets.

gymnanthous (jĭmnăn'thŭs) *a.* [Gk. *gymnos*, uncovered ; *anthos*, flower.] With no floral envelope ; achlamydeous.

gymnetrous (jĭmnē'trŭs) *a.* [Gk. *gymnos*, naked ; *etron*, abdomen.] Without an anal fin.

gymnoarian (jĭm'nōā'rĭăn) *a.* [Gk. *gymnos*, naked ; *oarion*, small egg.] *Appl.* gonads when naked, or not enclosed in coelomic sacs. *Opp.* cystoarian.

gymnoblastic (jĭm'nöblăs'tĭk) *a.* [Gk. *gymnos*, naked ; *blastos*, bud.] Without hydrothecae and gonothecae ; *appl.* certain Coelenterata.

gymnocarpic (jĭm'nökâr'pĭk) *a.* [Gk. *gymnos*, uncovered ; *karpos*, fruit.] With naked fruit ; *appl.* lichens with uncovered apothecia, mosses with expanded hymenium ; gymnocarpous.

gymnocidium (jĭm'nösĭd'ĭŭm) *n.* [Gk. *gymnos*, uncovered ; *oikos*, house ; *idion*, *dim.*] A basal swelling of certain moss capsules.

gymnocyte (jĭm′nösīt) *n.* [Gk. *gymnos*, uncovered ; *kytos*, hollow.] A cell without a defining cell-wall, *opp.* lepocyte.

gymnocytode (jĭm′nösī′tōd) *n.* [Gk. *gymnos*, naked ; *kytos*, hollow ; *eidos*, form.] Cytode without cell-wall or nucleus.

gymnogenous (jĭmnŏj′ënŭs) *a.* [Gk. *gymnos*, naked ; *genos*, offspring.] Naked when born ; *appl.* birds.

gymnogynous (jĭmnŏj′ĭnŭs) *a.* [Gk. *gymnos*, naked ; *gyne*, female.] With exposed ovary.

gymnoplast (jĭm′nöplăst) *n.* [Gk. *gymnos*, naked ; *plastos*, formed.] Protoplasm without definite formation or cell-wall.

gymnopterous (jĭmnŏp′tërŭs) *a.* [Gk. *gymnos*, naked ; *pteron*, wing.] Having bare wings, without scales ; *appl.* insects.

gymnorhinal (jĭm′nörī′năl) *a.* [Gk. *gymnos*, naked ; *rhis*, nose.] With nostril region not covered by feathers, as in some birds.

gymnosomatous (jĭm′nösō′mătŭs) *a.* [Gk. *gymnos*, naked ; *soma*, body.] Having no shell or mantle, as certain molluscs.

gymnospermous (jĭmnöspĕr′mŭs) *a.* [Gk. *gymnos*, uncovered ; *sperma*, seed.] Having seeds not enclosed in a true ovary, as conifers.

gymnospore (jĭm′nöspōr) *n.* [Gk. *gymnos*, naked ; *sporos*, seed.] A naked germ or spore not enclosed in a protective envelope.

gymnostomatous (jĭm′nöstŏm′ătŭs) *a.* [Gk. *gymnos*, naked ; *stoma*, mouth.] Naked-mouthed ; having no peristome, *appl.* mosses ; gymnostomous.

gynaecaner (jĭn′ēkā′nër) *n.* [Gk. *gyne*, woman ; *aner*, man.] A male ant resembling a female ; a gynaecomorphic male.

gynaeceum (jĭnēsē′ŭm) *n.* [Gk. *gynaikeie*, women's part of a house.] The female organs of a flower, the pistil, consisting of one or more carpels ; gynaecium, gynecium, gynoecium.

gynaecoid (jĭnē′koid) *n.* [Gk. *gyne*, woman ; *eidos*, form.] An egg-laying worker ant.

gynaecophore (jĭnē′köfōr) *n.* [Gk. *gyne*, woman ; *pherein*, to carry.] Canal or groove of certain worms, formed by inrolling of sides, in which the female is carried ; gynaecophoric or gynaecophoral groove.

gynander (jĭnăn′dër) *n.* [Gk. *gyne*, female ; *aner*, male.] A gynandromorph.

gynandrism (jĭnăn′drĭzm) *n.* [Gk. *gyne*, woman ; *aner*, man.] Hermaphroditism.

gynandromorph (jĭnăn′drömôrf) *n.* [Gk. *gyne*, woman ; *aner*, man ; *morphe*, form.] An individual exhibiting a spatial mosaic of male and female characters ; *cf.* intersex.

gynandromorphism (jĭnăn′drömôrfĭzm). [Gk. *gyne*, woman ; *aner*, man ; *morphe*, form.] Condition of being a gynandromorph or manifesting a mosaic of male and female sexual characters, as having one side characteristically male, the other female.

gynandrophore (jĭnăn′dröfōr) *n.* [Gk. *gyne*, woman ; *aner*, man ; *pherein*, to carry.] An axial prolongation bearing a sporophyll ; a gonophore bearing both stamens and gynoecium.

gynandrosporous (jĭnăn′dröspō′rŭs) *a.* [Gk. *gyne*, woman ; *aner*, man ; *sporos*, seed.] With androspores adjoining the oogonium, as in some algae.

gynandrous (jĭnăn′drŭs) *a.* [Gk. *gyne*, woman ; *aner*, man.] Having stamens fused with pistils, as in some orchids.

gynantherous (jĭnăn′thërŭs) *a.* [Gk. *gyne*, woman ; *anthos*, flower.] Having stamens converted into pistils.

gynase (jī′nās) *n.* [Gk. *gyne*, woman.] A female-determining factor in the form of an enzyme or hormone.

gynatrium (jĭnā′trĭŭm) *n.* [Gk. *gyne*, woman ; L. *atrium*, entrance-hall.] Female genital pouch or vestibulum, of certain insects.

gyne (jĭn′ē) *n.* [Gk. *gyne*, woman.] A female ant.

gynecium,—gynoecium, *q.v.*

gynetype (jĭn′ētīp) *n.* [Gk. *gyne*, woman; *typos*, pattern.] Type specimen of the female of a species.

gynic (jĭn′ĭk) *a.* [Gk. *gyne*, woman.] Female, *opp.* andric.

gynobase (jĭn′ōbās) *n.* [Gk. *gyne*, woman; L. *basis*, base.] A gynoecium-bearing receptacle of certain plants; condition in which style appears to arise from ovary.

gynobasic style,—a style arising from base of carpel.

gynodioecious (jĭnōdīē′sĭŭs) *a.* [Gk. *gyne*, woman; *dis*, twice; *oikos*, house.] *Appl.* plants producing female or hermaphrodite flowers only.

gynoecium (jĭnē′sĭŭm) *n.* [Gk. *gyne*, woman; *oikos*, house.] The female organs of a flower; gynaeceum.

gynogenesis (jĭ′nōjĕn′ēsĭs) *n.* [Gk. *gyne*, woman; *genesis*, descent.] Development from eggs penetrated by the spermatozoon but not embodying its nucleus, as in some nematodes.

gynogonidia (jĭ′nōgŏnĭd′ĭă) *n. plu.* [Gk. *gyne*, woman; *gonidion*, small seed.] Female sexual elements formed after repeated division of parthenogonidia in Mastigophora.

gynomerogony (jĭ′nōmĕrŏg′ōnĭ) *n.* [Gk. *gyne*, female; *meros*, part; *gone*, generation.] The development of an egg fragment, obtained before fusion with male nucleus, and containing maternal chromosomes only.

gynomonoecious (jĭ′nōmŏnē′sĭŭs) *a.* [Gk. *gyne*, woman; *monos*, alone; *oikos*, house.] *Appl.* plants with pistillate and hermaphrodite flowers only.

gynophore (jĭ′nōfōr) *n.* [Gk. *gyne*, woman; *pherein*, to carry.] A stalk supporting the ovary; elongation of thalamus between stamens and pistil; female gonophore.

gynosporangium (jĭn′ōspōrăn′jĭŭm) *n.* [Gk. *gyne*, woman; *sporos*, seed; *anggeion*, vessel.] Female sporangium; megasporangium.

gynospore (jĭ′nōspōr) *n.* [Gk. *gyne*, female; *sporos*, seed.] Female spore; megaspore; embryo-sac.

gynostegium (jĭn′ōstē′jĭŭm) *n.* [Gk. *gyne*, woman; *stege*, roof.] A protective covering for a gynoecium.

gynostemium (jĭn′ōstē′mĭŭm) *n.* [Gk. *gyne*, woman; *stemon*, warp.] The column composed of united pistil and stamens in orchids.

gypsophil (jĭp′sōfĭl) *a.* [Gk. *gypsos*, chalk, gypsum; *philein*, to love.] Thriving in soils containing chalk or gypsum; gypsophilous; calcicolous, calciphil.

gypsophyte (jĭp′sōfīt) *n.* [Gk. *gypsos*, chalk, gypsum; *phyton*, plant.] A gypsophil plant; calcicole, calcipete, calciphile, calciphyte.

gyral (jī′răl) *a.* [L. *gyrus*, circle.] *Pert.* a gyrus; *pert.* circular or spiral movement.

gyration (jīrā′shŭn) *n.* [L. *gyrare*, to revolve.] Rotation, as of cells; a whorl of a spiral shell.

gyre (jīr) *n.* [Gk. *gyros*, L. *gyrus*, circle.] Circular movement; spiral coiling, as of chromatids.

gyrencephalic (jī′rĕnkĕfăl′ĭk, -sĕf-) *a.* [Gk. *gyros*, circle; *engkephalos*, brain.] Having cerebral convolutions; gyrencephalous. *Opp.* lissencephalic.

gyri,—*plu.* of gyrus.

gyrochrome (jī′rōkrōm) *a.* [Gk. *gyros*, circle; *chroma*, colour.] With Nissl granules arranged in a circle, *appl.* certain neurones.

gyroma (jĭrō′mă) *n.* [Gk. *gyros*, circle.] A discoid or knob-like apothecium of certain lichens; annulus, *q.v.*, of ferns.

gyrose (jī′rōs) *a.* [L. *gyrare*, to revolve.] With undulating lines; sinuous.

gyrus (jī′rŭs) *n.* [L. *gyrus*, circle.] A cerebral convolution; a ridge winding between two grooves.

H

habenula (hăbĕn'ūlă) *n.* [L. *habena*, strap.] A name *appl.* certain band-like structures. *a.* Habenular; *appl.* a commissure of epithalamus.

habitat (hăb'ĭtăt) *n.* [L. *habitare*, to inhabit.] The locality or external environment in which a plant or animal lives.

habitat space,—the habitable part of space or area available for establishing a population.

habituation (hăbĭt'ūā'shŭn) *n.* [L. *habituare*, to bring into a habit.] The adjustment, effected in a cell or in an organism, by which subsequent contacts of the same stimulus produce diminishing effects.

habitus (hăb'ĭtŭs) *n.* [L. *habitus*, appearance.] The general appearance or conformation characteristic of a plant or an animal; constitutional tendency.

hadal (hā'dăl) *a.* [Gk. *hades*, unseen.] *Appl.* or *pert.* abyssal deeps below 6000 metres.

hadrocentric (hăd'rösĕn'trĭk) *a.* [Gk. *hadros*, thick; *kentron*, centre.] With phloem surrounding xylem.

hadrome (hăd'rōm) *n.* [Gk. *hadros*, thick.] Conducting tissue of xylem; hadromestome.

Haeckel's law [*E. H. Haeckel*, German zoologist]. Biogenetic law; recapitulation theory, *q.v.*

haem (hēm) *n.* [Gk. *haima*, blood.] A blood substance, oxidising to haematin; $C_{34}H_{32}O_4N_4Fe$.

haemachrome (hē'măkrōm) *n.* [Gk. *haima*, blood; *chromos*, colour.] Colouring matter found in blood.

haemacyte (hē'măsīt) *n.* [Gk. *haima*, blood; *kytos*, hollow.] A blood corpuscle.

haemad (hē'măd) *adv.* [Gk. *haima*, blood; L. *ad*, to.] Situated on same side of vertebral column as heart.

haemal (hē'măl) *a.* [Gk. *haima*, blood.] *Pert.* blood or blood-vessels; situated on same side of vertebral column as heart.

haemamoeba (hē'mămē'bă) *n.* [Gk. *haima*, blood; *amoibe*, change.] Protozoon with an amoeboid trophozoitic stage parasitic in a red blood-corpuscle.

haemangioblast (hēmăn'jĭöblăst) *n.* [Gk. *haima*, blood; *anggeion*, vessel; *blastos*, bud.] A blood island, *q.v.*

haemapoietic (hē'măpoiĕt'ĭk) *a.* [Gk. *haima*, blood; *poiein*, to form.] Blood-forming; haemopoietic.

haemapophysis (hē'măpŏf'ĭsĭs) *n.* [Gk. *haima*, blood; *apo*, from; *phyein*, to grow.] One of plate-like or spine-like processes growing from the latero-ventral surfaces of a vertebral centrum.

haematal (hĕm'ătăl) *a.* [Gk. *haima*, blood.] *Pert.* blood or blood-vessels.

haematid (hĕm'ătĭd) *n.* [Gk. *haima*, blood.] Red blood-corpuscle.

haematin (hĕm'ătĭn) *n.* [Gk. *haima*, blood.] A pigment formed by decomposition of haemoglobin, containing iron and having the property of carrying oxygen; protohaem; $C_{34}H_{33}O_5N_4Fe$.

haematobic (hĕm'ătō'bĭk) *a.* [Gk. *haima*, blood; *bios*, life.] Living in blood.

haematobium (hĕm'ătō'bĭŭm) *n.* [Gk. *haima*, blood; *bios*, life.] An organism living in blood.

haematoblast (hĕm'ătöblăst) *n.* [Gk. *haima*, blood; *blastos*, bud.] A cell that will develop into a red blood-corpuscle; thrombocyte; blood platelet.

haematochrome (hĕm'ătökrōm) *n.* [Gk. *haima*, blood; *chroma*, colour.] A carotenoid red pigment of certain algae.

haematocryal (hĕm'ătökrī'ăl) *a.* [Gk. *haima*, blood; *kryos*, cold.] Cold-blooded.

haematocyanin (hĕm'ătösī'ănĭn) *n.* [Gk. *haima*, blood; *kyanos*, dark blue.] Haemocyanin, *q.v.*

haematocytozoon (hĕm'ătösī'tözō'ŏn) *n.* [Gk. *haima*, blood; *kytos*, hollow; *zoon*, animal.] An intracorpuscular blood parasite.

haematodocha (hĕm'ătŏdŏk'ă) *n.* [Gk. *haima*, blood; *doche*, receptacle.] A fibro-elastic bag at base of palpal organ in Araneae.

haematogen (hĕm'ătöjĕn) *n.* [Gk. *haima*, blood; *genos*, birth.] A nucleoprotein containing iron.

haematogenesis (hĕm'ătöjĕn'ĕsĭs) *n.* [Gk. *haima*, blood; *genesis*, descent.] The formation of blood.

haematogenous (hĕm'ătŏj'ënŭs) *a.* [Gk. *haima*, blood; *genos*, birth.] Formed in blood; derived from blood.

haematoidin (hĕm'ătoid'ĭn) *n.* [Gk. *haima*, blood; *eidos*, form.] An iron-free derivative of haemoglobin, forming crystals in blood clots, and identical with bilirubin.

haematolysis (hĕm'ătŏl'ĭsĭs) *n.* [Gk. *haima*, blood; *lysis*, loosing.] Haemolysis, *q.v.*

haematophagous (hĕm'ătŏf'ăgŭs) *a.* [Gk. *haima*, blood; *phagein*, to eat.] Feeding on blood, or obtaining nourishment from blood.

haematophyte (hĕm'ătöfīt) *n.* [Gk. *haima*, blood; *phyton*, plant.] Any vegetable micro-organism in blood.

haematopoiesis, — haematogenesis, haemopoiesis.

haematoporphyrin (hĕm'ătöpôr'fĭrĭn) *n.* [Gk. *haima*, blood; *porphyra*, purple.] An iron-free pigment formed by decomposition of haematin; $C_{34}H_{33}O_6N_4$.

haematosis (hĕm'ătō'sĭs) *n.* [Gk. *haimatoein*, to change to blood.] Blood-formation.

haematothermal (hĕm'ătöthĕr'măl) *a.* [Gk. *haima*, blood; *thermos*, warm.] Warm-blooded.

haematozoon (hĕm'ătözō'ŏn) *n.* [Gk. *haima*, blood; *zoon*, animal.] Any animal parasitic in blood.

haemerythrin (hēm'ĕrĭth'rĭn) *n.* [Gk. *haima*, blood; *erythros*, red.] A red respiratory pigment of corpuscles in body fluid of sipunculids and some annelids; haemoerythrin.

haemic (hē'mĭk) *a.* [Gk. *haima*, blood.] *Pert.* blood.

haemin (hē'mĭn) *n.* [Gk. *haima*, blood.] Haem; chloride formed in blood clot: $C_{34}H_{32}O_4N_4FeCl$.

haemoblast (hē'möblăst) *n.* [Gk. *haima*, blood; *blastos*, bud.] A cell which gives rise to an erythroblast; haematoblast.

haemochromes (hē'mökrōmz) *n.plu.* [Gk. *haima*, blood; *chroma*, colour.] Blood pigments, as haemoglobin, haemocyanin, chlorocruorin, erythrocruorin, haemoerythrin.

haemochromogen (hē'mökrō'möjĕn) *n.* [Gk. *haima*, blood; *chroma*, colour; *genos*, birth.] A chromoprotein produced by alkali and reduction of haemoglobin.

haemoclastic (hē'möklăs'tĭk) *a.* [Gk. *haima*, blood; *klastos*, broken.] Breaking down blood cells, *appl.* tissues. *Opp.* haemoplastic.

haemocoele (hē'mösēl) *n.* [Gk. *haima*, blood; *koilos*, hollow.] An expanded portion of the blood system which replaces the true coelom.

haemoconia (hē'mökŏn'ĭă) *n.* [Gk. *haima*, blood; *konis*, dust.] Minute fat droplets entering or leaving cells; chylomicrons, *q.v.*

haemocyanin (hē'mösī'ănĭn) *n.* [Gk. *haima*, blood; *kyanos*, dark blue.] A haemoglobin-like blood pigment containing copper instead of iron, in molluscs, crustaceans, and some arachnids.

haemocyte (hē'mösīt) *n.* [Gk. *haima*, blood; *kytos*, hollow.] A blood cell, as in insects.

haemocytoblast (hē'mösī'töblăst) *n.* [Gk. *haima*, blood; *kytos*, hollow; blastos, bud.] Primitive stem cell from which all blood cells are derived; a lymphoid haemoblast; lymphoidocyte.

haemocytolysis (hē-mösītŏl'ĭsĭs) *n.* [Gk. *haima*, blood; *kytos*, hollow; *lyein*, to dissolve.] Breaking up of red blood-corpuscles by solution.

haemocytotrypsis (hē'mösī'tötrĭp'sĭs) *n.* [Gk. *haima*, blood; *kytos*, hollow; *tribein*, to rub.] Breaking up of blood-corpuscles by pressure.

haemoerythrin (hē'möĕrĭth'rĭn) *n.* [Gk. *haima*, blood ; *erythros*, red.] A red respiratory pigment in certain invertebrates ; haemerythrin.

haemofuscin (hē'möfŭs'sĭn) *n.* [Gk. *haima*, blood ; L. *fuscus*, tawny.] A yellow blood pigment deposited under various pathological conditions.

haemogenesis,—haematogenesis.

haemoglobin (hē'möglō'bĭn) *n.* [Gk. *haima*, blood ; L. *globus*, sphere.] The red respiratory pigment of blood of vertebrates, consisting of haematin united to globin.

haemohistioblast (hē'möhĭs'tĭöblăst) *n.* [Gk. *haima*, blood ; *histion*, tissue ; *blastos*, bud.] A free macrophage in blood, especially of veins.

haemoid (hē'moid) *a.* [Gk. *haima*, blood ; *eidos*, form.] Resembling blood.

haemolymph (hē'mölĭmf) *n.* [Gk. *haima*, blood ; L. *lympha*, water.] A fluid found in coelom of some invertebrates, regarded as equivalent to blood and lymph of higher forms ; *appl.* nodes : modified lymph nodes containing blood.

haemolysin (hē'mŏlī'sĭn) *n.* [Gk. *haima*, blood ; *lyein*, to dissolve.] A substance developed in or added to blood serum, capable of destroying red blood-corpuscles.

haemolysis (hēmŏl'ĭsĭs) *n.* [Gk. *haima*, blood ; *lysis*, loosing.] The lysis or solution of red blood-corpuscles ; erythrocytolysis ; laking.

haemophilia (hēm'öfĭl'ĭă) *n.* [Gk. *haima*, blood ; *philos*, loving.] Absence of ready coagulation of shed blood, a sex-linked hereditary characteristic.

haemoplasmodium (hē'möplăzmō'dĭŭm, -plăs-) *n.* [Gk. *haima*, blood ; *plasma*, mould.] A unicellular parasite of blood.

haemoplastic (hē'möplăs'tĭk) *a.* [Gk. *haima*, blood ; *plastos*, formed.] Blood-forming ; haemopoietic. *Opp.* haemoclastic.

haemopoiesis (hē'möpoiēs'ĭs) *n.* [Gk. *haima*, blood ; *poiesis*, making.] The formation and development of blood cells.

haemopoietic (hē'möpoiĕt'ĭk) *a.* [Gk. *haima*, blood ; *poietikos* productive]. Blood-forming ; *pert.* haemopoiesis ; haemoplastic.

haemopsonin (hēmŏp'sönĭn) *n.* [Gk. *haima*, blood ; *opsonein*, to cater.] An opsonin for erythrocytes.

haemorrhoidal (hĕmöroid'ăl) *a.* [Gk. *haima*, blood ; *rhein*, to flow.] Rectal, *appl.* blood-vessels, nerve.

haemosiderin (hēmösĭd'ērĭn) *n.* [Gk. *haima*, blood ; *sideros*, iron.] A yellow pigment of blood giving an iron reaction.

haemostatic (hē-möstăt'ĭk) *a.* [Gk. *haima*, blood ; *statikos*, causing to stand.] *Appl.* membrane crossing joint between trochanter and femur in autotomy of limb of some arthropods.

haemotoxin (hē'mötŏk'sĭn) *n.* [Gk. *haima*, blood ; *toxikon*, poison.] A toxin which produces haemolysis.

haemotropic (hē'mötrŏp'ĭk) *a.* [Gk. *haima*, blood ; *trope*, turn.] Affecting or acting upon blood.

haemozoin (hē'mözō'ĭn) *n.* [Gk. *haima*, blood ; *zoon*, animal.] Granules of a black pigment, the residue from digestion of haemoglobin by malarial parasites.

haerangium (hērăn'jĭŭm) *n.* [L. *haerere*, to cling ; Gk. *anggeion*, vessel.] The apparatus for collecting and dispersing spores in Haerangiomycetes, an adhesive droplet containing spores being held by the tenaculum, *q.v.*

hair (hār) *n.* [A.S. *haer.*] Any epidermal filamentous outgrowth consisting of one or more cells, varied in shape ; a thread-like or filamentous outgrowth of epidermis of animals ; a setum, *q.v.*

hair cells,—sensory cells in organ of Corti.

hair follicle,—tubular sheath formed by invagination of epidermis and surrounding base of hair.

half-inferior,—having ovary but partially adherent to calyx.

half-spindle,—unipolar spindle, as in meiosis of some insects.

half-terete,—rounded on one side, flat on the other.

halibios,—halobios.

haliplankton,—haloplankton, *q.v.*

hallachrome (hăl'ăkrōm) *n.* [*Halla*, an annelid; Gk. *chroma*, colour.] A red pigment or respiratory catalyst in skin of Halla, derived from tyrosine, formed by oxidation of dopa, and oxidised to melanin; $C_9H_7O_4N$.

Haller's organ [*G. Haller*, German zoologist]. A tarsal chemoreceptor in ticks.

hallux (hăl'ŭks) *n.* [L. *hallux*, great toe.] First digit of hind-limb.

halm,—haulm.

halobios (hăl'ōbī'ŏs) *n.* [Gk. *hals*, sea; *bios*, life.] Sum total of organisms living in the sea.

halolimnic (hăl'ōlĭm'nĭk) *a.* [Gk. *hals*, sea; *limne*, marsh.] *Pert.* marine organisms modified to live in fresh water.

halophilous (hălŏf'ĭlŭs) *a.* [Gk. *hals*, salt; *philein*, to love.] Salt-loving; thriving in presence of salt; halophilic.

halophyte (hăl'ōfīt) *n.* [Gk. *hals*, salt; *phyton*, plant.] A shore plant; plant capable of thriving on salt-impregnated soils.

haloplankton (hăl'ōplăng'ktŏn) *n.* [Gk. *hals*, sea; *plangktos*, wandering.] The organisms drifting in the sea; haliplankton.

halosere (hăl'ōsēr) *n.* [Gk. *hals*, salt; L. *serere*, to put in a row.] A plant succession originating in a saline area.

haloxene (hăl'ōksēn) *a.* [Gk. *hals*, salt; *xenos*, guest.] Tolerating salt water.

halteres (hăltē'rēz) *n. plu.* [Gk. *halter*, weight.] A pair of small capitate bodies representing rudimentary posterior wings in Diptera; balancers, poisers.

hamate (hā'māt) *a.* [L. *hamatus*, hooked.] Hooked or hook-shaped at the tip; hamose; uncinate.

hamatum (hāmā'tŭm) *n.* [L. *hamatus*, hooked.] The unciform bone in the carpus, probably corresponding to fourth and fifth distalia of a typical pentadactyl limb.

hamiform (hā'mĭfôrm) *a.* [L. *hamus*, hook; *forma*, shape.] Hook-shaped; unciform.

hamirostrate (hā'mĭrŏs'trāt) *a.* [L. *hamus*, hook; *rostrum*, beak.] Having a hooked beak.

hamose,—hamate.

hamstrings,—tendons of insertion of the posterior femoral muscles, *i.e.*, of semitendinosus, semimembranosus, and biceps.

hamula (hăm'ūlă) *n.* [L. *hamulus*, little hook.] Retinaculum of insects; fused ventral appendages acting with caudal furcula in springtails or Collembola; hamulus, *q.v.*

hamular,—hooked; hook-like.

hamulate (hăm'ūlāt) *a.* [L. *hamulus*, little hook.] Having small hook-like processes.

hamulus (hăm'ūlŭs) *n.* [L. *hamulus*, little hook.] A hooklet, or hook-like process, as of lacrimal, hamate, and pterygoid bones, and of osseous spiral lamina at apex of cochlea; minute hook-like process on distal barbules which aid in interlocking of feather barbs; retinaculum of Hymenoptera.

hamus (hā'mŭs) *n.* [L. *hamus*, hook.] Hooked part of uncus in male Lepidoptera.

hapaxanthous (hăp'ăksăn'thŭs) *a.* [Gk. *hapax*, once; *anthos*, flower.] With only a single flowering period; hapaxanthic, *opp.* pollakanthic.

haplobiont (hăp'lōbī'ŏnt) *n.* [Gk. *haploos*, simple; *bion*, living.] An organism characterised by one kind of individual. *Opp.* diplobiont.

haplocaulescent (hăp'lōkôlĕs'ĕnt) *a.* [Gk. *haploos*, simple; L. *caulis*, stem.] With a simple axis, *i.e.* capable of producing seed on the main axis.

haplochlamydeous (hăp'lōklămĭd'ēŭs) *a.* [Gk. *haploos*, simple; *chlamys*, cloak.] Having rudimentary leaves in connection with sporophylls.

haplo-diploid (hăp'lödĭp'loid) *a.* [Gk. *haploos*, simple; *diploos*, double; *eidos*, form.] *Appl.* sex-differentiation in which the male is haploid, the female diploid.

haplodont (hăp'lödŏnt) *a.* [Gk. *haploos*, simple; *odous*, tooth.] Having molars with simple crowns.

haploid (hăp'loid) *a.* [Gk. *haploos*, simple; *eidos*, form.] Having the number of chromosomes characteristic of mature germ-cells for the organism in question; *appl.* the typical gametic number of chromosomes after meiosis. *n.* Organism having one genome; *cf.* diploid.

haplometrosis,—monometrosis.

haplometrotic,—monometrotic.

haplomitosis (hăp'lömītō'sĭs) *n.* [Gk. *haploos*, simple; *mitos*, thread.] Type of cell division where nuclear granules form chromospires which withdraw in two groups or divide transversely in the middle.

haplomycelium (hăp'lömīsē'lĭŭm) *n.* [Gk. *haploos*, simple; *mykes*, fungus.] Haploid mycelium.

haplont (hăp'lŏnt) *n.* [Gk. *haploos*, simple; *on*, being.] An organism having haploid somatic nuclei.

haploperistomous (hăp'löpĕrĭs'tömŭs) *a.* [Gk. *haploos*, simple; *peri*, around; *stoma*, mouth.] Having a single peristome; having a peristome with a single row of teeth, *appl.* mosses; haploperistomic.

haplopetalous (hăp'löpĕt'ălŭs) *a.* [Gk. *haploos*, simple; *petalon*, leaf.] With a single row of petals.

haplophase (hăp'löfāz) *n.* [Gk. *haploos*, simple; *phasis*, aspect.] Stage in life-history of an organism when nuclei are haploid; gametophyte phase.

haplophyte (hăp'löfīt) *n.* [Gk. *haploos*, simple; *phyton*, plant.] A haploid plant or gametophyte. *Opp.* diplophyte or sporophyte.

haploptile (hăp'lötīl, -ptīl) *n.* [Gk. *haploos*, simple; *ptilon*, feather.] Single neossoptile, without rachis, formed by precocious development of the barbs of the teleoptile.

haplosis (hăplō'sĭs) *n.* [Gk. *haploos*, simple.] Halving of the chromosome number during meiosis; reduction and disjunction.

haplostemonous (hăp'löstĕm'önŭs) *a.* [Gk. *haploos*, simple; *stemon*, warp.] Having one whorl of stamens.

haplostromatic (hăp'löstrōmăt'ĭk) *a.* [Gk. *haploos*, simple; *stroma*, bedding.] *Appl.* fungi having little or no entostroma, perithecia being formed in ectostroma. *Opp.* diplostromatic.

haplotype (hăp'lötīp) *n.* [Gk. *haploos*, simple; *typos*, pattern.] The only species in a genus originally, and thereby becoming a genotype.

haplozygous (hăplŏz'ĭgŭs) *a.* [Gk. *haploos*, simple; *zygon*, yoke.] *Appl.* genes in haploid organisms; hemizygous.

haptera (hăp'tĕră) *n. plu.* [Gk. *haptein*, to fasten.] Holdfasts, special disc-like outgrowths from the stem-like portion of certain algae, which serve as organs of attachment. *Sing.* hapteron.

haptic (hăp'tĭk) *a.* [Gk. *haptein*, to touch.] *Pert.* touch; *appl.* stimuli and reactions.

haptogen (hăp'töjĕn) *a.* [Gk. *haptein*, to fasten; *-genes*, producing.] *Appl.* a limiting membrane of solidified protein which prevents miscibility.

haptomonad (hăp'tömŏn'ăd) *n.* [Gk. *haptein*, to fasten; *monas*, unit.] An attached form of certain parasitic Flagellata; *cf.* nectomonad.

haptophores (hăp'töfōrz) *n. plu.* [Gk. *haptein*, to fasten; *pherein*, to carry.] The combining qualities of the molecule of a toxin, lysin, opsonin, precipitin, or agglutinin; *cf.* toxophores.

haptospore (hăp'töspōr) *n.* [Gk. *haptein*, to fasten; *sporos*, seed.] An adhesive spore; plasmaspore.

haptotropic (hăp'tötrŏp'ĭk) *a.* [Gk. *haptein*, to touch; *trope*, turn.] *Appl.* curvature of a plant organ due to contact stimulus; thigmotropic.

haptotropism (hăptŏt′röpĭzm) *n.* [Gk. *haptein*, to touch ; *trope*, turn.] Response to contact stimulus, as in tentacles, tendrils, stems.

haptotype (hăp′tötīp) *n.* [Gk. *haptein*, to touch ; *typos*, pattern.] An icotype collected with the holotype but possibly taken from another plant.

Harderian gland [*J. J. Harder*, Swiss anatomist]. An accessory lacrimal gland of third eyelid or nictitating membrane.

harlequin lobe,—a testicular lobe with cells differing from those of other lobes, in certain Hemiptera.

harmonic suture,—an articulation formed by apposition of edges or surfaces, as between palatine bones.

harmosis (hârmō′sĭs) *n.* [Gk. *harmosis*, fitting.] Arrangement and adaptation in response to a stimulus.

harmozone (hârmō′zōn) *n.* [Gk. *harmozo*, I arrange.] One of the hormones which influence growth and nutrition.

harpagones (hâr′păgō′nēz) *n.plu.* [L. *harpago*, hook.] Claspers or valves of certain male insects ; a pair of sclerites between harpes and claspers in mosquitoes ; harpes in Lepidoptera.

harpes (hâr′pēz) *n. plu.* [Gk. *harpe*, sickle.] Chitinous processes between the claspers of mosquitoes ; claspers or valves of Lepidoptera.

Hartig net, — network of hyphae between cortical cells of roots in ectotrophic mycorrhiza.

Hassall's concentric corpuscles [*A. H. Hassall*, English physician]. Epithelial cell nests in medulla of thymus.

hastate (hăs′tāt) *a.* [L. *hasta*, spear.] Spear-shaped, more or less triangular with the two basal lobes divergent ; *appl.* leaf-markings.

Hatschek's nephridium [*B. Hatschek*, Austrian zoologist]. A nephridium between notochord and preoral pit in Cephalochorda.

Hatschek's pit,—a mucin-secreting gland in roof of oral cavity in Cephalochorda ; preoral pit.

haulm (hôm) *n.* [A.S. *healm.*] The stem of such plants as peas ; the stem of a grass.

haustellate (hôs′tēlāt) *a.* [L. *haurire*, to drain.] Having a proboscis adapted for sucking.

haustellum (hôstĕl′ŭm) *n.* [L. *haurire*, to drain.] A proboscis adapted for sucking.

haustoria,—*plu.* of haustorium.

haustorial (hôstō′rĭăl) *a.* [L. *haurire*, to drink.] *Pert.* or resembling a haustorium.

haustorium (hôstō′rĭŭm) *n.* [L. *haurire*, to drink.] An outgrowth of stem, root, or hyphae of certain parasitic plants, which serves to draw food from the host plant ; sucker ; an outgrowth of embryo-sac which extends to nutritive tissue in certain non-parasitic plants.

haustra (hôs′tră) *n.plu.* [L. *haustrum*, drawer.] Recesses of sacculations of the colon, between plicae semilunares. *Sing.* haustrum.

Haversian canals [*C. Havers*, English anatomist]. Small canals in bone, in which lie blood-capillaries, nerve, and lymph-space.

Haversian fringes,—synovial villi.

Haversian system,—a Haversian canal, the surrounding concentric lamellae and lacunae with canaliculi.

H Cl cells,—parietal cells of stomach, which secrete hydrochloric acid.

H-disc,—lighter region in anisotropic band of myofibrillae ; Hensen's disc.

head-cap,—apical part or galea of head of spermatozoon ; perforatorium.

head-case,—the outer hard covering of insect head.

head-cell,—one of the cells on manubrium of antheridium of Chara.

head-kidney,—the pronephric portion of kidney, in vertebrates usually represented only in embryo ; a nephridium usually developed in cephalic segment of invertebrates.

heart (hârt) *n.* [A.S. *heorte.*] A hollow muscular organ with varying number of chambers which by rhythmic contraction keeps up circulation of blood ; core or central portion of a tree or fruit.

heart-wood,—the darker, harder, central wood of trees ; duramen.

heat (hēt) *n.* [A.S. *haetu.*] A kind of energy manifested in various ways ; the sensation of warmth produced by stimulation of special organs ; the period of sexual desire.

heat spot,—a special area on the skin at which nerve endings sensitive to heat are found.

hectocotylus (hĕk'tökŏt'ĭlŭs) *n.* [Gk. *hekaton*, hundred ; *kotylos*, cup.] One of the arms of a male cephalopod, specialised to effect transference of sperms.

hedonic (hēdŏn'ĭk) *a.* [Gk. *hedone*, pleasure.] *Appl.* skin glands of certain reptiles, which secrete musk and are specially active at rutting season.

heel (hēl) *n.* [A.S. *hela.*] Hinder or posterior tarsal portion of foot ; talon or talonid of a tooth ; a spinule at base of tibia in Hymenoptera.

Heidenhain, demilunes of,—*see* demilunes.

hekistotherm (hē'kĭstöthĕrm) *n.* [Gk. *hekistos*, least ; *therme*, heat.] A plant that thrives with the minimum of heat, as alpine plants.

Heister's valve [*L. Heister*, German anatomist]. Spiral valve in neck of gall-bladder.

helcotropism (hĕlkŏt'röpĭzm) *n.* [Gk. *helkein*, to draw down ; *trepein*, to turn.] Tendency to respond to stimulus of gravity ; geotropism.

helices,—*plu.* of helix.

helicine (hĕl'ĭsĭn) *a.* [Gk. *helix*, spiral.] Spiral ; convoluted ; *appl.* certain convoluted and dilated arteries in penis ; *pert.* outer rim of pinna.

helicoid (hĕl'ĭkoid) *a.* [Gk. *helix*, spiral ; *eidos*, like.] Spiral ; shaped like a snail's shell ; *pert.* type of sympodial branching in which sympodium consists of fork branches of same side.

helicoid cyme,—an inflorescence produced by suppression of successive axes on same side, thus causing the sympodium to be spirally twisted ; bostryx.

helicorubin (hĕl'ĭköroob'ĭn) *n.* [L. *helix*, spiral ; *ruber*, red.] A red pigment of gut of pulmonate gastropods.

helicospore (hĕl'ĭköspōr) *n.* [Gk. *helix*, spiral ; *sporos*, seed.] A convolute or spiral spore.

helicotrema (hĕl'ĭkötrē'mă) *n.* [Gk. *helix*, spiral ; *trema*, hole.] A small opening near summit of cochlea by which the scalae vestibuli and tympani communicate.

heliophil (hē'lĭöfĭl) *a.* [Gk. *helios*, sun ; *philein*, to love.] Adapted for relatively high intensity of light ; heliophilic, heliophilous. *Opp.* heliophobic, skiophil.

heliophobic,—skiophil, *q.v.*

heliophyll (hē'lĭöfĭl) *n.* [Gk. *helios*, sun ; *phyllon*, leaf.] A plant having isolateral leaves. *Opp.* skiophyll.

heliophyte (hē'lĭöfīt) *n.* [Gk. *helios*, sun ; *phyton*, plant.] A sun plant, *opp.* shade plant or skiaphyte.

heliosis (hē'lĭō'sĭs) *n.* [Gk. *helios*, sun.] Production of discoloured spots or markings on leaves through concentration of sun on them ; solarisation.

heliotaxis (hē'lĭötăk'sĭs) *n.* [Gk. *helios*, sun ; *taxis*, arrangement.] Locomotor or other response to stimulus of sunlight.

heliotropism (hē'lĭŏt'röpĭzm) *n.* [Gk. *helios*, sun ; *trepein*, to turn.] Curvature of organisms or certain parts in response to the stimulus of sunlight.

helix (hē'lĭks) *n.* [Gk. *helix*, spiral.] A spiral ; the coiled spiral arrangement of certain structures in invertebrates ; the outer rim of external ear.

helmet (hĕl′mĕt) *n.* [A.S. *helm*; *helan*, to cover.] The process of bill of hornbills; the bony plates covering head of certain extinct fishes; the galea of flowers and of insects.

helminthoid (hĕlmĭn′thoid) *a.* [Gk. *helmins*, worm; *eidos*, shape.] Shaped like a worm; vermiform.

helminthology (hĕl′mĭnthŏl′ŏjĭ) *n.* [Gk. *helmins*, worm; *logos*, discourse.] The study of the natural history of worms; the study of parasitic flatworms and roundworms.

helophyte (hĕl′ŏfīt) *n.* [Gk. *helos*, marsh; *phyton*, plant.] A marsh plant; a cryptophyte growing in soil saturated with water.

helotism (hĕl′ŏtĭzm) *n.* [Gk. *heilotes*, serf, from *Helos*, Laconian town.] Symbiosis in which the one organism enslaves the other and forces it to labour in its behalf, *e.g.* in lichens, in some species of ants.

hema-,—*see* haema-.

heme,—haem.

hemelytron (hĕmĕl′ĭtrŏn) *n.* [Gk. *hemi*, half; *elytron*, sheath.] Proximally hardened forewing of certain insects; elytron of certain worms; hemelytrum.

hemera (hēmĕr′ă) *n.* [Gk. *hemera*, day.] The time during which fossiliferous strata constituting a zone of sedimentary rocks were deposited.

hemeranthous (hēmĕrăn′thŭs) *a.* [Gk. *hemera*, day; *anthos*, flower.] Flowering by day; hemeranthic.

hemerophyte (hē′mĕrŏfīt) *n.* [Gk. *hemeros*, tame; *phyton*, plant.] A cultivated plant.

hemerythrin,—haemerythrin.

hemibasidium (hĕm′ĭbăsĭd′ĭŭm) *n.* [Gk. *hemi*, half; *basis*, base; *idion*, *dim.*] The promycelium of the Ustilaginales.

hemibathybial (hĕm′ĭbăthĭb′ĭăl) *a.* [Gk. *hemi*, half; *bathys*, deep; *bios*, life.] *Pert.* plankton between littoral and bathybial zones.

hemibranch (hĕm′ĭbrăngk) *n.* [Gk. *hemi*, half; *brangchia*, gills.] Gill with gill filaments on one side only; half-gill.

hemicellulase (hĕm′ĭsĕl′ūlās) *n.* [Gk. *hemi*, half; L. *cellula*, small cell.] An enzyme which effects hydrolysis of a hemicellulose, occurring in endosperm, fungi, and certain invertebrates.

hemicellulose (hĕm′ĭsĕl′ūlōs) *n.* [Gk. *hemi*, half; L. *cellula*, small cell.] One of several polysaccharides, chemically unrelated to cellulose, occurring as cell wall constituents in cotyledons, endosperms, and woody tissues, and serving as reserve food.

hemicephalous (hĕm′ĭkĕf′ălŭs, -sĕf-), *a.* [Gk. *hemi*, half; *kephale*, head.] *Appl.* insect larvae with reduced head.

hemichlamydeous (hĕm′ĭklămĭd′ëŭs) *a.* [Gk. *hemi*, half; *chlamys*, cloak.] Having ovuliferous scale inverted and bearing nucellus.

hemichordate (hĕm′ĭkôr′dāt) *a.* [Gk. *hemi*, half; *chorde*, string.] Possessing a rudimentary notochord.

hemicryptophyte (hĕm′ĭkrĭp′tŏfīt) *n.* [Gk. *hemi*, half; *kryptos*, hidden; *phyton*, plant.] A plant with dormant buds in the soil surface, the aerial shoots surviving for a season only.

hemicyclic (hĕm′ĭsĭ′klĭk) *a.* [Gk. *hemi*, half; *kyklos*, round.] With some floral whorls cyclic, others spiral.

hemielytron,—hemelytron, *q.v.*

hemiepiphyte (hĕm′ĭĕp′ĭfīt) *n.* [Gk. *hemi*, half; *epi*, upon; *phyton*, plant.] A plant whose seeds germinate on another plant, but later send roots to the ground.

hemigamy (hĕmĭg′ămĭ) *n.* [Gk. *hemi-*, half; *gamos*, marriage.] Activation of ovum by male nucleus without nuclear fusion; semigamy.

hemignathous (hĕmĭg′năthŭs) *a.* [Gk. *hemi*, half; *gnathos*, jaw.] Having one jaw shorter than the other, as in some fishes and birds.

hemikaryon (hĕm′ĭkăr′ĭŏn) *n.* [Gk. *hemi*, half; *karyon*, kernel.] A nucleus with gametic or haploid number of chromosomes; a pronucleus.

hemikaryotic (hĕm′ĭkărĭŏt′ĭk) *a.* [Gk. *hemi*, half; *karyon*, kernel.] *Pert.* hemikaryon; haploid.

hemimetabolic (hĕm′ĭmĕtăbŏl′ĭk) *a.* [Gk. *hemi*, half; *metabole*, change.] Having an incomplete or partial metamorphosis, as certain insects.

hemiparasite (hĕm′ĭpăr′ăsīt) *n.* [Gk. *hemi*, half; *parasitos*, parasite.] A partial or facultative parasite.

hemiparasitic (hĕm′ĭpăr′ăsĭt′ĭk) *a.* [Gk. *hemi*, half; *para*, beside; *sitos*, food.] *Pert.* a plant which is capable of carrying on photosynthesis, but not sufficiently to supply all food material.

hemipenis (hĕm′ĭpē′nĭs) *n.* [Gk. *hemi*, half; L. *penis*, penis.] One of the paired copulatory organs in lizards and snakes.

hemipneustic (hĕm′ĭnū′stĭk, -pnū-) *a.* [Gk. *hemi*, half; *pnein*, to breathe.] With one or more pairs of spiracles closed.

hemipterygoid (hĕm′ĭptĕr′ĭgoid) *n.* [Gk. *hemi*, half; *pteryx*, wing; *eidos*, form.] In neognath birds, part of pterygoid which fuses with palatine.

hemisaprophyte (hĕm′ĭsăp′röfīt) *n.* [Gk. *hemi*, half; *sapros*, decayed; *phyton*, plant.] A plant living partly by photosynthesis, partly by obtaining food from humus.

hemisome (hĕm′ĭsōm) *n.* [Gk. *hemi*, half; *soma*, body.] The symmetrical half of an animal about a median vertical plane.

hemisphere (hĕm′ĭsfēr) *n.* [Gk. *hemi*, half; *sphaira*, globe.] One of the cerebral or cerebellar hemispheres.

hemispore (hĕm′ĭspōr) *n.* [Gk. *hemi*, half; *sporos*, seed.] A protoconidium, *q.v.*, of dermatophytes.

hemisystole (hĕm′ĭsĭs′tölē) *n.* [Gk. *hemi*, half; *systellein*, to contract.] Contraction of one ventricle of the heart.

hemitropous (hĕmĭt′röpŭs) *a.* [Gk. *hemi*, half; *trope*, turn.] Turned half round, having an ovule with hilum on one side and micropyle, etc., opposite in a plane parallel to placenta.

hemixis (hĕmĭk′sĭs) *n.* [Gk. *hemi*, half; *mixis*, mingling.] Fragmentation and reorganisation of macronucleus without involving micronucleus, in Paramecium.

hemizygous (hĕmĭz′ĭgŭs) *a.* [Gk. *hemi*, half; *zygon*, yoke.] *Appl.* genes in haploid organisms; *appl.* genes without alleles in normal diploid organisms; haplozygous.

hemo-,—*see* haemo-.

Henle's layer [*F. G. J. Henle*, German anatomist]. Outermost stratum of nucleated cubical cells in inner root-sheath of a hair-follicle.

Henle's loop,—loop of a kidney tubule within apical portion of pyramid.

Henle's sheath,—perineurium, or its prolongation surrounding branches of a nerve.

Hensen's cells [*V. Hensen*, German histologist]. Columnar supporting cells on basilar membrane, external to outer phalangeal cells in organ of Corti.

Hensen's line,—a disc dividing the darker portion of a sarcomere into two parts; mesophragma, Q line.

Hensen's node,—the primitive node, *q.v.*

Hensen's stripe,—a band of interlacing fibrils on under surface of tectorial membrane of Corti's organ.

hepar (hē′pâr) *n.* [Gk. *hepar*, liver.] Liver, or an organ having a similar function.

heparin (hē′părĭn) *n.* [Gk. *hepar*, liver.] Substance present in liver and some other tissues, which inhibits formation, or action, of thrombin.

hepatic (hĕpăt′ĭk) *a.* [Gk. *hepar*, liver.] *Pert.*, like, or associated with the liver; *pert.* liverworts.

hepaticology (hĕp′ătĭkŏl′öjĭ) *n.* [Gk. *hepar*, liver; *logos*, discourse.] The study of Hepaticae or liverworts.

hepatobiliary (hĕp′ătöbĭlĭărĭ) *a.* [Gk. *hepar*, liver; L. *bilis*, bile.] *Appl.* a fibrous capsule enclosing hepatic vessels and bile duct, Glisson's capsule.

hepatocolic (hĕp′ătökŏl′ĭk) *a.* [Gk. *hepar*, liver; *colon*, large intestine.] *Pert.* liver and colon.

hepatocystic (hĕp′ătösĭs′tĭk) *a.* [Gk. *hepar*, liver; *kystis*, bladder.] *Pert.* liver and gall-bladder.

hepatoduodenal (hĕp′ătödū′ödē′năl) *a.* [Gk. *hepar*, liver; L. *duodeni*, twelve each.] *Pert.* liver and duodenum.

hepatoenteric (hĕp′ătöĕntĕr′ĭk) *a.* [Gk. *hepar*, liver; *enteron*, gut.] Of or *pert.* liver and intestine.

hepatogastric (hĕp′ătögăs′trĭk) *a.* [Gk. *hepar*, liver; *gaster*, stomach.] *Pert.* liver and stomach.

hepatopancreas,—digestive gland in many invertebrates, supposed to perform a function similar to that of liver and of pancreas in higher forms.

hepatoportal (hĕp′ătöpôr′tăl) *a.* [Gk. *hepar*, liver; L. *porta*, gate.] *Pert.* or designating portal circulation of liver.

hepatorenal (hĕp′ătörē′năl) *a.* [Gk. *hepar*, liver; L. *renes*, kidneys.] *Pert.* liver and kidney.

hepatoumbilical (hĕp′ătöŭmbĭl′ĭkăl) *a.* [Gk. *hepar*, liver; L. *umbilicus*, navel.] Joining liver and umbilicus.

heptagynous (hĕptăj′ĭnŭs) *a.* [Gk. *hepta*, seven; *gyne*, female.] With seven pistils.

heptamerous (hĕptăm′ërŭs) *a.* [Gk. *hepta*, seven; *meros*, part.] Having whorls of flowers in sevens.

heptandrous (hĕptăn′drŭs) *a.* [Gk. *hepta*, seven; *aner*, man.] Having seven stamens.

heptarch (hĕp′târk) *a.* [Gk. *hepta*, seven; *arche*, beginning.] Having seven initial groups of xylem.

heptastichous (hĕptăs′tĭkŭs) *a.* [Gk. *hepta*, seven; *stichos*, row.] Arranged in seven rows; *appl.* leaves.

herb (hĕrb) *n.* [L. *herba*, green crop.] A seed plant without woody stem.

herbaceous (hĕrbā′shŭs) *a.* [L. *herbaceus*, grassy.] *Pert.* or being a herb, or similarly formed.

herbivorous (hërbĭv′örŭs) *a.* [L. *herba*, green crop; *vorare*, to devour.] Eating or subsisting on herbs.

Herbst's corpuscle [*E. F. Herbst*, German anatomist]. A simple type of Pacinian corpuscle, in birds.

hercogamy (hērkŏg′ămĭ) *n.* [Gk. *herkos*, barrier; *gamos*, union.] The condition in which self-fertilisation is impossible; also herkogamy.

hereditary (hērĕd′ĭtărĭ) *a.* [L. *hereditas*, heirship.] Transmissible from parent to offspring, as characteristics, physical or mental.

heredity (hērĕd′ĭtĭ) *n.* [L. *hereditas*, heirship.] The organic relation between successive generations; germinal constitution.

heritability (hĕr′ĭtăbĭl′ĭtĭ) *n.* [L.L. *hereditabilis*, that may be inherited.] Capacity for being transmitted from one generation to another; hereditary or genotypic variance expressed as percentage of total variance in the feature examined.

herkogamy,—hercogamy.

hermaphrodite (hĕrmăf′rödīt) *n.* [Gk. *hermaphroditos*, combining both sexes.] An organism with both male and female reproductive organs. *a.* Hermaphroditic.

hermaphroditism (hĕrmăf′rŏdĭtĭzm) *n.* [Gk. *hermaphroditos*, combining both sexes.] The condition of having both male and female reproductive organs in one individual.

hermetism (hĕrmē′tĭzm) *n.* [Gk. *Hermes*.] The angiocarpic condition of fungi; angiocarpy.

herpetology (hĕr′pĕtŏl′öjĭ) *n.* [Gk. *herpeton*, reptile; *logos*, discourse.] That part of zoology dealing with the structure, habits and classification of reptiles.

hesperidin (hĕspĕr′ĭdĭn) *n.* [Gk. *Hesperides*.] Vitamin P, a bioflavonoid, active principle of citrin, affecting permeability of capillaries.

hesperidium (hĕs′pērĭd′ĭŭm) *n.* [Gk. *Hesperides*, sisters guarding the golden apples given by Gaia.] A superior, many-celled, few-seeded indehiscent fruit, having epicarp and mesocarp joined together, and endocarp projecting into interior as membranous partitions which divide the pulp into chambers; *e.g.* orange.

hesthogenous (hĕsthŏj′ĕnŭs) *n.* [Gk. *hesthes*, clothes; *-genes*, born.] Covered with down at hatching; dasypaedic.

heteracanthous (hĕt′ĕrăkăn′thŭs) *a.* [Gk. *heteros*, other; *akantha*, spine.] Having the spines in dorsal fin asymmetrical.

heteractinal (hĕt′ĕrăk′tĭnăl) *a.* [Gk. *heteros*, other; *aktis*, ray.] *Pert.* nail-like spicules having disc of six to eight rays in one plane, and a stout ray at right angles to these.

heterandrous (hĕt′ĕrăn′drŭs) *a.* [Gk. *heteros*, other; *aner*, man.] With stamens of different length or shape.

heterauxesis (hĕt′ĕrôksē′sĭs) *n.* [Gk. *heteros*, other; *auxesis*, growth.] Irregular or asymmetrical growth of organs; relative growth rate of parts of an organism; heterogonic or allometric growth; bradyauxesis and tachyauxesis, *q.v.*

heterauxin,—heteroauxin, *q.v.*

heteraxial (hĕt′ĕrăk′sĭăl) *a.* [Gk. *heteros*, other; *axis*, axis.] With three unequal axes.

heterecious,—heteroecious.

heteroagglutinin (hĕt′ĕröăgloot′ĭnĭn) *n.* [Gk. *heteros*, other; L. *agglutinare*, to glue to.] Fertilisin or agglutinin of eggs which reacts on sperm of different species; *cf.* isoagglutinin.

heteroauxin (hĕt′ĕröôk′sĭn) *n.* [Gk. *heteros*, other; *auxein*, to grow.] A growth-promoting hormone, extracted from fungi; heterauxin; β-indolyl-acetic acid, $C_{10}H_9O_2N$.

heterobasidium (hĕt′ĕröbăsĭd′ĭŭm) *n.* [Gk. *heteros*, other; *basis*, base; *idion*, *dim.*] A septate basidium composed of a hypobasidium and epibasidium. *Opp.* homobasidium.

heteroblastic (hĕt′ĕröblăs′tĭk) *a.* [Gk. *heteros*, other; *blastos*, bud.] With indirect development.

heterobrachial (hĕt′ĕröbrā′kĭăl) *a.* [Gk. *heteros*, other; L. *brachium*, arm.] *Pert.* chromosome arms on either side of centromere; pericentric.

heterocarpous (hĕt′ĕrökâr′pŭs) *a.* [Gk. *heteros*, other; *karpos*, fruit.] Bearing two distinct types of fruit.

heterocaryo-,—*see* heterokaryo-.

heterocellular (hĕt′ĕrösĕl′ūlăr) *a.* [Gk. *heteros*, other; L. *cellula*, small cell.] Composed of cells of more than one type. *Opp.* homocellular.

heterocephalous (hĕt′ĕrökĕf′ălŭs, -sĕf-) *a.* [Gk. *heteros*, other; *kephale*, head.] Having pistillate flowers on separate heads from staminate.

heterocercal (hĕt′ĕrösĕr′kăl) *a.* [Gk. *heteros*, other; *kerkos*, tail.] Having vertebral column terminating in upper lobe of caudal fin, which is usually larger than lower.

heterocercy (hĕt′ĕrösĕr′sĭ) *n.* [Gk. *heteros*, other; *kerkos*, tail.] Condition of having a heterocercal tail.

heterochlamydeous (hĕt′ĕröklămĭd′-ëŭs) *a.* [Gk. *heteros*, other; *chlamys*, cloak.] Having a calyx differing from corolla in colour, texture, etc.

heterochromatic (hĕt′ĕrökrōmăt′ĭk) *a.* [Gk. *heteros*, other; *chroma*, colour.] *Pert.* heterochromatin; *appl.* chromosomal regions liable to become heteropycnotic. *Opp.* euchromatic.

heterochromatin (hĕt′ĕrökrō′mătĭn) *n.* [Gk. *heteros*, other; *chroma*, colour]. Chromatin retaining a high nucleic acid content and regulating nucleic acid metabolism in nucleus and cytoplasm.

heterochromatism (hĕt′ĕrökrō′măt-ĭzm) *n.* [Gk. *heteros*, other; *chroma*, colour.] Change of colour, as seasonal colour change in an inflorescence.

heterochromaty,—differential staining.

heterochromia (hĕt'ërökrō'myă) *n.* [Gk. *heteros*, other; *chroma*, colour.] Difference in colour of parts normally of one colour, as of irides of a pair of eyes.

heterochromosome (hĕt'ërökrō'mösōm) *n.* [Gk. *heteros*, other; *chroma*, colour; *soma*, body.] A chromosome other than an ordinary or typical one; sex-chromosome; allosome. *Opp.* autosome, euchromosome.

heterochromous (hĕt'ërökrō'mŭs) *a.* [Gk. *heteros*, other; *chroma*, colour.] Differently coloured; *appl.* disc and marginal florets. *Opp.* homochromous.

heterochronism (hĕt'ërŏk'rönĭzm) *n.* [Gk. *heteros*, other; *chronos*, time.] Departure from typical sequence in time of formation of organs; heterochrony.

heterochrosis (hĕt'ërökrō'sĭs) *n.* [Gk. *heteros*, other; *chrosis*, colouring.] Abnormal coloration.

heteroclinous (hĕt'ëröklī'nŭs) *a.* [Gk. *heteros*, other; *kline*, bed.] Heterocephalous, *q.v.*

heterocoelous (hĕt'ërösē'lŭs) *a.* [Gk. *heteros*, other; *koilos*, hollow.] *Pert.* vertebrae with saddle-shaped articulatory centra; concavoconvex.

heterocont,—heterokont.

heterocysts (hĕt'ërösĭsts) *n.plu.* [Gk. *heteros*, other; *kystis*, bladder.] Clear cells occurring at intervals on filaments of certain algae, marking limits of hormogonia.

heterodactylous (hĕt'ërödăk'tĭlŭs) *a.* [Gk. *heteros*, other; *daktylos*, digit.] With the first and second toes turned backwards.

heterodont (hĕt'ërödŏnt) *a.* [Gk. *heteros*, other; *odous*, tooth.] Having the teeth differentiated for various purposes. *Opp.* homodont.

heterodromous (hĕt'ërŏd'römŭs) *a.* [Gk. *heteros*, other; *dramein*, to run.] Having genetic spiral of stem leaves turning in different direction to that of branch leaves.

heteroecious (hĕt'ërē'sĭŭs) *a.* [Gk. *heteros*, other; *oikos*, house.] Passing different stages of life history in different hosts; exhibiting heteroecism; metoecious, metoxenous.

heterogamete (hĕt'ërögămēt') *n.* [Gk. *heteros*, other; *gametes*, spouse.] One of dissimilar conjugating gametes; an anisogamete.

heterogametic (hĕt'ërögămĕt'ĭk) *a.* [Gk. *heteros*, other; *gametes*, spouse.] Elaborating two kinds of gametes in equal numbers; having unequal pair of sex chromosomes, XY or WZ; *appl.* sex that is heterozygous; reproducing sexually; digametic; *cf.* homogametic.

heterogamous (hĕt'ërŏg'ămŭs) *a.* [Gk. *heteros*, other; *gamos*, marriage.] With unlike gametes; having two types of flowers; having indirect pollination methods.

heterogamy (hĕt'ërŏg'ămĭ) *n.* [Gk. *heteros*, other; *gamos*, offspring.] Alternation of two sexual generations, one being true sexual, the other parthenogenetic; condition of having, or union of, gametes of different size and structure; anisogamy.

heterogangliate (hĕt'ërögăng'glĭāt) *a.* [Gk. *heteros*, other; *gangglion*, ganglion.] With widely separated and asymmetrically placed nerve-ganglia.

heterogenesis (hĕt'ëröjĕn'ësĭs) *n.* [Gk. *heteros*, other; *genesis*, descent.] Spontaneous generation; alternation of generations.

heterogenetic (hĕt'ëröjënĕt'ĭk) *a.* [Gk. *heteros*, other; *genesis*, descent.] Descended from different ancestral stock; *pert.* heterogenesis.

heterogenous (hĕt'ërŏj'ënŭs) *a.* [Gk. *heteros*, other; *genes*, produced.] Having a different origin; not originating in the body; *pert.* heterogeny.

heterogeny (hĕt'ërŏj'ënĭ) *n.* [Gk. *heteros*, other; *genos*, generation.] Having several distinct generations succeeding one another in a regular series.

heterogonic (hĕt'ërögŏn'ĭk) *a.* [Gk. *heteros*, other; *gonos*, produce.] Differing in developmental or growth rate; allometric.

heterogonous (hĕt′ĕrŏg′ŏnŭs) *a.* [Gk. *heteros*, other; *gonos*, birth.] *Pert.* heterogenesis, or heterogony.

heterogony (hĕt′ĕrŏg′ŏnĭ) *n.* [Gk. *heteros*, other; *gonos*, birth.] Condition of having two, or three, kinds of flowers differing in length of stamen; alternation of generations; allometry, *q.v.*

heterogynous (hĕt′ĕrŏj′ĭnŭs) *a.* [Gk. *heteros*, other; *gyne*, woman.] With two types of females.

heteroicous,—heteroecious.

heterokaryon (hĕt′ĕrōkăr′ĭŏn) *n.* [Gk. *heteros*, other; *karyon*, nucleus.] An individual having heterokaryotic cells; a cell formed by fusion of hyphal cells, the haploid nuclei remaining separate.

heterokaryosis (hĕt′ĕrōkărĭō′sĭs) *n.* [Gk. *heteros*, other; *karyon*, nucleus.] Presence of genetically dissimilar nuclei within individual cells; heterokaryotic condition.

heterokaryote (hĕt′ĕrōkăr′ĭōt) *a.* [Gk. *heteros*, other; *karyon*, nucleus.] Having two distinct types of nuclei.

heterokaryotic (hĕt′ĕrōkărĭŏt′ĭk) *a.* [Gk. *heteros*, other; *karyon*, nucleus.] Having genetically dissimilar nuclei, in a multinucleate cell, or in different cells of a hypha; heterokaryote.

heterokinesis (hĕt′ĕrōkĭnē′sĭs) *n.* [Gk. *heteros*, other; *kinein*, to move.] Qualitative or differential division of chromosomes.

heterokont (hĕt′ĕrōkŏnt) *a.* [Gk. *heteros*, other; *kontos*, punting-pole.] Having flagella or cilia of unequal length. *Opp.* isokont.

heterolecithal (hĕt′ĕrōlĕs′ĭthăl) *a.* [Gk. *heteros*, other; *lekithos*, yolk.] Having unequally distributed deutoplasm.

heterologous (hĕt′ĕrŏl′ŏgŭs) *a.* [Gk. *heteros*, other; *logos*, relation.] Of different origin; derived from a different species; differing morphologically, *appl.* alternating generations; *appl.* various substances, *e.g.* agglutinins, affecting other than species of origin; *cf.* homologous.

heterology (hĕt′ĕrŏl′ŏjĭ) *n.* [Gk. *heteros*, other; *logos*, relation.] Non-correspondence of parts owing to different origin or different elements.

heterolysis (hĕt′ĕrŏl′ĭsĭs) *n.* [Gk. *heteros*, other; *lysis*, loosing.] Cell or tissue disintegration by action of exogenous agents or enzymes. *Opp.* autolysis.

heterolytic (hĕt′ĕrōlĭt′ĭk) *a.* [Gk. *heteros*, other; *lyein*, to dissolve.] Causing or *pert.* heterolysis. *Opp.* autolytic.

heteromallous (hĕt′ĕrŏmăl′ŭs) *a.* [Gk. *heteros*, other; *mallos*, lock of wool.] Spreading in different directions.

heteromastigote (hĕt′ĕrōmăstī′gōt) *a.* [Gk. *heteros*, other; *mastix*, lash.] Having two different types of flagella; heteromastigate.

heteromerous (hĕt′ĕrŏm′ĕrŭs) *a.* [Gk. *heteros*, other; *meros*, part.] Having, or consisting of, an unequal number of parts, *appl.* whorls, tarsi, etc.; having a stratified thallus.

heterometabolic (hĕt′ĕrōmĕtăbŏl′ĭk) *a.* [Gk. *heteros*, other; *metabole*, change.] Having incomplete metamorphosis.

heteromorphic (hĕt′ĕrōmôr′fĭk) *a.* [Gk. *heteros*, other; *morphe*, shape.] Having different forms at different times; *appl.* chromosomes of different size and shape, or chromosome pairs differing in size; *appl.* alternation of diploid and haploid phases in morphologically dissimilar generations, antithetic; heteromorphous, *q.v.*

heteromorphism (hĕt′ĕrōmôr′fĭzm) *n.* [Gk. *heteros*, other; *morphe*, shape.] The state or quality of being heteromorphic.

heteromorphosis (hĕt′ĕrōmôr′fōsĭs) *n.* [Gk. *heteros*, other; *morphosis*, shaping.] Production of a part in an abnormal position; regeneration, when the new part is different from that removed; *cf.* homoeosis.

heteromorphous (hĕt′ĕrōmôr′fŭs) *a.* [Gk. *heteros*, other; *morphe*, shape.] *Pert.* an irregular structure, or departure from the normal.

heteronereis (hĕt′ërōnē′rēĭs) *n.* [Gk. *heteros*, other; *Nereis*, Nereid.] A free-swimming dimorphic sexual stage of Nereis and other marine worms.

heteronomous (hĕt′ërŏn′ōmŭs) *a.* [Gk. *heteros*, other; *nómos*, law.] Subject to different laws of growth; specialised on different lines. [Gk. *heteros*, other; *nomós*, department.] *Appl.* segmentation into dissimilar segments.

heteropelmous (hĕt′ërōpĕl′mŭs) *a.* [Gk. *heteros*, other; *pelma*, sole of foot.] Having flexor tendons of toes bifid.

heteropetalous (hĕt′ërōpĕt′ălŭs) *a.* [Gk. *heteros*, other; *petalon*, leaf.] With dissimilar petals.

heterophagous (hĕt′ërŏf′ăgŭs) *a.* [Gk. *heteros*, other; *phagein*, to eat.] Having young in altrices condition.

heterophil (hĕt′ërōfĭl) *a.* [Gk. *heteros*, other; *philos*, loving.] *Appl.* non-specific antigens and antibodies present in an organism, affording natural immunity; *appl.* granular leucocytes which show interspecific differences in their reaction to stains. *n.* Polymorphonuclear leucocyte.

heterophyadic (hĕt′ërōfīăd′ĭk) *a.* [Gk. *heteros*, other; *phyas*, shoot.] Producing separate shoots, one vegetative, one reproductive.

heterophyllous (hĕt′ërōfĭl′ŭs) *a.* [Gk. *heteros*, other; *phyllon*, leaf.] Bearing foliage leaves of different shape on different parts of the same plant; having lamellae of different size or shape, as some agarics.

heterophylly,—heterophyllous condition.

heterophyte (hĕt′ërōfīt) *n.* [Gk. *heteros*, other; *phyton*, plant.] A plant obtaining nourishment from dead or living organisms, or from their products; a heterotrophic, saprophytic, or parasitic plant. *Opp.* autophyte.

heterophytic (hĕt′ërōfĭt′ĭk) *a.* [Gk. *heteros*, other; *phyton*, plant.] With two kinds of spores, borne by different sporophytes; *cf.* homophytic.

heteroplanogametes (hĕt′ërōplăn′ōgămēts′) *n. plu.* [Gk. *heteros*, other; *planos*, wandering; *gametes*, spouse.] Motile gametes that are unlike one another.

heteroplasia (hĕt′ërōplā′sĭă) *n.* [Gk. *heteros*, other; *plassein*, to mould.] The development of one tissue from another of a different kind.

heteroplasm (hĕt′ërōplăzm) *n.* [Gk. *heteros*, other; *plasma*, mould.] Tissue formed in abnormal places.

heteroplasma (hĕt′ërōplăzmă) *n.* [Gk. *heteros*, other; *plasma*, mould.] Plasma from a different species used as a medium for tissue culture; *cf.* autoplasma, homoplasma.

heteroplastic (hĕt′ërōplăs′tĭk) *a.* [Gk. *heteros*, other; *plastos*, formed.] *Appl.* grafts of unrelated material; *appl.* transplantation between individuals of different species or genera, *opp.* homoioplastic; *cf.* xenoplastic.

heteroploid (hĕt′ëröploid) *a.* [Gk. *heteros*, other; *haploos*, onefold.] Having an extra chromosome through non-disjunction of a pair in meiosis; not having a multiple of the basic haploid number of chromosomes. *n.* An organism having heteroploid nuclei.

heteroproteose (hĕt′ërōprō′tēōs) *n.* [Gk. *heteros*, other; *protos*, first.] One of primary products formed by action of gastric juices on other hydrolysing agents on proteins; propeptone.

heteropycnosis (hĕt′ërōpĭknō′sĭs) *n.* [Gk. *heteros*, other; *pyknos*, dense.] Condensation of sex-chromosome during growth-period stages of gonia and cytes; condition of chromosome region or of chromosomes synthesising more or less nucleic acid than remainder of chromosome set.

heteropycnotic (hĕt′ërōpĭknŏt′ĭk) *a.* [Gk. *heteros*, other; *pyknos*, dense.] *Appl.* chromosome manifesting heteropycnosis.

heterorhizal (hĕt′ërörī′zăl) *a.* [Gk. *heteros*, other ; *rhiza*, root.] With roots coming from no determinate point.

heterosexual (hĕt′ërösĕk′sūăl) *a.* [Gk. *heteros*, other ; L. *sexus*, sex.] Of, or *pert.* the opposite sex ; *appl.* hormones, etc.

heterosis (hĕt′ërō′sĭs) *n.* [Gk. *heteros*, other.] Cross-fertilisation ; hybrid vigour, result of heterozygosis.

heterosomal (hĕt′ërösō′măl) *a.* [Gk. *heteros*, other ; *soma*, body.] Occurring in, or *pert.*, different bodies ; *appl.* rearrangements in two or more chromosomes of a set.

heterosome (hĕt′ërösōm) *n.* [Gk. *heteros*, other ; *soma*, body.] A heterochromosome.

heterosporangic (hĕt′ëröspŏrăn′jĭk) *a.* [Gk. *heteros*, other ; *sporos*, seed ; *anggeion*, vessel.] Bearing two kinds of spores in separate sporangia.

heterosporous (hĕt′ërŏs′pörŭs, hĕt-ëröspō′rŭs) *a.* [Gk. *heteros*, other ; *sporos*, seed.] Producing two kinds of spores ; heterosporic.

heterospory (hĕt′ërŏs′pörĭ) *n.* [Gk. *heteros*, other ; *sporos*, seed.] The condition of being heterosporous ; the production of megaspores and microspores.

heterostemonous (hĕt′ëröstĕm′önŭs) *a.* [Gk. *heteros*, other ; *stemon*, stamen.] With unlike stamens.

heterostrophy (hĕt′ërŏs′tröfĭ) *n.* [Gk. *heteros*, other ; *strophe*, turning.] The condition of being coiled in a direction opposite to normal.

heterostyled (hĕt′ëröstī′ld) *a.* [Gk. *heteros*, other ; *stylos*, pillar.] Having unlike or unequal styles ; heterostylic.

heterostyly (hĕt′ëröstī′lĭ) *n.* [Gk. *heteros*, other ; *stylos*, pillar.] Condition of being heterostyled.

heterosynapsis (hĕt′ërösĭnăp′sĭs) *n.* [Gk. *heteros*, other ; *synapsis*, union.] Pairing of two dissimilar chromosomes ; *cf.* homosynapsis.

heterotaxis (hĕt′ërötăk′sĭs) *n.* [Gk. *heteros*, other ; *taxis*, arrangement.] Abnormal or unusual arrangement of organs or parts.

heterothallic (hĕt′ëröthăl′ĭk) *a.* [Gk. *heteros*, other ; *thallos*, young shoot.] Requiring branches of two distinct mycelia to form a zygospore; *appl.* moulds ; *cf.* homothallic.

heterothallism,—heterothallic condition.

heterothermal (hĕt′ëröthĕr′măl) *a.* [Gk. *heteros*, other ; *therme*, heat.] *Appl.* animals whose temperature varies with that of the surrounding medium ; poikilothermal. *Opp.* homoiothermal.

heterotic (hĕt′ërŏt′ĭk) *a.* [Gk. *heteros*, other.] *Pert.* heterosis ; *appl.* vigour.

heterotomy (hĕt′ërŏt′ömĭ) *n.* [Gk. *heteros*, other ; *temnein*, to cut.] Condition of having parts of perianth whorls unequal or dissimilar ; irregular dichotomy in Crinoidea.

heterotopy (hĕt′ërŏt′öpĭ) *n.* [Gk. *heteros*, other ; *topos*, place.] Displacement ; abnormal habitat.

heterotrichous (hĕt′ërŏt′rĭkŭs) *a.* [Gk. *heteros*, other ; *thrix*, hair.] Having two types of cilia ; having thallus consisting of prostrate and erect filaments, as certain algae.

heterotrophic (hĕt′ërötrŏf′ĭk) *a.* [Gk. *heteros*, other ; *trophe*, nourishment.] Getting nourishment from organic substances ; *appl.* parasitic plants ; *opp.* autotrophic.

heterotropic chromosome, — sex-chromosome, *q.v.*

heterotropous (hĕt′ërŏt′röpŭs) *a.* [Gk. *heteros*, other ; *trepein*, to turn.] *Pert.* ovule with hilum and micropyle at opposite ends in a plane parallel to placenta ; heterotropic.

heterotype (hĕt′ërötīp) *n.* [Gk. *heteros*, other ; *typos*, pattern.] First meiotic division.

heterotypic (hĕt′ërötĭp′ĭk) *a.* [Gk. *heteros*, other ; *typos*, pattern.] *Pert.* mitotic division in which daughter chromosomes remain united and form rings ; *appl.* first or reduction division in meiosis ; *cf.* homeotypic.

heterotypical (hĕt′ĕrōtĭp′ĭkăl) *a.* [Gk. *heteros*, other; *typos*, pattern.] *Appl.* a genus comprising species that are not truly related.

heteroxenous (hĕt′ĕrōzĕn′ŭs, -ŏk′sē-nŭs) *a.* [Gk. *heteros*, other; *xenos*, host.] Occurring on or infesting more than one kind of host; heteroecious.

heterozygosis (hĕt′ĕrōzĭgō′sĭs) *n.* [Gk. *heteros*, other; *zygon*, yoke.] Descent from two different species, varieties, or races.

heterozygote (hĕt′ĕrōzī′gōt) *n.* [Gk. *heteros*, other; *zygon*, yoke.] An organism having alternative forms of a gene; an impure dominant; a heterozygous organism.

heterozygous (hĕtĕrŏz′ĭgŭs) *a.* [Gk. *heteros*, other; *zygon*, yoke.] Bearing two dissimilar alternative genetical factors.

hexacanth (hĕk′săkănth) *a.* [Gk. *hex*, six; *akantha*, thorn.] Having six hooks; *appl.* embryo of certain flat-worms.

hexactinal (hĕk′săk′tĭnăl) *a.* [Gk. *hex*, six; *aktis*, ray.] With six rays.

hexactine (hĕk′săk′tĭn) *n.* [Gk. *hex*, six; *aktis*, ray.] A spicule with six equal and similar rays meeting at right angles.

hexactinian (hĕk′săktĭn′ĭăn) *a.* [Gk. *hex*, six; *aktis*, ray.] With tentacles or mesenteries in multiples of six.

hexacyclic (hĕk′săsī′klĭk) *a.* [Gk. *hex*, six; *kyklos*, circle.] Having floral whorls consisting of six parts.

hexagynous (hĕksăj′ĭnŭs) *a.* [Gk. *hex*, six; *gyne*, woman.] Having six pistils.

hexamerous (hĕksăm′ĕrŭs) *a.* [Gk. *hex*, six; *meros*, part.] Occurring in sixes, or arranged in sixes.

hexandrous (hĕksăn′drŭs) *a.* [Gk. *hex*, six; *aner*, man.] Having six stamens.

hexapetaloid (hĕk′săpĕt′ăloid) *a.* [Gk. *hex*, six; *petalon*, petal; *eidos*, form.] With petaloid perianth of six parts.

hexapetalous (hĕk′săpĕt′ălŭs) *a.* [Gk. *hex*, six; *petalon*, petal. Having six petals.

hexaphyllous (hĕk′săfĭl′ŭs) *a.* [Gk. *hex*, six; *phyllon*, leaf.] Having six leaves.

hexaploid (hĕk′săploid) *a.* [Gk. *hex*, six; *haploos*, simple; *eidos*, form.] With six sets of chromosomes. *n.* An organism having six times the monoploid chromosome number.

hexapod (hĕk′săpŏd) *a.* [Gk. *hex*, six; *pous*, foot.] *Pert.* animal with six legs. *n.* An insect.

hexapterous (hĕksăp′tĕrŭs) *a.* [Gk. *hex*, six; *pteron*, wing.] Having six wing-like processes or expansions.

hexarch (hĕk′sârk) *a.* [Gk. *hex*, six; *arche*, beginning.] Having six radiating vascular strands; *appl.* roots.

hexasepalous (hĕk′săsĕp′ălŭs) *a.* [Gk. *hex*, six; F. *sépale*, sepal.] Having six sepals.

hexaspermous (hĕk′săspĕr′mŭs) *a.* [Gk. *hex*, six; *sperma*, seed.] Having six seeds.

hexasporous (hĕk′săspō′rŭs) *a.* [Gk. *hex*, six; *sporos*, seed.] Having six spores.

hexastemonous (hĕk′săstĕm′ŏnŭs) *a.* [Gk. *hex*, six; *stemon*, stamen.] Having six stamens; hexandrous.

hexaster (hĕksăs′tĕr) *n.* [Gk. *hex*, six; *aster*, star.] A variety of hexactine in which the rays branch and produce star-shaped figures.

hexastichous (hĕksăs′tĭkŭs) *a.* [Gk. *hex*, six; *stichos*, row.] Having the parts arranged in six rows.

hexicology (hĕk′sĭkŏl′ŏjĭ) *n.* [Gk. *hexis*, habit; *logos*, discourse.] Bionomics.

hexuronic acid,—ascorbic acid or vitamin C.

hiatus (hīā′tŭs) *n.* [L. *hiare*, to gape.] Any large opening.

hibernaculum (hī′bĕrnăk′ūlŭm) *n.* [L. *hibernaculum*, winter-quarters.] A winter bud; specially modified winter bud in fresh-water Polyzoa.

hibernal (hībĕr′năl) *a.* [L. *hibernus*, wintry.] Of the winter; hiemal.

hibernate (hī′bĕrnāt) *v.* [L. *hibernus*, wintry.] To pass the winter in a resting state.

hibernating glands,—lymph glands of richly vascularised fatty tissue occurring in some rodents and insectivores.

hidrosis (hīdrō′sĭs) *n.* [Gk. *hidros*, sweat.] Excretion of sweat; perspiration.

hiemal (hī′ĕmăl) *a.* [L. *hiems*, winter.] *Pert.* winter; *appl.* aspect of a community.

Highmore's antrum [*N. Highmore*, English surgeon]. The maxillary sinus, which communicates with the middle meatus of the nose.

Highmore's body,—corpus highmoreanum, mediastinum testis.

hilar (hī′lăr) *a.* [L. *hilum*, trifle.] Of or *pert.* a hilum; *appl.* appendix of spores.

hiliferous (hīlĭf′ĕrŭs) *a.* [L. *hilum*, trifle; *ferre*, to carry.] Having a hilum.

hilum (hī′lŭm) *n.* [L. *hilum*, trifle.] Scar on ovule where it was attached to placenta; eye of seed; nucleus of starch grain; small notch, opening, or depression, usually where vessels, nerves, etc., enter, of kidney, lung, spleen, etc.; also hilus.

hind brain,—rhombencephalon, that portion of brain derived from third embryonic vesicle.

hind gut,—diverticulum of yolk-sac extending into tail-fold in human embryo; posterior portion of alimentary tract.

hind-kidney,—metanephros.

hinge-cells,—large epidermal cells which, by changes in turgor, control rolling and unrolling of a leaf.

hinge-joint,—a joint in which articulatory surfaces are so moulded as to permit motion in one plane only; ginglymus.

hinge-ligament,—the tough elastic substance joining the two valves of a bivalve shell.

hinge-line,—the line of articulation of the two valves in a bivalve shell.

hinge-tooth,—one of the projections found on the hinge-line in bivalves.

hinoid (hī′noid) *a.* [Gk. *his*, nerve; *eidos*, form.] With parallel veins at right angles to mid-rib, *appl.* leaf-type.

hip-joint,—the ball-and-socket joint between femur and hip-girdle.

hippocampal (hĭp′ökăm′păl) *a.* [Gk. *hippos*, horse; *kampe*, bend.] *Pert.* the hippocampus.

hippocampus (hĭp′ökăm′pŭs) *n.* [Gk. *hippos*, horse; *kampe*, bend.] Part of rhinencephalon forming an eminence extending throughout length of floor of inferior cornu of lateral ventricle; hippocampus major.

hippocampus minor,—calcar avis.

hippocrepian (hĭp′ökrē′pĭăn) *a.* [Gk. *hippos*, horse; *krepis*, shoe.] Shaped like a horse-shoe; hippocrepiform.

hippuric (hĭpū′rĭk) *a.* [Gk. *hippos*, horse; *ouron*, urine.] Obtained from horse's urine; *appl.* acid, benzoyl glycine, $C_9H_9O_3N$, synthesised by kidney and present in urine of herbivorous animals.

hirsute (hĭrsūt′) *a.* [L. *hirsutus*, shaggy.] Covered with hair-like feathers, *appl.* birds; having stiff, hairy bristles or covering.

hirudin (hĭrū′dĭn) *n.* [L. *hirudo*, leech.] A substance, obtained in solution from buccal glands of leech, which prevents clotting of blood by inhibiting action of thrombin on fibrinogen.

His' bundle [*W. His*, German anatomist]. Band of muscle fibres, with nerve fibres, connecting auricles and ventricles of heart; atrioventricular or auriculoventricular bundle; Gaskell's bridge.

hispid (hĭs′pĭd) *a.* [L. *hispidus*, rough.] Having stiff hairs, spines, or bristles.

histamine (hĭs′tămĭn) *n.* [Gk. *histos*, tissue; *ammoniakon*, resinous gum.] Product of the basic amino acid and food constituent histidine, in ergot and animal tissues, stimulates autonomic nervous system, gastric juice secretion, and capillary dilatation; $C_5H_9N_3$.

histioblast (hĭs'tĭöblăst) *n.* [Gk. *histion*, tissue ; *blastos*, bud.] An immature histiocyte.

histiocyte (hĭs'tĭösīt) *n.* [Gk. *histion*, tissue ; *kytos*, hollow.] A primitive blood cell giving rise to a monocyte ; a monocyte of reticular origin, or a clasmatocyte derived from endothelium, a reticulo-endothelial cell ; fixed macrophage in loose connective tissue ; adventitial cell ; rhagiocrine cell.

histiogenic,—histogenic.

histioid (hĭs'tĭoid) *a.* [Gk. *histion*, web ; *eidos*, form.] Like a web, arachnoid ; tissue-like.

histiomonocyte (hĭs'tĭömŏn'ösīt) *n.* [Gk. *histion*, tissue ; *monos*, alone ; *kytos*, hollow.] An endothelial cell of certain capillaries and associated with the histiocytic metabolic system.

histiotypic (hĭs'tĭötĭp'ĭk) *a.* [Gk. *histion*, tissue ; *typos*, pattern.] *Appl.* uncontrolled or unorganised growth of cells, in tissue culture. *Opp.* organotypic.

histoblast (hĭs'töblăst) *n.* [Gk. *histos*, tissue ; *blastos*, bud.] A unit of tissue ; imaginal disc.

histochemistry (hĭs'tökĕm'ĭstrĭ) *n.* [Gk. *histos*, tissue ; *chemeia*, transmutation.] The chemistry of animal tissues.

histocyte (hĭs'tösīt) *n.* [Gk. *histos*, tissue ; *kytos*, hollow.] Tissue cell as distinguished from germ cell.

histogenesis (hĭs'töjĕn'ësĭs) *n.* [Gk. *histos*, tissue; *genesis*, descent.] Formation and development of tissue.

histogenic (hĭs'töjĕn'ĭk) *a.* [Gk. *histos*, tissue ; *-genes*, producing.] Tissue-producing ; *appl.* the separate merismatic layers in a stratified growing point.

histogenous,—produced in or from tissue ; *appl.* cavities, conidia, etc.

histogens (hĭs'töjënz) *n. plu.* [Gk. *histos*, tissue ; *gennaein*, to produce.] Tissue-producing zones or layers : plerome, periblem, dermatogen, and calyptrogen.

histohaematin (hĭs'töhĕ̄m'ătĭn) *n.* [Gk. *histos*, tissue ; *haima*, blood.] An intracellular haemin compound ; a cytochrome.

histology (hĭstŏl'öjĭ) *n.* [Gk. *histos*, tissue ; *logos*, discourse.] The science which treats of the detailed structure of animal or plant tissues ; microscopic morphology ; histomorphology.

histolysis (hĭstŏl'ĭsĭs) *n.* [Gk. *histos*, tissue ; *lyein*, to dissolve.] The dissolution of organic tissues ; process by which most of pupal internal organs dissolve into creamy fluid, except certain cells round which new imaginal tissues are formed.

histometabasis (hĭs'tömĕtăb'ăsĭs) *n.* [Gk. *histos*, tissue ; *metabasis*, alteration.] Fossilisation with retention of the detailed structure of plant or animal tissues.

histone (hĭs'tōn) *n.* [Gk. *histos*, tissue.] A protein constituent of cell nuclei, thymus, blood corpuscles, and lymph glands.

histophyly (hĭstöfī'lĭ) *n.* [Gk. *histos*, tissue ; *phyle*, tribe.] Phylogenetic history of a group of cells.

histoteleosis (hĭs'tötĕlē'ōsĭs) *n.* [Gk. *histos*, tissue ; *teleios*, full-grown.] The completion of functional differentiation of tissue cells.

histotrophic (hĭs'tötrŏf'ĭk) *a.* [Gk. *histos*, tissue ; *trephein*, to nourish.] *Pert.* or connected with tissue formation or repair.

histozoic (hĭs'tözō'ĭk) *a.* [Gk. *histos*, tissue ; *zoon*, animal.] Living within tissues ; *appl.* trophozoitic stage of certain Sporozoa.

histozyme (hĭs'tözīm) *n.* [Gk. *histos*, tissue ; *zyme*, leaven.] An enzyme found in kidneys of certain animals, and in fungi capable of decomposing hippuric acid ; hippuricase.

hock (hŏk) *n.* [A.S. *hoh*, heel.] The tarsal joint, or its region ; hough.

holandric (hŏlăn'drĭk) *a.* [Gk. *holos*, whole ; *aner*, male.] *Pert.* holandry ; transmitted from male to male through the Y-chromosome ; *appl.* sex-linked characters.

holandry (hŏlăn'drĭ) *n.* [Gk. *holos*, whole ; *aner*, male.] The condition of having full number of testes, as two pairs in Oligochaeta ; *cf.* meroandry.

holarctic (hŏlârk'tĭk) *a.* [Gk. *holos*, whole ; *Arktos*, Great Bear.] *Appl.* or *pert.* a zoogeographical region including northern parts of the Old and New Worlds or palaearctic and nearctic sub-regions.

holard (hŏlârd') *n.* [Gk. *holos*, whole ; *ardo*, I water.] Total water content of soil ; *cf.* chresard, echard.

holaspidean (hŏl'ăspĭd'ēăn) *a.* [Gk. *holos*, whole ; *aspis*, shield.] With single series of large scales on posterior aspect of tarso-metatarsus.

holcodont (hŏl'kŏdŏnt) *a.* [Gk. *holkos*, furrow ; *odous*, tooth.] Having the teeth in a long continuous groove.

holdfast,—a sucker or disc-like extension of a thallus, primarily for attachment, as appressorium, hapteron, hyphopodium, stomatopodium.

holobasidium (hŏl'ŏbăsĭd'ĭŭm) *n.* [Gk. *holos*, whole ; *basis*, base ; *idion*, *dim.*] A basidium not divided by septa.

holobenthic (hŏl'ŏbĕn'thĭk) *a.* [Gk. *holos*, whole ; *benthos*, depths.] Living in depths of sea throughout life.

holoblastic (hŏl'ŏblăs'tĭk) *a.* [Gk. *holos*, whole ; *blastos*, bud.] *Pert.* eggs with total cleavage.

holobranch (hŏl'ŏbrăngk) *n.* [Gk. *holos*, whole ; *brangchia*, gills.] A gill in which gill filaments are borne on both sides.

holocarpic (hŏl'ŏkâr'pĭk) *a.* [Gk. *holos*, whole ; *karpos*, fruit.] Having the fruit-body formed by the entire thallus ; *appl.* fungi without rhizoids or haustoria, living in host cell, as certain Phycomycetes. *Opp.* eucarpic.

Holocene (hŏl'ŏsēn) *a.* [Gk. *holos*, whole ; *kainos*, recent.] Recent geological epoch following Pleistocene ; postglacial age.

holochlamydate (hŏl'ŏklăm'ĭdāt) *a.* [Gk. *holos*, whole ; *chlamys*, cloak.] Having no notch on mantle margin.

holochroal (hŏl'ŏkrō'ăl) *a.* [Gk. *holos*, whole ; *chros*, close.] Having eyes with globular or biconvex lenses closely crowded together, so that cornea is continuous over whole eye.

holocrine (hŏl'ŏkrīn) *a.* [Gk. *holos*, whole ; *krinein*, to separate.] *Appl.* glands in which secretory cells disintegrate and form part of secretion, as sebaceous glands ; *cf.* apocrine, merocrine.

holocyclic (hŏl'ŏsĭk'lĭk) *a.* [Gk. *holos*, whole ; *kyklos*, circle.] *Pert.* or completing alternation of sexual and parthenogenetic generations.

holodikaryotic (hŏl'ŏdī'kărĭŏt'ĭk) *a.* [Gk. *holos*, whole ; *dis*, double ; *karyon*, nucleus.] Having a pair of nuclei and lacking a haploid phase.

holoenzyme (hŏl'ŏĕn'zīm) *n.* [Gk. *holos*, whole ; *en*, in ; *zyme*, leaven.] An enzyme consisting of an apo-enzyme and co-enzyme, neither of which is active by itself.

hologametes (hŏl'ŏgamēts') *n. plu.* [Gk. *holos*, whole ; *gametes*, spouse.] Fully developed protozoa taking part in syngamy. *Opp.* merogametes.

hologamy (hŏlŏg'ămĭ) *n.* [Gk. *holos*, whole ; *gamos*, marriage.] Macrogamy ; condition of having gametes similar to somatic cells.

hologastrula (hŏl'ŏgas'troolă) *n.* [Gk. *holos*, whole ; *gaster*, stomach.] Gastrula formed from holoblastic egg.

holognathous (hŏlŏg'năthŭs) *a.* [Gk. *holos*, whole ; *gnathos*, jaw.] Having the jaw in a single piece.

hologonidium,—soredium, *q.v.*

hologynic (hŏlŏjĭn'ĭk) *a.* [Gk. *holos*, whole ; *gyne*, woman.] Transmitted direct from female to female ; *appl.* sex-linked characters.

holomastigote (hŏl'ŏmăs'tĭgōt) *a.* [Gk. *holos*, whole ; *mastix*, whip.] Having one type of flagellum scattered evenly over the body.

holometabolic (hŏl′ömĕtăbŏl′ĭk) *a.* [Gk. *holos*, whole; *metabole*, change.] Having complete metamorphosis.

holometabolism (hŏl′ömĕtăb′ölĭzm) *n.* [Gk. *holos*, whole; *metabole*, change.] State of having complete metamorphosis. *Opp.* hemimetabolism.

holomorphosis (hŏl′ömôr′fōsĭs) *n.* [Gk. *holos*, whole; *morphe*, shape.] Regeneration in which the entire part is replaced.

holonephridia,—meganephridia, *q.v.*

holonephros (hŏl′önĕf′rŏs) *n.* [Gk. *holos*, whole; *nephros*, kidney.] The hypothetical continuous excretory organ.

holoparasite (hŏl′öpăr′ăsīt) *n.* [Gk. *holos*, whole; *parasitos*, parasite.] A parasite which cannot exist independently of a host; obligate parasite.

holophyte (hŏl′öfīt) *n.* [Gk. *holos*, whole; *phyton*, plant.] Any green or phototrophic independent plant.

holophytic (hŏl′öfĭt′ĭk) *a.* [Gk. *holos*, whole; *phyton*, plant.] Obtaining the whole of its food after the manner of a plant; phototrophic. *Opp.* holozoic.

holoplankton (hŏl′öplăngktŏn) *n.* [Gk. *holos*, whole; *plangktos*, wandering.] The marine or fresh-water organisms which complete their life cycle while drifting with the surrounding water.

holoplanktonic (hŏl′öplăngktŏn′ĭk) *a.* [Gk. *holos*, whole; *plangktos*, wandering.] Living near the surface of sea, or of lake, throughout life; *pert.* holoplankton.

holopneustic (hŏl′önū′stĭk) *a.* [Gk. *holos*, whole; *pnein*, to breathe.] With all spiracles open for respiration.

holoptic (hŏlŏp′tĭk) *a.* [Gk. *holos*, whole; *ops*, eye.] Having eyes of two sides meeting in a coadapted line of union. *Opp.* dichoptic.

holorhinal (hŏl′örī′năl) *a.* [Gk. *holos*, whole; *rhines*, nostrils.] Having nares with posterior margin rounded. *Opp.* schizorhinal.

holosaprophyte (hŏl′ösăp′röfīt) *n.* [Gk. *holos*, whole; *sapros*, rotten; *phyton*, plant.] Any obligate saprophyte.

holoschisis (hŏlŏs′kĭsĭs) *n.* [Gk. *holos*, whole; *schizein*, to cut.] Amitosis.

holosericeous (hŏl′ösĕrĭsh′ŭs) *a.* [Gk. *holos*, whole; L.L. *sericeus*, silken.] Completely covered with silky hairlike structures; having a silky lustre or sheen.

holostomatous (hŏl′östŏm′ătŭs) *a.* [Gk. *holos*, whole; *stoma*, mouth.] With margin of aperture entire.

holostyly (hŏl′östī′lĭ) *n.* [Gk. *holos*, whole; *stylos*, pillar.] Primitive condition of jaw suspension in some fishes.

holosystolic (hŏl′ösĭstŏl′ĭk) *a.* [Gk. *holos*, whole; *systole*, contraction.] *Pert.* complete systole.

holotrichous (hŏlŏt′rĭkŭs) *a.* [Gk. *holos*, whole; *thrix*, hair.] Having a uniform covering of cilia over the body.

holotype (hŏl′ötīp) *n.* [Gk. *holos*, whole; *typos*, pattern.] The single specimen chosen for designation of a new species.

holozoic (hŏl′özō′ĭk) *a.* [Gk. *holos*, whole; *zoon*, animal.] Obtaining the whole of its food after the manner of animals; ingulfing solid food particles. *Opp.* holophytic.

homacanth (hŏm′ăkănth) *a.* [Gk. *homos*, same; *akantha*, spine.] Having spines of dorsal fin symmetrical.

homaxonic (hŏmăksŏn′ĭk) *a.* [Gk. *homos*, same; *axon*, axis.] Built up around equal axes; homaxial.

homeo-, *also* homoeo-, homoio-.

homeochronous,—homochronous.

homeokinesis (hŏm′ëökĭnē′sĭs) *n.* [Gk. *homoios*, alike; *kinein*, to move.] Mitosis with equal division of chromatinic elements to daughter nuclei.

homeostasis (hŏmëŏs′tăsĭs) *n.* [Gk. *homoios*, alike; *stasis*, standing.] The balance of nature; maintenance of equilibrium between organism and environment; the constancy of the internal environment of the body, as in birds and mammals.

homeostat (hŏm′ëöstăt) *n.* [Gk. *homoios*, alike; *statos*, standing.] Any cytoplasmic or non-genic carrier of a heritable character.

homeosynapsis,—homosynapsis, *q.v.*

homeotely (hŏm′ëŏt′ëlĭ) *n.* [Gk. *homoios*, alike; *telos*, end.] Evolution from homologous parts, but with less close resemblance.

homeotypic (hŏm′ēōtĭp′ĭk) *a.* [Gk. *homoios*, alike; *typos*, character.] *Appl.* second division in meiosis, similar to typical mitosis; *cf.* heterotypic.

homeozoic (hŏm′ēözō′ĭk) *a.* [Gk. *homoios*, alike; *zoon*, animal.] *Pert.* a region or series of regions with identical fauna.

homobasidium (hŏm′öbăsĭd′ĭŭm) *n.* [Gk. *homos*, same; *basis*, base; *idion*, *dim.*] A typical non-septate basidium. *Opp.* heterobasidium.

homobium (hŏmō′bĭŭm) *n.* [Gk. *homos*, same; *bios*, life.] The interdependence and mutual life of fungus and alga in lichens.

homoblastic (hŏm′öblăs′tĭk) *a.* [Gk. *homos*, same; *blastos*, bud.] Having direct embryonic development; arising from similar cells.

homobrachial (hŏm′öbrā′kĭăl) *a.* [Gk. *homos*, same; L. *brachium*, arm.] *Pert.* the same chromosome arm; paracentric.

homocarpous (hŏm′ökâr′pŭs) *a.* [Gk. *homos*, same; *karpos*, fruit.] Bearing one kind of fruit.

homocellular (hŏm′ösĕl′ūlar) *a.* [Gk. *homos*, same; L. *cellula*, small cell.] Composed of cells of one type only. *Opp.* heterocellular.

homocercal (hŏm′ösĕr′kăl) *a.* [Gk. *homos*, same; *kerkos*, tail.] Having a tail with equal or nearly equal lobes, and axis ending near middle of base.

homocerebrin (hŏm′ösĕr′ëbrĭn) *n.* [Gk. *homos*, same; L. *cerebrum*, brain.] A substance identical with cerebrin.

homochlamydeous (hŏm′öklămĭd′-ëŭs) *a.* [Gk. *homos*, same; *chlamys*, cloak.] Having outer and inner perianth whorls alike.

homochromous (hŏm′ökrō′mŭs) *a.* [Gk. *homos*, same; *chroma*, colour.] Of one colour; *appl.* capitular florets. *Opp.* heterochromous.

homochronous (hömŏk′rönŭs) *a.* [Gk. *homos*, same; *chronos*, time.] Occurring at the same age or period, in successive generations.

homodermic (hŏm′ödĕr′mĭk) *a.* [Gk. *homos*, same; *derma*, skin.] Sprung from same embryonic layer.

homodont (hō′mödŏnt) *a.* [Gk. *homos*, same; *odous*, tooth.] Having the teeth all alike, not differentiated; isodont. *Opp.* heterodont.

homodromous (hömŏd′römŭs) *a.* [Gk. *homos*, same; *dramein*, to run.] Having genetic spiral alike in direction in stem and branches; moving or acting in the same direction.

homodynamic (hŏm′ödĭnăm′ĭk) *a.* [Gk. *homos*, same; *dynamis*, power.] Developing without resting stages; *appl.* insects not requiring a diapause for further development; *pert.* homodynamy; acting upon the production of the same phenotypic effects at the same time; *appl.* genes.

homodynamy (hŏm′ödī′nămĭ) *n.* [Gk. *homos*, same; *dynamis*, power.] Metameric homology.

homoeandrous (hŏmēăn′drŭs) *a.* [Gk. *homoios*, alike; *aner*, male.] Having uniform stamens.

homoecious (hŏmē′sĭŭs) *a.* [Gk. *homos*, same; *oikos*, abode.] Occupying the same host or shelter during the life cycle.

homoeo-,—*also* homeo, homoio.

homoeologous (hŏmēŏl′ögŭs) *a.* [Gk. *homoios*, like; *logos*, relation.] *Appl.* chromosomes having in part the same sequence of genes; partly homologous.

homoeologue, — a homoeologous chromosome.

homoeomerous (hŏm′ēŏm′ërŭs) *a.* [Gk. *homoios*, like; *meros*, part.] With or consisting of similar parts.

homoeomorphic (hŏm′ēömôr′fĭk) *a.* [Gk. *homoios*, like; *morphe*, form.] Resembling in shape or structure; exhibiting convergence.

homoeosis (hŏmē'ōsĭs) *n.* [Gk. *homoiosis*, likeness.] Assumption by one part of likeness to another part, as modification of antenna into foot, or of petal into stamen ; metamorphy.

homoeotype (hŏm'ēōtīp) *n.* [Gk. *homoios*, alike : *typos*, pattern.] A specimen authoritatively stated to be identical with the holotype, lectotype, paratypes, or syntypes of its species.

homoeozoic (hŏ'mēōzō'ĭk) *a.* [Gk. *homoios*, alike ; *zoe* life.] Characterised by similar forms of life ; *appl.* areas or zones.

homogametic (hŏm'ŏgămĕt'ĭk) *a.* [Gk. *homos*, same ; *gametes*, spouse.] Having homogametes or gametes of one type ; *appl.* sex possessing two X-chromosomes ; *cf.* heterogametic, digametic.

homogamous (hŏmŏg'ămŭs) *a.* [Gk. *homos*, same ; *gamos*, marriage.] Characterised by homogamy.

homogamy (hŏmŏg'ămĭ) *a.* [Gk. *homos*, same ; *gamos*, marriage.] Inbreeding due to some type of isolation ; condition of having flowers all alike, having stamens and pistils mature at same time.

homogangliate (hŏm'ŏgăng'lĭāt) *a.* [Gk. *homos*, same ; *ganglion*, knot.] Having ganglia of nerve loops symmetrically arranged.

homogen (hō'mŏjĕn) *n.* [Gk. *homos*, same ; *genos*, race.] One of a group having a common origin ; one of a series of identically derived parts.

homogenesis (hŏm'ŏjĕn'ĕsĭs) *n.* [Gk. *homos*, same ; *genesis*, descent.] The type of reproduction in which like begets like.

homogenetic (hŏm'ŏjĕnĕt'ĭk) *a.* [Gk. *homos*, same ; *genesis*, descent.] Having the same origin ; *pert.* homogenesis ; *appl.* pairing of homologous chromosomes.

homogenous (hŏmŏj'ĕnŭs) *a.* [Gk. *homos*, same ; *genos*, race.] More or less alike owing to descent from common stock ; *appl.* graft from another animal of same species.

homogeny (hŏmŏj'ĕnĭ) *n.* [Gk. *homos*, same ; *genos*, race.] Correspondence between parts due to common descent ; the same genotypical structure ; homogeneity.

homoglandular (hŏm'ŏglăn'dūlăr) *a.* [Gk. *homos*, same ; L. *glandula*, small acorn.] Of or *pert.* the same gland.

homogony (hŏmŏg'ŏnĭ) *n.* [Gk. *homos*, same ; *gonos*, offspring.] Condition of having one type of flower with equally long stamens and pistil.

homoio-,—*also* homeo-, homoeo-.

homoiochlamydeous (hŏmoi'ŏ-klămĭd'ēŭs) *a.* [Gk. *homoios*, like ; *chlamys*, cloak.] With sepals and petals similar ; homochlamydeous.

homoiomerous (hŏmoiŏm'ĕrŭs) *a.* [Gk. *homoios*, like ; *meros*, part.] Having algae distributed equally through fungoid mycelium in a lichen.

homoioplastic (hŏmoi'ŏplăs'tĭk) *a.* [Gk. *homoios*, like ; *plastos*, formed.] *Appl.* transplantation between individuals of the same species ; homeoplastic.

homoiosmotic (hŏmoi'ŏsmŏt'ĭk) *a.* [Gk. *homoios*, like ; *osmos*, impulse.] *Appl.* organisms with constant internal osmotic pressure ; euryhaline, *q.v.*

homoiothermal (hŏmoi'ŏthĕr'măl) *a.* [Gk. *homoios*, like ; *thermos*, hot.] Having a more or less constant body temperature ; warm-blooded ; homoeothermal, homoiothermic, homothermal, homothermic, homothermous. *Opp.* poikilothermal.

homoiotransplantation,—transplantation of tissue or organ from one organism to another, possibly unrelated ; *cf.* autotransplantation.

homolecithal (hŏm'ŏlĕs'ĭthăl) *a.* [Gk. *homos*, same ; *lekithos*, yolk.] Having little deutoplasm, which is equally distributed.

homolog,—homologue.

homologous (hŏmŏl'ŏgŭs) *a.* [Gk. *homologos*, agreeing.] Resembling in structure and origin ; *appl.* alternating generations ; *appl.* various substances, *e.g.* agglutinins affecting organisms of same species only; *appl.* chromosomes with the same sequence of genes; *appl.* genes determining the same character, *e.g.* eye colour. *Cf.* heterologous, antithetic.

homologue (hŏm′ŏlŏg) *n.* [Gk. *homologos*, agreeing.] One of a series of structures similar in structure and origin; a homologous agent.

homology (hŏmŏl′ŏjĭ) *a.* [Gk. *homologia*, agreement.] Similarity in structure and development of organ or parts.

homomallous (hŏm′ŏmăl′ŭs) *a.* [Gk. *homos*, same; *mallos*, lock of wool.] Curving uniformly to one side; *appl.* leaves.

homomorphic (hŏm′ŏmôr′fĭk) *a.* [Gk. *homos*, same; *morphe*, form.] Of similar size or structure; *pert.*, or exhibiting, homomorphism; *appl.* chromosome pairs; *cf.* heteromorphic.

homomorphism (hŏm′ŏmôr′fĭzm) *n.* [Gk. *homos*, same; *morphe*, shape.] The condition of having perfect flowers of only one type; hemimetabolism; similarity of larva and adult.

homomorphosis (hŏm′ŏmôr′fōsĭs) *n.* [Gk. *homos*, same; *morphosis*, shaping.] Condition of having a newly regenerated part like the part removed.

homonomic (hŏm′ŏnŏm′ĭk) *a.* [Gk. *homos*, same; *nomos*, law.] Having the same behaviour; *appl.* affinity, as of tissues combining, *e.g.* vascular anastomoses, or complementary affinity, as in adrenal medulla and cortex; homonomous, *q.v.*

homonomous (hŏmŏn′ŏmŭs) *a.* [Gk. *homos*, same; *nomós*, department.] *Appl.* segmentation into similar segments. [Gk. *nómos*, law.] Following same stages or process, as of development or growth.

homonomy (hŏmŏn′ŏmĭ) *n.* [Gk. *homos*, same; *nómos*, law.] The homology existing between parts arranged on transverse axes; homodynamy.

homonym (hŏm′ŏnĭm) *n.* [Gk. *homos*, same; *onyma*, name.] A name preoccupied, and therefore unsuitable according to law of priority.

homopetalous (hŏm′ŏpĕt′ălŭs) *a.* [Gk. *homos*, same; *petalon*, petal.] Having all the petals alike.

homophyadic (hŏm′ŏfīăd′ĭk) *a.* [Gk. *homos*, same; *phyas*, shoot.] Producing only one kind of shoot.

homophylic (hŏm′ŏfīl′ĭk) *a.* [Gk. *homos*, same; *phyle*, race.] Resembling one another owing to a common ancestry.

homophyllous (hŏm′ŏfĭl′ŭs) *a.* [Gk. *homos*, same; *phyllon*, leaf.] Bearing leaves all of one kind.

homophytic (hŏm′ŏfĭt′ĭk) *a.* [Gk. *homos*, same; *phyton*, plant.] With two kinds of spores, or one bisexual type, borne by a single sporophyte; *cf.* heterophytic.

homoplasma (hŏm′ŏplăz′mă) *n.* [Gk. *homos*, same; *plasma*, mould.] Plasma from another animal of same species used as a medium for tissue culture; *cf.* autoplasma, heteroplasma.

homoplasmic (hŏm′ŏplăz′mĭk) *a.* [Gk. *homos*, same; *plasma*, mould.] Having the same general form; *pert.* homoplasma.

homoplast (hŏm′ŏplăst) *n.* [Gk. *homos*, same; *plastos*, moulded.] An organ or organism formed of similar plastids; coenobium; catallact.

homoplastic (hŏm′ŏplăs′tĭk) *a.* [Gk. *homos*, same; *plastos*, moulded.] *Pert.* homoplasty; *appl.* graft made into individual of same species; *cf.* autoplastic.

homoplastid,—homoplast.

homoplasty (hŏm′ŏplăs′tĭ) *n.* [Gk. *homos*, same; *plastos*, moulded.] Convergence; resemblance in form of structure between different organs or organisms due to evolution along similar lines; also homoplasy; isotely.

homopolar (hŏm′ŏpō′lăr) *a.* [Gk. *homos*, same; *polos*, pole.] Having both ends of an axis alike.

homopterous (hömŏp'tërŭs) *a.* [Gk. *homos*, same; *pteron*, wing.] Having the wings alike.

homorhizal (hŏm'örī'zăl) *a.* [Gk. *homos*, same; *rhiza*, root.] Not having an antiapical root, as Pteridophyta. *Opp.* allorhizal.

homosomal (hŏm'ösō'măl) *a.* [Gk. *homos*, same; *soma*, body.] Occurring in, or *pert.*, the same body; *appl.* rearrangements restricted to a single chromosome.

homosporangic (hŏm'öspörăn'jĭk) *a.* [Gk. *homos*, same; *sporos*, seed; *anggeion*, vessel.] Bearing spores of one kind or of two kinds in one sporangium.

homosporous (hŏmöspō'rŭs) *a.* [Gk. *homos*, same; *sporos*, seed.] Producing only one kind of spore; homosporic; isosporous.

homostyled (höm'östīld) *a.* [Gk. *homos*, same; *stylos*, pillar.] With uniform styles; homogonous.

homosynapsis (hŏm'ösĭnăp'sĭs) *n.* [Gk. *homos*, same; *synapsis*, union.] Pairing of two homologous chromosomes; *cf.* heterosynapsis.

homotaxial (hŏm'ötăk'sĭăl) *a.* [Gk. *homos*, same; *taxis*, arrangement.] Containing the same assemblage of species, *appl.* fossiliferous deposits.

homotaxis (hŏm'ötăk'sĭs) *n.* [Gk. *homos*, same; *taxis*, arrangement.] Similar assemblage or succession of species or types in different regions or strata, not necessarily contemporaneous; homotaxy.

homothallic (hŏm'öthăl'ĭk) *a.* [Gk. *homos*, same; *thallos*, young shoot.] Forming zygospores from two branches of the same mycelium; *appl.* moulds. *Opp.* heterothallic.

homothermous, — homoiothermal.

homotropous (hömŏt'röpŭs) *a.* [Gk. *homos*, same; *trope*, turn.] Erect; having micropyle and chalaza at opposite ends; *appl.* ovules.

homotypic (hŏmötĭp'ĭk) *a.* [Gk. *homos*, same; *typos*, pattern.] Homeotypic, *q.v.*; *pert.* or exhibiting homotypy.

homotypy (hŏm'ötīpĭ) *n.* [Gk. *homos*, same; *typos*, pattern.] Equality of structures along main axis of body; serial homology; reversed symmetry; enantiomorphic condition, *q.v.*

homoxylous (hŏm'özī'lŭs) *a.* [Gk. *homos*, same; *xylon*, wood.] *Appl.* wood without vessels and consisting of tracheids.

homozygosis (hŏm'özĭgō'sĭs) *n.* [Gk. *homos*, same; *zygon*, yoke.] Condition of having a given genetical factor in the duplex condition, and producing gametes of only one kind as regards that factor.

homozygote (hŏm'özī'gōt) *n.* [Gk. *homos*, same; *zygon*, yoke.] An organism in which characters are stable, resulting from union of gametes bearing similar genes.

homozygous (hŏm'özī'gŭs) *a.* [Gk. *homos*, same; *zygon*, yoke.] Having identical genes for a given character; exhibiting or *pert.* homozygosis; *pert.* homozygote.

homunculus (hömŭn'kūlŭs) *n.* [L. *homunculus*, little man.] The small miniature of human foetus supposed to be in spermatozoon, according to Animalculists; homonculus; a human dwarf normally proportioned.

honey-dew, — a sugary exudation found on leaves of many plants; a viscous fluid secreted by mycelium of ergot; a sweet secretion produced by certain insects, *e.g.*, by aphids.

hooded (hood'ëd) *a.* [A.S. *hōd.*] Bearing a hood-like petal; cucullate; rolled up like a cone of paper, as certain leaves; having head conspicuously and differently coloured from rest of body; having crests on head; having wingshaped expansions on neck, as in cobra.

hook-glands,—paired longitudinal glands uniting anteriorly to form head gland in Pentastomida.

hordeaceous (hôr'dëā'shŭs) *a.* [L. *hordeum*, barley.] *Pert.* or resembling barley.

horiodimorphism (hō'rĭödīmôr'fĭzm) *n.* [Gk. *horios*, in season; *dis*, twice; *morphe*, shape.] Seasonal dimorphism.

horizon (hŏrī'zŏn) *n.* [Gk. *horizon*, bounding.] Soil layer of a more or less well-defined character; a layer of deposit characterised by definite fossil species and formed at a definite time.

horizontal (hŏr'ĭzŏn'tăl) *a.* [Gk. *horizon*, bounding.] Growing in a plane at right angles to primary axis.

horme (hôr'mē) *n.* [Gk. *horme*, impetus.] Purposive behaviour; conation; urge or drive in living cells or organisms; élan vital.

hormesis (hôrmē'sĭs) *n.* [Gk. *hormaein*, to excite.] Stimulation by a non-poisonous dose of a toxic substance or agent.

hormocyst (hôr'mösĭst) *n.* [Gk. *hormos*, chain; *kystis*, bladder.] A modified thick-walled hormogonium, in some blue-green algae.

hormogonium (hôr'mögō'nĭŭm) *n.* [Gk. *hormos*, chain; *gone*, generation.] That portion of an algal filament between two heterocysts, which, breaking away, acts as a reproductive body; hormogone.

hormones (hôrmōnz) *n. plu.* [Gk. *hormaein*, to excite.] Substances normally produced in cells and necessary for the proper functioning of other distant cells to which they are conveyed and of the body as a whole; internal secretions of ductless glands which pass into blood vessels by osmosis; exciting agents, *opp.* chalones; internal secretions in plants, as auxins, *q.v.*

hormonic (hôrmŏn'ĭk) *a.* [Gk. *hormaein*, to excite.] *Pert.* hormones; *appl.* excitatory internal secretions, *opp.* chalonic.

hormonopoiesis (hôrmō'nöpoiē'sĭs) *n.* [Gk. *hormaein*, to excite; *poiesis*, making.] The production of hormones.

hormoproteins (hôr'möprō'tēĭnz) *n. plu.* [Gk. *hormaein*, to excite; *proteion*, first.] Proteins or protein derivatives secreted by endocrines.

hormospore (hôr'möspōr) *n.* [Gk. *hormos*, chain; *sporos*, seed.] A spore dividing into microgonidi as of some lichens.

horn (hôrn) *n.* [A.S. *horn.*] The process on head of many animals; any projection resembling a horn; anterior part of each uterus when posterior parts are united to form median corpus uteri; a tuft of feathers as in owl; a spine in fishes; a tentacle in snails; an awn; any pointed projection or process in plants; cornu.

horn core,—the os cornu, fusing with frontal bone, over which fits hollow horn of ruminants.

horodimorphism, — horiodimorphism, *q.v.*

horotelic (hōrötĕl'ĭk) *a.* [Gk. *hora*, right time; *telos*, fulfilment.] Evolving at the standard rate; *cf.* bradytelic, tachytelic.

Hortega cells [*P. de R. Hortega*, Spanish histologist]. Phagocytic neuroglial cells or microglia.

host (hōst) *n.* [L. *hospes*, host.] Any organism in which another organism spends part or the whole of its existence, and from which it derives nourishment or gets protection; an organism which receives grafted or transplanted tissue.

hough, *see* hocks.

house (hows) *n.* [A.S. *hūs.*] The external gelatinous-like covering secreted by certain tunicates.

Houston's valves [*J. Houston*, Irish surgeon]. Semilunar transverse folds of mucous membrane in the rectum; plicae transversales recti.

humeral (hū'mĕrăl) *a.* [L. *humerus*, shoulder.] *Pert.* shoulder region; *pert.* the anterior basal angle of insect wing, *appl.* a cross vein; one of horny plates on plastron of chelonians.

humerus (hū'mĕrŭs) *n.* [L. *humerus*, shoulder.] The bone of the upper arm.

humicolous (hūmĭk'ölŭs) *a.* [L. *humus*, soil; *colere*, to dwell.] Soil-inhabiting; growing in or on soil.

humistratous (hū'mĭstrā'tŭs) *a.* [L. *humus*, soil; *sternere*, to spread.] Spreading over surface of ground.

humoral (hū'mörăl) *a.* [L. *humor*, moisture.] *Appl.* theory of immunity ascribing to body fluids the power to resist infection.

humour (hū'mŏr) *n.* [L. *humor*, moisture.] Any fluid or juice; the fluid of the eye.

humus (hū'mŭs) *n.* [L. *humus*, earth.] A dark material formed by decomposition of vegetable or animal matter and constituting organic part of soils.

husk (hŭsk) *n.* [M.E. *huske*.] The outer coating of various seeds.

Huxley's layer [*T. H. Huxley*, English zoologist]. The middle layer of polyhedral cells in inner root-sheath of hair.

hyaline (hī'ălĭn) *a.* [Gk. *hyalos*, glass.] Clear; transparent; free from inclusions.

hyalodermis (hī'ălödĕr'mĭs) *n.* [Gk. *hyalos*, glass; *derma*, skin.] Tissue of large, empty and absorptive cells in Sphagnum.

hyalogen (hī'ălöjĕn) *n.* [Gk. *hyalos*, glass; *-genes*, producing.] Any of substances found in animal tissues which are insoluble and related to mucoids.

hyaloid (hī'ăloid) *a.* [Gk. *hyalos*, glass; *eidos*, form.] Glassy; transparent.

hyaloid artery,—from central artery of retina through hyaloid canal to back of lens, in foetal eye.

hyaloid canal,—through vitreous body of eye, from optic nerve to back of lens.

hyaloid fossa,—anterior concavity of vitreous body, receptacle of crystalline lens.

hyaloid membrane,—delicate membrane enveloping vitreous body of eye.

hyalomere (hī'ălömēr) *n.* [Gk. *hyalos*, glass; *meros*, part.] The clear homogeneous part of a blood platelet, *opp.* chromomere.

hyalomucoid (hī'ălömū'koid) *n.* [Gk. *hyalos*, glass; L. *mucus*, mucus; Gk. *eidos*, like.] One of the non-phosphorised gluco-proteids in vitreous humour.

hyaloplasm (hī'ălöplăzm) *n.* [Gk. *hyalos*, glass; *plasma*, mould.] Ground substance of cell as distinguished from microsomes, or from reticulum or spongioplasm; ectoplasm or peripheral zone in plant cells; also hyaloplasma.

hyalopterous (hī'ălŏp'tērŭs) *a.* [Gk. *hyalos*, glass; *pteron*, wing.] Having transparent wings.

hyalosome (hī'ălösōm) *n.* [Gk. *hyalos*, glass; *soma*, body.] A nucleolar-like body in a cell-nucleus, only slightly stainable by nuclear or plasma stains.

hyalosporous (hī'ălöspō'rŭs, hī'ălŏs'pörŭs) *a.* [Gk. *hyalos*, glass; *sporos*, seed.] Having colourless spores or conidia.

hybrid (hī'brĭd) *n.* [L. *hibrida*, cross.] Any cross-bred animal or plant; heterozygote. *a.* Cross-bred; heterozygous.

hybrid incapacitation, — hybrid sterility and inviability, inclusively.

hybrid swarms,—populations consisting of descendants of species hybrids, as at borders between geographical areas populated by these species.

hybridisation (hī'brĭdīzā'shŭn) *n.* [L. *hibrida*, cross.] Act or process of hybridising; state of being hybridised; cross-fertilisation.

hybridise (hī'brĭdīz) *v.* [L. *hibrida*, cross.] To interbreed, to cross, to produce hybrids.

hybridism (hī'brĭdĭzm) *n.* [L. *hibrida*, cross.] The state or quality of being a hybrid.

hydathode (hī'dăthōd) *n.* [Gk. *hydatos*, of water; *hodos*, way.] An epidermal structure specialised for secretion, or for exudation, of water; water stoma.

hydatid (hī'dătĭd) *n.* [Gk. *hydatis*, watery vesicle.] Any vesicle or sac filled with clear watery fluid; sac containing encysted stages of larval tapeworms; vestige of Müllerian duct constituting appendix of testis, hydatid of Morgagni; stalked appendix of epididymis.

hydatiform (hī'dătĭfôrm) *a.* [Gk. *hydatis*, watery vesicle ; L. *forma*, shape.] Resembling a hydatid.

hydatigenous (hī'dătĭj'ēnŭs) *a.* [Gk. *hydatis*, watery vesicle ; *-genes*, producing.] Producing or forming hydatids.

hydranth (hī'drănth) *n.* [Gk. *hydor*, water ; *anthos*, flower.] A nutritive zooid in a hydroid colony.

hydrarch (hī'drârk) *n.* [Gk. *hydor*, water ; *arche*, beginning.] *Appl.* seres progressing from hydric towards mesic conditions.

hydric (hī'drĭk) *a.* [Gk. *hydor*, water.] Characterised by an abundant supply of moisture, *appl.* plants, environment.

hydroanemophilous (hī'dröănĕmŏf'ĭlŭs) *a.* [Gk. *hydor*, water ; *anemos*, wind ; *philos*, loving.] *Pert.* or having spores which are discharged after moistening of spore-producing structures, and become air-borne.

hydrocaulis (hī'drökôl'ĭs) *n.* [Gk. *hydor*, water ; L. *caulis*, stalk.] The branching vertical portion of coenosarc in a hydroid colony.

hydrobiology (hī'dröbīŏl'öjĭ) *n.* [Gk. *hydor*, water ; *bios*, life ; *logos*, discourse.] The study of the life of aquatic plants and animals.

hydrochoric (hī'drökō'rĭk) *a.* [Gk. *hydor*, water ; *chorein*, to spread.] Dispersed by water ; dependent on water for dissemination.

hydrocircus (hī'drösĕr'kŭs) *n.* [Gk. *hydor*, water ; *kirkos*, circle.] The hydrocoelic ring surrounding mouth in echinoderms.

hydrocladia (hī'drö'klăd'ĭă) *n. plu.* [Gk. *hydor*, water ; *kladion*, twig.] The secondary branches of a hydrocaulis.

hydrocoel (hī'drösēl) *n.* [Gk. *hydor*, water ; *koilos*, hollow.] The water-vascular system in echinoderms.

hydrocryptophyte, — hydrophyte, *q.v.*

hydrocyst (hī'drösĭst) *n.* [Gk. *hydor*, water ; *kystis*, bladder.] A dactylozooid.

hydroecium (hīdrē'sĭŭm) *n.* [Gk. *hydor*, water ; *oikos*, house.] A closed tube at upper end of a siphonophore ; an infundibulum.

hydroid (hī'droid) *n.*, *a.* [Gk. *hydor*, water ; *eidos*, form.] Elongated empty cell in central cylinder of mosses ; a tracheid ; the polyp of Hydrozoa.

hydrolysis (hīdrŏl'ĭsĭs) *n.* [Gk. *hydor*, water ; *lyein*, to dissolve.] The reaction between a chemical compound and the hydrogen and hydroxyl ions of water.

hydrome (hī'drōm) *n.* [Gk. *hydor*, water ; *mestos*, full.] Any tissue that conducts water ; also hydrom.

hydromegatherm (hī'drömĕg'ăthĕrm) *n.* [Gk. *hydor*, water ; *megas*, great ; *therme*, heat.] A plant which must have much moisture and heat to develop fully.

hydromorph (hī'drömŏrph) *n.* [Gk. *hydor*, water ; *morphe*, form.] A plant having the form and structure of a hydrophyte.

hydromorphic (hīdrömôr'fĭk) *a.* [Gk. *hydor*, water ; *morphe*, form.] Structurally adapted to an aquatic environment, as organs of water plants ; *appl.* or *pert.* soils permanently containing a surplus of water.

hydronasty (hī'drönăs'tĭ) *n.* [Gk. *hydor*, water ; *nastos*, close-pressed.] Plant movement induced by changes in atmospheric humidity.

hydrophilous (hī'drŏf'ĭlŭs) *a.* [Gk. *hydor*, water ; *philein*, to love.] Pollinated through agency of water.

hydrophobe (hī'dröfōb) *a.* [Gk. *hydor*, water ; *phobos*, fear.] Avoiding or repelling water ; *appl.* hairs of certain aquatic insects.

hydrophoric (hī'dröfŏr'ĭk) *a.* [Gk. *hydrophoros*, carrying water.] *Appl.* canal, the madreporic or stone canal, *q.v.*

hydrophyllium (hī'dröfĭl'ĭŭm) *n.* [Gk. *hydor*, water ; *phyllon*, leaf.] One of leaf-like transparent bodies arising above and partly covering the sporosacs in a siphonophore.

hydrophyte (hī'dröfīt) *n.* [Gk. *hydor*, water ; *phyton*, plant.] An aquatic plant ; *cf.* hygrophyte.

hydrophyton (hīdröfī'tŏn) *n.* [Gk. *hydor*, water ; *phyton*, plant.] A complete hydroid colony, root-like organ, stem and branches.

hydroplanula (hī'dröplăn'ūlă) *n.* [Gk. *hydor*, water ; L. *planus*, flat.] Stages between planula and actinula in larval history of coelenterates.

hydropolyp (hī'dröpŏl'ĭp) *n.* [Gk. *hydor*, water ; F. *polype*, polyp.] A polyp of a hydroid colony ; a hydrula.

hydroponics (hī'dröpŏn'ĭks) *n.* [Gk. *hydor*, water ; *ponos*, exertion.] The science and art of crop production in liquid culture media ; *cf.* water culture.

hydropore (hī'dröpōr) *n.* [Gk. *hydor*, water ; *poros*, opening.] The opening into right hydrocoel in echinoderm larvae.

hydropote (hī'dröpōt) *n.* [Gk. *hydropotes*, water-drinker.] A cell or cell - group, in some submerged leaves, easily permeable by water and salts.

hydropyle (hīdrŏp'ĭlē) *n.* [Gk. *hydor*, water ; *pyle*, gate.] Specialised area in cuticular membrane of embryo, for passage of water, as in grasshoppers.

hydrorhabd (hī'dröräbd) *n.* [Gk. *hydor*, water ; *rhabdos*, rod.] A rhabdosome, in graptolites.

hydrorhiza (hī'drörī'ză) *n.* [Gk. *hydor*, water ; *rhiza*, root.] The creeping root-like portion of coenosarc of a hydroid colony.

hydrosere (hī'drösēr) *n.* [Gk. *hydor*, water ; L. *serere*, to put in a row.] A plant succession originating in a wet environment.

hydrosome (hī'drösōm) *n.* [Gk. *hydor*, water ; *soma*, body.] The conspicuously hydra-like stage in a coelenterate life-history ; hydrosoma.

hydrospire (hī'dröspīr) *n.* [Gk. *hydor*, water ; L. *spira*, coil.] The folds on the stereom of blastoids, being respiratory structures.

hydrostatic (hī'dröstăt'ĭk) *a.* [Gk. *hydor*, water ; *statikos*, causing to stand.] *Appl.* organs of flotation, as air sacs in aquatic larvae of insects.

hydrostome (hī'dröstōm) *n.* [Gk. *hydor*, water ; *stoma*, mouth.] The mouth of a hydroid polyp.

hydrotaxis (hī'drötăk'sĭs) *n.* [Gk. hydor, water ; *taxis*, arrangement.] Response of organisms to stimulus of moisture.

hydrotheca (hī'dröthē'kă) *n.* [Gk. *hydor*, water ; *theke*, cup.] Cup-like structure into which the polyp may withdraw, in many coelenterates.

hydrotropic (hī'drötrŏp'ĭk) *a.* [Gk. *hydor*, water ; *trope*, turn.] *Appl.* curvature of a plant organ towards a greater degree of moisture.

hydrotropism (hī'drŏt'röpĭzm) *n.* [Gk. *hydor*, water ; *trepein*, to turn.] Response to stimulus of water.

hydroxycobalamin,—vitamin B_{12b}.

hydrula (hī'droolă) *n.* [Gk. *hydor*, water.] Hypothetical simple polyp.

hyetal (hī'ëtăl) *a.* [Gk. *hyetos*, rain.] *Pert.* rain ; *pert.* precipitation.

hygiene (hī'jēn) *n.* [Gk. *hygieinos*, healthful.] That part of biology dealing with health preservation.

hygric (hī'grĭk) *a.* [Gk. *hygros*, wet.] Humid ; tolerating, or adapted to, humid conditions. *Opp.* xeric.

hygrochasy (hī'grökā'sĭ) *n.* [Gk. *hygros*, wet ; *chasis*, separation.] Dehiscence of seed vessels when induced by moisture ; *cf.* xerochasy.

hygrokinesis (hī'grökīnē'sĭs) *n.* [Gk. *hygros*, wet ; *kinesis*, movement.] Movement in response to change in humidity.

hygrophilous (hīgrŏf'ĭlŭs) *a.* [Gk. *hygros*, wet ; *philein*, to love.] Inhabiting moist or marshy places.

hygrophyte (hī'gröfīt) *n.* [Gk. *hygros*, wet ; *phyton*, plant.] A plant which thrives in plentiful moisture ; *cf.* hydrophyte.

hygroplasm (hī'gröplăzm) *n.* [Gk. *hygros*, wet ; *plasma*, mould.] The more liquid part of protoplasm, *opp.* stereoplasm.

hygroscopic (hī'grŏskŏp'ĭk) *a.* [Gk. *hygros*, wet; *skopein*, to regard.] Sensitive to, or retaining, moisture.

hylion (hī'lĭŏn) *n.* [Gk. *hyle*, wood; *on*, being.] Forest climax; hylium.

hylogamy (hīlŏg'ămĭ) *n.* [Gk. *hyle*, material; *gamos*, marriage.] The fusion of gametes, *opp.* somatogamy; syngamy.

hylophagous (hīlŏf'ăgŭs) *a.* [Gk. *hyle*, wood; *phagein*, to eat.] Eating wood; *appl.* certain insects.

hylophyte (hī'lŏfīt) *n.* [Gk. *hyle*, wood; *phyton*, plant.] A plant growing in woods.

hylotomous (hī'lŏt'ŏmŭs) *a.* [Gk. *hyle*, wood; *temnein*, to cut.] Wood-cutting; *appl.* certain insects.

hymen (hī'mĕn) *n.* [Gk. *hymen*, membrane.] Thin fold of mucous membrane at orifice of vagina.

hymenial (hīmē'nĭăl) *a.* [Gk. *hymen*, skin.] *Pert.* hymenium.

hymeniferous (hī'mĕnĭf'ĕrŭs) *a.* [Gk. *hymen*, skin; L. *ferre*, to carry.] Having a hymenium.

hymeniform (hī'mĕnĭfôrm) *a.* [Gk. *hymen*, skin; L. *forma*, form.] Formed like a palisade of club-shaped cells; *appl.* cuticle of fleshy fungi.

hymenium (hīmē'nĭŭm) *n.* [Gk. *hymen*, skin.] The outermost layer of mushroom lamellae, or of other fungi, consisting of spore-producing cells interspersed with barren cells or paraphyses.

hymenoid (hī'mĕnoid) *a.* [Gk. *hymen*, membrane; *eidos*, form.] Membranoid; membranous; resembling a hymenium; hymeniform.

hymenophore (hī'mĕnŏfōr) *n.* [Gk. *hymen*, skin; *pherein*, to carry.] The hymenial portion of sporophore of a fungus.

hymenopodium (hī'mĕnŏpō'dĭŭm) *n.* [Gk. *hymen*, membrane; *pous*, foot.] The tissue between trama and subhymenium, as in cup fungi and agarics.

hymenopterous (hī'mĕnŏp'tĕrŭs) *a.* [Gk. *hymen*, skin; *pteron*, wing.] Having membranous wings; *appl.* certain insects.

hyobranchial (hī'ŏbrăng'kĭăl) *a.* [Gk. *Υ*; *brangchia*, gills.] *Pert.* hyoid and branchial arches.

hyoepiglottic (hī'ŏĕpĭglŏt'ĭk) *a.* [Gk. *Υ*; *epi*, upon; *glotta*, tongue.] Connecting hyoid and epiglottis.

hyoglossal (hī'ŏglŏs'ăl) *a.* [Gk. *Υ*; *glossa*, tongue.] *Pert.* tongue and hyoid; *appl.* membrane and muscle.

hyoid (hī'oid) *a.* [Gk. *hyoeides*, *Υ*-shaped.] *Pert.* or designating a bone or series of bones lying at base of tongue and developed from hyoid arch of embryo; *appl.* a sclerite enclosing pharynx in some insects; hyoidean. *n.* The hyoid bone.

hyoidean (hīoid'ēăn) *a.* [Gk. *hyoeides*, *Υ*-shaped.] *Pert.* or associated with the hyoid arch or bone; *appl.* a branch of first efferent branchial vessel, or of lingual artery; *appl.* nerve, the posterior post-trematic nerve.

hyoideus (hīoid'ēŭs) *n.* [Gk. *hyoeides*, *Υ*-shaped.] A nerve which supplies mucosa of mouth and muscles of hyoid region.

hyomandibular (hī'ŏmăndĭb'ūlăr) *a.* [Gk. *Υ*; L. *mandibulum*, jaw.] *Pert.* hyoid and mandible; *pert.* dorsal segment of hyoid arch in fishes.

hyomental (hī'ŏmĕn'tăl) *a.* [Gk. *Υ*; L. *mentum*, chin.] *Pert.* hyoid and chin.

hyoplastron (hī'ŏplăs'trŏn) *n.* [Gk. *Υ*; F. *plastron*, breast-plate.] The second lateral plate in plastron of Chelonia.

hyostapes (hī'ŏstā'pēz) *n.* [Gk. *Υ*; L.L. *stapes*, stirrup.] Lower portion of columellar primordium which gives rise to part of columella in some reptiles.

hyosternum (hī'ŏstĕr'nŭm) *n.* [Gk. *Υ*; *sternon*, breast.] Hyoplastron.

hyostylic (hī'ŏstīl'ĭk) *a.* [Gk. *Υ*; *stylos*, pillar.] Having jaw articulated to skull by hyomandibular or corresponding part; exhibiting hyostyly; *cf.* autostylic.

hyosymplecticum (hī'ŏsĭmplĕk'tĭkŭm) *n.* [Gk. *Y*; *symplektos*, plaited together.] The cartilaginous primordium from which hyomandibular and symplecticum are derived.

hyothyroid (hī'ŏthī'roid) *a.* [Gk. *Y*; *thyreos*, shield; *eidos*, like.] *Pert.* hyoid bone and thyroid cartilage of larynx; *appl.* ligaments, membrane.

hypallelomorph (hīp'ălēl'ŏmôrf) *n.* [Gk. *hypo*, under; *allelon*, of one another; *morphe*, form.] Allelomorphs which under certain conditions are themselves compound.

hypandrium (hīpăn'drĭŭm) *n.* [Gk. *hypo*, under; *aner*, male.] Subgenital plate or ninth abdominal sternite of certain insects.

hypanthium (hīpăn'thĭŭm) *n.* [Gk. *hypo*, under; *anthos*, flower.] Any enlargement of the torus.

hypanthodium (hīp'ănthō'dĭŭm) *n.* [Gk. *hypo*, under; *anthodes*, like flowers.] An inflorescence with concave capitulum on whose walls the flowers are arranged.

hypantrum (hīpăn'trŭm) *n.* [Gk. *hypo*, under; *antron*, cave.] Notch on vertebrae of certain reptiles for articulation with hyposphene.

hypapophysis (hīp'ăpŏf'ĭsĭs) *n.* [Gk. *hypo*, under; *apo*, upon; *phyein*, to grow.] A ventral process on a vertebral centrum.

hyparterial (hīp'ârtē'rĭăl) *a.* [Gk. *hypo*, under; L. *arteria*, artery.] Situated below an artery; *appl.* branches of bronchi below pulmonary artery.

hypaxial (hĭpăk'sĭăl) *a.* [Gk. *hypo*, under; L. *axis*, axis.] Ventral; below vertebral column; *appl.* muscles.

hyperapophysis (hī'pĕrăpŏf'ĭsĭs) *n.* [Gk. *hyper*, above; *apo*, from; *phyein*, to grow.] A postero-lateral process of dorsal side of vertebra.

hyperchromasy (hī'pĕrkrō'măsĭ) *n.* [Gk. *hyper*, above; *chroma*, colour.] A relatively superabundant supply of chromatin to cytoplasm in a cell.

hyperchromatosis (hī'pĕrkrō'mătōsĭs) *n.* [Gk. *hyper*, above; *chroma*, colour.] Excess of nuclear substance in a cell previous to division.

hypercoracoid (hī'pĕrkŏr'ăkoid) *a.* [Gk. *hyper*, above; *korax*, crow; *eidos*, form.] *Pert.* or designating upper bone at base of pectoral fin in fishes.

hypercyesis (hī'pĕrsīē'sis) *n.* [Gk. *hyper*, above; *kyesis*, conception.] Superfoetation; additional fertilisation in a mammal already pregnant.

hyperfeminisation,—condition of a feminised male with female characteristics exaggerated, as in small size and weight.

hypergamesis (hī'pĕrgămē'sĭs) *n.* [Gk. *hyper*, above; *gamos*, marriage.] Process of absorption by female of excess spermatozoa.

hypermasculinisation, — condition of a masculinised female with male characteristics exaggerated, as in large proportions, appearance of male secondary sexual characters.

hypermetamorphosis (hī'pĕrmĕt'ămôr'fōsĭs) *n.* [Gk. *hyper*, above; *meta*, after; *morphosis*, shaping.] A protracted and thoroughgoing metamorphosis; metamorphosis involving two or more distinct types of larval instar, in certain insects.

hypermorphosis (hī'pĕrmôr'fōsĭs) *n.* [Gk. *hyper*, above; *morphosis*, shaping.] The development of additional characters, in comparison with the adult ancestral stage.

hyperparasite (hī'pĕrpăr'ăsīt) *n.* [Gk. *hyper*, above; *para*, beside; *sitos*, food.] A parasite which is parasitic on or in another parasite.

hyperphalangy (hī'pĕrfăl'ănjĭ) *n.* [Gk. *hyper*, above; *phalangx*, line of battle.] Condition of having digits with more than normal number of phalanges.

hyperpharyngeal (hī'pĕrfărĭn'jēăl) *a.* [Gk. *hyper*, above; *pharyngx*, gullet.] Dorsally to the pharynx; *appl.* gill or bar in Salpidae.

hyperpituitarism (hī'pĕrpĭtū'ĭtărĭzm) *n.* [Gk. *hyper*, above; L. *pituita*, phlegm.] Overaction of pituitary gland, resulting in gigantism or giantism; hyperhypophysism.

hyperplasia (hī′pĕrplā′siă) *n.* [Gk. *hyper*, above ; *plassein*, to mould.] Overgrowth ; excessive or hyperplastic development due to increase in number of cells ; *cf.* hypertrophy.

hyperploid (hī′pĕrploid) *a.* [Gk. *hyper*, above ; *haploos*, onefold ; *eidos*, form.] Aneuploid with extra chromosomes, *opp.* hypoploid.

hyperpnoea (hī′pĕrpnē′ă) *n.* [Gk. *hyper*, above ; *pnoe*, breath.] Rapid breathing due to insufficient supply of oxygen.

hypersensitivity (hī′pĕrsĕn′sĭtĭv′ĭtĭ) *n.* [Gk. *hyper*, above ; L. *sentire*, to feel.] A condition of being unduly sensitive to a stimulus.

hypertely (hīpĕr′tĕlĭ) *n.* [Gk. *hyper*, above ; *telos*, end.] Excessive imitation in colour or pattern, being of problematical utility ; overdevelopment, as canines of Babirusa ; hypertelia.

hypertensin,—angiotonin, *q.v.*

hypertonia (hī′pĕrtō′nĭă) *n.* [Gk. *hyper*, above ; *tonos*, tone.] Excessive tonicity.

hypertrophy (hīpĕr′trŏfĭ) *n.* [Gk. *hyper*, above ; *trophe*, nourishment.] Excessive growth due to increase in size of cells ; *cf.* hyperplasia.

hypha (hī′fă) *n.* [Gk. *hyphe*, web.] The thread-like element or filament of vegetative mycelium of a fungus ; filamentous cell in medulla of an algal thallus.

hyphal,—of, or *pert.*, hyphae or a hypha.

hyphasma (hĭfăz′mă) *n.* [Gk. *hyphasma*, thing woven.] A barren mycelium ; a cord of mycelium.

hyphodrome (hī′fŏdrōm) *a.* [Gk. *hyphe*, web ; *dromos*, course.] Running throughout the tissues ; *appl.* thick leaves where veins are not visible from surface.

hyphopodium (hīfŏpō′dĭŭm) *n.* [Gk. *hyphe*, web ; *pous*, foot.] A hyphal branch with enlarged terminal cell or haustorium for attaching the hypha, as in some Ascomycetes.

hyphostroma,—mycelium.

hypnobasidium, — sclerobasidium, *q.v.*

hypnocyst (hĭp′nŏsĭst) *n.* [Gk. *hypnos*, sleep ; *kystis*, bladder.] Cyst in which contained organism simply rests ; dormant cyst.

hypnody (hĭp′nŏdĭ) *n.* [Gk. *hypnodia*, sleepiness.] The long resting period of certain larval forms.

hypnogenic (hĭp′nŏjĕn′ĭk) *a.* [Gk. *hypnos*, sleep ; *-genes*, producing.] Sleep-inducing ; *appl.* influences which tend to produce hypnosis.

hypnosperm (hĭp′nŏspĕrm) *n.* [Gk. *hypnos*, sleep ; *sperma*, seed.] A hypnospore.

hypnosporangium (hĭp′nŏspŏrăn′jĭŭm) *n.* [Gk. *hypnos*, sleep ; *sporos*, seed ; *anggeion*, vessel.] A sporangium containing resting spores.

hypnospore (hĭp′nŏspōr) *n.* [Gk. *hypnos*, sleep ; *sporos*, seed.] A resting spore ; a zygote that remains in a quiescent condition during winter.

hypnote (hĭp′nōt) *n.* [Gk. *hypnos*, sleep.] An organism in a dormant condition.

hypnozygote (hĭp′nŏzĭgōt) *n.* [Gk. *hypnos*, sleep ; *zygotos*, yoked.] A zygote that becomes encysted, thereby constituting a hypnospore, *e.g.* oospore, zygospore.

hypoachene (hī′pŏākēn′) *n.* [Gk. *hypo*, under ; *a*, not ; *chainein*, to gape.] Achene developed from an inferior ovary.

hypoarion (hī′pŏā′rĭŏn) *n.* [Gk. *hypo*, under ; *oarion*, little egg.] A small lobe below the optic lobes of most teleosts.

hypobasal (hī′pŏbā′săl) *n.* [Gk. *hypo*, under ; *basis*, base.] The lower segment of a developing ovule, which ultimately gives rise to the root. *Opp.* epibasal.

hypobasidium (hī′pŏbăsĭd′ĭŭm) *n.* [Gk. *hypo*, under ; *basis*, base ; *idion*, *dim.*] Basal cell or part of a heterobasidium, in which nuclei unite, and which gives rise to an epibasidium ; a probasidium.

hypobenthos (hī′pŏbĕn′thos) *n.* [Gk. under ; *benthos*, depths of the sea.] The fauna of the sea-bottom below 500 fathoms.

hypoblast (hī'pöblăst) *n.* [Gk. *hypo*, under; *blastos*, bud.] The inner germ-layer in a gastrula.

hypoblastic (hī'pöblăs'tĭk) *a.* [Gk. *hypo*, under; *blastos*, bud.] *Pert.*, or derived from, the inner germ-layer; endodermal.

hypobranchial (hī'pöbrăng'kĭăl) *a.* [Gk. *hypo*, under; *brangchia*, gills.] *Pert.* lower or fourth segment of branchial arch.

hypocarp (hī'pökârp) *n.* [Gk. *hypo*, under; *karpos*, fruit.] A fleshy modified peduncle of certain fruits, as cashew-apple.

hypocentrum (hī'pösĕn'trŭm) *n.* [Gk. *hypo*, under; *kentron*, centre.] A transverse cartilage that arises below nerve cord and forms part of vertebral centrum.

hypocercal (hī'pösĕr'kăl) *a.* [Gk. *hypo*, under; *kerkos*, tail.] Having notochord terminating in lower lobe of caudal fin.

hypocerebral (hī'pösĕr'ëbrăl) *a.* [Gk. *hypo*, under; L. *cerebrum*, brain.] *Appl.* ganglion of stomatogastric system, linked to frontal and ventricular ganglia, also to corpora cardiaca.

hypochilium (hī'pökī'lĭŭm) *n.* [Gk. *hypo*, under; *cheilos*, lip.] The lower portion of lip of an orchid.

hypochondrium (hĭp'ökŏn'drĭŭm) *n.* [Gk. *hypo*, under; *chondros*, cartilage.] Abdominal region lateral to epigastric and above lumbar.

hypochord (hī'pökôrd) *n.* [Gk. *hypo*, under; *chorde*, cord.] A transitory subnotochordal rod in anamniotes.

hypochordal (hī'pökôr'dăl) *a.* [Gk. *hypo*, under; *chorde*, cord.] Below the notochord; *appl.* lower lobe of caudal fin; *appl.* bar of mesodermal tissue developing into ventral arch of atlas and amalgamating with fibrocartilages in other cervical vertebrae.

hypocleidium (hī'pöklīdĭ'ŭm) *n.* [Gk. *hypo*, under; *kleidion*, little key.] The interclavicle.

hypocone (hī'pökōn) *n.* [Gk. *hypo*, under; *konos*, cone.] Postero-internal cusp of upper molar; the part posterior to girdle in Dinoflagellata, *opp.* epicone.

hypoconid (hī'pökō'nĭd) *n.* [Gk. *hypo*, under; *konos*, cone.] Postero-buccal cusp of lower molar.

hypoconule (hīpökŏn'ūl) *n.* [Gk. *hypo*, under; *konos*, cone.] Fifth or distal cusp of upper molar.

hypoconulid (hī'pökŏn'ūlĭd) *n.* [Gk. *hypo*, under; *konos*, cone.] Postero-mesial cusp of lower molar.

hypocoracoid (hī'pökŏr'ăkoid) *a.* [Gk. *hypo*, under; *korax*, crow; *eidos*, form.] *Pert.* lower bone at base of pectoral fin in fishes.

hypocotyl (hī'pökŏt'ĭl) *n.* [Gk. *hypo*, under; *kotyle*, cup.] That portion of stem below cotyledons in an embryo.

hypocotyledonary (hī'pökŏt'ĭlē'dŏnărĭ) *a.* [Gk. *hypo*, under; *kotyledon*, hollow.] Below the cotyledons.

hypocrateriform (hĭ̄p'ökrātĕr'ĭfôrm) *a.* [Gk. *hypo*, under; *krater*, bowl; L. *forma*, shape.] Saucer-shaped; having a gamopetalous corolla with long narrow tube, and limbs at right angles to tube; hypocraterimorphous.

hypodactylum (hī'pödăk'tĭlŭm) *n.* [Gk. *hypo*, under; *daktylos*, digit.] The under surface of a bird's toes.

hypoderma (hī'pödĕr'mă) *n.* [Gk. *hypo*, under; *derma*, skin.] Hypodermis; tissue just under epidermis in plants; hypoderm.

hypodermal (hī'pödĕr'măl) *a.* [Gk. *hypo*, under; *derma*, skin.] *Pert.* hypoderma; *pert.* hypodermis.

hypodermalia (hī'pödĕrmā'lĭă) *n. plu.* [Gk. *hypo*, under; *derma*, skin.] Sponge spicules situated just below the derma or skin.

hypodermic (hī'pödĕr'mĭk) *a.* [Gk. *hypo*, under; L. *dermis*, skin.] *Pert.* parts just under the skin.

hypodermis (hī'pödĕr'mĭs) *n.* [Gk. *hypo*, under; L. *dermis*, skin.] The cellular layer lying beneath and secreting the cuticle of Annulata, Arthropoda, etc.; hypoblast, *q.v.*; hypoderma, *q.v.*

hypodicrotic (hī'pōdīkrŏt'ĭk) *a.* [Gk. *hypo*, under; *di*, two; *krotein*, to beat.] Having two arterial beats for the one cardiac.

hypogaean,—hypogeal.

hypogastric (hĭp'ŏgăs'trĭk) *a.* [Gk. *hypo*, under; *gaster*, stomach.] *Pert.* lower median region of abdomen; *appl.* artery, vein, plexus, etc.

hypogastrium (hĭp'ŏgăs'trĭŭm) *n.* [Gk. *hypo*, under; *gaster*, stomach.] Lower median region of abdomen.

hypogastroid,—hypoischium, *q.v.*

hypogeal (hī'pŏjē'ăl) *a.* [Gk. *hypo*, under; *ge*, earth.] Undergound; *appl.* stems, etc.; also hypogean.

hypogenesis (hī'pŏjĕn'ĕsĭs) *n.* [Gk. *hypo*, under; *genesis*, origin.] Development without occurrence of alternation of generations.

hypogenous (hīpŏj'ĕnŭs) *a.* [Gk. *hypo*, under; *-genes*, produced.] Growing on lower surface of anything.

hypogeous (hī'pŏjē'ŭs) *a.* [Gk. *hypo*, under; *ge*, earth.] Growing or maturing under the soil surface.

hypoglossal (hī'pŏglŏs'ăl) *n.* [Gk. *hypo*, under; *glossa*, tongue.] The twelfth paired cranial nerve, distributed to base of tongue.

hypoglottis (hī'pŏglŏt'ĭs) *n.* [Gk. *hypo*, under; *glotta*, tongue.] The under part of tongue; a division of labium of beetles.

hypognathous (hīpŏg'năthŭs) *a.* [Gk. *hypo*, under; *gnathos*, jaw.] Having the lower jaw slightly longer than the upper; with mouth-parts ventral, *appl.* head of insects.

hypogynium (hī'pŏjĭn'ĭŭm) *n.* [Gk. *hypo*, under; *gyne*, female.] Structure supporting ovary in such plants as sedges.

hypogynous (hīpŏj'ĭnŭs) *a.* [Gk. *hypo*, under; *gyne*, female.] Inserted below the gynoecium, and not adherent; immediately below oogonium, *appl.* antheridium, as in some Peronosporales.

hypohyal (hī'pŏhī'ăl) *n.* [Gk. *hypo*, under; *hyoeides*, *Y*-shaped.] The hyoid element lying between ceratohyal and basihyal.

hypoischium (hī'pŏĭs'kĭŭm) *n.* [Gk. *hypo*, under; *ischion*, hip.] A small bony rod passing backwards from ischiadic symphysis and supporting ventral cloacal wall; hypogastroid; os cloacae.

hypolemmal (hī'pŏlĕm'ăl) *a.* [Gk. *hypo*, under; *lemma*, peel.] Beneath the sarcolemma; *appl.* arborisation of an axis cylinder in a motor plate.

hypolimnion (hī'pŏlĭmnī'ŏn, -lĭm'-nyŏn) *n.* [Gk. *hypo*, under; *limne*, lake.] The water between the thermocline and bottom of lakes. *Opp.* epilimnion.

hypomeral (hī'pŏm'ĕrăl) *a.* [Gk. *hypo*, under; *meros*, part.] Hypomeric; *appl.* slender bones among lower trunk muscles in some fishes.

hypomere (hī'pŏmēr) *n.* [Gk. *hypo*, under; *meros*, part.] Lower or lateral plate zone of coelomic pouches.

hypomeron (hīpŏm'ĕrŏn) *n.* [Gk. *hypo*, under; *meros*, part.] The lateral inflexed side of a coleopterous prothorax.

hypomorph (hī'pŏmôrf) *n.* [Gk. *hypo*, under; *morphe*, form.] A gene having a smaller effect than its wild-type allelomorph.

hyponasty (hī'pŏnăstĭ) *n.* [Gk. *hypo*, under; *nastos*, close-pressed.] The state of growth in a flattened structure in which the under surface grows more vigorously than the upper.

hyponeural (hī'pŏnū'răl) *a.* [Gk. *hypo*, under; *neuron*, nerve.] *Appl.* system of radial and transverse motor nerves in echinoderms.

hyponome (hī'pŏnōm) *n.* [Gk. *hyponomos*, water-pipe.] The funnel of Cephalopoda.

hyponychium (hī'pŏnĭk'ĭŭm) *n.* [Gk. *hypo*, under; *onyx*, nail.] Layer of epidermis on which nail rests.

hyponym (hī'pŏnĭm) *n.* [Gk. *hypo*, under; *onyma*, name.] A generic name not founded on a type species.

hypoparatype (hī′pŏpăr′ătīp) *n.* [Gk. *hypo*, under; *para*, beside; *typhos*, pattern.] A specimen originally indicating a new species, but not chosen as a type specimen; *cf.* holotype, paratype.

hypopetalous (hī′pŏpĕt′ălŭs) *a.* [Gk. *hypo*, under; *petalon*, leaf.] Having corolla inserted below, and not adherent to, gynoecium.

hypophamine,—*see* pitocin, pitressin.

hypophare (hī′pŏfār) *n.* [Gk. *hypo*, under; *pharos*, cloth.] Lower part of sponge, in which there are no chambers; *cf.* spongophare.

hypopharyngeal (hī′pŏfărĭn′jēăl) *a.* [Gk. *hypo*, under; *pharyngx*, pharynx.] *Pert.* or situated below or on lower surface of pharynx.

hypopharynx (hī′pŏfăr′ĭngks) *n.* [Gk. *hypo*, under; *pharyngx*, pharynx.] The lingua of many insects; in mosquitoes, an outgrowth from base of labium which bears the salivary groove or duct.

hypophloeodal (hī′pŏflē′ŏdăl) *a.* [Gk. *hypo*, under; *phloios*, bark.] Living or growing under bark.

hypophragm (hī′pŏfrăm) *n.* [Gk. *hypo*, under; *phragma*, protection.] Operculum or epiphragm closing the opening of shell in some gastropods.

hypophyllium (hī′pŏfĭl′ĭŭm) *n.* [Gk. *hypo*, under; *phyllon*, leaf.] A scale-like leaf below a cladophyll; base of stipulate leaf, forming abscission layer.

hypophyllous (hī′pŏfĭl′ŭs) *a.* [Gk. *hypo*, under; *phyllon*, leaf.] Located or growing under a leaf.

hypophysectomy (hī′pŏfĭsĕk′tŏmĭ) *n.* [Gk. *hypo*, under; *physis*, growth; *ek*, out; *temnein*, cut.] Excision or removal of the pituitary gland.

hypophysial (hī′pŏfĭz′ĭăl) *a.* [Gk. *hypo*, under; *physis*, growth.] *Pert.* the hypophysis.

hypophysin (hīpŏf′ĭsĭn) *n.* [Gk. *hypo*, under; *physis*, growth.] Pituitary extract.

hypophysis (hīpŏf′ĭsĭs) *n.* [Gk. *hypo*, under; *physis*, growth.] The pituitary body; also hypophyseos; the olfactory pit in the lancelet; the last cell of the suspensor; the cell from which root-tip arises in dicotyledons.

hypopituitarism (hī′pŏpĭtū′ĭtărĭzm) *n.* [Gk. *hypo*, under; L. *pituita*, phlegm.] Deficiency of pituitary gland, resulting in a type of infantilism; hypohypophysism.

hypoplasia (hī′pŏplā′sĭă) *n.* [Gk. *hypo*, under; *plasis*, formation.] Developmental deficiency; hypoplastic development; deficient growth.

hypoplastron (hī′pŏplăs′trŏn) *n.* [Gk. *hypo*, under; F. *plastron*, breastplate.] The third lateral bony plate in plastron of Chelonia.

hypopleuron (hī′pŏploor′ŏn) *n.* [Gk. *hypo*, under; *pleuron*, side.] Region below metapleuron in insects.

hypoploid (hī′pŏploid) *a.* [Gk. *hypo*, under; *haploos*, onefold; *eidos*, form.] Aneuploid with fewer chromosomes; lacking one chromosome of the complement. *Opp.* hyperploid.

hypopneustic (hī′pŏnū′stĭk) *a.* [Gk. *hypo*, under; *pnein*, to breathe.] Having a reduced number of spiracles; *appl.* modified tracheal system in certain insects.

hypopodium (hī′pŏpō′dĭŭm) *n.* [Gk. *hypo*, under; *podion*, little foot.] Basal portion of a leaf, including stalk; style of carpel.

hypoproct (hī′pŏprŏkt) *n.* [Gk. *hypo*, under; *proktos*, anus.] Medial prolongation of terminal abdominal segment beneath the anus, in Diplopoda and some Insecta.

hypopteron (hī′pŏp′tĕrŏn) *n.* [Gk. *hypo*, under; *pteron*, feather.] Axillary feather in birds.

hypoptilum (hī′pŏp′tĭlŭm) *n.* [Gk. *hypo*, under; *ptilon*, down.] The aftershaft, *q.v.*

hypopus (hī′pŏpŭs) *n.* [Gk. *hypo*, under; *pous*, foot.] Cyst-like stage of Tyroglyphidae.

hypopyge (hī′pŏpī′jē) *n.* [Gk. *hypo*, under; *pyge*, rump.] Clasping organ of male dipterous insect; also hypopygium.

hyporadiolus (hī′pörădī′ölŭs) *n.* [Gk. *hypo*, under; L. *radiolus*, small rod.] A barbule of aftershaft of a feather.

hyporadius (hī′pörăd′ĭŭs) *n.* [Gk. *hypo*, under; L. *radius*, rod.] A barb of aftershaft of a feather.

hyporhachis (hī′pörā′kĭs) *n.* [Gk. *hypo*, under; *rhachis*, spine.] The stem of aftershaft of a feather; also hyporachis.

hyposkeletal (hī′pöskĕl′ëtăl) *a.* [Gk. *hypo*, under; *skeletos*, hard.] Lying beneath or internally to endoskeleton.

hyposomite (hī′pösō′mīt) *n.* [Gk. *hypo*, under; *soma*, body.] Ventral part of a body segment, as in Amphioxus.

hyposphene (hī′pösfēn) *n.* [Gk. *hypo*, under; *sphen*, wedge.] A wedge-shaped process on neural arch of vertebra of certain reptiles, which fits into hypantrum.

hypostasis (hīpŏs′tăsĭs) *n.* [Gk. *hypo*, under; *stasis*, standing.] Sediment or deposit, as of blood; recessiveness of non-allelomorphic characters; *cf.* epistasis.

hypostatic (hī′pöstăt′ĭk) *a.* [Gk. *hypo*, under; *stasis*, standing.] *Appl.* the recessive of two characters whose genes are not at the same time allelomorphs; exhibiting condition of hypostasis; *cf.* epistatic; *pert.* a sediment.

hypostereom (hī′pöstĕr′ëŏm) *n.* [Gk. *hypo*, under; *stereoma*, basis.] The third or inner layer of thecal plates, of Cystidea; the inner layer of integument, of Crinoidea.

hypostoma (hīpŏs′tömă) *n.* [Gk. *hypo*, under; *stoma*, mouth.] The fold bounding posterior margin of oral aperture in crustaceans; labrum or median preoral plate in trilobites; oral projection or manubrium of a hydrozoan; anteroventral region of insect head; ventral mouth part of ticks; hypostome.

hypostomatic (hī′pöstŏmăt′ĭk) *a.* [Gk. *hypo*, under; *stoma*, mouth.] Situated beneath stomata of plant epidermis; *appl.* chamber or cavity.

hypostomatous (hī′pöstŏm′ătŭs) *a.* [Gk. *hypo*, under; *stoma*, mouth.] Having stomata on under surface; having mouth placed on lower or ventral side.

hypostracum (hīpŏs′trăkŭm) *n.* [Gk. *hypo*, under; *ostrakon*, shell.] Inner primary layer or endocuticle of exoskeleton in Acarina.

hypostroma (hī′pöstrō′mă) *n.* [Gk. *hypo*, under; *stroma*, bedding.] Basal part of a fungal stroma; entostroma, *q.v.* *Cf.* epistroma.

hypotarsus (hī′pötâr′sŭs) *n.* [Gk. *hypo*, under; L. *tarsus*, ankle.] The calcaneum of a bird.

hypothalamus (hī′pöthăl′ămŭs) *n.* [Gk. *hypo*, under; *thalamos*, chamber.] Region below thalamus, and structures forming greater part of floor of third ventricle.

hypothallus (hī′pöthăl′ŭs) *n.* [Gk. *hypo*, under; *thallos*, young shoot.] Layer bearing sporangia in Myxomycetes; a sclerotium; undifferentiated hyphal growth, or marginal outgrowth, in lichens.

hypotheca (hīpöthē′kă) *n.* [Gk. *hypo*, under; *theke*, box.] Theca covering hypocone in Dinoflagellata; younger half of frustule in diatoms.

hypothecium (hīpöthē′sĭŭm, -shĭŭm) *n.* [Gk. *hypo*, under; *theke*, box.] The layer of dense hyphal threads below the thecium in lichens; subhymenium.

hypothenar (hī′pöthĕn′ăr) *a.* [Gk. *hypo*, under; *thenar*, palm of hand.] *Pert.* the prominent part of palm of hand above base of little finger.

hypothetical units, — the ultimate component parts of protoplasm; ultracellular units ranking between the molecule and the cell; also called variously, physiological units, pangens, gemmules, biophores, bioblasts, somacules, idiosomes, plasomes, micellae, plastidules, inotagmata, idioblasts, biogens, gemmae, microzymas, genes, gens, primordia.

hypotonic (hī'pötŏn'ĭk) *a.* [Gk. *hypo*, under; *tonos*, tension.] Having a lower osmotic pressure than that of another fluid, as of serum.

hypotrematic (hī'pötrēmăt'ĭk) *a.* [Gk. *hypo*, under; *trema*, pore.] *Appl.* the lower lateral bar of branchial basket of lamprey.

hypotrichous (hīpŏt'rĭkŭs) *a.* [Gk. *hypo*, under; *thrix*, hair.] Having cilia mainly restricted to under surface; with deficient hair.

hypotrochanteric (hī'pötrŏk'ăntĕr'ĭk) *a.* [Gk. *hypo*, under; *trochanter*, runner.] Beneath the trochanter.

hypotympanic (hī'pötĭmpăn'ĭk) *a.* [Gk. *hypo*, under; L. *tympanum*, drum.] Situated below the tympanum; *pert.* quadrate.

hypotype (hī'pötīp) *n.* [Gk. *hypo*, under; *typos*, pattern.] Any specimen described or figured in order to amplify or correct the identification of a species; plesiotype, *q.v.*

hypovalve (hī'pövălv) *n.* [Gk. *hypo*, under; L. *valva*, fold.] The antapical part of envelope in certain Dinoflagellata; hypocone.

hypoxanthine (hī'pözăn'thĭn) *n.* [Gk. *hypo*, under; *xanthos*, yellow.] A crystalline nitrogenous substance found in glandular and muscle tissue and in some seeds; $C_5H_4ON_4$.

hypozygal (hīpŏz'ĭgăl) *n.* [Gk. *hypo*, under; *zygon*, yoke.] Lower ossicle of a syzygial pair bearing no pinnule.

hypsiloid,—ypsiloid.

hypsodont (hĭp'södŏnt) *a.* [Gk. *hypsos*, height; *odous*, tooth.] *Pert.* or designating teeth with high crowns and short roots; hypselodont.

hypsophyll (hĭp'söfĭl) *n.* [Gk. *hypsi*, high; *phyllon*, leaf.] Any leaf beneath the sporophylls; bract, or bracteole.

hypural (hīpū'răl) *a.* [Gk. *hypo*, under; *oura*, tail.] *Pert.* a bony structure, formed by fused haemal spines of last few vertebrae, which supports caudal fin in certain fishes.

hysteranthous (hĭstërăn'thŭs) *a.* [Gk. *hysteros*, coming after; *anthos*, flower.] Leafing after appearance of flowers.

hysterectomy (hĭs'tĕrĕk'tömĭ) *n.* [Gk. *hystera*, womb; *ek*, out; *temnein*, to cut.] Excision of the uterus.

hysteresis (hĭstĕr'ēsĭs) *n.* [Gk. *hysteresis*, late arrival.] Lag in one of two associated processes or phenomena; lag in adjustment of external form to internal stresses, as in chromosome during spiralisation.

hysterochroic (hĭs'tërökrō'ĭk) *a.* [Gk. *hysteros*, later; *chros*, colour.] Gradually discolouring from base to tip; *appl.* ageing fruit-bodies.

hysterogenic (hĭs'tëröjĕn'ĭk) *a.* [Gk. *hysteros*, later; *genos*, birth.] Of later development or growth.

hysterophyte (hĭs'töröfīt) *n.* [Gk. *hysteros*, inferior; *phyton*, plant.] Saprophyte, *q.v.*; any parasitic fungus.

hysterosoma (hĭs'tërösō'mă) *n.* [Gk. *hysteros*, after; *soma*, body.] Part of body posterior to proterosoma and comprising metapodosoma and opisthosoma in Acarina.

hysterotely (hĭs'tërŏt'ëlĭ) *n.* [Gk. *hysteros*, after; *telos*, completion.] The retention or manifestation of larval characters in pupa or imago, or of pupal characters in imago; metathetely, *opp.* prothetely.

hyther (hīth'ër) *n.* [Gk. *hy*(*dor*), water; *ther*(*me*), heat.] Combined effect of moisture and temperature on an organism.

I

ichnite (ĭk'nīt) *n.* [Gk. *ichnos*, track.] A fossil footprint; ichnolite.

ichthyic (ĭk'thiĭk) *a.* [Gk. *ichthys*, fish.] *Pert.* or characteristic of fishes; ichthyoid.

ichthyodont (ĭk'thĭödŏnt) *n.* [Gk. *ichthys*, fish; *odous*, tooth.] A fossil tooth of fish.

ichthyodorulite (ĭk′thĭödŏr′ūlīt) *n.* [Gk. *ichthys*, fish ; *dory*, spear ; *lithos*, stone.] A fossil dermal or fin spine of fish.

ichthyoid, (ĭk′thĭoid) *a.* [Gk. *ichthys*, fish ; *eidos*, form.] Fish-like ; ichthyic.

ichthyolite (ĭk′thĭölīt) *n.* [Gk. *ichthys*, fish ; *lithos*, stone.] A fossil fish or part of one.

ichthyology (ĭkthĭŏl′öjĭ) *n.* [Gk. *ichthys*, fish ; *logos*, discourse.] The study of fishes.

ichthyopterygia (ĭk′thĭöptërĭj′ĭă) *n. plu.* [Gk. *ichthys*, fish ; *pteryx*, wing or fin.] Paired fish fins.

iconotype (īkō′nötīp) *n.* [Gk. *eikon*, image ; *typos*, pattern.] Representation, drawing or photograph, of a type.

icosandrous (ī′kösăn′drŭs) *a.* [Gk. *eikosi*, twenty ; *aner*, man.] Having twenty or more stamens.

icotype (ī′kōtīp) *n.* [Gk. *eikon*, image ; *typos*, pattern.] A representative specimen used for identification of a species.

id (ĭd) *n.* [Gk. *idios*, distinct.] A hypothetical structural unit ; the chromomere ; the instincts, collectively.

idant (ĭdănt) *n.* [Gk. *idios*, distinct.] A unit resulting from an aggregation of ids ; the chromosome.

identical (īdĕnt′ĭkăl) *a.* [L. *idem*, the same.] *Appl.* progeny having the same genes, as monozygotic twins ; *appl.* points on retina corresponding to those of the other eye.

ideoglandular (īdēöglăn′dūlăr) *a.* [Gk. *idein*, to see ; L. *glandula*, small acorn.] *Pert.* glandular activity induced by a mental image.

ideomotor (īdēömō′tŏr) *a.* [Gk. *idein*, to see ; L. *movere*, to move.] *Pert.* unwilled movement in response to a mental image.

ideotype (īdēötīp) *n.* [Gk. *idein*, to see ; *typos*, pattern.] Specimen, other than a topotype, named by the author who has described the species to which it belongs.

ideovascular (īdēövăs′kūlăr) *a.* [Gk. *idein*, to see ; L. *vasculum*, small vessel.] *Pert.* circulatory changes induced by a mental image.

idioandrosporous (ĭd′ĭöăndröspō′rŭs) *a.* [Gk. *idios*, distinct ; *aner*, male ; *sporos*, seed.] With androspores formed on filaments that do not bear oogonia.

idiobiology (ĭd′ĭöbīŏl′öjĭ) *n.* [Gk. *idios*, personal ; *bios*, life ; *logos*, discourse.] Biology of an individual organism ; autobiology.

idioblast (ĭd′ĭöblăst) *n.* [Gk. *idios*, distinct ; *blastos*, bud.] A hypothetical unit, *q.v.* ; plant cell containing oil, gum, calcium carbonate, or other product and which differs from the surrounding parenchyma.

idiocalyptrosome (ĭd′ĭökălĭp′trösōm) *n.* [Gk. *idios*, distinct ; *kalyptra*, covering ; *soma*, body.] Outer zone derived from idiosphaerosome in sperm cells.

idiochromatin (ĭd′ĭökrō′mătĭn) *n.* [Gk. *idios*, distinct ; *chroma*, colour.] Temporarily dormant generative chromatin ; *cf.* trophochromatin.

idiochromidia (ĭd′ĭökrōmĭd′ĭă) *n. plu.* [Gk. *idios*, distinct ; *chroma*, colour.] Sporetia ; generative chromidia ; *cf.* trophochromidia.

idiochromosome (ĭd′ĭökrō′mösōm) *n.* [Gk. *idios*, distinct ; *chroma*, colour ; *soma*, body.] A sex chromosome.

idiocryptosome (ĭd′ĭökrĭp′tösōm) *n.* [Gk. *idios*, distinct ; *kryptos*, hidden ; *soma*, body.] Inner zone derived from idiosphaerosome in sperm cells.

idiogram (ĭd′ĭögrăm) *n.* [Gk. *idios*, distinct ; *gramma*, drawing.] A diagrammatic representation of a characteristic chromosomal constitution.

idiomuscular (ĭd′ĭömŭs′kūlăr) *a.* [Gk. *idios*, peculiar ; L. *musculus*, muscle.] *Appl.* contraction of a degenerated muscle artificially stimulated.

idiophthartosome (ĭd′ĭöfthâr′tösōm) *n.* [Gk. *idios*, distinct ; *phthartos*, transitory ; *soma*, body.] The idiozome remnant.

idioplasm (ĭd'ĭöplăzm) *n.* [Gk. *idios*, distinct; *plasma*, mould.] Chromatin; the generative or germinal part of a cell; *cf.* trophoplasm.

idiosoma (ĭdĭösō'mă) *n.* [Gk. *idios*, distinct; *soma*, body.] The body, prosoma and opisthosoma, of Acarina.

idiosome (ĭd'ĭösōm) *n.* [Gk. *idios*, distinct; *soma*, body.] A hypothetical unit, *q.v.*; sphere or region of cytoplasm differing in viscosity from remainder of cell and surrounding the centriole or centrosome; idiozome, *q.v.*

idiosphaerosome (ĭd'ĭösfē'rösōm) *n.* [Gk. *idios*, distinct; *sphaira*, globe; *soma*, body.] Acrosome; central granule of idiosphaerotheca.

idiosphaerotheca (ĭd'ĭösfē'röthē'kă) *n.* [Gk. *idios*, distinct; *sphaira*, globe; *theke*, case.] Acroblast; vesicle containing acrosome in sperm cells.

idiothalamous (ĭd'ĭöthăl'ămŭs) *a.* [Gk. *idios*, distinct; *thalamos*, room.] *Appl.* lichens in which various parts are differently coloured from thallus.

idiothermous (ĭd'ĭöthĕr'mŭs) *a.* [Gk. *idios*, personal; *thermos*, hot.] Warm-blooded; homoiothermal.

idiotrophic (ĭd'ĭötrŏf'ĭk) *a.* [Gk. *idios*, personal; *trophe*, nourishment.] Capable of selecting food.

idiotype (ĭd'ĭötīp) *n.* [Gk. *idios* personal; *typos*, pattern.] Individual genotype.

idiovariation,—mutation, *q.v.*

idiozome (ĭd'ĭözōm) *n.* [Gk. *idios*, distinct; *zoma*, girdle.] In spermatogenesis a separated portion of archoplasm which ultimately becomes head-cap of spermatozoon; centrotheca; a cell-body of auxocytes containing the centrioles.

I-disc,—singly refracting or isotropic band in myofibrillae.

idorgan (ĭd'ôrgăn) *n.* [Gk. *idios*, distinct; *organon*, instrument.] A purely morphological multicellular unit which does not possess the features of a soma.

ileac (ĭl'ëăk) *a.* [Gk. *eilo*, to roll up.] *Pert.* ileum; ileal; *appl.* arteries, lymph-glands.

ileocaecal (ĭl'ëösē'kăl) *a.* [L. *ileum*, groin; *caecus*, blind.] *Pert.* ileum and caecum; *appl.* fossae, folds.

ileocolic (ĭl'ëökŏl'ĭk) *a.* [L. *ileum*, groin; Gk. *kolon*, colon.] *Pert.* ileum and colon; *appl.* artery, lymph-glands.

ileum (ĭl'ëŭm) *n.* [L. *ileum*, groin.] Lower part of small intestine; anterior part of hind-gut in insects.

iliac (ĭl'ĭăk) *a.* [L. *ilia*, flanks.] *Pert.* ilium, a pelvic bone; *appl.* artery, fossa, furrow, tuberosity, vein, etc.; *appl.* muscle, iliacus, from upper part of iliac fossa to side of tendon of psoas major; *appl.* processes of ischiopubic plate; forming base for pelvic fins.

iliocaudal (ĭl'ĭökô'dăl) *a.* [L. *ilia*, flanks; *cauda*, tail.] Connecting ilium and tail; *appl.* muscle.

iliococcygeal (ĭl'ĭökŏksĭj'ëăl) *a.* [L. *ilia*, flanks; Gk. *kokkyx*, cuckoo.] *Pert.* ileum and coccyx; *appl.* a muscle.

iliocostal (ĭl'ĭökŏs'tăl) *a.* [L. *ilia*, flanks; *costa*, rib.] In region of ilia and ribs; *appl.* several muscles.

iliofemoral (ĭl'ĭöfĕm'öräl) *a.* [L. *ilia*, flanks; *femur*, thigh.] *Pert.* ilium and femur; *appl.* a ligament.

iliohypogastric (ĭl'ĭöhī'pögăs'trĭk) *a.* [L. *ilia*, flanks; Gk. *hypo*, under; *gaster*, stomach.] *Pert.* ilium and lower anterior part of abdomen; *appl.* a nerve.

ilio-inguinal (ĭl'ĭöĭng'gwĭnăl) *a.* [L. *ilia*, flanks; *inguen*, groin.] In the region of ilium and groins; *appl.* a nerve.

ilio-ischiadic (ĭl'ĭöĭskĭăd'ĭk) *a.* [L. *ilia*, flanks; Gk. *ischion*, hip.] *Appl.* fenestra between ilium and ischium when these are fused at both ends.

iliolumbar (ĭl'ĭölŭm'băr) *a.* [L. *ilia*, flanks; *lumbus*, loin.] In region of ilium and loins; *appl.* artery, ligament, vein.

iliopectineal (ĭl'ĭöpĕktĭn'ëăl) *a.* [L. *ilia*, flanks; *pecten*, crest.] *Appl.*

an eminence marking point of union of ilium and pubis ; *appl.* fascia.

iliopsoas (ĭl'ĭösō'ăs, -psō'ăs) *n.* [L. *ilia*, flanks ; Gk. *psoa*, loins.] Iliacus and psoas major considered as one muscle.

iliotibial (ĭl'ĭötĭb'ĭăl) *a.* [L. *ilia*, flanks ; *tibia*, shin.] *Appl.* tract or band of muscle at lower end of thigh.

iliotrochanteric (ĭl'ĭötrōkăntĕr'ĭk) *a.* [L. *ilia*, flanks ; Gk. *trochanter*, runner.] Uniting ilium and trochanter of femur ; *appl.* a ligament.

ilium (ĭl'ĭŭm) *n.* [L. *ilium*, flank.] That part of hip-bone supporting the flank ; dorsal bone of pelvic arch.

illuvial (ĭlū'vĭăl) *a.* [L. *in*, into ; *luere*, to wash.] *Appl.* lower soil layers or B horizon.

imaginal (ĭmăj'ĭnăl) *a.* [L. *imago*, image.] *Pert.* an imago ; *appl.* larval discs, patches of cells from which new organs develop.

imago (ĭmā'gō) *n.* [L. *imago*, image.] The last or adult stage in insect metamorphosis ; the perfect insect.

imbibition (ĭm'bĭbĭsh'ŭn) *n.* [L. *in*, into ; *bibere*, to drink.] Absorption of fluids, as of water by roots.

imbricate (ĭm'brĭkāt) *a.* [L. *imbricare*, to tile.] Having parts overlapping each other like roof-tiles ; *appl.* scales, plates, bud-scales, bracts.

imbrication lines,—parallel growth lines of dentine ; contour lines of Owen.

imitative (ĭm'ĭtātĭv) *a.* [L. *imitari*, to imitate.] *Appl.* form, structure, habit, colouring, etc., assumed for protection or aggression.

immaculate (ĭmăk'ūlāt) *a.* [L. *in*, not ; *macula*, spot.] Without spots or marks of different colour.

immarginate (ĭmâr'jĭnāt) *a.* [L. *in*, not ; *margo*, edge.] Without a distinct margin.

immune body,—heat-stable antibody or lysin ; amboceptor, *q.v.*

immunise (ĭmūnīz', ĭm'ūnīz) *v.* [L. *immunis*, free.] To render invulnerable to a toxin, usually by injecting the toxin in small quantities at short intervals, without appearance of severe symptoms.

immunity (ĭmū'nĭtĭ) *n.* [L. *immunis*, free.] An organism's resistance, natural or acquired, to the onset of pathological conditions from infection, natural or artificial, by micro-organisms or their products.

impar (ĭm'pâr) *a.* [L. *impar*, unequal.] Not paired ; not existing in pairs ; azygous.

imparidigitate (ĭmpăr'ĭdĭj'ĭtāt) *a.* [L. *impar*, unequal ; *digitus*, finger.] Having an odd number of digits.

imparipinnate (ĭmpăr'ĭpĭn'āt) *a.* [L. *impar*, unequal ; *pinna*, wing.] Unequally pinnate ; pinnate with an odd terminal leaflet.

impedicellate (ĭmpĕd'ĭsĕlāt) *a.* [L. *in*, not ; *pediculus*, small foot.] Without short or slender stalks ; not having pedicels.

imperfect (ĭmpĕr'fĕkt) *a.* [L. *imperfectus*, unfinished.] Incomplete ; *appl.* fungi lacking the sexual spore stage.

imperforate (ĭmpĕr'förāt) *a.* [L. *in*, not ; *per*, through ; *foratus*, bored.] Not pierced ; *appl.* foraminiferous shells without fine pores in addition to principal opening.

impervious (ĭmpĕr'vĭŭs) *a.* [L. *in*, not ; *pervius*, passable.] Not permeable ; *appl.* nostrils with septum between nasal cavities.

implant (ĭm'plănt) *n.* [L. *in*, into ; *plantare*, to plant.] An organ or part transplanted to an abnormal position ; a graft.

implantation cone,—cone of origin, *q.v.*

implex (ĭm'plĕks) *n.* [L. *implexus*, plaited.] Endoplica or infolding of integument for muscle attachment in insects.

importation (ĭmpôrtā'shŭn) *n.* [L. *importare*, to carry into.] Ingestion by sinking of food into protoplasm of captor, as in certain protozoa.

impregnation (ĭm′prĕgnā′shŭn) *n.* [L. *impraegnare*, to fertilise.] Transference of spermatozoa from male to body of female; insemination.

impressio (ĭmprĕs′ĭō) *n.* [L. *impressio*, impression.] Impression or concavity in one organ or structure where in contact with another, as of surface of liver in contact with stomach, etc.

impuberal (ĭmpū′bĕrăl) *a.* [L. *impubes*, under age.] Prepubertal; sexually immature.

impulse (ĭm′pŭls) *n.* [L. *impulsus*, driven.] Self-propagated disturbance induced by excitation.

inantherate (ĭnăn′thĕrāt) *a.* [L. *in*, not; Gk. *antheros*, flowering.] Without anthers; anantherous.

inappendiculate (ĭn′ăpĕndĭk′ūlāt) *a.* [L. *in*, not; *appendicula*, small appendage.] Without appendages.

inarticulate (ĭnârtĭk′ūlāt) *a.* [L. *in*, not; *articulatus*, jointed.] Not segmented; not jointed.

inaxon (ĭnăk′sŏn) *n.* [Gk. *is*, fibre; *axon*, axis.] A nerve-cell with axis-cylinder branching at a distance from it.

inbreeding,—breeding through a succession of parents belonging to the same stock, or very nearly related.

Inca bones, — distinct portions of interparietal, found in skulls of former Peruvians; os interparietale.

incaliculate (ĭnkălĭk′ūlāt) *a.* [L. *in*, not; *caliculus*, small flower-cup.] Wanting a calicle.

incasement theory, — preformation theory, *q.v.*

incisal (ĭnsī′săl) *a.* [L. *incidere*, to cut into.] Cutting, as edge of a tooth.

incised (ĭnsīzd′) *a.* [L. *incisus*, cut into.] With deeply notched margin.

incisiform (ĭnsī′zĭfôrm) *a.* [L. *incisus*, cut into; *forma*, shape.] Incisor-shaped.

incisive (ĭnsī′sĭv) *a.* [L. *incisus*, cut into.] *Pert.* or in region of incisors; *appl.* bones, foramina, fossa.

incisor (ĭnsī′sŏr) *a.* [L. *incisus*, cut into.] Adapted for cutting, *appl.* mammalian premaxillary teeth. *n.* A crest or ridge of palatine process of maxilla.

incisura (ĭnsīsū′ră) *n.* [L. *incidere*, to cut into.] Notch, depression, or indentation, as in bone, stomach, liver, etc.

included (ĭnklood′ĕd) *a.* [L. *includere*, to shut in.] Having stamens and pistils not protruding beyond corolla; not exserted.

inclusion bodies,—intracellular particles, as pigment granules, mitochondria, Golgi bodies, microsomes, viruses, etc.

incomplete metamorphosis, — insect metamorphosis in which young are hatched in general adult form and develop without quiescent stage.

incongruent (ĭnkŏng′grooĕnt) *a.* [L. *incongruens*, not suiting.] Not suitable or fitting; *appl.* surface of joints which do not fit properly.

incoordination (ĭn′kōôr′dĭnā′shŭn) *n.* [L. *in*, not; *cum*, together; *ordo*, order.] Want of co-ordination; irregularity of movement due to loss of muscle control.

incrassate (ĭnkrăs′āt) *a.* [L. *incrassare*, to thicken.] Thickened; becoming thicker.

incretion (ĭnkrē′shŭn) *n.* [L. *in*, into; *cretus*, separated.] Internal secretion; autacoid.

incrustation (ĭnkrŭstā′shŭn) *n.* [L. *in*, into; *crusta*, shell.] Fossilisation by encasement in mineral substance.

incubation (ĭn′kūbā′shŭn) *n.* [L. *incubare*, to lie on.] The hatching of eggs by means of heat, natural or artificial; period between infection and appearance of symptoms induced by parasitic organisms.

incubatorium (ĭn′kūbătō′rĭŭm) *n.* [L. *incubare*, to lie on.] Temporary pouch surrounding mammary area, in which egg of Echidna is hatched.

incubous (ĭn′kūbŭs) *a.* [L. *incubare*, to lie on.] *Appl.* leaves so arranged that the base of each is covered by upper portion of next lower.

incudal (ĭn'kūdăl) *a.* [L. *incus*, anvil.] *Pert.* the incus ; *appl.* fold, fossa.

incudate (ĭnkū'dāt) *a.* [L. *incus*, anvil.] *Appl.* type of rotifer mastax with large and hooked rami and reduced mallei.

incumbent (ĭnkŭm'bĕnt) *a.* [L. *incumbere*, to lie upon.] Lying upon ; bent downwards to lie along a base ; *appl.* cotyledons so folded that flat sides are next radicle ; *appl.* hairs or spines applied lengthwise to their base ; *appl.* insect wings resting on abdomen.

incurrent (ĭnkŭr'ĕnt) *a.* [L. *in*, into ; *currere*, to run.] Leading into ; afferent ; *appl.* ectoderm - lined canals which admit water, in sponges ; *appl.* inhalant siphons of molluscs.

incurvate (ĭnkŭr'vāt) *a.* [L. *incurvus*, bent.] Curved inwards or bent back ; incurved, inflected.

incurvation (ĭn'kŭrvā'shŭn) *n.* [L. *incurvare*, to curve.] The doubling back on itself of a structure or organ, as of a spirochaete about to divide.

incus (ĭn'kŭs) *n.* [L. *incus*, anvil.] Part of a rotifer mastax ; the anvil-shaped ear ossicle of mammals.

indeciduate (ĭn'dēsĭd'ūāt) *a.* [L. *in*, not ; *decidere*, to fall down.] Non-caducous ; with maternal part of placenta not coming away at birth.

indeciduous (ĭn'dēsĭd'ūūs) *a.* [L. *in*, not ; *decidere*, to fall down.] Persistent ; not falling off at maturity ; everlasting ; evergreen.

indefinite (ĭndĕf'ĭnĭt) *a.* [L. *in*, not ; *definitus*, limited.] Not limited ; not determinate ; of no fixed number ; racemose, *q.v.*

indehiscent (ĭn'dēhĭs'ĕnt) *a.* [L. *in*, not ; *dehiscens*, gaping.] Not splitting at maturity ; *appl.* certain fruits.

indeterminate (ĭn'dētĕr'mĭnāt) *a.* [L. *in*, not ; *determinare*, to limit.] Indefinite ; undefined ; not classified.

indeterminate growth,—growth of stem, branch or shoot not limited or stopped by development of a terminal bud ; indefinite prolongation and subdivision of an axis.

indeterminate inflorescence,—growth of a floral axis by indefinite branching because unlimited by development of a terminal bud.

index,—the forefinger or digit next to the thumb ; a number or formula expressing ratio of one quantity to another.

indicators,—species characteristic of climatic, soil and other conditions in a particular region or habitat ; dominant species in a biotope.

indigenous (ĭndĭj'ĕnŭs) *a.* [L. *indigena*, native.] Belonging to the locality ; not imported ; native.

individual (ĭn'dĭvĭd'ūăl) *a.* [L. *in*, not ; *dividuus*, divisible.] *Pert.* a single example or unit, as individual variations of colour. *n.* A person or zooid of distinctive function of a hydrozoan colony.

individualism,—symbiosis in which the two parties together form what appears to be a single organism.

individuation,—development of interdependent functional units, as in colony formation ; organisation of morphogenetic processes ; regional or tissue differentiation ; process of developing into an individual.

indole-acetic acid,—*see* heteroauxin.

induced movement, — movement dictated and influenced by external stimulus, as plant curvature.

induction (ĭndŭk'shŭn) *n.* [L. *inducere*, to lead in.] Act or process of causing to occur ; process whereby a cell or tissue influences neighbouring cells or tissues ; lowering by one reflex of the threshold of another, spinal induction.

inductive stimulus,—an external stimulus which influences growth or behaviour of an organism.

indumentum (ĭn'dūmĕn'tŭm) *n.* [L. *indumentum*, covering.] The plumage of birds ; a hairy covering.

induplicate (ĭndū'plĭkāt) *a.* [L. *in*, in ; *duplex*, double.] In vernation, having bud-leaves bent or rolled without overlapping ; in aestivation, having bud sepals or petals folded inwards at points of contact.

induplicative (ĭndū′plĭkātĭv) *a.* [L. *in*, in; *duplex*, double.] *Appl.* vernation or aestivation with induplicate foliage or floral leaves respectively.

indurescent (ĭn′dūrĕs′ĕnt) *a.* [L. *indurescere*, to harden.] Becoming firmer or harder.

indusia,—*plu.* of indusium.

indusial (ĭndū′zĭăl) *a.* [L. *induere*, to put on.] Containing larval insect cases, as certain limestones; *pert.* the indusium.

indusiate (ĭndū′zĭāt) *a.* [L. *induere*, to put on.] Having an enveloping case, *appl.* insect larvae; having an indusium.

indusiform (ĭndū′zĭfôrm) *a.* [L. *induere*, to put on; *forma*, shape.] Resembling an indusium.

indusium (ĭndū′zĭŭm) *n.* [L. *induere*, to put on.] An outgrowth of plant epiderm covering and protecting a sorus, as in ferns; outgrowth hanging from top of stipe in certain fungi; cup-like fringe of hairs surrounding a stigma; an insect larva case; the supracallosal gyrus of the rhinencephalon, indusium griseum.

induviae (ĭndū′vĭē) *n. plu.* [L. *induviae*, garments.] Scale-leaves; leaves which remain attached to stem after withering.

induviate (ĭndū′vĭāt) *a.* [L. *induviae*, garments.] Covered with scale-leaves or induviae.

inequilateral (ĭnĕk′wĭlăt′ĕrăl) *a.* [L. *in*, not; *aequus*, equal; *latus*, side.] Having two sides unequal; having unequal portions on either side of a line drawn from umbo to gape of a bivalve shell.

inequilobate (ĭnĕk′wĭlō′bāt) *a.* [L. *in*, not; *aequus*, equal; *lobus*, lobe.] With lobes of unequal size.

inequivalve (ĭnĕk′wĭvălv) *a.* [L. *in*, not; *aequus*, equal; *valvae*, folding doors.] Having two valves of shell unequal; *appl.* molluscs.

inerm (ĭnĕrm′) *a.* [L. *inermis*, unarmed.] Without means of defence and offence; without spines; inermous.

inert (ĭnĕrt′) *a.* [L. *iners*, inactive.] Physiologically inactive; *appl.* heterochromatic region of chromosome with paucity of active genes.

inferior (ĭnfē′rĭŏr) *a.* [L. *inferior*, lower.] *Appl.* lower placed of two, farther down axis; growing or arising below another organ.

inferoanterior (ĭn′fĕröăntē′rĭŏr) *a.* [L. *inferus*, beneath; *anterior*, in front.] Below and in front.

inferobranchiate (ĭn′fĕröbrăng′kĭāt) *a.* [L. *inferus*, beneath; Gk. *brangchia*, gills.] With gills under margin of mantle, as in certain molluscs.

inferolateral (ĭn′fĕrölăt′ĕrăl) *a.* [L. *inferus*, beneath; *latus*, side.] Below and at or towards the side.

inferomedian (ĭn′fĕrömē′dĭăn) *a.* [L. *inferus*, beneath; *medius*, middle.] Below and about the middle.

inferoposterior (ĭn′fĕröpŏstē′rĭŏr) *a.* [L. *inferus*, beneath; *posterior*, behind.] Below and behind.

inferradial (ĭn′fĕrrā′dĭăl) *n.* [L. *inferus*, beneath; *radius*, radius.] Lower part of transversely bisected radials of certain fossil crinoids.

inflected (ĭnflĕk′tĕd) *a.* [L. *inflectere*, to bend in.] Curved or abruptly bent inwards or towards the axis; inflexed.

inflorescence (ĭn′flörĕs′ĕns) *n.* [L. *inflorescere*, to begin to blossom.] A flowering or putting forth blossoms; method in which flowers are arranged on an axis.

influents (ĭn′flooĕnts) *n. plu.* [L. *influere*, to flow into.] The animals present in a plant community, or those primarily dependent and acting upon the dominant plant species.

infra-axillary (ĭn′frăăk′sĭlărĭ) *a.* [L. *infra*, below; *axilla*, armpit.] Branching off below the axil.

infrabasal (ĭn′frăbā′săl) *n.* [L. *infra*, below; *basis*, base.] One of a series of plates, perradial in position, below the basals in crinoids.

infrabranchial (ĭn'frăbrăng'kĭăl) *a.* [L. *infra*, below; *branchiae*, gills.] Below the gills; *appl.* part of pallial chamber.

infracentral (ĭn'frăsĕn'trăl) *a.* [L. *infra*, below; *centrum*, centre.] Below a vertebral centrum.

infraciliature (ĭn'frăsĭl'ĭătūr) *n.* [L. *infra*, below; *cilia*, eyelashes.] The structures or organellae just below the cilia, consisting of kinetia, in Ciliata.

infraclavicle (ĭn'frăklăv'ĭkĕl) *n.* [L. *infra*, below; *clavicula*, little key.] Membrane bone occurring in pectoral girdle of some fishes.

infraclavicular (ĭn'frăklăvĭk'ūlăr) *a.* [L. *infra*, below; *clavicula*, small key.] Beneath the clavicle; *appl.* branches of brachial plexus; *appl.* fossa or triangle between deltoid and pectoralis major.

infracortical (ĭn'frăkôr'tĭkăl) *a.* [L. *infra*, below; *cortex*, bark.] Beneath the cortex.

infracostal (ĭn'frăkŏs'tăl) *a.* [L. *infra*, below; *costa*, rib.] Beneath the ribs; *appl.* muscles.

infradentary (ĭn'frădĕn'tărĭ) *a.* [L. *infra*, below; *dens*, tooth.] Beneath the dentary bone.

infraglenoid (ĭn'frăglē'noid) *a.* [L. *infra*, below; Gk. *glene*, socket; *eidos*, like.] Below glenoid cavity; *appl.* a tuberosity.

infrahyoid (ĭnfrăhī'oid) *a.* [L. *infra*, below; Gk. *hyoeides*, *Y*-shaped.] Beneath the hyoid; *appl* muscles.

infralabial (ĭn'frălā'bĭăl) *a.* [L. *infra*, below; *labium*, lip.] Beneath the lower lip.

inframarginal (ĭnfrămâr'jĭnăl) *a.* [L. *infra*, below; *margo*, margin.] Under the margin, or marginal structure; *appl.* a cerebral convolution; *appl.* certain plates on carapace of Chelonia below marginals; *appl.* lower of two series of plates round margin of stelleroid arms and discs.

inframaxillary (ĭn'frămăksĭl'ărĭ) *a.* [L. *infra*, below; *maxilla*, jaw.] Beneath maxilla; *appl.* nerves.

infranasal (ĭn'frănā'zăl) *n.* [L. *infra*, below; *nasus*, nose.] An additional nasal element in some Theromorpha.

infraorbital (ĭn'frăôr'bĭtăl) *a.* [L. *infra*, below; *orbis*, eye-socket.] Beneath the orbit; *appl.* artery, canal, foramen, groove, nerve, glands, etc.

infrapatellar (ĭn'frăpătĕl'ăr) *a.* [L. *infra*, below; *patella*, knee-cap.] *Appl.* pad of fat beneath patella; *appl.* bursa between tibia and ligamentum patellae.

infrarostral (ĭn'frărŏs'trăl) *a.* [L. *infra*, below; *rostrum*, snout.] Beneath a rostrum; *appl.* paired cartilages, derived from Meckel's cartilage, of lower part of suctorial mouth of tadpoles.

infrascapular (ĭn'frăskăp'ūlăr) *a.* [L. *infra*, below; *scapula*, shoulder-blade.] Beneath the scapula; *appl.* artery.

infraspecific (ĭn'frăspĕsĭf'ĭk) *a.* [L. *infra*, below; *species*, particular kind.] *Pert.* a subdivision of a species, as subspecies and varieties.

infraspinatous (ĭn'frăspīnā'tŭs) *a.* [L. *infra*, below; *spina*, spine.] Beneath the spine; beneath scapular spine; *appl.* muscle, fossa; infraspinous.

infrastapedial (ĭn'frăstăpē'dĭăl) *a.* [L. *infra*, below; *stapes*, stirrup.] Beneath stapes of ear; *appl.* part of columella.

infrasternal (ĭn'frăstĕr'năl) *a.* [L. *infra*, below; *sternum*, breast-bone.] Below the breast-bone; *appl.* notch superficially at lower end of sternum.

infratemporal (ĭn'frătĕm'pŏrăl) *a.* [L. *infra*, below; *tempora*, temples.] Beneath the temporal bone; *appl.* a crest and fossa.

infratrochlear (ĭn'frătrŏk'lēăr) *a.* [L. *infra*, below; *trochlea*, pulley.] Beneath the trochlea; *appl.* a nerve given off from nasociliary nerve.

infructescence (ĭn'frŭktĕs'ĕns) *n.* [L. *in*, into; *fructus*, fruit.] An inflorescence matured into a fruit; a composite or confluent fruit.

infundibula,—*plu.* of infundibulum; passages surrounded by air-cells in the lung.

infundibular (ĭn′fŭndĭb′ūlăr) *a.* [L. *infundibulum*, funnel.] Funnel-shaped; *appl.* an abdominal muscle; *appl.* corolla; infundibuliform; choanoid, *q.v.*; *pert.* infundibulum.

infundibulin (ĭnfŭndĭb′ūlĭn) *n.* [L. *infundibulum*, funnel.] An extract of posterior pituitary lobe causing decrease in renal water excretion; antidiuretin; infundin.

infundibulum (ĭn′fŭndĭb′ūlŭm) *n.* [L. *infundibulum*, funnel.] Any funnel-shaped organ or structure; *appl.* part of brain, of ethmoid bone, of right ventricle, etc.; conus arteriosus; a cephalopod siphon; part of bird's oviduct; flattened stomach-like cavity of ctenophore; septal funnel in Scyphozoa.

infuscate (ĭnfŭs′kāt) *a.* [L. *in*, into; *fuscus*, dark.] Tinged to appear dark, as insect wings.

infusoriform (ĭn′fūsō′rĭfôrm) *a.* [L. *infusus*, poured into; *forma*, shape.] Resembling an infusorian; *appl.* embryonic forms of Coelentera; *appl.* male form of Dicyemidae.

infusorigen (ĭn′fūsō′rĭjĕn) *n.* [L. *infusus*, poured into; *genos*, offspring.] A gastrula-like phase in development of certain Mesozoa.

ingest (ĭnjĕst′) *v.* [L. *ingestus*, taken in.] To convey food material into the alimentary canal or food-cavity.

ingesta (ĭnjĕs′tă) *n. plu.* [L. *ingestus*, taken in.] The sum-total of substances taken in by the body. *Opp.* egesta.

ingestion (ĭnjĕs′tĭŏn) *n.* [L. *ingestus*, taken in.] The swallowing or taking in of food-material.

ingluvies (ĭngloov′ĭēz) *n.* [L. *ingluvies*, crop.] The crop of a bird; a dilatation of oesophagus; the rumen.

inguinal (ĭng′gwĭnăl) *a.* [L. *inguen*, groin.] In region of groin.

inguinal ring,—*see* abdominal ring.

inguino-abdominal,—in region of abdomen and groin.

inguino-crural,—in region of groin and leg.

inhalant (ĭnhā′lănt) *a.* [L. *in*, into; *halare*, to breathe.] Adapted for inspiring or drawing in, as terminal pores of incurrent canals in sponges, or siphons in molluscs.

inhibin (ĭnhĭb′ĭn) *n.* [L. *inhibere*, to restrain.] A testicular hormone depressing gonadotrophic activity of prehypophysis.

inhibition (ĭn′hĭbĭsh′ŏn) *n.* [L. *inhibere*, to restrain.] Prohibition, or checking, of an action or process.

inhibitory (ĭnhĭb′ĭtŏrĭ) *a.* [L. *inhibere*, to restrain.] *Appl.* nerves which control movement or secretion.

inion (ĭn′ĭŏn) *n.* [Gk. *inion*, back of head.] The external protuberance of occipital bone.

initial (ĭnĭsh′ăl) *n.* [L. *initium*, beginning.] A cell which initiates differentiation of tissues, as in apical meristem, vascular cambium, etc.; histogen cell, primordial cell.

ink sac,—in Sepia, a pear-shaped body in wall of mantle cavity which contains the ink gland, secreting a black substance, ink or sepia, ejection of which is a means of defence.

innate (ĭn′nāt) *a.* [L. *innatus*, inborn.] Inherited; basifixed, *appl.* anther with filament attached only to base.

innervation (ĭn′nĕrvā′shŭn) *n.* [L. *in*, into; *nervus*, sinew.] Nerve-distribution; vital nerve force.

innidiation (ĭn′nĭdĭā′shŭn) *n.* [L. *in*, into; *nidus*, nest.] Colonisation or development of cells or organisms in a part of the body to which they have been transferred by metastasis, *q.v.*

innominate (ĭnnŏm′ĭnāt) *a.* [L. *in*, not; *nomen*, name.] Nameless; *appl.* various arteries and veins.

innominate artery, — truncus brachiocephalicus.

innominate bone,—the hip-bone or lateral half of pelvic girdle; os coxae, os innominatum.

innominate veins,—left and right brachiocephalic veins.

innovation (ĭn'övā'shŭn) *n.* [L. *innovare*, to renew.] A growth or shoot of mosses which develops into a new plant by dying-off of portion of parent-plant behind it ; basal vegetative shoot of grasses.

inocomma (ī'nökŏm'ă) *n.* [Gk. *is*, fibre ; *komma*, clause.] Portion of muscle fibril between telophragmata or Z discs ; inokomma ; sarcomere.

inocular (ĭnŏk'ūlăr) *a.* [L. *in*, into ; *oculus*, eye.] *Appl.* antennae inserted close to eye.

inoculum (ĭnŏk'ūlŭm) *n.* [L. *inoculare*, to engraft.] The cells, bacteria, spores, etc. introduced into a medium for cultures.

inocyte (ī'nösīt) *n.* [Gk. *is*, fibre ; *kytos*, hollow.] Elongated cell of fibrous tissue.

inogen (ī'nöjĕn) *n.* [Gk. *is*, fibre ; *gennaein*, to produce.] A nitrogenous substance of muscle tissue.

inoperculate (ĭn'ŏpĕr'kūlāt) *a.* [L. *in*, un- ; *operculum*, lid.] Without a lid or operculum.

inophragma (ī'nöfrăg'mă) *n.* [Gk. *is*, fibre ; *phragma*, fence.] The transverse membrane through adjacent myofibrillae ; mesophragma and telophragma ; M and Z lines bisecting A-and I-discs.

inosculate (ĭnŏs'kūlāt) *v.* [L. *in*, in ; *osculari*, to kiss.] To intercommunicate or unite, as vessels, ducts, etc. ; to anastomose.

inositol,—carbohydrate present in cells, the lipotropic anti-alopecia factor of bios, *q.v.* ; $C_6H_{12}O_6$.

inotagmata (ī'nötăg'mătă) *n. plu.* [Gk. *is*, fibre ; *tagma*, arrangement.] Hypothetical units, *q.v.*

inquiline (ĭn'kwĭlīn) *n.* [L. *inquilinus*, tenant.] Animal living in home of another and getting share of its food ; partner in commensalism ; an insect developing in gall produced by an insect of another species, being detrimental to the latter.

inscriptions, tendinous, — three fibrous bands crossing the rectus abdominis muscle.

insectivorous (ĭn'sĕktĭv'örŭs) *a.* [L. *insectum*, cut into ; *vorare*, to devour.] Insect-eating ; *appl.* certain animals and carnivorous plants.

insemination (ĭn'sĕmĭnā'shŭn) *n.* [L. *in*, in ; *seminatio*, sowing.] The introduction of semen or spermatozoa into female genital tract.

inserted (ĭnsĕr'tĕd) *a.* [L. *in*, in ; *serere*, to join.] United by natural growth.

insertion (ĭnsĕr'shŭn) *n.* [L. *insertus*, joined.] Point of attachment of organs, as of muscles, leaves ; point on which force of a muscle is applied.

insertional,—*appl.* translocation in which the portion between two breaks of a chromosome is transferred to a break in another chromosome ; *cf.* shift.

insessorial (ĭn'sĕsō'rĭăl) *a.* [L. *insidere*, to sit upon.] Adapted for perching.

insistent (ĭnsĭs'tĕnt) *a.* [L. *insistere*, to stand upon.] *Appl.* hind toe, of certain birds, whose tip only reaches the ground.

insolation (ĭnsölā'shŭn) *n.* [L. *in*, into ; *sol*, sun.] Exposure to sun's rays.

inspiration (ĭnspĭrā'shŭn) *n.* [L. *inspirare*, to inhale.] The act of drawing air into the lungs ; absorption of oxygen by plants.

instaminate (ĭnstăm'ĭnāt) *a.* [L. *in*, not ; *stamen*, thread.] Not bearing stamens.

instar (ĭn'stăr) *n.* [L. *instar*, form.] Insect at a particular stage between moults.

instipulate (ĭnstĭp'ūlāt) *a.* [L. *in*, not ; *stipula*, stalk.] Without stipules ; estipulate, exstipulate.

insula (ĭn'sūlă) *n.* [L. *insula*, island.] Island of Reil, a triangular eminence lying deeply in lateral fissure of temporal lobe ; islet of Langerhans, *q.v.* ; a blood island, *q.v.*

insulin (ĭn'sūlĭn) *n.* [L. *insula*, island.] The anti-diabetic endocrine product of pancreas, formed in β-cells of islets of Langerhans ; $C_{45}H_{69}O_{14}N_{11}S \cdot 3H_2O$.

integrifolious (ĭntĕg′rĭfō′lĭŭs) *a.* [L. *integer*, whole ; *folium*, leaf.] With entire leaves.

integripallial (ĭntĕg′rĭpăl′ĭăl), **integripalliate** (ĭntĕg′rĭpăl′ĭāt) *a.* [L. *integer*, whole ; *pallium*, mantle.] Having an unbroken pallial line ; *appl.* shells of molluscs with small or no siphons.

integument (ĭntĕg′ūmĕnt) *n.* [L. *integumentum*, covering.] A covering, investing, or coating structure or layer ; coat of ovule ; integumentum.

interacinous (ĭn′tĕrăs′ĭnŭs) *a.* [L. *inter*, between ; *acinus*, grape.] Among alveoli of a racemose gland ; interacinar.

interalveolar (ĭn′tĕrăl′vēŏlăr) *a.* [L. *inter*, among ; *alveolus*, small cavity.] Among alveoli ; *appl.* cell islets.

interamb (ĭntĕrămb′) *n.* [L. *inter*, between ; *ambulare*, to walk.] Interambulacral area.

interambulacral (ĭn′tĕrămbūlā′krăl) *a.* [L. *inter*, between ; *ambulare*, to walk.] *Appl.* area of echinoderm test between two ambulacral areas. *n.* A plate of that area.

interambulacrum (ĭn′tĕrămbūlā′krŭm) *n.* [L. *inter*, between ; *ambulare*, to walk.] The area between two ambulacral areas.

interarticular (ĭn′tĕrârtĭk′ūlăr) *a.* [L. *inter*, between ; *articulus*, joint.] Between articulating parts of bones ; *appl.* certain ligaments and fibro-cartilages.

interatrial (ĭn′tĕrā′trĭăl) *a.* [L. *inter*, between ; *atrium*, hall.] *Appl.* groove and septum separating the two atria of the heart.

interauricular (ĭn′tĕrôrĭk′ūlăr) *a.* [L. *inter*, between ; *auricula*, little ear.] Between auricles of heart.

interaxillary (ĭn′tĕrăk′sĭlărĭ) *a.* [L. *inter*, between ; *axilla*, armpit.] Placed between the axils.

interbrachial (ĭn′tĕrbrā′kĭăl) *a.* [L. *inter*, between ; *brachium*, arm.] Between arms, rays, or brachial plates.

interbrain,—diencephalon.

interbranchial (ĭn′tĕrbrăng′kĭăl) *a.* [L. *inter*, between ; *branchiae*, gills.] *Appl.* septum between successive gill slits.

interbreed (ĭn′tĕrbrēd′) *v.* [L. *inter*, between ; A.S. *brod*, brood.] To cross different varieties of plants or animals.

intercalare (ĭn′tĕrkăl′ărē) *n.* [L. *intercalaris*, inserted.] In many fishes and fossil amphibians, an additional element in the vertebra.

intercalarium (ĭn′tĕrkălā′rĭŭm) *n.* [L. *intercalaris*, inserted.] The third Weberian ossicle.

intercalary (ĭn′tĕrkăl′ărĭ, ĭntĕr′kălărĭ) *a.* [L. *intercalaris*, inserted.] Inserted between others ; *appl.* meristematic layers between masses of permanent tissue ; *appl.* growth elsewhere than at growing point ; *appl.* veins between main veins of insect wings ; *appl.* plates in Dinoflagellata ; *appl.* bands in diatoms ; *appl.* cartilage between neural arches, interneural or interdorsal plate.

intercapitular (ĭn′tĕrkăpĭt′ūlăr) *a.* [L. *inter*, between ; *capitulum*, little head.] Between capitula ; *appl.* veins of fingers and toes.

intercarotid (ĭn′tĕrkărŏt′ĭd) *a.* [L. *inter*, between ; Gk. *karos*, deep sleep.] Between carotid arteries.

intercarpal (ĭn′tĕrkâr′păl) *a.* [L. *inter*, between ; *carpus*, wrist.] Among or between carpal bones ; *appl.* joints.

intercarpellary (ĭn′tĕrkâr′pĕlărĭ) *a.* [L. *inter*, between ; Gk. *karpos*, fruit.] Between the carpels.

intercartilaginous (ĭn′tĕrkârtĭlăj′ĭnŭs) *a.* [L. *inter*, between ; *cartilago*, gristle.] Between cartilages.

intercavernous (ĭn′tĕrkăv′ĕrnŭs) *a.* [L. *inter*, between ; *caverna*, cavern.] *Appl.* sinuses connecting cavernous sinuses, part of ophthalmic veins.

intercellular (ĭn′tĕrsĕl′ūlăr) *a.* [L. *inter*, between ; *cellula*, little cell.] Among or between cells, as spaces in meristem, biliary passages among liver-cells, plexus of dendrites between sympathetic ganglion cells, etc.

intercentral (ĭn′tërsĕn′trăl) *a.* [L. *inter*, between ; *centrum*, centre.] Uniting, or between, two centra.

intercentrum (ĭn′tërsĕn′trŭm) *n.* [L. *inter*, between ; *centrum*, centre.] A second central ring in an embolomerous vertebra.

interchange,—mutual or reciprocal translocation, in chromosomes.

interchondral (ĭn′tërkôn′drăl) *a.* [L. *inter*, between ; Gk. *chondros*, cartilage.] *Appl.* articulations and ligaments between costal cartilages.

interchromosomal (ĭn′tërkrō′mösō′măl) *a.* [L. *inter*, between ; Gk. *chroma*, colour ; *soma*, body.] Between chromosomes ; *appl.* fibrils playing part in the beginning of cell-wall formation in plants.

intercingular (ĭn′tërsĭng′gūlăr) *a.* [L. *inter*, between ; *cingulum*, girdle.] *Appl.* area of longitudinal groove between parts of a spiral girdle, in certain Dinoflagellata.

interclavicle (ĭn′tërklăv′ĭkl) *n.* [L. *inter*, between ; *clavicula*, small key.] The episternum ; a median ventral bone between clavicles.

interclavicular (ĭn′tërklăvĭk′ūlăr) *a.* [L. *inter*, between ; *clavicula*, small key.] Between the clavicles ; *appl.* a ligament.

interclinoid (ĭn′tërklī′noid) *a.* [L. *inter*, between ; Gk. *kline*, bed ; *eidos*, form.] Joining clinoid processes ; *appl.* fibrous process or ligament.

intercolumnar (ĭn′tërkŏlŭm′năr) *a.* [L. *inter*, between ; *columna*, column.] Between columnar structures, as certain abdominal muscle fibres.

intercondyloid (ĭn′tërkŏn′dĭloid) *a.* [L. *inter*, between ; Gk. *kondylos*, knob ; *eidos*, form.] Between condyles ; *appl.* an eminence of tibia, and fossae of femur and tibia.

intercostal (ĭn′tërkŏs′tăl) *a.* [L. *inter*, between ; *costa*, rib.] Between the ribs, as arteries, glands, membranes, nerves, veins, muscles ; between ribs of leaf, mericarp, etc.

intercostobrachial (ĭn′tërkŏs′tŏbrā′kĭăl) *a.* [L. *inter*, between ; *costa*, rib ; *brachium*, arm.] *Appl.* lateral branch of second intercostal nerve which supplies upper arm ; intercostohumeral.

intercoxal (ĭn′tërkŏk′săl) *a.* [L. *inter*, between ; *coxa*, hip.] Between the coxae or proximal limb-joints of arthropods ; *appl.* plate, etc.

intercrescence (in′tërkrĕs′ëns) *n.* [L. *inter*, between ; *crescere*, to grow.] A growing into each other, as of tissues.

intercrural (ĭn′tërkroo′răl) *a.* [L. *inter*, between ; *crus*, leg.] *Appl.* intercolumnar tendinous fibres arching across external oblique muscles.

intercuneiform (ĭn′tërkūnē′ĭfôrm) *a.* [L. *inter*, between ; *cuneus*, wedge ; *forma*, shape.] Connecting the three cuneiform bones of the ankle ; *appl.* articulations and ligaments.

interdeferential (ĭn′tërdĕfërĕn′shăl) *a.* [L. *inter*, between ; *deferre*, to carry down.] Between the vasa deferentia.

interdigital (ĭn′tërdĭj′ĭtăl) *a.* [L. *inter*, between ; *digitus*, finger.] Between digits ; *appl.* glands.

interfascicular (ĭn′tërfăsĭk′ūlăr) *a.* [L. *inter*, between ; *fasciculus*, small bundle.] Situated between the fascicles or vascular bundles ; *appl.* cambium.

interfemoral (ĭn′tërfĕm′öräl) *a.* [L. *inter*, between ; *femur*, thigh bone.] Between the thighs.

interference (ĭn′tërfē′rĕns) *n.* [L. *inter*, between ; *ferire*, to strike.] The lessened probability of crossing-over in the neighbourhood of a previous crossing-over.

interfertile (ĭn′tërfĕr′tĭl) *a.* [L. *inter*, between ; *fertilis*, fertile.] Able to interbreed.

interfilamentar (ĭn′tërfĭlămĕn′tăr) *a.* [L. *inter*, between ; F. *filament*, from L. *filum*, thread.] *Appl.* junctions or horizontal bars connecting molluscan gill filaments.

interfilar (ĭn′tërfī′lăr) *a.* [L. *inter*, between ; *filum*, thread.] *Appl.* ground-substance of protoplasm, as opposed to reticulum.

interfoliaceous (ĭn′tĕrfōlĭā′shŭs) *a.* [L. *inter*, between; *folium*, leaf.] Situated or arising between two opposite leaves; interfoliar.

interfrontal (ĭn′tĕrfrŭn′tăl) *n.* [L. *inter*, between; *frons*, forehead.] An unpaired median bone between frontals and nasals in Eryops.

interganglionic (ĭn′tĕrgăngglĭŏn′ĭk) *a.* [L. *inter*, between; Gk. *ganglion*, little tumour.] Connecting two ganglia, as nerve cords or strands.

intergemmal (ĭn′tĕrjĕm′ăl), *a.* [L. *inter*, between; *gemma* bud.] Between taste buds; *appl.* nerve fibres.

intergeneric (ĭn′tĕrjĕnĕr′ĭk) *a.* [L. *inter*, between; *genus*, kind.] Between genera; *appl.* hybridisation.

intergenital (ĭn′tĕrjĕn′ĭtăl) *a.* [L. *inter*, between; *genitalis*, generative.] Between the genitals; *appl.* certain echinoderm plates.

interglacial (ĭn′tĕrglā′sĭăl) *a.* [L. *inter*, between; *glacies*, ice.] *Appl.* or *pert.* ages between glacial ages, particularly of the Pleistocene epoch.

interglobular (ĭntĕrglŏb′ūlăr) *a.* [L. *inter*, between; *globulus*, small globe.] *Appl.* a series of spaces towards outer surface of dentine, due to imperfect calcification.

intergular (ĭn′tĕrgū′lăr) *n.* [L. *inter*, between; *gula*, gullet.] A paired or unpaired plate in front of gulars in Chelonia.

interhyal (ĭn′tĕrhī′ăl) *n.* [L. *inter*, between; Gk. *hyoeides*, Υ-shaped.] A small bone between hyomandibular and rest of hyoid of some higher vertebrates.

interkinesis (ĭn′tĕrkĭnē′sĭs) *n.* [L. *inter*, between; Gk. *kinesis*, movement.] Interphase; resting stage between two mitotic divisions of a cell.

interlamellar (ĭn′tĕrlămĕl′ăr) *a.* [L. *inter*, between; *lamella*, thin plate.] *Appl.* vertical bars of tissue joining gill lamellae of molluscs; *appl.* compartments of lung-book in scorpions and spiders; *appl.* spaces between lamellae or gills of agarics.

interlaminar (ĭn′tĕrlăm′ĭnăr) *a.* [L. *inter*, between; *lamina*, thin plate.] Uniting laminae; between laminae.

interlobar (ĭn′tĕrlō′băr) *a.* [L. *inter*, between; L.L. *lobus*, lobe.] Between lobes; *appl.* sulci and fissures dividing cerebral hemispheres into lobes.

interlobular (ĭn′tĕrlŏb′ūlăr) *a.* [L. *inter*, between; *lobulus*, small lobe.] Occurring between lobules; *appl.* kidney arteries, vessels of liver, etc.

interlocular (ĭn′tĕrlŏk′ūlăr) *a.* [L. *inter*, between; *loculus*, compartment.] Between loculi.

interloculus (ĭn′tĕrlŏk′ūlŭs) *n.* [L. *inter*, between; *loculus*, compartment.] Space between two loculi.

intermandibular (ĭn′tĕrmăndĭb′ūlăr) *a.* [L. *inter*, between; *mandibulum*, jaw.] Between rami of mandibles.

intermaxilla (ĭn′tĕrmăksĭl′ă) *n.* [L. *inter*, between; *maxilla*, jaw.] Bone between maxillae; the premaxilla.

intermaxillary (ĭn′tĕrmăksĭl′ărĭ) *a.* [L. *inter*, between; *maxilla*, jaw.] Between maxillae; *pert.* premaxillae; *appl.* gland in nasal septum of certain amphibians and reptiles.

intermediary (ĭn′tĕrmē′dĭărĭ) *a.* [L. *inter*, between; *medius*, middle.] Acting as a medium; *appl.* nerve-cells receiving impulses from afferent cells and transmitting them to efferent cells.

intermediate (ĭn′tĕrmē′dĭăt) *a.* [L. *inter*, between; *medius*, middle.] Occurring between two points or parts; *appl.* a nerve-mass, certain areas of brain, ribs, etc.

intermediate disc,—a thin doubly refracting disc in the middle of the singly refracting disc of myofibrils in striated muscle; Dobie's line, Krause's membrane, plasmophore, telophragma, Z-disc.

intermediate host,—host intervening between two others in life-history of certain parasites, as Limnaea in life-history of Fasciola.

intermedin (ĭn'tĕrmē'dĭn) *n.* [L. *inter*, between; *medius*, middle.] Hormone obtained from pars intermedia of the pituitary gland; B substance; melanocyte-stimulating hormone.

intermedium (ĭn'tĕrmē'dĭŭm) *n.* [L. *inter*, between; *medius*, middle.] A small bone of carpus and tarsus.

intermesenteric (ĭn'tĕrmĕs'ĕntĕr'ĭk, -mĕz-) *a.* [L. *inter*, between; Gk. *mesos*, middle; *enteron*, gut.] Occurring between mesenteries; *appl.* spaces in sea-anemones.

intermitotic (ĭn'tĕrmĭtŏt'ĭk) *n.* [L. *inter*, between; Gk. *mitos*, thread.] A cell with individual life between mitoses causing its origin and division into daughter cells; *cf.* postmitotic.

intermuscular (ĭn'tĕrmŭs'kūlăr) *a.* [L. *inter*, between; *musculus*, muscle.] Between or among muscle fibres.

intermyotomic (ĭn'tĕrmī'ŏtŏm'ĭk) *a.* [L. *inter*, between; Gk. *mys*, muscle; *tome*, cutting.] *Appl.* vertebra formed of caudals of one somite and cranials of next posterior; *cf.* intrasegmental.

internal (ĭntĕr'năl) *a.* [L. *internus*, within.] Located on inner side; nearer middle axis; located or produced within.

internal secretion,—endocrine secretion; hormone.

internal spiral,—coil within a single chromatid, as between prophase and anaphase.

internasal (ĭn'tĕrnā'zăl) *a.* [L. *inter*, between; *nasus*, nose.] Between nostrils; *appl.* plate, septum, gland.

interneural (ĭn'tĕrnū'răl) *a.* [L. *inter*, between; Gk. *neuron*, nerve.] Between neural processes, arches or spines; *appl.* sharp bones attached to dorsal fin rays; *appl.* intercalary cartilages.

interneurone (ĭn'tĕrnū'rŏn) *n.* [L. *inter*, between; Gk. *neuron*, nerve.] An internuncial neurone or relay cell; interneuron.

internodal (ĭn'tĕrnō'dăl) *a.* [L. *inter*, between; *nodus*, knot.] *Pert.* part between two nodes.

internode (ĭn'tĕrnōd) *n.* [L. *inter*, between; *nodus*, knot.] The part between two successive nodes or joints, as of plant stem, of medullated nerve fibre; non-genetic segment of a chromosome.

internodia (ĭn'tĕrnō'dĭă) *n. plu.* Phalanges.

internum (ĭntĕr'nŭm) *n.* [L. *internus*, inward.] Inner region or medulla of a mitochondrium or of Golgi apparatus; or of acroblast.

internuncial (ĭn'tĕrnŭn'sĭăl) *a.* [L. *inter*, between; *nuntius*, messenger.] Intercommunicating, as paths of transmission or nerve fibres; *appl.* neurone interposed between afferent and efferent nerve cells, association neurone.

interoceptor (ĭn'tĕrŏsĕp'tŏr) *n.* [L. *internus*, inside; *capere*, to take.] A receptor which receives stimuli from within the body; end-organ for visceral sensibility.

interocular (ĭn'tĕrŏk'ūlăr) *a.* [L. *inter*, between; *oculus*, eye.] Placed between the eyes.

interoperculum (ĭn'tĕrŏpĕr'kūlŭm) *n.* [L. *inter*, between; *operculum*, lid.] A membrane bone of operculum of Teleostomi and Dipnoi, attached to mandible; interopercle.

interoptic (ĭn'tĕrŏp'tĭk) *a.* [L. *inter*, between; Gk. *optikos*, *pert.* sight.] Between optic lobes.

interorbital (ĭn'tĕrôr'bĭtăl) *a.* [L. *inter*, between; *orbis*, eye-socket.] Between the orbits; *appl.* septum of tropibasic skull; *appl.* sinus.

interosculant (ĭn'tĕrŏs'kūlănt) *a.* [L. *inter*, between; *osculari*, to kiss.] Possessing characters common to two or more groups or species.

interosseous (ĭn'tĕrŏs'ēŭs) *a.* [L. *inter*, between; *os*, bone.] Occurring between bones; *appl.* arteries, membranes, muscles, nerves.

interparietal (ĭn'tĕrpărī'ĕtăl) *a.* [L. *inter*, between; *paries*, wall.] In many vertebrates a bone arising between parietals and supraoccipital.

interpeduncular (ĭn′tërpĕdŭng′kūlăr) *a.* [L. *inter*, between ; *pedunculus*, little foot.] *Appl.* fossa between cerebral peduncles, and a ganglion.

interpetaloid (ĭn′tërpĕt′ăloid) *a.* [L. *inter*, between ; Gk. *petalon*, leaf ; *eidos*, form.] Between petaloid areas of an echinoderm test.

interpetiolar (ĭn′tërpĕt′ĭōlăr) *a.* [L. *inter*, between ; *petiolus*, little foot.] Situated between petioles or bases of opposite leaves.

interphalangeal (ĭn′tërfălăn′jēăl) *a.* [L. *inter*, between ; Gk. *phalangx*, line of battle.] *Appl.* articulations between successive phalanges.

interphase (ĭn′tërfāz) *n.* [L. *inter*, between ; Gk. *phasis*, aspect.] Resting stage between first and second mitotic divisions ; interkinesis.

interplacental (ĭn′tërplăsĕn′tăl) *a.* [L. *inter*, between ; *placenta*, flat cake.] Between placentae.

interpleural (ĭn′tërploo′răl) *a.* [L. *inter*, between ; Gk. *pleuron*, side.] Between pleurae.

interpleurite (ĭn′tërploor′īt) *n.* [L. *inter*, between ; Gk. *pleuron*, side.] A small sclerite between sclerites of the pleura ; intersegmental pleural sclerite.

interpositional growth,—of cells, by interposition between neighbouring cells without loss of contact ; intrusive growth. *Opp.* sliding growth.

interpubic (ĭn′tërpū′bĭk) *a.* [L. *inter*, between ; *pubes*, mature.] *Appl.* the fibrocartilaginous lamina between pubic bones.

interracial (ĭn′tër-rā′sĭăl) *a.* [L. *inter*, between ; *radix*, root.] Between races or breeds ; *appl.* hybridisation, differences, etc.

interradial (ĭn′tër-rā′dĭăl) *a.* [L. *inter*, between ; *radius*, radius.] *Pert.* an interradius.

interradium (ĭn′tër-rā′dĭŭm) *n.* [L. *inter*, between ; *radius*, radius.] The area between two radii of any radially symmetrical animal.

interradius (ĭn′tër-rā′dĭŭs) *n.* [L. *inter*, between ; *radius*, radius.] The radius of a radiate animal halfway between two perradii.

interramal (ĭn′tër-rā′măl) *a.* [L. *inter*, between ; *ramus*, branch.] Between branches or rami.

interramicorn (ĭn′tër-rām′ĭkôrn) *n.* [L. *inter*, between ; *ramus*, branch ; *cornu*, horn.] A piece of a bird's bill beyond mandibular rami forming the gonys.

interrenal (ĭn′tër-rē′năl) *a.* [L. *inter*, between ; *renes*, kidneys.] Between the kidneys ; *appl.* veins.

interrenal body,—a gland, situated between kidneys of elasmobranchs, representing the adrenal cortex of higher vertebrates.

interrupted (ĭn′tër-rŭp′tĕd) *a.* [L. *inter*, between ; *rumpere*, to break.] With continuity broken ; irregular ; asymmetrical.

interruptedly pinnate, — pinnate with pairs of small leaflets occurring between larger ones.

interscapular (ĭn′tërskăp′ūlăr) *a.* [L. *inter*, between ; *scapula*, shoulder-blade.] Between the shoulder-blades ; *appl.* feathers ; *appl.* brown fatty tissue, so-called hibernating gland, as in some rodents.

intersegmental (ĭn′tërsĕgmĕn′tăl) *a.* [L. *inter*, between ; *segmentum*, piece.] Between segments ; between spinal segments, *appl.* axons, septa.

intersegmentalia (ĭn′tërsĕg′mĕntā′-lĭă) *n. plu.* [L. *inter*, between ; *segmentum*, piece.] Sclerites between adjacent body segments in insects, as intertergites, interpleurites, intersternites.

interseptal (ĭn′tërsĕp′tăl) *a.* [L. *inter*, between ; *septum*, fence.] *Pert.* spaces between septa or partitions.

intersex (ĭn′tërsĕks) *n.* [L. *inter*, between ; *sexus*, sex.] An organism with characteristics intermediate between typical male and typical female of its species ; an organism first developing as a male or female, then as an individual of the opposite sex ; a sex mosaic in time ; *cf.* gynandromorph.

interspecific (ĭn′tĕrspēsĭf′ĭk) *a.* [L. *inter*, between; *species*, kind.] Between distinct species; *appl.* crosses, as mule, hinny, cattalo, tigron; *appl.* selection.

intersphincteric (ĭn′tĕrsfĭngktĕr′ĭk) *a.* [L. *inter*, between; Gk. *sphingkter*, tight band.] Between sphincters; *appl.* groove of anal canal.

interspicular (ĭn′tĕrspĭk′ūlăr) *a.* [L. *inter*, between; *spiculum*, sharp point.] Occurring between spicules.

interspinal (ĭn′tĕrspī′năl) *a.* [L. *inter*, between; *spina*, spine.] Occurring between spinous processes or between spines; *appl.* bones, muscles, ligaments.

interspinous,—interspinal.

interstapedial (ĭn′tĕrstăpē′dĭăl) *a.* [L. *inter*, between; *stapes*, stirrup.] *Appl.* a part of columella of ear.

intersterility (ĭn′tĕrstĕrĭl′ĭtĭ) *n.* [L. *inter*, between; *sterilis*, unfruitful.] Incapacity for interbreeding.

intersternal (ĭn′tĕrstĕr′năl) *a.* [L. *inter*, between; *sternum*, breastbone.] Between the sterna; *appl.* ligaments connecting manubrium and body of sternum.

intersternite (ĭn′tĕrstĕr′nīt) *n.* [L. *inter*, between; *sternum*, breastbone.] A sternal sclerite between thoracic segments of insects; intersegmental sternite; a furcasternite, *q.v.*

interstitial (ĭn′tĕrstĭsh′ĭăl) *a.* [L. *inter*, between; *sistere*, to set.] Occurring in interstices or spaces; *appl.* growth; *appl.* lamellae between Haversian systems; *appl.* cells within tissues, *e.g.* within gonad tissues; *appl.* soil-water.

intertemporal (ĭn′tĕrtĕm′pŏrăl) *n.* [L. *inter*, between; *tempora*, temples.] A paired membrane bone, part of sphenoid complex, fusing with alisphenoids; dermosphenotic.

intertentacular (ĭn′tĕrtĕntăk′ūlăr) *a.* [L. *inter*, between; *tentaculum*, feeler.] Between tentacles; *appl.* a ciliated tube opening at base of tentacles and connecting coelom and exterior, found in Molluscoidea.

intertergal (ĭn′tĕrtĕr′găl) *a.* [L. *inter*, between; *tergum*, back.] Between tergites or dorsal sclerites.

intertergite (ĭn′tĕrtĕr′jīt) *n.* [L. *inter*, between; *tergum*, back.] A small sclerite between dorsal sclerites; intersegmental tergal sclerite.

intertidal (ĭn′tĕrtī′dăl) *a.* [L. *inter*, between; A.S. *tid*, time.] *Appl.* shore organisms living between high- and low-water marks.

intertrabecula (ĭn′tĕrtrăbĕk′ūlă) *n.* [L. *inter*, between; *trabecula*, little beam.] A separate plate between the trabeculae anteriorly, in some birds.

intertragic (ĭntĕrtrăj′ĭk) *a.* [L. *inter*, between; Gk. *tragos*, goat.] *Appl.* notch between tragus and antitragus.

intertrochanteric (ĭn′tĕrtrŏkăntĕr′ĭk) *a.* [L. *inter*, between; Gk. *trochanter*, runner.] Between trochanters; *appl.* crest, line.

intertrochlear (ĭn′tĕrtrŏk′lēăr) *a.* [L. *inter*, between; *trochlea*, pulley.] *Appl.* an ulnar ridge fitting into a groove of the humerus.

intertubercular (ĭn′tĕrtūbĕr′kūlăr) *a.* [L. *inter*, between; *tuberculum*, small hump.] *Appl.* plane of body through tubercles of iliac crests; *appl.* sulcus between tubercles of humerus.

intervaginal (ĭn′tĕrvăj′ĭnăl) *a.* [L. *inter*, between; *vagina*, sheath.] Between sheaths; *appl.* space.

intervarietal (ĭn′tĕrvărī′ĕtăl) *a.* [L. *inter*, between; *varius*, diverse.] *Appl.* crosses between two distinct varieties of a species.

interventricular (ĭn′tĕrvĕntrĭk′ūlăr) *a.* [L. *inter*, between; *ventricula*, small cavity.] Between ventricles; *appl.* foramen between third and lateral ventricles, foramen of Monro.

intervertebral (ĭn′tĕrvĕr′tĕbrăl) *a.* [L. *inter*, between; *vertebra*, vertebra.] Occurring between vertebrae; *appl.* discs, fibrocartilages, foramina, veins.

intervillous (ĭn′tërvĭl′ŭs) *a.* [L. *inter*, between; *villi*, hairs.] Occurring between villi; *appl.* spaces in trophoblastic network filled with maternal blood.

interxylary (ĭn′tërzī′lărĭ) *a.* [L. *inter*, between; Gk. *xylon*, wood.] Between xylem strands; *appl.* phloem.

interzonal (ĭn′tërzō′năl) *a.* [L. *inter*, between; *zona*, belt.] Between two zones; *appl.* spindle fibres uniting groups of daughter chromosomes in anaphase of mitosis.

interzooecial (ĭn′tërzōē′sĭăl) *a.* [L. *inter*, between; *zoon*, animal; *oikos*, house.] Occurring among zooecia.

intestinal (ĭntĕs′tĭnăl, ĭntĕstī′năl) *a.* [L. *intestina*, entrails.] *Pert.* intestines; *appl.* glands, villi, etc.

intestine (ĭntĕs′tĭn) *n.* [L. *intestina*, entrails.] Part of alimentary canal from pylorus to anus, or part corresponding to this.

intextine (ĭntĕk′stĭn) *n.* [L. *intus*, within; *exter*, without.] An inner membrane of an extine.

intima (ĭn′tĭmă) *n.* [L. *intimus*, innermost.] The innermost lining membrane of a part or organ; tunica intima.

intine (ĭn′tĭn) *n.* [L. *intus*, within.] The inner covering membrane of a pollen grain, or of a spore. *Opp.* extine.

intrabiontic (ĭn′trăbīŏn′tĭk) *a.* [L. *intra*, within; Gk. *bios*, life; *on*, being.] *Appl.* a process of selection occurring in a living unit.

intrabulbar,—intragemmal, *q.v.*

intracapsular (ĭn′trăkăp′sūlăr) *a.* [L. *intra*, within; *capsula*, small chest.] Contained within a capsule; *appl.* protoplasm of Radiolaria; *appl.* dendrites.

intracardiac (ĭn′trăkâr′dĭăk) *a.* [L. *intra*, within; Gk. *kardia*, heart.] Endocardiac, *q.v.*

intracartilaginous (ĭn′trăkâr′tĭlăj′ĭnŭs) *a.* [L. *intra*, within; *cartilago*, gristle.] Inside the cartilage; *appl.* ossification; endochondral.

intracellular (ĭn′trăsĕl′ūlăr) *a.* [L. *intra*, within; *cellula*, small room.] Within the cell.

intracortical (ĭn′trăkôr′tĭkăl) *a.* [L. *intra*, within; *cortex*, rind.] Within the cortex; uniting parts of brain cortex.

intra-epithelial (ĭn′trăĕpĭthē′lĭăl) *a.* [L. *intra*, within; Gk. *epi*, upon; *thele*, nipple.] Occurring in epithelium; *appl.* glands, usually mucous.

intrafascicular (ĭn′trăfăsĭk′ūlăr) *a.* [L. *intra*, within; *fasciculus*, little bundle.] Within a vascular bundle.

intrafoliaceous (ĭn′trăfōlĭā′shŭs) *a.* [L. *intra*, within; *folium*, leaf.] *Appl.* stipules encircling stem and forming a sheath; ochreate.

intrafusal (ĭn′trăfū′zăl) *a.* [L. *intra*, within; *fusus*, spindle.] *Appl.* fasciculi and fibres connected respectively with neurotendinous and neuromuscular spindles.

intragemmal (ĭn′trăjĕm′ăl) *a.* [L. *intra*, within; *gemma*, bud.] Within a taste-bud; *appl.* nerve fibres, spaces.

intraglobular (ĭn′trăglŏb′ūlăr) *a.* [L. *intra*, within; *globulus*, globule.] Occurring within a globule or corpuscle.

intrajugular (ĭn′trăjŭg′ūlăr) *a.* [L. *intra*, within; *jugulum*, throat.] *Appl.* a process in middle of jugular notch of occipital bone.

intralamellar (ĭn′trălămĕl′ăr) *a.* [L. *intra*, within; *lamella*, thin plate.] Within a lamella; *appl.* trama of gill-bearing fungi.

intralobular (ĭn′trălŏb′ūlăr) *a.* [L. *intra*, within; *lobulus*, small lobe.] Occurring within lobules; *appl.* veins draining liver lobules.

intramembranous (ĭn-trămĕm′brănŭs) *a.* [L. *intra*, within; *membrana*, film.] Within a membrane; *appl.* bone development.

intramolecular (ĭn′trămŏlĕk′ūlăr) *a.* [L. *intra*, within; F. *molécule*, small particle.] *Appl.* plant respiration from splitting up of complex substances within the cell.

intranuclear (ĭn′trănū′klēăr) *a.* [L. *intra*, within; *nucleus*, kernel.]

Within the nucleus ; *appl.* spindles, fibres, etc.

intraparietal (ĭn'trăpărī'ĕtăl) *a.* [L. *intra*, within ; *paries*, wall.] Enclosed within an organ ; within parietal lobe, as sulcus, etc.

intrapetalous (ĭn'trăpĕt'ălŭs) *a.* [L. *intra*, within ; Gk. *petalon*, leaf.] Situated in a petaloid area, in echinoderms.

intrapetiolar (ĭn'trăpĕt'ĭōlăr) *a.* [L. *intra*, within ; *petiolus*, little foot.] Within the petiole base expansion.

intrapleural (ĭn'trăploo'răl) *a.* [L. *intra*, within ; Gk. *pleuron*, side.] Within the thoracic cavity.

intrasegmental (ĭn'trăsĕgmĕn'tăl) *a.* [L. *intra*, within ; *segmentum*, part.] *Appl.* vertebra formed of cranial and caudal elements of same original myotome ; *cf.* intermyotomic.

intraselection (ĭn'trăsēlĕk'shŭn) *n.* [L. *intra*, within ; *selectio*, choice.] Selection within an organ, of cells fittest to survive.

intrasexual (ĭn'trăsĕk'sūăl) *a.* [L. *intra*, within ; *sexus*, sex.] *Appl.* selection of competing individuals of the same sex.

intraspecific (ĭn'trăspĕsĭf'ĭk) *a.* [L. *intra*, within ; *species*, particular kind ; *facere*, to make.] Within a species ; *appl.* selection of individuals.

intraspicular (ĭn'trăspĭk'ūlăr) *a.* [L. *intra*, within ; *spicula*, small spike.] Having spicules completely embedded in spongin.

intrastelar (ĭn'trăstē'lăr) *a.* [L. *intra*, within ; Gk. *stele*, pillar.] Within the stele of a stem or root ; *appl.* ground tissue, bundles, etc.

intratarsal (ĭn'trătâr'săl) *a.* [L. *intra*, within ; *tarsus*, ankle.] Within the tarsus ; *appl.* joint of reptilian limb between rows of tarsal bones.

intrathyroid (ĭn'trăthī'roid) *a.* [L. *intra*, within ; Gk. *thyreos*, shield ; *eidos*, form.] *Appl.* a cartilage joining laminae of thyroid cartilage during infancy.

intrauterine (ĭn'trăū'tĕrīn) *a.* [L. *intra*, within ; *uterus*, womb.] Within the uterus.

intravaginal (ĭn'trăvăj'ĭnăl) *a.* [L. *intra*, within ; *vagina*, sheath.] Within vagina ; contained within a sheath, as grass branches.

intravascular (ĭn'trăvăs'kūlăr) *a.* [L. *intra*, within ; *vasculum*, small vessel.] Within blood-vessels.

intraventricular (ĭn'trăvĕntrĭk'ūlăr) *a.* [L. *intra*, within ; *ventriculus*, small cavity.] Within a ventricle ; *appl.* caudate nucleus of corpus striatum, seen within ventricle of brain.

intravesical (ĭn'trăvĕs'ĭkăl) *a.* [L. *intra*, within ; *vesica*, bladder.] Within the bladder.

intravitelline (ĭn'trăvĭtĕl'ĭn) *a.* [L. *intra*, within ; *vitellus*, egg-yolk.] Within the yolk of an egg.

intraxylary (ĭn'trăzī'lărĭ) *a.* [L. *intra*, within ; Gk. *xylon*, wood.] Within wood or xylem.

intrazonal (ĭn'trăzō'năl) *a.* [L. *intra*, within ; *zona*, belt.] Within a zone ; *appl.* soils characteristic of locally limited soil-forming conditions, differing from prevalent or normal soils of the region or zone.

intrinsic (ĭntrĭn'sĭk) *a.* [L. *intrinsecus*, inwards.] Inward ; inherent ; *appl.* inner muscles, as of tongue, of syrinx, etc. ; *appl.* cycles, in population of a species, owing to coaction within or between species ; *appl.* rate of natural increase in a stabilised population having a balanced age distribution ; *appl.* brightness sensation due to differential retinal response to different wave-lengths. *Opp.* extrinsic.

introitus (ĭntrō'ĭtŭs) *n.* [L. *introitus*, entry.] An opening or orifice.

intromittent (ĭn'trōmĭt'ĕnt) *a.* [L. *intro*, within ; *mittere*, to send.] Adapted for inserting ; *appl.* male copulatory organs.

introrse (ĭntrôrs') *a.* [L. *introrsus*, inwards.] Turned inwards or towards axis ; of anthers, opening on side next pistil.

introvert (ĭn'trōvĕrt) *n.* [L. *intro*, within ; *vertere*, to turn.] That which is capable of involution, as anterior region of body of certain zooids, of certain annulates, mouth extremity of certain molluscs. (ĭn'trövĕrt') *v.* To turn, bend, or draw inwards.

intrusive growth,—*see* interpositional growth.

intussusception (ĭn'tŭssŭsĕp'shŭn) *n.* [L. *intus*, within; *suscipere*, to receive.] Growth in surface-extent or volume by intercalation of particles among those already present. *Opp.* accretion; *cf.* apposition.

inulase (ĭn'ūlās) *n.* [L. *inula*, elecampane.] A plant enzyme which hydrolyses inulin into laevulose.

inulin (ĭn'ūlĭn) *n.* [L. *inula*, elecampane.] A carbohydrate occurring in rhizomes and roots of many plants, and forming laevulose when hydrolysed; dahlia starch; $(C_6H_{10}O_5)_x$.

inuncate (ĭnŭng'kāt) *a.* [L. *inuncatus*, hooked together.] Covered with barbed hairs; glochidiate.

invaginate (ĭnvăj'ĭnāt) *v.* [L. *in*, into; *vagina*, sheath.] To involute or draw into a sheath; *appl.* insinking of wall of a cavity or vessel. *a.* Introverted; enclosed in a sheath; concave.

invagination (ĭnvăj'ĭnā'shŭn) *n.* [L. *in*, into; *vagina*, sheath.] Involution; introversion; gastrula-formation by infolding of blastula wall; ingestion by temporarily transformed periplast-like ectoplasm in certain Protozoa.

inversion (ĭnvër'shŭn) *n.* [L. *invertere*, to turn upside down.] Reversal in order of genes, or reversal of a chromosome segment, within the chromosome as a whole; a turning inward, inside out, or upside-down of a part.

invertase (ĭnvĕr'tās) *n.* [L. *invertere*, to turn into.] A plant enzyme which converts cane sugar into dextrose and laevulose; invertin; sucrase.

invertebrate (ĭnvĕr'tĕbrāt) *a.* [L. *in*, not; *vertebra*, joint.] Back-boneless; without spinal column.

investing bones,—membrane bones.

investment (ĭnvĕst'mĕnt) *n.* [L. *in*, in; *vestire*, to clothe.] Outer covering of a part, organ, animal, or plant.

involucel (ĭnvŏl'ūsĕl) *n.* [*Dim.* of L. *involucrum*, covering.] The small bracts at base of a secondary umbel; a partial involucre.

involucellate (ĭnvŏl'ūsĕl'āt) *a.* [*Dim.* of L. *involucrum*, covering.] Bearing involucels.

involucellum,—involucel.

involucral (ĭn'vŏlū'krăl) *a.* [L. *involucrum*, covering.] *Pert.* or like an involucre.

involucrate (ĭn'vŏlū'krāt) *a.* [L. *involucrum*, covering.] Bearing involucres.

involucre (ĭn'vŏlū'kër) *n.* [L. *involucrum*, covering.] Bracts forming whorl at base of a condensed inflorescence, as of capitulum and umbel; a group of leaves surrounding antheridial and archegonial groups in bryophytes; involucrum.

involucret,—involucel, *q.v.*

involucrum (ĭn'vŏlū'krŭm) *n.* [L. *involucrum*, covering.] In Hydromedusae, protective cup into which nematocysts can be spirally retracted; metanotum of Orthoptera; periosteal layer formed around dead portion of bone, in certain diseased conditions; an involucre, *q.v.*

involuntary (ĭnvŏl'ŭntărĭ) *a.* [L. *in*, not; *voluntas*, wish.] Not under control of will; *appl.* plain unstriped muscles, as of alimentary canal, and to their movements.

involute (ĭn'vŏlūt) *a.* [L. *involutus*, rolled up.] Of leaves, having the edges rolled inwards at each side; of shells, closely coiled.

involution (ĭn'vŏlū'shŭn) *n.* [L. *involutus*, rolled up.] Reduction to normal of enlarged, modified, or deformed conditions; decrease in size, or structural and functional changes, as in old age; *appl.* forms that have become deformed in structure, but not to such an extent as to be incapable of recovery; a rolling inwards, as of leaves; movement of cells to interior in a certain type of gastrulation; resting, *appl.* spores, stage, etc.

iodophilic (ī'ōdŏfĭl'ĭk) *a.* [Gk. *ioeides*, violet-like; *philos*, loving.] Staining darkly in iodine solution; *appl.* certain cytoplasmic inclusions and vacuoles; iodinophilous.

iodopsin (ī'ōdŏpsĭn) *n.* [Gk. *ioeides*, violet; *opsis*, sight.] Visual violet of retinal cones, a photo-sensitive protein-vitamin A compound.

iodothyrin (ī'ōdŏthī'rĭn) *n.* [Gk. *ioeides*, violet; *thyreos*, shield.] An iodine compound in the colloid material of thyroid gland.

iodothyroglobulin (ī'ōdŏthī'rŏglŏb'-ūlĭn) *n.* [Gk. *ioeides*, violet; *thyreos*, shield; L. *globus*, globe.] Compound of iodothyrin and nucleoprotein extractable hormone of the thyroid gland.

ipsilateral (ĭp'sĭlăt'ĕrăl) *a.* [L. *ipse*, same; *latus*, side.] *Pert.* or situated on the same side, *opp.* contralateral.

iridal (ī'rĭdăl) *a.* [Gk., L. *iris*, rainbow.] *Pert.* the iris; iridial.

iridial angle,—filtration angle of eye: an angular recess between cornea and anterior surface of iris.

iridocytes (ĭr'ĭdōsīts) *n. plu.* [Gk. *iris*, rainbow; *kytos*, hollow.] Guanin granules, bodies or plates, of which the reflecting tissue of skin of fishes and reptiles is composed; iridescent cells in integument of Sepia.

iridomotor (ĭr'ĭdōmō'tŏr) *a.* [L. *iris*, rainbow; *movere*, to move.] Connected with movements of iris.

iridophores,—iridocytes, *q.v.*

iris (ī'rĭs) *n.* [L. *iris*, rainbow.] A thin, circular, contractile and vascular disc of eye between cornea and lens, and surrounding the pupil; a marking immediately encircling the pupil of an ocellus, as on wing of some Lepidoptera.

iris cells,—pigment cells surrounding cone and retinula of an ommatidium.

irradiation (ĭr'rădĭā'shŭn) *n.* [L. *in*, into; *radius*, ray.] Treatment with rays, as ultra-violet rays, X-rays, etc.; the spreading of an effect of a stimulus; spreading of an excitatory process; apparent enlargement of objects, due to difference in illumination.

irritability (ĭr'ĭtăbĭl'ĭtĭ) *n.* [L. *irritare*, to provoke.] Power of receiving external impressions, and reacting to them, inherent in living matter.

irritant (ĭr'ĭtănt) *n.* [L. *irritare*, to provoke.] An external stimulus which provokes a response.

irrorate (ĭrrō'rāt) *a.* [L. *irrorare*, to bedew.] Covered as if by minute droplets; dotted with minute colour markings, as wings of certain butterflies.

isadelphous (īsădĕl'fŭs) *a.* [Gk. *isos*, equal; *adelphos*, brother.] With equal number of stamens in two phalanges.

isandrous (īsăn'drŭs) *a.* [Gk. *isos*, equal; *aner*, male.] Having similar stamens, their number equalling that of the sections of the corolla.

isantherous (īsăn'thĕrŭs) *a.* [Gk. *isos*, equal; *antheros*, flowering.] Having equal anthers.

isanthous (īsăn'thŭs) *a.* [Gk. *isos*, equal; *anthos*, flower.] Having uniform or regular flowers.

isauxesis (īsôksē'sĭs) *n.* [Gk. *isos*, equal; *auxesis*, growth.] Growth of a part at the same rate as that of the whole; ontogenetic heterauxesis.

ischiadic (ĭs'kĭăd'ĭk), **ischial** (ĭs'kĭăl) *a.* [Gk. *ischion*, hip.] *Pert.* or in region of hip; *appl.* artery, vein, process of ischiopubic plate.

ischiocapsular (ĭs'kĭōkăp'sūlăr) *a.* [Gk. *ischion*, hip; L. *capsula*, little chest.] *Appl.* a ligament joining capsular ligament and hip.

ischiocavernosus (ĭs'kĭōkăv'ĕrnō'sŭs) *a.* [Gk. *ischion*, hip; L. *cavus*, hollow.] *Appl.* muscle between hip and corpora cavernosa; erector of penis, or of clitoris.

ischioflexorius (ĭs'kĭōflĕksō'rĭŭs) *n.* [Gk. *ischion*, hip; L. *flexus*, bent.] Posterior thigh muscle in salamander, corresponding to semimembranosus.

ischiopodite (ĭs'kĭŏpödīt) *n.* [Gk. *ischion*, hip; *pous*, foot.] Proximal joint of walking legs of certain Crustacea, or of maxillipedes.

ischiopubic (ĭs'kĭöpū'bĭk) *a.* [Gk. *ischion*, hip; L. *pubes*, adult.] *Appl.* a gap or fenestra between ischium and pubis; *appl.* a median cartilaginous plate with median and lateral processes, in Dipnoi.

ischiopubis (ĭs'kĭöpū'bĭs) *n.* [Gk. *ischion*, hip; L. *pubis*, adult.] The ischium of pterodactyls, pubis being excluded from acetabulum; a fused ischium and pubis.

ischiorectal (ĭs'kĭörĕk'tăl) *a.* [Gk. *ischion*, hip; L. *rectus*, straight.] *Pert.* ischium and rectum; *appl.* fossa and muscles.

ischium (ĭs'kĭŭm) *n.* [Gk. *ischion*, hip.] The ventral and posterior bone of each half of pelvic girdle of vertebrates except fishes; an ischiopodite.

isidia (īsĭd'ĭă) *n. plu.* [Gk. *isis*, plant; *idion*, *dim.*] Coral-like soredia on surface of some lichens. *Sing.* isidium.

isidiferous (ī'sĭdĭf'ërŭs) *a.* [Gk. *isis*, plant; L. *ferre*, to bear.] Bearing isidia; isidophorous.

isidioid (īsĭd'ĭoid) *a.* [Gk. *isis*, plant; *idion*, *dim.*; *eidos*, like.] Like an isidium.

isidium,—*sing.* of isidia.

island of Reil [*J. C. Reil*, German anatomist]. Insula, *q.v.*

islets of Langerhans [*P. Langerhans*, German anatomist]. Spherical or oval bodies scattered throughout the pancreas, concerned in metabolism of sugar in body; endocrine portion of pancreas.

isoagglutinin (ī'söăgloot'ĭnĭn) *n.* [Gk. *isos*, equal; L. *agglutinare*, to glue to.] Fertilizin or agglutinin of eggs which reacts on sperm of same species; *cf.* heteroagglutinin.

isoagglutinogen (ī'söăglootĭn'öjĕn), **isohaemagglutinogen** (ī'söhēm'ăglootĭn'öjĕn) *n.* [Gk. *isos*, equal; *haima*, blood; *genos*, birth; L. *agglutinare*, to glue to.] Substance producing agglutination of erythrocytes within the same blood group.

isoalleles (ī'söălēlz') *n. plu.* [Gk. *isos*, equal; *allelon*, one another.] Different alleles which produce the same phenotypic effect in the homozygote.

isobilateral (ī'söbīlăt'ërăl) *a.* [Gk. *isos*, equal; L. *bis*, twice; *latus*, side.] *Appl.* a form of bilateral symmetry where a structure is divisible in two planes at right angles.

isoblabe (ī'söblā'bē) *n.* [Gk. *isos*, equal; *blabe*, damage.] A line connecting points, on a map, indicating the same degree of damage, infestation, or infection by a harmful agent or pathogenic species.

isobryonic (ī'söbrĭŏn'ĭk) *a.* [Gk. *isos*, equal; *bryein*, to proliferate.] Developing equally, as lobes of dicotyledonous embryo; isobryous.

isocarpous (ī'sökâr'pŭs) *a.* [Gk. *isos*, equal; *karpos*, fruit.] Having carpels and perianth divisions equal in number.

isocercal (ī'sösĕr'kăl) *a.* [Gk. *isos*, equal; *kerkos*, tail.] With vertebral column ending in median line of caudal fin.

isochela (ī'sökē'lă) *n.* [Gk. *isos*, equal; *chele*, claw.] A chela with two parts equally developed; a two-pronged or anchor-shaped spicule in certain sponges.

isochromosome (ī'sökrō'mösōm) *n.* [Gk. *isos*, equal; *chroma*, colour; *soma*, body.] Chromosome with identical arms united in a median centromere; metacentric derived from telocentric chromosome.

isochromous (ī'sökrō'mŭs) *a.* [Gk. *isos*, equal; *chroma*, colour.] Equally tinted; uniformly coloured; isochromatic, isochroous.

isocont,—isokont.

isocortex (ī'sökôr'tĕks) *n.* [Gk. *isos*, equal; L. *cortex*, bark.] The part of cerebral cortex made up of six layers of nerve-cells. *Opp.* allocortex.

isocytic (ī'sösĭt'ĭk) *a.* [Gk. *isos*, equal; *kytos*, hollow.] With all cells equal.

isodactylous (ī′södăk′tĭlŭs) *a.* [Gk. *isos*, equal; *daktylos*, finger.] Having all digits of equal size.

isodemic (īsödĕm′ĭk) *a.* [Gk. *isos*, equal; *demos*, people.] With, or *pert.*, populations composed of an equal number of individuals; *appl.* lines on a map which pass through points representing equal population density.

isodiametric (ī′södīămĕt′rĭk) *a.* [Gk. *isos*, equal; *dia*, through; *metron*, measure.] Having equal diameters; *appl.* cells or other structures; *appl.* rounded or polyhedral cells.

isodont (ī′södŏnt) *a.* [Gk. *isos*, equal; *odous*, tooth.] Having teeth all equal.

isodynamic (ī′södĭnăm′ĭk) *a.* [Gk. *isos*, equal; *dynamis*, power.] Of equal strength; providing the same amount of energy; *appl.* foods.

isogametangiogamy (ī′sögămētăn′jĭŏg′ămĭ) *n.* [Gk. *isos*, equal; *gametes*, spouse; *anggeion*, vessel; *gamos*, marriage.] The union of similar gametangia.

isogamete (ī′sögămēt′) *n.* [Gk. *isos*, equal; *gametes*, spouse.] One of a pair of undifferentiated gametes.

isogamous (īsŏg′ămŭs) *a.* [Gk. *isos*, equal; *gamos*, marriage.] Having the gametes alike.

isogamy (īsŏg′ămĭ) *n.* [Gk. *isos*, equal; *gamos*, marriage.] Union of similar gametes, or of similar unicells.

isogenes (ī′söjēnz) *n. plu.* [Gk. *isos*, equal; *genos*, descent.] Lines on a map which connect points where same gene frequency is found.

isogenetic (ī′söjĕnĕt′ĭk) *a.* [Gk. *isos*, equal; *genesis*, descent.] Arising from the same or a similar origin; of the same genotype; isogenous.

isogenic (īsöjĕn′ĭk) *a.* [Gk. *isos*, equal; *genos*, race.] Homozygous.

isogenomatic (ī′söjĕnömăt′ĭk) *a.* [Gk. *isos*, equal; *genos*, race.] Containing similar sets of chromosomes; *appl.* nuclei; isogenomic.

isognathous (īsŏg′năthŭs) *a.* [Gk. *isos*, equal; *gnathos*, jaw.] Having both jaws alike.

isogonal (īsŏg′önăl) *a.* [Gk. *isos*, equal; *gonia*, angle.] Forming equal angles; *appl.* branching.

isogonic (ī′sögŏn′ĭk) *a.* [Gk. *isos*, equal; *gonos*, offspring.] Producing similar individuals from differing stocks. [Gk. *gonia*, angle.] Isogonal.

isogynous (īsŏj′ĭnŭs) *a.* [Gk. *isos*, equal; *gyne*, woman.] Having similar gynoecia or pistils.

isokont (ī′sökŏnt) *a.* [Gk. *isos*, equal; *kontos*, punting-pole.] Having flagella or cilia of the same length. *Opp.* heterokont.

isolate (ī′sölāt) *n.* [It. *isola*, from; L. *insula*, island.] A breeding group restricted by isolation.

isolateral (ī′sölăt′ĕrăl) *a.* [Gk. *isos*, equal; L. *latus*, side.] Having equal sides; *appl.* leaves with palisade tissue on both sides.

isolation (īsölā′shŭn) *n.* [L. *insula*, island.] Separation from others; prevention of mating between breeding groups owing to spatial, topographical, ecological, phenological, physiological, genetic, or other barriers

isolecithal (ī′sölĕs′ĭthăl) *a.* [Gk. *isos*, equal; *lekithos*, yolk.] *Appl.* ova with yolk granules distributed nearly equally throughout egg substance.

isomar,—isophane, *q.v.*

isomastigote (ī′sömăstī′gōt) *a.* [Gk. *isos*, equal; *mastix*, whip.] Having flagella of equal length; isokont.

isomere (ī′sömēr) *n.* [Gk. *isos*, equal; *meros*, part.] A homologous structure or part.

isomerogamy,—isogamy, *q.v.*

isomerous (īsŏm′ĕrŭs) *a.* [Gk. *isos*, equal; *meros*, part.] Having equal numbers of different parts; *appl.* flowers with same number of parts in each whorl; exhibiting isomery.

isometry (īsŏm′ĕtrĭ) *n.* [Gk. *isos*, equal; *metron*, measure.] Growth of a part at the same rate as the standard or the whole.

isomorphic (ī'sömôr'fĭk) *a.* [Gk. *isos*, equal; *morphe*, shape.] Superficially alike; isomorphous; *appl.* alternation of diploid and haploid phases in morphologically similar generations.

isomorphism (ī'sömôr'fĭzm) *n.* [Gk. *isos*, equal; *morphe*, shape.] Apparent similarity of individuals of different race or species.

isomyaric (ī'sömĭăr'ĭk) *a.* [Gk. *isos*, equal; *mys*, muscle.] With adductor muscles equal in size; isomyarian.

isonym (ī'sönĭm) *n.* [Gk. *isos*, equal; *onyma*, name.] A new name, of species, etc., based upon the oldest name or basinym.

isopedin (īsŏp'ēdĭn) *n.* [Gk. *isopedos*, level.] Inner layer of laminated bony material in cosmoid and ganoid fish scales.

isopetalous (ī'söpĕt'ălŭs) *a.* [Gk. *isos*, equal; *petalon*, leaf.] Having similar petals.

isophagous (īsŏf'ăgŭs) *a.* [Gk. *isos*, equal; *phagein*, to eat.] Feeding on one or allied species; *appl.* fungi.

sophane (ī'söfān) *n.* [Gk. *isos*, equal; *phainein*, to show.] A line connecting all places within a region at which a biological phenomenon, *e.g.* flowering of a plant, occurs at the same time; isomar, phenocontour.

isophene (ī'söfēn) *n.* [Gk. *isos*, equal; *phainein*, to show.] A contour line delimiting area corresponding to a given frequency of a variant form; phenocontour.

isophenous (ī'söfē'nŭs) *a.* [Gk. *isos*, equal; *phainein*, to show.] Being of the same phenotype.

isophytoid (ī'söfī'toid) *a.* [Gk. *isos*, equal; *phyton*, plant; *eidos*, form.] An 'individual' of a compound plant not differentiated from the rest.

isoplankt (ī'söplăngkt) *n.* [Gk. *isos*, equal; *plangktos*, wandering.] Line representing, on a map, distribution of equal amounts of plankton, or of particular plankton species.

isoploid (ī'söploid) *a.* [Gk. *isos*, equal; *aploos*, onefold.] With an even number of chromosome sets in somatic cells. *n.* An isoploid individual.

isopodous (īsŏp'ödŭs) *a.* [Gk. *isos*, equal; *pous*, foot.] Having the legs alike and equal.

isopogonous (ī'söpō'gōnŭs) *a.* [Gk. *isos*, equal; *pogon*, beard.] Of feathers, having the two webs equal and similar.

isopolyploid (ī'söpŏl'ĭploid) *a.*, *n.* [Gk. *isos*, equal; *polys*, many; *aploos*, onefold; *eidos*, form.] Polyploid with an even number of chromosome sets, as tetraploid, hexaploid, octoploid, etc.

isopygous (ī'sŏp'ĭgŭs) *a.* [Gk. *isos*, equal; *pyge*, rump.] With pygidium and cephalon of equal size; *appl.* trilobites.

isospore (ī'söspōr) *n.* [Gk. *isos*, equal; *sporos*, seed.] An agamete produced by schizogony. *Opp.* anisospore.

isosporous (īsŏs'pörŭs, īsöspō'rŭs) *a.* [Gk. *isos*, equal; *sporos*, seed.] Having spores of one kind only; homosporous.

isostemonous (īsöstĕm'önŭs) *a.* [Gk. *isos*, equal; L. *stemon*, warp.] Having stamens equal in number to that of sepals or of petals.

isotelic (ī'sötĕl'ĭk) *a.* [Gk. *isos*, equal; *telos*, end.] Exhibiting, or tending to produce, the same effect; homoplastic; *appl.* food factors that can replace each other; *pert.* isotely.

isotels (ī'sötĕlz) *n. plu.* [Gk. *isos*, equal; *telos*, end.] Substances having the same physiological, *e.g.* nutritional, effect.

isotely,—homoplasty, *q.v.*

isotomy (īsŏt'ömĭ) *n.* [Gk. *isos*, equal; *temnein*, to cut.] Bifurcation repeated in a regular manner, as in crinoid brachia.

isotonic (īsötŏn'ĭk) *a.* [Gk. *isos*, equal; *tonos*, strain.] Of equal tension; having equal osmotic pressure; iso-osmotic.

isotonicity (ī'sötönĭs'ĭtĭ) *n.* [Gk. *isos*, equal; *tonos*, tone.] Normal tension under pressure or stimulus.

isotopic (ī'sötŏp'ĭk) *a.* [Gk. *isos*, equal; *topos*, place.] *Pert.* isotopes, chemical elements having the same atomic number and identical chemical properties, but differing in atomic weight.

isotropic (ī'sötrŏp'ĭk) *a.* [Gk. *isos*, equal; *tropikos*, turning.] Singly refracting in polarised light, *appl.* the light stripes of voluntary muscle fibres; *opp.* anisotropic; symmetrical around longitudinal axis; not influenced in any one direction more than another, *appl.* growth rate; without pre-determined axes, as eggs; isotropous.

isotropy (īsŏt'röpĭ) *n.* [Gk. *isos*, equal; *trepein*, to turn.] Absence of predetermined axes in eggs.

isotype (ī'sötīp) *n.* [Gk. *isos*, equal; *typos*, pattern.] A specimen collected from the same plant as the holotype and at the same time; type of plant or animal common to two or more areas or regions.

isozoic (ī'sözō'ĭk) *a.* [Gk. *isos*, equal; *zoon*, animal.] Inhabited by similar forms of animal life.

isozooid (ī'sözō'oid) *n.* [Gk. *isos*, equal; *zoon*, animal; *eidos*, like.] A zooid similar to parent stock.

isthmiate (ĭsth'mĭăt) *a.* [Gk. *isthmos*, neck.] Connected by an isthmus-like part.

isthmus (ĭsth'mŭs) *n.* Gk. *isthmos*, neck.] A narrow structure connecting two larger parts, as those of aorta, acoustic meatus, limbic lobe, prostate, thyroid, etc., or between semi-cells; junction between perikaryon and axon-base.

iter (ĭt'ĕr) *n.* [L. *iter*, way.] A passage or canal, as those of middle ear, brain, etc.; an aqueduct.

ivory (ī'vörĭ) *n.* [L. *ebur*, ivory. through F. *ivoire*.] Dentine of teeth, usually that of elephant's tusks and similar structures, formed from odontoblasts.

ixocomous (ĭksŏk'ömŭs) *a.* [Gk. *ixos*, mistletoe; *kome*, hair.] *Pert.* or formed by viscous or slimy hyphae, as surface of certain fungi.

ixoderm (ĭks'ödĕrm) *n.* [Gk. *ixos*, mistletoe; *derma*, skin.] A layer of hyphae that have become viscous, covering the pileus of certain fungi; ixotrichoderm.

J

Jacob's membrane [*A. Jacob*, Irish ophthalmologist]. Layer of rods and cones of retina; bacillary layer.

Jacobson's cartilage [*L. L. Jacobson*, Danish anatomist]. Vomeronasal cartilage supporting Jacobson's organ.

Jacobson's nerve, — tympanic branch of the glossopharyngeal nerve.

Jacobson's organ,—a diverticulum of olfactory organ in many vertebrates, often developing into an epithelium-lined sac opening into mouth; vomeronasal organ.

jactitation (jăktĭtā'shŭn) *n.* [L. *jactare*, to toss.] Process of scattering seeds by censer mechanism, *q.v.*

jaculator (jăk'ūlātör) *n.* [L. *jaculator*, shooter.] A placental process, usually hooked, of certain fruits.

jaculatory (jăk'ūlătörĭ) *a.* [L. *jaculatorius*, throwing.] Darting out; capable of being emitted.

jaculatory duct,—portion of vas deferens which is capable of being protruded, in many animals.

jaculiferous (jăk'ūlĭf'ërŭs) *a.* [L. *jaculum*, a dart; *ferre*, to carry.] Bearing dart-like spines.

jarovization (yâr'övĭzā'shŭn) *n.* [Russ. *yarovizatsya*, from *yarovoi*, vernal.] Vernalisation, *q.v.*

jaw (jô) *n.* [Akin to *chaw*, *chew*.] A structure, of vertebrates, supported by bone or cartilage, naked or sheathed in horn, or bearing teeth or horny plates, forming part of mouth, and helping to open or shut it; a similarly placed structure in invertebrates.

jaw foot,—maxillipede of Arthropoda.

J-disc,—isotropic or I-disc, *q.v.*

jecoral (jĕk'ŏrăl) *a.* [L. *jecur*, liver.] Of or *pert.* the liver.

jecorin (jĕk'ŏrĭn) *n.* [L. *jecur*, liver.] A lecithin-like substance or phosphatide present in liver and other organs of the body.

jejunum (jējoon'ŭm) *n.* [L. *jejunus*, empty.] Part of small intestine between duodenum and ileum.

jelly of Wharton [*T. Wharton*, English anatomist]. The gelatinous connective tissue surrounding the vessels of umbilical cord.

Johnston's organ [*C. Johnston*, British entomologist]. A statical or chordotonal organ in second segment of insect antenna.

joint (joint) *n.* [O.F. *joindre*, from L. *jungere*, to join.] Place of union or separation of two parts, as between bones; articulation; a node; portion between two nodes or joints.

Jordan's organ [*K. Jordan*, zoologist]. The chaetosemata.

juba (joob'ă) *n.* [L. *juba*, mane.] A mane; a loose panicle.

jubate (joob'āt) *a.* [L. *jubatus*, maned.] With mane-like growth.

jugal (joog'ăl) *n.* [L. *jugum*, yoke.] The malar bone, between maxilla and squamosal. *a. Pert.* a jugum.

jugate (joog'āt) *a.* [L. *jugum*, yoke.] Having pairs of leaflets; furnished with a jugum.

jugular (jŭg'ūlăr, joog'ūlăr) *a.* [L. *jugulum*, collar-bone.] *Pert.* neck or throat; *appl.* veins, foramen, fossa, etc.; *appl.* nerve, the hyoidean or posterior post-trematic nerve; *appl.* ventral fish-fins beneath and in front of pectoral fins.

jugulum (joog'ūlŭm) *n.* [L. *jugulum*, collar-bone.] The foreneck region of a bird's breast; in insects, the jugum of wing.

jugum (joog'ŭm) *n.* [L. *jugum*, yoke.] A pair of opposite leaflets; ridge on mericarp of umbelliferous plants; small lobe on posterior border of fore-wing of certain moths; ridge or depression connecting two structures; union of lesser sphenoidal wings in first year after birth.

Jurassic (joorăs'ĭk) *a.* [*Jura* mountains.] *Pert.* or *appl.* Mesozoic period between Triassic and Cretaceous.

juvenal (joo'vēnăl) *a.* [L. *juvenalis*, youthful.] Youthful; *appl.* plumage replacing nestling-down of first plumage.

juvenile hormone,—secreted by corpus allatum and inhibiting development of adult characters, in certain insects; neotenin.

juvenile leucocyte,—a metamyelocyte in circulation before maturation.

juxta (jŭk'stă) *n.* [L. *juxta*, close to.] A ring-walled structure supporting sheath of aedeagus.

juxtaglomerular (jŭk'stăglŏmĕr'ūlăr) *a.* [L. *juxta*, close to; *glomerare*, to form into a ball.] *Appl.* cells surrounding arteriole of glomerulus of kidney.

juxtamedullary (jŭk'stămĕdŭl'ărĭ) *a.* [L. *juxta*, close to; *medulla*, marrow.] Near medulla; *appl.* inner portion of zona reticularis of adrenal glands.

juxtanuclear (jŭk'stănū'klēăr) *a.* [L. *juxta*, close to; *nucleus*, kernel.] *Appl.* bodies: basophil deposits in cytoplasm of vitamin D-deficient parathyroid cells.

K

kaino-,—*see* caeno-.

kako-,—*see* caco-.

kalidium (kălĭd'ĭŭm) *n.* [*Dim.* of Gk. *kalia*, hut.] A form of sporocarp, or cystocarp.

kalymma (kăl'ĭmă) *n.* [Gk. *kalymma*, covering.] Vacuolated part of outer layer of certain radiolarians.

kalymmocytes (kăl'ĭmŏsīts) *n. plu.* [Gk. *kalymma*, covering; *kytos*, cell.] In ascidians, certain follicle-cells which migrate into the egg after maturation.

karyaster (kărĭăs'tĕr) *n.* [Gk. *karyon*, nut, nucleus; *aster*, star.] A star-shaped group of chromosomes.

karyenchyma (kărĭĕng'kĭmă) *n.* [Gk. *karyon*, nucleus; *engchyma*, infusion.] Nuclear sap; achromatin; karyochylema.

karyoclasis (kărĭŏk'lăsĭs) *n.* [Gk. *karyon*, nucleus; *klasis*, breaking.] Breaking down of a cell-nucleus.

karyogamy (kărĭŏg'ămĭ) *n.* [Gk. *karyon*, nucleus; *gamos*, marriage.] Union and interchange of nuclear material.

karyokinesis (kăr'ĭōkĭnē'sĭs) *n.* [Gk. *karyon*, nucleus; *kinesis*, movement.] Indirect cell-division; mitosis.

karyology (kăr'ĭŏl'ōgĭ) *n.* [Gk. *karyon*, nucleus; *logos*, discourse.] Nuclear cytology.

karyolymph (kăr'ĭōlĭmf') *n.* [Gk. *karyon*, nucleus; L. *lympha*, water.] Nuclear sap; karyenchyma.

karyolysis (kăr'ĭŏl'ĭsĭs) *n.* [Gk. *karyon*, nucleus; *lyein*, to loosen.] Supposed dissolution of the nucleus in mitosis; liquefaction of nuclear membrane. *a.* karyolytic.

karyomere (kăr'ĭōmēr) *n.* [Gk. *karyon*, nucleus; *meros*, part.] In mitosis, a small vesicle into which a chromosome is converted in one type of nuclear construction; karyomerite.

karyomicrosome (kăr'ĭōmī'krōsōm) *n.* [Gk. *karyon*, nucleus; *mikros*, small; *soma*, body.] A nuclear granule.

karyomite (kăr'ĭōmīt) *n.* [Gk. *karyon*, nucleus; *mitos*, thread.] A chromosome.

karyomitome (kăr'ĭōmĭtōm') *n.* [Gk. *karyon*, nucleus; *mitoma*, network.] The nuclear thread-work.

karyomitosis (kăr'ĭōmĭtō'sĭs) *n.* [Gk. *karyon*, nucleus; *mitos*, thread.] Indirect nuclear division; mitosis.

karyon (kăr'ĭŏn) *n.* [Gk. *karyon*, nucleus.] The cell-nucleus.

karyophans (kăr'ĭōfănz') *n. plu.* [Gk. *karyon*, nucleus; *phainein*, to appear.] Microsomes or nucleus-like granules surrounded by an ovoid matrix, which form the spironeme and axoneme in stalk of infusoria.

karyophore (kăr'ĭōfōr) *n.* [Gk. *karyon*, nucleus; *pherein*, to bear.] System of ectoplasmic fibrils or membranes for mooring the nucleus, in certain ciliates.

karyoplasm (kăr'ĭōplăzm) *n.* [Gk. *karyon*, nucleus; *plasma*, mould.] Nucleoplasm, the nuclear substance; *cf.* cytoplasm.

karyorhexis (kăr'ĭōrĕk'sĭs) *n.* [Gk. *karyon*, nucleus; *rhexis*, breaking.] Fragmentation of the cell nucleus; karyoschisis.

karyosome (kăr'ĭōsōm) *n.* [Gk. *karyon*, nucleus; *soma*, body.] A nucleolus of the 'net-knot' type; a chromosome; a special aggregation of chromatin in resting nucleus; the cell-nucleus itself; *cf.* plasmosome.

karyosphere (kăr'ĭōsfēr) *n.* [Gk. *karyon* nucleus; *sphaira*, globe.] The large nucleolus from which arise all or most of the chromosomes of Protista.

karyota (kărĭō'tă) *n. plu.* [Gk. *karyon*, nucleus.] Nucleated cells.

karyotheca (kăr'ĭōthē'kă) *n.* [Gk. *karyon*, nucleus; *theke*, covering.] The nuclear membrane.

karyotin (kăr'ĭōtĭn) *n.* [Gk. *karyon*, nucleus.] Chromatin; nuclear substance.

karyotype (kăr'ĭōtīp) *n.* [Gk. *karyon*, nucleus; *typos*, pattern.] Group of individuals with the same chromosome number and similar linear arrangement of genes in homologous chromosomes; chromosome complement of such a group.

kata-,—*also* cata-.

katabolism (kătăb'ōlĭzm) *n.* [Gk. *kata*, down; *bole*, throw.] The destructive chemical processes in living organisms, *opp.* anabolism.

katabolite (kătăb'ōlīt) *n.* [Gk. *kata*, down; *bole*, throw.] Any product of katabolism, *e.g.* urea.

katagenesis (kăt'ăjĕn'ĕsĭs) *n.* [Gk. *kata*, down; *genesis*, descent.] Retrogressive evolution.

katakinetic (kăt'ăkĭnĕt'ĭk) *a.* [Gk. *kata*, down ; *kinein*, to move.] *Appl.* process leading to discharge of energy ; *cf.* anakinetic.

katakinetomeres (kăt'ăkĭnĕt'ömērz) *n. plu.* [Gk. *kata*, down ; *kinein*, to move ; *meros*, part.] Unreactive, stable, atoms or molecules.

kataphase (kăt'ăfāz) *n.* [Gk. *kata*, down ; *phasis*, appearance.] The stages of mitosis from formation of chromosomes to division of cell ; *cf.* anaphase.

kataphoresis (kăt'ăförē'sĭs) *n.* [Gk. *kata*, down ; *pherein*, to carry.] Transfer of fluids through a membrane from anode to kathode ; electrical osmosis.

kataphoric (kătăfŏr'ĭk) *a.* [Gk. *kata*, down; *pherein*, to carry.] *Appl.* passive action, the result of lethargy.

kataplexy (kăt'ăplĕksĭ) *n.* [Gk. *kata*, down ; *plessein*, to strike.] Condition of an animal feigning death ; maintenance of a postural reflex induced by restraint or shock ; cataplexis ; *cf.* catalepsis.

katastate (kăt'ăstăt, kătăs'tăt) *n.* [Gk. *kata*, down ; *stasis*, state.] Any product of katabolic activity of protoplasm ; katabolite.

katatrepsis (kăt'ătrĕp'sĭs) *n.* [Gk. *kata*, down ; *trepein*, to turn.] Stage of decreasing movement in blastokinesis.

katatropic (kăt'ătrŏp'ĭk) *a.* [Gk. *kata*, down ; *tropikos*, turning.] Turning downwards.

katharobic (kăthărŏb'ĭk) *a.* [Gk. *katharos*, pure ; *bios*, life.] Living in clean waters, *appl.* Protista. *Opp.* saprobic.

kathodic (kăthŏd'ĭk) *a.* [Gk. *kathodos*, descent.] Not arising in conformity with genetic spiral ; *appl.* leaves.

kation (kăt'ĭŏn, kătī'ŏn) *n.* [Gk. *kata*, down ; *ienai*, to go.] A positively charged ion which moves towards kathode or negative pole ; *opp.* anion.

Keber's organ [*G. A. F. Keber*, German zoologist]. Pericardial glands in lamellibranchs.

keel (kēl) *n.* [A.S. *ceol*, ship.] The carina on breast-bone of flying birds ; boat-shaped structure formed by two anterior petals of Leguminosae ; ridge on blade or on other parts of grasses.

kenanthy (kĕnăn'thĭ) *n.* [Gk. *kenos*, empty ; *anthos*, flower.] Non-development of stamens and pistils of a flower.

kenenchyma (kĕnĕng'kĭmă) *n.* [Gk. *kenos*, empty ; *engchyma*, infusion.] A tissue devoid of its living contents, as cork.

keph-,—*see* ceph-.

keraphyllous (kĕrăfĭl'ŭs) *a.* [Gk. *keras*, horn ; *phyllon*, leaf.] *Appl.* layer of a hoof between horny and sensitive parts.

keratin (kĕr'ătĭn) *n.* [Gk. *keras*, horn.] A scleroprotein forming the basis of epidermal structures such as horns, nails, hairs.

keratinisation (kĕr'ătĭnīzā'shŭn) *n.* [Gk. *keras*, horn.] State of becoming horny ; *appl.* cells of epiderm developing in a horny material.

keratinolytic (kĕr'ătĭnölĭt'ĭk) *a.* [Gk. *keras*, horn ; *lyein*, to dissolve.] Hydrolysing keratin ; *appl.* enzymes, as produced by dermatophytes.

keratinophilic (kĕr'ătĭnöfĭl'ĭk) *a.* [Gk. *keras*, horn ; *philos*, loving.] Growing on a horny or keratinised substrate ; *appl.* certain fungi.

keratogenous (kĕrătŏj'ënŭs) *a.* [Gk. *keras*, horn ; *-genes*, producing.] Horn-producing.

keratohyalin (kĕr'ătöhī'ălĭn) *n.* [Gk. *keras*, horn ; *hyalos*, glass.] Substance contained in stratum lucidum of skin.

keratoid (kĕr'ătoid) *a.* [Gk. *keras*, horn ; *eidos*, form.] Horny ; resembling horn.

keratose (kĕr'ătōs) *a.* [Gk. *keras*, horn.] Having horny fibres in skeleton, as certain sponges.

kernel (kĕr'nĕl) *n.* [A.S. *cyrnel*, small grain.] The inner part of a seed containing the embryo.

ketogenic hormone,—a prepituitary principle which influences fat metabolism.

key-fruit,—winged achenes hanging in clusters, as of Acer and Fraxinus.

key gene,—oligogene, *q.v.*

kidney (kĭd′nē) *n.* [A.S. *cwith*, womb; *neere*, kidney.] Nephros; paired organ which elaborates and excretes urine.

kinaesthesis (kĭn′ēsthē′sĭs) *n.* [Gk. *kinein*, to move; *aisthesis*, perception.] Perception of movement due to stimulation of muscles, tendons, and joints; proprioception.

kinaesthetic (kĭn′ēsthĕt′ĭk) *a.* [Gk. *kinein*, to move; *aisthesis*, perception.] *Pert.* sense of movement or muscular effort; *appl.* sense, area.

kinase (kī′nās) *n.* [Gk. *kinein*, to move.] A substance which transforms zymogens to enzymes.

kinesiodic (kĭn′ēsĭŏd′ĭk) *a.* [Gk. *kinesis*, movement; *hodos*, way.] *Pert.* motor nerve paths; *cf.* kinesodic.

kinesis (kĭnē′sĭs) *n.* [Gk. *kinesis*, movement.] Random movement; locomotor reactions depending on intensity of stimulus; variation in linear or angular velocity.

kinesodic (kĭn′ēsŏd′ĭk) *a.* [Gk. *kinesis*, movement; *hodos*, way.] Conveying motor impulses.

kinetia,—*plu.* of kinetium.

kinetic (kĭnĕt′ĭk) *a.* [Gk. *kinein*, to move.] Active; *appl.* function of movement, *opp.* static; energy employed in producing or changing motion; *appl.* division centre in cell-division.

kinetium (kĭnē′shĭŭm, -tĭŭm) *n.* [Gk. *kinein*, to move.] A row of kinetosomes with a kinetodesma; kinety.

kinetoblast (kĭnē′töblăst) *n.* [Gk. *kinein*, to move; *blastos*, bud.] Outer ciliated investment of aquatic larvae with special locomotor properties.

kinetochore (kĭnē′tökōr) *n.* [Gk. *kinein*, to move; *choros*, place.] Spindle-attachment or -insertion region; centromere.

kinetodesma (kĭnē′tödĕs′mă) *n.* [Gk. *kinein*, to move; *desma*, bond.] A fibril alongside a row of kinetosomes in Ciliata.

kinetogenesis (kĭnē′töjĕn′ēsĭs) *n.* [Gk. *kinein*, to move; *genesis*, descent.] The evolution theory that animal structures have been produced by animal movements.

kinetomeres (kĭnē′tömērz) *n. plu.* [Gk. *kinein*, to move; *meros*, part.] Molecules or atoms, reactive or stable, ana- and kata-kinetomeres.

kinetonema (kĭnē′tönē′mă) *n.* [Gk. *kinein*, to move; *nema*, thread.] Part of the chromonema associated with spindle-attachment region or centromere.

kinetonucleus (kĭnē′tönū′klëŭs) *n.* [Gk. *kinein*, to move; L. *nucleus*, kernel.] The secondary nucleus, kinetoplast, or parabasal body, in forms such as trypanosomes, in close connection with flagellum and undulating membrane; *cf.* trophonucleus.

kinetoplasm (kĭnē′töplăzm) *n.* [Gk. *kinein*, to move; *plasma*, something formed.] An iron-containing nucleo-protein forming a source of energy to Nissl granules.

kinetoplast (kĭnē′töplăst) *n.* [Gk. *kinein*, to move; *plastos*, formed.] Composite body formed by union of parabasal body with blepharoplast in some Mastigophora.

kinetosome (kĭnē′tösōm) *n.* [Gk. *kinein*, to move; *soma*, body.] One of a group of granules occupying the polar plate region in moss sporogenesis; a self-duplicating granule at the base of a cilium in Ciliata.

kinetospore (kīnē′töspōr) *n.* [Gk. *kinein*, to move; *sporos*, seed.] A zoospore in its physiological aspect.

kinety,—kinetium.

kinoplasm (kī′nöplăzm) *n.* [Gk. *kinein*, to move; *plasma*, mould.] The substance of attraction-sphere, astral rays, and spindle-fibres; archiplasm; ergastoplasm.

kinoplasmosomes (kī′nöplăz′mösōmz) *n. plu.* [Gk. *kinein*, to move; *plasma*, form; *soma*, body.] Phragmoplast fibres seen at periphery of cell plate.

klado-,—clado-, *q.v.*

klasma-plates (klăz'mă-plāts) *n. plu.* [Gk. *klasma*, fragment; L. *platus*, flat.] Small parts of compound ambulacral plates separated by growth pressure, in echinoids.

kleisto-,—*also* cleisto-, *q.v.*

kleistogamous (klīstŏg'ămŭs) *a.* [Gk. *kleistos*, closed; *gamos*, marriage.] Fertilised in closed flowers.

kleronomous (klērŏn'ŏmŭs) *a.* [Gk. *kleronomos*, heir.] Inherited; *appl.* paths in nervous system.

klinokinesis (klī'nŏkĭnē'sĭs) *n.* [Gk. *klinein*, to slope; *kinesis*, movement.] Change in rate of change of direction, or angular velocity, due to intensity of stimulation; *cf.* kinesis.

klon,—clone, *q.v.*

knee (nē) *n.* [A.S. *cneow*, knee.] Genu; joint between femur and tibia; root-process of certain swamp-inhabiting trees.

knephoplankton (nĕf'ŏplăngk'tŏn) *n.* [Gk. *knephas*, twilight; *plangktos*, wandering.] Plankton living at depths between thirty and five hundred metres; *cf.* phaoplankton, skotoplankton.

knot (nŏt) *n.* [A.S. *cnotta*, knot.] In wood, base of branch surrounded by new layers of wood and hardened by pressure; in nuclear meshwork, small particles of chromatin where meshes cross.

koino-,—coeno-, *q.v.*

Kölliker's canal [*R. A. von Kölliker*, Swiss zoologist]. A canal leading from otocyst towards exterior, as in certain Cephalopoda.

kolyone (kō'lĭōn) *n.* [Gk. *kolyein*, to hinder.] Substance elaborated in, and conveyed from, a tissue or organ, which lessens or inhibits function of other tissues.

kolytic (kōlĭ'tĭk) *a.* [Gk. *kolytikos*, hindering.] Inhibiting; inhibitory.

komma (kŏm'ă) *n.* [Gk. *komma*, clause.] Sarcomere; inocomma.

koniocortex (kŏn'ĭŏkôr'tĕks) *n.* [Gk. *konis*, dust; L. *cortex*, bark.] Granular part of cortex, characteristic of sensory areas of brain.

Kovalevsky's canal [*P. Kovalesvkii*, Russian embryologist]. The neurenteric canal.

Krause's end-bulbs, — *see* end-bulbs.

Krause's glands [*K. F. T. Krause*, German anatomist]. Accessory lacrimal glands with ducts opening into fornix of conjunctiva.

Krause's membrane [*W. J. F. Krause*, German anatomist]. The single or double row of dots in the light transverse band of striated muscle; telophragma, Z-disc.

Kupffer cells [*K. W. von Kupffer*, German anatomist]. Stellate macrophages of liver sinuses.

kyano-,—cyano-, *q.v.*

kyogenic (kīŏjĕn'ĭk) *a.* [Gk. *kyesis*, pregnancy; *genos*, descent.] *Appl.* prepituitary hormone stimulating secretion of progestin by corpora lutea.

kyto-,—cyto-, *q.v.*

L

labella (lăbĕl'ă) *n.* [L. *labellum*, small lip.] Paraglossa of insects; *plu.* of labellum.

labellate (lăbĕl'āt) *a.* [L. *labellum*, small lip.] Furnished with labella or small lips.

labelloid (lăbĕl'oid) *a.* [L. *labellum*, small lip; Gk. *eidos*, form.] Like a labellum.

labellum (lăbĕl'ŭm) *n.* [L. *labellum*, small lip.] The lower petal, morphologically posterior, of an orchid; two fused lateral staminodes, as in flower of Zingiberaceae; small lobe beneath labrum, or labial palp, in insects; proboscis lobe.

labia (lā'bĭă) *n. plu.* [L. *labium*, lip.] Lips; lip-like structures.

labia cerebri,—margins of cerebral hemispheres overlapping corpus callosum.

labia majora,—outer lips of vulva.

labia minora,—inner lips of vulva.

labial (lā'bĭăl) *a.* [L. *labium*, lip.] *Pert.* or resembling a lip, or labium.

labial palp,—lobe-like structure near mouth of molluscs ; jointed appendage on labium of insects.

labiate (lā'bĭăt) *a.* [L. *labium*, lip.] Lip-like; possessing lips or thickened margins ; having limb of calyx or corolla so divided that one portion overlaps the other.

labiatiflorous (lā'bĭătĭflō'rŭs) *a.* [L. *labium*, lip ; *flos*, flower.] Having the corolla divided into two lip-like portions.

labidophorous (lăb'ĭdŏf'ŏrŭs) *a.* [Gk. *labis*, forceps ; *pherein*, to carry.] Possessing pincer-like organs.

labiella (lā'bĭĕl'ă) *n.* [L. *labium*, lip.] A mouth-part of Myriopoda.

labile (lā'bĭl, lăb'ĭl) *a.* [L. *labilis*, apt to slip.] Readily undergoing change ; unstable ; *appl.* genes that are constantly mutating.

labiodental (lā'bĭōdĕn'tăl) *a.* [L. *labium*, lip ; *dens*, tooth.] *Pert.* lip and teeth ; *appl.* an embryonic lamina; *appl.* labial surface of tooth.

labiosternite (lā'bĭōstĕr'nīt) *n.* [L. *labium*, lip ; *sternum*, breast-bone.] A median area between palpigers of insect head.

labiostipes (lā'bĭōstī'pēz) *n.* [L. *labium*, lip ; *stipes*, stalk.] A portion of basal part of insect labium.

labipalp (lā'bĭpălp) *n.* [L. *labium*, lip ; *palpare*, to feel.] Labipalpus, labial palp of insects.

labium (lā'bĭŭm) *n.* [L. *labium*, lip.] A lip, or lip-shaped structure ; the fused second maxillae of insects. *Plu.* labia.

labral (lā'brăl) *a.* [L. *labrum*, lip.] *Pert.* a labrum.

labrocyte (lăb'rōsīt) *n.* [Gk. *labros*, greedy ; *kytos*, hollow.] A mast cell.

labrum (lā'brŭm) *n.* [L. *labrum*, lip.] Anterior lip of certain arthropods ; hypostoma of trilobites ; outer margin of mouth of gastropod shell ; ring of fibrocartilage, ambon, *q.v.*

labyrinth (lăb'ĭrĭnth) *n.* [L. *labyrinthus*, labyrinth.] The complex internal ear, bony or membranous ; lateral mass of air-cells of ethmoidal bone ; portions of kidney cortex with uriniferous tubules ; tracheal tympanum.

labyrinthodont (lăb'ĭrĭn'thōdŏnt) *a.* [Gk. *labyrinthos*, labyrinth ; *odous*, tooth.] Having teeth with great complexity of dentine arrangement.

lac (lăk) *n.* [Persian, *lak*, lacquer.] A resinous secretion of lac glands of certain Coccidae, composition depending on the food plant.

laccate (lăk'āt) *a.* [It. *lacca*, varnish.] Appearing as if varnished.

lacerated (lăs'ĕrātĕd) *a.* [L. *lacerare*, to tear.] Having margin or apex deeply cut into irregular lobes.

lacertiform (lăsĕr'tĭfôrm) *a.* [L. *lacerta*, lizard ; *forma*, shape.] Having the shape of a lizard.

lacertus (lăsĕr'tŭs) *n.* [L. *lacertus*, arm-muscle.] Lacertus fibrosus, aponeurosis of tendon of biceps muscle of the arm ; bicipital fascia.

lachry-,—lacri-.

lacinia (lăsĭn'ĭă) *n.* [L. *lacinia*, flap.] Segment of an incised leaf ; slender projection from margin of a thallus ; extension of posterior margin of proglottis over anterior part of following proglottis ; inner division of endopodite or stipes of maxilla of insects ; fimbria, *q.v.*

laciniate (lăsĭn'ĭāt) *a.* [L. *lacinia*, flap.] Irregularly incised, as petals ; fringed ; *appl.* a ligament of the ankle, the internal annular ligament.

laciniform (lăsĭn'ĭfôrm) *a.* [L. *lacinia*, flap ; *forma*, shape.] Shaped like lacinia ; fringe-like.

lacinula (lăsĭn'ūlă) *n.* [L. *lacinia*, *dim.*, flap.] Small lacinia ; inflexed sharp point of petal.

lacinulate (lăsĭn'ūlāt) *a.* [L. *lacinia*, *dim.*, flap.] Having lacinulae.

lacrimal (lăk'rĭmăl) *a.* [L. *lacrima*, tear.] Secreting or *pert.* tears ; *pert.* or situated near lacrimal organ ; *appl.* artery, bone, duct, glands, nerve, papillae, sac ; also lachrymal.

lacrimiform (lăk'rĭmĭfôrm) *a.* [L. *lacrima*, tear; *forma*, shape.] Tear-shaped; lacrimaeform, lacrioid, lachrimiform, lachrymiform, dacryoid; *appl.* spores, etc.

lacrimonasal (lăk'rĭmönā'zăl) *a.* [L. *lacrima*, tear; *nasus*, nose.] *Pert.* lacrimal and nasal bones or duct.

lacrimose (lăk'rĭmōs) *a.* [L. *lacrimosus*, tearful.] Bearing tear-shaped appendages, as gills of certain fungi.

lactalbumin (lăk'tălbū'mĭn) *n.* [L. *lac*, milk; *albumen*, egg-white.] An albumin found in milk.

lactase (lăk'tās) *n.* [L. *lac*, milk.] An intestinal enzyme converting lactose into glucose and galactose; also found in certain plants.

lactation (lăktā'shŭn) *n.* [L. *lac*, milk.] Secretion of milk in mammary glands; period during which milk is secreted.

lacteals (lăk'tëălz) *n. plu.* [L. *lac*, milk.] Chyliferous or lymphatic vessels of small intestine; ducts which carry latex.

lactescent (lăktĕs'ënt) *a.* [L. *lactescere*, to turn to milk.] Producing milk; yielding latex.

lactic (lăk'tĭk) *a.* [L. *lac*, milk.] *Pert.* milk; *appl.* bacilli, acid.

lactifer,—laticifer, *q.v.*

lactiferous (lăktĭf'ërŭs) *a.* [L. *lac*, milk; *ferre*, to carry.] Forming or carrying milk; carrying latex.

lactochrome (lăk'tökrōm) *n.* [L. *lac*, milk; Gk. *chroma*, colour.] A nitrogenous colouring matter in milk; lactoflavin, *q.v.*

lactoflavin (lăk'töflā'vĭn) *n.* [L. *lac*, milk; *flavus*, yellow.] Vitamin B_2; riboflavin, *q.v.*; $C_{17}H_{20}O_6N_4$.

lactogenic (lăk'töjĕn'ĭk) *a.* [L. *lac*, milk; Gk. *-genes*, producing.] *Pert.*, or stimulating, secretion of milk; *appl.* a prepituitary hormone inducing secretion of milk in mammals and of crop milk in the pigeon; *appl.* interval between parturition and ovulation, or between parturition and menstruation.

lactoglobulin (lăk'töglŏb'ūlĭn) *n.* [L. *lac*, milk; *globulus*, *dim.* of *globus*, globe.] The specific protein of milk, insoluble in water; lactalbumin.

lactoproteid (lăk'töprō'tëĭd) *n.* [L. *lac*, milk; Gk. *proteion*, first; *eidos*, form.] Any milk proteid.

lactose (lăk'tōs) *n.* [L. *lac*, milk.] Milk-sugar, $C_{12}H_{22}O_{11}$.

lacuna (lăkū'nă) *n.* [L. *lacuna*, cavity.] A space between cells; sinus; urethral follicle; cavity in bone; small cavity or depression on surface in lichens; a leaf gap. *Plu.* lacunae.

lacunar,—having, resembling, or *pert.* lacunae.

lacunate (lăkū'nāt) *a.* [L. *lacuna*, cavity.] Lacunar; *pert.* lacunae; *appl.* collenchyma, with cell-walls thickened where bordering intercellular spaces.

lacunose (lăkū'nōs) *a.* [L. *lacuna*, cavity.] Having many cavities; pitted.

lacunosorugose (lăkū'nōsöroo'gōs) *a.* [L. *lacuna*, cavity; *rugosus*, wrinkled.] Having deep furrows or pits, as some seeds and fruits.

lacunula (lăkū'nūla) *n.* [L. *Dim.* of *lacuna*, a hollow.] A minute cavity or lacuna; a minute air space, as in grey hair.

lacus lacrimalis,—the triangular space between eyelids which contains lacrimal caruncle and receives tears from orifices of the lacrimal ducts.

lacustrine (lăkŭs'trĭn) *a.* [L. *lacus*, lake.] *Pert.*, or living in or beside, lakes.

laeotropic (lē'ötrŏp'ĭk) *a.* [Gk. *laios*, left; *trope*, turning.] Inclined, turned, or coiled to the left; laeotropous, sinistral.

laevulose (lē'vūlōs) *n.* [L. *laevus*, left.] Fruit-sugar; fructose, $C_6H_{12}O_6$.

lagena (lăgē'nă, lăjē'nă) *n.* [L. *lagena*, flask.] Apical portion of the cochlear duct or scala media.

lageniform (lăgē'nĭfôrm, lăjē'nĭfôrm) *a.* [L. *lagena*, flask; *forma*, shape.] Shaped like a flask.

lagoena,—lagena.

lagopodous (lăgŏp′ŏdŭs) *a.* [Gk. *lagos*, hare ; *pous*, foot.] Possessing hairy or feathery feet.

Lamarckian (lămârk′ĭăn) *a.* [*J.-B. de Lamarck*, French biologist]. Of or *pert.* theories put forward by Lamarck.

Lamarckism (lămârk′ĭzm) *n.* The evolution theory of Lamarck, embodying the principle that acquired characteristics are transmissible.

lambda (lăm′dă) *n.* [Gk. Λ, lambda.] The junction of lambdoid and sagittal sutures.

lambdoid (lăm′doid] *a.* [Gk. Λ, lambda ; *eidos*, form.] Λ-shaped ; *appl.* the cranial suture joining occipital and parietal bones.

lamella (lămĕl′ă) *n.* [L. *lamella*, small plate.] Any thin plate- or scale-like structure ; the gill of an agaric.

lamellar (lămĕl′ăr), **lamellate** (lăm′ĕlāt) *a.* [L. *lamella*, small plate.] Composed of, or possessing thin plates.

lamellated corpuscles,—Pacinian corpuscles, *q.v.*

lamellibranchiate (lămĕl′ĭbrăng′kiāt) *a.* [L. *lamella*, small plate ; *branchiae*, gills.] Having plate-like gills on each side ; with bilaterally compressed symmetrical body, like a bivalve.

lamellicorn (lămĕl′ĭkôrn) *a.* [L. *lamella*, small plate ; *cornu*, horn.] Having antennal joints expanded into flattened plates.

lamelliferous (lăm′ĕlĭf′ĕrŭs) *a.* [L. *lamella*, small plate ; *ferre*, to carry.] Having small plates or scales.

lamelliform (lămĕl′ĭfôrm) *a.* [L. *lamella*, small plate ; *forma*, shape.] Plate-like.

lamellirostral (lămĕl′ĭrŏs′trăl) *a.* [L. *lamella*, small plate ; *rostrum*, beak.] Having inner edges of bill bearing lamella-like ridges.

lamelloid,—lamelliform.

lamina (lăm′ĭnă) *n.* [L. *lamina*, plate.] A thin layer, or scale ; blade of leaf ; one of thin plate-like expansions of sensitive tissue which fit into grooves on inside of horse-hoof.

lamina basalis,—a thin membrane on inner surface of lamina choriocapillaris.

lamina choriocapillaris,—capillary plexus constituting inner layer of choroid.

lamina cribrosa,—cribriform plate, *q.v.* ; membraneous portion of sclera at site of attachment of optic nerve and with perforations for axons of ganglion cells of retina.

lamina fusca,—inner layer of sclera, adjoining lamina suprachoroidea.

lamina papyracea,—plate or os planum of ethmoidal bone, forming part of medial wall of orbit.

lamina perpendicularis,—median process of mesethmoid or ethmoid forming proximal or bony part of nasal septum.

lamina suprachoroidea,—delicate tissue or membrane between choroid and sclera.

lamina terminalis,—thin layer of grey matter forming anterior boundary of third ventricle of brain.

lamina vasculosa,—outer layer of choroid beneath suprachoroid membrane.

lamina vitrea,—lamina basalis.

laminar (lăm′ĭnăr), **laminiform** (lăm′ĭnĭfôrm) *a.* [L. *lamina*, plate ; *forma*, shape.] Consisting of plates or thin layers ; laminous.

laminarian (lămĭnā′rĭăn) *a.* [*Laminaria*, a genus of brown seaweeds.] *Appl.* zone between low water to about fifteen fathoms.

lamination (lăm′ĭnā′shŭn) *n.* [L. *lamina*, plate.] The formation of thin plates or layers ; arrangement in layers, as nerve cells of cerebral cortex.

laminiplantar (lăm′ĭnĭplăn′tăr) *a.* [L. *lamina*, plate ; *planta*, sole of foot.] Having scales of metatarsus meeting behind in a smooth ridge.

lanate (lā′nāt) *a.* [L. *lana*, wool.] Woolly ; covered with short hair-like processes giving woolly appearance to surface.

lance-linear (lăns′-lĭn′ëăr) *a.* [L. *lancea,* lance; *linea,* line.] Between lanceolate and linear in form.

lance-oblong (lăns′-ŏb′lŏng) *a.* [L. *lancea,* lance; *oblongus,* oblong.] Oblong with tapering ends.

lanceolate (lăn′sëölāt) *a.* [L. *lanceola,* little lance.] Slightly broad, or tapering, at base and tapering to point; lance-shaped.

lance-oval (lăns′-ō′văl), **lance-ovate** (lăns′-ō′vāt) *a.* [L. *lancea,* lance; *ovalis,* oval.] Having a shape intermediate between lanceolate and oval.

lancet (lăn′sët) *n.* [F. *lancette,* from L. *lancea,* lance.] One of the paired parts, ventral to stylet, of sting in Hymenoptera.

lancet - plates, — plates supporting water-vascular vessels of Blastoidea.

Landolt's fibre [*E. Landolt,* French ophthalmologist]. Free end of outer processes of cone-bipolar cells in inner nuclear layer of retina.

Langerhans' cell [*P. Langerhans,* German anatomist]. Melanoblast.

Langerhans, follicles of,—*see* follicles.

Langerhans, islets of,—*see* islets.

Langhans' cells [*T. Langhans,* German histologist]. Giant cells of inner layer of trophoblast or layer of Langhans.

languet, languette (lăngget′) *n.* [F. *languette,* small tongue.] A process on branchial sac of ascidians.

laniary (lān′ĭărĭ) *a.* [L. *laniare,* to tear to pieces.] Term *appl.* to canine tooth.

lantern,—*see* Aristotle's lantern.

lanthanin (lănthā′nĭn) *n.* [Gk. *lanthanein,* to conceal.] Oxychromatin; linin, *q.v.*

lanuginous (lănū′jĭnŭs) *a.* [L. *lanugo,* down.] Covered with down; lanuginose.

lanugo (lănū′gō) *n.* [L. *lanugo,* down.] The downy covering on a foetus, begins to be shed before birth.

lapidicolous (lăp′ĭdĭk′ölŭs) *a.* [L. *lapis,* stone; *colere,* to cultivate.] *Appl.* animals that live under stones.

lapillus (lăpĭl′ŭs) *n.* [L. *lapillus,* pebble.] A small otolith in utriculus of teleosts.

lappaceous (lăpā′shŭs) *a.* [L. *lappa,* bur.] Like a bur; prickly.

lappet (lăp′ët) *n.* [A.S. *laeppa,* loose hanging part.] One of paired lobes extending downwards from distal end of stomodaeum in jelly-fish; lobe of a sea-anemone gullet; wattle of a bird.

larmier (lâr′myër) *n.* [F. *larme,* tear.] Tear pit; saccus lacrimalis.

larva (lâr′vă) *n.* [L. *larva,* ghost.] An embryo which becomes self-sustaining and independent before it has assumed the characteristic features of its parents.

larval (lâr′văl) *a.* [L. *larva,* ghost.] *Pert.* a larva; in the larval stage.

larviform (lâr′vĭfôrm) *a.* [L. *larva,* ghost; *forma,* shape.] Shaped like a larva.

larviparous (lârvĭp′ărŭs) *a.* [L. *larva,* ghost; *parere,* to produce.] Producing live larvae.

larvivorous (lârvĭv′örŭs) *a.* [L. *larva,* ghost; *vorare,* to devour.] Larva-eating.

larvule (lâr′vūl) *n.* [L. *larvula,* small larva.] Young larva.

laryngeal (lărĭn′jëăl) *a.* [Gk. *laryngx,* upper part of windpipe.] *Pert.* or near the larynx; *appl.* artery, vein, nerve, etc.

laryngeal prominence,—subcutaneous projection of the thyroid cartilage in front of the throat; Adam's-apple, pomum Adami.

laryngopharynx (lărĭng′göfăr′ĭngks) *n.* [Gk. *laryngx,* larynx; *pharyngx,* gullet.] Part of pharynx between soft palate and oesophagus.

laryngotracheal (lărĭng′götrā′këăl) *a.* [Gk. *laryngx,* windpipe; L. *trachea,* trachea.] *Pert.* larynx and trachea; *appl.* embryonic groove and tube.

larynx (lăr′ĭngks) *n.* [Gk. *laryngx,* larynx.] The organ of voice in most vertebrates, except birds.

lasso (lăs′ō) *n.* [Sp. *lazo,* noose.] A contractile filamentous noose used in trapping nematodes by certain soil fungi.

lasso-cells,—filamented hemispherical adhesive cells, investing tentacles of Ctenophora; colloblasts.

lata-type,—a mutant with one or more supernumerary chromosomes as compared with its parent (from *Oenothera lata*).

latebra (lăt′ëbră) *n.* [L. *latebra*, hiding-place.] The bulb or flask-shaped mass of white yolk in eggs.

latebricole (lăt′ĕbrĭkōl) *a.* [L. *latebra*, hiding-place; *colere*, to inhabit.] Inhabiting holes.

latent (lā′tĕnt) *a.* [L. *latens*, hidden.] Lying dormant but capable of development under favourable circumstances; *appl.* buds, resting stages, characters.

latent bodies,—the resting stage of certain Haemoflagellata.

latent period,—the time interval between completion of presentation of a stimulus and the beginning of a reaction; reaction time.

lateral (lăt′ërăl) *a.* [L. *latus*, side.] *Pert.* or situated at a side, or at a side of an axis.

lateral chain theory,—*see* side-chain.

lateral line,—longitudinal line at each side of body of fishes, marking position of sensory cells.

lateral mesenteries, — the mesenteries of Zoantharia, excluding directive or dorsal and ventral pairs.

lateralia (lătërā′lĭă) *n. plu.* [L. *latus*, side.] The lateral plates of Cirripedia.

laterigrade (lăt′ërĭgrād) *a.* [L. *latus*, side; *gradus*, step.] Walking sideways, as a crab.

laterinerved (lăt′ërinĕrvd′) *a.* [L. *latus*, side; *nervus*, sinew.] With lateral veins.

laterite (lăt′ërīt) *n.* [L. *later*, brick.] *Appl.* tropical red soils containing alumina and iron oxides and little silica owing to leaching under hot, moist conditions.

laterocranium (lăt′ërōkrā′nĭŭm) *n.* [L. *latus*, side; *cranium*, skull.] Area of insect head comprising genae and postgenae.

latero-sensory (lăt′ërōsĕn′sōrĭ) *a.* [L. *latus*, side; *sensus*, sense.] *Appl.* system of lateral sense-organs in fishes, or lateral line system.

laterosternites (lăt′ëröstĕr′nīts) *n. plu.* [L. *latus*, side; *sternum*, breastbone.] Sclerites at side of eusternum, as in Dermaptera and Isoptera.

laterotergites (lăt′ërötĕr′jīts) *n. plu.* [L. *latus*, side; *tergum*, back.] Small sclerites adjoining tergum of abdominal segments in some crustaceans and insects.

latex (lā′tĕks) *n.* [L. *latex*, a liquid.] A milky, or clear, sometimes coloured, juice or emulsion of diverse composition found in some plants, as in spurges, rubber trees, certain agarics, etc.

laticifer (lătĭs′ĭfër) *n.* [L. *latex*, a liquid; *ferre*, to carry.] Any latex-containing cell, series of cells, or duct.

laticiferous (lăt′ĭsĭf′ërŭs) *a.* [L. *latex*, a liquid; *ferre*, to carry.] Conveying latex; *appl.* cells, tissue, vessels.

latiplantar (lăt′ĭplăn′tăr) *a.* [L. *latus*, broad; *planta*, sole of foot.] Having hinder tarsal surface rounded.

latirostral (lăt′ĭrŏs′trăl) *a.* [L. *latus*, broad; *rostrum*, beak.] Broad-beaked.

latiseptate (lăt′ĭsĕp′tāt) *a* [L *latus*, broad; *septum*, septum.] Having a broad septum in the silicula.

latitudinal furrow,—one running round a segmenting egg above and parallel to the equatorial.

Laurer-Stieda canal,—a canal leading from junction of oviduct and vitelline duct to opening on dorsal surface in trematodes.

laurinoxylon (lôr′ĭnözī′lŏn) *n.* [L. *laurus*, laurel; Gk. *xylon*, wood.] Any fossil wood; lithoxyle.

law of acceleration,—the generalisation that organs of greater importance develop more quickly.

lax (lăks) *a.* [L. *laxus*, loose.] Loose, as *appl.* panicle.

layer of Langhans [*T. Langhans*, German histologist]. Cytotrophoblast.

leader (lē′dër) *n.* [A.S. *laedan*, to lead.] Highest shoot or part of trunk of a tree.

leaf (lēf) *n.* [A.S. *leaf*, leaf.] An expanded outgrowth of a stem, usually green.

leaf-buttress,—lateral prominence on shoot axis, due to underlying leaf primordium, representing leaf-base.

leaf-cushions,—prominent persistent leaf-bases, furnishing diagnostic characters in certain extinct plants.

leaf-gap,—mesh of stelar network, corresponding to site of leaf attachment in ferns; gap in vascular cylinder of stem, a parenchymatous region associated with leaf-traces; lacuna.

leaflet,—a small leaf; individual unit of a compound leaf.

leaf-stalk,—petiole.

leaf-trace,—vascular bundles extending from stem bundles to leaf-base. *Cf.* girdle bundles.

leberidocytes (lĕbērĭ'dösīts) *n. plu.* [Gk. *leberis*, exuvia; *kytos*, hollow.] Cells containing glycogen, and developing from and regressing to leucocytes, found in blood of Arachnida at moulting.

lechriodont (lĕk'rĭödŏnt') *a.* [Gk. *lechrios*, crosswise; *odous*, tooth.] With vomerine and pterygoid teeth in a row nearly transverse.

lecithalbumin (lĕs'ĭthălbū'mĭn) *n.* [Gk. *lekithos*, egg-yolk; L. *albumen*, white of egg.] A substance, consisting of albumin and lecithin, of various body organs.

lecithelles (lĕs'ĭthĕlz) *n. plu.* [Gk. *lekithos*, egg-yolk.] Yolk granules in hypoblastic or other lecithoblasts.

lecithin (lĕs'ĭthĭn) *n.* [Gk. *lekithos*, egg-yolk.] A phosphorised fat or phospholipide of cell-protoplasm.

lecithoblast (lĕs'ĭthöblăst) *n.* [Gk. *lekithos*, egg-yolk; *blastos*, bud.] In developing eggs, the yolk-containing blastomeres.

lecithocoel (lĕs'ĭthösēl) *n.* [Gk. *lekithos*, egg-yolk; *koilos*, hollow.] Segmentation cavity of holoblastic eggs.

lectoallotype (lĕk'töăl'ötīp) *n.* [Gk. *lektos*, chosen; *allos*, other; *typos*, pattern.] A specimen of the opposite sex to that of the lectotype and subsequently chosen from the original material.

lectotype (lĕk'tötīp) *n.* [Gk. *lektos*, chosen; *typos*, pattern.] A specimen chosen from syntypes to designate type of species.

legume (lĕg'ūm) *n* [L. *legumen*, pulse.] Dehiscent one-celled, two-valved seed-vessel, as pod of pea or bean; lomentum, *q.v.*

legumin (lĕgū'mĭn) *n.* [L. *legumen*, pulse.] A globulin in seeds of Leguminosae; vegetable casein.

leiotrichous (līŏt'rĭkŭs) *a.* [Gk. *leios*, smooth; *thrix*, hair.] Having straight hair; leiothric.

leiotropic,—laeotropic, *q.v.*

leipsanenchyma (līp'săněng'kĭma) *n.* [Gk. *leipsanon*, remnant; *engchyma*, infusion.] Part of primordial tissue of a carpophore, located between stipe and pileus; lipsanenchyma.

lemma (lĕm'ă) *n.* [Gk. *lemma*, husk.] A valve or flowering glume; lower or outer palea, bract with axillary flower.

lemniscus (lĕmnĭs'kŭs) *n.* [Gk. *lemniskos*, ribbon.] One of paired club-shaped organs at base of acanthocephalan proboscis; a fillet of fibres on each side of cerebral peduncles.

lenitic (lēnĭt'ĭk) *a.* [L. *lenis*, smooth.] Lentic, *q.v.*

lens (lĕnz) *n.* [L. *lens*, lentil.] A transparent part of eye, which focuses rays of light on retina; crystalline lens; modified portion of cornea in front of each element of a compound eye; modified cells of luminescent organ in certain fishes.

lentic (lĕn'tĭk) *a.* [L. *lentus*, slow.] *Appl.* or *pert.* standing water; living in swamp, pond, or lake; lenitic. *Opp.* lotic.

lenticel (lĕn'tĭsĕl) *n.* [L. *lens*, lentil.] Ventilating pore in angiosperm stems or roots; canal in cork; a lenticular gland.

lenticula (lĕntĭk'ūlă) *n.* [L. *lenticula*, *dim.* of *lens*, lentil.] A spore case in certain fungi; a lenticel; a lentigo or freckle.

lenticular,—shaped like a double-convex lens; lentiform; *appl.* glands, lymphoid structures between pyloric glands. *n.* Tip of incus articulating with stapes, often ossified as a separate unit.

lenticulate (lĕntĭk'ūlāt) *a.* [L. *lens*, lentil.] Meeting in a sharp point; depressed, circular, and frequently ribbed.

lentiform (lĕn'tĭfôrm) *a.* [L. *lens*, lentil; *forma*, shape.] Lentil-shaped; lenticular; *appl.* nucleus, the extraventricular portion of corpus striatum.

lentigerous (lĕntĭj'ërŭs) *a.* [L. *lens*, lentil; *gerere*, to bear.] Furnished with a lens.

lentiginose (lĕntĭj'ĭnōs), **lentiginous** (lĕntĭj'ĭnŭs) *a.* [L. *lentigo*, freckle.] Freckled; speckled; bearing numerous small dots.

lento-capillary point,—point, just above wilting coefficient, at which flow of water towards root hairs is impeded on account of surface tension resistance.

leotropic,—laeotropic, *q.v.*

lepidodendroid (lĕp'ĭdödĕn'droid) *a.* [Gk. *lepis*, scale; *dendron*, tree; *eidos*, form.] *Pert.* Lepidodendron; having scale-like leaf-scars.

lepidoid (lĕp'ĭdoid) *a.* [Gk. *lepis*, scale; *eidos*, form.] Resembling a scale or scales.

lepidomorial,—*pert.*, or composed of, lepidomoria.

lepidomorium (lĕp'ĭdömŏr'ĭŭm) *n.* [Gk. *lepis*, scale; *morion*, constituent part.] Small scale, or unit of composite scale, with bony base and conical or conoid crown of dentine, containing pulp cavity and sometimes covered with enamel.

lepidophyte (lĕp'ĭdöfīt) *n.* [Gk. *lepis*, scale; *phyton*, plant.] A fossil plant of fern family.

lepidopterous (lĕp'ĭdŏp'tërŭs) *a.* [Gk. *lepis*, scale; *pteron*, wing.] Having wings covered with minute overlapping scales; *pert.* moths, butterflies.

lepidosis (lĕp'ĭdō'sĭs) *n.* [Gk. *lepis*, scale.] Character and arrangement of scales of animals.

lepidosteoid (lĕp'ĭdŏs'tëoid) *a.* [Gk. *lepis*, scale; *osteon*, bone; *eidos*, form.] *Appl.* a ganoid scale lacking cosmine.

lepidote (lĕp'ĭdōt) *a.* [Gk. *lepidotos*, scaly.] Covered with minute scales.

lepidotic (lĕp'ĭdō'tĭk) *a.* [Gk. *lepidotos*, scaly.] *Appl.* an acid found in wings of some Lepidoptera.

lepidotrichia (lĕp'ĭdötrĭk'ĭă) *n. plu.* [Gk. *lepis*, scale; *thrix*, hair.] The bony actinotrichia of teleosts.

lepocyte (lĕp'ösīt) *n.* [Gk. *lepis*, husk; *kytos*, hollow.] A cell with a defining cell-wall, *opp.* gymnocyte.

lepospondylous (lĕp'öspŏn'dĭlŭs) *a.* [Gk. *lepis*, husk; *sphondylos*, vertebra.] Having amphicoelous, or hour-glass shaped, vertebrae.

leptocentric (lĕp'tösĕn'trĭk) *a.* [Gk. *leptos*, slender; *kentron*, centre.] *Appl.* concentric bundle with central leptome.

leptocephaloid (lĕp'tökĕf'ăloid, -sĕf-) *a.* [Gk. *leptos*, slender; *kephale*, head; *eidos*, form.] Resembling or having the shape of eel larvae.

leptocercal (lĕp'tösĕr'kăl) *a.* [Gk. *leptos*, slender; *kerkos*, tail.] With long slender tapering tail, as some fishes; leptocercous, *appl.* protozoa.

leptocystidium (lĕp'tösĭstĭd'ĭŭm) *n.* [Gk. *leptos*, thin; *kystis*, bladder; *idion*, *dim.*] A thin-walled cystidium, as in many agarics.

leptodactylous (lĕp'tödăk'tĭlŭs) *a.* [Gk. *leptos*, slender; *daktylos*, finger.] Having slender digits.

leptodermatous (lĕp'tödĕr'mătŭs) *a.* [Gk. *leptos*, thin; *derma*, skin.] Thin-skinned; *appl.* various thecae; leptodermic, leptodermous.

leptoid (lĕp'toid) *n.* [Gk. *leptos*, slender; *eidos*, form.] One of the thin-walled cortical cells forming strand projecting into the central cylinder of rhizome in mosses; a tubular cell in stem of certain pteridophytes.

leptome (lĕp'tōm) *n.* [Gk. *leptos*, slender.] Phloem-like part of vascular tissue of plant stems; leptomestome; bast; also leptom.

leptomeninges (lĕp'tömĕnĭn'jēz) *n. plu.* [Gk. *leptos*, thin; *meningx*, membrane.] The pia mater and arachnoid membrane.

leptonema (lĕp'tönē'mă) *n.* [Gk. *leptos*, slender; *nema*, thread.] Fine unpaired chromosome thread at leptotene.

leptophloem (lĕp'töflō'ëm) *n.* [Gk. *leptos*, slender; *phloios*, smooth bark.] Rudimentary bast tissue.

leptophyllous (lĕp'töfĭl'ŭs) *a.* [Gk. *leptos*, slender; *phyllon*, leaf.] With slender leaves; having a small leaf area, under 25 square millimetres.

leptosome (lĕp'tösōm) *a.* [Gk. *leptos*, slender; *soma*, body.] Tall and slender; *opp.* eurysome.

leptosporangiate (lĕp'töspörăn'jĭăt) *a.* [Gk. *leptos*, slender; *sporos*, seed; *anggeion*, vessel.] With sporogenous tissue developing from outer cell of periclinal division. *Opp.* eusporangiate.

leptostroterate (lĕp'töstrō'tĕrāt) *a.* [Gk. *leptos*, slender; *strotos*, covered.] With ambulacral plates narrow and crowded together, as in certain Stelleroidea.

leptotene (lĕp'tötēn) *n.* [Gk. *leptos*, slender; *tainia*, band.] Early stage of the prophase of meiosis where chromatin is in form of fine threads.

leptotichous (lĕp'tötĭ'kŭs) *a.* [Gk. *leptos*, thin; *teichos*, wall.] Thin-walled; *appl.* plant tissue.

leptotrombicula (lĕp'tötrŏmbĭk'ūlă) *n.* [Gk. *leptos*, slender; It. *tromba*, trumpet.] The larval form of a trombicula.

leptoxylem (lĕp'tözī'lëm) *n.* [Gk. *leptos*, slender; *xylon*, wood.] Rudimentary wood tissue.

lepto-zygotene (lĕp'tözĭg'ötēn) *a.* [Gk. *leptos*, slender; *zygon*, yoke; *tainia*, band.] *Appl.* transition stage between leptonema and zygonema.

leptus (lĕp'tŭs) *n.* [Gk. *leptos*, small.] The six-legged larva of mites.

lethal (lē'thăl) *a.* [L. *letum*, death.] Causing death; of a parasite, fatal or deadly in relation to a particular host; *appl.* a hereditary factor which so influences development that the individual is rendered non-viable. *n.* A lethal factor.

lethality (lēthăl'ĭtĭ) *n.* [L. *letum*, death.] The ratio of fatal cases to total number of cases affected by a disease or other harmful agency.

leuceine (lū'sēĭn) *n.* [Gk. *leukos*, white.] An amino-acid formed during decomposition of proteids.

leucine (lū'sĭn) *n.* [Gk. *leukos*, white.] Amino-caproic acid found as a constituent of pancreatic juice and of various tissues and organs, also of some plants; $C_6H_{13}O_2N$.

leucism (lū'sĭzm, loo-) *n.* [Gk. *leukos*, white.] The presence of white plumage or pelage in animals with pigmented eyes and skin.

leucite (lū'sīt) *n.* [Gk. *leukos*, white.] A colourless plastid.

leuco-,—*also* leuko-.

leucoblast (lū'köblăst, loo-) *n.* [Gk. *leukos*, white; *blastos*, bud.] A colourless blood-corpuscle in development.

leucocarpous (lū'kökâr'pŭs, loo-) *a.* [Gk. *leukos*, white; *karpos*, fruit.] With the fruit white.

leucocyan (lū'kösī'ăn, loo-) *n.* [Gk. *leukos*, white; *kyanos*, dark blue.] A pigment found in certain algae.

leucocyte (lū'kösīt, loo-) *n.* [Gk. *leukos*, white; *kytos*, hollow.] An amoebocyte; a colourless blood-corpuscle; leukocyte.

leucocytogenesis (lū'kösī'töjĕn'ësĭs, loo-) *n.* [Gk. *leukos*, white; *kytos*, hollow; *genesis*, descent.] Leucocyte formation; leucopoiesis.

leucocytoid,—histiocyte, *q.v.*

leucophore (lū'köfōr, loo-) *n.* [Gk. *leukos*, white; *pherein*, to bear.] A yellow-pigment-bearing cell; guanophore, iridocyte.

leucoplastids (lū'köplăs'tĭdz, loo-) *n. plu.* [Gk. *leukos*, white; *plastos*, formed ; *idion, dim.*] Colourless plastids from which amylo-, chloro-, and chromoplastids arise.

leucoplasts (lū'köplăsts, loo-) *n. plu.* [Gk. *leukos,* white ; *plastos,* formed.] Colourless granules of plant cytoplasm, *opp.* chromoplasts ; leucoplastids.

leucopoiesis (lū'köpoiē'sĭs, loo-) *n.* [Gk. *leukos,* white ; *poiesis,* making.] The formation of white blood corpuscles.

leucopsin (lūkŏp'sĭn, loo-) *n.* [Gk. *leukos,* white ; *opsis,* sight.] Visual white, formed from visual yellow ; vitamin A alcohol.

leucopterin(e) (lū'kŏp'tĕrĭn, loo-) *n.* [Gk. *leukos,* white ; *pteron,* wing.] A white wing pigment of certain Lepidoptera ; $C_{19}H_{19}O_{11}N_{15}$.

leucosin (lū'kōsĭn, loo-) *n.* [Gk. *leukos,* white.] An albumin found in various cereals.

leuko-,—*see* leuco-.

levator (lĕvā'tŏr) *n.* [L. *levare,* to raise.] A name given to muscles serving to raise an organ or part. *Opp.* depressor.

levigate (lĕv'ĭgāt) *v.* [L. *levigare,* to make smooth.] To smoothen. *a.* Made smooth.

levulose,—laevulose, *q.v.*

Leydig's cells [*F. von Leydig,* German anatomist]. Cells in testicular interstitial tissue.

Leydig's duct,—the Wolffian duct.

Leydig's organs,—minute organs on antennae of arthropods, supposed to be organs of smell.

liana (lĭân'ă), **liane** (lĭân') *n.* [F. *liane,* from L. *ligare,* to bind.] Any luxuriant woody climbing plant of tropical or semi-tropical forests.

Lias (lī'ăs) *n.* [*layers.*] Marine and estuarine deposits of Jurassic period, containing remains of cycads, insects, ammonites, saurians, and other fossils.

liber (lī'bĕr) *n.* [L. *liber,* inner bark.] Inner bark ; bast.

libido (lĭbī'dŏ) *n.* [L. *libido,* desire.] Excitation within body associated with instinct ; sexual energy ; psychic energy ; horme, *q.v.* ; élan vital.

libriform (lī'brĭfôrm) *a.* [L. *liber,* inner bark ; *forma,* shape.] Resembling bast ; *appl.* fibres, woody, later becoming septate.

lichenin (lī'kĕnĭn) *n.* [Gk. *leichen,* lichen.] A polysaccharide found in Cetraria islandica and other lichens, hydrolysed by the enzyme lichenase ; lichenine, lichen starch, moss starch.

lichenism (lī'kĕnĭzm) *n.* [Gk. *leichen,* lichen.] Symbiotic relationship between fungi and algae.

lichenoid (lī'kĕnoid) *a.* [Gk. *leichen,* lichen ; *eidos,* form.] Resembling a lichen.

lichenology (lī'kĕnŏl'öjĭ) *n.* [Gk. *leichen,* lichen ; *logos,* discourse.] The study of lichens.

Lieberkühn's crypts [*J. N. Lieberkühn,* German anatomist]. Tubular glands of the small intestine.

Liebig's law [*J. von Liebig,* German chemist]. The food element least plentiful in proportion to the requirements of plants limits their growth ; law of the minimum, *q.v.*

lien (lī'ĕn) *n.* [L. *lien,* spleen.] Spleen.

lienal (līē'năl) *a.* [L. *lien,* spleen.] *Pert.* spleen ; *appl.* artery, vein, nerve plexus ; splenic.

lienculus (līĕn'kūlŭs) *n.* [*Dim.* of L. *lien,* spleen.] An accessory spleen.

lienogastric (līē'nögăs'trĭk) *a.* [L. *lien,* spleen ; *gaster,* stomach.] *Pert.* spleen and stomach ; *appl.* artery supplying spleen and parts of stomach and pancreas ; *appl.* vein of hepatic portal system.

lienorenal,—*see* phrenicolienal.

life-cycle,—the various phases through which an individual species passes to maturity.

life zone,—a biome, *q.v.* ; a subdivision of a biome, as temperature, distribution, community, etc., zones.

ligament (lĭg'ămĕnt) *n.* [L. *ligamentum,* bandage.] A strong fibrous band of tissue connecting two or more moveable bones.

ligamenta flava,—yellow elastic ligaments connecting laminae of adjoining vertebrae.

ligneous (lĭg'nëŭs) *a.* [L. *lignum*, wood.] Woody; of nature of wood.

lignescent (lĭgnĕs'ënt) *a.* [L. *lignescere*, to become woody.] Developing the characters of woody tissue.

lignicolous (lĭgnĭk'ölŭs) *a.* [L. *lignum*, wood; *colere*, to inhabit.] Growing on or in wood.

lignification (lĭg'nĭfĭkā'shŭn) *n.* [L. *lignum*, wood; *facere*, to form.] Wood-formation; thickening of plant cell-walls by deposition of lignin.

lignin (lĭg'nĭn) *n.* [L. *lignum*, wood.] A complex substance which, associated with cellulose, causes the thickening of plant cell-walls, and so forms wood.

lignivorous (lĭgnĭv'örŭs) *a.* [L. *lignum*, wood; *vorare*, to devour.] Eating wood; *appl.* various insects.

lignocellulose (lĭg'nösĕl'ūlōs) *n.* [L. *lignum*, wood; *cellula*, little cell.] Essential constituent of woody tissue, lignin and cellulose combined.

lignose (lĭg'nōs) *n.* [L. *lignum*, wood.] A variety of cellulose.

ligula (lĭg'ūlă) *n.* [L. *ligula*, little tongue.] A band or taenia of white matter in dorsal wall of fourth ventricle; median structure between labial palps of insects; lobe of parapodium in certain annelids; ligule, *q.v.*; lingula, *q.v.*

ligulate (lĭg'ūlāt) *a.* [L. *ligula*, little tongue.] Having or *pert.* ligules; strap-shaped, as ray florets of Compositae.

ligule (lĭg'ūl) *n.* [L. *ligula*, little tongue.] A membranous outgrowth at junction of blade and leaf-sheath or petiole; small scale on upper surface of leaf-base in Lepidodendreae, Selaginellaceae, and Isoëtes; a tongue-shaped corolla, as of certain florets.

liguliflorous (lĭg'ūlĭflō'rŭs) *a.* [L. *ligula*, little tongue; *flos*, flower.] Having ligulate flowers only.

limacel (lī'măsĕl) *n.* [F., from L. *limax*, slug.] Concealed vestigial shell of slugs; limacelle.

limaciform (lĭmăs'ĭfôrm) *a.* [L. *limax*, slug; *forma*, shape.] Like a slug; slug-shaped.

limacine (lĭm'ăsĭn) *a.* [L. *limax*, slug.] *Pert.* slugs.

limb (lĭm) *n.* [A.S. *lim*, limb.] Branch; arm; leg; wing; expanded portion of unguiculate petal.

limbate (lĭm'bāt) *a.* [L. *limbus*, border.] With a border; bordered and having a differently coloured edge.

limbic (lĭm'bĭk) *a.* [L. *limbus*, border.] Bordering; *appl.* a cerebral lobe, including hippocampal and cingulate gyri.

limbous (lĭm'bŭs) *a.* [L. *limbus*, border.] *Appl.* overlapping sutures.

limbus (lĭm'bŭs) *n.* [L. *limbus*, border.] Any border if distinctly marked off by colour or structure.

limen (lī'mĕn) *n.* [L. *limen*, threshold.] Threshold, minimum stimulus, or quantitative difference in stimulation, that is perceptible; boundary, as between vestibule of nostril and nasal cavity, limen nasi.

limicolous (līmĭk'ölŭs) *a.* [L. *limus*, mud; *colere*, to dwell.] Living in mud.

liminal (lĭm'ĭnăl) *a.* [L. *limen*, threshold.] *Pert.* a threshold; *appl.* stimulus; *appl.* sensation.

limited,—*appl.* chromosomes in germinal, not in somatic, nuclei.

limitrophic (lī'mĭtrŏf'ĭk) *a.* [Gk. *limos*, hunger; *trophe*, nourishment.] *Pert.* or controlling nutrition.

limivorous (līmĭv'örŭs) *a.* [L. *limus*, mud; *vorare*, to devour.] Mud-eating; *appl.* certain aquatic animals which swallow mud.

limnetic (lĭmnĕt'ĭk) *a.* [Gk. *limne*, marshy lake.] Living in, or *pert.*, marshes or lakes; *appl.* zone of deep water between surface and compensation depth.

limnobiology (lĭm'nöbīŏl'öjĭ) *n.* [Gk. *limne*, lake; *bios*, life; *logos*, discourse.] The study of life in standing fresh waters.

limnobios (lĭm′nöbī′ŏs) *n.* [Gk. *limne*, lake; *bios*, life.] Life in fresh water; fresh-water plants and animals collectively.

limnocryptophyte (lĭm′nökrĭp′töfīt) *n.* [Gk. *limne*, marsh; *kryptos*, hidden; *phyton*, plant.] A helophyte or marsh plant; limnophyte.

limnology (lĭmnŏl′öjĭ) *n.* [Gk. *limne*, marshy lake; *logos*, discourse.] Science dealing with biological and other phenomena *pert.* inland waters; the study of standing waters.

limnophilous (lĭmnŏf′ĭlŭs) *a.* [Gk. *limne*, marsh; *philein*, to love.] Living in fresh-water marshes; also limnobiotic.

limnophyte (lĭm′nöfīt) *n.* [Gk. *limne*, marshy lake; *phyton*, plant.] A pond plant; a helophyte.

limnoplankton (lĭm′nöplăng′ktŏn) *n.* [Gk. *limne*, marshy lake; *plangktos*, wandering.] The floating animal and plant life in fresh-water lakes, ponds, and marshes. *Opp.* haloplankton.

limosphere (lĭm′ösfēr) *n.* [Gk. *limen*, receptacle; *sphaira*, globe.] A spherical body containing a vacuole, situated near blepharoplast in spermiogenesis of some mosses.

linea (lĭn′ëă) *n.* [L. *linea*, line.] A line-like structure or mark.

linear (lĭn′ëăr) *a.* [L. *linea*, line.] *Pert.* or in a line; tape- or thread-like; asthenic, *appl.* constitutional type.

linear-ensate,—between linear and ensiform in shape.

linear - lanceolate,—between linear and lanceolate in shape.

linear-oblong, between linear and oblong in shape.

linellae (lĭnĕl′ē) *n. plu.* [L. *linella*, fine thread.] A system of filaments in certain Sarcodina holding together the xenophya.

lineolate (lĭn′ëölāt) *a.* [L. *linea*, line.] Marked by fine lines or striae.

lingua (lĭng′gwă) *n.* [L. *lingua*, tongue.] The floor of mouth in mites; hypopharynx of insects; a tongue, or tongue-like structure.

lingual (lĭng′gwăl) *a.* [L. *lingua*, tongue.] *Pert.* tongue; *appl.* artery, gyrus, nerve, vein, etc.; *appl.* radula of molluscs.

linguiform (lĭng′gwĭfôrm) *a.* [L. *lingua*, tongue; *forma*, shape.] Tongue-shaped.

lingula (lĭng′gūlă) *n.* [L. *lingula*, little tongue.] A small tongue-like process of bone or other tissue, as of cerebellum or sphenoid; a genus of brachiopods; ligula, *q.v.*

lingulate,—ligulate, *q.v.*

linin (lī′nĭn) *n.* [L. *linum*, flax.] The substance of achromatinic or oxyphilic reticulum of cell-nucleus.

lininoplast (lĭn′ĭnöplăst) *n.* [L. *linum*, flax; Gk. *plastos*, moulded.] Plasmosome, *q.v.*

linkage (lĭng′kĕj) *n.* [A.S. *hlince*, link.] Tendency of certain hereditary factors to remain associated through several generations; gametic coupling.

Linnaean (lĭnē′ăn) *a.* [*C. Linné* or *Linnaeus*, Swedish naturalist]. *Pert.* or designating the system of classification established by Linnaeus.

linneon (lĭnē′ŏn) *n.* [*C. Linné*, Swedish naturalist]. Linnaean or taxonomic species.

lipase (lĭp′ās) *n.* [Gk. *lipos*, fat.] A lipolytic or fat-splitting enzyme, found in blood and in various plant and animal organs, and in various seeds.

lip-cell,—a sporangium cell at the point of dehiscence.

lipides (lĭp′īdz) *n. plu.* [Gk. *lipos*, fat.] Heterogeneous compounds soluble in fats and their solvents, including fats, waxes, chromolipides, sterols, glycolipides, phospholipides; lipids; *cf.* lipoids.

lipines (lĭp′īnz) *n. plu.* [Gk. *lipos*, fat.] Compound lipides, including phospholipides and cerebrosides; lipins.

lipochondria (lĭp′ökŏn′drĭă) *n. plu.* [Gk. *lipos*, fat; *chondros*, grain.] Lipoid granules in the Golgi zone; Golgi presubstance.

lipochrin (lĭpō′krĭn) *a.* [Gk. *lipos*, fat; *ochros*, sallow.] *Appl.* yellow lipoid droplet, fading by light, in unpigmented base of retinal cell.

lipochroic (lĭp′ökrō′ĭk) *a.* [Gk. *lipos*, fat; *chros*, colour.] With pigment in oil droplets.

lipochromes (lĭp′ökrōmz) *n. plu.* [Gk. *lipos*, fat; *chroma*, colour.] A more or less indefinite group of plant and animal pigments, as carotins, luteins, chlorophane, rhodophane, xanthophane, zooerythrin, etc.

lipoclastic (lĭp′öklăs′tĭk) *a.* [Gk. *lipos*, fat; *klastos*, broken.] Fat-splitting; lipolytic; *appl.* enzymes.

lipofuscin (lĭp′öfŭs′sĭn) *n.* [Gk. *lipos*, fat; L. *fuscus*, dusky.] A yellowish-brown pigment in cytoplasm of some nerve-cells.

lipogastry (lī′pögăs′trĭ) *n.* [Gk. *leipesthai*, to be lacking; *gaster*, stomach.] Temporary obliteration of gastral cavity, as in some sponges.

lipogenous (lĭpŏj′ënŭs) *a.* [Gk. *lipos*, fat; *genos*, birth.] Fat-producing.

lipohumour (lĭp′öhū′mŏr) *n.* [Gk. *lipos*, fat; L. *humor*, moisture.] A fat-soluble substance produced by nerves and acting on chromatophores.

lipoid (lĭp′oid) *a.* [Gk. *lipos*, fat; *eidos*, form.] Resembling a fatty substance. *n.* A lipide; one of various fat-soluble substances occurring in plants and animals, as a sterol, carotene, terpene.

lipolysis (lĭpŏl′ĭsĭs) *n.* [Gk. *lipos*, fat; *lysis*, loosing.] The dissolution of fat.

lipolytic (lĭp′ölĭt′ĭk) *a.* [Gk. *lipos*, fat; *lyein*, to dissolve.] Capable of dissolving fat; fat-reducing.

lipomerism (līpŏm′ërĭzm) *n.* [Gk. *leipesthai*, to be lacking; *meros*, part.] Suppression of segmentation, or coalescence of segments, as in crustaceans.

lipopalingenesis (lī′pöpăl′ĭnjĕn′ësĭs) *n.* [Gk. *leipesthai*, to be lacking; *palin*, anew; *genesis*, descent.] The omission of some stage or stages in phylogeny.

lipophore (lĭp′öfōr) *n.* [Gk. *lipos*, fat; *-phoros*, -bearing.] A wandering cell originating in neural crest and containing a lipochrome.

lipoproteins (lĭp′öprō′tëĭnz) *n. plu.* [Gk. *lipos*, fat; *proteion*, first.] Proteins united with fatty compounds.

lipostomy (līpŏs′tömĭ) *n.* [Gk. *leipesthai*, to be lacking; *stoma*, mouth.] Temporary obliteration of mouth or osculum.

lipotropic (lĭpötrŏp′ĭk) *a.* [Gk. *lipos*, fat; *trope*, turn.] Influencing fat metabolism; accelerating removal of fat.

lipoxanthins,—lipochromes.

lipoxenous (lĭpözĕn′ŭs, lĭpŏk′sënŭs) *a.* [Gk. *lipein*, to abandon; *xenos*, host.] Leaving the host before completion of development.

lipsanenchyma,—leipsanenchyma.

lirella (lĭrĕl′ă) *n.* [L. *lira*, furrow.] A linear apothecium of lichens.

lissencephalous (lĭs′ĕnkĕf′ălŭs, -sĕf-) *a.* [Gk. *lissos*, smooth; *engkephalos*, brain.] Having few or no convolutions of the brain; lissencephalic.

lissoflagellate (lĭs′öflăj′ëlāt) *a.* [Gk. *lissos*, smooth; L. *flagellum*, whip.] Having no collar surrounding base of flagellum.

lithite (lĭth′īt) *n.* [Gk. *lithos*, stone.] A calcareous secretion found in connection with ear, or with otocysts, lithocysts, and tentaculocysts, sensory organs of many invertebrates.

lithocarp (lĭth′ökârp) *n.* [Gk. *lithos*, stone; *karpos*, fruit.] Fossil fruit or carpolith.

lithocysts (lĭth′ösĭsts) *n. plu.* [Gk. *lithos*, stone; *kystis*, bladder.] Minute sacs or grooves, containing lithites, found in various invertebrates; enlarged cells of plant epidermis, in which cystoliths are formed.

lithodesma (lĭth′ödĕs′mă) *n.* [Gk. *lithos*, stone; *desma*, bond.] A small plate, shelly in nature, found in certain bivalves.

lithodomous (lĭthŏd′ömŭs) *a.* [Gk. *lithos*, stone; *domos*, house.] Living in rock-holes or clefts.

lithogenous (lĭthŏj′ënŭs) *a.* [Gk. *lithos*, stone; *-genes*, producing.] Rock-forming, or rock-building, as certain corals.

lithophagous (lĭthŏf′ăgŭs) *a.* [Gk. *lithos*, stone; *phagein*, to eat.] Stone-eating, as birds; rock-burrowing, as some molluscs and sea-urchins.

lithophilous (lĭthŏf′ĭlŭs) *a.* [Gk. *lithos*, stone; *philein*, to love.] Growing on stones or rocks; saxicoline.

lithophyll (lĭth′öfĭl) *n.* [Gk. *lithos*, stone; *phyllon*, leaf.] A fossil leaf, or leaf-impression.

lithophyte (lĭth′öfīt) *n.* [Gk. *lithos*, stone; *phyton*, plant.] Plant growing on rocky ground.

lithosere (lĭth′ösēr) *n.* [Gk. *lithos*, stone; L. *serere*, to put in a row.] A plant succession originating on rock surfaces.

lithosol (lĭth′osŏl) *n.* [Gk. *lithos*, stone; *solum*, soil.] A shallow soil largely composed of incompletely weathered rock fragments.

lithotomous (lĭthŏt′ömŭs) *a.* [Gk. *lithos*, stone; *temnein*, to cut.] Stone-boring, as certain molluscs.

litoral (lĭt′öräl) *a.* [L. *litus*, sea-shore.] Growing or living at or near the sea-shore; *appl.* zone between high and low water marks; also *appl.* cells, fixed macrophages, lining sinuses of reticular tissues and the wall of lymph channels; littoral.

Littré's glands [*A. Littré*, French surgeon]. Urethral mucous glands.

lituate (lĭt′ūăt) *a.* [L. *lituus*, augur's staff.] Forked, with prongs curving outwards.

liver (lĭv′ër) *n.* [A.S. *lifer*, liver.] The bile-secreting gland of vertebrates; digestive gland of some invertebrates.

liver factor,—vitamin B_{12}, anti-pernicious anaemia factor.

liver-pancreas,—an organ in molluscs and crustaceans, combining functions of liver and pancreas.

lobar (lō′băr) *a.* [L.L. *lobus*, lobe.] Of or *pert.* a lobe.

lobate (lō′bāt) *a.* [L.L. *lobus*, lobe.] Divided into lobes; lobose.

lobe (lōb) *n.* [L.L. *lobus*, from Gk. *lobos*, lobe.] Any rounded projection of an organ; lobus; a flap-like structure on toes of certain birds.

lobed (lōbd) *a.* [Gk. *lobos*, lobe.] Having margin cut up into rounded divisions by incisions which reach less than half-way to mid-rib.

lobopodia (lŏb′öpō′dĭă) *n. plu.* [Gk. *lobos*, lobe; *pous*, foot.] Blunt pseudopodia of Protozoa.

lobose (lŏb′ōs) *a.* [Gk. *lobos*, lobe.] Divided into lobes; lobate.

lobular (lŏb′ūlăr) *a.* [Gk. *lobos*, lobe.] Like or *pert.* small lobes.

lobulate (lŏb′ūlāt) *a.* [Gk. *lobos*, lobe.] Divided into small lobes

lobule (lŏb′ūl) *n.* [*Dim.* of L.L. *lobus*, lobe.] A small lobe or subdivision of a lobe; lobulus.

lobus (lō′bŭs) *n.* [L.L. *lobus*, lobe.] Lobe; portion of an organ, as of glands and brain, delimited by fissures or septa.

local sign,—characteristic quality of a tactile or other sensation associated with point of stimulation.

localisation (lō′kălĭzā′shŭn) *n.* [L. *localis*, local.] Determination of a position; restriction to a limited area; restriction of pairing and chiasma formation at pachytene to one part of the chromosome.

localisation of function,—reference to different parts of brain as communicating centres of various senses.

localisation of sensation,—identification on surface of body of exact spot affected.

locellus (lösĕl′ŭs) *n.* [L. *locellus* from *locus*, place.] A small compartment of an ovary.

lociation (lŏsĭā′shŭn) *n.* [L. *locus*, place.] Local differences in abundance or proportion of dominant species; local faciation.

locomotor rods,—hooked or knobbed rods for crawling, on ventral surface of certain Nematoda.

locular (lŏk′ūlăr) *a.* [L. *loculus*, little place.] Containing, or composed of loculi; loculate.

locule,—loculus.
loculi,—*plu.* of loculus.
loculicidal (lŏk'ūlĭsī'dăl) *a.* [L. *loculus*, compartment; *caedere*, to cut.] Dehiscent dorsally down middle of carpels.
loculus (lŏk'ūlŭs) *n.* [L. *loculus*, compartment.] A small chamber or cavity; cavity in stroma, containing asci; cavity of an ovary or of an anther; cavity between septa in certain Coelenterata; chamber of foraminiferal shell.
locus (lō'kŭs) *n.* [L. *locus*, place.] Position of gene in the chromosome; location of a stimulus.
locusta (lökŭs'tă) *n.* [L. *locusta*, locust.] Spikelet of grasses; a locust.
lodicule (lŏd'ĭkūl) *n.* [L. *lodicula*, coverlet.] A scale at base of ovary in grasses, supposed to represent part of a perianth.
lodix (lō'dĭks) *n.* [L. *lodix*, blanket.] A ventral sclerite of seventh abdominal segment, covering genital plate, in Lepidoptera.
logotype (lŏg'ötīp) *n.* [Gk. *logos*, word; *typos*, pattern.] A genotype by subsequent designation, not originally described as such.
loma (lō'ma) *n.* [Gk. *loma*, hem.] A thin membranous flap forming a fringe round an opening; fringe of toe in birds.
lomastome (lō'măstōm) *a.* [Gk. *loma*, hem; *stoma*, mouth.] Having margin of lip recurved or reflected.
loment,—lomentum.
lomentaceous (lō'mëntā'shŭs) *a.* [L. *lomentum*, bean meal.] *Pert.*, resembling, or having lomenta.
lomentum (lōmĕn'tŭm) *n.* [L. *lomentum*, bean meal.] A legume or pod constricted between seeds; loment.
long-day,—*appl.* plants in which the flowering period is hastened by a relatively long photoperiod, ordinarily more than 12 hours.
longicorn (lŏn'jĭkôrn) *a.* [L. *longus*, long; *cornu*, horn.] Having long antennae; *appl.* certain beetles.
longipennate (lŏn'jĭpĕn'āt) *a.* [L. *longus*, long; *penna*, wing.] Having long wings, or long feathers.
longirostral (lŏn'jĭrŏs'trăl) *a.* [L. *longus*, long; *rostrum*, beak.] With a long beak; longirostrate.
longisection (lŏn'jĭsĕk'shŭn) *n.* [L. *longus*, long; *sectio*, cut.] Longitudinal section; section along or parallel to a longitudinal axis. *Opp.* transection.
loop cell,—dome cell, *q.v.*
loph (lŏf) *n.* [Gk. *lophos*, crest.] Crest which may connect cones in teeth and so form a ridge.
lophiostomate (lŏf'ĭŏs'tömāt) *a.* [Gk. *lophion*, small crest; *stoma*, mouth.] With crested conceptacle-opening.
lophobranchiate (lŏf'öbrăng'kĭāt) *a.* [Gk. *lophos*, crest; *brangchia*, gills.] With tufted gills.
lophocaltrops (lŏf'ökăl'trŏps) *n.* [Gk. *lophos*, crest; A.S. *coltraeppe*, kind of thistle.] A sponge spicule with rays crested or branched.
lophocercal (lŏf'ösër'kăl) *a* [Gk. *lophos*, crest; *kerkos*, tail.] Having a rayless caudal fin like a ridge round end of vertebral column.
lophodont (lŏf'ödŏnt) *a.* [Gk. *lophos*, crest; *odous*, tooth.] Having transverse ridges on the cheek-teeth grinding surface.
lophophore (lŏf'öfōr) *n.* [Gk. *lophos*, crest; *pherein*, to carry.] A horse-shoe-shaped tentacle-supporting organ in Polyzoa and Brachiopoda.
lophoselenodont (lŏf'ösëlē'nödŏnt) *a.* [Gk. *lophos*, crest; *selene*, moon; *odous*, tooth.] Having cheek-teeth ridged with crescentic cuspid ridges on grinding surface.
lophosteon (lŏfŏs'tëŏn) *n.* [Gk. *lophos*, crest; *osteon*, bone.] The keel-ridge of a sternum.
lophotriaene (lŏf'ötrī'ēn) *n.* [Gk. *lophos*, crest; *triaina*, trident.] Lophocaltrops, *q.v.*
lophotrichous (lŏfŏt'rĭkŭs) *a.* [Gk. *lophos*, tuft; *thrix*, hair.] Having long whip-like flagella; with a tuft of flagella at one pole; *appl.* bacteria; lophotrichate, lophotrichic.
loral (lō'răl) *a.* [L. *lorum*, thong.] *Pert.* or situated at the lore.

lorate (lō'rāt) *a.* [L. *lorum*, thong.] Strap-shaped.

lore (lōr) *n.* [L. *lorum*, thong.] Space between bill and eyes in birds.

Lorenzini's ampullae,—ampullary temperature receptors of rostrum in elasmobranchs.

lorica (lōrī'kă, lōr'ĭkă) *n.* [L. *lorica*, corselet.] A protective external case found in rotifers, infusorians, and diatoms.

loricate (lō'rĭkāt) *a.* [L. *lorica*, corselet.] Covered with protective shell or scales.

lorication moment,—the occasion of deposition of silica or calcium carbonate for an entire skeleton at one time; dictyotic moment.

lorulum (lō'rūlŭm) *n.* [L. *dim.* of *lorum*, thong.] The small strap-shaped and branched thallus of certain lichens.

lorum (lō'rŭm) *n.* [L. *lorum*, thong.] The piece of under jaw on which submentum lies in certain insects; dorsal plate protecting pedicle in spiders.

lotic (lō'tĭk) *a.* [L. *lotum*, flowed over.] *Appl.* or *pert.* running water; living in brook or river. *Opp.* lentic.

Louis, angle of [*A. Louis*, French surgeon]. Angulus Ludovici or sternal angle.

loxodont (lŏk'södŏnt) *a.* [Gk. *loxos*, oblique; *odous*, tooth.] Having molar teeth with shallow grooves between the ridges.

luciferase (loos'ĭfĕrās) *n.* [L. *lux*, light; *ferre*, to carry.] An oxidising enzyme which acts on luciferin, causing luminescence; photogenin.

luciferin (loos'ĭfĕrĭn) *n.* [L. *lux*, light; *ferre*, to carry.] Intracellular or extracellular substance oxidised by luciferase, causing luminescence; photophelein.

lucifugal (lūsĭf'ūgăl, loo-) *a.* [L. *lucifugus*, avoiding the light.] Shunning light; *appl.* fruit-body of certain fungi; lucifugous; photophobic. *Opp.* lucipetal.

lucipetal (lūsĭp'ĕtăl, loo-) *a.* [L. *lux*, light; *petere*, to seek.] Requiring light; photophilous. *Opp.* lucifugal.

lumbar (lŭm'băr) *a.* [L. *lumbus*, loin.] *Pert.* or near the region of the loins; *appl.* artery, vein, vertebrae, plexus, gland, etc.

lumbocostal (lŭm'bōkŏs'tăl) *a.* [L. *lumbus*, loin; *costa*, rib.] *Pert.* loins and ribs; *appl.* arch, ligament.

lumbosacral (lŭm'bōsā'krăl) *a.* [L. *lumbus*, loin; *sacrum*, sacred.] *Pert.* loins and sacrum; *appl.* nerve and trunk, plexus.

lumbrical (lŭm'brĭkăl) *a.* [L. *lumbricus*, earth-worm.] Lumbriciform; *appl.* four small muscles in palm of hand and in sole of foot: lumbricales, *sing.* lumbricalis.

lumbriciform (lŭmbrĭs'ĭfôrm) *a.* [L. *lumbricus*, earth-worm; *forma*, shape.] Like a worm in appearance.

lumbricoid,—lumbriciform.

lumen (lū'mĕn, loo-) *n.* [L. *lumen*, light.] The cavity of a tubular part or organ; central cavity of a plant cell.

luminescent organs, — specialised organs for the production of light, found in various plant and animal organisms.

lumirhodopsin (lū'mĭrōdŏp'sĭn, loo-) *n.* [L. *lumen*, light; Gk. *rhodon*, rose; *opsis*, sight.] Transient orange-red product of the bleaching of rhodopsin by light, is converted into metarhodopsin.

lunar (lū'năr, loo-) *a.* [L. *luna*, moon.] *Appl.* carpal bone, os lunare or lunatum, also called semilunar and intermedium; lunate.

lunate (lū'nāt, loo-) *a.* [L. *luna*, moon.] Somewhat crescent-shaped, semilunar.

lunatum,—semilunar bone.

lunette (lūnĕt') *n.* [F. *lunettes*, spectacles.] Transparent lower eyelid of snakes.

lung (lŭng) *n.* [A.S. *lunge*, lung.] The paired or single respiratory organ of air-breathing higher animal forms.

lung-book,—the respiratory organ of scorpions and spiders, formed like a purse with numerous compartments.

lunula (lū'nūlă, loo-) *n.* [L. *lunula*, small moon.] Lunule.

lunular (lū'nūlăr, loo-) *a.* [L. *lunula*, small moon.] With crescent-shaped marking; lunulate.

lunule (lū'nūl, loo-) *n.* [L. *lunula*, small moon.] A crescent-shaped structure or marking; lunula; small crescentic sclerite, the frontal lunule, above antennal bases in certain Diptera; white opaque portion of nail near root.

lunulet (lū'nūlĕt, loo-) *n.* [L. *lunula*, small moon.] A small lunule.

lupulin (lū'pūlĭn, loo'pūlĭn) *n.* [L. *lupus*, hop.] The resinous glandular scales of hops; an organic compound, bitter and acrid, obtained from these; $C_{26}H_{38}O_4$.

luteal (lū'tēăl, loo-) *a.* [L. *luteus*. orange-yellow.] *Pert.* or like cells of corpus luteum; *appl.* lutein and paralutein cells; *appl.* hormone: progesterone.

lutein (lū'tēĭn, loo-) *n.* [L. *luteus*, orange-yellow.] The yellow lipochrome pigment of egg-yolk and corpus luteum; $C_{40}H_{56}O_2$.

lutein cells,—modified granulosa cells during formation of corpus luteum; follicular lutein cells, *opp.* lutein cells of theca interna.

luteination,—luteinisation.

luteinisation (lū'tēĭnīzā'shŭn, loo-) *n.* [L. *luteus*, orange-yellow.] The formation of corpus luteum.

luteinising hormone,—a pituitary hormone which stimulates theca-lutein cell formation and interstitial cells of testis; LH, prolan B.

luteosterone,—progesterone, progestin.

luteotrophic (lū'tēōtrŏf'ĭk) *a.* [L. *luteus*, orange-yellow; Gk. *trophe*, nourishment.] *Appl.* hormone which assists in maintaining corpus luteum, and may also be lactogenic.

lutteorophin, — luteotrophic hormone; luteotropin, prolactin; LTH.

Luys, nucleus of,—corpus subthalamicum of hypothalamus.

lychnidiate (lĭknĭd'ĭāt) *a.* [Gk. *lychnidion*, small lamp.] Luminous.

lycopene (lī'köpēn) *n.* [L.L. *lycopersicum*, tomato, from Gk. *lykopersikon*.] The red carotenoid pigment of fruits of tomato, rose, etc.; lycopin; $C_{40}H_{56}$.

lygophil (lī'göfĭl) *a.* [Gk. *lyge*, shadow; *philos*, friend.] Preferring shade or darkness.

lymph (lĭmf) *n.* [L. *lympha*, water.] An alkaline colourless fluid contained in lymphatic vessels.

lymph heart,—contractile expansion of a lymph vessel where it opens into a vein, in many vertebrates.

lymphatic (lĭmfăt'ĭk) *a.* [L. *lympha*, water.] *Pert.* or conveying lymph.

lymphocyte (lĭm'fösīt) *n.* [L. *lympha*, water; Gk. *kytos*, hollow.] A small mononuclear colourless corpuscle of blood and lymph.

lymphogenic (lĭm'föjĕn'ĭk) *a.* [L. *lympha*, water; Gk. *-genes*, producing.] Produced in lymph-glands.

lymphogenous (lĭmfŏj'ēnŭs) *a.* [L. *lympha*, water; Gk. *-genes*, producing.] Lymph-forming.

lymphoid (lĭm'foid) *a.* [L. *lympha*, water; Gk. *eidos*, form.] *Appl.* retiform tissue with meshes largely occupied by lymph corpuscles; adenoid.

lymphoidocyte (lĭm'foidösīt) *n.* [L. *lympha*, water; Gk. *eidos*, form; *kytos*, hollow.] Haemocytoblast.

lymphomonocyte (lĭm'fömŏn'ösīt) *n.* [L. *lympha*, water; Gk. *monos*, single; *kytos*, hollow.] A large mononuclear leucocyte.

lymphomyelocyte (lĭm'fömī'ēlösīt) *n.* [L. *lympha*, water; Gk. *myelos*, marrow; *kytos*, hollow.] Myeloblast.

lyochromes (lī'ökrōmz) *n. plu.* [Gk. *lyein*, to loose; *chroma*, colour.] Water-soluble yellow cell pigments, or flavins, including vitamin B_2.

lyocytosis (lī'ösĭtō'sĭs) *n.* [Gk. *lyein*, to loose; *kytos*, hollow.] Histolysis by extra-cellular digestion, as in insect metamorphosis.

Lyonnet's glands,—paired accessory silk glands in lepidopterous larvae; Filippi's glands.

lyophil (lī'öfĭl) *a.* [Gk. *lyein*, to loose; *philos*, loving.] *Appl.* solutions which, after evaporation to dryness, go readily into solution again on addition of fluid; *cf.* lyophobe.

lyophobe (lī'öfōb) *a.* [Gk. *lyein*, to loose; *phobos*, fear.] *Appl.* solutions which, after evaporation to dryness, remain as a solid; *cf.* lyophil.

lyotropic (līötrŏp'ĭk) *a.* [Gk. *lyein*, to loose; *trope*, turn.] *Appl.* solutions which are dependent on changes in the solvent itself.

lyra (lī'ră) *n.* [Gk. *lyra*, lyre.] Triangular lamina or psalterium joining lateral parts of fornix, marked with fibres as a lyre; a lyrate pattern as on some bones; a series of chitinous rods forming part of the stridulating organ in certain spiders.

lyrate (lī'rāt) *a.* [Gk. *lyra*, lyre.] Lyre-shaped; *appl.* certain leaves.

lyriform (lĭr'ĭfôrm) *a.* [L. *lyra*, lyre; *forma*, shape.] Lyre-shaped; *appl.* a sensory organ, the lyra, in spiders.

lysactinic (līsăktĭn'ĭk) *a.* [Gk. *lysis*, loosing; *aktis*, ray.] Of Stelleroidea, having podia limited to lower half of body instead of continued to apical plates; *cf.* desmactinic.

lysigenic,—lysigenous.

lysigenous (līsĭj'ënŭs) *a.* [Gk. *lysis*, loosing; *-genes*, producing.] *Appl.* formation of tissue cavities caused by degeneration and breaking down of cell-walls in centre of mass.

lysin (lī'sĭn) *n.* [Gk. *lysis*, loosing.] Any substance capable of causing dissolution or lysis of cells or bacteria.

lysine (lī'sēn) *n.* [Gk. *lysis*, loosing.] A diamino-acid, constituent of some plant proteins, a dietary factor, and cleavage product of certain animal proteins; $C_6H_{14}O_2N_2$.

lysis (lī'sĭs) *n.* [Gk. *lysis*, loosing.] Breaking down or dissolution of compounds or cells, as by enzymes.

lysogenesis (lī'söjĕn'ësĭs) *n.* [Gk. *lysis*, loosing; *genesis*, descent.] The action of lysins.

lysogenous,—lysigenous.

lysosomes (lī'sösōmz) *n. plu.* [Gk. *lysis*, loosing; *soma*, body.] Particles in cytoplasm, smaller than mitochondria, consisting of a membrane enclosing several enzymes; mitochondria B, light mitochondria.

lysozyme (lī'sözīm) *n.* [Gk. *lysis*, loosing; *zyme*, leaven.] A globulin found in mammalian tissue secretions, white of egg, and some micro-organisms, and having mucolytic and bactericidal properties.

lytic (lĭt'ĭk) *a.* [Gk. *lyein*, to break down.] *Pert.* lysis; *pert*, a lysin.

lytta (lĭt'ă) *n.* [Gk. *lytta*, madness.] A vermiform structure of muscle, fatty and connective tissue, or cartilage, under the tongue of mammals; cantharis, a blister-beetle.

M

macerate (măs'ërāt) *v.* [L. *macerare*, to soften.] To wear away or to isolate parts of a tissue or organ; to soften and wear away by digestion or other means.

machopolyp (măk'öpŏl'ĭp) *n.* [Gk. *mache*, fight; *polys*, many; *pous*, foot.] A nematophore, of certain Hydromedusae, provided with cnidoblasts or adhesive globules.

macrander (măkrăn'der) *n.* [Gk. *makros*, large; *aner*, male.] A large male plant.

macrandrous (măkrăn'drŭs) *a.* [Gk. *makros*, large; *aner*, male.] Having large male plants or elements.

macraner (măk'rănër) *n.* [Gk. *makros*, large; *aner*, male.] Male ant of unusually large size.

macrergate (măkrĕr'gāt) *n.* [Gk. *makros*, large; *ergates*, worker.] Worker ant of unusually large size.

macro-,—*also see* mega-.

macrobiotic (măk'röbīŏt'ĭk) *a.* [Gk. *makros*, long; *bios*, life.] Long-lived; life-prolonging.

macroblast (măk'röblăst) *n.* [Gk. *makros*, large; *blastos*, bud.] A large cell or corpuscle; a young normoblast.

macrocarpous (măk'rökâr'pŭs) *a.* [Gk. *makros*, large; *karpos*, fruit.] Producing large fruit.

macrocentrosome (măk'rösĕn'trösōm) *n.* [Gk. *makros*, large; *kentron*, centre; *soma*, body.] Centrosome and central granule, or entosphere.

macrocephalous (măk'rökĕf'ălŭs, -sĕf-) *a.* [Gk. *makros*, large; *kephale*, head.] Having the cotyledons thickened; big-headed.

macrochaeta (măk'rökē'tă) *n.* [Gk. *makros*, large; *chaite*, hair.] A large bristle, as on body of certain insects.

macrocnemic (măk'röknē'mĭk) *a.* [Gk. *makros*, large; *kneme*, tibia.] *Appl.* Zoanthidae having the sixth protocneme or primary pair of mesenteries perfect.

macroconidium (măk'rökŏnĭd'ĭŭm) *n.* [Gk. *makros*, large; *konis*, dust; *idion*, *dim.*] A large asexual spore or conidium.

macroconjugant (măk'rökŏn'joogănt) *n.* [Gk. *makros*, large; L. *conjugare*, to unite.] The larger individual of a conjugating pair.

macrocyclic (măk'rösīk'lĭk) *a.* [Gk. *makros*, large; *kyklos*, circle.] Having a complete or a long cycle; with both gametophyte and sporophyte stages. *Opp.* microcyclic.

macrocyst (măk'rösĭst) *n.* [Gk. *makros*, large; *kystis*, bladder.] A large reproductive cell of certain fungi; a large cyst or case, as for spores.

macrocystidium (măk'rösĭstĭd'ĭŭm) *n.* [Gk. *makros*, large; *kystis*, bladder; *idion*, *dim.*] A long cystidium-like structure in some Gasteromycetes.

macrocytase (măk'rösī'tās) *n.* [Gk. *makros*, large; *kytos*, hollow.] The enzyme of macrophages or endothelial cells.

macrodactylous (măk'rödăk'tĭlŭs) *a.* [Gk. *makros*, long; *daktylos*, finger.] With long digits.

macrodont (măk'rödŏnt) *a.* [Gk. *makros*, large; *odous*, tooth.] With large teeth.

macro-elements,—elements required and occurring in relatively large quantities as natural constituents of living organisms or tissues; major elements, macronutrients. *Opp.* minor elements, microelements, trace-elements.

macroevolution (măk'röēvölū'shŭn) *n.* [Gk. *makros*, large; L. *evolvere*, to unroll.] Evolutionary processes extending through geological eras; large-scale evolution of new genera and species owing to mutations resulting in marked changes in chromosome pattern and reaction system. *Opp.* microevolution.

macrogamete (măk'rögamēt') *n.* [Gk. *makros*, large: *gametes*, spouse.] The larger of two conjugants, usually considered as equivalent to ovum or female conjugant.

macrogametocyte (măk'rögămē'tösīt) *n.* [Gk. *makros*, large; *gametes*, spouse; *kytos*, hollow.] The mother-cell of a macrogamete, considered female; term used mainly in connection with Protista.

macrogamy (măkrŏg'ămĭ) *n.* [Gk. *makros*, large; *gamos*, marriage.] Syngamy between full-grown individuals of a species, as in Actinophrys; hologamy.

macroglia (măkrŏglī'ă) *n. plu.* [Gk. *makros*, large; *glia*, glue.] Astrocytes or true neuroglia; astroglia and oligodendroglia.

macroglossate (măk'röglŏs'āt) *a.* [Gk. *makros*, large; *glossa*, tongue.] Furnished with a large tongue.

macrognathic (măk'rönăth'ĭk) *a.* [Gk. *makros*, large; *gnathos*, jaw.] Having specially developed jaws.

macrogonidium (măk'rögŏnĭd'ĭum) *n.* [Gk. *makros*, large; *gone*, generation; *idion*, *dim.*] A large gonidium.

macrogyne (măk'röjĭnē) *n.* [Gk. *makros*, large; *gyne*, woman.] Female ant of unusually large size.

macroleucocyte (măk'rölū'kŏsīt, -loo-) *n.* [Gk. *makros*, large; *leukos*, white; *kytos*, hollow.] A chromophil leucocyte, developed from a proleucocyte.

macromere (măk'römēr) *n.* [Gk. *makros*, large; *meros*, part.] In cleavage of telolecithal eggs, a larger cell of lower hemisphere.

macromerozoite (măk'römĕrözō'īt) *n.* [Gk. *makros*, large; *meros*, part; *zoon*, animal.] One of many divisions produced by macroschizont stage of Sporozoa.

macromesentery (măk'römĕs'ĕntĕrĭ, -mĕz-) *n.* [Gk. *makros*, large; *mesos*, middle; *enteron*, gut.] One of the larger complete mesenteries of Anthozoa.

macromitosome (măk'römī'tösōm) *n.* [Gk. *makros*, large; *mitos*, thread; *soma*, body.] The paranucleus, as in Lepidoptera.

macromutation (măk'römūtā'shŭn) *n.* [Gk. *makros*, large; L. *mutare*, to change.] Simultaneous mutation of a number of different characters.

macromyelon (măk'römī'ĕlŏn) *n.* [Gk. *makros*, long; *myelos*, marrow.] The medulla oblongata.

macronotal (măk'rönō'tăl) *a.* [Gk. *makros*, large; *noton*, back.] With large thorax, as a queen ant.

macront (măk'rŏnt) *n.* [Gk. *makros*, large; *on*, being.] The larger of two sets of cells formed after schizogony in Neosporidia, the macront giving rise to macrogametes.

macronucleocyte (măk'rönū'klëösīt) *n.* [Gk. *makros*, large; L. *nucleus*, kernel; Gk. *kytos*, hollow.] A leucocyte having a relatively large nucleus; chromophil leucocyte of insects.

macronucleus (măk'rönū'klëŭs) *n.* [Gk. *makros*, large; L. *nucleus*, kernel.] The larger of two nuclei in a cell, usually supposed to be of a vegetative or somatic nature; meganucleus.

macronutrients,—macro-elements.

macrophage (măk'röfāj) *n.* [Gk. *makros*, large; *phagein*, to eat.] A large phagocytic cell, fixed or wandering; a large mononuclear leucocyte; a histiocyte, clasmatocyte, pericyte, etc.

macrophagous (măkrŏf'ăgŭs) *a.* [Gk. *makros*, large; *phagein*, to eat.] Feeding on relatively large masses of food, *opp.* microphagous.

macrophyllous (măk'röfĭl'ŭs) *a.* [Gk. *makros*, large; *phyllon*, leaf.] Having large leaves or leaflets.

macroplankton (măk'röplăng'ktŏn) *n.* [Gk. *makros*, large; *plangkton*, wandering.] The larger organisms drifting with the surrounding water, as jelly-fish, etc., *opp.* microplankton and nanoplankton.

macropodous (măkrŏp'ödŭs) *a.* [Gk. *makros*, long; *pous*, foot.] Having a long stalk, as a leaf or leaflet; having hypocotyl large in proportion to rest of embryo; long-footed.

macropterous (măkrŏp'tĕrŭs) *a.* [Gk. *makros*, large; *pteron*, wing.] With unusually large fins or wings; fully winged, *opp.* brachypterous.

macropyrenic (măk'röpīrē'nĭk) *a.* [Gk. *makros*, large; *pyren*, fruit stone.] With nuclei markedly larger than average for the species or other group. *n.* A macropyrenic individual.

macroschizogony (măk'röskĭzŏg'-önĭ) *n.* [Gk. *makros*, large; *schizein*, to cleave; *gone*, generation.] Method of multiplication of macroschizonts; schizogony giving rise to large merozoites.

macroschizont (măk'röskĭz'ŏnt) *n.* [Gk. *makros*, large; *schizein*, to cleave; *on*, being.] Stage in life-cycle of certain Haemosporidia developed from sporozoite, and giving rise to macromerozoites.

macrosclereids (măk'rösklē'rëĭdz) *n. plu.* [Gk. *makros*, large; *skleros*, hard; *eidos*, form.] Relatively large columnar sclereids, as in coat of certain seeds.

macroscopic (măk'röskŏp'ĭk) *a.* [Gk. *makros*, large; *skopein*, to view.] Visible by the naked eye.

macrosepalous (măk′rösĕp′ălŭs) *a.* [Gk. *makros*, large; F. *sépale*, sepal.] With specially large sepals.

macroseptum (măk′rösĕp′tŭm) *n.* [Gk. *makros*, large; L. *septum*, inclosure.] A primary or perfect septum of Anthozoa.

macrosiphon (măkrösī′fŏn) *n.* [Gk. *makros*, large; *siphon*, tube.] Large internal siphon of certain cephalopods.

macrosmatic (măk′rŏsmăt′ĭk) *a.* [Gk. *makros*, large; *osme*, smell.] With well-developed sense of smell.

macrosomatous (măk′rösō′mătŭs) *a.* [Gk. *makros*, large; *soma*, body.] Possessing abnormally large body.

macrosome (măk′rösōm) *n.* [Gk. *makros*, large; *soma*, body.] A large alveolar sphere or granule in protoplasm.

macrosplanchnic (măk′rösplăngk′-nĭk) *a.* [Gk. *makros*, large; *splangchnon*, entrail.] Large-bodied and short-legged.

macrosporangiophore (măk′röspör-ăn′jĭöfōr) *n.* [Gk. *makros*, large; *sporos*, seed; *anggeion*, vessel; *pherein*, to bear.] A structure bearing a macrosporangium.

macrosporangium (măk′röspörăn′-jĭŭm) *n.* [Gk. *makros*, large; *sporos*, seed; *anggeion*, vessel.] A sporangium developing macrospores or megaspores.

macrospore (măk′röspōr) *n.* [Gk. *makros*, large; *sporos*, seed.] A large anisospore or gamete of Sarcodina; a larger spore of heterosporous plants; embryo-sac; megaspore.

macrosporophore (măk′röspō′röfōr) *n.* [Gk. *makros*, large; *sporos*, seed; *pherein*, to bear.] A leafy lobe developing macrosporangia.

macrosporophyll (măk′röspŏr′öfĭl) *n.* [Gk. *makros*, large; *sporos*, seed; *phyllon*, leaf.] Macrosporophore; carpel.

macrosporozoite (măk′röspŏr′özō′īt) *n.* [Gk. *makros*, large; *sporos*, seed; *zoon*, animal.] A larger endogamous sporozoite of Sporozoa.

macrostomatous (măk′röstŏm′ătŭs) *a.* [Gk. *makros*, large; *stoma*, mouth.] With very large mouth.

macrostylospore (măk′röstī′löspōr) *n.* [Gk. *makros*, large; *stylos*, pillar; *sporos*, seed.] A large spore-like stalked body.

macrostylous (măk′röstī′lŭs) *a.* [Gk. *makros*, long; *stylos*, pillar.] With long styles.

macrotherm (măk′röthĕrm) *n.* [Gk. *makros*, large; *therme*, heat.] A tropical plant; macrothermophyte, megatherm.

macrotous (măkrō′tŭs) *a.* [Gk. *makros*, large; *ous*, ear.] With large ears.

macrotrichia (măk′rötrĭk′ĭă) *n. plu.* [Gk. *makros*, large; *thrix*, hair.] The larger setae on body or wings of insects.

macrotype (măk′rötīp) *n.* [Gk. *makros*, large; *typos*, a type.] A modified arrangement of mesenteries containing more macromesenteries than normal microtype, in Anthozoa.

macrozoogonidium (măk′rözō′ögŏn-ĭd′ĭŭm) *n.* [Gk. *makros*, large; *zoon*, animal; *gone*, generation; *idion*, *dim.*] A large zoogonidium.

macrozoospore (măk′rözō′öspōr) *n.* [Gk. *makros*, large; *zoon*, animal; *sporos*, seed.] Large motile spore.

macruric (măkroor′ĭk) *a.* [Gk. *makros*, long; *oura*, tail.] Long-tailed; macrural, macrurous.

macula (măk′ūlă) *n.* [L. *macula*, spot.] A spot or patch of colour; a small pit or depression; a tubercle; neuroepithelial area of membranous labyrinth, as in sacculus, utriculus, ampullae, and cochlear duct.

macula cribrosa,—area on wall of vestibule of ear, perforated for passage of auditory nerve filaments.

macula germinitiva,—the germinal spot, nucleolus of an ovum.

macula lutea,—yellow spot of retina, an oval yellowish area in centre of posterior part of retina at point of most perfect vision.

macular (măk'ūlăr) *a.* [L. *macula*, spot.] *Pert.* a macula; *pert.* macula lutea.

maculate (măk'ūlāt), **maculiferous** (măk'ūlĭf'ĕrŭs), **maculose** (măk'-ūlōs) *a.* [L. *macula*, spot.] Spotted.

maculation (măk'ūlā'shŭn) *n.* [L. *maculare*, to spot.] The arrangement of spots on a plant or an animal.

madescent (mădĕs'sĕnt) *a.* [L. *madescere*, to become wet.] Becoming moist; slightly moist.

madid (măd'ĭd) *a.* [L. *madidus*, moist.] Moist; wet.

madrepore (măd'rĕpōr) *n.* [F. *madrépore*—from L. *mater*, mother; Gk. *poros*, friable stone.] A branching stony coral; plate at external opening of stone canal in echinoderms.

madreporic (măd'rĕpŏr'ĭk) *a.* [F. *madrépore*, madrepore.] *Pert.* a madrepore or madreporite; *appl.* body, plate, tubercle, canal.

madreporic canal—hydrophonic or stone canal, *q.v.*

madreporite (mădrĕp'ōrīt) *n.* [F. *madrépore*, madrepore.] A flat circular or pentagonal grooved, perforated plate at end of an interambulacral area, or between two such areas in Echinoidea, or between rays in Asteroidea; a modified genital plate.

Magendie's foramen [*F. Magendie*, French physiologist]. Median aperture in roof of fourth ventricle, connecting the latter with subarachnoid cavities; metapore.

maggot (măg'ŏt) *n.* [M.E. *magot*, grub.] The worm-like insect larva, without appendages or distinct head, as that of the blowfly.

magnum,—capitatum, *q.v.*

maiosis,—meiosis, *q.v.*

mala (mā'lă) *n.* [L. *mala*, cheek.] Part of maxilla of some insects, of mandible of certain myriopods; part of exterior of lower jaw of birds; cheek; malar bone.

malacoid (măl'ăkoid) *a.* [Gk. *malakos*, soft; *eidos*, form.] Soft in texture.

malacology (măl'ăkŏl'ŏjĭ) *n.* [Gk. *malakos*, soft; *logos*, discourse.] The study of molluscs.

malacophilous (măl'ăkŏf'ĭlŭs) *a.* [Gk. *malakos*, soft; *philein*, to love.] Pollinated by agency of gastropods.

malacopterous (măl'ăkŏp'tĕrŭs) *a.* [Gk. *malakos*, soft; *pteron*, wing.] Soft-finned.

malacostracous (măl'ăkŏs'trăkŭs) *a.* [Gk. *malakos*, soft; *ostrakon*, shell.] Soft-shelled.

Malagasy (mălăgăs'ĭ) *a.* *Appl.* or *pert.* the zoogeographical subregion including Madagascar and adjacent islands.

malar (mā'lăr) *a.* [L. *mala*, cheek-bone.] *Pert.* or in region of cheek. *n.* The jugal or zygomatic bone.

malaxation (mălăksā'shŭn) *n.* [Gk. *malassein*, to soften.] Compression of mandibles, or chewing, as by wasps.

male (māl) *a.* [L. *mas*, male.] *Pert.* masculine organism; *appl.* organs of reproduction, as testes, or stamens; symbol ♂.

male pronucleus,—nucleus of spermatozoon.

malella (mălĕl'ă) *n.* [L.L. *dim.* of L. *mala*, jaw.] Distal toothed process of outer stipes of deutomala in certain Myriopoda.

malleate (măl'ēāt) *a.* [L. *malleus*, hammer.] Hammer-shaped; *appl.* a type of trophi of rotifer gizzard.

malleoincudal (măl'ēōĭnkū'dăl) *a.* [L. *malleus*, hammer; *incus*, anvil.] *Pert.* malleus and incus of ear.

malleolar (mălē'ŏlăr) *n.* [L. *dim.* of *malleus*, hammer.] The vestigial fibula of ruminants. *a. Pert.* or in region of malleolus; *appl.* arteries, folds, sulcus.

malleolus (mălē'ŏlŭs) *n.* [L. *dim.* of *malleus*, hammer.] Medial and lateral malleolus, lower extremity prolongations of tibia and fibula respectively; one of the club- or racket-shaped appendages on basal segments of hind legs of Solpugidæ.

malleoramate (mălʹëörāʹmāt) *a.* [L. *malleus*, hammer ; *ramus*, branch.] *Appl.* type of trophi with looped manubrium and toothed incus in rotifer gizzard.

malleus (mălʹëŭs) *n.* [L. *malleus*, hammer.] A part of rotifer mastax or gizzard ; one of the chain of auditory ossicles of mammals ; one of the Weberian ossicles of fishes.

mallochorion (mălʹökŏrʹĭŏn) *n.* [Gk. *mallos*, wool ; *chorion*, skin.] The primitive mammalian chorion.

malloplacenta (mălʹōplăsĕnʹta) *n.* [Gk. *mallos*, wool ; L. *placenta*, flat cake.] Non-deciduate placenta with villi evenly distributed, as in cetaceans and some ungulates.

Malpighian (mălpĭgʹĭăn) *n.* [*M. Malpighi*, Italian anatomist]. Discovered by or named after Malpighi.

Malpighian body or **corpuscle,**—in spleen, a nodular mass of lymphoid tissue ensheathing the smaller arteries ; in kidney, a glomerulus of convoluted capillary blood-vessels enclosed in a dilatation of uriniferous tubule.

Malpighian layer,—basal layer of epidermis next to true skin ; rete Malpighii.

Malpighian pyramids,—medullary pyramids of kidney.

Malpighian tubules,—thread-like excretory tubes leading into posterior part of gut of insects.

maltase (môlʹtās) *n.* [A.S. *mealt*, malt.] An enzyme which converts malt-sugar into grape-sugar.

maltose (môlʹtōs) *n.* [A.S. *mealt*, malt.] Malt-sugar, formed from starch by ptyalin and amylase ; $C_{12}H_{12}O_{11}$.

mamelon (mămʹëlŏn) *n.* [F. *mamelon*, from L. *mamilla*, nipple.] Small pimple-like structure in centre of tubercle of echinoid interambulacral plate ; papilla forming nucellus in cycads.

mamilla (mămĭlʹă) *n.* [L. *mamilla*, nipple.] A nipple ; a nipple-shaped structure ; mammilla.

mamillary bodies,—corpora mamillaria or albicantia, *q.v.*

mamillary process or **tubercle,**—superior tubercle connected with transverse process of lower thoracic vertebrae.

mamillate (mămʹĭlāt) *a.* [L. *mamilla*, nipple.] Studded with small protuberances.

mamma (mămʹă) *n.* [L. *mamma*, breast.] Milk-secreting organ of female mammals.

mammal (mămʹăl) *n.* [L. *mamma*, breast.] An animal of a class of vertebrates of which the females suckle the young.

mammalogy (mămălʹöjĭ) *n.* [L. *mamma*, breast ; Gk. *logos*, discourse.] The study of mammals.

mammary (mămʹărĭ) *a.* [L. *mamma*, breast.] *Pert.* the breast ; *appl.* arteries, veins, glands, tubules, etc.

mammiferous (mămĭfʹërŭs) *a.* [L. *mamma*, breast ; *ferre*, to bear.] Developing mammae ; milk-secreting ; mammalian.

mammiform (mămʹĭfôrm) *a.* [L. *mamma* breast ; *forma*, shape.] Breast-shaped ; *appl.* pileus of certain fungi.

mammilla,—mamilla, *q.v.*

mammogenic (mămʹöjĕnʹĭk) *a.* [L. *mamma*, breast ; Gk. *gennaein*, to produce.] *Appl.* pi uitary hormone complex which promotes growth of the lobe-alveolar and duct systems of the mammary gland.

manchette (mănshĕtʹ) *n.* [F. *manchette*, cuff.] Membrane enveloping the cytoplasm surrounding the axial filament of a spermatid ; armilla or superior annulus in certain fungi.

mandible (mănʹdĭbl) *n.* [L. *mandibulum*, jaw.] The lower jaw of vertebrates, either a single bone or composed of several ; a paired mouth appendage of arthropods ; mandibulum.

mandibular (măndĭbʹūlăr) *a.* [L. *mandibulum*, jaw.] *Pert.* the lower jaw ; *appl.* arch, canal, foramen, fossa, nerve, notch.

mandibulate (măndĭbʹūlāt) *a.* [L. *mandibulum*, jaw.] Having a lower jaw ; having functional jaws ; having mandibles.

mandibuliform (măndĭb'ūlĭfôrm) *a.* [L. *mandibulum*, jaw; *forma*, shape.] Resembling, or used as a mandible; *appl.* certain insect maxillae.

mandibulohyoid (măndĭb'ūlōhī'oid) *a.* [L. *mandibulum*, jaw; Gk. *hyoeides*, Υ-shaped.] In region of mandible and hyoid.

mandibulomaxillary (măndĭb'ūlōmăksĭl'ărĭ) *a.* [L. *mandibulum*, jaw; *maxilla*, jaw.] *Pert.* maxillae and mandibles of arthropods.

manducation (măn'dūkā'shŭn) *n.* [L. *manducare*, to chew.] Chewing; mastication.

manicate (măn'ĭkāt) *a.* [L. *manicatus*, sleeved.] Covered with entangled hairs or matted scales.

manna (măn'ă) *n.* [Gk. *manna*, manna.] Hardened exudation of bark of certain trees; honey-dew secreted by certain Coccidae.

mannose (măn'ōs) *n.* [Gk. *manna*, manna.] A sugar of various plants; $C_6H_{12}O_6$.

manocyst (mā'nösĭst) *n.* [L. *manare*, to proceed from; Gk. *kystis*, pouch.] A receptive oogonial papilla reaching the antheridium, as in Phytophthora.

manoxylic (mănözī'lĭk) *a.* [Gk. *manos*, slack; *xylon*, wood.] Having soft loose wood, as Cycadales. *Opp.* pycnoxylic.

mantle (măn'tl) *n.* [L. *mantellum*, cloak.] Outer soft fold of integument next shell of molluscs; pallium; sheath of spongoblast cells; body-wall of ascidians; scapulars and wing coverts of birds; ocrea, *q.v.*

mantle cavity,—a space between the mantle and body proper.

mantle cell,—a cell of tapetum or investing tissue of a sporangium.

mantle fibres,—the spindle-fibres of a fully formed spindle.

mantle layer,—a layer of embryonic medulla spinalis representing the future gray columns.

mantle lobes,—dorsal and ventral flaps of mantle in bivalves.

manual (măn'ūăl) *n.* [L. *manus*, hand.] A wing-quill borne on manus of birds; remex primarius, primary feather.

manubrial (mănū'brĭăl) *a.* [L. *manubrium*, handle.] *Pert.* a manubrium; handle-shaped.

manubrium (mănū'brĭŭm) *n.* [L. *manubrium*, handle.] A cell projecting inwards from shield of an antheridial globule of thallophytes; a hypostome or conical elevation at distal end of a hydrozoan polyp; clapper-like portion hanging down from under surface of medusae; handle-like part of malleus of ear; handle of malleus of mastax; presternum or anterior part of sternum; basal part of furcula in Collembola.

manus (măn'ŭs) *n.* [L. *manus*, hand.] Hand, or part of fore-limb corresponding to it, as found in vertebrates from Amphibia onwards.

manyplies,—omasum or psalterium, third chamber of stomach of ruminants — so-called from its folded structure.

marcescent (mărsĕs'ĕnt) *a.* [L. *marcescere*, to wither.] Withering but not falling off; *appl.* a calyx or corolla persisting after fertilisation.

marcid (mâr'sĭd) *a.* [L. *marcidus*, withered.] Withered; shrivelled.

marginal (mâr'jĭnăl) *a.* [L. *margo*, edge.] *Pert.* at or near the margin, edge, or border; *appl.* veil, a secondary growth of edge of pileus, in agarics and boletes; *appl.* a form of nervation; *appl.* a convolution of frontal lobe; *appl.* a type of placenta; *appl.* plates round margin of chelonian carapace.

marginalia (mâr'jĭnā'lĭă) *n. plu.* [L. *margo*, edge.] Prostalia or defensive spicules on body surface round osculum.

marginate (mâr'jĭnāt) *a.* [L. *margo*, edge.] Having a distinct margin in structure or colouring.

marginella (mâr'jĭnĕl'ă) *n.* [*Dim.* of L. *margo*, edge.] Ring formed by part of cutis proliferating beyond margin of lamellae, in certain fungi with an exposed hymenium.

marginicidal (mâr'jĭnĭsī'dăl) *a.* [L. *margo*, edge; *caedere*, to cut.] Dehiscing by line of union of carpels.

marginiform (mâr'jĭnĭfôrm) *a.* [L. *margo*, edge; *forma*, shape.] Like a margin or border in appearance or structure.

marginirostral (mâr'jĭnĭrŏs'trăl) *a.* [L. *margo*, edge; *rostrum*, beak.] Forming the edges of a bird's bill.

marita (mărī'tă, marē'tă) *n.* [L. *maritus*, conjugal.] Sexually mature stage in helminth life history.

marital (măr'ĭtăl) *a.* [L. *maritus*, conjugal.] *Pert.* marita; producing fertilised eggs, *appl.* trematodes.

marker,—an identifying factor; a gene of known location and effect which makes possible the determination of the distribution of other, less conspicuously effective, genes.

marmorate (mâr'mörāt) *a.* [L. *marmor*, marble.] Of marbled appearance.

marrow (măr'ō) *n.* [A.S. *mearg*, pith.] Connective tissue filling up cylindrical cavities in bodies of long bones, and spaces of cancellous tissue, differing in composition in different bones; medulla ossium; pith of certain plants; vegetable marrow.

marrow-brain,—myelencephalon.

marsupial (mârsū'pĭăl) *a.* [L. *marsupium*, pouch.] *Pert.* a marsupium; pouch-bearing, as a kangaroo; *appl.* bones of pelvic girdle in certain mammals.

marsupium (mârsū'pĭŭm) *n.* [L. *marsupium*, pouch.] Any pouch-like structure in which the young of an animal complete their development, such as abdominal pouch of marsupials; gill cavities of bivalves; recess formed by diverging spines and a supporting membrane in stelleroids; structure protecting the acrocyst in Sertularia; a nursing-sac surrounding certain archegonia.

Martinotti cells,—pyramidal nerve-cells of cerebral cortex, with axons directed to the peripheral plexiform or molecular layer.

mask (măsk) *n.* [F. *masque*, mask.] A hinged prehensile structure, corresponding to adult labium, peculiar to dragon-fly nymph.

masked (măs'kd) *a.* [F. *masque*, mask.] Personate, *appl.* corolla; concealed, *appl.* fat of cell which is not evident microscopically.

massa intermedia,—grey matter connecting thalami across third ventricle; middle commissure.

masseter (măsē'tĕr) *n.* [Gk. *masseter*, one that chews.] Muscle which raises lower jaw and assists in chewing.

masseteric (măs'ētĕr'ĭk) *a.* [Gk. *masseter*, one that chews.] *Pert.* or near masseter muscle of cheek; *appl.* artery, vein, nerve.

massive (măs'ĭv) *a.* [L. *massa*, mass.] Bulky; heavy; compacted; *appl.* nuclei deficient in nuclear sap.

massula (măs'ūlă) *n.* [L. *massula*, small mass.] A mass of microspores in a sporangium of certain pteridophytes; a massed group of microspores in orchids.

mast cells,—spheroid or ovoid cells of very granular protoplasm, numerous in connective tissue where fat is being laid down; Mastzellen of Ehrlich.

mastax (măs'tăks) *n.* [Gk. *mastax*, jaws.] The gizzard or pharyngeal mill of rotifers.

mastication (măs'tĭkā'shŭn) *n.* [L. *masticare*, to chew.] Process of chewing food with teeth till reduced to small pieces or to a pulp.

masticatory stomach,—the gastric mill or stomodaeal apparatus of crustaceans, for grinding and straining food material.

mastidion (măstĭd'ĭŏn) *n.* [Gk. *mastos*, breast; *idion*, *dim.*] Nipple-like protuberance on paturon, in some spiders.

mastigium (măstĭj'ĭŭm) *n.* [Gk. *mastigion*, little whip.] Defensive posterior lash of certain larvae.

mastigobranchia (măstīgöbrăng'kĭă) *n.* [Gk. *mastix*, whip;

brangchia, gills.] Epipodite of adult Decapoda, a bilobed membranous lamina extending upwards between gills.

mastigosome (măstī′gösōm′) *n.* [Gk. *mastix*, whip; *soma*, body.] A blepharoplast.

mastoid (măs′toid) *a.* [Gk. *mastos*, breast; *eidos*, form.] Nipple-shaped; *appl.* a process of temporal bone, cells, foramen, fossa, notch.

mastoideosquamous (măstoid′ëö-skwā′mŭs) *a.* [Gk. *mastos*, breast; *eidos*, like; L. *squama*, scale.] *Pert.* mastoid and squamous parts of temporal bone.

mastoidohumeralis (măstoid′öhū-mërā′lĭs) *a.* [Gk. *mastos*, breast; *eidos*, like; L. *humerus*, humerus.] A muscle of certain quadrupeds, connecting mastoid and humerus.

masto-occipital (măs′tö-ŏksĭp′ĭtăl) *a.* [Gk. *mastos*, breast; L. *occiput*, occiput.] *Pert.* occipital bone and mastoid process of temporal.

mastoparietal (măs′töpărī′ëtăl) *a.* [Gk. *mastos*, breast; L. *paries*, wall.] *Pert.* parietal bone and mastoid process of temporal.

mastotympanic (măs′tötĭmpăn′ĭk) *a.* [Gk. *mastos*, breast; *tympanon*, drum.] *Appl.* part of tympanic cavity's boundary in certain reptiles.

mating types,—groups, the individuals of which do not conjugate with individuals of other groups, as of ciliates.

matriclinous (măt′rĭklī′nŭs) *a.* [L. *mater*, mother; Gk. *klinein*, to bend.] With hereditary characteristics more maternal than paternal; matroclinic, matroclinal.

matrix (mā̆t′rĭks) *n.* [L. *mater*, mother.] Ground substance of connective tissue; part beneath body and root of nail; uterus; body upon which lichen or fungus grows; envelope of chromatid; substance in which a fossil is embedded.

matroclinal,—matriclinous, *q.v.*

mattula (măt′ūlă) *n.* [L. *matta*, mat.] Fibrous network covering petiole bases of palms.

maturation (măt′ūrā′shŭn) *n.* [L. *maturus*, ripe.] Ripening; completion of germ-cell development, consisting of reduction of chromatin; meiosis, reduction of chromosomes from somatic or diploid to genetic or haploid number.

Mauthner's cells [*L. Mauthner*, Austrian physician]. A layer between medullary sheath and neurolemma of nerve fibre.

maxilla (măksĭl′ă) *n.* [L. *maxilla*, jaw.] The upper jaw; part of upper jaw behind premaxilla; an appendage of most arthropods, posterior to mandible, modified in various ways in adaptation to function and requirements.

maxillary (măksĭl′ărĭ) *a.* [L. *maxilla*, jaw.] *Pert.* or in region of maxilla or upper jaw; *appl.* artery, nerve, process, sinus, tuberosity, vein, etc.

maxillary glands, — paired renal organs opening at base of maxilla in Crustacea.

maxilliferous (măk′sĭlĭf′ërŭs) *a.* [L. *maxilla*, jaw; *ferre*, to carry.] Bearing maxillae.

maxilliform (măksĭl′ĭfôrm) *a.* [L. *maxilla*, jaw; *forma*, shape.] Like a maxilla.

maxillipede (măksĭl′ĭpēd) *n.* [L. *maxilla*, jaw; *pes*, foot.] An appendage, in one, two, or three pairs, posterior to maxillae in arthropods; also maxilliped.

maxillodental (măksĭl′ödĕn′tăl) *a.* [L. *maxilla*, jaw; *dens*, tooth.] *Pert.* jaws and teeth.

maxillojugal (măksĭl′öjoo′găl) *a.* [L. *maxilla*, jaw; *jugum*, yoke.] *Pert.* jaw and jugal bone.

maxillolabial (măksĭl′ölā′bĭăl) *a.* [L. *maxilla*, jaw; *labium*, lip.] *Pert.* maxilla and labium; *appl.* dart in ticks.

maxillomandibular (măksĭl′ömăn-dĭb′ūlăr) *a.* [L. *maxilla*, jaw; *mandibulum*, jaw.] *Appl.* arch forming jaws of primitive fishes; *pert.* maxilla and mandible.

maxillopalatal (măksĭl'öpăl'ătăl) *a.* [L. *maxilla*, jaw; *palatus*, palate.] *Pert.* jaw and palatal bones; *appl.* a maxillary process of birds; maxillopalatine.

maxillopharyngeal (măksĭl'öfărĭn'jëăl) *a.* [L. *maxilla*, jaw; Gk. *pharyngx*, gullet.] *Pert.* lower jaw and pharynx.

maxillopremaxillary (măksĭl'öprēmăksĭl'ărĭ) *a.* [L. *maxilla*, jaw; *pre*, before.] *Pert.* whole of upper jaw; *appl.* jaw when maxilla and premaxilla are fused.

maxilloturbinal (măksĭl'ötŭr'bĭnăl) *a.* [L. *maxilla*, jaw; *turbo*, whorl.] *Pert.* maxilla and turbinals. *n.* A bone arising from lateral wall of nasal cavity, which supports sensory epithelium.

maxillula (măksĭl'ūlă) *n.* [L. *dim.* of *maxilla*, jaw.] A first maxilla in Crustacea when there are more pairs than one; an appendage between mandible and first maxilla in primitive insects.

maxim (măk'sĭm) *n.* [L. *maximus*, greatest.] An ant of the large worker type or of the soldier caste, *opp.* minim.

mazaedium (măzē'dĭŭm) *n.* [Gk. *maza*, cake; *idion*, *dim.*] A coat formed by ends of paraphyses and their secretions, covering hymenium of certain Ascomycetes; a fruit-body of certain lichens; mazedium.

mazic (mā'zĭk) *a.* [Gk. *maza*, cake.] Placental; *pert.* placenta.

M-chromosome, — a microchromosome; or, a mediocentric chromosome.

M-disc,—a line in middle of Hensen's line, *q.v.*

meatus (mēā'tŭs) *n.* [L. *meatus*, passage.] A passage or channel, as acoustic, nasal, etc.

mechanism (mĕk'ănĭzm) *n.* [Gk. *mechane*, machine.] The view that all vital phenomena are due to physical and chemical laws.

mechanocyte (mĕk'ănösīt) *n.* [Gk. *mechane*, contrivance; *kytos*, hollow]. A cell derived from bone, cartilage, connective tissue, tendon, or muscle; a supporting cell; a fibrocyte.

mechanoreceptor (mĕk'ănörēsĕp'tŏr) *n.* [Gk. *mechane*, contrivance; L. *recipere*, to receive.] A specialised structure sensitive to contact, pressure, or gravity.

Meckel's cartilage or **rod** [*J. F. Meckel, junior*, German anatomist]. The lower jaw of lower vertebrates, and in higher vertebrates, the axis round which membrane bones of jaw are arranged and formed.

Meckel's ganglion [*J. F. Meckel, senior*, German anatomist]. The sphenopalatine ganglion.

meconidium (mē'kōnĭd'ĭŭm) *n.* [Gk. *mekon*, poppy; *idion*, *dim.*] Sessile or pedicellate extracapsular medusa usually lying on top of gonangium of certain hydroids.

meconium (mēkō'nĭŭm) *n.* [Gk. *mekon*, poppy.] Waste products of a pupa or other embryonic form; contents of intestine of a new-born mammal.

media (mē'dĭă) *n.* [L. *medius*, middle.] A middle structure, such as a layer of tissue, a central nervure; *plu.* mediae. *Plu.* of medium.

mediad (mē'dĭăd) *adv.* [L. *medius*, middle; *ad*, to.] Towards but not quite in the middle line or axis.

medial (mē'dĭăl) *a.* [L. *medius*, middle.] Situated in the middle. *n.* The middle vein of wing of insects.

median (mē'dĭăn) *a.* [L. *medius*, middle.] Lying or running in axial plane; intermediate; middle. *n.* The middle variate when variates are arranged in order of magnitude.

median nerve,—nerve arising from union of medial and lateral cord of brachial plexus, with branches in forearm.

mediastinal (mē'dĭăstī'năl) *a.* [L. *mediastinus*, medial.] *Pert.* or in region of mediastinum; *appl.* cavity, arteries, glands, pleura.

mediastinum (mē'dĭăstī'nŭm) *n.* [L. *mediastinus*, medial.] Space between right and left pleura in and near median sagittal thoracic plane; incomplete vertical septum of testis, Highmore's body.

mediator (mē′dĭātŏr) *n.* [L. *medius*, middle.] A nerve cell maintaining relation between receptor and effector; amboceptor.

mediocentric (mē′dĭōsĕn′trĭk) *a.* [L. *medius*, middle; *centrum*, centre.] Having a medial, or mediad, centromere; *appl.* chromosome.

Medio-Columbian,—Sonoran, *q.v.*

mediocubital (mē′dĭōkū′bital) *n.* [L. *medius*, middle; *cubitalis*, of elbow.] A cross-vein between posterior media and cubitus of insect wing.

mediodorsal (mē′dĭōdôr′săl) *a.* [L. *medius*, middle; *dorsum*, back.] In the dorsal middle line.

mediopalatine (mē′dĭōpăl′ătĭn) *a.* [L. *medius*. middle; *palatus*, palate.] Between palatal bones; *appl.* a cranial bone of some birds.

mediopectoral (mē′dĭōpĕk′tŏrăl) *a.* [L. *medius*, middle; *pectus*, breast.] *Appl.* middle part of sternum.

mediostapedial (mē′dĭōstăpē′dĭăl) *n.* [L. *medius*, middle; *stapes*, stirrup.] *Pert.* that portion of columella auris external to stapes.

mediotarsal (mē′dĭōtâr′săl) *a.* [L. *medius*, middle; *tarsus*, ankle.] Between tarsal bones.

medioventral (mē′dĭōvĕn′trăl) *a.* [L. *medius*, middle; *venter*, belly.] In the middle ventral line.

mediproboscis (mē′dĭprōbŏs′ĭs) *n.* [L. *medius*, middle; Gk. *proboskis*, trunk.] Middle portion of insect proboscis, part of ligula.

medithorax (mē′dĭthō′răks) *n.* [L. *medius*, middle; Gk. *thorax*, chest.] Middle part of the thorax; the mesothorax of insects.

medium (mē′dĭŭm) *n.* [L. *medium*, middle.] Any of the structures through which a force acts, as refracting media of eye-ball; substance in which cultures are reared or tissues propagated.

medulla (mĕdŭl′ă) *n.* [L. *medulla*, marrow, pith.] Marrow of bones; central part of an organ or tissue; pith or central portion of stem.

medulla oblongata, — posterior portion of brain continuous with medulla spinalis or spinal cord.

medullary (mĕdŭl′ărĭ) *a.* [L. *medulla*, pith.] *Pert.* or in region of medulla; *appl.* axis, artery, lamina, membrane, bone, spaces, canal, etc.

medullary canal,—hollow cylindrical portion of a long bone containing marrow; the neurocoel; neural tube.

medullary groove,—a groove on surface of medullary plate, bounded by folds which grow and coalesce, converting groove into a canal, the neurocoel.

medullary keel,—a downward growth towards archenteron, the rudiment of central nervous system in development of certain primitive vertebrates.

medullary layer,—a thick subcortical layer of the thallus of some lichens.

medullary membrane,—lining of cavity in long bones; endosteum, internal periosteum.

medullary phloem, — internal phloem in a bicollateral bundle, as in Cucurbitaceae.

medullary plate,—plate-like formation of ectoderm cells bordering blastopore of early embryo; neural plate, earliest rudiment of nervous system.

medullary rays — a number of strands of connective tissue extending between pith and pericycle.

medullary sheath,—a ring of protoxylem round pith of certain stems; a layer of white substance, composed of myelin, surrounding axis cylinder of medullated nerve-fibre.

medullary velum,—valve of Vieussens, *q.v.*

medullated (mĕd′ŭlātĕd) *a.* [L. *medulla*, pith.] Provided with pith, or with a medullary sheath.

medullated nerve-fibres,—fibres of brain and spinal cord, consisting of axis-cylinder or neuraxis of primitive fibrillae, surrounded by medullary sheath, in turn covered by delicate neurilemma.

medulliblasts (mēdŭl′ĭblăsts) *n. plu.* [L. *medulla*, marrow; Gk. *blastos*, bud.] Cells of embryonic nervous tissue which give rise to neuroblasts and spongioblasts.

medullispinal (mēdŭl′ĭspī′năl) *a.* [L. *medulla*, pith; *spina*, spine.] Of the spinal cord.

medusa (mēdū′să) *n.* [Gk. *Medousa*, one who rules.] A jelly-fish.

medusiform (mēdū′sĭfôrm) *a.* [Gk. *Medousa*, Medusa; L. *forma*, shape.] Like a medusa or jelly-fish.

medusoid (mēdū′soid) *n.* [Gk. *Medousa*, Medusa; *eidos*, like.] A medusa-like free-swimming gonophore of Hydrozoa. *a.* Like a jelly-fish or medusa.

medusome (mēdū′sōm) *n.* [Gk. *Medousa*, Medusa; *soma*, body.] Medusoid stage in life-history of Obelia.

mega-,—*also see* macro-.

megacephalic (mĕg′ăkĕfăl′ĭk, -sĕf-) *a.* [Gk. *megas*, large; *kephale*, head.] With abnormally large head; having a cranial capacity of over 1450 c.c.; *cf.* mesocephalic, microcephalic.

megagamete (mĕg′ăgămēt′) *n.* [Gk. *megas*, large; *gametes*, spouse.] A rounded cell regarded as an ovum or its equivalent, developed from a megagametocyte after a process akin to maturation; macrogamete.

megagametocyte (mĕg′ăgămē′tösīt) *n.* [Gk. *megas*, large; *gametes*, spouse; *kytos*, hollow.] A cell developed from a merozoite, and itself giving rise to a megagamete.

megagametogenesis (mĕg′ăgămētöjĕn′ĕsĭs) *n.* [Gk. *megas*, great; *gametes*, spouse; *genesis*, descent.] Development of megagametes or ova.

megagametophyte (mĕg′ăgămē′töfīt) *n.* [Gk. *megas*, large; *gametes*, spouse; *phyton*, plant.] The female gametophyte developed from a megaspore, *opp.* microgametophyte.

megakaryocyte (mĕg′ăkăr′ĭösīt) *n.* [Gk. *megas*, large; *karyon*, nut; *kytos*, hollow.] An amoeboid giant cell of bone-marrow, with one large annular lobulated nucleus, containing a number of nucleoli.

megalaesthetes (mĕg′ălēsthēt′ēz) *n. plu.* [Gk. *megalon*, great; *aisthetes*, perceiver.] Sensory organs, sometimes in form of eyes, in Placophora.

megalecithal,—*see* megalolecithal.

megaloblast (mĕg′ălöblăst) *n.* [Gk. *megalos*, greatly; *blastos*, bud.] A primitive large erythroblast.

megalogonidum (mĕg′ălögŏnĭd′ĭŭm) *n.* [Gk. *megalos*, greatly; *gonos*, offspring; *idion*, *dim.*] A large gonidium.

megalolecithal (mĕg′ălölĕs′ĭthăl) *a.* [Gk. *megalos*, greatly; *lekithos*, yolk.] Containing much yolk, as telolecithal eggs; megalecithal.

megalopic (mĕg′ălŏp′ĭk) *a.* [Gk. *megalos*, greatly; *ops*, eye.] Belonging to the megalops stage.

megalopore (mĕg′ălöpōr) *n.* [Gk. *megalon*, great; *poros*, channel.] Pore in dorsal plates of Chiton, for placing a megalaesthete in direct communication with exterior.

megalops (mĕg′ălŏps) *n.* [Gk. *megalos*, greatly; *ops*, eye.] A larval stage of certain Crustacea, as crabs, conspicuous by large stalked eyes; megalopa.

megalospheric (mĕg′ălösfĕr′ĭk) *a.* [Gk. *megalos*, greatly; *sphaira*, globe.] Of polythalamous foraminifer shells, having a megalosphere or large initial chamber; megaspheric.

megamere (mĕg′ămēr) *n.* [Gk. *megas*, large; *meros*, part.] One of the large cells formed after primary divisions of a developing ovum.

megameric (mĕg′ămĕr′ĭk) *a.* [Gk. *megas*, large; *meros*, part.] With relatively large parts; *appl.* chromosomes with large heterochromatic regions; *pert.* megameres.

meganephridia (mĕg′ănĕfrĭd′ĭă) *n. plu.* [Gk. *megas*, large; *nephros*, kidney; *idion*, *dim.*] Large nephridia, occurring as one pair per segment; holonephridia.

meganucleus (mĕg′ănū′klēŭs) *n.* [Gk. *megas*, large; L. *nucleus*, kernel.] The larger or vegetative nucleus of infusoria; macronucleus; trophonucleus.

megaphanerophyte (mĕg′ăfăn′ërōfīt) *n.* [Gk. *megas*, large; *phaneros*, manifest; *phyton*, plant.] Tree exceeding 30 metres in height.

megaphyllous (mĕg′ăfĭl′ŭs) *a.* [Gk. *megas*, large; *phyllon*, leaf.] Having relatively large leaves.

megasclere (mĕg′ăsklēr) *n.* [Gk. *megas*, large; *skleros*, hard.] Skeletal spicule of general supporting framework of sponges. *Opp.* microsclere.

megasome,—macrosome, *q.v.*

megasorus (mĕg′ăsō′rŭs) *n.* [Gk. *mega*, large; *soros*, heap.] A sorus containing megasporangia, *opp.* microsorus.

megasporangium (mĕg′ăspōrăn′jĭŭm) *n.* [Gk. *megas*, large; *sporos*, seed; *anggeion*, vessel.] A macrospore-producing sporangium; ovule.

megaspore (mĕg′ăspōr) *n.* [Gk. *megas*, great; *sporos*, seed. A larger-sized spore of dimorphic forms in reproduction by spore-formation; larger spore of heterosporous plants, regarded as female; gynospore; embryo-sac cell of seed plant; macrospore.

megasporocyte (mĕg′ăspŏr′ōsīt) *n.* [Gk. *megas*, large; *sporos*, seed; *kytos*, hollow.] The embryo-sac mother-cell, diploid cell in ovary that undergoes meiosis, producing four haploid megaspores.

megasporophyll (mĕg′ăspŏr′ōfĭl) *n.* [Gk. *megas*, great; *sporos*, seed; *phyllon*, leaf.] A spore-bearing leaf developing megasporangia; carpel.

megatherm (mĕg′ăthĕrm) *n.* [Gk. *megas*, great; *therme*, heat.] A tropical plant; a plant requiring moist heat.

megazooid (mĕg′ăzō′oid) *n.* [Gk. *megas*, great; *zoon*, animal; *eidos*, form.] The larger zooid resulting from binary or other fission.

megazoospore (mĕg′ăzō′ōspōr) *n.* [Gk. *megas*, great; *zoon*, animal; *sporos*, seed.] A large zoospore, as in reproduction of certain Radiolaria; a zoogonidium of certain Algae.

megistotherm (mĕj′ĭstōthĕrm, mĕg-) *n.* [Gk. *megistos*, greatest; *therme*, heat.] A plant that thrives at a more or less uniformly high temperature.

Mehlis' glands,—acinous glands surrounding the ootype; shell gland of trematodes.

Meibomian glands [*H. Meibom*, German anatomist]. The tarsal glands, modified sebaceous glands of the eyelids, the ducts opening on the free margins.

meiocyte (mī′ōsīt) *n.* [Gk. *meion*, smaller; *kytos*, hollow.] A reproductive cell prior to meiosis; auxocyte, *q.v.*

meiogenic (mī′ōjĕn′ĭk) *a.* [Gk. *meion*, smaller; *gene*, descent.] Promoting nuclear division.

meiogyrous (mī′ōjī′rŭs) *a.* [Gk. *meion*, less; *gyros*, circle.] Slightly coiled inwards.

meiolecithal (mī′ōlĕs′ĭthăl) *a.* [Gk. *meion*, less; *lekithos*, yolk.] Having little yolk, as homolecithal and isolecithal eggs.

meiomery (mīŏm′ërĭ) *n.* [Gk. *meion*, smaller; *meros*, part.] Condition of having fewer than the normal number of parts.

meiophylly (mī′ōfĭl′ĭ) *n.* [Gk. *meion*, smaller; *phyllon*, leaf.] Suppression of one or more leaves in a whorl.

meiosis (mīō′sĭs) *n.* [Gk. *meion*, smaller.] Process of reduction division of germ-cell chromosomes from diploid to haploid number at maturation; also maiosis.

meiosporangium (mī′ōspōrăn′jĭŭm) *n.* [Gk. *meion*, less; *sporos*, seed; *anggeion*, vessel.] A thick-walled diploid sporangium, producing haploid zoospores; *cf.* mitosporangium.

meiospore (mī'öspōr) *n.* [Gk. *meion*, less; *sporos*, seed.] A uninucleate haploid zoospore produced in a meiosporangium; *cf.* mitospore.

meiostemonous (mī'östĕm'önŭs) *a.* [Gk. *meion*, smaller; *stemon*, spun thread.] Having fewer stamens than petals or sepals.

meiotaxy (mī'ötăk'sĭ) *n.* [Gk. *meion*, smaller; *taxis*, arrangement.] Suppression of whorl or set of organs.

meiotherm (mī'öthĕrm) *n.* [Gk. *meion*, less; *therme*, heat.] A plant that thrives in a cool-temperate environment.

meiotic (mīŏt'ĭk) *a.* [Gk. *meion*, smaller.] *Appl.* reduction division; *pert.* meiosis.

Meissner's corpuscles [*G. Meissner*, German histologist]. Tactile corpuscles, associated with sense of pain, in skin of digits, lips, nipple, and certain other areas.

Meissner's plexus, a gangliated plexus of nerve fibres in submucous coat of small intestine.

melanin (mĕl'ănĭn) *n.* [Gk. *melas*, black.] Black or dark-brown pigment; *cf.* eumelanin, phaeomelanin, dopa, haemozoin; $C_{77}H_{98}O_{33}N_{14}S$.

melaniridosome (mĕl'ănĭr'ĭdösōm) *n.* [Gk. *melas*, black; *iris*, rainbow; *soma*, body.] A pigment body consisting of a melanophore and associated iridocytes in corium of fishes.

melanism (mĕl'ănĭzm) *n.* [Gk. *melas*, black.] Excessive development of black pigment.

melanoblast (mĕl'änöblăst) *n.* [Gk. *melas*, black; *blastos*, bud.] A cell of rete mucosum giving rise to melanin formation in the Malpighian layer of epidermis.

melanocyte (mĕl'ănösīt) *n.* [Gk. *melas*, black; *kytos*, hollow.] A black pigmented lymphocyte.

melanocyte-stimulating hormone, —intermedin; MSH.

melanogenesis (mĕl'ănöjĕn'ĕsĭs) *n.* [Gk. *melas*, black; *genesis*, origin.] The formation of melanin.

melanophore (mĕl'ănöfōr) *n.* [Gk. *melas*, black; *pherein*, to bear.] A black pigment cell.

melanosoma (mĕl'ănösō'mă) *n.* [Gk. *melas*, black; *soma*, body.] Dark, pigment mass associated with ocellus, as in certain Dinoflagellata.

melanospermous (mĕl'ănöspĕr'mŭs) *a.* [Gk. *melas*, black; *sperma*, seed.] *Appl.* seaweeds with dark-coloured spores.

melanotic (mĕl'ănŏt'ĭk) *a.* [Gk. *melas*, black.] Having black pigment unusually developed.

meliphagous (mĕlĭf'ăgŭs) *a.* [Gk. *meli*, honey; *phagein*, to eat.] Feeding on honey; mellivorous.

melliferous (mĕlĭf'ërŭs) *a.* [L. *mel*, honey; *ferre*, to carry.] Honey-producing.

mellisugent (mĕl'ĭsū'jënt) *a.* [L. *mel*, honey; *sugere*, to suck.] Honey-sucking.

mellivorous (mĕlĭv'örŭs) *a.* [L. *mel*, honey; *vorare*, to devour.] Honey-eating; meliphagous.

member (mĕm'bër) *n.* [L. *membrum*, member.] A limb or organ of the body; a well-defined part or organ of a plant.

membrana (mĕmbrâ'nă) *n.* [L. *membrana*, membrane.] A thin film, skin, or layer of tissue covering a part of animal or plant; a thin covering of cells or of unicellular organisms; a membrane.

membranaceous (mĕm'brănā'sëŭs) *a.* [L. *membrana*, membrane.] Of the consistency, or having the structure, of a membrane.

membrane bone,—a bone developing directly in membrane without passing through a cartilage stage.

membranella (mĕm'brănĕl'ă) *n.* [L. *membrana*, membrane.] An undulating membrane formed by fusion of rows of cilia, in some protozoa; ciliated band, in tornaria.

membraniferous (mĕm'brănĭf'ërŭs) *a.* [L. *membrana*, membrane; *ferre*, to carry.] Enveloped in or bearing a membrane.

membranoid (mĕm'brănoid) *a.* [Gk. *membrana*, membrane; *eidos*, form.] Resembling a membrane.

membranous (mĕm′brănŭs) *a.* [L. *membrana*, membrane.] Resembling or consisting of membrane; pliable and semitransparent.

membranous cranium,—a mesenchymal investment enclosing brain.

membranous labyrinth, — internal ear, separated from bony cavities by perilymph, and itself containing endolymph.

membranous vertebral column,—continuous sheath of mesoderm enveloping notochord and neural tube.

membranula (mĕmbrăn′ūlă) *n.* [L. *dim.* of *membrana*, membrane.] A concrescence of cilia, as in certain infusoria.

membranule (mĕm′brănūl) *n.* [L. *dim.* of *membrana*, membrane.] A small opaque space close to body of insect, in anal area of wing of some dragonflies.

menacme (mĕnăk′mē) *n.* [Gk. *men*, month; *akme*, prime.] The interval between first and final menstruation; life between menarche and menopause.

menadione,—vitamin K_3, present in green vegetables and other foods, essential to formation of prothrombin; $C_{11}H_8O_2$.

menarche (mĕnâr′kē) *n.* [Gk. *men*, month; *arche*, beginning.] First menstruation; age at first menstruation.

Mendelian,—*pert.* character which behaves according to results of Mendel's law, manifesting allelomorphic inheritance.

Mendelian population,—a group of interbreeding individual organisms, a species being the most extensive.

Mendelism,—a law or rule governing inheritance of characters in plants and animals, discovered by *Gregor Mendel.* This principle deals with inheritance of 'unit characters,' presence or absence of one or other of a pair of contrasting characters, dominant and recessive. It also shows that offspring of organisms with a pair of contrasting characters will exhibit these in a definite ratio, and it is extended to deal with groups of characters.

meningeal (mēnĭn′jēăl) *a.* [Gk. *meningx*, membrane.] *Pert.* or in region of meninges; *appl.* arteries, veins, nerves, etc.

meninges (mĕnĭn′jēz) *n. plu.* [Gk. *meningx*, membrane.] The three membranes enclosing brain and spinal cord, from without inwards: dura mater, arachnoid, and pia mater.

meningocyte (mĕnĭng′gōsīt) *n.* [Gk. *meningx*, membrane; *kytos*, hollow.] A phagocytic cell of the subarachnoid space.

meningosis (mĕn′ĭnggō′sĭs) *n.* [Gk. *meningx*, membrane.] Attachment by means of membranes.

meningospinal (mĕnĭng′gōspī′năl) *a.* [Gk. *meningx*, membrane; L. *spina*, spine.] *Pert.* spinal cord membranes.

meninx,—*sing.* of meninges.

meninx primaria,—membrane representing dura mater, as in Anura.

meninx primitiva,—a single membrane surrounding the central nervous system, as in Cyclostomata and Elasmobranchii.

meninx secundaria,—a pigmented membrane representing pia mater and arachnoid, as in Anura.

meniscus (mēnĭs′kŭs) *n.* [Gk. *meniskos*, small moon.] Interarticular fibro-cartilage found in joints exposed to violent concussion; semilunar cartilage; intervertebral disc; a tactile disc, being terminal expansion of axis cylinder in tactile corpuscles. *Plu.* menisci.

menopause (mē′nōpôz) *n.* [Gk. *men*, month; *pausi*, ending.] Climacterical cessation of menstruation. *Cf.* climacteric.

menotaxis (mĕn′ōtăk′sĭs) *n.* [Gk. *menein*, to remain; *taxis*, arrangement.] Compensatory movements to maintain a given direction of body axis in relation to sensory stimuli; maintenance of visual axis during locomotion.

mensa (mĕn′să) *n.* [L. *mensa*, table.] Chewing surface of tooth.

menses (mĕn′sēz) *n.plu.* [L. *menses*, months.] The fluid discharged during menstruation ; catamenia.

menstrual (mĕn′strooăl) *a.* [L. *menstrualis*, monthly.] Monthly ; catamenial : of or *pert.* menses ; lasting for a month, as flower.

menstruation (mĕn′strooā′shŭn) *n.* [L. *mensis*, month ; *struere*, to flow.] Periodic discharge from uterus of various vertebrates, chiefly higher mammals.

mental (mĕn′tăl) *a.* [L. *mentum*, chin.] *Pert.* or in region of chin ; *appl.* foramen, nerve, spines, tubercle, muscle ; *appl.* scale or plate of fish and of reptile ; *pert.* mentum of insects. [L. *mens*, mind.] *Pert.* the mind.

mentigerous (mĕntĭj′ĕrŭs) *a.* [L. *mentum*, chin ; *gerere*, to carry.] Supporting or bearing the mentum.

mentomeckelian (mĕn′tōmĕkē′lĭăn) *a.* [L. *mentum*, chin ; *J. F. Meckel, junior*, German anatomist]. *Appl.* a cartilage bone, present in a few lower vertebrates, at either side of mandibular symphysis.

mentum (mĕn′tŭm) *n.* [L. *mentum*, chin.] The chin ; medial part of gnathochilarium in Diplopoda ; region of labium between prementum and submentum in insects ; projection between head and foot of some gastropods.

mere (mēr) *n.* [Gk. *meros*, part.] A part ; a blastomere, *q.v.*

mericarp (mĕr′ĭkârp) *n.* [Gk. *meris*, part ; *karpos*, fruit.] A one-seeded indehiscent part of a schizocarp, as of a cremocarp.

mericlinal (mĕrĭklī′năl) *a.* [Gk. *meris*, part ; *klinein*, to bend.] Partly periclinal, *appl.* chimaera with inner tissue of one species only partly surrounded by outer tissue of the other.

meridional canal,—in ctenophores, a canal into which adradial canals open.

meridional furrow,—a longitudinal furrow extending from pole to pole of a segmenting egg.

merisis (mĕr′ĭsĭs) *n.* [Gk. *meris*, division.] Increase in size owing to cell division ; *cf.* auxesis.

merism,—metamerism, *q.v.*

merismatic (mĕr′ĭsmăt′ĭk) *a.* [Gk. *merismos*, partition.] Dividing or separating into cells or segments ; meristematic, *q.v.*

merismoid (mĕrĭs′moid) *a.* [Gk. *merismos*, partition ; *eidos*, like.] With branched pileus.

merispore (mĕr′ĭspōr) *n.* [Gk. *meris*, part ; *sporos*, seed.] A segment or spore of a multicellular spore-body.

meristele (mĕr′ĭstēlē) *n.* [Gk. *meris*, part ; *stele*, pillar.] A separate part of a monostelic stem passing outwards from stele to leaves ; the branch of a stele supplying a leaf.

meristem (mĕr′ĭstĕm) *n.* [Gk. *meristos*, divided.] Tissue formed of cells all capable of diversification, as found at growing points ; merismatic or meristematic tissue.

meristematic (mĕr′ĭstĕmăt′ĭk) *a.* [Gk. *meristos*, divided.] *Pert.* or consisting of meristem ; *appl.* tissue, cells of growing point ; merismatic.

meristematic ring,—tube of meristematic tissue between cortex and pith, subtending the apical meristem and giving rise to vascular tissues.

meristic (mĕrĭs′tĭk) *a.* [Gk. *meristos*, divided.] Segmented ; divided off into parts ; differing in number of parts.

meristic variation, — changes in number of parts or segments, and in geometrical relations of the parts ; *cf.* substantive variation.

meristogenetic (mĕrĭs′tōjĕnĕt′ĭk) *a.* [Gk. *meristos*, divided ; *genesis*, descent.] Developing from meristem ; developing from a single hyphal cell or a group of contiguous cells ; meristogenous.

merithallus (mĕ′rĭthăl′ŭs) *n.* [Gk. *meris*, part ; *thallos*, young shoot.] A stem unit ; an internode.

Merkel's corpuscle [*F. S. Merkel*, German anatomist]. A tactile receptor, in skin and in submucosa of mouth.

mermaid's purse,—horny, floating or fixed, egg-envelope of elasmobranchs.

mermithaner (mĕrmīth′ănër) *n.* [Gk. *mermis*, cord; *aner*, male.] Male ant parasitised by Mermis.

mermithergate (mĕr′mīthĕr′gāt) *n.* [Gk. *mermis*, cord; *ergates*, worker.] An enlarged worker ant parasitised by Mermis.

mermithogyne (mĕrmī′thöjĭn′ē) *n.* [Gk. *mermis*, cord; *gyne*, female.] Female ant parasitised by Mermis.

meroandry (mĕröăn′drĭ) *n.* [Gk. *meros*, part; *aner*, male.] The condition of having a reduced number of testes, as a single pair in certain Oligochaeta; *cf.* holandry.

meroblast (mĕr′öblăst) *n.* [Gk. *meros*, part; *blastos*, bud.] Intermediate stage between schizont and merozoite in some Sporozoa; a meroblastic ovum.

meroblastic (mĕr′öblăs′tĭk) *a.* [Gk. *meros*, part; *blastos*, bud.] *Appl.* ova which undergo only partial segmentation or cleavage in development; developing from part of the oosphere only.

merocerite (mērŏs′ĕrīt) *n.* [Gk. *meros*, thigh; *keras*, horn.] The fourth segment of crustacean antennae.

merocrine (mĕr′ökrĭn) *a.* [Gk. *meros*, part; *krinein*, to separate.] *Appl.* glands in which secreting cells are able to function repeatedly, as sudoriferous and lactiferous glands. *Opp.* holocrine.

merocytes (mĕr′ösīts) *n. plu.* [Gk. *meros*, part; *kytos*, hollow.] Nuclei formed by repeated division of supernumerary sperm-nuclei, as in egg of selachians, reptiles, and birds; schizonts, *q.v.*

merogametes (mĕr′ögămēts′) *n. plu.* [Gk. *meros*, part; *gametes*, spouse.] Protozoan individuals specialised for syngamy; microgametes. *Opp.* hologametes.

merogamy,—microgamy, *q.v.*

merogastrula (mĕr′ögăs′troolă) *n.* [Gk. *meros*, part; *dim.* of *gaster*, stomach.] The gastrula formed from a meroblastic ovum.

merogenesis (mĕr′öjĕn′ĕsĭs) *n.* [Gk. *meros*, part; *genesis*, descent.] Formation of parts; segmentation.

merogeny,—merogony, *q.v.*

merognathite (mērŏg′năthīt) *n.* [Gk. *meros*, thigh; *gnathos*, jaw.] Fourth segment of crustacean mouth-part.

merogony (mĕrŏg′önĭ) *n.* [Gk. *meros*, part; *gone*, generation.] Development of normal young of small size, from part of an egg, in which there was no female pronucleus.

meroistic (mĕrōĭs′tĭk) *a.* [Gk. *meros*, part; *oon*, egg.] *Appl.* ovariole containing nutritive or nurse cells; *cf.* acrotrophic, polytrophic.

merokinesis (mĕr′ökĭnē′sĭs) *n.* [Gk. *meros*, part; *kinesis*, movement.] Formation and division of a thread-like chromosome in the karyomeres.

merome (mĕrōm) *n.* [Gk. *meros*, part]. A body segment; somite, metamere.

meromorphosis (mĕr′ömôr′fōsĭs) *n.* [Gk. *meros*, part; *morphosis*, shaping.] Regeneration of a part with the new part less than that lost.

meron (mē′rŏn) *n.* [Gk. *meros*, upper thigh.] Posterior portion of coxa of insects; sclerite between middle and hind coxae, or immediately above hind coxa, in Diptera; meseusternum.

meronephridia,—micronephridia.

meront (mĕrŏnt′) *n.* [Gk. *meros*, part; *on*, being.] Any unit produced by cleavage or schizogony; a uninucleate schizont-stage in Neosporidia, succeeding the planont-stage.

meroplankton (mĕr′öplăng′ktŏn) *n.* [Gk. *meros*, part; *plangktos*, wandering.] Plankton living only part-time near the surface; temporary plankton, consisting mainly of eggs and larvae; seasonal plankton.

meropodite (mē′röpödīt′) *n.* [Gk. *meros*, upper thigh; *pous*, foot.] Fourth segment of thoracic appendage in crustaceans; femur in spiders.

meros,—meropodite.

merosomatous (mĕr'ösōm'ătŭs) *a.* [Gk. *meros*, part; *soma*, body.] *Appl.* ascidiozooids divided into two regions, thorax and abdomen.

merosome (mĕr'ösōm) *n.* [Gk. *meros*, part; *soma*, body.] A body segment, somite, or metamere.

merosporangium (mĕr'öspörăn'jĭŭm) *n.* [Gk. *meros*, part; *sporos*, seed; *anggeion*, vessel.] Outgrowth from the apex of a sporangiophore, producing a row of spores, as in certain Mucorales.

merosthenic (mē'rŏsthĕn'ĭk) *a.* [Gk. *meros*, upper thigh; *sthenos*, strength.] With unusually developed hind-limbs.

merotomy (mĕrŏt'ömĭ) *n.* [Gk. *meros*, part; *temnein*, to cut.] Segmentation or division into parts.

merotype (mĕr'ötīp) *n.* [Gk. *meros*, part; *typos*, pattern.] Part of the same perennial plant or vegetatively propagated animal from which a holotype was taken.

merozoite (mĕr'özō'īt) *n.* [Gk. *meros*, part; *zoon*, animal.] Division-product of a schizont in Sporozoa.

merozoon (mĕr'özō'ŏn) *n.* [Gk. *meros*, part; *zoon*, animal.] A fragment of a unicellular animal containing part of the macronucleus, obtained by artificial division.

merrythought,—furcula of birds, formed by coalesced clavicles.

merus,—meropodite, *q.v.*

Méry's glands [*J. Méry*, French anatomist]. Bulbo-urethral glands.

mesad,—mediad, mesiad.

mesadenia (mĕsădē'nĭă) *n. plu.* [Gk. *mesos*, middle; *aden*, gland.] Mesodermal accessory genital glands in insects; *cf.* ectadenia.

mesal,—medial, mesial.

mesamoeboid (mĕs'ămē'boid) *a.* [Gk. *mesos*, middle; *amoibe*, change; *eidos*, form.] *Appl.* nucleated cells of blood islands from which blood corpuscles are derived.

mesanepimeron (mĕsăn'ĕpĭmē'rŏn, mēz-) *n.* [Gk. *mesos*, middle; *ana*, up; *meros*, upper thigh.] Sclerite above epimeron and below wing base, in Diptera.

mesanepisternum,—mesepisternum.

mesarch (mĕs'ârk) *a.* [Gk. *mesos*, middle; *arche*, beginning.] *Appl.* xylem having metaxylem developing in all directions from the protoxylem, characteristic of ferns; having the protoxylem surrounded by metaxylem; beginning in a mesic environment, *appl.* seres.

mesaticephalic (mĕs'ătĭkĕfăl'ĭk,-sĕf-) *a.* [Gk. *mesatos*, mid; *kephale*, head.] Having a cephalic index of 75 to 80; mesocephalic.

mesaxonic (mĕs'ăksŏn'ĭk) *a.* [Gk. *mesos*, middle; *axon*, axis.] With the line dividing the foot, passing up the middle digit.

mesectoderm (mĕsĕk'töděrm) *n.* [Gk. *mesos*, middle; *ektos*, outside; *derma*, skin.] Parenchyma formed of descendants of ectodermal cells which migrated inwards.

mesembryo (mĕsĕm'brĭö) *n.* [Gk. *mesos*, middle; *embryon*, embryo.] The blastula.

mesencephalon (mĕs'ĕnkĕf'ălŏn, -sĕf-) *n.* [Gk. *mesos*, middle; *en*, in; *kephale*, head.] The mid-brain, comprising corpora quadrigemina (bigemina), cerebral peduncles, and aqueduct of Sylvius.

mesenchyma (mĕsĕng'kĭmă), **mesenchyme** (mĕsĕng'kīm) *n.* [Gk. *mesos*, middle; *engchein*, to pour in.] A mass of tissue, intermediate between ectoderm and endoderm of a gastrula.

mesendoderm (mĕsĕn'dödĕrm) *n.* [Gk. *mesos*, middle; *endon*, within; *derma*, skin.] Cells lying posteriorly to lip of blastopore, partly invaginated with endoderm in gastrulation, in development of some molluscs.

mesenterial (mĕs'ĕntē'rĭăl, mĕz-) *a.* [Gk. *mesos*, middle; *enteron*, gut.] *Pert.* a mesentery; *appl.* filaments of Actinozoa.

mesenteric (mĕs'ĕntĕr'ĭk) *a.* [Gk. *mesos*, middle; *enteron*, gut.] *Pert.* a mesentery; *appl.* arteries, glands, nerves, veins, etc.

mesenteriole (mĕs'ĕntē'rĭōl) *n.* [L. *dim.* of *mesenterium*, mesentery.] A fold of peritoneum derived from mesentery, and retaining vermiform process or appendix in position.

mesenterium,—mesentery, *q.v.*

mesenteron (mĕsĕn'tĕrŏn, mēz-) *n.* [Gk. *mesos*, middle ; *enteron*, gut.] The main digestive cavity of Actinozoa and other Coelentera ; portion of alimentary canal lined by endoderm ; mid-gut.

mesentery (mĕs'ĕntĕrĭ, mĕz-) *n.* [L. *mesenterium*, mesentery.] A peritoneal fold serving to hold viscera in position ; a muscular partition extending inwards from body-wall in coelenterates.

mesentoderm,—mesendoderm.

mesepimeron (mĕs'ĕpĭmē'rŏn, mĕz-) *n.* [Gk. *mesos*, middle ; *epi*, upon ; *meros*, upper thigh.] The epimeron of insect mesothorax; meskatepimeron in Diptera.

mesepisternum (mĕs'ĕpĭstĕr'nŭm) *n.* [Gk. *mesos*, middle ; *epi*, upon ; *sternon*, breast.] Meso-episternum, sclerite below anterior spiracle in Diptera ; mesanepisternum.

mesepithelium,—mesothelium.

mesethmoid (mĕsĕth'moid, mēz-) *a.* [Gk. *mesos*, middle ; *ethmos*, sieve ; *eidos*, form.] Between the two ectethmoid bones ; *appl.* ethmoid plate of cranium when it ossifies ; median cranial bone of vertebrates.

mesiad (mĕz'ĭăd) *adv.* [Gk. *mesos*, middle ; L. *ad*, to.] Towards or near the middle plane.

mesial (mē'zĭăl), **mesian** (mē'zĭăn) *a.* [Gk. *mesos*, middle.] In the middle vertical or longitudinal plane.

mesic (mĕs'ĭk, mē'zĭk) *a.* [Gk. *mesos*, middle.] Conditioned by temperate moist climate, neither xeric nor hydric.

meskatepimeron (mĕskăt'ĕpĭmē'rŏn) *n.* [Gk. *mesos*, middle ; *kata*, down ; *epi*, upon ; *meros*, upper thigh.] Sclerite posterior to mesosternal area, the mesepimeron of Diptera.

meskatepisternum (mĕskăt'ĕpĭstĕr'nŭm) *n.* [Gk. *mesos*, middle ; *kata*, down ; *epi*, upon ; *sternon*, chest.] Sclerite between root of wing and under-side of mesothorax, the sternopleura or mesosternal area of Diptera.

mesoappendix,—mesenteriole.

mesoarion,—mesovarium, *q.v.*

mesobenthos (mĕs'öbĕn'thŏs, mēz-) *n.* [Gk. *mesos*, middle ; *benthos*, depths.] Animal and plant life of sea-bottom when depth is between 100 and 500 fathoms.

mesoblast (mĕs'öblăst, mēz-) *n.* [Gk. *mesos*, middle ; *blastos*, bud.] The mesoderm or middle layer of an embryo ; mesoblastema.

mesoblastic (mĕs'öblăs'tĭk, mēz-) *a.* [Gk. *mesos*, middle ; *blastos*, bud.] *Pert.* or developing from middle layer of an embryo.

mesobranchial (mĕs'öbrăng'kĭăl, mēz-) *a.* [Gk. *mesos*, middle ; *brangchia*, gills.] *Pert.* middle gill-region, as in Crustacea.

mesobronchus (mĕs'öbrŏng'kŭs, mēz-) *n.* [Gk. *mesos*, middle ; *brongchos*, windpipe.] In birds, the main trunk of a bronchus giving rise to secondary bronchi.

mesocaecum (mĕs'ösē'kŭm, mēz-) *n.* [Gk. *mesos*, middle ; L. *caecus*, blind.] The mesentery connected with the caecum.

mesocardium (mĕs'ökâr'dĭŭm, mēz-) *n.* [Gk. *mesos*, middle ; *kardia*, heart.] An embryonic mesentery binding heart to pericardial walls ; part of pericardium enclosing veins (venous m.) or aorta (arterial m.) ; mesocardial ligament or gubernaculum cordis.

mesocarp (mĕs'ökârp, mēz-) *n.* [Gk. *mesos*, middle ; *karpos*, fruit.] The middle layer of the pericarp.

mesocentrous (mĕs'ösĕn'trŭs, mēz-) *a.* [Gk. *mesos*, middle; *kentron*, centre.] Ossifying from a median centre.

mesocephalic (mĕs'ökĕf'ălĭk, mē'zösĕf'ălĭk) *a.* [Gk. *mesos*, middle ; *kephale*, head.] Having a cranial capacity of between 1350 and 1450 c.c. ; *cf.* megacephalic, microcephalic.

mesocerebrum,—deuterocerebrum.

mesochilium (mĕs'ŏkī'lĭŭm, mēz-) *n.* [Gk. *mesos*, middle; *cheilos*, lip.] The middle portion of labellum of orchids.

mesochiton (mĕs'ŏkī'tŏn, mēz-) *n.* [Gk. *mesos*, middle; *chiton*, coat.] Middle layer of oogonial wall, between endochiton and exochiton, as in Fucales; mesochite.

mesocoel (mĕs'ŏsēl, mēz-) *n.* [Gk. *mesos*, middle; *koilos*, hollow.] Middle portion of coelomic cavity; the second of three main parts of coelom of molluscs; cavity of mesencephalon, aqueduct of Sylvius or iter.

mesocolic (mĕs'ŏkŏl'ĭk, mēz-) *a.* [Gk. *mesos*, middle; *kolon*, large intestine.] *Pert.* mesocolon; *appl.* lymph glands.

mesocolon (mĕs'ŏkō'lŏn, mēz-) *n.* [Gk. *mesos*, middle; *kolon*, large intestine.] A mesentery or fold of peritoneum attaching colon to dorsal wall of abdomen.

mesocoracoid (mĕs'ŏkŏr'ăkoid, mēz-) *a.* [Gk. *mesos*, middle; *korax*, crow; *eidos*, form.] Situated between hyper- and hypo-coracoid; *appl.* middle part of coracoid arch of certain fishes.

mesocotyl (mĕs'ŏkŏt'ĭl, mēz-) *n.* [Gk. *mesos*, middle; *kotyle*, cup.] Part of axis between scutellum and coleoptile.

mesocycle (mĕs'ŏsīkl, mēz-) *n.* [Gk. *mesos*, middle; *kyklos*, circle.] A layer of tissue between xylem and phloem of a monostelic stem; part of conjunctive tissue of stele.

mesodaeum (mĕs'ŏdē'ŭm, mēz-) *n.* [Gk. *mesos*, middle; *odaios*, *pert.* way.] Endodermal part of embryonic digestive tract, between stomodaeum and proctodaeum.

mesoderm (mĕs'ŏdĕrm, mēz-) *n.* [Gk. *mesos*, middle; *derma*, skin.] The mesoblast or embryonic layer lying between ectoderm and endoderm.

mesodermal (mĕs'ŏdĕr'măl, mēz-) *a.* [Gk. *mesos*, middle; *derma*, skin.] *Pert.*, derived, or developing from mesoderm; mesodermic.

mesodesm (mĕs'ŏdĕzm, mēz-) *n.* [Gk. *mesos*, middle; *desma*, bond.] Part of mesocycle.

mesodont (mĕs'ŏdŏnt, mēz-) *a.* [Gk. *mesos*, middle; *odous*, tooth.] *Appl.* stag-beetles having a medium development of mandible projections.

meso-ectodermal, — ectomesodermal, *q.v.*; ectomesogloeal, *q.v.*

meso-episternum,—mesepisternum.

mesogaster (mĕs'ŏgăs'tĕr, mēz-) *n.* [Gk. *mesos*, middle; *gaster*, stomach.] The mesentery or fold of peritoneum supporting the stomach.

mesogastric (mĕs'ŏgăs'trĭk, mēz-) *a.* [Gk. *mesos*, middle; *gaster*, stomach.] *Pert.* a mesogaster or mesogastrium, or to middle gastric region.

mesogastrium (mĕs'ŏgăs'trĭŭm, mēz-) *n.* [Gk. *mesos*, middle; *gaster*, stomach.] Mesentery connecting stomach with dorsal abdominal wall in embryo; middle abdominal region.

mesoglia (mĕsŏglī'ă, mēz-) *n.* [Gk. *mesos*, middle; *gloia*, glue.] Mesodermal phagocytic interstitial cells of nervous system; of Hortega: microglia; of Robertson: oligodendroglia.

mesogloea (mĕs'ŏglē'ă, mēz-) *n.* [Gk. *mesos*, middle; *gloia*, glue.] An intermediate non-cellular gelatinous layer in sponges and coelenterates.

mesognathion (mĕs'ŏnăth'ĭŏn, mēz-) *n.* [Gk. *mesos*, middle; *gnathos*, jaw.] The lateral segment of premaxilla, bearing lateral incisor.

mesohepar (mĕs'ŏhē'păr, mēz-) *n.* [Gk. *mesos*, middle; *hepar*, liver.] Mesentery supporting liver.

mesohydrophytic (mĕs'ŏhī'drŏfĭtĭk, mēz-) *a.* [Gk. *mesos*, middle; *hydor*, water; *phyton*, plant.] Growing in temperate regions but requiring much moisture.

mesolamella (mĕs'ŏlămĕl'ă, mēz-) *n.* [Gk. *mesos*, middle; L. *lamella*, thin plate.] A thin mesogloeal layer between ocellus and gastrodermis in jelly-fish.

mesolecithal (mĕs′ŏlĕs′ĭthăl, mēz-) *a.* [Gk. *mesos*, middle ; *lekithos*, yolk.] Having a moderate yolk content ; *cf.* centrolecithal.

mesology (mĕsŏl′ŏjĭ, mēz-) *n.* [Gk. *mesos*, middle ; *logos*, discourse.] The study of relations between organism and environment ; bionomics.

mesome (mĕs′ōm, mēz′ōm) *n.* [Gk. *mesos*, middle.] The axis regarded as a morphological unit of plants.

mesomere (mĕs′ŏmēr, mēz-) *n.* [Gk. *mesos*, middle ; *meros*, part.] Middle zone of coelomic pouches in embryo ; mesoblastic somite or protovertebra ; medial branch of phallic lobe in insects.

mesometrium (mĕs′ŏmē′trĭŭm, mēz-) *n.* [Gk. *mesos*, middle ; *metra*, uterus.] The mesentery of uterus and connecting tubes.

mesomitosis (mĕs′ŏmĭtō′sĭs, mēz-) *n.* [Gk. *mesos*, middle ; *mitos*, thread.] Mitosis within nuclear membrane, without co-operation of cytoplasmic elements ; *cf.* metamitosis.

mesomorph (mĕs′ŏmôrf, mēz-) *n.* [Gk. *mesos*, middle ; *morphe*, form.] A mesomorphic animal ; a mesomorphic plant, usually a mesophyte.

mesomorphic (mĕs′ŏmôr′fĭk, mēz-) *a.* [Gk. *mesos*, middle ; *morphe*, form.] Having form, structure, or size normal or intermediate between extremes ; mesoplastic.

mesomyodian (mĕs′ŏmīō′dĭăn, mēz-) *a.* [Gk. *mesos*, middle ; *mys*, muscle ; *eidos*, form.] *Appl.* birds with muscles of syrinx attached to middle of bronchial semi-rings.

meson (mĕs′ŏn, mē′zŏn) *n.* [Gk. *mesos*, middle.] The central plane, or region of it.

mesonephric (mĕs′ŏnĕf′rĭk, mēz-) *a.* [Gk. *mesos*, middle ; *nephros*, kidney.] *Pert.* mesonephros, or mid-kidney ; *appl.* duct, tubules.

mesonephridium (mĕs′ŏnĕfrĭd′ĭŭm, mēz-) *n.* [Gk. *mesos*, middle ; *nephros*, kidney ; *idion*, *dim.*] A nephridium or excretory organ of certain invertebrates, derived from mesoblast.

mesonephros (mĕs′ŏnĕf′rŏs, mēz) *n.* [Gk. *mesos*, middle ; *nephros*, kidney.] Intermediate part of excretory organ in vertebrate embryos ; Wolffian body.

mesonotum (mĕs′ŏnō′tŭm, mēz-) *n.* [Gk. *mesos*, middle ; *noton*, back.] Dorsal part of insect mesothorax.

mesoparapteron (mĕs′ŏpărăp′tĕrŏn, mēz-) *n.* [Gk. *mesos*, middle ; *para*, beside ; *pteron*, wing.] A small sclerite of mesothorax of some insects.

mesopetalum (mĕs′ŏpĕt′ălŭm, mēz-) *n.* [Gk. *mesos*, middle ; *petalon*, leaf.] Labellum or lip of an orchid.

mesophanerophyte (mĕs′ŏfăn′ĕrŏfīt, mēz-) *n.* [Gk. *mesos*, middle ; *phaneros*, manifest ; *phyton*, plant.] Tree from 8 to 30 metres in height.

mesophil (mĕs′ŏfĭl, mēz-) *a.* [Gk. *mesos*, middle ; *philein*, to love.] Thriving at moderate temperatures, at between 20° and 40° C. when *appl.* bacteria ; mesophilic ; mesic, *q.v.* *n.* Mesophile.

mesophloem (mĕs′ŏflō′ĕm, mēz-) *n.* [Gk. *mesos*, middle ; *phloios*, smooth bark.] Middle or green bark ; mesophloeum.

mesophragma (mĕs′ŏfrăg′mă, mēz-) *n.* [Gk. *mesos*, middle ; *phragma*, fence.] A chitinous piece descending into interior of insect body with post-scutellum for base ; M or Hensen's line, *q.v.*

mesophryon (mĕsŏf′rĭŏn, mēz-) *n.* [Gk. *mesos*, middle ; *ophrys*, eyebrow.] The elevated median head-region or glabella of trilobites.

mesophyll (mĕs′ŏfĭl, mēz-) *n.* [Gk. *mesos*, middle ; *phyllon*, leaf.] The internal parenchyma of a leaf.

mesophyte (mĕs′ŏfīt, mēz-) *n.* [Gk. *mesos*, middle ; *phyton*, plant.] A plant thriving in temperate climate with normal amount of moisture.

mesoplankton (mĕs′ŏplăng′ktŏn, mēz-) *n.* [Gk. *mesos*, middle ; *plangktos*, wandering.] Drifting animal and plant life from a hundred fathoms downwards ; drifting organisms of medium size ; *cf.* megaloplankton, microplankton, nanoplankton.

mesoplast (mĕs′ŏplăst, mēz-) *n.* [Gk. *mesos*, middle; *plastos*, moulded.] A cell nucleus.

mesoplastic (mĕs′ŏplăs′tĭk, mēz-) *a.* [Gk. *mesos*, middle; *plastos*, moulded.] Having a normal or average form; mesomorphic; *appl.* constitutional type.

mesoplastron (mĕs′ŏplăs′trŏn, mēz-) *n.* [Gk. *mesos*, middle; F. *plastron*, breast-plate.] Plate between hyo- and hypo-plastron of certain turtles.

mesopleurite (mĕs′ŏploo′rīt, mēz-) *n.* [Gk. *mesos*, middle; *pleura*, side.] Lateral mesothoracic sclerite, as in Diptera.

mesopleuron (mĕs′ŏploo′rŏn, mēz-) *n.* [Gk. *mesos*, middle; *pleura*, side.] A lateral part of insect mesothorax; a mesopleurite.

mesopodial (mĕs′ŏpō′dĭăl, mēz-) *a.* [Gk. *mesos*, middle; *pous*, foot.] Having a supporting structure, such as a stipe, in a central position; *pert.* a mesopodium.

mesopodium (mĕs′ŏpō′dĭŭm, mēz-) *n.* [Gk. *mesos*, middle; *pous*, foot.] Leaf-stalk or petiole region of leaf; middle part of molluscan foot; the metacarpus or metatarsus.

mesopostscutellum (mĕs′ŏpōst′-skūtĕl′ŭm, mēz-) *n.* [Gk. *mesos*, middle; L. *post*, after; *scutellum*, small shield.] Postscutellum of mesothorax in insects.

mesopraescutum (mĕs′ŏprēskū′tŭm, mēz-) *n.* [Gk. *mesos*, middle; L. *prae*, before; *scutum*, shield.] Praescutum of mesothorax in insects; mesoprescutum.

mesopterygium (mĕs′ŏtĕrĭj′ĭŭm, mēz-) *n.* [Gk. *mesos*, middle; *pterygion*, little wing or fin.] The middle of three basal pectoral fin-cartilages in recent elasmobranchs.

mesopterygoid (mĕs′ŏtĕr′ĭgoid, mēz-) *n.* [Gk. *mesos*, middle; *pteryx*, wing; *eidos*, form.] The middle of three pterygoid bone elements of teleosts; the ectopterygoid.

mesoptile (mĕs′ŏtīl, mēz-, -ptīl) *n.* [Gk. *mesos*, middle; *ptilon*, feather.] Prepenna following protoptile and succeeded by metaptile or by teleoptile.

mesorchium (mĕsôr′kĭŭm, mēz-) *n.* [Gk. *mesos*, middle; *orchis*, testicle.] Mesentery supporting testis.

mesorectum (mĕs′ŏrĕk′tŭm, mēz-) *n.* [Gk. *mesos*, middle; L. *rectus*, straight.] Mesentery supporting rectum.

mesorhinal (mĕs′ŏrī′năl, mēz-) *a.* [Gk. *mesos*, middle; *rhines*, nostrils.] Between nostrils.

mesorhinium (mĕs′ŏrĭn′ĭŭm, mēz-) *n.* [Gk. *mesos*, middle; *rhis*, nose.] The internarial surface region of a bird's bill.

mesosalpinx (mĕs′ŏsăl′pĭngks, mēz-) *n.* [Gk. *mesos*, middle; *salpingx*, trumpet.] The portion of broad ligament enclosing uterine tube.

mesoscapula (mĕs′ŏskăp′ūlă, mēz-) *n.* [Gk. *mesos*, middle; L. *scapula*, shoulder-blade.] Scapular spine.

mesoscutellum (mĕs′ŏskūtĕl′ŭm, mēz-) *n.* [Gk. *mesos*, middle; L. *scutellum*, small shield.] Scutellum of insect mesothorax.

mesoscutum (mĕs′ŏskū′tŭm, mēz-) *n.* [Gk. *mesos*, middle; L. *scutum*, shield.] Scutum of insect mesothorax.

mesosoma (mĕs′ŏsō′mă, mēz-) *n.* [Gk. *mesos*, middle; *soma*, body.] Middle part of body; praeabdomen of Arthropoda.

mesosome (mĕs′ŏsōm, mēz-) *n.* [Gk. *mesos*, middle; *soma*, body.] A phallosome, *q.v.*

mesosperm (mĕs′ŏspĕrm, mēz-) *n.* [Gk. *mesos*, middle; *sperma*, seed.] Integument investing nucellus of ovule.

mesospore (mĕs′ŏspōr, mēz-), *n.* [Gk. *mesos*, middle; *sporos*, seed.] A unicellular teleutospore in certain rust fungi; a resting-spore or amphispore.

mesosporium (mĕs′ŏspō′rĭŭm, mēz-) *n.* [Gk. *mesos*, middle; *sporos*, seed.] The intermediate of three spore coats.

mesostate (mĕs′östāt, mēz-) *n.* [Gk. *mesos*, middle; *stasis*, standing.] Intermediate stage in metabolism.

mesostereom (mĕs′östĕr′ëŏm, mēz-) *n.* [Gk. *mesos*, middle; *stereos*, solid.] The middle layer of thecal plates of Cystidea.

mesosternebra (mĕs′östĕr′nĕbră, mēz-) *n.* [Gk. *mesos*, middle; *sternon*, breast-bone.] A part of developing mesosternum.

mesosternum (mĕs′östĕr′nŭm, mēz-) *n.* [Gk. *mesos*, middle; L. *sternum*, breast-bone.] Middle part of sternum of vertebrates; gladiolus; sternum of mesothorax of insects; mesosternal area, episternum of mesothorax, or meskatepisternum of Diptera.

mesostethium (mĕs′östē′thĭŭm, mēz-) *n.* [Gk. *mesos*, middle; *stethos*, chest.] A mesosternum.

mesostylous (mĕs′östī′lŭs, mēz-) *a.* [Gk. *mesos*, middle; *stylos*, pillar.] Having styles of intermediate length; *appl.* heterostylous flowers.

mesotarsal (mĕs′ötâr′săl, mēz-) *a.* [Gk. *mesos*, middle; L. *tarsus*, ankle-joint.] *Pert.* mesotarsus.

mesotarsus (mĕs′ötâr′sŭs, mēz-) *n.* [Gk. *mesos*, middle; L. *tarsus*, ankle-joint.] A middle-limb tarsus of insects.

mesotergum (mĕsötĕr′gŭm, mēz-) *n.* [Gk. *mesos*, middle; L. *tergum*, back.] Median arched portion or axis of trilobite body.

mesothecium (mĕs′öthē′sĭŭm, mēz-) *n.* [Gk. *mesos*, middle; *theke*, cup.] The middle investing layer of an anther-sac; lichen thecium.

mesotheic (mĕs′öthē′ĭkē, mz-) *a.* [Gk. *mesos*, middle; *theinai*, to render.] Neither highly susceptible nor entirely resistant to parasites or infection.

mesothelium (mĕs′öthē′lĭŭm, mēz-) *n.* [Gk. *mesos*, middle; *thele*, nipple.] Mesoderm bounding primitive coelom and giving rise to muscular and connective tissue; epithelium of mosoblastic origin.

mesotherm (mĕs′öthĕrm, mēz-) *n.* [Gk. *mesos*, middle; *therme*, heat.] Plant thriving in moderate heat.

mesothoracic (mĕs′öthōrăs′ĭk, mēz-) *a.* [Gk. *mesos*, middle; *thorax*, chest.] *Pert.* or in region of mesothorax; *appl.* a spiracle, of insects.

mesothorax (mĕs′öthō′răks, mēz-) *n.* [Gk. *mesos*, middle; *thorax*, chest.] The middle segment of thoracic region of insects.

mesotic (mĕsō′tĭk, mēz-) *a.* [Gk. *mesos*, middle; *ous*, ear.] *Appl.* paired chondrocranial cartilages in birds, between parachordal and acrochordal; also basiotic.

mesotriaene (mĕs′ötrī′ēn, mēz-) *n.* [Gk. *mesos*, middle; *triaina*, trident.] Aberrant type of triaene spicule.

mesotrochal (mĕsŏt′rökăl, mēz-) *a.* [Gk. *mesos*, middle; *trochos*, wheel.] *Appl.* an annulate larva with circlet of cilia round middle of body.

mesotrophic (mĕs′ötrŏf′ĭk, mēz-) *a.* [Gk. *mesos*, middle; *trophe*, nourishment.] Mixotrophic, *q.v.*; providing a moderate amount of nutrition, *appl.* environment.

mesotropic (mĕs′ötrŏp′ĭk, mēz-) *a.* [Gk. *mesos*, middle; *tropikos*, turning.] Turning or directed toward the middle or toward the median plane.

mesotympanic (mĕs′ötĭmpăn′ĭk, mēz-) *n.* [Gk. *mesos*, middle; *tympanon*, drum.] Symplectic; a bone in suspensory apparatus of lower jaw in fishes.

mesovarium (mĕs′övā′rĭŭm, mēz-) *n.* [Gk. *mesos*, middle; L. *ovarium*, ovary.] Mesentery of ovary; suspensory mesentery in fishes.

mesoventral (mĕs′övĕn′trăl, mēz-) *a.* [Gk. *mesos*, middle; L. *venter*, belly.] In middle ventral region.

Mesozoic (mĕs′özō′ĭk, mēz-) *a.* [Gk. *mesos*, middle; *zoe*, life.] *Appl.* or *pert.* secondary geological era, the age of reptiles.

mestome (mĕs′tōm) *n.* [Gk. *mestos*, filled.] A vascular bundle, including hadrome and leptome.

metabasis (mĕtăb'ăsĭs) *n.* [Gk. *metabasis*, alteration.] Transition; change, as of symptoms.

metabiosis (mĕt'ăbīō'sĭs) *n.* [Gk. *meta*, after; *biosis*, a living.] Condition in which one organism lives only after another has prepared its environment and has died; changed condition of living resulting from an external cause, as bacterial mutations due to radiation.

metabolic (mĕt'ăbŏl'ĭk) *a.* [Gk. *metabole*, change.] Changeable; *appl.* chemical changes occurring in the living organism; influencing metabolism, *appl.* hormones; formed during metabolism; metamorphosing.

metabolin,—metabolite, *q.v.*

metabolism (mĕtăb'ŏlĭzm) *n.* [Gk. *metabole*, change.] The chemical change, constructive and destructive, occurring in living organisms.

metabolite (mĕtăb'ŏlīt) *n.* [Gk. *metabole*, change.] Any product of metabolism.

metaboly (mĕtăb'ŏlĭ) *n.* [Gk. *metabole*, change.] Change, particularly of shape, as in Eugleninae.

metabranchial (mĕt'ăbrăng'kĭăl) *a.* [Gk. *meta*, after; *brangchia*, gills.] *Pert.* or in region of posterior gill region.

metacarpal (mĕt'ăkâr'păl) *a.* [Gk. *meta*, after; *karpos*, wrist.] *Pert.* metacarpus; *appl.* bones, articulations, etc. *n.* A primary wing-quill in the metacarpal region.

metacarpophalangeal (mĕt'ăkâr'pŏfălăn'jēăl) *a.* [Gk. *meta*, after; *karpos*, wrist; *phalangx*, series.] *Appl.* articulations between metacarpals and phalanges.

metacarpus (mĕt'ăkâr'pŭs) *n.* [Gk. *meta*, after; *karpos*, wrist.] The skeletal part of hand between wrist and fingers, consisting typically of five cylindrical bones.

metacele,—metacoel.

metacentric (mĕt'ăsĕn'trĭk) *a.* [Gk. *meta*, among; *kentron*, centre.] Having the centromere at or near the middle, *appl.* chromosomes; *cf.* acrocentric, telocentric. *n.* A metacentric or V-shaped chromosome; isochromosome.

metacercaria (mĕt'ăsĕrkā'rĭă) *n.* [Gk. *meta*, after; *kerkos*, tail.] A cercaria after encystment; adolescaria.

metacerebrum,—tritocerebrum.

metacestode (mĕt'ăsĕs'tōd) *n.* [Gk. *meta*, after; *kestos*, girdle; *eidos*, form.] Bladder-worm, encysted stage of a cestode; plerocestoid; plerocercoid.

metachroic (mĕtăkrō'ĭk) *a.* [Gk. *meta*, change of; *chros*, colour.] Changing colour, as older tissue in fungi.

metachromasis (mĕt'ăkrō'măsĭs) *n.* [Gk. *meta*, change of; *chroma*, colour.] Condition of certain tissues and cell components which, treated with basic aniline stains, show other than the fundamental colour constituent; metachromasy.

metachromatic (mĕt'ăkrōmăt'ĭk) *a.* [Gk. *meta*, change of; *chroma*, colour.] *Appl.* substances characterised by metachromasy; *appl.* granules of reserve food substances which stain with basic dyes, in bacteria and algal cells; *appl.* minute bodies in protoplasm of certain hyphal cells, Woronin bodies.

metachromatinic grains,—chromatoid bodies found in cells, very similar to chromatin in properties and characteristics.

metachrome, — a metachromatic granule.

metachromy (mĕt'ăkrō'mĭ) *n.* [Gk. *meta*, change of; *chroma*, colour.] Change in colour, as of flowers.

metachronic (mĕt'ăkrŏn'ĭk) *a.* [Gk. *metachronos*, done afterwards.] One acting after the other; *appl.* rhythm of movement of cilia.

metachrosis (mĕt'ăkrō'sĭs) *n.* [Gk. *meta*, change of; *chrosis*, colouring.] Ability to change skin colour by expansion or contraction of pigment cells.

metacneme (mĕt'ăknēmē) *n.* [Gk. *meta*, after; *kneme*, tibia.] A secondary mesentery of Zoantharia.

metacoel (mĕt'ăsēl) *n.* [Gk. *meta*, after; *koilos*, hollow.] The posterior part of coelom of molluscs; anterior extension of fourth ventricle of brain.

metacone (mĕt'ăkōn) *n.* [Gk. *meta*, after; *konos*, cone.] Postero-external cusp of upper molar.

metaconid (mĕt'ăkō'nĭd) *n.* [Gk. *meta*, after; *konos*, cone.] Postero-internal cusp of lower molar.

metaconule (mĕt'ăkō'nūl) *n.* [Gk. *meta*, after; *konos*, cone.] Posterior secondary cusp of upper molar.

metacoracoid (mĕt'ăkŏr'ăkoid) *n.* [Gk. *meta*, after; *korax*, crow; *eidos*, form.] Posterior part of coracoid.

metacromion (mĕt'ăkrō'mĭŏn) *n.* [Gk. *meta*, after; *akros*, summit; *omos*, shoulder.] Posterior branch-process of acromion-process of scapular spine.

metacyclic (mĕt'ăsī̆k'lĭk) *a.* [Gk. *meta*, after; *kyklos*, circle.] *Appl.* final infective forms, of certain parasitic protozoa, which pass on to next host.

metadiscoidal (mĕt'ădĭskoid'ăl) *a.* [Gk. *meta*, after; *diskos*, disc; *eidos*, form.] *Appl.* placenta in which villi are at first scattered and later restricted to a disc, as in man and monkeys.

metadromous (mĕtăd'römŭs) *a.* [Gk. *meta*, after; *dromos*, running.] With primary veins of segment arising from upper side of mid-rib.

meta-episternum, — metepisternum.

metaesthetism (mĕtēsthē'tĭzm) *n.* [Gk. *meta*, after; *aisthetos*, perceptible by senses.] Doctrine that "consciousness is a product of evolution of matter and force."

metagastric (mĕt'ăgăs'trĭk) *a.* [Gk. *meta*, after; *gaster*, stomach.] *Pert.* posterior gastric region.

metagastrula (mĕt'ăgăs'troolă) *n.* [Gk. *meta*, after; *gaster*, stomach.] A modified form of gastrula.

metagenesis (mĕt'ăjĕn'ësĭs) *n.* [Gk. *meta*, after; *genesis*, descent.] Alternation of sexual and asexual generations; *cf.* heterogenesis.

metagnathous (mëtăg'năthŭs) *a.* [Gk. *meta*, change of; *gnathos*, jaw.] Having mouth parts for biting in the larval stage and for sucking in the adult, as certain insects; having the points of the beak crossed, as crossbills.

metagyny (mëtăj'ĭnĭ, mĕt'ăgī'nĭ) *n.* [Gk. *meta*, afterwards; *gyne*, female.] Protandry.

metakinesis (mĕt'ăkīnē'sĭs) *n.* [Gk. *meta*, after; *kinein*, to move.] Middle stage of mitosis, during which chromosomes are grouped in equatorial plate; movement of chromosomes between prophase and metaphase; hypothetical quality of organisms which has the potentiality of evolving into consciousness.

metaleptic (mĕt'ălĕp'tĭk) *a.* [Gk. *metalepsis*, participation.] Associated in a process or action; operating together; synergic.

metallic (mĕtăl'ĭk) *a.* [Gk. *metallon*, mine.] Iridescent; *appl.* colours due to interference by fine striae or thin lamellae, as in insects.

metaloph (mĕt'ălŏf) *n.* [Gk. *meta*, after; *lophos*, crest.] The posterior crest of a molar, uniting metacone, metaconule, and hypocone.

metamere (mĕt'ămēr) *n.* [Gk. *meta*, after; *meros*, part.] A body segment.

metameric (mĕt'ămĕr'ĭk) *a.* [Gk. *meta*, after; *meros*, part.] *Pert.* metamerism or segmentation.

metamerised (mĕt'ămërīzd) *a.* [Gk. *meta*, after; *meros*, part.] Segmented.

metamerism (mĕt'ămërĭzm) *n.* [Gk. *meta*, after; *meros*, part.] The condition of a body divided up into segments more or less alike; segmentation; zonal symmetry.

metamitosis (mĕt'ămĭtō'sĭs) *n.* [Gk. *meta*, after; *mitos*, thread.] Mitosis in which cytoplasmic and nuclear elements are both affected; *cf.* mesomitosis.

metamorphosis (mĕt′ămôr′fōsĭs) *n.* [Gk. *meta*, change of; *morphe*, form.] Change of form and structure undergone by an animal from embryo to adult stage, as in insects; transformation of one structure into another, as of stamens into petals; interference with normal symmetry in flowers; internal chemical change.

metamps (mĕt′ămps) *n. plu.* [Gk. *meta*, change of; *morphe*, form.] Different forms of same species, as in certain sponges.

metamyelocyte (mĕtămī′ëlösīt) *n.* [Gk. *meta*, beyond; *myelos*, marrow; *kytos*, hollow.] A myelocyte with horseshoe-shaped nucleus before transformation into a leucocyte.

metanauplius (mĕt′ănôp′lĭŭs) *n.* [Gk. *meta*, after; L. *nauplius*, kind of shell-fish.] Larval stage of Crustacea, succeeding nauplius stage.

metandry (mĕtăn′drĭ) *n.* [Gk. *meta*, after; *aner*, male.] Meroandry with retention of posterior pair of testes only, *opp.* proandry; protogyny, *opp.* protandry.

metanephric (mĕt′ănĕf′rĭk) *a.* [Gk. *meta*, after; *nephros*, kidney.] *Pert.* or in region of hind-kidney.

metanephros (mĕt′ănĕf′rŏs) *n.* [Gk. *meta*, after; *nephros*, kidney.] The organ arising behind mesonephros and replacing it as functional kidney of fully-developed Amniota.

metanotum (mĕt′ănō′tŭm) *n.* [Gk. *meta*, after; *noton*, back.] Notum or tergum of insect metathorax.

metanucleus (mĕt′ănū′klëŭs) *n.* [Gk. *meta*, after; L. *nucleus*, kernel.] Egg-nucleolus after extrusion from germinal vesicle.

metapeptone (mĕt′ăpĕp′tōn) *n.* [Gk. *meta*, after; *peptos*, digested.] A product of action of gastric juice on albumins.

metaphase (mĕt′ăfāz) *n.* [Gk. *meta*, after; *phainein*, to appear.] The stage in mitosis or meiosis in which chromosomes are split up in equatorial plate.

metaphery (mĕtăf′ërĭ) *n.* [Gk. *meta*, change of; *herein*, to bear.] Displacement of organs.

metaphloem (mĕt′ăflō′ëm) *n.* [Gk. *meta*, after; *phloios*, inner bark.] The phloem of secondary xylem.

metaphragma (mĕt′ăfrăg′mă) *n.* [Gk. *meta*, after; *phragma*, fence.] An internal metathoracic septum in insects.

metaphysis (mĕtăf′ĭsĭs) *n.* [Gk. *meta*, besides; *physis*, growth.] Paraphysis, *q.v.*, of fungi; vascular part of diaphysis adjoining epiphyseal cartilage.

metaphyte (mĕt′ăfīt) *n.* [Gk. *meta*, after; *phyton*, plant.] A multicellular plant, *opp.* protophyte.

metaplasia (mĕt′ăplā′sĭă) *n.* [Gk. *meta*, change of; *plasis*, moulding.] Conversion of tissue from one form to another, as in ossification.

metaplasis (mĕtăp′lăsĭs) *n.* [Gk. *meta*, after; *plasis*, moulding.] The mature period in life of an individual.

metaplasm (mĕt′ăplăzm) *n.* [Gk. *meta*, after; *plasma*, mould.] Lifeless or ergastic ingredients of protoplasm, *opp.* to living material or organoids.

metaplastic (mĕt′ăplăs′tĭk) *a.* [Gk. *meta*, after; *plastos*, moulded.] *Pert.* metaplasia; *pert.* metaplasm.

metaplastic or **metaplasmic bodies**,—grains of protoplasm which are stages or products of metabolism and not true protoplasm.

metapleural (mĕt′ăploo′răl) *a.* [Gk. *meta*, after; *pleura*, side.] Posteriorly and laterally situated; *pert.* metapleure; *pert.* metapleuron.

metapleure (mĕt′ăploor) *n.* [Gk. *meta*, after; *pleura*, side.] An abdominal or ventro-lateral fold of integument of certain primitive Chordata.

metapleuron (mĕt′ăploor′ŏn) *n.* [Gk. *meta*, after; *pleura*, side.] The pleuron of insect metathorax.

metapneustic (mĕt′ănū′stĭk, -pnū′-) *a.* [Gk. *meta*, after; *pneuma*, breath.] *Appl.* insect larvae with only the terminal pair of spiracles.

metapodeon (mĕt′ăpŏd′ēŏn), **metapodeum** (mĕt′ăpō′dēŭm) *n.* [Gk. *meta*, after ; *pous*, foot.] That part of insect abdomen behind petiole or podeon.

metapodial (mĕt′ăpō′dĭăl) *a.* [Gk. *meta*, after ; *pous*, foot.] *Pert.* a metapodeon or to a metapodium.

metapodium (mĕt′ăpō′dĭŭm) *n.* [Gk. *meta*, after ; *pous*, foot.] Posterior portion of molluscan foot ; portion of foot between tarsus and digits ; in four-footed animals, metacarpus and metatarsus.

metapodosoma (mĕt′ăpŏdŏsō′mă) *n.* [Gk. *meta*, after ; *pous*, foot ; *soma*, body.] Body region bearing third and fourth pair of legs in Acarina.

metapolar cells,—second circlet of cells of polar cap of rhombogen of Rhombozoa.

metapophysis (mĕt′ăpŏf′ĭsĭs) *n.* [Gk. *meta*, after ; *apo*, from ; *phyein*, to grow.] A prolongation of a vertebral articular process developed in certain vertebrates ; mamillary process.

metapore (mĕt′ăpōr) *n.* [Gk. *meta*, after ; *poros*, channel.] The medial aperture in roof of fourth ventricle of brain ; Magendie's foramen.

metapostscutellum (mĕt′ăpōst′skūtĕl′ŭm) *n.* [Gk. *meta*, after ; L. *post*, after ; *scutellum*, small shield.] Postscutellum of insect metathorax.

metapraescutum (mĕt′ăprēskū′tŭm) *n.* [Gk. *meta*, after ; L. *prae*, before ; *scutum*, shield.] Praescutum of insect metathorax.

metapterygium (mĕt′ătĕrĭj′ĭŭm) *n.* [Gk. *meta*, after ; *pterygion*, little wing.] The posterior basal fin-cartilage, pectoral or pelvic, of recent elasmobranchs.

metapterygoid (mĕt′ătĕr′ĭgoid) *n.* [Gk. *meta*, after ; *pteryx*, wing ; *eidos*, form.] Posterior of three pterygoid elements in certain lower vertebrates.

metaptile (mĕt′ătīl, -ptīl) *n.* [Gk. *meta*, after ; *ptilon*, feather.] A plumose penna or feather ; *cf.* mesoptile, teleoptile.

metarachis (mĕt′ărā′kĭs) *n.* [Gk. *meta*, after ; *rhachis*, spine.] Face of Pennatulacea which coincides with sulcar aspect of terminal zooid —so-called dorsal surface.

metarhodopsin (mĕt′ărōdŏp′sĭn) *n.* [Gk. *meta*, after ; *rhodon*, rose ; *opsis*, sight.] Transient orange product of lumirhodopsin, dissociating into trans vitamin A, aldehyde and scotopsin.

metarteriole (mĕt′ârtē′rĭōl) *n.* [Gk. *meta*, besides ; L.L. *arteriola*, small artery.] Branch of an arteriole between arteriole and arterial capillaries.

metarubricyte (mĕt′ăroob′rĭsīt) *n.* [Gk. *meta*, after ; L. *ruber*, red ; Gk. *kytos*, hollow.] Normoblast.

metascutellum (mĕt′ăskūtĕl′ŭm) *n.* [Gk. *meta*, after ; L. *scutellum*, small shield.] Scutellum of insect metathorax.

metascutum (mĕt′ăskū′tŭm) *n.* [Gk. *meta*, after ; L. *scutum*, shield.] Scutum of insect metathorax.

metaseptum (mĕt′ăsĕp′tŭm) *n.* [Gk. *meta*, after ; L. *septum*, partition.] A secondary or subsequently formed septum ; a protoplasmic partition.

metasicula (mĕt′ăsĭk′ūlă) *n.* [Gk. *meta*, after ; L. *sicula*, small dagger.] Part of the sicula from which the first theca buds laterally, in graptolites.

metasitism (mĕt′ăsĭtĭzm) *n.* [Gk. *meta*, after ; *sitos*, food.] A cannibalistic mode of life.

metasoma (mĕt′ăsō′mă) *n.* [Gk. *meta*, after ; *soma*, body.] The six terminal segments of opisthosoma of Eurypterida ; posterior body-region of Arachnoidea ; postabdomen ; abdomen, as of woodlice.

metasomatic (mĕt′ăsōmăt′ĭk) *a.* [Gk. *meta*, after ; *soma*, body.] *Pert.* or situated in metasoma.

metasperm (mĕt′ăspĕrm) *n.* [Gk. *meta*, after ; *sperma*, seed.] A plant having seeds in a closed ovary ; an angiosperm.

metasporangium (mĕt'ăspŏrăn'jĭŭm) *n.* [Gk. *meta*, after; *sporos*, seed; *anggeion*, vessel.] A sporangium containing resting spores, as in Bacillaceae.

metastasis (mĕtăs'tăsĭs) *n.* [Gk. *metastasis*, removal.] Metabolism; transference of function from one organ to another; transport of bacteria by the circulatory system.

metastatic life history,—that of certain Trematoda in which the young form, after entering intermediate host, metamorphoses into adult, after which intermediate host is swallowed by final host.

metasternum (mĕt'ăstĕr'nŭm) *n.* [Gk. *meta*, after; L. *sternum*, breastbone.] The sternum of insect metathorax; sternum of fourth segment of podosoma in Acarina; posterior sternal part, or xiphisternum, of Anura; xiphoid or ensiform process, posterior part of sternum of higher vertebrates.

metasthenic (mĕt'ăsthĕn'ĭk) *a.* [Gk. *meta*, after; *sthenos*, strength.] With well-developed posterior part of body.

metastigmate (mĕt'ăstĭg'māt) *a.* [Gk. *meta*, after; *stigma*, mark.] Having posterior tracheal openings or stigmata, as in mites.

metastoma (mĕtăs'tŏ'mă) *n.* [Gk. *meta*, after; *stoma*, mouth.] The two-lobed lower lip of Crustacea; 'hypopharynx' of Myriopoda; median plate behind mouth in Palaeostraca; metastome.

metastructure (mĕt'ăstrŭk'tūr) *n.* [Gk. *meta*, after; L. *struere*, to build.] Ultramicroscopic organisation.

metasyndesis (mĕt'ăsĭn'dēsĭs) *n.* [Gk. *meta*, after; *syndesis*, bond.] Telosyndesis, *q.v.*

metatarsal (mĕt'ătâr'săl) *a.* [Gk. *meta*, after; L. *tarsus*, ankle.] In region of metatarsus; *appl.* arteries, veins, etc.; *pert.* metatarsal bones.

metatarsophalangeal (mĕt'ătâr'sŏ-fălăn'jēăl) *a.* [Gk. *meta*, after; L. *tarsus*, ankle; Gk. *phalangx*, troop.] *Appl.* articulations between metatarsus and phalanges of foot.

metatarsus (mĕt'ătâr'sŭs) *n.* [Gk. *meta*, after; L. *tarsus*, ankle.] Part of foot between tarsus and toes; first joint of tarsus in insects; first dactylopodite or basitarsus in spiders.

metathalamus (mĕt'ăthăl'ămŭs) *n.* [Gk. *meta*, after; *thalamos*, chamber.] The geniculate bodies of the thalamencephalon.

metatherian (mĕt'ăthē'rĭăn) *a.* [Gk. *meta*, beyond; *therion*, small animal.] *Appl.* marsupials, with short-term placenta and later development in marsupium.

metathetely (mĕt'ăthĕt'ĕlĭ) *n.* [Gk. *metatheein*, to run behind; *telos*, completion.] Hysterotely.

metathorax (mĕt'ăthō'răks) *n.* [Gk. *meta*, after; *thorax*, chest.] Posterior segment of insect thorax.

metatracheal (mĕt'ătrā'kēăl) *a.* [Gk. *meta*, between; L.L. *trachia*, windpipe.] *Appl.* wood, with xylem parenchyma located independently of the vessels.

metatroch (mĕt'ătrŏk) *n.* [Gk. *meta*, after; *trochos*, wheel.] In a trochophore, a circular band of cilia behind the mouth.

metatrophic (mĕt'ătrŏf'ĭk) *a.* [Gk. *meta*, change of; *trophe*, nourishment.] Living on both nitrogenous and carbonaceous organic matter.

metatympanic,—entotympanic, *q.v.*

metatype (mĕt'ătīp) *n.* [Gk. *meta*, after; *typos*, image.] A topotype of the same species as the holotype or lectotype.

metaxenia (mĕt'ăzē'nĭă) *n.* [Gk. *meta*, after; *xenia*, hospitality.] Physiological effect of pollen upon maternal tissue.

metaxylem (mĕt'ăzī'lĕm) *n.* [Gk. *meta*, after; *xylon*, wood.] Secondary xylem with many thick-walled cells.

metazoaea (mĕt'ăzōē'ă) *n.* [Gk. *meta*, after; *zoe*, life.] A larval stage of Crustacea between zoaea and megalopa stages.

metazonite (mĕt'ăzōnīt) *n.* [Gk. *meta*, after; *zone*, girdle.] The posterior ring of a diplosomite. *Opp.* prozonite.

metazoon (mĕt′ăzō′ŏn) *n.* [Gk. *meta*, after; *zoon*, animal.] A multicellular animal; metazoan; a metazoan excluding Parazoa.
metembryo (mĕtĕm′brĭö) *n.* [Gk. *meta*, towards; *embryon*, embryo.] The gastrula.
metencephalon (mĕt′ĕnkĕf′ălŏn, -sĕf-) *n.* [Gk. *meta*, after; *en*, in; *kephale*, head.] Part of hind-brain, consisting of cerebellum, pons, and intermediate part of fourth ventricle; or hind-brain.
metenteron (mĕtĕn′tĕrŏn) *n.* [Gk. *meta*, after; *enteron*, gut.] Intermesenteric chamber of sea-anemone or other coelenterate.
metepencephalon, — rhombencephalon or hind-brain.
metepimeron (mĕt′ĕpĭmē′rŏn) *n.* [Gk. *meta*, after; *epi*, upon; *meros*, upper thigh.] Epimeron of insect metathorax.
metepisternum (mĕt′ĕpĭstĕr′nŭm) *n.* [Gk. *meta*, after; *epi*, upon; *sternon*, breast-bone.] Episternum of insect metathorax; meta-episternum.
metestrum,—metoestrus, *q.v.*
methaemoglobin (mĕt-hē′möglō′bĭn) *n.* [Gk. *meta*, after; *haima*, blood; L. *globus*, globe.] An oxidation product of haemoglobin; HbO, HbOH.
metochy (mĕt′ŏkĭ) *n.* [Gk. *metoche*, sharing.] Relationship between a neutral guest insect and its host.
metoecious (mĕtē′sĭŭs) *a.* [Gk. *meta*, after; *oikos*, house.] Metoxenous or heteroecious; with two hosts.
metoestrus (mĕtē′strŭs) *n.* [Gk. *meta*, after; *oistros*, gadfly.] The luteal phase, period when activity subsides after oestrus; metoestrum.
metope (mĕt′ōpē) *n.* [Gk. *metopon*, forehead.] The middle frontal portion of a crustacean.
metopic (mĕtŏp′ĭk) *a.* [Gk. *metopon*, forehead.] *Pert.* forehead; *appl.* frontal suture.
metopion (mĕtō′pĭŏn) *n.* [Gk. *metopion*, forehead.] Point on forehead where mid-sagittal plane intersects line connecting frontal eminences.
metosteon (mĕtŏs′tēŏn) *n.* [Gk. *meta*, after; *osteon*, bone.] A posterior sternal ossification in birds.
metovum (mĕtō′vŭm) *n.* [Gk. *meta*, after; L. *ovum*, egg.] An egg-cell surrounded by nutritive material.
metoxenous (mĕtŏk′sēnŭs) *a.* [Gk. *meta*, after; *xenos*, guest.] Parasitic on different hosts at different stages in life-history; heteroecious.
metra (mē′tră) *n.* [Gk. *metra*, womb.] The uterus.
metraterm (mē′trătĕrm) *n.* [Gk. *metra*, womb; *terma*, end.] Terminal portion of uterus in trematodes.
metrocyte (mē′trösīt) *n.* [Gk. *meter*, mother; *kytos*, hollow.] A cell that has originated other cells by division; mother-cell.
metrogonidium (mē′trögŏnĭd′ĭŭm) *n.* [Gk. *meter*, mother; *dim.* of *gone*, seed.] A gonidium which produces new gonidia by division, in lichens.
metula (mē′tūlă) *n.* [*Dim.* of L. *meta*, end-post.] A spore-bearing branch having flask-shaped outgrowths, as in certain fungi.
M-factor,—a certain antigen in erythrocytes of higher animals.
micella (mĭsĕl′ă) *n.* [L. *dim.* of *mica*, morsel.] Hypothetical unit, *q.v.*; an orderly aggregate of chain-like molecules.
micraesthetes (mīkrēsthē′tēz) *n.plu.* [Gk. *mikros*, small; *aisthetes*, perceiver.] The smaller sensory organs of Placophora.
micrander (mīkrăn′dĕr) *n.* [Gk. *mikros*, small; *aner*, male.] A dwarf male, as of certain green algae.
micraner (mī′krănĕr) *n.* [Gk. *mikros*, small; *aner*, male.] A dwarf male ant.
micrergate (mīkrĕr′gāt) *n.* [Gk. *mikros*, small; *ergates*, worker.] A dwarf worker ant.
micro-aerophiles, — organisms requiring less oxygen than is present in the air.
microbe (mī′krōb) *n.* [Gk. *mikros*, small; *bios*, life.] A bacterium; a micro-organism.

microbiology (mī'kröbīŏl'öjĭ) *n.* [Gk. *mikros*, small ; *bios*, life ; *logos*, discourse.] Biology of microscopic organisms.

microbion,—microbe.

microbiophagy (mī'kröbīŏf'ăjĭ) *n.* [Gk. *mikros*, small ; *bios*, life ; *phagein*, to consume.] Destruction or lysis of micro-organisms by a phage.

microbiota (mī'kröbīō'tă) *n.* [Gk. *mikros*, small ; *bionai*, to live.] Flora and fauna composed of microscopical organisms.

microblast (mī'kröblăst) *n.* [Gk. *mikros*, small ; *blastos*, bud.] An erythroblast smaller than normal.

microcaltrops (mī'krökăl'trŏps) *n.* [Gk. *mikros*, small ; A.S. *coltraeppe*, kind of thistle.] A primitive tetraxon, or euaster with four persistent rays.

microcentrosome,—centriole.

microcentrum (mī'krösĕn'trŭm) *n.* [Gk. *mikros*, small ; *kentron*, centre.] The dynamic centre of a cell, composed of centrosomes ; kinetonucleus.

microcephalic (mī'krökĕfăl'ĭk, -sĕf-) *a.* [Gk. *mikros*, small ; *kephale*, head.] With abnormally small head ; having a cranial capacity of under 1350 c.c. ; *cf.* megacephalic, mesocephalic.

microchaeta (mī'krökē'tă) *n.* [Gk. *mikros*, small ; *chaeta*, hair.] A small bristle, as on body of certain insects.

microchromosome (mī'krökrō'mösōm) *n.* [Gk. *mikros*, small ; *chroma*, colour ; *soma*, body.] A chromosome considerably smaller than the other chromosomes of the same type of nucleus ; M-chromosome.

microconidium (mī'krökŏnĭd'ĭŭm) *n.* [Gk. *mikros*, small ; *konis*, dust ; *idion*, *dim.*] A comparatively small conidium.

microconjugant (mī'krökŏn'joogănt) *n.* [Gk. *mikros*, small ; L. *conjugare*, to unite.] A motile ciliated free-swimming conjugant or gamete which attaches itself to a macroconjugant and fertilises it.

microcyclic (mī'krösīk'lĭk) *a.* [Gk. *mikros*, small ; *kyklos*, circle.] Having a simple or short cycle ; with haplophase or gametophyte stage only. *Opp.* macrocyclic.

microcyst (mī'krösĭst) *n.* [Gk. *mikros*, small ; *kystis*, bladder.] A resting-spore stage of slime fungi.

microcytase (mī'krösī'tās) *n.* [Gk. *mikros*, small ; *kytos*, hollow.] The enzyme of microphages or smaller leucocytes.

microcytes (mī'krösīts) *n. plu.* [Gk. *mikros*, small ; *kytos*, hollow.] Blood-corpuscles about half the size of erythrocytes, numerous in diseased conditions.

microdont (mī'krödŏnt) *a.* [Gk. *mikros*, small ; *odous*, tooth.] With comparatively small teeth.

micro-elements, — trace-elements, *q.v.*

microevolution (mī'kröēvölū'shŭn) *n.* [Gk. *mikros*, small ; L. *evolvere*, to unroll.] Evolutionary processes that can be noticed within a relatively brief period, as during a human life-time ; evolution due to gene mutation and recombination. *Opp.* macro-evolution.

microfilaria (mī'kröfĭlā'rĭă) *n.* [Gk. *mikros*, small ; L. *filum*, thread.] The embryo of a Filaria.

microgamete (mī'krögămēt') *n.* [Gk. *mikros*, small ; *gametes*, spouse.] The smaller of two conjugant gametes, regarded as male.

microgametoblast (mī'krögămē'töblăst) *n.* [Gk. *mikros*, small ; *gametes*, spouse ; *blastos*, bud.] Intermediate stage between microgametocyte and microgamete in certain Sporozoa.

microgametocyte (mī'krögămē'tösīt) *n.* [Gk. *mikros*, small ; *gametes*, spouse ; *kytos*, hollow.] Cell developed from merozoite in certain protozoa, giving rise to microgametes.

microgametogenesis (mī'krögămē'töjĕn'ësĭs) *n.* [Gk. *mikros*, small ;

gametes, spouse ; *genesis*, descent.] Development of microgametes or spermatozoa.

microgametophyte (mī'krögămē'töfīt) *n.* [Gk. *mikros*, small ; *gametes*, spouse ; *phyton*, plant.] The male gametophyte developed from a microspore, *opp.* megagametophyte.

microgamy (mīkrŏg'ămĭ) *n.* [Gk. *mikros*, small ; *gamos*, marriage.] Syngamy between smallest individuals produced by fission or gemmation, as in Foraminifera ; merogamy.

microglia (mīkröglĭ'ă, mī'krōglē'ă) *n. plu.* [Gk. *mikros*, small ; *glia*, glue.] Mesodermal phagocytic cells in grey and white nervous matter ; mesoglia.

microgonidium (mī'krögŏnĭd'ĭŭm) *n.* [Gk. *mikros*, small ; *gonos*, offspring ; *idion*, *dim.*] A comparatively small gonidium ; a male gamont or gametocyte.

microgyne (mī'kröjĭnē) *n.* [Gk. *mikros*, small ; *gyne*, female.] Dwarf female ant.

microhabitat (mī'kröhăb'ĭtăt) *n.* [Gk. *mikros*, small ; L. *habitare*, to inhabit.] The immediate special environment of an organism, a small place in the general habitat ; *cf.* niche.

microhenad (mī'kröhĕn'ăd) *n.* [Gk. *mikros*, small ; *henas*, unit.] A filter-passer.

microlecithal (mī'krölĕs'ĭthăl) *a.* [Gk. *mikros*, small ; *lekithos*, yolk.] Containing little yolk.

microleucoblast (mī'krölū'köblăst, -loo-) *n.* [Gk. *mikros*, small ; *leukos*, white ; *blastos*, bud.] Myeloblast.

microleucocyte (mī'krölū'kösīt, -loo-) *n.* [Gk. *mikros*, small ; *leukos*, white ; *kytos*, hollow.] A small amoebocyte.

micromere (mī'krömēr) *n.* [Gk. *mikros*, small ; *meros*, part.] A cell of upper or animal hemisphere in meroblastic and other eggs.

micromerozoite (mī'krömĕr'özōīt) *n.* [Gk. *mikros*, small ; *meros*, part ; *zoon*, animal.] Cell derived from microschizont and developing into gametocyte in Haemosporidia.

micromesentery (mī'krömĕs'ĕntĕrĭ, -mĕz-) *n.* [Gk. *mikros*, small ; *mesos*, middle ; *enteron*, gut.] A secondary incomplete mesentery in Zoantharia.

micromutation (mī'krömūtā'shŭn) *n.* [Gk. *mikros*, small ; L. *mutare*, to change.] Mutation at only one gene locus ; genovariation, point mutation, transgenation.

micromyelocyte (mī'krömī'ĕlösīt) *n.* [Gk. *mikros*, small ; *myelos*, marrow ; *kytos*, hollow.] A small heterophil myelocyte.

micron (mī'krŏn) *n.* [Gk. *mikros*, small.] Micromillimetre, one-thousandth part of a millimetre ; symbol : μ.

micronemic (mī'krönē'mĭk) *a.* [Gk. *mikros*, small ; *nema*, thread.] *Pert.* or having small hyphae ; micronemeous.

micronephridia (mī'krönĕfrĭd'ĭă) *n. plu.* [Gk. *mikros*, small ; *nephros*, kidney ; *idion*, *dim.*] Small nephridia ; meronephridia.

micront (mī'krŏnt) *n.* [Gk. *mikros*, small ; *on*, being.] A small cell formed by schizogony, itself giving rise to microgametes.

micronucleocyte (mī'krönū'klēösīt) *n.* [Gk. *mikros*, small ; L. *nucleus*, kernel ; Gk. *kytos*, hollow.] An amoebocyte with a relatively small nucleus.

micronucleus (mī'krönū'klēŭs) *n.* [Gk. *mikros*, small ; L. *nucleus*, kernel.] The smaller, reproductive nucleus of many protozoa, in close proximity to meganucleus ; gononucleus.

micro-nutrients,—substances essential to health of organisms, but required in minute quantity ; *e.g.* trace elements, *q.v.*

micro-organism (mī'krö-ôr'gănĭzm) *n.* [Gk. *mikros*, small ; *organon*, instrument.] A microscopic organism ; microbe ; protist.

microparasite (mī'kröpăr'ăsīt) *n.* [Gk. *mikros*, small ; *para*, beside ; *sitos*, food.] A parasite of microscopic size.

microphages (mī'kröfā'jëz) *n. plu.* [Gk. *mikros*, small; *phagein*, to eat.] Chiefly the polymorphonuclear heterophil leucocytes.

microphagic (mī'kröfăj'ĭk) *a.* [Gk. *mikros*, small; *phagein*, to eat.] Feeding on minute organisms or particles, *appl.* protozoa; microphagous, feeding on small prey, *appl.* agnathous fishes. *Opp.* macrophagous.

microphagocyte (mī'kröfăg'ösīt) *n.* [Gk. *mikros*, small; *phagein*, to eat; *kytos*, hollow.] A microphage or small phagocyte of blood.

microphanerophyte (mī'kröfăn'ëröfīt) *n.* [Gk. *mikros*, small; *phaneros*, manifest; *phyton*, plant.] Tree or shrub from 2 to 8 metres in height.

microphil (mī'kröfĭl) *a.* [Gk. *mikros*, small; *philein*, to love.] Tolerating only a narrow range of temperature, *appl.* certain bacteria; microphilic. *n.* Microphile.

microphyllous (mī'kröfĭl'ŭs) *a.* [Gk. *mikros*, small; *phyllon*, leaf.] With small leaves.

microphyte (mī'kröfīt) *n.* [Gk. *mikros*, small; *phyton*, plant.] Any microscopic plant.

microphytology (mī'kröfītŏl'öjĭ) *n.* [Gk. *mikros*, small; *phyton*, plant; *logos*, discourse.] Science of microphytes; bacteriology.

microplankton (mī'kröplăng'ktŏn) *n.* [Gk. *mikros*, small; *plangktos*, wandering.] Small organisms drifting with the surrounding water, somewhat larger than those of nanoplankton, *q.v.*

micropodous (mīkrŏp'ödŭs) *a.* [Gk. *mikros*, small; *pous*, foot.] With rudimentary or small foot or feet.

micropore (mī'kröpōr) *n.* [Gk. *mikros*, small; *poros*, channel.] A small pore in a Chiton shell, containing a sense-organ.

micropterism (mīkrŏp'tërĭzm) *n.* [Gk. *mikros*, small; *pteron*, wing.] Condition of having unusually small wings, as in some insects.

micropterous (mīkrŏp'tërŭs) *a.* [Gk. *mikros*, small; *pteron*, wing.] Having small hind wings invisible till tegmina are expanded, as in some insects; with small or rudimentary fins.

micropyle (mī'kröpīl) *n.* [Gk. *mikros*, small; *pyle*, gate.] Aperture for admission of pollen-tube at ovule apex; aperture between hilum and point of radicle; small opening in cyst wall of macrogamete, for entry of microgamete; pore of oocyst; aperture in egg-membrane for admission of spermatozoon; pore in spongin-coat of sponges for escape of gemmules.

micropyle apparatus,—raised processes or porches, sometimes of elaborate structure, developed round micropyle of certain insect eggs.

micropyrenic (mī'kröpīrē'nĭk) *a.* [Gk. *mikros*, small; *pyren*, fruit-stone.] With nuclei markedly smaller than average for the species or other group. *n.* A micropyrenic individual.

microrhabdus (mī'krörăb'dŭs) *n.* [Gk. *mikros*, small; *rhabdos*, rod.] Minute monaxon or rod-like spicule.

microschizogony (mī'kröskĭzŏg'önĭ) *n.* [Gk. *mikros*, small; *schizein*, to cleave; *gonos*, birth.] Schizogony resulting in small merozoites.

microschizont (mī'kröskĭzŏnt') *n.* [Gk. *mikros*, small; *schizein*, to cut; *onta*, beings.] A male schizont of certain protozoa.

microsclere (mī'kröskIēr) *n.* [Gk. *mikros*, small; *skleros*, hard.] One of small spicules found lying scattered in tissues of sponges. *Opp.* megasclere.

microseptum (mī'krösĕp'tŭm) *n.* [Gk. *mikros*, small; L. *septum*, partition.] An incomplete mesentery of Zoantharia.

microsere (mī'kröSēr) *n.* [Gk. *mikros*, small; L. *serere*, to put in a row.] A successional series of plant communities in a microhabitat.

microsmatic (mī'krŏsmăt'ĭk) *a.* [Gk. *mikros*, small; *osme*, smell.] With feebly-developed sense of smell.

microsome (mī'krösōm) *n.* [Gk. *mikros*, small; *soma*, body.] Granule of protoplasm as opposed to ground-substance; a minute particle or vesicle in cytoplasm, containing a number of enzymes and partaking in the protein synthesis of the cell.

microsorus (mī'krösōrŭs) *n.* [Gk. *mikros*, small; *soros*, heap.] A sorus containing microsporangia, *opp.* megasorus.

microspecies (mī'kröspē'shēz) *n.* [Gk. *mikros*, small; L. *species*, particular kind.] A small species, or subspecies, with little variability; Jordanon.

microsphere (mī'krösfēr) *n.* [Gk. *mikros*, small; *sphaira*, globe.] The initial chamber of Foraminifera when very small; centrosphere.

microspheric (mī'krösfĕr'ĭk) *a.* [Gk. *mikros*, small; *sphaira*, globe.] *Appl.* foraminifera when initial chamber of shell is small.

microsplanchnic (mī'kröspläng k'nĭk) *a.* [Gk. *mikros*, small; *splangchnon*, entrail.] Small-bodied and long-legged.

microsporangium (mī'kröspörăn'jĭŭm) *n.* [Gk. *mikros*, small; *sporos*, seed; *anggeion*, vessel.] A sporangium bearing a number of microspores; pollen sac or anther lobe of phanerogams.

microspore (mīkröspōr) *n.* [Gk. *mikros*, small; *sporos*, seed.] The spore developed in a microsporangium of heterosporous plants; the cell from which a pollen grain develops; a pollen grain; androspore; the smaller anisospore of Sarcodina.

microsporocyte (mī'kröspō'rösīt) *n.* [Gk. *mikros*, small; *sporos*, seed; *kytos*, hollow.] The pollen mother cell which produces microspores resulting from two meioses.

microsporophore (mī'kröspō'röfōr) *n.* [Gk. *mikros*, small; *sporos*, seed; *pherein*, to bear.] A microsporangium.

microsporophyll (mī'kröspō'röfĭl) *n.* [Gk. *mikros*, small; *sporos*, seed; *phyllon*, leaf.] A microsporangium-bearing leaf; stamen.

microsporozoite (mī'kröspō'rözō'īt) *n.* [Gk. *mikros*, small; *sporos*, seed; *zoon*, animal.] A smaller endogenous sporozoite of Sporozoa.

microstome (mī'kröstōm) *n.* [Gk. *mikros*, small; *stoma*, mouth.] A small opening or orifice.

microstrobilus (mī'kröströb'ĭlŭs) *n.* [Gk. *mikros*, small; *strobilos*, cone.] A small cone, as in cycads.

microstylospore (mī'kröstī'löspōr) *n.* [Gk. *mikros*, small; *stylos*, pillar; *sporos*, seed.] A comparatively small stylospore.

microstylous (mī'kröstīl'ŭs) *a.* [Gk. *mikros*, small; *stylos*, pillar.] Having short styles; *appl.* heterostylous flowers.

microtaxonomy (mī'krötăksŏn'ömĭ) *n.* [Gk. *mikros*, small; *taxis*, arrangement; *nomos*, law.] Classification and its principles as applied to subspecies, varieties, or races.

microteliospore (mī'krötĕl'ĭöspōr) *n.* [Gk. *mikros*, small; *telos*, end; *sporos*, seed.] A spore produced in a microtelium.

microtelium (mī'krötĕl'ĭŭm) *n.* [Gk. *mikros*, small; *telos*, end.] Sorus of microcyclic rust fungi.

microtherm (mī'kröthĕrm) *n.* [Gk. *mikros*, small; *therme*, heat.] A plant of the cold temperate zone.

microtrichia (mī'krötrĭk'ĭă) *n. plu.* [Gk. *mikros*, small; *thrix*, hair.] Small hairs without basal articulation on insect wings.

microtype (mī'krötīp) *n.* [Gk. *mikros*, small; L. *typus*, type.] Normal mesentery arrangement of Anthozoa; *cf.* macrotype.

microzoid (mī'krözō'ĭd) *n.* [Gk. *mikros*, small; *zoon*, animal; *idion*, *dim.*] Male gamete, as in algae.

microzooid (mī'krözō'oid) *n.* [Gk. *mikros*, small; *zoon*, animal; *eidos*, form.] A free-swimming motile ciliated bud of Vorticella and other protozoa.

microzoon (mī'krözō'ŏn) *n.* [Gk. *mikros*, small; *zoon*, animal.] A microscopic animal.

microzoospore (mī′krözō′öspōr) *n.* [Gk. *mikros*, small; *zoon*, animal; *sporos*, seed.] Small planogamete; small anisospore of Radiolaria.

microzyma (mī′krözī′mă) *n.* [Gk. *mikros*, small; *zyme*, leaven.] A hypothetical ultimate unit, *q.v.*

microzyme (mī′krözīm) *n.* [Gk. *mikros*, small; *zyme*, leaven.] A micro-organism of fermenting or decomposing liquids.

micton (mĭk′tŏn) *n.* [Gk. *miktos*, mixed; *on*, being.] A species resulting from interspecific hybridisation and of which the individuals are interfertile.

micturition (mĭk′tūrĭsh′ŭn) *n.* [L. *mingere*, to void water.] Act of voiding contents of urinary bladder; urination.

mid-body,—a cell plate or group of granules in equatorial region of spindle in anaphase of mitosis.

mid-brain,—middle zone of primitive or embryonic brain; mesencephalon of adults.

middle lamella,—the layer derived from the cell plate, and covered on both sides by cellulose in formation of the wall of a plant cell.

mid-rib—the large central vein of a leaf, continuation of the petiole.

midriff (mĭd′rĭf) *n.* [A.S. *mid*, middle; *hrif*, belly.] The diaphragm or muscular partition between thoracic and abdominal cavities.

Miescher's tubes [*J. F. Miescher*, Swiss pathologist]. Rainey's tubes, *q.v.*

migration (mīgrā′shŭn) *n.* [L. *migrare*, to transfer.] Change of habitat, according to season, climate, food-supply, etc., of birds, reindeer, bats, certain fishes, insects, etc.; movements of plants into a new area.

migratory cell,—an amoeboid cell or leucocyte of blood; wandering cell.

miliary (mĭl′ĭărĭ) *a.* [L. *milium*, millet.] Of granular appearance; consisting of small and numerous grain-like parts.

milk-teeth,—first dentition of mammals, shed after or before birth; deciduous teeth.

milk-tubes,—laticiferous vessels.

milt (mĭlt) *n.* [A.S. *milte*, spleen.] The spleen; testis of fishes.

mimetic (mĭmĕt′ĭk) *a.* [Gk. *mimetikos*, imitative.] *Pert.* or exhibiting mimicry.

mimic (mĭm′ĭk) *v.* [Gk. *mimikos*, imitating.] To assume, usually for protection, the habits, colour, or structure of another organism.

mimicry (mĭm′ĭkrĭ) *n.* [Gk. *mimikos*, imitating.] Assumption of resemblance in colour or structure as a means of self-protection; camouflage.

minim (mĭn′ĭm) *n.* [L. *minimus*, least.] An ant of the smallest worker caste.

minimum, law of the,—that factor for which an organism or species has the narrowest range of tolerance or adaptability limits its existence; extension of Liebig's law, *q.v.*

minimus (mĭn′ĭmŭs) *n.* [L. *minimus*, least.] Fifth digit of hand or foot.

minor elements,—trace-elements, *q.v.*

Miocene (mī′ösēn) *n.* [Gk. *meion*, less; *kainos*, recent.] A Tertiary geological epoch, between Oligocene and Pliocene.

miostemonous,—meiostemonous.

miotic,—meiotic, *q.v.*; myotic, *q.v.*

miracidium (mīr′ăsĭd′ĭŭm) *n.* [Gk. *dim.* of *meirakion*, stripling.] The ciliated embryo or youngest stage in life-history of a trematode.

miscegenation (mĭs′sējĕnā′shŭn) *n.* [L. *miscere*, to mix; *genus*, race.] Interbreeding between races or varieties.

misogamy (mīsŏg′ămĭ) *n.* [Gk. *misein*, to hate; *gamos*, marriage.] Antagonism to mating; reproductive isolation.

Mississippian, — Lower Carboniferous in North America.

miter,—mitra.

mitochondria (mī'tŏkŏn'drĭă) *n. plu.* [Gk. *mitos*, thread; *chondros*, grain.] Granular, rod-shaped, or filamentous organellae in cytoplasm, varying in different tissues and functioning in cell respiration and nutrition; chondriosomes, and numerous other synonyms.

mitochondria B,—lysosomes, *q.v.*

mitochondrial sheath,—an envelope containing mitochondrial granules sheathing spiral thread of spermatozoan body or connecting-piece.

mitochondrion,—*sing.* of mitochondria.

mitogenetic (mī'tŏjĕnĕt'ĭk) *a.* [Gk. *mitos*, thread; *genesis*, descent.] Inducing cell division; *appl.* influence inducing mitosis in apical meristem and emanating from the same or another apical meristem; *appl.* radiation, Gurwitsch or M-rays, from living matter and supposed to induce mitosis.

mitome (mī'tōm) *n.* [Gk. *mitos*, thread.] Reticulum of cell-protoplasm, *opp.* ground-substance.

mitoschisis (mĭtŏs'kĭsĭs) *n.* [Gk. *mitos*, thread; *schizein*, to cleave.] Indirect nuclear division; mitosis.

mitosis (mĭtō'sĭs) *n.* [Gk. *mitos*, thread.] Indirect or karyokinetic nuclear division, with chromosome-formation, spindle-formation, with or without centrosome activity; *opp.* amitosis; *cf.* meiosis.

mitosome (mī'tŏsōm) *n.* [Gk. *mitos*, thread; *soma*, body.] A body arising from spindle-fibres of secondary spermatocytes, eventually said to form connecting piece and tail envelope of spermatozoon; the spindle-remnant; *cf.* paranucleus.

mitosporangium (mī'tŏspŏrăn'jĭŭm) *n.* [Gk. *mitos*, thread; *sporos*, seed; *anggeion*, vessel.] A thin-walled diploid sporangium, producing zoospores by mitoses; *cf.* meiosporangium.

mitospore (mī'tŏspōr) *n.* [Gk. *mitos*, thread; *sporos*, seed.] A uninucleate diploid zoospore produced in a mitosporangium; *cf.* meiospore.

mitotic (mĭtŏt'ĭk) *a.* [Gk. *mitos*, thread.] *Pert.* or produced by mitosis; *appl.* division, figure.

mitotic index,—the number of cells simultaneously in the process of division, out of a total of one thousand cells.

mitotin (mī'tŏtĭn) *n.* [Gk. *mitos*, thread.] Substance supposed to act with an enzyme mitotase in generating mitogenetic radiation.

mitra (mī'tră) *n.* [L. *mitra*, head-band.] A helmet-shaped part of calyx or corolla: the mitriform pileus of certain fungi.

mitral cells,—pyramidal cells with thick basal dendrites, found in molecular layer of olfactory bulb.

mitral valve,—bicuspid valve of the left auriculo-ventricular orifice of the heart.

mitriform (mĭt'rĭfôrm) *a.* [L. *mitra*, head-band; *forma*, shape.] Mitre-shaped.

mixipterygium (mĭk'sĭptĕrĭj'ĭŭm) *n.* [Gk. *mixis*, mixing; *pterygion*, little wing or fin.] Clasper of male elasmobranchs, medial lobe of pelvic fin.

mixis (mĭk'sĭs) *n.* [Gk. *mixis*, mingling.] The union of sexual cells; karyogamy and karyomixis; fertilisation.

mixochimaera (mĭk'sŏkĭmē'ră) *n.* [Gk. *mixis*, mingling; *chimaira*, monster.] A heterokaryotic hypha.

mixochromosome (mĭk'sŏkrō'mŏsōm) *n.* [Gk. *mixis*, mixing; *chroma*, colour; *soma*, body.] The new chromosome formed by fusion of a pair, in syndesis or synapsis; zygosome.

mixoploidy (mĭk'sŏploĭdĭ) *n.* [Gk. *mixis*, mixing; *haploos*, onefold; *eidos*, form.] Condition of having cells or tissues with different chromosome numbers in the same individual, as in a chimaera or mosaic.

mixote (mĭk'sōt) *n.* [Gk. *mixis*, mingling.] The product of fusion of reproductive cells whether of gametes or of gametoids; zygote, *q.v.*; zygotoid, *q.v.*

mixotrophic (mĭk'sötrŏf'ĭk) *a.* [Gk. *mixis*, mixing ; *trephein*, to nourish.] Combining holophytic with saprophytic nutrition ; obtaining part of nourishment from an outside source ; partly parasitic.

mnemic (nē'mĭk) *a.* [Gk. *mneme*, memory.] *Appl.* theory which attributes hereditary phenomena to latent memory of past generations.

mnemotaxis (nē'mötăk'sĭs) *n.* [Gk. *mneme*, memory ; *taxis*, arrangement.] Locomotion directed by memory stimulus, as returning to a feeding place and homing.

moderator (mŏd'ĕrātör) *n.* [L. *moderator*, regulator.] Band of muscle checking excessive distention of right ventricle, as in heart of some mammals.

modification (mŏd'ĭfĭkā'shŭn) *n.* [L. *modus*, measure ; *facere*, to make.] A phenotypic change due to environment or function.

modifier (mŏd'ĭfīĕr) *n.* [L. *modus*, measure ; *facere*, to make.] A factor which modifies the effect of another factor ; a gene which modifies function of a gene at a different locus.

modiolus (mödī'ölŭs) *n.* [L. *modiolus*, small measure.] The conical central axis of cochlea of ear ; the convergence of muscle fibres close to the angle of the mouth.

modulation (mŏd'ūlā'shŭn) *n.* [L. *modulatus*, measured.] Dedifferentiation and redifferentiation of cells during definitive tissue development; alteration in cells, produced by environmental stimuli, without impairment of their essential character.

modulator (mŏd'ūlātör) *n.* [L. *modulatus*, measured.] A band of the spectrum, localised in the red-yellow, green, and blue regions, which evokes colour sensation ; a physiological unit of colour reception ; *cf.* dominator.

molar (mō'lăr) *a.* [L. *molere*, to grind.] Adapted for grinding, as *appl.* teeth ; *appl.* buccal glands.

molecular hypothesis,—the supposition that muscle and nerve are composed of molecules or particles, like the molecules of a magnet, with positive and negative surfaces.

molecular layer,—external layer of cortex of cerebrum and cerebellum ; a layer of olfactory bulb ; plexiform layer.

Moll's glands,—modified sudoriferous glands between follicles of eyelashes, ciliary glands.

molluscoid (mŏlŭs'koid) *a.* [L. *molluscus*, soft ; Gk. *eidos*, like.] Resembling a mollusc ; characteristic of a mollusc ; *pert.* Molluscoidea.

molt,—*see* moult, ecdysis.

monacanthid (mŏn'ăkăn'thĭd) *a.* [Gk. *monos*, alone ; *akantha*, thorn.] With one row of ambulacral spines, as certain starfishes.

monactinal (mŏnăk'tĭnăl) *a.* [Gk. *monos*, single ; *aktis*, ray.] *Appl.* a monactine or single-rayed spicule.

monactinellid (mŏnăk'tĭnĕl'ĭd) *a.* [Gk. *monos*, single ; *aktis*, ray.] Containing uniaxial spicules only, as certain sponges.

monad (mŏn'ăd) *n.* [Gk. *monas*, unit.] A primitive organism or organic unit ; flagellula form of a protozoan ; single cell, instead of tetrad, produced by a spore mother-cell owing to meiotic anomaly.

monadelphous (mŏnădĕl'fŭs) *a.* [Gk. *monos*, single ; *adelphos*, brother.] Having stamens united into one bundle by union of filaments.

monadiform (mŏnăd'ĭfôrm) *a.* [Gk. *monas*, unit ; L. *forma*, shape.] Like a flagellate protozoan.

monamniotic (mŏn'ămnĭŏt'ĭk) *a.* [Gk. *monos*, single ; *amnion*, foetal membrane.] Having one amnion ; *appl.* uniovular twins.

monandrous (mŏnăn'drŭs) *a.* [Gk. *monos*, alone ; *aner*, male.] Having only one stamen ; having only one male mate.

monarch (mŏn'ârk] *a.* [Gk. *monos*, alone ; *arche*, beginning.] With only one protoxylem bundle.

monaster (mŏnăs'tĕr) *n.* [Gk. *monos*, alone ; *aster*, star.] The single aster of monocentric mitosis.

monaxial (mŏnăk'sĭăl) *a*. [Gk. *monos*, alone; *axon*, axis.] Having one line of axis; uniaxial; having inflorescence developed on primary axis.

monaxon (mŏnăk'sŏn) *n*. [Gk. *monos*, alone; *axon*, axis.] A type of spicule built upon a single axis; a monaxonic nerve cell.

monaxonic (mŏn'ăksŏn'ĭk) *a*. [Gk. *monos*, alone; *axon*, axis.] Elongate; *appl*. types of protozoa with one long body-axis; with one axon, *appl*. nerve cell.

monecious,—monoecious, *q.v*.

monembryonic (mŏnĕm'brĭŏn'ĭk) *a*. [Gk. *monos*, alone; *embryon*, foetus.] Producing one embryo at a time.

monergic (mŏnĕr'jĭk) *a*. [Gk. *monos*, alone; *energos*, active.] Having one energid; consisting of one nucleated cell.

monestrous,—monoestrous, *q.v*.

monilicorn (mŏnĭl'ĭkôrn) *a*. [L. *monile*, necklace; *cornu*, horn.] Having antennae with appearance of a chain of beads.

moniliform (mŏnĭl'ĭfôrm) *a*. [L. *monile*, necklace; *forma*, shape.] Arranged like a chain of beads; monilioid, *appl*. spores; toruloid, *appl*. hyphae; constricted at regular intervals, *appl*. nucleus of certain infusoria; with contractions and expansions alternately, as branches of certain roots.

moniliospore (mŏnĭl'ĭōspōr) *n*. [L. *monile*, necklace; Gk. *sporos*, seed.]. Any spore of a moniliform series.

monimostylic (mŏn'ĭmŏstĭ'lĭk) *a*. [Gk. *monimos*, fixed; *stylos*, pillar.] Exhibiting monimostyly, or having quadrate united to squamosal, and sometimes to other bones, as in certain reptiles; *cf*. streptostylic.

monoblast (mŏn'ōblăst) *n*. [Gk. *monos*, alone; *blastos*, bud.] A cell, as in spleen, that develops into a monocyte.

monocardian (mŏn'ōkâr'dĭăn) *a*. [Gk. *monos*, alone; *kardia*, heart.] Having one auricle and ventricle.

monocarp (mŏn'ōkârp) *n*. [Gk. *monos*, alone; *karpos*, fruit.] A monocarpic plant.

monocarpellary (mŏn'ōkâr'pĕlărĭ) *a*. [Gk. *monos*, single; *karpos*, fruit.] Containing a single carpel.

monocarpic (mŏn'ōkâr'pĭk) *a*. [Gk. *monos*, alone; *karpos*, fruit.] Dying after bearing fruit once.

monocarpous (mŏn'ōkâr'pŭs) *a*. [Gk. *monos*, alone; *karpos*, fruit.] Having one ovary developed from the gynoecium.

monocaryon,—monokaryon.

monocellular,—unicellular.

monocentric (mŏnōsĕn'trĭk) *a*. [Gk. *monos*, single; *kentron*, centre.] Having, derived from, or *pert*. a single centre; with a single centromere.

monocephalous (mŏn'ōkĕf'ălŭs, -sĕf-) *a*. [Gk. *monos*, alone; *kephale*, head.] With one capitulum only.

monocercous (mŏn'ōsĕr'kŭs) *a*. [Gk. *monos*, single; *kerkos*, tail.] With one flagellum, as certain protozoa; uniflagellate.

monocerous (mŏnŏs'ĕrŭs) *a*. [Gk. *monos*, single; *keras*, horn.] Having one horn only.

monochasium (mŏn'ōkā'zĭŭm) *n*. [Gk. *monos*, alone; *chasis*, division.] A cymose inflorescence with main axes producing one branch each.

monochlamydeous (mŏn'ōklămĭd'-ēŭs) *a*. [Gk. *monos*, alone; *chlamys*, cloak.] Apetalous; having calyx but no corolla.

monochorionic (mŏn'ōkōrĭŏn'ĭk) *a*. [Gk. *monos*, single; *chorion*, skin.] Having a single chorion; *appl*. uniovular twins.

monochromatic (mŏn'ōkrōmăt'ĭk) *a*. [Gk. *monos*, single; *chroma*, colour.] Having but one colour; unicoloured; colour-blind, seeing brightness but no hue.

monochronic (mŏn'ōkrŏnĭk) *a*. [Gk. *monos*, alone; *chronos*, time.] Occurring or originating only once.

monociliated (mŏn'ōsĭl'ĭātĕd) *a*. [Gk. *monos*, single; L. *cilium*, eyelid.] Having one flagellum; uniflagellate.

monoclinous (mŏn'ŏklī'nŭs) *a.* [Gk. *monos*, alone; *kline*, couch.] Hermaphrodite, having stamens and pistil in each flower; having gametangium and oogonium originating from the same hypha.

monocondylar (mŏn'ŏkŏn'dĭlăr) *a.* [Gk. *monos*, single; *kondylos*, knuckle.] Having a single occipital condyle, as skull of reptiles and birds; monocondylic, monocondylous.

monocont,—monokont.

monocotyledonous (mŏnŏkŏt'ĭlē'dŏnŭs) *a.* [Gk. *monos*, alone; *kotyledon*, cup-shaped hollow.] Having one cotyledon, or embryo-lobe.

monocratic (mŏn'ŏkrăt'ĭk) *a.* [Gk. *monos*, single; *kratos*, power.] With the four spores of a tetrad being of the same sex. *Opp.* dicratic.

monocrepid (mŏn'ŏkrēp'ĭd) *a.* [Gk. *monos*, alone; *krepis*, foundation.] *Appl.* a desma formed by secondary silica deposits on a monaxial spicule.

monocule (mŏnŏk'ūl) *n.* [Gk. *monos*, single; L. *oculus*, eye.] A one-eyed animal, as certain insects and crustaceans.

monocyclic (mŏn'ŏsĭk'lĭk) *a.* [Gk. *monos*, alone; *kyklos*, circle.] Having one cycle; with a single whorl; annual, *appl.* herbs.

monocystic (mŏn'ŏsĭs'tĭk) *a.* [Gk. *monos*, single; *kystis*, bag.] With one stage of encystation.

monocytes (mŏn'ŏsīts) *n. plu.* [Gk. *monos*, alone; *kytos*, hollow.] The group of white blood corpuscles including large mononuclear and transition cells; endothelial leucocytes; histiocytes.

monodactylous (mŏn'ŏdăk'tĭlŭs) *a.* [Gk. *monos*, alone; *daktylos*, finger.] With one digit, or one claw, only.

monodelphic (mŏnŏdĕl'fĭk) *a.* [Gk. *monos*, single; *delphys*, womb.] Having uteri more or less united, as in placental mammals; having a single uterus, as *appl.* certain nematodes.

monodelphous,—monadelphous, *q.v.*

monodesmic (mŏn'ŏdĕs'mĭk, -dĕz-) *a.* [Gk. *monos*, single; *desmos*, bond.] *Appl.* scales formed of fused lepidomoria with continuous covering layer of dentine, as some placoid scales.

monodont (mŏn'ŏdŏnt) *a.* [Gk. *monos*, single; *odous*, tooth.] Having one persistent tooth, as male narwhal with one long tusk.

monoecious (mŏnē'sĭŭs) *a.* [Gk. *monos*, single; *oikos*, house.] Ambisexual; with male and female flowers on same plant; with sex organs on one gametophyte; hermaphrodite; having either microsporangia or megasporangia on one sporophyte.

monoestrous (mŏnē'strŭs) *a.* [Gk. *monos*, single; *oistros*, gadfly.] Having one oestrous period in a sexual season; *cf.* polyoestrous.

monofactorial,—unifactorial, *q.v.*

monogamous (mŏnŏg'ămŭs) *a.* [Gk. *monos*, single; *gamos*, marriage.] Consorting with one mate only.

monoganglionic (mŏn'ŏgăng'glĭŏnĭk) *a.* [Gk. *monos*, single; *gangglion*, little tumour.] Having a single ganglion.

monogastric (mŏn'ŏgăs'trĭk) *a.* [Gk. *monos*, single; *gaster*, stomach.] With only one gastric cavity; with one venter, *appl.* muscles.

monogenesis (mŏn'ŏjĕn'ĕsĭs) *n.* [Gk. *monos*, single; *genesis*, descent.] Asexual reproduction; theory of development of all organisms from single cells; origin of a new form at one place or period.

monogenetic (mŏn'ŏjĕnĕt'ĭk) *a.* [Gk. *monos*, alone; *genesis*, descent.] Reproducing asexually; direct, as *appl.* reproduction; monogenic.

monogenic (mŏn'ŏjĕn'ĭk) *a.* [Gk. *monos*, single; *genos*, sex.] Producing offspring consisting of one sex; either arrhenogenic or thelygenic; controlled by a single gene.

monogenomic (mŏn'ŏjĕnŏm'ĭk) *a.* [Gk. *monos*, single; *genos*, offspring.] Having a single set of chromosomes.

monogenous (mŏnŏj'ĕnŭs) *a.* [Gk. *monos,* alone ; *genos,* offspring.] Asexual, as *appl.* reproduction.

monogeny (mŏnŏj'ĕnĭ) *n.* [Gk. *monos,* single ; *genos,* sex.] Production of offspring consisting of one sex; arrhenogeny and thelygeny.

monogoneutic (mŏn'ŏgŏnū'tĭk) *a.* [Gk. *monos,* single ; *goneuein,* to produce.] Breeding once a year.

monogonoporous (mŏn'ŏgŏnŏp'ŏrŭs) *a.* [Gk. *monos,* alone ; *gonos,* offspring ; *poros,* channel.] Having one genital pore common to both male and female organs, as in certain Turbellaria.

monogony (mŏnŏg'ŏnĭ) *n.* [Gk. *monos,* alone ; *gonos,* offspring.] Asexual reproduction, including schizogony and gemmation.

monogynoecial (mŏn'ŏjĭnē'sĭăl) *a.* [Gk. *monos,* alone ; *gyne,* female ; *oikos,* house.] Developing from one pistil ; monogynaecial.

monogynous (mŏnŏj'ĭnŭs) *a.* [Gk. *monos,* alone ; *gyne,* female.] Having one pistil only ; consorting with but one female.

monohybrid (mŏn'ŏhībrĭd) *n.* [Gk. *monos,* alone ; L. *hybrida,* mongrel.] A hybrid offspring of parents differing in one character. *a.* Heterozygous for a single pair of factors.

monokaryon (mŏn'ŏkăr'ĭŏn) *n.* [Gk. *monos,* alone ; *karyon,* nut.] A nucleus with a single centriole.

monokont (mŏn'ŏkŏnt) *a.* [Gk. *monos,* single ; *kontos,* punting-pole.] Uniflagellate.

monolayer (mŏn'ŏlā'ĕr) *n.* [Gk. *monos,* single ; A.S. *lecgan,* to lie.] A single homogeneous layer of units, as of molecules, cells, etc. ; monomolecular layer.

monolocular,—unilocular.

monolophous (mŏn'ŏlŏf'ŭs) *a.* [Gk. *monos,* alone ; *lophos,* crest.] *Appl.* spicules with one ray forked or branched like a crest.

monomastigate (mŏn'ŏmăs'tĭgāt), **monomastigote** (mŏn'ŏmăst'īgōt) *a.* [Gk. *monos,* single ; *mastix,* whip.] Having one flagellum, as certain Protista.

monomeniscous (mŏn'ŏmēnĭs'kŭs) *a.* [Gk. *monos,* alone ; *meniskos,* small moon.] Having an eye with only one lens.

monomeric (mŏn'ŏmĕr'ĭk) *a.* [Gk. *monos,* alone ; *meros,* part.] *Pert.* one segment ; derived from one part ; bearing a dominant gene at only one of two loci.

monomerosomatous (mŏn'ŏmĕr'-ŏsōm'ătŭs) *a.* [Gk. *monos,* alone ; *meros,* part ; *soma,* body.] Having body-segments all fused together, as in certain insects.

monomerous (mŏnŏm'ĕrŭs) *a.* [Gk. *monos,* alone ; *meros,* part.] Consisting of one part only ; *appl.* flower-whorls.

monometrosis (mŏn'ŏmē'trŏsĭs) *n.* [Gk. *monos,* alone ; *meter,* mother.] Colony foundation by one female, as by queen in some social Hymenoptera. *Opp.* pleometrosis.

monomial (mŏnō'mĭăl) *a.* [Gk. *monos,* single ; L. *nomen,* name.] *Appl.* a name or designation consisting of one term only ; *cf.* binomial.

monomorphic (mŏn'ŏmôr'fĭk) *a.* [Gk. *monos,* single ; *morphe,* form.] Developing with no or very slight change of form from stage to stage, as certain protozoa and insects ; *cf.* polymorphic ; producing spores of one kind only.

monomyaric (mŏn'ŏmīă'rĭk) *a.* [Gk. *monos,* alone ; *mys,* muscle.] With posterior adductor only, anterior adductor being aborted ; *appl.* certain bivalves ; monomyarian.

mononeuronic (mŏn'ŏnūrŏn'ĭk) *a.* [Gk. *monos,* single ; *neuron,* nerve.] With one nerve ; *appl.* chromatophores with single type of innervation.

monont (mŏn'ŏnt) *n.* [Gk. *monos,* alone ; *on,* being.] A single individual reproducing without conjugation, *opp.* sporont or zygote.

mononuclear (mŏn'ŏnū'klēăr) *a.* [Gk. *monos,* single ; L. *nucleus,* kernel.] With one nucleus only ; uninuclear. *n.* A mononuclear leucocyte.

mononychous (mŏnŏn′ĭkŭs) *a.* [Gk. *monos*, single; *onyx*, claw.] Having a single or uncleft claw.

mononym (mŏn′önĭm) *n.* [Gk. *monos*, single; *onyma*, name.] A designation consisting of one term only; name of a monotypic genus.

monopetalous (mŏn′öpĕt′ălŭs) *a.* [Gk. *monos*, alone; *petalon*, leaf.] Having one petal only; having petals united all round; *cf.* gamopetalous.

monophagous (mŏnŏf′ăgŭs) *a.* [Gk. *monos*, alone; *phagein*, to eat.] Subsisting on one kind of food; *appl.* Sporozoa living permanently in a single cell; *appl.* caterpillars feeding on plants of one genus only; *cf.* stenophagous; *appl.* insects restricted to one species or variety of food plant; *cf.* oligophagous.

monophasic (mŏn′öfā′zĭk) *a.* [Gk. *monos*, alone; *phainein*, to appear.] *Appl.* condensed life cycle of some trypanosomes, lacking the active stage; *cf.* diphasic.

monophyletic (mŏn′öfīlĕt′ĭk) *a.* [Gk. *monos*, alone; *phyle*, tribe.] Derived from a single common parent form; *Opp.* oligophyletic, polyphyletic.

monophyllous (mŏn′öfĭl′ŭs) *a.* [Gk. *monos*, alone; *phyllon*, leaf.] Having one leaf only; unifoliate; having a one-piece calyx.

monophyodont (mŏn′öfī′ödŏnt) *a.* [Gk. *monos*, alone; *phyein*, to produce; *odous*, tooth.] Having only one set of teeth, the milk dentition being absorbed in foetal life or absent altogether.

monoplacid (mŏn′öplăs′ĭd) *a.* [Gk. *monos*, alone; *plax*, flat plate.] With one plate only, of any kind.

monoplacula (mŏn′öplăk′ūlă) *n.* [Gk. *monos*, alone; *plax*, flat plate.] A single-layered placula.

monoplanetic (mŏn′öplănĕt′ĭk) *a.* [Gk. *monos*, alone; *planetes*, wanderer.] With one stage of motility in life-history; *appl.* formation of zoospores in certain fungi, *opp.* diplanetic; monoplanetary.

monoplanetism (mŏn′öplăn′ĕtĭzm) *n.* [Gk. *monos*, alone; *planetes*, wanderer.] Condition of having one period of motility in one life-history, as of zoospores in some fungi.

monoplastic (mŏn′öplăs′tĭk) *a.* [Gk. *monos*, alone; *plastos*, formed.] Persisting in one form.

monoploid (mŏn′öploid) *a.* [Gk. *monos*, alone; *haploos*, simple; *eidos*, form.] Having one set of chromosomes, true haploid; in a polyploid series, having the basic haploid chromosome number. *n.* A monoploid organism.

monoplont,—haplont, *q.v.*

monopodal (mŏnŏp′ödăl) *a.* [Gk. *monos*, single; *pous*, foot.] Having one supporting structure; with one pseudopodium.

monopodial (mŏn′öpō′dĭăl) *a.* [Gk. *monos*, alone; *pous*, foot.] Branching from one primary axis acropetally.

monopodium (mŏn′öpō′dĭŭm) *n.* [Gk. *monos*, alone; *pous*, foot.] A single main or primary axis from which all main lateral branches develop.

monopolar,—unipolar, *q.v.*

monopyrenous (mŏn′öpīrē′nŭs) *a.* [Gk. *monos*, alone; *pyren*, kernel.] Single-stoned, as a fruit.

monorchic (mŏnôr′kik) *a.* [Gk. *monos*, single; *orchis*, testis.] Having one testis.

monorefringent (mŏn′örēfrĭn′jĕnt) *a.* [Gk. *monos*, single; L. *refringere*, to break off.] Singly refracting; isotropic.

monorhinal (mŏn′örī′năl) *a.* [Gk. *monos*, alone; *rhines*, nostrils.] Having only one nostril, as Cyclostomata; *pert.* one nostril.

monosaccharides (mŏn′ösăk′ărīdz) *n. plu.* [Gk. *monos*, single; L. *saccharum*, sugar.] Simple sugars, *e.g.* glucose, fructose, galactose.

monosepalous (mŏn′ösĕp′ălŭs) *a.* [Gk. *monos*, alone; F. *sépale*, sepal.] Having a single sepal; having all sepals united into one; *cf.* gamosepalous.

monosiphonic (mŏn′ösīfŏn′ĭk) *a.* [Gk. *monos*, alone; *siphon*, tube.] Having tubes of a hydrocaulis distinct from one another, as in certain hydromedusae; having a single central tube in filament, as in certain algae; monosiphonous.

monosome (mŏn′ösōm) *n.* [Gk. *monos*, alone; *soma*, body.] The unpaired accessory or X-chromosome.

monosomic (mŏn′ösōmĭk) *a.* [Gk. *monos*, alone; *soma*, body.] Diploid with one chromosome missing.

monospermous (mŏn′öspĕr′mŭs) *a.* [Gk. *monos*, single; *sperma*, seed.] One-seeded; monospermic.

monospermy (mŏn′öspĕr′mĭ) *n.* [Gk. *monos*, single; *sperma*, seed.] Normal fertilisation by entrance of one sperm only into an ovum.

monospondylic (mŏn′öspŏndĭl′ĭk) *a.* [Gk. *monos*, alone; *sphondylos*, vertebra.] *Appl.* vertebrae without intercentra.

monosporangium (mŏn′öspörăn′jĭŭm) *n.* [Gk. *monos*, alone; *sporos*, seed; *anggeion*, vessel.] A sporangium producing simple spores.

monospore (mŏn′öspōr) *n.* [Gk. *monos*, alone; *sporos*, seed.] A simple or undivided spore.

monosporic (mŏn′öspŏr′ĭk) *a.* [Gk. *monos*, single; *sporos*, seed.] *Pert.* or originating from a single spore; monosporial.

monosporous (mŏn′ŏspōrŭs, mŏnŏs′pörŭs) *a.* [Gk. *monos*, alone; *sporos*, seed.] Having only one spore or a simple spore.

monostachyous (mŏn′östăk′ĭŭs) *a.* [Gk. *monos*, alone; *stachys*, corn-ear.] With only one spike.

monostele (mŏn′östē′lē) *n.* [Gk. *monos*, alone; *stele*, column.] An axis stele when only one is the direct continuation of plerome.

monostelic (mŏn′östĕl′ĭk) *a.* [Gk. *monos*, alone; *stele*, column.] Having a single stele or central cylinder running through whole axis.

monosterigmatic (mŏn′östĕrĭgmăt′ĭk) *a.* [Gk. *monos*, alone; *sterigma*, support.] Having a single sterigma; *appl.* fungi.

monostichous (mŏnŏs′tĭkŭs). *a.* [Gk. *monos*, single; *stichos*, row.] Arranged in one row; along one side of an axis.

monostigmatous (mŏn′östĭg′mătŭs) *a.* [Gk. *monos*, single; *stigma*, mark.] With one stigma only.

monostylous (mŏn′östī′lŭs) *a.* [Gk. *monos*, alone; *stylos*, pillar.] Having one style only.

monosy (mŏn′ösĭ) *n.* [Gk. *monos*, alone.] Separation of parts normally fused.

monosymmetrical (mŏn′ösĭmĕt′rĭkăl) *a.* [Gk. *monos*, alone; *symmetria*, due proportion.] Having only one plane of bilateral symmetry; zygomorphic.

monothalamous (mŏn′öthăl′ămŭs) *a.* [Gk. *monos*, single; *thalamos*, chamber.] Unilocular; single-chambered; monothalamic; *appl.* fruits formed from single flowers; having one gynoecium; *appl.* galls; *appl.* shells of foraminifera and other protozoa.

monothecal (mŏn′öthē′kăl) *a.* [Gk. *monos*, alone; *theke*, box.] Having one loculus; single-chambered.

monothelious (mŏn′öthē′lĭŭs) *a.* [Gk. *monos*, alone; *thelys*, female.] *Appl.* a female consorting with more than one male.

monotocous (mŏnŏt′ökŭs) *a.* [Gk. *monos*, single; *tokos*, offspring.] Uniparous, having one offspring at a birth; monocarpic, *q.v.*

monotrichous (mŏnŏt′rĭkŭs) *a.* [Gk. *monos*, single; *thrix*, hair.] Having only one flagellum at one pole; monotrichic, monotrichate.

monotrochal (mŏnŏt′rökăl) *a.* [Gk. *monos*, single; *trochos*, wheel.] Having a prototroch only, as trochosphere of certain Polychaeta.

monotrochous (mŏnŏt′rökŭs) *a.* [Gk. *monos*, alone; *trochos*, wheel.] Having a single-piece trochanter, as in most stinging Hymenoptera.

monotrophic (mŏn′ötrŏf′ĭk) *a.* [Gk. *monos*, alone; *trophe*, nourishment.] Subsisting on one kind of food.

monotype (mŏn′ōtīp) *n.* [Gk. *monos*, alone; *typos*, type.] Single type which constitutes species or genus; a unique holotype.

monotypic (mŏn′ōtĭp′ĭk) *a.* [Gk. *monos*, alone; *typos*, type.] *Pert.* monotype; having only one species, *appl.* genus; having no subspecies, *appl.* species; haplotypic, *opp.* polytypic.

monovalent,—univalent.

monovoltine,—univoltine.

monoxenous (mŏnŏks′ēnŭs, mŏnōzĕn′ŭs) *a.* [Gk. *monos*, alone; *xenos*, host.] Inhabiting one host only, *appl.* parasites; *cf.* heteroxenous.

monoxylic (mŏn′ōzī′lĭk) *a.* [Gk. *monos*, alone; *xylon*, wood.] Having wood formed as a continuous ring, *appl.* stems.

monozoic (mŏn′ōzō′ĭk) *a.* [Gk. *monos*, alone; *zoon*, animal.] Producing one sporozoite only; *appl.* archispores forming only one sporozoite on liberation from cyst.

monozygotic (mŏn′ōzīgŏt′ĭk) *a.* [Gk. *monos*, alone; *zygotes*, yoked.] Developing from one fertilised ovum, as identical twins; monozygous; uniovular.

Monro, foramen of, [*A. Monro*, Scottish anatomist]. The interventricular foramen.

mons pubis,—prominence due to subcutaneous fatty tissue in front of symphysis pubis; mons Veneris.

montane (mŏn′tān) *a.* [L. *montanus*, *pert.* mountains.] *Pert.* mountains; *appl.* flora and fauna; monticolous.

Montgomery's glands [*W. F. Montgomery*, Irish physician]. Areolar glands of nipple, prominent during lactation.

monticolous (mŏntĭk′ōlŭs) *a.* [L. *mons*, mountain; *colere*, to inhabit.] Inhabiting mountainous regions.

monticulus (mŏntĭk′ūlŭs) *n.* [L. *dim. mons*, mountain.] Largest part of superior vermis of cerebellum.

mores (mō′rēz) *n. plu.* [L. *mos*, wont.] Groups of organisms preferring the same habitat, having the same reproductive season, and agreeing in their general reactions to the physical environment.

Morgagni, columns of [*G. B. Morgagni*, Italian anatomist]. Rectal columns, *q.v.*

Morgagni, hydatid of,—*see* hydatid.

moriform (mô′rĭfôrm) *a.* [L. *morum*, mulberry; *forma*, form.] Formed in a cluster resembling aggregate fruit; shaped like a mulberry.

morphallaxis (môrfăl′ăksĭs) *n.* [Gk. *morphe*, form; *allaxis*, changing.] Transformation of one part into another, in regeneration of parts, *opp.* epimorphosis; gradual growth or development into a particular form.

morphogenesis (môr′fōjĕn′ēsĭs) *n.* [Gk. *morphe*, form; *genesis*, descent.] The development of shape; origin and development of organs or parts of organisms.

morphogenetic (môr′fōjēnĕt′ĭk) *a.* [Gk. *morphe*, form; *genesis*, descent.] *Pert.* morphogenesis; *appl.* internal secretions which influence growth and nutrition of organs or organisms.

morphogenic hormone,—the chemical substance released by the primary organiser in development; evocator.

morphogens (môr′fōjĕnz) *n. plu.* [Gk. *morphe*, form; *gennaein*, to produce.] Substances interacting in presence of an evocator, and determining the pattern of embryonic development.

morphogeny,—morphogenesis.

morphologic index,—ratio expressing relation of trunk to limbs.

morphology (môrfŏl′ōjĭ) *n.* [Gk. *morphe*, form; *logos*, discourse.] The science of form and structure of plants and animals, as distinct from consideration of functions.

morphon (môr′fŏn) *n.* [Gk. *morphe*, form; *on*, being.] A definitely formed individual, *opp.* a bion.

morphoplasm (môr′fōplăzm) *n.* [Gk. *morphe*, form; *plasma*, formation.] Formative protoplasm; kinoplasm; protoplasmic reticulum, *opp.* cell sap.

morphoplasy (môr'föplā'sĭ) *n.* [Gk. *morphe*, form; *plassein*, to mould.] Formative potentiality of a growing organism.

morphosis (môr'fōsĭs, môrfō'sĭs) *n.* [Gk. *morphosis*, form.] The manner of development of part or organism.

morphotic (môrfŏt'ĭk) *a.* [Gk. *morphosis*, form.] Formative; tissue-building; *pert.* morphosis.

morphotype (môr'fötīp) *n.* [Gk. *morphe*, form; *typos*, pattern.] Type specimen of one of the forms of a polymorphic species.

Morren's glands [*C. F. A. Morren*, Belgian zoologist]. Calciferous glands of earth-worms.

morula (môr'ūlă) *n.* [L. *morum*, mulberry.] A solid cellular globular mass, the first result of ovum segmentation; stage in development preceding gastrula; a globular aggregation of developing male gametes, a sperm morula; a coelomocyte containing refractive globules, morula-shaped cell.

morulation (môrūlā'shŭn) *n.* [L. *morum*, mulberry.] Morula formation by segmentation.

morulit (môr'ūlĭt) *n.* [L. *morum*, mulberry.] Nucleolus or karyosome,

mosaic (mōzā'ĭk) *n.* [It. *mosaica.* mosaic.] Hybrid having unblended parental allelomorphic characters; chimaera; a virus disease of plants; *appl.* theory that each ommatidium in compound eye of arthropods receives a portion of an image, the several portions being integrated as the total image by the brain.

moschate (mŏs'kāt) *a.* [Gk. *moschos*, musk.] Having or resembling the odour of musk; musky.

moss-fibres,—nerve fibres branching around cells of internal layer of cerebellar cortex.

mossy cells,—protoplasmic astrocytes.

motoneuron (mō'tönū'rŏn) *n.* [L. *movere*, to move; Gk. *neuron*, nerve.] A motor neurone, *q.v.*

motor (mō'tŏr) *a.* [L. *movere*, to move.] *Pert.* or connected with movement; *appl.* nerves, etc.

motor areas,—areas of brain where motion is correlated.

motor end-organ,—terminal ramification of axis-cylinder in striated muscle; less correctly, end-plate.

motor neurones,—nerve cells concerned in regulation of movement.

motor oculi,—the third cranial nerve.

motor unit,—a motor neurone and associated muscle fibres.

motorium (mötō'rĭŭm) *n.* [L. *movere*, to move.] Motor areas; part of nervous system where motorial sense is localised.

moult (mōlt) *v.* [L. *mutare*, to change.] To cast or shed periodically the outer covering, whether of feathers, hair, skin, or horns. *n.* The process of shedding; ecdysis.

moulting glands,—ecdysial glands, *q.v.*

moulting hormone,—secreted by ecdysial glands or cells in dorsal region of protocerebrum, in Arthropoda; ecdysone.

mouth part,—a head or mouth appendage of arthropods.

M-rays,—mitogenetic rays.

mucedinous (mūsĕd'ĭnŭs) *a.* [L.L. *mucedo*, mould, from L. *mucus*, mucus.] Having loosely spaced white filaments, like a mould fungus.

mucid (mū'sĭd) *a.* [L. *mucidus*, mouldy.] Mouldy; slimy.

mucific (mūsĭf'ĭk) *a.* [L. *mucus*, mucus; *facere*, to make.] Mucus-secreting.

muciform (mū'sĭfôrm) *a.* [L. *mucus*, mucus; *forma*, shape.] Resembling mucus.

mucigen (mū'sĭjĕn) *n.* [L. *mucus*, mucus; Gk. *-genes*, producing.] The substance of granules in cells of mucous membrane; mucinogen.

mucilage (mū'sĭlĕj) *n.* [L. *mucus*, mucus.] A substance of varying composition, hard when dry, swelling and slimy when moist, produced in cell-walls of certain plants.

mucilaginous (mū'sĭlăj'ĭnŭs) *a.* [L. *mucus*, mucus.] *Pert.*, containing, resembling, or composed of mucilage; *appl.* certain glands of joints; *appl.* cells, ducts, canals, slits.

mucin (mū'sĭn) *n.* [L. *mucus*, mucus.] A glycoprotein of mucus, occurring in, or secreted by, certain cells and glands.

mucinogen (mūsĭn'öjĕn) *n.* [L. *mucus*, mucus; Gk. *-genes*, producing.] A substance producing mucin, occurring in granules of mucous gland cells.

muciparous (mūsĭp'ărŭs) *a.* [L. *mucus*, mucus; *parere*, to beget.] Mucus-secreting.

mucocellulose (mū'kösĕl'ūlōs) *n.* [L. *mucus*, mucus; *cellula*, small cell.] Cellulose mixed with mucous substance, as in some seeds and fruits.

mucocutaneous (mū'kökūtā'nëŭs), **mucodermal** (mū'ködĕr'măl) *a.* [L. *mucus*, mucus; *cutis*, skin; Gk. *derma*, skin.] *Pert.* skin and mucous membrane.

mucoid (mū'koid) *a.* [L. *mucus*, mucus; Gk. *eidos*, like.] *Pert.* or caused by mucus or mucilage; *appl.* degeneration, tissue. *n.* A mucoprotein of cartilage, bone, tendon, etc.

mucoproteins (mū'köprō'tëĭnz) *n. plu.* [L. *mucus*, mucus; Gk. *protos*, first.] Compounds of protein with a carbohydrate, include mucins and mucoids; glucoproteins or glycoproteins.

mucosa (mūkō'să) *n.* [L. *mucus*, mucus.] A mucous membrane.

mucoserous (mū'kösē'rŭs) *a.* [L. *mucus*, mucus; *serum*, whey.] Secreting mucus and body fluid.

mucous (mū'kŭs) *n.* [L. *mucus*, mucus.] Secreting, containing, or *pert.* mucus; *appl.* glands, membranes, sheaths, tissue.

mucro (mū'krō) *n.* [L. *mucro*, sharp point.] A stiff or sharp point abruptly terminating an organ; a small awn; pointed keel or sterile third carpel, as in pine, posterior tip of cuttle-bone; a projection below orifice in Polyzoa; distal part of furcula in Collembola.

mucronate (mū'krönāt) *a.* [L. *mucro*, sharp point.] Abruptly terminated by a sharp spine; mucroniferous.

mucronulate (mūkrŏn'ūlāt) *a.* [L. *mucro*, sharp point.] Tipped with small mucro.

mucronule (mū'krönūl) *n.* [L. *mucro*, sharp point.] A small mucro.

muculent (mū'kŭlĕnt) *a.* [L. *mucus*, mucus.] Like mucus; containing mucus; mucilaginous.

mucus (mū'kŭs) *n.* [L. *mucus*, mucus.] The slimy, glairy substance secreted by goblet cells of a mucous membrane or by mucous cells of a gland.

mulberry body,—morula, *q.v.*

Müllerian bodies [*F. Müller*, German naturalist]. Structures containing albuminous and oily substances in trichilium, eaten by tropical ants.

Müllerian ducts [*J. Müller*, German anatomist]. Paramesonephric ducts, arising on lateral aspects of mesonephric or Wolffian ducts.

Müllerian eminence [*J. Müller*, German anatomist]. A colliculus or elevation of ventral part of cloaca at entrance of Müllerian ducts and between openings of Wolffian ducts.

Müller's fibres [*H. Müller*, German anatomist]. Neuroglial fibres forming framework supporting nervous layers of retina; sustentacular or radial fibres of Müller.

Müller's larva [*J. Müller*, German zoologist]. Ciliated larva of Polycladida; cephalotrocha.

Müller's muscle [*H. Müller*, German anatomist]. A plain muscle across inferior orbital fissure; a plain muscle of eyelids.

multangular (mŭltăng'gūlăr) *a.* [L. *multus*, many; *angulus*, angle.] *Appl.* two carpal bones, greater and lesser multangulum, respectively trapezium and trapezoid.

multaxial,—multiaxial.

multiarticulate (mŭl'tĭârtĭk'ūlāt) *a.* [L. *multus*, many; *articulus*, joint.] With many articulations; many-jointed; polyarthric.

multiaxial (mŭl'tĭăk'sĭăl) *a.* [L. *multus*, many; *axis*, axis.] Having or *pert.* several axes.

multicamerate (mŭl'tĭkăm'ĕrāt) *a.* [L. *multus*, many; *camera*, chamber.] Multilocular; with many chambers.

multicapsular (mŭl′tĭkăp′sūlăr) *a.* [L. *multus*, many; *capsula*, little chest.] With many capsules.
multicarinate (mŭl′tĭkăr′ĭnāt) *a.* [L. *multus*, many; *carina*, keel.] Having many carinae or ridges.
multicarpellary (mŭl′tĭkâr′pĕlărĭ) *a.* [L. *multus*, many; Gk. *karpos*, fruit.] Having many carpels; polycarpellary.
multicellular (mŭl′tĭsĕl′ūlăr) *a.* [L. *multus*, many; *cella*, cell.] Many-celled; consisting of more than one cell.
multicentral (mŭl′tĭsĕn′trăl) *a.* [L. *multus*, many; *centrum*, centre.] With more than one centre of growth or development.
multiciliate (mŭl′tĭsĭl′ĭāt) *n.* [L. *multus*, many; *cilium*, eyelid.] With some or many cilia.
multicipital (mŭl′tĭsĭp′ĭtăl) *a.* [L. *multus*, many; *caput*, head.] With many heads or branches arising from one point.
multicostate (mŭl′tĭkŏs′tāt) *a.* [L. *multus*, many; *costa*, rib.] With many ribs or veins; with many ridges.
multicuspid (mŭl′tĭkŭs′pĭd) *a.* [L. *multus*, many; *cuspis*, spear-head.] With several cusps or tubercles; *appl.* molar teeth.
multidentate (mŭl′tĭdĕn′tāt) *a.* [L. *multus*, many; *dens*, tooth.] With many teeth, or indentations.
multidigitate (mŭl′tĭdĭj′ĭtāt) *a.* [L. *multus*, many; *digitus*, finger.] Many-fingered.
multifactorial (mŭl′tĭfăktō′ryăl) *a.* [L. *multus*, many; *facere*, to make.] *Pert.* or controlled by a number of genes; polygenic.
multifarious (mŭl′tĭfā′rĭŭs) *a.* [L. *multifarius*, manifold.] Arranged in numerous series or rows; polystichous.
multifid (mŭl′tĭfĭd) *a.* [L. *multus*, many; *findere*, to cleave.] Having many clefts or divisions.
multiflagellate (mŭl′tĭflăj′ĕlāt) *a.* [L. *multus*, many; *flagellum*, whip.] Furnished with several or many flagella; polymastigote, *q.v.*
multiflorous (mŭl′tĭflō′rŭs) *a.* [L. *multus*, many; *flos*, flower.] Bearing many flowers.
multifoliate (mŭl′tĭfō′lĭāt) *a.* [L. *multus*, many; *folium*, leaf.] With many leaves.
multifoliolate (mŭl′tĭfō′lĭōlāt) *a.* [L. *multus*, many; *foliolum*, small leaf.] With many leaflets.
multiform (mŭl′tĭfôrm) *a.* [L. *multus*, many; *forma*, form.] Occurring in, or containing, different forms; *appl.* layer: inner cell-lamina of cerebral cortex; polymorphous.
multiganglionate (mŭl′tĭgăng′-glĭōnāt) *a.* [L. *multus*, many; Gk. *ganglion*, small tumour.] With several or many ganglia.
multigyrate (mŭl′tĭjī′rāt) *a.* [L. *multus*, many; *gyrus*, circle.] With many gyri; tortuous.
multijugate (mŭl′tĭjoog′āt) *a.* [L. *multus*, many; *jugum*, yoke.] Having many pairs of leaflets.
multilacunar (mŭl′tĭlăkū′năr) *a.* [L. *multus*, many; *lacuna*, cavity.] With many lacunae; having a number of leaf-gaps, *appl.* nodes.
multilaminate (mŭl′tĭlăm′ĭnāt) *a.* [L. *multus*, many; *lamina*, plate.] Composed of several or many laminae.
multilobate (mŭl′tĭlō′bāt) *a.* [L. *multus*, many; *lobus*, lobe.] Composed of many lobes; multilobar.
multilobulate (mŭl′tĭlŏb′ūlāt) *a.* [L. *multus*, many; *lobulus*, small lobe.] Having many lobules.
multilocular (mŭl′tĭlŏk′ūlăr) *a.* [L. *multus*, many; *loculus*, compartment.] Having many cells or chambers; *appl.* spore: sporidesm; multiloculate.
multinervate (mŭl′tĭnĕr′vāt) *a.* [L. *multus*, many; *nervus*, sinew.] With many nerves or nervures.
multinodal (mŭl′tĭnō′dăl) *a.* [L. *multus*, many; *nodus*, knot.] With many nodes; multinodate.
multinomial (mŭl′tĭnō′mĭăl) *a.* [L. *multus*, many; *nomen*, name.] *Appl.* a name or designation composed of several names or terms; *cf.* binomial, trinomial.

multinucleate (mŭl'tĭnū'klëāt) *a.* [L. *multus*, many; *nucleus*, kernel.] With several or many nuclei; polykaric.

multinucleolate (mŭl'tĭnūklē'ölāt) *a.* [L. *multus*, many; *nucleolus*, small kernel.] With more than one nucleolus.

multiovulate (mŭl'tĭō'vūlāt) *a.* [L. *multus*, many; *ovum*, egg.] With several or many ovules.

multiparous (mŭltĭp'ărŭs) *a.* [L. *multus*, many; *parere*, to beget.] Bearing several, or more than one, at a birth; developing several or many lateral axes.

multipennate (mŭl'tĭpĕn'āt) *a.* [L. *multus*, many; *penna*, feather.] *Appl.* muscle containing a number of extensions of its tendon of insertion.

multipinnate (mŭl'tĭpin'āt) *a.* [L. *multus*, many; *pinnatus*, feathered.] Divided into many lateral processes or leaflets; many times pinnate.

multiple corolla,—a corolla with two or more whorls of petals.

multiple diploid,—allopolyploid, *q.v.*

multiple factors,—genes having a joint or cumulative effect.

multiple fission,—repeated division; division into a large number of parts or spores.

multiplicate (mŭl'tĭplĭkāt) *a.* [L. *multiplicare*, to make manifold.] Consisting of many; having many folds or plicae.

multipolar (mŭl'tĭpō'lăr) *a.* [L. *multus*, many; *polus*, axis-end.] *Appl.* nerve-cells with more than two axis-cylinder processes; involving more than two poles, *appl.* mitosis, usually pathological.

multiporous (mŭl'tĭpō'rŭs) *a.* [L. *multus*, many; Gk. *poros*, passage.] Having many pores.

multiradiate (mŭl'tĭrā'dĭāt) *a.* [L. *multus*, many; *radius*, ray.] Many-rayed.

multiramose (mŭl'tĭrā'mōs) *a.* [L. *multus*, many; *ramus*, branch.] Much branched.

multiseptate (mŭl'tĭsĕp'tāt) *a.* [L. *multus*, many; *septum*, partition.] Having numerous partitions.

multiserial (mŭl'tĭsē'rĭăl) *a.* [L. *multus*, many; *series*, row.] Arranged in many rows; multiseriate; *appl.* xylem rays.

multispiral (mŭl'tĭspī'răl) *a.* [L. *multus*, many; *spira*, coil.] With many coils or whorls.

multisporous,—polysporous.

multistaminate (mŭl'tĭstăm'ĭnāt) *a.* [L. *multus*, many; *stamen*, thread.] Having several or many stamens.

multisulcate (mŭl'tĭsŭl'kāt) *a.* [L. *multus*, many; *sulcus*, furrow.] Much furrowed.

multitentaculate (mŭl'tĭtĕntăk'ūlāt) *a.* [L. *multus*, many; *tentaculum*, feeler.] Having many tentacles.

multituberculate (mŭl'tĭtūbĕr'kūlāt) *a.* [L. *multus*, many; *tuberculum*, small hump.] Having several or many small prominences.

multituberculy (mŭl'tĭtūbĕr'kūlĭ) *n.* [L. *multus*, many; *tuberculum*, small hump.] The theory that molar teeth are derived from forms with a number of tubercles.

multivalve (mŭl'tĭvălv) *n.* [L. *multus*, many; *valvae*, folding-doors.] A shell composed of more valves or pieces than two.

multivincular (mŭl'tĭvĭng'kūlăr) *a.* [L. *multus*, many; *vinculum*, fetter.] *Appl.* hinge of bivalve shell with several ligaments.

multivoltine (mŭl'tĭvŏl'tĭn) *a.* [L. *multus*, many; It. *volta*, turn.] Having more than one brood in a year; *appl.* silkworms.

multocular (mŭltŏk'ūlăr) *a.* [L. *multus*, many; *oculus*, eye.] Many-eyed.

multungulate (mŭltŭng'gūlāt) *a.* [L. *multus*, many; *ungula*, hoof.] Having the hoof in more than two parts.

mune (mūn) *n.* [L. *munus*, function.] A group of organisms with a characteristic behaviour response; mores, *q.v.*

mural (mū'răl) *a.* [L. *muralis*, of walls.] Constituting or *pert.* a wall, as cells or membranes.

muralium (mūrā'lĭŭm) *n.* [L. *muralis*, *pert.* a wall.] A structure formed by layers one cell thick, as of liver-cells.

muricate (mū'rĭkāt) *a.* [L. *muricatus*, having sharp points.] Formed with sharp points; covered with short sharp outgrowths; studded with oxalate crystals, *appl.* cystidia.

muriform (mū'rĭfôrm) *a.* [L. *murus*, wall; *forma*, shape.] Like a brick wall; *appl.* a parenchyma so arranged, occurring in medullary rays of dicotyledons and in corky formations; *appl.* arrangement of germinating spores; *appl.* spores; dictyospores.

muscicoline (mŭsĭk'ölĭn) *a.* [L. *muscus*, moss; *colere*, to inhabit.] Living or growing among or on mosses; muscicolous.

muscle (mŭsl) *n.* [L. *musculus*, muscle.] A mass of contractile fibres with motorial function; fleshy part of body, composed of muscular tissue.

muscle banners,—folds or plaits of mesogloea on sulcar aspects of anthozoan mesenteries, supporting retractor muscles.

muscle column,—sarcostyle.

muscle-spindle,—a sensory structure in muscle, consisting of a spindle-shaped connective tissue sheath containing small modified fibres and sensory nerve endings.

muscoid (mŭs'koid) *a.* [L. *muscus*, moss; Gk. *eidos*, form.] Moss-like; mossy; muscous.

muscology (mŭskŏl'öjĭ) *n.* [L. *muscus*, moss; Gk. *logos*, discourse.] The study of Musci or mosses; *cf.* bryology.

muscular (mŭs'kūlăr) *a.* [L. *musculus*, muscle.] *Pert.* or consisting of muscle; *appl.* sense, excitability, fibres, tissue, process, triangle, stomach, etc.

musculature (mŭs'kūlătūr) *n.* [L. *musculus*, muscle.] The system or arrangement of muscles as a whole.

musculocutaneous (mŭs'kūlökūtā'nëŭs) *a.* [L. *musculus*, muscle; *cutis*, skin.] *Pert.* muscles and skin; *appl.* limb veins and nerves supplying muscles and skin.

musculophrenic (mŭs'kūlöfrĕn'ĭk) *a.* [L. *musculus*, muscle; Gk. *phren*, midriff.] Supplying diaphragm and body-wall muscles; *appl.* an artery.

musculospiral (mŭs'kūlöspī'răl) *a.* [L. *musculus*, muscle; *spira*, coil.] *Appl.* radial nerve which passes spirally down humerus.

mushroom bodies,—corpora pedunculata or pedunculate bodies, *q.v.*

mushroom gland, — the seminal vesicles of certain insects, as cockroaches.

mutafacient (mūtăfăs'ĭënt, -shĭënt) *a.* [L. *mutare*, to change; *facere*, to make.] Inducing or aiding the creation of a mutation, as intracellular agents, mainly.

mutagenic (mū'tăjĕn'ĭk) *a.* [L. *mutare*, to change; Gk. *gennaein*, to generate.] Capable of inducing a mutation, as radiation, chemicals, or other extra-cellular agents.

mutant (mū'tănt) *n.* [L. *mutare*, to change.] An individual with transmissible characteristics different from those of the parent form. *a.* Exhibiting mutation.

mutate (mū'tāt, mūtāt'] *v.* [L. *mutare*, to change.] To undergo or exhibit mutation.

mutation (mūtā'shŭn) *n.* [L. *mutare*, to change.] Gradual variation towards a definite change of structure; a successional species or subspecies; a saltation or discontinuous variation; theory of De Vries that new forms, differing sufficiently to constitute a new variety, arise spontaneously and remain true.

mutator,—*appl.* genes which increase the general mutation rate.

mutilation (mū'tĭlāshŭn) *n.* [L. *mutilare*, to maim.] Loss of an essential part of a structure; amputation.

mutilous (mū'tĭlŭs) *a.* [L. *mutilus*, maimed.] Without defensive structures, as clawless, harmless, toothless, blunt.

mutualism (mū'tūălĭzm) *n.* [L. *mutuus*, exchanged.] A form of symbiosis in which both parties derive advantage without sustaining injury.

myarian (mīă'rĭăn) *a.* [Gk. *mys*, muscle.] *Appl.* classification according to musculature.

mycelioid (mīsē'lĭoid) *a.* [Gk. *mykes*, fungus; *eidos*, form.] Like mycelium.

mycelium (mīsē'lĭŭm) *n.* [Gk. *mykes*, fungus.] Network of filamentous cells or hyphae forming typical vegetative structure of fungi; mycele; spawn, as of mushroom.

myceloconidium,—stylospore.

mycetocyte (mīsē'tösīt) *n.* [Gk. *mykes*, fungus; *kytos*, hollow.] One of follicle-cells at posterior oocyte pole through which the egg of Aphides is infected by symbionts.

mycetogenetic (mīsē'töjĕnĕt'ĭk) *a.* [Gk. *mykes*, fungus; *genesis*, descent.] Produced by a fungus; mycetogenic.

mycetoid (mīsē'toid) *a.* [Gk. *mykes*, fungus; *eidos*, form.] Fungoid; fungus-like.

mycetology,—mycology, *q.v.*

mycetoma (mīsētō'mă) *n.* [Gk. *mykes*, fungus.] The mycetocytes collectively.

mycetophagous (mī'sētŏf'ăgŭs) *a.* [Gk. *mykes*, fungus; *phagein*, to eat.] Feeding on fungi; fungivorous.

mycin,—fungine, *q.v.*

mycina (mī'sĭnă) *n.* [Gk. *mykes*, fungus.] A spherical stalked apothecium of certain lichens.

mycobiota (mī'köbīō'tă) *n.* [Gk. *mykes*, fungus; *bios*, life.] The fungi of an area or region.

mycocecidium (mī'kösēsĭd'ĭŭm) *n.* [Gk. *mykes*, fungus; *kekis*, gall-nut.] Any gall caused by fungi.

mycoclera (mī'köklē'ră) *n.* [Gk. *mykes*, fungus; *kleros*, portion.] The mycelial covering of ectotrophic mycorrhiza.

mycocriny (mī'kökrī'nĭ) *n.* [Gk. *mykes*, fungus; *krinein*, to separate.] Chemical decomposition of plant debris by fungi.

mycoderm (mī'ködĕrm) *n.* [Gk. *mykes*, fungus; *derma*, skin.] A bacterial film during alcoholic fermentation.

mycoecotype (mī'köē'kötīp) *n.* [Gk. *mykes*, fungus; *oikos*, household; *typos*, pattern.] The habitat type of mycorrhizal and parasitic fungi.

mycoid (mī'koid) *a.* [Gk. *mykes*, fungus; *eidos*, form.] Like a fungus; fungoid, fungous.

mycology (mīkŏl'öjĭ) *n.* [Gk. *mykes*, fungus; *logos*, discourse.] That part of botany which deals with fungi; mycetology.

mycophthorous (mīköfthō'rŭs) *a.* [Gk. *mykes*, fungus; *phthoros*, destruction.] Fungus-destroying; *appl.* or *pert.* fungi parasitising other fungi.

mycoplasm (mī'köplăzm) *n.* [Gk. *mykes*, fungus; *plasma*, form.] A parasitic substance of cereal seeds, giving rise to rust fungus.

mycopremna (mī'köprĕm'nă) *n.* [Gk. *mykes*, fungus; *premnon*, stem.] A rhizome containing symbiotic fungi, as in some orchids.

mycorrhiza (mī'körī'ză) *n.* [Gk. *mykes*, fungus; *rhiza*, root.] Association of fungal mycelium with roots of a higher plant; mycorhiza.

mycorrhizic (mī'körī'zĭk) *a.* [Gk. *mykes*, fungus; *rhiza*, root.] Exhibiting the features of a mycorhiza; partially symbiotic; mycorhizic.

mycosterols (mī'köstĕr'ŏlz) *n. plu.* [Gk. *mykes*, fungus; *stereos*, solid; L. *oleum*, oil.] Sterols from cryptogams, especially fungi, as ergosterol, fucosterol, zymosterol, etc.; *cf.* phytosterols.

mycothallus (mī'köthăl'ŭs) *n.* [Gk. *mykes*, fungus; *thallos*, young shoot.] The assimilative body of fungi.

mycotrophic (mī'kötrŏf'ĭk) *a.* [Gk. *mykes*, fungus; *trophe*, nourishment.] *Appl.* plants living symbiotically with fungi.

mycteric (mĭktĕr'ĭk) *a.* [Gk. *mykter*, nose.] *Pert.* nasal cavities.

myelencephalon (mī'ĕlĕnkĕf'ălŏn, -sĕf-) *n.* [Gk. *myelos*, marrow; *engkephalos*, brain.] The posterior part of hind-brain, comprising medulla oblongata and lower part of fourth ventricle; after-brain.

myelin (mī'ĕlĭn) *n.* [Gk. *myelos*, marrow.] A highly refracting fatty material forming medullary sheath of nerve fibres.

myelination (mī'ĕlĭnā'shŭn) *n.* [Gk. *myelos*, marrow.] Acquisition of a medullary sheath; myelinisation.

myeloblast (mī'ĕlŏblăst) *n.* [Gk. *myelos*, marrow; *blastos*, bud.] An undifferentiated non-granular lymphoid cell of bone marrow; lymphomyelocyte.

myelobrachium, — restibrachium, *q.v.*

myelocoel (mī'ĕlŏsēl) *n.* [Gk. *myelos*, marrow; *koilos*, hollow.] The spinal cord canal.

myelocyte (mī'ĕlŏsīt) *n.* [Gk. *myelos*, marrow; *kytos*, hollow.] An amoeboid cell of bone marrow.

myeloic (mīĕlō'ĭk) *a.* [Gk. *myelos*, marrow.] *Appl.* and *pert.* cells which give rise to neutrophil or polymorphonuclear leucocytes.

myeloid (mī'ĕloid) *a.* [Gk. *myelos*, marrow; *eidos*, form.] Like marrow in appearance or structure; *appl.* cells, as megakaryocytes, monocytes, and parenchymal cells; resembling myelin, *appl.* granules at base of retinal pigment cells.

myelomere (mī'ĕlŏmēr) *n.* [Gk. *myelos*, marrow; *meros*, part.] A segment of the spinal cord.

myelon (mī'ĕlŏn) *n.* [Gk. *myelos*, marrow.] Spinal cord of Vertebrata.

myeloplast (mī'ĕlŏplăst) *n.* [Gk. *myelos*, marrow; *plastos*, formed.] A leucocyte of bone marrow.

myeloplax (mī'ĕlŏplăks) *n.* [Gk. *myelos*, marrow; *plax*, something flat.] A giant-cell of marrow and blood-forming organs; megalokaryocyte and osteoclast.

myelopoiesis (mī'ĕlŏpoiē'sĭs) *n.* [Gk. *myelos*, marrow; *poiesis*, making.] The formation and development of cells of bone marrow, as of granulocytes.

myelospongium (mī'ĕlŏspŏn'jĭŭm) *n.* [Gk. *myelos*, marrow; *sponggia*, sponge.] Interconnected spongioblasts which give rise to neuroglia.

myenteric (mīĕntĕr'ĭk) *a.* [Gk. *mys*, muscle; *enteron*, gut.] *Appl.* nerve plexus controlling movement of food towards anus, Auerbach's plexus; *appl.* reflex.

myenteron (mīĕn'tĕrŏn) *n.* [Gk. *mys*, muscle; *enteron*, gut.] The muscular coat of intestine.

myiasis (mī'yăsĭs) *n.* [Gk. *myia*, fly.] The invasion of living tissues by larvae of Diptera.

mylohyoid (mī'lŏhī'oid) *a.* [Gk. *myle*, mill; *hyoeides*, Υ-shaped.] In the region of hyoid bone and posterior part of mandible; *appl.* artery, groove, muscle, nerve.

myoalbumin (mī'ŏălbū'mĭn) *n.* [Gk. *mys*, muscle; L. *albumen*, white of egg.] An albumin product of muscle.

myoblast (mī'ŏblăst) *n.* [Gk. *mys*, muscle; *blastos*, bud.] A cell which develops into muscle fibre.

myocardium (mī'ŏkâr'dĭŭm) *n.* [Gk. *mys*, muscle; *kardia*, heart.] The muscular walls of the heart.

myochrome (mī'ŏkrōm) *n.* [Gk. *mys*, muscle; *chroma*, colour.] Any muscle-pigment.

myocoel (mī'ŏsēl) *n.* [Gk. *mys*, muscle; *koilos*, hollow.] Part of the coelom enclosed in a myotome.

myocomma (mī'ŏkŏm'ă) *n.* [Gk. *mys*, muscle; *komma*, clause.] A myoseptum or ligamentous connection between successive myomeres.

myocyte (mī'ŏsīt) *n.* [Gk. *mys*, muscle; *kytos*, hollow.] Contractile inner layer of ectoplasm of Gregarinina; a contractile cell; muscle cell.

myodome (mī'ŏdōm) *n.* [Gk. *mys*, muscle; *domos*, chamber.] A chamber containing the eye-muscles in some teleosts.

myodynamic (mī'ŏdĭnăm'ĭk) *a.* [Gk. *mys*, muscle; *dynamis*, power.] *Pert.* muscular force or contraction.

myoepicardial (mī'ŏĕpĭkâr'dĭăl) *a.* [Gk. *mys*, muscle; *epi*, upon; *kardia*, heart.] *Appl.* a mantle consisting of the mesocardium walls, destined to form the muscular and epicardial walls of the heart.

myoepithelial (mī'öĕpĭthē'lĭăl) *a.* [Gk. *mys*, muscle; *epi*, upon; *thele*, nipple.] *Pert.* muscle and epithelium; *appl.* epithelium cells with contractile outgrowths, as in coelenterates; *appl.* contractile cells of epithelial origin in salivary and sweat glands.

myofibrillae (mī'öfībrĭl'ē) *n. plu.* [Gk. *mys*, muscle; L. *fibrilla*, small fibre.] Contractile fibrils of muscular tissue; myofibrils.

myofilaments (mī'öfĭl'ăments) *n. plu.* [Gk. *mys*, muscle; L. *filum*, thread.] Thin thread-like components of a myofibrilla.

myogenic (mī'öjĕn'ĭk) *a.* [Gk. *mys*, muscle; *gennaein*, to produce.] Having origin in muscular cells, as heart-beat.

myoglobin (mī'öglō'bĭn) *n.* [Gk. *mys*, muscle; L. *globus*, globe.] Myohaematin.

myoglobulin (mī'öglŏb'ūlĭn) *n.* [Gk. *mys*, muscle; L. *globulus*, small globe.] A globulin of muscle.

myohaematin (mī'öhēm'ătĭn) *n.* [Gk. *mys*, muscle; *haima*, blood.] A pigment of muscular tissue, a cytochrome, *q.v.*

myoid (mī'oid) *a.* [Gk. *mys*, muscle; *eidos*, form.] Resembling or composed of muscular fibres; *appl.* striated cells or sarcolytes of thymus. *n.* Contractile proximal part or filament of rods and cones of retina.

myolemma (mī'ölĕm'ă) *n.* [Gk. *mys*, muscle; *lemma*, skin.] The sheath of muscle fibre; sarcolemma.

myology (mīŏl'öjĭ) *n.* [Gk. *mys*, muscle; *logos*, discourse.] The branch of anatomy dealing with muscles.

myomere (mī'ömēr) *n.* [Gk. *mys*, muscle; *meros*, part.] A muscle-segment divided off by connective tissue insertions or myocommata.

myometrial (mī'ömē'trĭăl) *a.* [Gk. *mys*, muscle; *metra*, uterus.] *Pert.* myometrium; *appl.* glandular tissue of uterus, supposed to produce a hormone affecting growth of mammary glands.

myometrium (mī'ömēt'rĭŭm) *n.* [Gk. *mys*, muscle; *metra*, uterus.] The muscular uterine wall.

myone (mīōn') *n.* [Gk. *myon*, muscular part.] Unit of muscle: individual muscle fibre.

myonema (mīönē'mă) *n.* [Gk. *mys*, muscle; *nema*, thread.] A minute contractile fibril of Protista; myoneme.

myoneural (mī'önū'răl) *a.* [Gk. *mys*, muscle; *neuron*, nerve.] Neuromyal, *q.v.*

myoneure (mī'önūr) *n.* [Gk. *mys*, muscle; *neuron*, nerve.] A motorial nerve-cell.

myonicity (mī'önĭs'ĭtĭ) *n.* [Gk. *mys*, muscle.] The contracting power of muscular tissue.

myophan (mī'öfăn) *a.* [Gk. *mys*, muscle; *phainein*, to appear.] Muscle-like; *appl.* striations in protozoa.

myophore (mī'öfōr) *n.* [Gk. *mys*, muscle; *pherein*, to bear.] A structure adapted for muscle attachment.

myophrisk (mī'öfrĭsk) *n.* [Gk. *mys*, muscle; *phrix*, ripple.] A myoneme or contractile element of protozoa.

myoplasm (mī'öplăzm) *n.* [Gk. *mys*, muscle; *plasma*, mould.] Contractile portion of muscle fibre, *opp.* sarcoplasm.

myopolar (mī'öpō'lăr) *a.* [Gk. *mys*, muscle; *polos*, axle-end.] *Pert.* muscular polarity.

myoproteid (mī'öprō'tēĭd) *n.* [Gk. *mys*, muscle; *protos*, first.] A globulin-like substance of fish muscle.

myoseptum (mī'ösĕp'tŭm) *n.* [Gk. *mys*, muscle; L. *septum*, partition.] A myocomma, *q.v.*

myosin (mī'ösĭn) *n.* [Gk. *mys*, muscle.] A globulin of dead muscular tissue; muscle-clot.

myosis (mīō'sĭs) *n.* [Gk. *myein*, to close.] Contraction of pupil of the eye.

myotasis (mī'ŏt'ăsĭs) *n.* [Gk. *mys*, muscle; *tasis*, tension.] Muscular tension or tonicity.

myotatic (mīötăt′ĭk) *a.* [Gk. *mys*, muscle; *tasis*, tension.] Causing or *pert.* myotasis; *appl.* stretch reflex.

myotic (mīŏt′ĭk) *a.* [Gk. *myein*, to close.] Causing or *pert.* myosis or pupillary contraction.

myotome (mī′ötōm) *n.* [Gk. *mys*, muscle; *tome*, cutting.] One of a series of hollow cubes formed in early vertebrate embryo; a muscular metamere of primitive vertebrates and segmented invertebrates.

myotonia (mīötō′nĭă) *n.* [Gk. *mys*, muscle; *tonos*, tension.] Muscular tension or tonicity.

myriosporous (mĭr′ĭöspō′rŭs) *a.* [Gk. *myrios*, numberless; *sporos*, seed.] Having very numerous spores; extremely polysporous.

myrmecochore (mĭr′mēkökō′rē) *n.* [Gk. *myrmex*, ant; *chorē*, farm.] An oily seed modified to attract, and be spread by, ants.

myrmecology (mĭr′mēkŏl′öji) *n.* [Gk. *myrmex*, ant; *logos*, discourse.] The study of ants.

myrmecophagous (mĭr′mēkŏf′ăgŭs) *a.* [Gk. *myrmex*, ant; *phagein*, to eat.] Ant-eating.

myrmecophil (mĭr′mēköfĭl) *n.* [Gk. *myrmex*, ant; *philos*, loving.] A guest insect in a nest of ants.

myrmecophilous (mĭr′mēkŏf′ĭlŭs) *a.* [Gk. *myrmex*, ant; *philos*, loving.] Pollinated by agency of ants; *appl.* fungi serving as food for ants; living with, or preying on, or mimicking ants, *appl.* spiders.

myrmecophobic (mĭr′mēköfŏb′ĭk) *a.* [Gk. *myrmex*, ant; *phobeisthai*, to flee.] Repelling ants; *appl.* certain plants equipped with glands, hairs, etc. that check ants.

myrmecophyte (mĭr′mēköfīt) *n.* [Gk. *myrmex*, ant; *phyton*, plant.] A myrmecophilous plant, or one that benefits from ant inhabitants and has special adaptations for housing them.

myrosin (mĭr′ösĭn) *n.* [Gk. *myron*, unguent.] Sinigrinase, an enzyme of Cruciferae, acting upon glucosides.

myrtiform (mĭr′tĭfôrm) *a.* [L. *myrtus*, myrtle; *forma*, shape.] *Appl.* incisive fossa.

mystacial (mĭstā′sĭăl) *a.* [Gk. *mystax*, moustache.] *Appl.* a pad of thickened skin on side of snout, and to tactile hairs or vibrissae.

mystax (mĭs′tăks) *n.* [Gk. *mystax*, moustache.] A group of hairs above mouth of certain insects; mystacial hairs.

myxamoeba (mĭk′sămē′bă) *n.* [Gk. *myxa*, slime; *amoibe*, change.] Mycetozoan spore in amoebula stage.

myxocyte (mĭk′sösīt) *n.* [Gk. *myxa*, slime; *kytos*, hollow.] Cell of mucous tissue.

myxoflagellate (mĭk′söflăj′ēlāt) *n.* [Gk. *myxa*, slime; L. *flagellum*, whip.] A flagellula or zoospore following myxamoeba stage in development of Myxomycetes or Mycetozoa.

myxopodium (mĭk′söpō′dĭŭm) *n.* [Gk. *myxa*, slime; *pous*, foot.] A slimy pseudopodium.

myxopterygium, — mixipterygium.

myxosporangium (mĭk′söspörăn′-jĭŭm) *n.* [Gk. *myxa*, slime; *sporos*, seed; *anggeion*, vessel.] A sporangium producing spores embedded in a slimy substance; fruit-body of Myxomycetes.

myxospore (mĭk′söspōr) *n.* [Gk. *myxa*, slime; *sporos*, seed.] A spore separated by a slimy disintegration of the hypha; slime spore; spore of Myxomycetes; a plasmaspore, *q.v.*

myzesis (mīzē′sĭs) *n.* [Gk. *myzein*, to suck.] Suction; sucking.

N

nacré (năkrā′) *a.* [F. *nacré*, having a pearly lustre.] *Appl.* the thick primary wall of sieve elements.

nacreous (nā′krēŭs) *a.* [Ar. *nakir*, hollowed.] Yielding or resembling mother-of-pearl or nacre.

nacrine (nā′krĭn) *n.* [Ar. *nakir*, hollowed.] Mother-of-pearl colour.

naiad (nī'ăd) *n.* [Gk. *naias*, water-nymph.] The nymph stage of hemimetabolic insects.

nail (nāl) *n.* [A.S. *naegel*, nail.] Terminal horny plate of finger or toe, or of beak; unguis.

nail bone,—terminal bone of finger or toe; ungual phalanx.

naked (nā'kĕd) *a.* [A.S. *nacod.*] Without a covering; *appl.* spores, seeds, etc.; *appl.* non-nuclear genes, as phage or virus.

nanander (nănăn'dĕr) *n.* [Gk. *nanos*, dwarf; *aner*, male.] A dwarf male; *appl.* plants; nannander.

nanism (nā'nĭzm) *n.* [Gk. *nanos*, dwarf.] Dwarfishness.

nanoid (nā'noid) *a.* [Gk. *nanos*, dwarf; *eidos*, form.] Dwarfish.

nanophanerophyte (năn'ŏfăn'ĕrŏfīt) *n.* [Gk. *nanos*, dwarf; *phaneros*, manifest; *phyton*, plant.] Shrub under 2 metres in height.

nanoplankton (năn'ŏplăng'ktŏn) *n.* [Gk. *nanos*, dwarf; *plangktos*, wandering.] Microscopic floating plant and animal organisms; nannoplankton; *cf.* microplankton.

nanous (nā'nŭs) *a.* [L. *nanus*, dwarf.] Dwarfed; dwarfish.

napiform (nā'pĭfôrm) *a.* [L. *napus*, turnip; *forma*, shape.] Turnip-shaped; *appl.* roots.

narcosis (nârkō'sĭs) *n.* [Gk. *narke*, numbness.] State of unconsciousness or stupor produced by a drug.

narcotic (nârkŏt'ĭk) *n.* [Gk. *narke*, numbness.] A drug which produces unconsciousness. *a. Pert.* or producing narcosis.

nares (nā'rēz) *n. plu.* [L. *nares*, nostrils.] Nostrils.

nares, anterior, — openings of olfactory organ to exterior; nostrils.

nares, posterior,—openings of olfactory organ into pharynx or throat; choanae.

narial (nā'rĭăl) *a.* [L. *nares*, nostrils.] *Pert.* the nostrils; *appl.* septum, the partition between nostrils.

naricorn (năr'ĭkôrn) *n.* [L. *nares*, nostrils; *cornu*, horn.] Terminal horny part of nostril of Turbinares; nasal scale.

nariform (năr'ĭfôrm) *a.* [L. *nares*, nostrils; *forma*, shape.] Shaped like nostrils.

narine,—narial.

naris,—*sing.* of nares.

nasal (nā'zăl) *a.* [L. *nasus*, nose.] *Pert.* the nose. *n.* Nasal scale, plate, or bone.

nasalis (năsā'lĭs) *n.* [L. *nasus*, nose.] Muscle drawing alae of the nose towards septum; compressor naris.

nasion (nā'zĭŏn) *n.* [L. *nasus*, nose.] Middle point of nasofrontal suture.

Nasmyth's membrane [*A. Nasmyth*, Scottish dentist]. Cuticula dentis, a transparent membrane over enamel of crown of a mammalian tooth.

nasoantral (nā'zŏăn'trăl) *a.* [L. *nasus*, nose; *antrum*, cavity.] *Pert.* nose and maxillary cavity.

nasobuccal (nā'zŏbŭk'ăl) *a.* [L. *nasus*, nose; *bucca*, cheek.] *Pert.* nose and cheek; *pert.* nose and mouth cavity.

nasociliary (nā'zŏsĭl'ĭărĭ) *a.* [L. *nasus*, nose; *cilia*, eyelashes.] *Appl.* branch of ophthalmic nerve, with internal and external nasal branches, and giving off the long ciliary and other nerves.

nasofrontal (nā'zŏfrŭn'tăl) *a.* [L. *nasus*, nose; *frons*, forehead.] *Appl.* part of superior ophthalmic vein which communicates with the angular vein.

nasolabial (nā'zŏlā'bĭăl) *a.* [L. *nasus*, nose; *labium*, lip.] *Pert.* nose and lip; *appl.* muscle; *appl.* groove and glands in Plethodontidae.

nasolacrimal (nā'zŏlăk'rĭmăl) *a.* [L. *nasus*, nose; *lacrima*, tear.] *Appl.* duct from lacrimal sac to inferior meatus of nose.

nasomaxillary (nā'zŏmăksĭl'ărĭ) *a.* [L. *nasus*, nose; *maxilla*, jaw.] *Pert.* nose and upper jaw.

naso-optic (nā'zŏŏp'tĭk) *a.* [L. *nasus*, nose; Gk. *optikos*, relating to sight.] *Appl.* an embryonic groove between nasal and maxillary processes.

nasopalatine (nā'zōpăl'ătīn) *a.* [L. *nasus*, nose; *palatus*, palate.] *Pert.* nose and palate. *Appl.* groove of vomer, recess in nasal septum, nerve, canal communicating with vomeronasal organ; nasopalatal.

nasopharyngeal (nā'zōfărĭn'jēăl) *a.* [L. *nasus*, nose; Gk. *pharyngx*, gullet.] *Pert.* nose and pharynx, or nasopharynx.

nasopharynx (nā'zōfăr'ĭngks) *n.* [L. *nasus*, nose; Gk. *pharyngx*, gullet.] That part of pharynx continuous with posterior nares; rhinopharynx.

nasoturbinal (nā'zōtŭr'bĭnăl) *a.* [L. *nasus*, nose; *turbo*, whorl.] *Appl.* outgrowths from lateral wall of nasal cavity increasing area of sensory surface.

nastic (năs'tĭk) *a.* [Gk. *nastos*, pressed close.] *Appl.* plant movements caused by diffuse stimuli, as chemo-, photo-, nycti-, traumato-, seismonasty.

nasus (nā'zŭs) *n.* [L. *nasus*, nose.] Nose; clypeus of insect head.

nasute (nāsūt') *a.* [L. *nasutus*, large-nosed.] *Appl.* a soldier termite with rostrum; nasutus.

natal (năt'ăl) *a.* [L. *nates*, buttocks.] *Pert.* the buttocks.

natality (nătăl'ĭtĭ) *n.* [L. *natalis*, *pert.* birth.] Birth-rate.

natant (nā'tănt) *a.* [L. *natare*, to swim.] Floating on water surface.

natatorial (năt'ătō'rĭăl), **natatory** (năt'ătōrĭ) *a.* [L. *natare*, to swim.] Formed or adapted for swimming.

native (nā'tĭv) *a.* [L. *natus*, born.] *Appl.* animals and plants which originated in district or area in which they live.

natural selection,—processes occurring in Nature which result in survival of fittest and elimination of individuals less well adapted to their environment.

nature (nā'tūr) *n.* [L. *natura*, nature.] Sum-total of inheritance, *opp.* nurture or environment.

nauplius (nô'plĭŭs) *n.* [L. *nauplius*, shell-fish.] The earliest larval stage of entomostracan crustaceans and certain shrimps.

nautiliform (nôt'ĭlĭfôrm) *a.* [L. *nautilus*, nautilus; *forma*, shape.] Shaped like a nautilus shell; nautiloid.

navel (nā'vĕl) *n.* [A.S. *nafela*, navel.] Place of attachment of umbilical cord to body of embryo; umbilicus.

navicular (năvĭk'ūlăr) *a.* [L. *navis*, *dim.*, ship.] Boat-shaped; scaphoid.

naviculare (năvĭk'ūlā'rē) *a.* [L. *navis*, *dim.*, ship.] The scaphoid radiale of mammalian carpus; tarsal bone between talus and cuneiform bones.

N-discs,—discs or bands on either side of Z-disc.

neala,—vannus, *q.v.*, of insect wing.

neallotype (nēăl'ōtīp) *n.* [Gk. *neos*, new; *allos*, other; *typos*, pattern.] A type specimen of the opposite sex to that of the specimen previously chosen for designation of a new species.

nealogy (nēăl'ōjĭ) *n.* [Gk. *neales*, youthful; *logos*, discourse.] The study of young animals.

neanic (nēăn'ĭk) *a.* [Gk. *neanikos*, youthful.] Adolescent; *appl.* larval phase preceding that of adult form.

Nearctic (nēârk'tĭk) *a.* [Gk. *neos*, new; *Arktos*, Great Bear.] *Appl.* or *pert.* a zoogeographical region, or sub-region of the holarctic region, comprising Greenland and North America, and including northern Mexico.

nebenkern (nā'bĕnkĕrn) *n.* [Ger. *neben*, near; *Kern*, nucleus.] Paranucleus, *q.v.*

nebenkörper (nā'bĕnkĕr'pĕr) *n.* [Ger. *neben*, near; *Körper*, body.] A body surrounded by oil-drops at hinder pole, of Pyrodinium.

necrobiosis (nĕk'rōbīō'sĭs) *n.* [Gk. *nekros*, dead; *biosis*, manner of life.] The activity of cells after death of an organism; continuance of certain vital functions after disorganisation of a cell.

necrocytosis (nĕk'rōsĭtō'sĭs) *n.* [Gk. *nekros*, dead; *kytos*, hollow.] Death of cells.

necrogenous (nĕkrŏj'ĕnŭs) *a.* [Gk. *nekros*, dead; *genos*, offspring.] Living or developing in dead bodies.

necrohormone (nĕk'röhôrmōn) *n.* [Gk. *nekros*, dead; *hormaein*, to excite.] Substance in tissue extracts or dead cells which may either kill living cells or induce mitosis.

necrophagous (nĕkrŏf'ăgŭs) *a.* [Gk. *nekros*, dead; *phagein*, to eat.] Feeding on dead bodies.

necrophilous,—necrophagous.

necrophoric (nĕk'röfŏr'ĭk) *a.* [Gk. *nekros*, dead; *pherein*, to carry.] Containing dead cells, *appl.* water-storing layers in lichens; carrying away dead bodies, *appl.* certain beetles; necrophoral, necrophorous.

necrosis (nĕkrō'sĭs) *n.* [Gk. *nekrosis*, deadness.] The death of cells or of tissues. *a.* Necrotic.

nectar (nĕk'tăr) *n.* [Gk. *nektar*, nectar.] Sweet substance secreted by special glands, nectaries, in flowers and in certain leaves; substance containing spores and attracting insects, produced by certain fungi, as on pycnidia.

nectar guides,—series of markings on petals of flowers, aiding insects in finding nectar, and at same time facilitating cross-fertilisation.

nectariferous (nĕk'tărĭf'ĕrŭs) *a.* [L. *nectar*, nectar; *ferre*, to carry.] Producing nectar, or having nectar-secreting structures.

nectarivorous (nĕk'tărĭv'örŭs) *a.* [L. *nectar*, nectar; *vorare*, to devour.] Nectar-sipping; *appl.* certain insects.

nectary (nĕk'tărĭ) *n.* [Gk. *nektar*, nectar.] A group of modified sub-epidermal cells of no definite position in a flower, less commonly in leaves, secreting nectar; a nectar gland; honey tube of aphids.

nectocalyx (nĕk'tökā'lĭks) *n.* [Gk. *nektos*, swimming; *kalyx*, cup.] A modified medusiform person adapted for swimming purposes found as part of a siphonophore colony.

nectocyst (nĕk'tösĭst) *n.* [Gk. *nektos*, swimming; *kystis*, bladder.] The cavity of a nectocalyx; nectosac.

nectomonad (nĕk'tömŏn'ăd) *n.* [Gk. *nektos*, swimming; *monas*, unit.] A free form of certain parasitic flagellates; *cf.* haptomonad.

necton,—nekton.

nectophore (nĕk'töfōr) *n.* [Gk. *nektos*, swimming; *pherein*, to carry.] A nectocalyx; that portion of common coenosarc on which nectocalyces are borne.

nectopod (nĕk'töpŏd) *n.* [Gk. *nektos*, swimming; *pous*, foot.] An appendage modified for swimming.

nectosome (nĕk'tösōm) *n.* [Gk. *nektos*, swimming; *soma*, body.] Upper or swimming part of a siphonophore.

nectozooid (nĕk'tözō'oid) *n.* [Gk. *nektos*, swimming; *zoon*, animal; *eidos*, form.] A nectocalyx.

Needham's sac,—spermatophore-sac, formed by dilatation of male genital duct, in certain cephalopods.

neencephalon,—neoencephalon.

negative tropism,—tendency to move away from the source of a stimulus.

nekton (nĕk'tŏn) *n.* [Gk. *nektos*, swimming.] The organisms swimming actively in water.

nema (nē'mă) *n.* [Gk. *nema*, thread.] A thread-like tubular projection at apex of graptolite sicula; a filament; a nematode.

nemathecium (nĕm'ăthē'sĭŭm) *n.* [Gk. *nema*, thread; *theke*, box.] A protuberance on thallus of thallophytes.

nemathybomes (nĕm'ăthĭb'ōmz) *n. plu.* [Gk. *nema*, thread; *hybos*, humped.] Mesogloeal parts containing developing nematocysts, as in Edwardsia.

nematoblast (nĕm'ătöblăst) *n.* [Gk. *nema*, thread; *blastos*, bud.] The cell from which a nematocyst develops.

nematocalyx (nĕm'ătökā'lĭks) *n.* [Gk. *nema*, thread; *kalyx*, cup.] The 'guard-polyp' of Plumularia, carrying nematocysts.

nematocyst (nĕm'ătösĭst) *n.* [Gk. *nema*, thread; *kystis*, bladder.] A stinging cell; cnida, cnidoblast.

nematogene (nĕm'ătŏjēn) *n.* [Gk. *nema*, thread; *genos*, offspring.] *Appl.* phase of Dicyemidae when their vermiform embryos escape from parent by perforating body wall. *Cf.* rhombogene.

nematogone (nĕm'ătŏgōnē) *n.* [Gk. *nema*, thread; *gone*, seed.] A thin-walled propagative cell in gemma of certain mosses.

nematoid (nĕm'atoid) *a.* [Gk. *nema*, thread; *eidos*, form.] Thread-like; filamentous.

nematology (nĕmătŏl'ŏjĭ) *n.* [Gk. *nema*, thread; *logos*, discourse.] The study of Nematoda; nematodology.

nematophore (nĕm'ătŏfōr) *n.* [Gk. *nema*, thread; *pherein*, to carry.] A nematocalyx.

nematophorous (nĕm'ătŏf'ŏrŭs) *a.* [Gk. *nema*, thread; *pherein*, to carry.] *Pert.* a nematophore.

nematosphere (nĕm'ătŏsfēr) *n.* [Gk. *nema*, thread; *sphaira*, globe.] The capitate end of a tentacle in certain sea-anemones.

nematozooid (nĕm'ătŏzō'oid) *n.* [Gk. *nema*, thread; *zoon*, animal; *eidos*, form.] A defensive zooid in Hydrozoa.

nemeous,—filamentous, nematoid.

nemic (nē'mĭk) *a.* [Gk. *nema*, thread.] *Pert.* a nema; *pert.* Nematoda.

nemorose (nĕm'ŏrōs) *a.* [L. *nemorosus*, sylvan.] Inhabiting open woodland places; nemoricole.

neoblast (nē'ŏblăst) *n.* [Gk. *neos*, new; *blastos*, bud.] One of the undifferentiated cells forming primordium of regeneration tissue in response to a wound stimulus.

neocarpy (nē'ŏkârpĭ) *n.* [Gk. *neos*, young; *karpos*, fruit.] Production of fruit by an otherwise immature plant.

neocerebellum (nē'ŏsĕr'ĕbĕl'ŭm) *n.* [Gk. *neos*, new; L. *dim.* of *cerebrum*, brain.] Cerebellar region which receives pontine fibres predominantly. *Opp.* palaeocerebellum.

neocortex,—neopallium.

Neo-Darwinism,—a revival of Darwin's doctrine of natural selection as chief factor in evolution, working on germinal variations, not on acquired characters.

neoencephalon (nē'ŏĕnkĕf'ălŏn, -sĕf-) *n.* [Gk. *neos*, young; *engkephalos*, brain.] The telencephalon or latest evolved anterior portion of brain.

Neogaea (nē'ŏjē'ă, -gâ'yă) *n.* [Gk. *neos*, new; *gaia*, earth.] Zoogeographical area comprising the neotropical region.

neogamous (nēŏg'ămŭs) *a.* [Gk. *neos*, young; *gamos*, marriage.] *Appl.* forms of protozoa exhibiting precocious association of gametocytes.

Neogene (nē'ŏjēn) *a.* [Gk. *neos*, young; *genos*, age.] *Pert.* or *appl.* the later Tertiary period, Miocene and Pliocene epochs.

neogenesis (nēŏ'jĕn'ĕsĭs) *n.* [Gk. *neos*, new; *genesis*, birth.] New tissue formation; regeneration.

Neo-Lamarckism, — a revival of Lamarck's doctrine of evolution, that inherited acquired characters formed inception of specific differences.

Neolaurentian (nē'ŏlôrĕn'shĭăn) *a.* [Gk. *neos*, young; *St Lawrence* River.] *Pert.* or *appl.* early Proterozoic era.

Neolithic (nē'ŏlĭth'ĭk) *a.* [Gk. *neos*, young; *lithos*, stone.] *Appl.* or *pert.* the newer, or polished, stone age.

neomorph (nē'ŏmôrf) *n.* [Gk. *neos*, new; *morphe*, form.] A structural variation from type; an allele which induces new reactions in developmental processes.

neomorphosis (nē'ŏmôr'fōsĭs) *n.* [Gk. *neos*, new; *morphosis*, change.] Regeneration in case where new part is unlike anything in body.

neonatal (nē'ŏnā'tăl) *a.* [Gk. *neos*, new; L. *natus*, born.] New-born; recently hatched or born.

neonychium (nē'ŏnĭk'ĭŭm) *n.* [Gk. *neos*, young; *onyx*, nail.] A soft pad enclosing each claw of embryo of unguiculate vertebrates and of some other mammals, to prevent tearing of foetal membranes; horny claw-pad in birds before hatching.

neopallium (nē'öpăl'ĭŭm) *n.* [Gk. *neos*, young; L. *pallium*, cloak.] In mammalian brain, the cerebral cortex, excluding hippocampus and pyriform lobe.

neoplasm (nē'öplăzm) *n.* [Gk. *neos*, new; *plasma*, formation.] New or added tissue, generally pathological.

neoptile (nē'ötīl, nē'öptīl) *n.* [Gk. *neos*, young; *ptilon*, feather.] A down feather; down; neossoptile.

neossoptile (nēŏs'ötīl, -ptīl) *n.* [Gk. *neossos*, nestling; *ptilon*, feather.] Feather of nestlings; down feather; neoptile.

neoteinia (nē'ötī'nĭă) *n.* [Gk. *neos*, young; *teinein*, to stretch.] The state of having development arrested to prolong immaturity; neoteny.

neoteinic (nē'ötī'nĭk) *a.* [Gk. *neos*, young; *teinein*, to stretch.] *Appl.* substitution royalties of termites which remain undeveloped in certain respects.

neotenin (nēötē'nĭn) *n.* [Gk. *neos*, young; *teinein*, to extend.] Hormone secreted by corpora allata which inhibits development of adult characteristics in young insects; juvenile hormone.

neoteny (nēŏt'ënĭ) *n.* [Gk. *neos*, young; *teinein*, to stretch.] Retention of larval characters beyond normal period, or occurrence of adult characteristics in larva.

neothalamus (nē'öthăl'ămŭs) *n.* [Gk. *neos*, new; *thalamos*, chamber.] The part of the thalamus with nuclei connected with association areas of the cerebral cortex.

neotropical (nē'ötrŏp'ĭkăl) *a.* [Gk. *neos*, new; *tropikos*, tropic.] *Appl.* or *pert.* a zoogeographical region consisting of Southern Mexico, Central and South America, and the West Indies.

neotype (nē'ötīp) *n.* [Gk. *neos*, new; *typos*, pattern.] A new type; a new holotype; a new type specimen from the original type locality.

neovirus (nē'övī'rŭs) *n.* [Gk. *neos*, new; L. *virus*, poison.] A virus directly formed by a mutant viroid. *Opp.* palaeovirus.

Neozoic (nē'özō'ĭk) *a.* [Gk. *neos*, young; *zoe*, life.] *Pert.* period from end of Mesozoic to present day.

nephric (nĕf'rĭk) *a.* [Gk. *nephros*, kidney.] *Pert.* kidney; renal.

nephridial (nĕfrĭd'ĭăl) *a.* [Gk. *nephros*, kidney; *idion*, *dim.*] Nephric, usually *appl.* the small excretory tubules in kidney; *pert.* excretory organ or nephridium of invertebrates.

nephridioblast (nĕfrĭd'ĭöblăst) *n.* [Gk. *nephros*, kidney; *idion*, *dim.*; *blastos*, bud.] An ectodermal cell which gives rise to a nephridium.

nephridiopore (nĕfrĭd'ĭöpōr) *n.* [Gk. *nephros*, kidney; *idion*, *dim.*; *poros*, passage.] The external opening of a nephridium.

nephridiostome (nĕfrĭd'ĭöstōm) *n.* [Gk. *nephros*, kidney; *idion*, *dim.*; *stoma*, mouth.] Ciliated coelomic opening of a nephridium.

nephridium (nĕfrĭd'ĭŭm) *n.* [Gk. *nephros*, kidney; *idion*, *dim.*] An excretory organ, usually that of invertebrates; embryonic kidney tubule of vertebrates.

nephroblast (nĕf'röblăst) *n.* [Gk. *nephros*, kidney; *blastos*, bud.] One of the embryonic cells which give rise ultimately to nephridia.

nephrocoel (nĕf'rösēl) *n.* [Gk. *nephros*, kidney; *koilos*, hollow.] The cavity of a nephrotome; nephrocoele.

nephrocytes (nĕf'rösīts) *n. plu.* [Gk. *nephros*, kidney; *kytos*, hollow.] Cells in sponges and insects which secrete waste and then migrate to surface of body to discharge; brown cells for storage and removal of waste products, as in ascidians.

nephrodinic (nĕf'rōdĭn'ĭk) *a.* [Gk. *nephros*, kidney; *odis*, labour.] Having one duct serving for both excretory and genital purposes.

nephrogenic (nĕf'röjĕn'ĭk) *a.* [Gk. *nephros*, kidney; *gennaein*, to produce.] *Pert.* development of kidney; *appl.* cord or column of fused mesodermal cells giving rise to tubules of mesonephros.

nephrogonoduct (něf′rŏgŏn′ŏdŭkt) *n.* [Gk. *nephros*, kidney; *gonos*, seed; L. *ducere*, to lead.] Excretory and genital duct in one.

nephroid (něf′roid) *a.* [Gk. *nephros*, kidney; *eidos*, form.] Kidney-shaped; reniform.

nephrolytic (něf′rŏlĭt′ĭk) *a.* [Gk. *nephros*, kidney; *lyein*, to dissolve.] *Pert.* or designating enzymatic action destructive to kidneys.

nephromere (něf′rŏmēr) *n.* [Gk. *nephros*, kidney; *meros*, part.] Nephrotome, *q.v.*

nephromixium (něf′rŏmĭk′sĭŭm) *n.* [Gk. *nephros*, kidney; *mixis*, mixing.] A compound excretory organ comprising flame cells and coelomic funnel.

nephron (něf′rŏn) *n.* [Gk. *nephros*, kidney.] Structural and functional unit of a kidney, including the renal corpuscle, convoluted tubules, and Henle's loop.

nephropore (něf′rŏpōr) *n.* [Gk. *nephros*, kidney; *poros*, passage.] A nephridiopore.

nephros (něf′rŏs) *n.* [Gk. *nephros*, kidney.] A kidney; usually the functional portion of a kidney.

nephrostoma (nĕfrŏ′stŏmă) *n.* [Gk. *nephros*, kidney; *stoma*, mouth.] The opening of a nephridial tubule into body cavity; nephrostome.

nephrotome (něf′rŏtōm) *n.* [Gk. *nephros*, kidney; *temnein*, to cut.] That part of a somite developing into an embryonic excretory organ; nephromere.

nepionic (nēpĭŏn′ĭk) *a.* [Gk. *nepios*, infant.] Postembryonic; infantile; during infancy; *appl.* phase in development or evolution.

nepionotype (nē′pĭŏnŏtīp) *n.* [Gk. *nepios*, infant: *typos*, pattern.] Type or type specimen of a larva of a species.

neritic (nērĭt′ĭk) *a.* [Gk. *nerites*, a mussel.] *Pert.* or living only in coastal waters, *opp.* oceanic.

neritopelagic (nē′rĭtŏpĕlăj′ĭk) *a.* [Gk. *Nereis*, Nereid; *pelagos*, sea.] *Pert.*, or inhabiting, the sea above continental shelf.

nervate (nĕr′vāt) *a.* [L. *nervus*, sinew.] Having nerves or veins.

nervation (nĕrvā′shŭn), **nervature** (nĕr′vătūr) *n.* [L. *nervus*, sinew.] The disposition of nerves or veins in a leaf or membranous wing.

nerve (nĕrv) *n.* [L. *nervus*, sinew.] One of numerous fibrous stimuli-transmitting cords connecting brain with all other parts of body; vein of insect wing; a vein of leaf.

nerve canal,—a canal for passage of nerve to pulp of a tooth.

nerve cell,—a cell characteristic of brain and nerve tissue; neurocyte, neurone.

nerve centre,—collection of nerve cells associated with a particular function.

nerve eminence,—a superficial group of cells in some fishes, acting as a sense organ and connected with lateral line system; neuromast.

nerve ending,—the terminal distal portion of a nerve, modified in various ways.

nerve fibres,—thread-like structures of which nerves are composed.

nerve net,—a reticulum of nerve cells and their processes connecting sensory cells and muscular elements, in coelenterates.

nerve pentagon,—five-sided nerve ring around mouth of echinoderms.

nervicolous (nĕrvĭk′ŏlŭs) *a.* [L. *nervus*, sinew; *colere*, to dwell.] Inhabiting or growing on leaf-veins; nervicole.

nerviduct (nĕr′vĭdŭkt) *n.* [L. *nervus*, sinew; *ducere*, to lead.] Passage for nerves in cartilage or bone.

nervimotion (nĕr′vĭmō′shŭn) *n.* [L. *nervus*, sinew; *movere*, to move.] Motion due to direct stimulus from nerves.

nervi nervorum,—branching nerve fibres with end-bulbs in epineurium.

nervous (nĕr′vŭs) *a.* [L. *nervus*, sinew.] *Pert.* nerves; *appl.* tissue composed of nerve fibres.

nervous system,—brain, spinal cord, nerves and all their branches taken collectively.

nervule (nĕr′vūl) *n*. [L. *dim*. of *nervus*, sinew.] Branch or terminal portion of nervure of insect wing.

nervuration (nĕr′vūrā′shŭn) *n*. [L. *nervus*, sinew.] Disposition of nervures ; neuration.

nervure (nĕr′vūr) *n*. [L. *nervus*, sinew.] One of rib-like structures which support membranous wings of insects, branches of tracheal system ; a leaf-vein.

nervus lateralis (nĕr′vŭs lăt′ĕrā′lĭs) *n*. [L. *nervus*, sinew ; *lateralis*, *pert*. side.] A branch of vagus nerve in fishes, connecting sensory lateral line with brain.

nervus terminalis (nĕr′vŭs tĕrmĭnā′lĭs) *n*. [L. *nervus*, sinew ; *terminalis*, bounding.] A cranial nerve associated with vomeronasal organ.

nessoptile,—neossoptile, *q.v.*

net knots,—karyosomes.

netrum (nĕt′rŭm) *n*. [A.S. *net*, meshwork.] The initial spindle of a dividing cell.

netted,—reticulate.

netted-veined,—with veins in form of a network.

nettling cells,—stinging cells in coelenterates ; nematocysts.

Neumann's sheath,—dentinal sheath surrounding dental canaliculi.

neurad (nū′răd) *adv*. [Gk. *neuron*, nerve ; L. *ad*, to.] Dorsally.

neural (nū′răl) *a*. [Gk. *neuron*, nerve.] *Pert*. or closely connected with nerves or nervous tissues.

neural arch,—arch formed on dorsal surface of vertebral centrum, by neural plates and neural spine, for passage of spinal cord.

neural canal,—canal formed by neural arches.

neural gland,—a body on ventral side of nerve ganglion in ascidians, presumable homologue of hypophysis in Craniata.

neural lobe,—infundibular process of pituitary gland or pars nervosa of neurohypophysis.

neural plates,—lateral members of a neural arch ; median row, usually of eight bony plates, in carapace of turtle.

neural shields,—horny shields above neural plates of turtles.

neural stalk,—infundibulum of neurohypophysis.

neurapophysis (nūrăpŏf′ĭsĭs) *n*. [Gk. *neuron*, nerve ; *apo*, from ; *phyein*, to grow.] The spinous process of a vertebra.

neuration (nūrā′shŭn) *n*. [Gk. *neura*, sinew.] Disposition of nervures ; nervation ; nervuration.

neuraxis (nūrăk′sĭs) *n*. [Gk. *neuron*, nerve ; L. *axis*, axle.] The cerebrospinal axis ; a neuraxon.

neuraxon (nūrăk′sŏn) *n*. [Gk. *neuron*, nerve ; *axon*, axle.] The central cylinder of a medullated nerve-fibre ; axis cylinder,

neurectoderm (nū′rĕktödĕrm) *n*. [Gk. *neuron*, nerve ; *ektos*, outside ; *derma*, skin.] The ectodermal cells forming the earliest rudiment of the nervous system, *opp*. skin ectoderm.

neurenteric (nūrĕntĕr′ĭk, nūrĕn′tĕrĭk) *a*. [Gk. *neuron*, nerve ; *enteron*, gut.] *Pert*. neurocoel and enteric cavity ; *appl*. canal, temporarily connecting posterior end of central canal of spinal cord with posterior end of enteric cavity.

neuric (nū′rĭk) *a*. [Gk. *neuron*, nerve.] *Pert*. nerves ; *pert*. nervous system ; neural.

neuricity (nūrĭs′ĭtĭ) *n*. [Gk. *neuron*, nerve.] Property peculiar to nerves.

neurilemma (nū′rĭlĕm′ă) *n*. [Gk. *neuron*, nerve ; *lemma*, skin.] Neurolemma, *q.v.* ; sheath of Henle, *q.v.*

neurility (nūrĭl′ĭtĭ) *n*. [Gk. *neuron*, nerve.] The stimuli-transmitting capacity of nerves.

neurite (nū′rīt) *n*. [Gk. *neuron*, nerve.] The axis-cylinder process ; axon, *q.v.*

neurobiotaxis (nū′röbī′ötăk′sĭs) *n*. [Gk. *neuron*, nerve ; *bios*, life ; *taxis*, arrangement.] Tendency of nerve fibres or ganglion cell groups to migrate, or growth of dendrites, towards source of most frequent stimulus.

neuroblasts (nū'röblăsts) *n. plu.* [Gk. *neuron*, nerve; *blastos*, bud.] Special epithelial cells from which nerve cells are formed.

neurocentral (nū'rösen'trăl) *a.* [Gk. *neuron*, nerve; L. *centrum*, centre.] *Appl.* two vertebral synchondroses persisting during first few years of human life.

neurochord (nū'rökôrd) *n.* [Gk. *neuron*, nerve; *chorde*, string.] A giant fibre, *q.v.*

neurocirrus (nū'rösĭr'ŭs) *n.* [Gk. *neuron*, nerve; L. *cirrus*, curl.] The cirrus of neuropodium of a polychaete annelid.

neurocoel (nū'rösēl) *n.* [Gk. *neuron*, nerve; *koilos*, hollow.] The cavity of central nervous system.

neurocranium (nū'rökrā'nĭŭm) *n.* [Gk. *neuron*, nerve; *kranion*, skull.] The cartilaginous or bony case containing the brain and capsules of special sense organs; *cf.* viscerocranium.

neurocrine (nū'rökrĭn) *a.* [Gk. *neuron*, nerve; *krinein*, to separate.] *Pert.* secretory function of nervous tissue or cells; neurosecretory. *n.* A substance or hormone liberated at nerve endings; neurohumor.

neurocyte (nū'rösīt) *n.* [Gk. *neuron*, nerve; *kytos*, hollow.] Nerve cell with its outgrowths; neurone.

neurocyton (nūrösī'tŏn) *n.* [Gk. *neuron*, nerve; *kytos*, hollow.] The body of a nerve cell; cyton.

neurodendron (nū'rödĕn'drŏn) *n.* [Gk. *neuron*, nerve; *dendron*, tree.] A dendrite.

neuro-epithelium (nū'rö-ĕpĭthe'lĭŭm) *n.* [Gk. *neuron*, nerve; *epi*, upon; *thele*, nipple.] Superficial layer of cells where specialised for a sense-organ.

neuro-fibrils (nū'röfī'brĭlz) *n. plu.* [Gk. *neuron*, nerve; L. *fibrilla*, fine fibre.] Exceedingly fine fibres of which a medullated nerve fibre is composed; fibrils in nerve cells, and extending into dendrites and axons; neurofibrillae.

neurogenesis (nū'röjĕn'ĕsĭs) *n.* [Gk. *neuron*, nerve; *genesis*, descent.] Nerve production.

neurogenic (nū'röjĕn'ĭk) *a.* [Gk. *neuron*, nerve; *genos*, birth.] Depending on discharge of nervous stimuli, as certain muscular contractions.

neuroglandular (nū'röglăn'dūlăr) *a.* [Gk. *neuron*, nerve; L. *glandula*, small acorn.] Having both nervous and glandular functions; *pert.* relation between nervous system and glands.

neuroglia (nūröglī'ă, nū-röglē'ă) *n. plu.* [Gk. *neuron*, nerve; *glia*, glue.] Cells, fibrous or protoplasmic, supporting nerve cells and nerve fibres; astrocytes and oligodendrocytes.

neurohumor (nū'röhū'mŏr) *n.* [Gk. *neuron*, nerve; L. *humor*, moisture.] Hormone produced by nervous tissue or associated glands which activates or inhibits other nervous tissue or its effectors; neurohormone.

neurohypophysis (nū'röhīpŏf'ĭsĭs) *n.* [Gk. *neuron*, nerve; *hypo*, under; *ph ein*, to grow.] The pars nervosa of posterior lobe and infundibulum of pituitary gland; neural lobe and stalk.

neuroid (nū'roid) *a.* [Gk. *neuron*, nerve; *eidos*, form.] Like a nerve; *appl.* intercellular conduction by non-nervous tissue; *appl.* intracellular transmission of stimuli, as in protozoa.

neurokeratin (nū'rökĕr'ătĭn) *n.* [Gk. *neuron*, nerve; *keras*, horn.] A pseudokeratin of nervous tissue.

neurolemma (nū'rölĕm'ă) *n.* [Gk. *neuron*, nerve; *lemma*, skin.] A delicate elastic membrane outside medullary sheath of nerve fibre; primitive sheath, nucleated sheath of Schwann.

neurology (nū'rŏl'öjĭ) *n.* [Gk. *neuron*, nerve; *logos*, discourse.] The study of the morphology, physiology, and pathology of the nervous system.

neurolymph (nū'rōlĭmf) *n.* [Gk. *neuron*, nerve; L. *lympha*, water.] Cerebrospinal fluid.

neuromasts (nū'rōmăsts) *n. plu.* [Gk. *neuron*, nerve; *mastos*, knoll.] Groups of sensory cells in lateral line system of fishes.

neuromere (nū'rōmēr) *n.* [Gk. *neuron*, nerve; *meros*, part.] A spinal segment corresponding in length to extent of attachment of pair of spinal nerves, a division of convenience, not structural; segmental ganglion of annelids and arthropods.

neuromery (nūrŏm'ĕrĭ) *n.* [Gk. *neuron*, nerve; *meros*, part.] Appearance of segmentation in developing nervous system.

neuromuscular (nū'rōmŭs'kūlăr) *a.* [Gk. *neuron*, nerve; L. *musculus*, muscle.] *Pert.* nerve and muscle; *appl.* muscle containing both striped and smooth fibres; neuromyal.

neuromyal (nū'rōmī'ăl) *a.* [Gk. *neuron*, nerve; *mys*, muscle.] Neuromuscular; *appl.* junction of end-plate and muscle as a functional unit.

neurone (nū'rōn) *n.* [Gk. *neuron*, nerve.] The nerve cell with its outgrowths, structural unit of the nervous system; neuron; neurocyte.

neuroneme (nū'rōnēm) *n.* [Gk. *neuron*, nerve; *nema*, thread.] A nerve fibril running parallel to a myoneme in an infusorian.

neuronephroblast (nū'rōnĕf'rōblăst) *n.* [Gk. *neuron*, nerve; *nephros*, kidney; *blastos*, bud.] One of cells derived from one of megameres, in segmenting egg of Clepsine, which later give rise to part of germinal bands from which nerve cord and nephridia develop.

neurophags (nū'rōfăgz) *n. plu.* [Gk. *neuron*, nerve; *phagein*, to eat.] Phagocytic cells that encroach upon and destroy nerve cells in old age.

neurophan (nū'rōfăn) *a.* [Gk. *neuron*, nerve; *phainein*, to appear.] Nervous, sensory; *appl.* supposed nervous fibrils of Ciliata.

neuropile (nū'rōpīl) *n.* [Gk. *neuron*, nerve; *pilos*, felt.] In ganglia, as of earthworm, a network of processes of association, motor, and sensory neurones; neuropil; neuropileus; punctate or plexiform intercellular substance of grey matter, forming layer of glial expansions and dendrites constituting the synaptic field; neuropilema.

neuroplasm (nū'rōplăzm) *n.* [Gk. *neuron*, nerve; *plasma*, form.] The undifferentiated portion or interfibrillar substance of cytoplasm of a neurone.

neuropodium (nū'rōpō'dĭŭm) *n.* [Gk. *neuron*, nerve; *pous*, foot.] Ventral lobe of polychaetan parapodium; terminal fibril of non-medullated nerve fibre.

neuropore (nū'rōpōr) *n.* [Gk. *neuron*, nerve; *poros*, passage.] Anterior opening of neurocoel to exterior.

neuropterous (nūrŏp'tĕrŭs) *a.* [Gk. *neuron*, nerve; *pteron*, wing.] Having wings with network of nervures; lace-winged.

neurosecretory (nū'rōsēkrē'tōrĭ) *a.* [Gk. *neuron*, nerve; L. *secernere*, to separate.] *Appl.* or *pert.* gland-like nerve cells.

neuroskeleton (nū'rōskĕl'ĕtŏn) *n.* [Gk. *neuron*, nerve; *skeletos*, dried up.] Endoskeleton.

neurosomes (nū'rōsōmz) *n. plu.* [Gk. *neuron*, nerve; *soma*, body.] Mitochondria of nerve cells.

neurosynapse (nū'rōsĭnăps') *n.* [Gk. *neuron*, nerve; *synapsis*, union.] Contiguity of nerve cells through terminal arborisations.

neurotendinous (nū'rōtĕn'dĭnŭs) *a.* [Gk. *neuron*, nerve; L. *tendere*, to stretch.] Concerning nerves and tendons.

neurotome,—neuromere.

neurotrophic (nū'rōtrŏf'ĭk) *a.* [Gk. *neuron*, nerve; *trephein*, to nourish.] Nourishing the nervous system.

neurotropic (nū'rōtrŏp'ĭk) *a.* [Gk. *neuron*, nerve; *trepein*, to turn.] *Pert.* neurotropism; acting upon nervous tissue; *appl.* viruses, bacteria, toxins, stains.

neurotropism (nūrŏt'rŏpĭzm) *n.* [Gk. *neuron*, nerve; *trepein*, to turn.] The attraction exerted by nervous tissue upon developing nerve tissue.

neurotubules,—delicate structures within axones, observed with the aid of an electron-microscope.

neurula (nū'rūlă) *n.* [Gk. *neuron*, nerve.] The stage in development of Chordata which coincides with formation of the medullary or neural tube.

neuston (nū'stŏn) *n.* [Gk. *neustos*, floating.] Organisms floating or swimming in surface water, or inhabiting surface film.

neuter (nū'tĕr) *a.* [L. *neuter*, of neither sex.] Sexless; having neither stamens nor pistils.

neutral (nū'trăl) *a.* [L. *neuter*, neither.] Neither male nor female; neither acid nor alkaline, $pH=7$; achromatic, as white, grey, and black; day-neutral, *q.v.*

neutrocyte (nū'trŏsīt) *n.* [L. *neutro*, to neither side; Gk. *kytos*, hollow.] A neutrophil leucocyte.

neutrophil (nū'trŏfĭl) *a.* [L. *neuter*, neither; Gk. *philein*, to love.] *Appl.* white blood corpuscles whose granules stain only with neutral stains; neutrophilic. *n.* A polymorphonuclear leucocyte.

N-factor,—a certain antigen in erythrocytes of higher animals.

niacin,—nicotinic acid, *q.v.*

niche (nĭch) *n.* [F. *niche*, from It. *nicchia*, recess in wall.] The place or status of an organism in its biotic environment; *cf.* microhabitat.

nicotinic acid,—the pellagra-preventive or P-P factor of vitamin B complex; niacin; $C_6H_5O_2N$.

nictitant (nĭk'tĭtănt) *a.* [L. *nictare*, to wink.] *Appl.* an ocellus with central lunate spot.

nictitating membrane,—third eyelid, a membrane which assists in keeping eye clean, in reptiles, birds, mammals.

nidamental (nĭd'ămĕn'tăl) *a.* [L. *nidamentum*, material for a nest.] *Appl.* glands which secrete material for an egg-covering.

nidation (nĭdā'shŭn) *n.* [L. *nidus*, nest.] The renewal of uterus lining between menstrual periods; embedding of fertilised ovum in uterine mucous membrane.

nidicolous (nĭdĭk'ŏlŭs) *a.* [L. *nidus*, nest; *colere*, to dwell.] Living in the nest for a time after hatching.

nidifugous (nĭdĭf'ūgŭs) *a.* [L. *nidus*, nest; *fugere*, to flee.] Leaving the nest soon after hatching.

nidulant (nĭd'ūlănt) *a.* [L. *dim.* of *nidus*, nest.] Partially surrounded or lying free in a hollow or cup-like structure.

nidulus (nĭd'ūlŭs) *n.* [L. *nidulus*, small nest.] A group of nerve-cell bodies in central nervous system; the nucleus from which a nerve originates.

nidus (nī'dŭs) *n.* [L. *nidus*, nest.] A nest; a nest-like hollow; a nucleus; a cavity for development of spores; nest of cells replacing epithelial cells of mid-gut in Orthoptera; focus or primary site of an infection.

nidus hirundinalis,—a fossa of cerebellum; nidus avis.

nigrescent (nīgrĕs'ĕnt) *a.* [L. *nigrescere*, to turn black.] Nearly black; blackish.

nipple (nĭpl) *n.* [*Dim.* of A.S. *nib*, for *neb*, nose.] Teat; mammary papilla; mamilla.

Nissl granules [*F. Nissl*, German neurologist]. Angular particles, consisting mainly of nucleoprotein, found in cytoplasm of unfatigued nerve cells; chromophil or tigroid bodies.

nisus (nī'sŭs) *n.* [L. *nisus*, effort.] Strong tendency; effort; muscular contraction for expulsion of eggs, young, or excreta.

nisus formativus (nī'sŭs fôrmătī'vŭs) *n.* [L. *nisus*, effort; *formare*, to form.] The tendency to reproduce.

nitid (nĭt'ĭd), **nitidous** (nĭt'ĭdŭs) *a.* [L. *nitidus*, shining.] Glossy.

nitrification (nī'trĭfĭkā'shŭn) *n.* [Gk. *nitron*, soda; L. *facere*, to make.] Oxidation of ammonia to nitrites and of nitrites to nitrates, as by action of bacteria.

nitrocobalamin,—vitamin B_{12c}.

nitrogenous (nītrŏj′ĕnŭs) *a.* [Gk. *nitron*, soda ; *genos*, descent.] *Pert.* or containing nitrogen.

nitrogenous equilibrium, — equilibrium of body maintained by equality of income and output of nitrogen.

nitrophilous (nītrŏf′ĭlŭs) *a.* [Gk. *nitron*, soda ; *philein*, to love.] Thriving in nitrogenous soils.

nitrophyte (nī′trŏfīt) *n.* [Gk. *nitron*, soda ; *phyton*, plant.] A nitrophilous plant.

nociceptive (nŏs′ĭsĕp′tĭv) *a.* [L. *nocere*, to hurt ; *capere*, to take.] *Appl.* stimuli which tend to injure tissue or induce pain ; *appl.* reflexes which protect from injury.

nociceptor (nŏsĭsĕp′tŏr) *n.* [L. *nocere*, to hurt ; *capere*, to take.] A receptor sensitive to injurious stimuli.

noctilucent (nŏk′tĭloo′sĕnt, -lū′-) *a.* [L. *nox*, night ; *lucere*, to shine.] Phosphorescent ; luminescent.

nocturnal (nŏktŭr′năl) *a.* [L. *nox*, night.] Seeking food and moving about at night only ; occurring at night.

nodal (nō′dăl) *a.* [L. *nodus*, knob.] *Pert.* a node or nodes.

node (nōd) *n.* [L. *nodus*, knob.] The knob or joint of a stem at which leaves arise ; aggregation of specialised cardiac cells, as atrioventricular and sinuatrial nodes ; a lymph gland ; one of the constrictions of medullary sheath or nodes of Ranvier ; nodus.

nodose (nŏd′ōs) *a.* [L. *nodus*, knob.] Having intermediate and terminal joints thicker than remainder ; having knots or swellings.

nodular (nŏd′ūlăr) *a.* [L. *nodulus*, *dim.* of *nodus*, knob.] *Pert.* a nodule or knot.

nodule (nŏd′ūl) *n.* [L. *nodulus*, *dim.* of *nodus*, knob.] A small knob-like structure, as root-nodule, lymphatic nodule ; anterior part of inferior vermis of cerebellum.

noduliferous (nŏd′ūlĭf′ĕrŭs) *a.* [L. *nodulus*, *dim.* of *nodus*, knob ; *ferre*, to carry.] Bearing nodules ; *appl.* roots of leguminous plants.

nodulus,—nodule.

nodus (nō′dŭs) *n.* [L. *nodus*, knob.] A node ; indentation near middle of anterior or costal margin of wing in Odonata.

noematic (nŏēmăt′ĭk) *a.* [Gk. *noema*, thought.] *Pert.* mental processes.

nomenclature (nō′mĕnklā′tūr, nōmĕn′klătūr) *n.* [L. *nomen*, name ; *calare*, to call.] System of naming plants, animals, organs, etc. ; binomial nomenclature.

nomogenesis (nō′mŏjĕn′ĕsĭs) *n.* [Gk. *nomos*, law ; *genesis*, descent.] View that development and evolution are governed by laws of development and not by environment.

non-conjunction,—failure of chromosome pairing.

non-deciduate,—indeciduate.

non-disjunction,—failure of a normal pair of chromosomes to separate at meiosis.

non-medullated, non-myelinated, *appl.* nerve fibres without medullary sheath ; amyelinate.

non-striated,—unstriped ; plain or involuntary, *appl.* muscle.

non-viable,—incapable of developing normally or of surviving parturition.

noosphere (nō′ŏsfēr) *n.* (Gk. *noos*, mind ; *sphaira*, globe.] The part of the globe containing living organisms as influenced by the human mind.

noradrenaline,—precursor of adrenaline ; norepinephrine.

norma (nôr′mă) *n.* [L. *norma*, rule.] View of the skull as a whole from certain points.

normoblasts (nôr′mŏblăsts) *n. plu.* [L. *norma*, rule ; Gk. *blastos*, bud.] Immature nucleated red blood corpuscles, derived from polychromatophil erythroblasts ; metarubricytes.

normocyte (nôr′mŏsīt) *n.* [L. *norma*, rule ; Gk. *kytos*, hollow.] The fully developed red blood corpuscle.

nosogenic (nŏs′öjĕn′ĭk) *a.* [Gk. *nosos*, disease; *gennaein*, to produce.] Causing disease; pathogenic.

nostrils (nŏs′trĭlz) *n. plu.* [A.S. *nosthyrl*, nostril.] The external openings of the nose; nares.

notal (nō′tăl) *a.* [Gk. *noton*, back.] Dorsal; *pert.* the back; *pert.* notum.

notate (nō′tāt) *a.* [L. *notatus*, marked.] Marked with lines or spots.

nothocline (nŏth′öklīn) *n.* [Gk. *nothos*, illegitimate; *klinein*, to slant.] The serial arrangement of characters or forms produced by crossing species; hybrid cline.

notocephalon (nō′tösĕf′ălŏn) *n.* [Gk. *noton*, back; *kephale*, head.] Dorsal shield of leg-bearing segments in certain Acarina; podosomatal plate; *cf.* notogaster.

notochord (nō′tökôrd) *n.* [Gk. *noton*, back; *chorde*, cord.] The dorsal supporting axis of lowest vertebrates, transitory in the others; chorda dorsalis.

notochordal (nō′tökôr′dăl) *a.* [Gk. *noton*, back; *chorde*, cord.] *Pert.* or enveloping notochord; *appl.* sheath, tissue, etc.

notocirrus (nō′tösĭr′ŭs) *n.* [Gk. *noton*, back; L. *cirrus*, curl.] Cirrus of notopodium of Polychaeta.

Notogaea (nō′töjē′ă, -gâ′yă) *n.* [Gk. *notos*, south; *gaia*, earth.] Zoogeographical area comprising Australian, New Zealand, and Pacific Ocean Islands regions, and formerly, neotropical region.

notogaster (nō′tögăs′tĕr) *n.* [Gk. *noton*, back; *gaster*, belly.] Posterior dorsal shield in certain Acarina; opisthosomatal plate; *cf.* notocephalon.

notogenesis (nō′töjĕn′ĕsĭs) *n.* [Gk. *noton*, back; *genesis*, origin.] Development of the notochord, and the associated stage of mesoderm differentiation.

notonectal (nō′tönĕk′tăl) *a.* [Gk. *noton*, back; *nektos*, swimming.] Swimming back downwards.

notopodium (nō′töpō′dĭŭm) *n.* [Gk. *noton*, back; *pous*, foot.] Dorsal lobe of polychaetan parapodium.

nototribe (nō′tötrīb) *a.* [Gk. *noton*, back; *tribein*, to rub.] *Appl.* flowers whose anthers and stigma touch back of insect as it enters calyx, a device for securing cross-fertilisation.

notum (nō′tŭm) *n.* [Gk. *noton*, back.] The dorsal portion of insect segment; tergum.

nucellus (nūsĕl′ŭs) *n.* [L. *dim.* of *nux*, nut.] Parenchymatous tissue between ovule or megaspore and its inner integument, and extending from chalaza at base to micropyle at apex.

nuchal (nū′kăl) *a.* [L.L. *nucha*, nape of neck.] *Pert.* nape of the neck; *appl.* two sense organs, regarded as olfactory, on prostomium of Chaetopoda; *appl.* thin cartilage between head and anterior dorsal part of mantle in decapod Cephalopoda; *appl.* anterior plate of chelonian carapace; *appl.* flexure of medulla oblongata. *n.* An unpaired posterior dorsal skull bone in Chondrostei.

nuciferous (nūsĭf′ĕrŭs) *a.* [L. *nux*, nut; *ferre*, to carry.] Nut-bearing.

nucivorous (nūsĭv′örŭs) *a.* [L. *nux*, nut; *vorare*, to devour.] Nut-eating.

nuclear (nū′klēăr) *a.* [L. *nucleus*, kernel.] *Pert.* a nucleus.

nuclear disc,—a star-like structure formed by chromosomes in equator of spindle during mitosis.

nuclear layer,—internal layer of cerebellar cortex; inner n.l. of retina, between inner and outer plexiform layers, and outer n.l., between outer plexiform layer and limiting membrane of layer of rods and cones.

nuclear membrane,—delicate membrane bounding a nucleus, formed from surrounding cytoplasm.

nuclear plate,—the equatorial plate.

nuclear spindle—a spindle-shaped structure formed of fine fibrils, in cytoplasm surrounding nucleus, a stage in mitosis.

nuclease (nū'klëās) *n.* [L. *nucleus*, kernel.] Enzyme of pancreatic and other cells.

nucleate (nū'klëāt) *a.* [L. *nucleus*, kernel.] Having a nucleus. *v.* To form into a nucleus. *n.* An ester or salt of nucleic acid.

nucleation (nūklëā'shŭn) *a.* [L. *nucleus*, kernel.] Nucleus formation.

nuclei,—*plu.* of nucleus.

nucleic (nū'klēĭk) *a.* [L. *nucleus*, kernel.] *Appl.* and *pert.* acids containing phosphorus, found in nuclei of cells.

nucleiform (nū'klēĭfôrm) *a.* [L. *nucleus*, kernel; *forma*, shape.] Shaped like a nucleus.

nuclein (nū'klēĭn) *n.* [L. *nucleus*, kernel.] A nucleoprotein found in nuclei,—yields a protein and nucleic acid by action of pancreatic juice; $C_{29}H_{49}O_{22}N_9P_3$.

nucleochylema (nū'klëökīlē'mă) *n.* [L. *nucleus*, kernel; Gk. *chylos*, juice.] Karyenchyma, nuclear sap.

nucleochyme,—karyenchyma, *q.v.*

nucleohyaloplasm (nū'klëöhī'ălöplăzm) *n.* [L. *nucleus*, kernel; Gk. *hyalos*, glass; *plasma*, mould.] The semi-fluid ground-substance of a nucleus; nuclear sap.

nucleoid (nū'klëoid) *a.* [L. *nucleus*, kernel; Gk. *eidos*, form.] Resembling a nucleus. *n.* A nucleus-like body occurring in certain blood corpuscles; a body taking part in bacterial cell division.

nucleolar (nūklē'ölăr) *a.* [L. *dim.* of *nucleus*, kernel.] *Pert.* a nucleolus.

nucleolar organiser,—granule, or a gene, which collects or secretes the nucleolus.

nucleolinus (nū'klēölī'nŭs) *n.* [*Dim.* of L. *nucleus*, kernel.] Small deeply staining intra-nucleolar granule which may divide in mitosis.

nucleolo-centrosome, — a nuclear body which may act as a centrosome during mitosis.

nucleolus (nūklē'ölŭs) *n.* [L. *nucleolus*, *dim.* of *nucleus* little kernel.] A rounded mass occurring in a nucleus; a plasmosome or a karyosome.

nucleolysis,—karyolysis.

nucleomicrosomes (nū'klëömī'krösōmz) *n. plu.* [L. *nucleus*, kernel; Gk. *mikros*, small; *soma*, body.] Nuclear chromatin granules.

nucleoplasm (nū'klëöplăzm) *n.* [L. *nucleus*, kernel; Gk. *plasma*, mould.] Reticular nuclear substance; karyoplasm; *cf.* cytoplasm.

nucleoprotein (nū'klëöprō'tëĭn) *n.* [L. *nucleus*, kernel; Gk. *protos*, first.] A compound of protein and nucleic acid, a constituent of cell nuclei.

nucleus (nū'klëŭs) *n.* [L. *nucleus*, kernel.] Complex spheroidal mass essential to life of most cells; mass of grey matter in central nervous system; a nidulus; centre of origin or hilum of starch grain; centre around which are formed the growth-rings of cycloid and ctenoid fish-scales; centre of perithecium in certain fungi; a protoconch, *q.v.*

nucleus ambiguus,—cells in medulla oblongata from which originate the motor fibres of glossopharyngeal and vagus, and of cerebral part of spinal accessory nerves.

nucleus pulposus,—the soft core of an intervertebral disc, remnant of notochord.

nuculanium (nū'kūlā'nĭŭm) *n.* [L. *nucula*, small nut.] A fleshy fruit, like a grape, differing from a berry in being superior.

nucule (nū'kūl) *n.* [L. *nucula*, small nut.] Nutlet; oogonium in Characeae.

nudibranchiate (nū'dĭbrăng'kĭāt) *a.* [L. *nudus*, naked; *branchiae*, gills.] Having gills not covered by a protective shell or membrane.

nudicaudate (nū'dĭkôd'āt) *a.* [L. *nudus*, naked; *cauda*, tail.] Having a tail not covered by hair or fur.

nudicaulous (nū'dĭkôl'ŭs) *a.* [L. *nudus*, naked; *caulis*, stem.] *Appl.* or having stems without leaves.

nudiflorous (nū'dĭflō'rŭs) *a.* [L. *nudus*, naked; *flos*, flower.] Having flowers without glands or hairs.

nudum (nū'dŭm) *n.* [L. *nudus*, naked.] Small bared area, as sensitive portion of antenna of butterflies.

Nuhn, glands of [*A. Nuhn*, German anatomist]. Anterior lingual glands or Blandin's glands.

nulliplex (nŭl'ĭplĕks) *a.* [L. *nullus*, none; *plexus*, interwoven.] Having recessive but no dominant genes for a given character, in polyploidy.

numerical,—*appl.* hybrid of parents that have different chromosome numbers.

nummulation (nŭm'ūlā'shŭn) *n.* [L. *nummus*, coin.] The tendency of red blood corpuscles to adhere together like piles of coins.

nummulitic (nŭm'ūlĭt'ĭk) *a.* [L. *nummus*, coin.] Like, *pert.*, or containing nummulites.

nuptial flight,—flight taken by queen bee when fertilisation takes place.

nurse cells,—single cells or layers of cells attached to or surrounding an egg-cell, for elaboration of food-material; trophocytes.

nurse generation,—an asexual budding generation of some Tunicata, in which phorozooids act as foster parents to later formed buds, the gonozooids.

nurture (nŭr'tūr) *n.* [O.F. *noriture*, nursing.] The sum-total of environmental influences, *opp.* nature.

nut (nŭt) *n.* [A.S. *knutu*, nut.] Dry, indehiscent one-celled fruit with hard pericarp; glans.

nutant (nū'tănt) *a.* [L. *nutare*, to nod.] Bent downwards; drooping.

nutation (nūtā'shŭn) *n.* [L. *nutare*, to nod.] Curvature or change of position in organs of a growing plant; slow rotating movement by pseudopodia.

nutlet (nŭt'lĕt) *n.* [*Dim.* of *nut.*] The stone formed in drupaceous fruits; achene of a schizocarp.

nutramins,—vitamins.

nutricism (nū'trĭsĭzm) *n.* [L. *nutrix*, nurse.] Symbiotic relationship with all the benefit to one partner.

nutrient (nū'trĭĕnt) *a.* [L. *nutrire*, to nourish.] Nourishing; *appl.* artery to marrow of bone, and foramen of entry. *n.* Food substance.

nutrilites (nū'trĭlīts) *n. plu.* [L. *nutrire*, to nourish.] Accessory organic food substances; bios; vitamins.

nutrition (nūtrĭsh'ŭn) *n.* [L. *nutrire*, to nourish.] The ingestion, digestion, and assimilation of food materials by animals and plants.

nutritive (nū'trĭtĭv) *a.* [L. *nutrire*, to nourish.] Concerned in function of nutrition; *appl.* yolk, polyp, zooid, plasma, etc.

nyctanthous (nĭktăn'thŭs) *a.* [Gk. *nyktos*, by night; *anthos*, flower.] Flowering at night.

nyctinasty (nĭk'tĭnăs'tĭ) *n.* [Gk. *nyktios*, nightly; *nastos*, pressed close.] Sleep movement of plants.

nyctipelagic (nĭk'tĭpĕlăj'ĭk) *a.* [Gk. *nyktios*, nightly; *pelagos*, sea.] Rising to surface of sea only at night.

nyctitropism (nĭk'tĭtrŏp'ĭzm, nĭktĭt'-rŏpĭzm) *n.* [Gk. *nyktios*, nightly; *trepein*, to turn.] Tendency of certain leaves to curve upwards at night; sleep movement; nyctinasty; nyctitropic curvature.

nymph (nĭmf) *n.* [Gk. *nymphe*, chrysalis.] A stage following the larval in insect metamorphosis; formerly: a pupa.

nymphae (nĭm'fē) *n. plu.* [Gk. *nymphe*, bride.] The labia minora; shell edges to which the hinge ligaments are attached, in bivalves; a pair of sclerites beneath epigynal plate in mites.

nymphal (nĭm'făl) *a.* [Gk. *nymphe*, chrysalis.] *Pert.* a nymph; *appl.* hormone secreted by corpus allatum during early stages and inhibiting premature metamorphosis.

nymphiparous,—pupiparous, *q.v.*

nymphochrysalis (nĭm'fŏkrĭs'ălis) *n.* [Gk. *nymphe*, pupa; *chrysallis*, from *chrysos*, gold.] Pupa-like resting stage between larval and nymphal form in certain mites.

nymphosis (nĭm'fōsĭs) *n.* [Gk. *nymphe*, chrysalis.] The process of changing into a nymph or a pupa.

O

oar-feathers, — the wing-feathers used in flight.

oarium,—ovarium, ovary.

obcompressed (ŏb'kŏmprĕst') *a.* [L. *ob*, towards; *comprimere*, to compress.] Flattened in a vertical direction.

obcordate (ŏbkôr'dāt) *a.* [L. *ob*, against; *cor*, heart.] Inversely heart-shaped; *appl.* leaves which have stalk attached to apex of heart.; obcordiform.

obcurrent (ŏbkŭr'ĕnt) *a.* [L. *ob*, against; *currere*, to run.] Converging, and attaching at point of contact.

obdiplostemonous (ŏbdĭplŏstē̆m'ŏnŭs) *a.* [L. *ob*, against; Gk. *diploos*, double; *stemon*, warp.] With outer series of stamens opposite petals.

obelion (ŏbē'lĭŏn) *n.* [Gk. *obelos*, a spit.] The point between parietal foramina, on sagittal suture.

obex (ŏb'ĕks) *n.* [L. *obex*, obstacle.] A triangular layer of grey matter, also a membranous ependymal layer, in roof of fourth ventricle; a limiting factor, *appl.* plant distribution. *Plu.* obices.

obimbricate (ŏbĭm'brĭkāt) *a.* [L. *ob*, reversely; *imbrex*, tile.] With regularly overlapping scales, with the overlapping ends downwards.

oblanceolate (ŏblăn'sēŏlāt) *a.* [L. *ob*, reversely; *lancea*, spear.] Inversely lanceolate.

obligate (ŏb'lĭgāt) *a.* [L. *obligatus*, bound.] Obligatory; limited to one mode of life or action; not optional; *appl.* aerobes, anaerobes; *appl.* sexual reproduction; *appl.* parthenogenesis; *appl.* saprophytes; *appl.* parasites which cannot exist independently of a host; *appl.* symbionts. *Opp.* facultative.

oblique (ŏblēk') *a.* [L. *obliquus*, slanting.] Placed obliquely; *appl.* septum forming ventral wall of thoracic air-sac in birds; *appl.* vein of left atrium, etc.; asymmetrical, *appl.* leaves; *appl.* cleavage: alternating or spiral.

obliquus (ŏblē'kwŭs) *n.* [L. *obliquus*, slanting.] An oblique muscle, as of ear, eye, head, abdomen.

obliterate (ŏblĭt'ĕrāt) *a.* [L. *obliteratus*, erased.] Indistinct or profuse; *appl.* markings on insects; suppressed.

oblongata,—medulla oblongata, *q.v.*

obovate (ŏbō'vāt) *a.* [L. *ob*, against; *ovum*, egg.] Inversely egg-shaped; *appl.* leaf with narrow end attached to stalk; *appl.* spores.

obovoid (ŏbō'void) *a.* [L. *ob*, against; *ovum*, egg; Gk. *eidos*, shape.] Inversely ovoid; roughly egg-shaped, with narrow end downwards.

obsolescence (ŏbsŏlĕs'ĕns) *n.* [L. *obsolescere*, to wear out.] The gradual reduction and consequent disappearance of a species; gradual cessation of a physiological process; a blurred portion of a marking on an animal.

obsolete (ŏb'sŏlēt) *a.* [L. *obsolescere*, to wear out.] Wearing out or disappearing; *appl.* any character that is becoming less and less distinct in each succeeding generation; *appl.* calyx united with ovary or reduced to a rim.

obsubulate (ŏbsū'būlāt) *a.* [L. *ob*, against; *subula*, awl.] Reversely awl-shaped or subulate; narrow and tapering from tip to base.

obtect (ŏbtĕkt') *a.* [L. *obtectus*, covered over.] *Appl.* pupa with wings and legs held to body. *Opp.* exarate.

obturator (ŏb'tūrā'tŏr) *a.* [L. *obturare*, to close.] *Pert.* any structure in neighbourhood of obturator foramen.

obturator foramen,—an oval foramen between ischium and os pubis.

obtuse (obtūs') *a.* [L. *obtusus*, blunt.] With blunt or rounded end; *appl.* leaves; *appl.* left margin of heart.

obtusilingual (ŏbtū'sĭlĭng'gwăl) *a.* [L. *obtusus*, blunt; *lingua*, tongue.] Short-tongued.

obumbrate (ŏbŭm'brāt) *a.* [L. *obumbrare*, to overshadow.] With some structure overhanging the parts so as partially to conceal them.

obverse (ŏbvĕrs') *a.* [L. *obvertere*, to turn round.] With base narrower than apex.

obvolute (ŏb'vŏlūt) *a.* [L. *obvolvere*, to wrap round.] Overlapping; *appl.* vernation when half of one leaf is wrapped round half of another similar leaf; half-equitant.

obvolvent (ŏbvŏl'vĕnt) *a.* [L. *obvolvere*, to wrap round.] Bent downwards and inwards; *appl.* wings, elytra of insects, etc.

occipital (ŏksĭp'ĭtăl) *a.* [L. *occiput*, back of head.] *Pert.* back part of head or occipital bones.

occipitalia (ŏk'sĭpĭtā'lĭă) *n. plu.* [L. *occiput*, back of head.] The group of parts of cartilaginous brain case forming back part of head; occipital bones.

occipito - atlantal (ŏksĭp'ĭtöătlăn'tăl) *a.* [L. *occiput*, back of head; Gk. *Atlas*, a Titan.] *Appl.* membrane closing gap between skull and neural arch of atlas in amphibians; *appl.* dorsal (posterior) and ventral (anterior) membranes between margin of foramen magnum and atlas in mammals; atlanto-occipital.

occipito-axial (ŏksĭp'ĭtöăk'sĭăl) *a.* [L. *occiput*, back of head; *axis*, axis.] *Appl.* ligament or membrana tectoria connecting occipital bone with axis or epistropheus.

occipitofrontal (ŏksĭp'ĭtöfrŭn'tăl) *a.* [L. *occiput*, back of head; *frons*, forehead.] *Appl.* longitudinal arc of skull; *appl.* fasciculus of long association-fibres between frontal and occipital lobes of cerebral hemispheres; *appl.* muscle, the epicranius.

occiput (ŏk'sĭpŭt, ŏk'sĭpoot) *n.* [L. *occiput*, back of head.] Occipital region of skull; dorsolateral region of insect head.

occlusal (ŏkloo'săl) *a.* [L. *occludere*, to shut in.] Contacting the opposing surface; *appl.* surfaces of teeth which touch those of the other jaw when jaws are closed.

occlusion (ŏkloo'zhŭn) *n.* [L. *occludere*, to shut in.] Overlapping of activation of motor neurones by simultaneous stimulation of several afferent nerves.

occlusor (ŏkloo'sŏr) *n.* [L. *occludere*, to shut in.] A closing muscle. *a. Appl.* muscles of an operculum or movable lid.

ocellar (ösĕl'ăr) *a.* [L. *ocellus*, little eye.] Of, or *pert.*, ocelli.

ocellate (ō'sĕlāt) *a.* [L. *ocellus*, little eye.] Like an eye or eyes; *appl.* markings on many animals.

ocellated,—having ocelli; having eye-like spots or markings.

ocellation (ŏs'ĕlā'shŭn) *n.* [L. *ocellus*, little eye.] Condition of having ocelli, or of having ocellate markings; ocellate marking.

ocelli,—*plu.* of ocellus.

ocelliferous,—ocellated.

ocellus (ösĕl'ŭs) *n.* [L. *ocellus*, little eye.] A simple single eye or eyespot found in many lower animals; an eye-like marking as in many insects, fishes, etc; a large cell of leaf epidermis, specialised for reception of light.

ochrea,—ocrea.

ochrophore (ō'kröfōr) *n.* [Gk. *ochros*, pale yellow; *pherein*, to bear.] A yellow pigment-bearing cell; iridocyte.

ocrea (ŏk'rēă,) *n.* [L. *ocrea*, greave.] A tubular sheath-like expansion at base of petiole; a sheath; partial covering of a stipe, formed by fragments of the disintegrated universal veil; ochrea.

ocreaceous (ŏk'rēā'shŭs) *a.* [L. *ocrea*, greave.] Ocrea-like; *appl.* various structures in plants and animals.

ocreate (ŏk'rēāt) *a.* [L. *ocrea*, greave.] Having an ocrea; booted, sheathed.

octactine (ŏktăk'tĭn) *n.* [Gk. *okta*, eight; *aktis*, ray.] A sponge spicule with eight rays, a modification of a hexactine.

octad (ŏk'tăd) *n.* [Gk. *okto*, eight.] A group of eight cells originating by division of a single cell.

octagynous (ŏktăj′ĭnŭs) *a.* [Gk. *okta*, eight; *gyne*, woman.] Having eight pistils.

octamerous (ŏktăm′ĕrŭs) *a.* [Gk. *okta*, eight; *meros*, part.] *Appl.* organs or parts of organs when arranged in eights; *appl.* parts of whorls of certain plants; *appl.* parts of certain Alcyonaria.

octandrous (ŏktăn′drŭs) *a.* [Gk. *okta*, eight; *aner*, man.] Having eight stamens.

octant (ŏk′tănt) *n.* [L. *octo*, eight.] One of eight cells formed by division of fertilised ovule in plants; one of units in eight-celled stage in segmentation of ovum.

octarch (ŏk′târk) *a.* [Gk. *okto*, eight; *arche*, element.] With eight vascular bundles.

octogynous,—octagynous.

octopetalous (ŏk′töpĕt′ălŭs) *a.* [Gk. *okto*, eight; *petalon*, leaf.] Having eight petals.

octophore (ŏk′töfōr) *n.* [Gk. *okto*, eight; *-phoros*, -bearing.] A modified ascus with eight spores arranged radially, as in Haerangiomycetes.

octoploid (ŏk′töploid) *a.* [Gk. *okto*, eight; *aploos*, onefold; *eidos*, form.] Having eight haploid chromosome sets in somatic cells. *n.* An octoploid organism.

octopod (ŏk′töpŏd) *a.* [Gk. *okto*, eight; *pous*, foot.] Having eight feet or arms.

octoradiate (ŏk′törā′dĭăt) *a.* [L. *octo*, eight; *radius*, spoke.] Having eight rays or arms.

octosepalous (ŏk′tösĕp′ălŭs) *a.* [L. *octo*, eight; F. *sépale*, sepal.] Having eight sepals.

octospore (ŏk′töspōr) *n.* [Gk. *okto*, eight; *sporos*, seed.] One of eight spores, as formed at end of carpogonial filaments, or in an octophore.

octosporous (ŏktŏs′pörŭs) *a.* [Gk. *okto*, eight; *sporos*, seed.] Having eight spores.

octostichous (ŏktŏs′tĭkŭs) *a.* [Gk. *okto*, eight; *stichos*, row.] Arranged in eight rows; having leaves in eights, in phyllotaxis.

octozoic (ŏk′tözō′ĭk) *a.* [Gk. *okto*, eight; *zoon*, animal.] *Appl.* a spore, of gregarines, containing eight sporozoites.

ocular (ŏk′ūlăr) *a.* [L. *oculus*, eye.] *Pert.* or perceived by the eye.

ocular lobe,—projecting thoracic lobe in some beetles.

ocular plates,—plates at end of ambulacral areas in sea-urchins.

oculate (ŏk′ūlāt) *a.* [L. *oculus*, eye.] Having eyes, or eye-like spots.

oculiferous (ŏk′ūlĭf′ĕrŭs), **oculigerous** (ŏk′ūlĭj′ĕrŭs) *a.* [L. *oculus*, eye; *ferre*, *gerere*, to carry.] Bearing eyes.

oculofrontal (ŏk′ūlöfrŭn′tăl) *a.* [L. *oculus*, eye; *frons*, forehead.] *Pert.* region of forehead and eye.

oculomotor (ŏk′ūlömō′tŏr) *a.* [L. *oculus*, eye; *movere*, to move.] Causing movements of eye-ball; *appl.* third cranial nerve.

oculonasal (ŏk′ūlönā′zăl) *a.* [L. *oculus*, eye; *nasus*, nose.] *Pert.* eye and nose.

oculus (ŏk′ūlŭs) *n.* [L. *oculus*, eye.] The eye; a leaf-bud in a tuber.

Oddi's sphincter [*R. Oddi*, Italian anatomist]. Muscle fibres surrounding duodenal end of common bile-duct.

odd-pinnate,—pinnate with one terminal leaflet.

odontoblast (ödŏn′töblăst) *n.* [Gk. *odous*, tooth; *blastos*, bud.] One of columnar cells on outside of dental pulp that form dentine; one of the cells giving rise to teeth of a radula.

odontobothrion (ödŏn′töbŏth′rĭŏn) *n.* [Gk. *odous*, tooth; *bothrion*, pit.] Tooth socket; alveolus dentis; phatne.

odontoclast (ödŏn′töklăst) *n.* [Gk. *odous*, tooth; *klan*, to break.] One of the large multinucleate cells that absorb roots of milk teeth.

odontogeny (ödŏntŏj′ĕnĭ) *n.* [Gk. *odous*, tooth; *gennaein*, to produce.] The origin and development of teeth.

odontoid (ödŏn′toid) *a.* [Gk. *odous*, tooth; *eidos*, form.] Tooth-like; *pert.* the odontoid process.

odontoid process,—dens, a tooth-like peg on axis round which atlas rotates, the centrum of atlas, which has first become free and finally fused with axis.

odontology (ödŏntŏl'öjĭ) *n.* [Gk. *odous*, tooth; *logos*, discourse.] Dental anatomy, histology, physiology, and pathology.

odontophore (ödŏn'töfōr) *n.* [Gk. *odous*, tooth; *pherein*, to carry.] The tooth-bearing organ in molluscs, including the radula, radula sac, cartilage, and muscles.

odontoplast (ödŏn'töplăst) *n.* [Gk. *odous*, tooth; *plastos*, moulded.] An odontoblast cell.

odontorhynchous,—lamellirostral.

odontosis (ödŏntō'sĭs) *n.* [Gk. *odous*, tooth.] Dentition; odontogeny.

odontostomatous (ödŏn'töstŏm'ătŭs) *a.* [Gk. *odous*, tooth; *stoma*, mouth.] Having tooth-bearing jaws.

odoriphore (ōd'ŏrĭfōr) *n.* [L. *odor*, smell; Gk. *pherein*, to carry.] A group of atoms responsible for the odour of a compound.

oecad (ē'kăd) *n.* [Gk. *oikade*, to one's home.] A form modified owing to habitat; a somatic modification; oecophene, ecad. *Opp.* phyad.

oecesis,—oikesis, *q.v.*

oecium (ē'sĭŭm) *n.* [Gk. *oikion*, abode.] The calcareous or chitinoid covering of a polyzooid.

oeco-,—*see also* eco-, oiko-.

oecoid (ē'koid) *n.* [Gk. *oikos*, house; *eidos*, form.] The stroma of a blood corpuscle; oikoid.

oecology (ēkŏl'öjĭ) *n.* [Gk. *oikos*, household; *logos*, discourse.] Ecology.

oecoparasite (ē'köpăr'ăsīt) *n.* [Gk. *oikos*, household; *parasitos*, parasite.] A parasite that can infect a healthy and uninjured host.

oecophene (ē'köfēn) *n.* [Gk. *oikos*, household; *phainein*, to appear.] Oecad, *q.v.*

oecotrophobiosis (ē'kötrŏföbīō'sĭs) *n.* [Gk. *oikos*, household; *trophe*, food; *biosis*, a living.] Trophallaxis, *q.v.*

oedematin (ēdē'mătĭn) *n.* [Gk. *oidema*, swelling.] The microsomes of ground-substance of nucleus.

oenocyte (ē'nösīt) *n.* [Gk. *oinos*, wine; *kytos*, hollow.] One of large cells from clusters which surround trachea and fat-body of insects and undergo changes in relation to moulting cycle.

oenocytoid (ē'nösī'toid) *n.* [Gk. *oinos*, wine; *kytos*, hollow; *eidos*, form.] One of rounded acidophil leucocytes in haemolymph of insects.

oesophageal (ēsŏf'ăjē'ăl, ēsŏfăj'ëăl) *a.* [Gk. *oisophagos*, gullet.] *Pert.* or near oesophagus, as ganglia.

oesophagus (ēsŏf'ăgŭs) *n.* [Gk. *oisophagos*, gullet.] That part of alimentary canal between pharynx and stomach, or part equivalent thereto.

oestradiol (ē'strădī'ŏl) *n.* [Gk. *oistros*, gadfly; *diolou*, together.] Ovarian hormone, transformed within organism to oestrone and oestriol; $C_{18}H_{24}O_2$.

oestrin,—oestrone, *q.v.*

oestriol,—one of the oestrogens in pregnancy urine; $C_{18}H_{24}O_3$.

oestrogen (ē'ströjĕn) *n.* [Gk. *oistros*, gadfly; *gennaein*, to produce.] A substance which induces oestrus; oestrogenic hormone.

oestrogenic (ē'ströjĕn'ĭk) *a.* [Gk. *oistros*, gadfly; *gennaein*, to produce.] Inducing oestrus; *appl.* hormones.

oestrone (ē'strōn) *n.* [Gk. *oistros*, gadfly.] The follicular oestrogenic hormone; oestrin, folliculin, theelin; $C_{18}H_{22}O_2$.

oestrous (ē'strŭs) *a.* [Gk. *oistros*, gadfly.] *Pert.* oestrus; oestrual.

oestrus (ē'strŭs) *n.* [Gk. *oistros*, gadfly.] The sexual heat of animals; rut; oestrum, oestruation.

offset,—a short prostrate branch which takes root at apex and develops new individuals.

offshoot,—lateral shoot from main stem.

oidia,—*plu.* of oidium.

oidiophore (ōĭd'ĭöfōr) *n.* [Gk. *oon*, egg; *idion*, *dim.*; *pherein*, to bear.] A hypha or hyphal structure bearing oidia.

oidiospore,—oidium.

oidium (ōĭd′ĭŭm) *n.* [Gk. *oon*, egg; *idion*, *dim.*] The conidial stage of some mildews; a thin-walled spore.

oike (oik′ē) *n.* [Gk. *oikein*, to have as one's abode.] Habitat; oikos.

oikesis (oik′ēsĭs) *n.* [Gk. *oikesis*, act of dwelling.] The establishment of organisms in a new habitat; ecesis (U.S.A.).

oikoid,—oecoid.

oikology,—ecology.

oikoplast (oik′öplăst) *n.* [Gk. *oikos*, house; *plastos*, moulded.] One of large glandular ectoderm cells which form gelatinous layer of appendicularians.

oikosite (oik′ösīt) *n.* [Gk. *oikos*, house; *sitos*, food.] A stationary or attached commensal or parasite.

oil gland,—a gland which secretes oil; the uropygial gland in birds.

oleaginous (ŏl′ëăj′ĭnŭs) *a.* [L. *oleaginus*, *pert.* olive.] Oily; *pert.*, containing, or producing oil.

olecranon (ōlĕk′rănŏn) *n.* [Gk. *olekranon*, point of elbow.] A large process at upper end of ulna.

oleiferous (ölēĭf′ërŭs) *a.* [L. *oleum*, oil; *ferre*, to carry.] Producing oil.

olein (ŏl′ēĭn) *n.* [L. *oleum*, oil.] A fat, liquid at ordinary temperatures, found in animal and vegetable tissues.

oleocyst (ŏl′ëösĭst) *n.* [L. *oleum*, oil; Gk. *kystis*, bladder.] A diverticulum of the nectocalyx.

oleosome,—elaioplast, *q.v.*

olfactory (ŏlfăk′törĭ) *a.* [L. *olfacere*, to smell.] *Pert.* sense of smell; *appl.* stimuli, structures, reactions.

olfactory lobe,—lobe projecting from anterior lower margin of cerebral hemispheres.

olfactory pit,—an olfactory organ of nature of a small pit or hollow; depression which later forms nasal passage.

olfactory spindle,—sensory cell structure associated with olfactory nerve in antennule of decapod crustaceans; lobus osphradicus.

oligacanthous (ŏl′ĭgăkăn′thŭs) *a.* [Gk. *oligos*, few; *akantha*, spine.] Bearing few spines.

oligandrous (ŏl′ĭgăn′drŭs) *a.* [Gk. *oligos*, few; *aner*, man.] Having few stamens; oligostemonous.

oligarch (ŏl′ĭgârk) *a.* [Gk. *oligos*, few; *arche*, beginning.] Having few vascular elements or bundles.

oligocarpous (ŏl′ĭgökâr′pŭs) *a.* [Gk. *oligos*, few; *karpos*, fruit.] Having few carpels.

Oligocene (ŏl′ĭgösēn) *n.* [Gk. *oligos*, few; *kainos*, recent.] A Tertiary geological epoch between Eocene and Miocene.

oligodendroglia (ŏl′ĭgödĕn′dröglī′ă, -dĕn′dröglē′ă) *n. plu.* [Gk. *oligos*, few; *dendron*, tree; *glia*, glue.] Adendritic neuroglia cells; oligoglia; oligodendrocytes; mesoglia.

oligodynamic (ŏl′ĭgödīnăm′ĭk) *a.* [Gk. *oligos*, few; *dynamis*, power.] Caused by small or minute forces; functioning in minute quantities.

oligogene (ŏl′ĭgöjēn) *n.* [Gk. *oligos*, few; *gene*, descent.] A qualitative gene or major mutant, *opp.* polygene.

oligogenic (ŏl′ĭgöjĕn′ĭk) *a.* [Gk. *oligos*, few; *gene*, descent.] Controlled by a few genes responsible for major heritable changes, *appl.* characters.

oligoglia (ŏl′ĭgöglī′ă, ŏl′ĭgöglē′a) *n.* [Gk. *oligos*, few; *glia*, glue.] Oligodendroglia.

oligolecithal (ŏl′ĭgölĕs′ĭthăl) *a.* [Gk. *oligos*, few; *lekithos*, egg-yolk.] Containing not much yolk.

oligolectic (ŏl′ĭgölĕk′tĭk) *a.* [Gk. *oligos*, few; *lektos*, chosen.] Selecting only a few; *appl.* insects visiting only a few different food-plants or flowers.

oligomerous (ŏl′ĭgŏm′ërŭs) *a.* [Gk. *oligos*, few; *meros*, part.] Having one or more whorls with fewer members than the rest.

oligonephrous (ŏl′ĭgönĕf′rŭs) *a.* [Gk. *oligos*, few; *nephros*, kidney.] Having few Malpighian tubules; *appl.* certain insects; oligonephric.

oligophagous (ŏl'ĭgŏf'ăgŭs) *a.* [Gk. *oligos*, few; *phagein*, to eat.] Restricted to a single order, family, or genus of food-plants, *appl.* insects; *cf.* monophagous.

oligophyletic (ŏl'ĭgöfīlĕt'ĭk) *a.* [Gk. *oligos*, few; *phyle*, tribe.] Derived from a few ancestral forms; *cf.* monophyletic, polyphyletic.

oligopod (ŏl'ĭgöpŏd) *a.* [Gk. *oligos*, few; *pous*, foot.] Furnished with few feet or legs; campodeiform.

oligopyrene (ŏl'ĭgöpīrēn') *a.* [Gk. *oligos*, few; *pyren*, fruit-stone.] *Appl.* certain spermatozoa with reduced number of chromosomes.

oligorhizous (ŏl'ĭgörī'zŭs) *a.* [Gk. *oligos*, few; *rhiza*, root.] Having few roots; *appl.* certain marsh plants.

oligospermous (ŏl'ĭgöspĕr'mŭs) *a.* [Gk. *oligos*, few; *sperma*, seed.] Bearing few seeds.

oligosporous (ŏl'ĭgöspō'rŭs) *a.* [Gk. *oligos*, few; *sporos*, seed.] Producing or having few spores.

oligostemonous (ŏl'ĭgöstĕm'önŭs) *a.* [Gk. *oligos*, few; *stemon*, thread.] Having few stamens; oligandrous.

oligotaxy (ŏl'ĭgötăk'sĭ) *n.* [Gk. *oligos*, few; *taxis*, arrangement.] Diminution in number of whorls.

oligothermic (ŏl'ĭgöthĕr'mĭk) *a.* [Gk. *oligos*, little; *therme*, heat.] Tolerating relatively low temperatures.

oligotokous (ŏl'ĭgŏt'ökŭs) *a.* [Gk. *oligos*, few; *tokos*, offspring.] Bearing few young.

oligotrophic (ŏl'ĭgötrŏf'ĭk) *a.* [Gk *oligos*, little; *trophe*, nourishment.] Providing, or *pert.*, inadequate nutrition; *opp.* eutrophic.

olistherozones (ŏlĭsthē'rözōnz) *n. plu.* [Gk. *olistheros*, sliding; *zone*, girdle.] Regions of incomplete splitting of chromatids, possibly due to nucleic acid deficiency; zones of differential reactivity.

oliva (ŏlī'vă), *n.* [L. *oliva*, olive.] A prominence on each side of anterior end of medulla just below pons; olive.

olivary (ŏl'ĭvărĭ) *a.* [L. *oliva*, olive.] *Pert.* the oliva, or olivary body; *pert.* certain nuclei of grey matter.

omasum (ōmā'sŭm) *n.* [L. *omasum*, paunch.] The psalterium or third division of a ruminant's stomach; manyplies.

ombrophil (ŏm'bröfĭl) *a.* [Gk. *ombros*, rain; *philein*, to love.] Adapted for rain, *appl.* plants, leaves.

omental (ōmĕn'tăl) *a.* [L. *omentum*, caul.] *Pert.* omentum or omenta.

omentum (ōmĕn'tŭm) *n.* [L. *omentum*, caul.] A fold ot peritoneum either free or acting as connecting link between viscera.

ommachromes,—ommatochromes.

ommateum (ŏmă'tēŭm) *n.* [Gk. *ommation*, little eye.] A compound eye.

ommatidium (ŏm'ătĭd'ĭŭm) *n.* [Gk. *ommation*, little eye; *idion*, *dim.*] One of component elements of a compound eye.

ommatochromes (ŏm'ătökrōmz) *n. plu.* [Gk. *omma*, eye; *chroma*, colour.] Eye-pigments.

ommatoids (ŏm'ătoidz) *n. plu.* [Gk. *omma*, eye; *eidos*, form.] Two or four light-coloured spots on last abdominal segment of Pedipalpi,—of disputed function.

ommatophore (ŏm'ătöfōr) *n.* [Gk. *omma*, eye; *pherein*, to bear.] A movable process bearing an eye.

omnicolous (ŏmnĭk'ölŭs) *a.* [L. *omnis*, all; *colere*, to dwell.] Capable of growing on different substrata; *appl.* lichens.

omnivorous (ŏmnĭv'örŭs) *a.* [L. *omnis*, all; *vorare*, to devour.] Eating both animal and vegetable tissue.

omohyoid (ō'möhī'oid) *a.* [Gk. *omos*, shoulder; *hyoeides*, Υ-shaped.] *Pert.* shoulder and hyoid; *appl.* a muscle.

omoideum (ōmoid'ëŭm) *n.* [Gk. *omos*, shoulder; *eidos*, shape.] Pterygoid bone of bird's skull.

omosternum (ō'möstĕr'nŭm) *n.* [Gk. *omos*, shoulder; L. *sternum*, breastbone.] Anterior element of amphibian sternum.

omphalic (ŏmfăl′ĭk) *a.* [Gk. *omphalos*, navel.] *Pert.* the umbilicus.

omphalodisc (ŏm′fălödĭsk) *n.* [Gk. *omphalos*, navel; *diskos*, disc.] An apothecium with a small central protuberance, as in certain lichens.

omphalodium,—omphaloidium.

omphalogenesis (ŏm′fălöjĕn′ësĭs) *n.* [Gk. *omphalos*, navel; *genesis*, descent.] Development of the umbilical vesicle and cord.

omphaloid (ŏm′făloid) *a.* [Gk. *omphalos*, navel; *eidos*, form.] Like a navel; having an umbilicus.

omphaloidium (ŏm′fălöĭd′ĭŭm) *n.* [Gk. *omphalos*, navel; *idion*, *dim.*] The scar at hilum of a seed, or hilum itself; omphalodium.

omphalomesenteric (ŏm′fălömĕs′ën-tĕr′ĭk, -mĕz-) *a.* [Gk. *omphalos*, navel; *mesenteron*, mid-gut.] *Pert.* umbilicus and mesentery; *appl.* arteries, veins, ducts.

oncosphere (ŏng′kösfēr) *n.* [Gk. *ongkos*, hook; *sphaira*, globe.] Larval stage of tapeworm preceding cysticercus; proscolex or six-hooked embryo stage of Cestoidea.

ontocycle (ŏn′tösī′kl) *n.* [Gk. *on*, being; *kyklos*, circle.] Evolution which in its later stages tends to produce forms exactly like those in the early stages.

ontogenesis (ŏn′töjĕn′ësĭs), **ontogeny** (ŏntŏj′ënĭ) *n.* [Gk. *on*, being; *genesis*, descent.] The history of development and growth of an individual; *cf.* phylogeny.

ontogenetic (ŏn′töjĕnĕt′ĭk) *a.* [Gk. *on*, being; *genesis*, descent.] *Pert.* ontogeny or development of an individual.

onychium (ŏnĭk′ĭŭm) *n.* [Gk. *onyx*, nail.] The layer below the nail; a pulvillus; a special false articulation to bear claws at end of tarsus in some spiders.

onychogenic (ŏn′ĭköjĕn′ĭk) *a.* [Gk. *onyx*, nail; *-genes*, producing.] Capable of producing a nail or nail-like substance; *appl.* material in nail matrix, and cells forming fibrous substance and cuticula of hairs.

onymy (ŏn′ĭmĭ) *n.* [Gk. *onyma*, name.] Nomenclature; applying onyms or technical names.

ooangium,—archegonium.

ooapogamy (ō′öăpŏg′ămĭ) *n.* [Gk. *oon*, egg; *apo*, away; *gamos*, marriage.] Diploid or somatic parthenogenesis.

ooblastema (ō′öblăstē′mă) *n.* [Gk. *oon*, egg; *blastos*, bud.] The egg after fertilisation.

oocarp (ō′ökârp) *n.* [Gk. *oon*, egg; *karpos*, fruit.] Oospore.

oocyst (ō′ösĭst) *n.* [Gk. *oon*, egg; *kystis*, bladder.] Cyst formed round two conjugating gametes in Sporozoa; pseudonavicella.

oocyte (ō′ösīt) *n.* [Gk. *oon*, egg; *kytos*, hollow.] An egg before formation of first polar body; in protozoa, a stage in 'female' conjugant before it prepares for fertilisation.

oocytin (ō′ösī′tĭn) *n.* [Gk. *oon*, egg; *kytos*, hollow.] Substance extracted from spermatozoa which has a fertilising and agglutinating effect on ova of same species.

ooecium (ōē′sĭŭm) *n.* [Gk. *oon*, egg; *oikos*, house.] An ovicell, or brood pouch.

oogamete (ō′ögămēt′) *n.* [Gk. *oon*, egg; *gametes*, spouse.] An oosphere of Sporozoa.

oogamous (ōŏg′ămŭs) *a.* [Gk. *oon*, egg; *gamos*, marriage.] Having sexually differentiated gametes; *pert.* oogamy.

oogamy (ōŏg′ămĭ) *n.* [Gk. *oon*, egg; *gamos*, marriage.] The union of a non-motile female gamete or egg-cell and a male gamete.

oogenesis (ō′öjĕn′ësĭs) *n.* [Gk. *oon*, egg; *genesis*, descent.] Formation, development, and maturation of the female gamete or ovum.

oogloea (ō′öglē′ă) *n.* [Gk. *oon*, egg; *gloia*, glue.] Egg cement.

oogone,—oogonium.

oogonial (ō′ögō′nĭăl) *a.* [Gk. *oon*, egg; *gonos*, begetting.] *Pert.* the oogonium.

oogonium (ō′ögō′nĭŭm) *n.* [Gk. *oon*, egg; *gonos*, begetting.] The female reproductive organ in certain thallophytes ; the mother egg-cell.

ooid (ō'oid) *a.* [Gk. *oon*, egg ; *eidos*, form.] Egg-shaped ; oval.

ookinesis (ō'ökĭnē'sĭs) *n.* [Gk. *oon*, egg ; *kinein*, to move.] The karyokinetic stages of nucleus in maturation and fertilisation of eggs.

ookinete (ō'ökĭnēt') *n.* [Gk. *oon*, egg ; *kinein*, to move.] The motile worm-shaped stage of the zygote in certain protozoa.

oolemma (ō'ölĕm'ă) *n.* [Gk. *oon*, egg ; *lemma*, husk.] The vitelline membrane of an egg ; the zona pellucida.

oology (ōŏl'öji) *n.* [Gk. *oon*, egg ; *logos*, discourse.] The study of eggs, particularly those of birds.

oophore (ō'öfōr) *n.* [Gk. *oon*, egg; *pherein*, to bear.] Ovary; oophyte, *q.v.*

oophoridium (ō'öfŏrĭd'ĭŭm) *n.* [Gk. *oon*, egg ; *pherein*, to bear ; *idion*, *dim.*] The megasporangium in certain plants.

oophoron,—ovary.

oophyte (ō'öfīt) *n.* [Gk. *oon*, egg ; *phyton*, plant.] The sexual generation in such plants as liverworts ; gametophyte.

ooplasm (ō'öplăzm) *n.* [Gk. *oon*, egg ; *plasma*, mould.] Cytoplasm or cell substance of an egg.

ooplast (ō'öplăst) *n.* [Gk. *oon*, egg ; *plastos*, formed.] An unfertilised ovum ; oosphere.

oopod (ō'öpŏd) *n.* [Gk. *oon*, egg ; *pous*, foot.] A component part of sting or ovipositor.

ooporphyrin (ō'öpôr'fĭrĭn) *n.* [Gk. *oon*, egg ; *porphyra*, purple.] A pigment of egg-shell of birds ; haematoporphyrin.

oosome (ō'ösōm) *n.* [Gk. *oon*, egg ; *soma*, body.] Spherical body in egg supposed to pass later to germ-cells ; germ track determinant or polar plasm.

oosperm (ō'öspĕrm) *n.* [Gk. *oon*, egg; *sperma*, seed.] A fertilised egg.

oosphere (ō'ösfēr) *n.* [Gk. *oon*, egg; *sphaira*, globe.] An egg before fertilisation ; a female gamete.

oospore (ō'öspōr) *n.* [Gk. *oon*, egg ; *sporos*, seed.] The zygote or fertilised egg-cell ; encysted zygote in certain protozoa.

oostegite (ō'östĕjīt) *n.* [Gk. *oon*, egg ; *stege*, roof.] A plate-like structure on basal portion of thoracic limb in certain Crustacea, which helps to form a receptacle for the egg.

oostegopod (ō'östĕg'öpŏd) *n.* [Gk. *oon*, egg ; *stege*, roof ; *pous*, foot.] A thoracic foot bearing an oostegite.

ootheca (ō'öthē'ka) *n.* [Gk. *oon*, egg ; *theke*, case.] A sporangium ; an egg-case, as in insects.

ootid (ō'ötĭd) *n.* [Gk. *oon*, egg ; *idion*, *dim.*] On analogy of spermatid, one of four parts into which egg divides at maturation.

ootocoid (ō'ötökoid) *a.* [Gk. *oon*, egg ; *tokos*, delivery ; *eidos*, form.] Giving birth to young at a very early stage, and then carrying them in a marsupium.

ootocous (ōŏt'ökŭs) *a.* [Gk. *oon*, egg ; *tokos*, delivery.] Egg-laying.

ootype (ō'ötīp) *n.* [Gk. *oon*, egg ; *typos*, mould.] Part of oviduct receiving ducts from shell- and yolk-glands, in flat-worms.

ooze (ooz) *n.* [A.S. *wase*, mud.] A deposit containing skeletal parts of minute organisms and covering large areas of ocean bottom ; soft mud.

oozoite (ō'özō'īt) *n.* [Gk. *oon*, egg ; *zoon*, animal.] Asexual parent, in tunicates.

oozooid (ō'özō'oid) *n.* [Gk. *oon*, egg ; *zoon*, animal ; *eidos*, form.] Any individual developed from an egg.

opercle,—operculum.

opercula,—*plu.* of operculum.

opercular (öpĕr'kūlăr) *n.* [L. *operculum*, lid.] Posterior bone of fish operculum. *a. Pert.* operculum ; *appl.* dehiscing antheridial cell, as in ferns.

operculate (öpĕr'kūlāt) *a.* [L. *operculum*, lid.] Having a lid, as the capsule of mosses ; calyptrate ; having a covering for gills, as most fishes ; operculiferous.

operculiform (ŏpĕr'kūlĭfôrm') *a.* [L. *operculum*, lid; *forma*, shape.] Lid-like.

operculigenous (ŏpĕr'kūlĭj'ënŭs) *a.* [L. *operculum*, lid; Gk. *gennaein*, to produce.] Producing or forming a lid.

operculum (ŏpĕr'kūlŭm) *n.* [L. *operculum*, lid.] A lid or covering flap, as at apex of an ascus, or of capsules of mosses; sepaline and petaline bud-cover, shed at flowering as in Eucalyptus; a convolution covering island of Reil; gill-cover of fishes; flap covering of nostrils and ears in some birds; lid-like structure or epiphragm closing mouth of shell in some gastropods; movable plates in shell of barnacle; first pair of abdominal appendages in Limulus and scorpions; small plate covering opening of a lung book in spiders; egg-cap, opened by emerging insect; chitinous lid of orifice in Polyzoa.

opesia (ŏpē'sĭă) *n.* [Gk. *ope*, hole.] Membranous aperture below orifice in Polyzoa.

ophiocephalous (ŏf'ĭŏkĕf'ălŭs, -sĕf-) *a.* [Gk. *ophis*, serpent; *kephale*, head.] *Appl.* larval pedicellariae of echinoids.

ophiopluteus (ŏf'ĭŏploot'ëŭs) *n.* [Gk. *ophis*, serpent; L. *pluteus*, shed.] The pluteus larva of Ophiuroidea.

ophiuroid (ŏfĭū'roid) *a.* [Gk. *ophis*, serpent; *oura*, tail; *eidos*, form.] Resembling or *pert.* a brittle-star; *appl.* cells: multiradiate or spiculate sclereids, astrosclereids.

ophryon (ŏf'rĭŏn, ŏfrī'ŏn) *n.* [Gk. *ophrys*, brow.] Point of junction of median line of face with a line across narrowest part of forehead.

ophthalmic (ŏfthăl'mĭk) *a.* [Gk. *ophthalmos*, eye.] *Pert.* eye; *appl.* a division of trigeminal nerve; *appl.* an artery arising from internal carotid; *appl.* inferior and superior veins of orbit.

ophthalmophore,—ommatophore, *q.v.*

ophthalmopod (ŏfthăl'mŏpŏd) *n.* [Gk. *ophthalmos*, eye; *pous*, foot.] Eye-stalk, as of decapod crustaceans.

opisthaptor (ŏpĭsthăp'tŏr) *n.* [Gk. *opisthe*, behind; *haptein*, to fasten.] Posterior sucker or disc in trematodes.

opisthial (ŏpĭs'thĭăl) *a.* [Gk. *opisthe*, behind.] Posterior; *appl.* pore or stomatal margin.

opisthion (ŏpĭs'thĭŏn) *n.* [Gk. *opisthe*, behind.] Median point of posterior margin of foramen magnum.

opisthocoelous (ŏpĭs'thŏsē'lŭs) *a.* [Gk. *opisthe*, behind; *koilos*, hollow.] Having the centrum concave behind; *appl.* vertebrae.

opisthocont,—opisthokont.

opisthodetic (ŏpĭs'thŏdĕt'ĭk) *a.* [Gk. *opisthe*, behind; *detos*, bound.] Lying posterior to beak or umbo; *appl.* ligaments in some bivalve shells; *cf.* parivincular.

opisthogenesis (ŏpĭs'thŏjĕn'ësis) *n.* [Gk. *opisthe*, behind; *genesis*, origin.] Development of segments or markings proceeding forward from the posterior end of the body.

opisthoglossal (ŏpĭs'thŏglŏs'ăl) *a.* [Gk. *opisthe*, behind; *glossa*, tongue.] Having tongue fixed in front, free behind.

opisthognathous (ŏpĭsthŏg'năthŭs) *a.* [Gk. *opisthe*, behind; *gnathos*, jaw.] Having retreating jaws.

opisthogoneate (ŏpĭs'thŏgŏn'ëăt) *a.* [Gk. *opisthe*, behind; *gone*, generation.] Having the genital aperture at hind end of body, as Chilopoda. *Opp.* progoneate.

opisthokont (ŏpĭs'thŏkŏnt) *a.* [Gk. *opisthe*, behind; *kontos*, punting-pole.] With flagellum or flagella at posterior end.

opisthonephros (ŏpĭs'thŏnĕf'rŏs) *n.* [Gk. *opisthe*, behind; *nephros*, kidney.] A renal organ of embryo, consisting of meso- and metanephric series of tubules.

opisthosoma (ŏpĭs'thŏsō'mă) *n.* [Gk. *opisthe*, behind; *soma*, body.] Posterior body region, as in Trilobita and Arachnoidea.

opisthotic (ŏp′ĭsthō′tĭk) *a.* [Gk. *opisthe*, behind; *ous*, ear.] *Pert.* inferior posterior bony element of otic capsule.

opisthure (ŏpĭsthūr′) *n.* [Gk. *opisthe*, behind; *oura*, tail.] The projecting tip of vertebral column.

opponens (ŏpō′nĕnz) *a.* [L. *opponere*, to oppose.] *Appl.* muscles which cause digits to approach one another.

opposite (ŏp′özĭt) *a.* [L. *opponere*, to oppose.] *Appl.* leaves which are opposite one another at same level on stem.

opsigenes (ŏpsĭj′ënēz) *n. plu.* [Gk. *opse*, late; *-genes*, born.] Structures formed or becoming functional long after birth.

opsonic (ŏpsŏn′ĭk) *a.* [Gk. *opsonein*, to cater.] *Pert.*, or affected by, opsonin; bacteriotropic.

opsonin (ŏp′sönĭn) *n.* [Gk. *opsonein*, to cater.] A constituent of blood which helps phagocytes to destroy invading bacteria; bacteriotropin.

optic (ŏp′tĭk) *a.* [Gk. *opsis*, sight.] *Pert.* vision.

optic axis,—line between central points of anterior and posterior curvature or poles of eye-ball.

optic bulb,—peripheral expansion of the embryonic optic vesicle, later invaginated to form the optic cup which gives rise to the retina.

optic disc,—region of entrance of optic nerve in retina; blind spot.

optic lobes,—part of brain intimately connected with optic tracts; corpora bigemina, *q.v.*

optic nerves,—second pair of cranial nerves.

optic rod,—rhabdome, *q.v.*

opticociliary (ŏp′tĭkösĭl′ĭărĭ) *a.* [Gk. *opsis*, sight; L. *cilia*, eyelashes.] *Pert.* optic and ciliary nerves.

opticon (ŏp′tĭkŏn) *n.* [Gk. *opsis*, sight.] Inner zone of optic lobes of insects.

opticopupillary (ŏp′tĭköpū′pĭlărĭ) *a.* [Gk. *opsis*, sight; L. *pupilla*, pupil of eye.] *Pert.* optic nerve and pupil.

optimum (ŏp′tĭmŭm) *n.* [L. *optimus*, best.] The most suitable degree of environmental factor for full development of organism concerned; point at which best response can be obtained.

optoblast (ŏp′töblăst) *n.* [Gk. *opsis*, sight; *blastos*, bud.] Nerve-cell of ganglionic layer of retina.

optocoel (ŏp′tösēl) *n.* [Gk. *opsis*, sight; *koilos*, hollow.] The cavity in optic lobes of brain.

optogram (ŏp′tögrăm) *n.* [Gk. *opsis*, sight; *graphein*, to write.] The image impressed on retina by action of light on visual purple.

ora (ō′ra) *n.* [L. *ora*, boundary.] A margin, as ora serrata: wavy border of retina, where nervous elements cease. *n. plu.* [L. *os*, mouth.] Mouths.

orad (ō′răd) *a.* [L. *os*, mouth; *ad*, to.] Towards the mouth or mouth region.

oral (ō′răl) *a.* [L. *os*, mouth.] *Pert.* or belonging to mouth; on side on which mouth lies, *opp.* aboral.

orbicular (ôrbĭk′ūlăr) *a.* [L. *orbis*, orb.] Round or shield-shaped with petiole attached to centre, *appl.* leaves; surrounding, *appl.* eye muscles; annular, *appl.* ligament of head of radius.

orbicularis (ôrbĭk′ūlā′rĭs) *a.* [L. *orbis*, orb.] *Appl.* a muscle whose fibres surround an opening.

orbiculate (ôrbĭk′ūlāt) *a.* [L. *orbiculatus*, rounded.] Nearly circular in outline; *appl.* leaves; *appl.* pileus.

orbit (ôr′bĭt) *n.* [L. *orbita*, circuit.] Bony cavity in which eye is situated; skin round eye of bird; hollow in arthropod cephalothorax where eye-stalk arises; conspicuous zone, or rim, of head-capsule, around compound eye of insects.

orbital (ôr′bĭtăl) *a.* [L. *orbita*, circuit.] *Pert.* the orbit.

orbitomalar (ôr′bĭtömā′lăr) *a.* [L. *orbita*, circuit; *mala*, cheek.] *Pert.* orbit and malar bone.

orbitonasal (ôr′bĭtönā′zăl) *a.* [L. *orbita*, circuit; *nasus*, nose.] *Pert.* orbit and nasal portions of adjoining bones.

orbitosphenoid (ôr′bĭtŏsfē′noid) *a.* [L. *orbita*, circuit; Gk. *sphen*, wedge; *eidos*, form.] *Pert.* paired cranial elements lying between presphenoid and frontal.

orchitic (ôrkĭt′ĭk) *a.* [Gk. *orchis*, testis.] Testicular; *pert.* testicle.

orculaeform (ôr′kūlĭfôrm) *a.* [L.L. *orcula*, *dim.* of L. *orca*, cask; *forma*, shape.] Cask-shaped; *appl.* spores of certain lichens.

order (ôr′dĕr) *n.* [L. *ordo*, order.] In classification, group of organisms closely allied, ranking between family and class.

ordinate (ôr′dĭnāt) *a.* [L. *ordinatus*, arranged.] Having markings arranged in rows.

ordinatopunctate (ôr′dĭnā′tŏpŭng′-ktāt) *a.* [L. *ordinatus*, arranged; *punctum*, prick.] Indicating serial presence of dots, etc.

Ordovician (ôr′dŏvĭsh′ĭăn) *a.* [L. *Ordovices*, tribe of North Wales.] *Pert.* or *appl.* period of Palaeozoic era between Cambrian and Silurian.

organ (ôr′găn) *n.* [Gk. *organon*, implement.] Any part or structure of an organism adapted for a special function or functions.

organ of Corti, or organon spirale,—Corti's organ, *q.v.*

organ of Valenciennes,—paired lamellated organ in female nautilus.

organellae (ôrgănĕl′ē) *n. plu.* [Gk. *organon*, instrument.] The various parts of a cell; organoids.

organic (ôrgăn′ĭk) *a.* [Gk. *organon*, instrument.] *Pert.*, derived from, or showing the peculiarities of a living organism; *pert.* carbon compounds.

organicism (ôrgăn′ĭsĭzm) *n.* [Gk. *organon*, instrument.] The co-operation or competition of cells, tissues, and organs and their reciprocal modifying action; the integration of an organism as a unit; the interblending of events within the organism.

organific (ôr′gănĭf′ĭk) *a.* [L. *organum*, instrument; *facere*, to make.] Producing an organism; making an organised structure.

organisation centre,—organiser.

organised (ôr′gănīzd) *a.* [Gk. *organon*, instrument.] Exhibiting characteristics of, or behaving like an organism; *appl.* growth resembling normal growth, in tissue culture, *opp.* unorganised growth of cells migrating from cut tissue.

organiser (ôr′gănīzĕr) *n.* [Gk. *organos*, fashioning.] A part of an embryo which provides a stimulus for the direction of morphological development and differentiation of other parts; *cf.* evocator.

organism (ôr′gănĭzm) *n.* [Gk. *organon*, instrument.] Any living animal or plant; anything capable of carrying on life processes.

organismic (ôr′gănĭs′mĭk) *a.* [Gk. *organon*, instrument.] *Appl.*, or *pert.*, factors or processes involved in integrating and maintaining individuality of an organism.

organogen (ôr′gănŏjĕn) *n.* [Gk. *organon*, instrument; *gennaein*, to produce.] Any of the elements C, H, O, N, also S, P, Cl.

organogenesis (ôr′gănŏjĕn′ĕsĭs) *n.* [Gk. *organon*, instrument; *genesis*, descent.] Formation and development of organs; organogeny.

organography (ôr′gănŏg′răfĭ) *n.* [Gk. *organon*, instrument; *graphein*, to write.] The description of organs in a living organism.

organoid (ôr′gănoid) *n.* [Gk. *organon*, instrument; *eidos*, form.] A formed morphological element in protoplasm; cell organ. *Opp.* metaplasm.

organoleptic (ôr′gănŏlĕp′tĭk) *a.* [Gk. *organon*, instrument; *lambanein*, to take hold of.] Capable of receiving, or of making, an impression.

organology (ôr′gănŏl′ŏjĭ) *n.* [Gk. *organon*, instrument; *logos*, discourse.] The study of organs of plants and animals.

organon spirale,—Corti's organ.

organonomy (ôr′gănŏn′ŏmĭ) *n.* [Gk. *organon*, instrument; *nomos*, law.] The laws that deal with life or living organisms.

organonymy (ôr'gănŏn'ĭmĭ) *n.* [Gk. *organon*, instrument; *onyma*, name.] The nomenclature of organs.

organophyly (ôr'gănŏfī'lĭ) *n.* [Gk. *organon*, instrument; *phyle*, tribe.] The phylogeny of organs.

organoplastic (ôr'gănŏplăs'tĭk) *a.* [Gk. *organon*, organ; *plassein*, to form.] Capable of forming, or producing, an organ; *pert.* formation of organs.

organotrophic (ôr'gănŏtrŏf'ĭk) *a.* [Gk. *organon*, instrument; *trephein*, to nourish.] *Pert.* formation and nourishment of organs.

organotypic (ôr'gănŏtĭp'ĭk) *a.* [Gk. *organon*, instrument; *typos*, pattern.] *Appl.* growth under somatic control; organised. *Opp.* histiotypic.

organule (ôr'gănūl) *n.* [L. *organum*, instrument.] A cell or element of an organism, or of an organ.

orgasm (ôr'găzm) *n.* [Gk. *organ*, to swell.] Immoderate excitement; turgescence of an organ.

Oriental (ōrĭĕn'tăl) *a.* [L. *orientalis*, eastern.] *Appl.* or *pert.* a zoogeographical region including India, Ceylon, Indo-China to Malaya and East Indies eastwards to Roma.

orientation (ō'rĭĕntā'shŭn) *n.* [L. *oriens*, rising of sun.] Alteration in position shown by organs or organisms under stimulus; relative disposition; arrangement of chromosomes with centromeres lying axially in relation to spindle.

orifice (ŏr'ĭfĭs) *n.* [L. *os*, mouth; *facere*, to make.] Mouth or aperture; opening of a tube, duct, etc.; orificium.

original (ŏrĭj'ĭnăl) *a.* [L. *origo*, origin.] *Pert.* beginning; *appl.* wild species from which cultivated have been derived.

ornis (ôr'nĭs) *n.* [Gk. *ornis*, bird.] Bird fauna of a region; avifauna.

ornithic (ôrnĭth'ĭk) *a.* [Gk. *ornis*, bird.] *Pert.* birds.

ornithichnite (ôrnĭth'ĭknīt) *n.* [Gk. *ornis*, bird; *ichnos*, track.] The fossil track or foot-print of a bird.

ornithine (ôr'nĭthĭn) *n.* [Gk. *ornis*, bird.] Diamino-valeric acid, found in excreta of birds; $C_5H_{12}O_2N_2$.

ornithocopros (ôr'nĭthŏkŏp'rŏs) *n.* [Gk. *ornis*, bird; *kopros*, dung.] The dung of birds.

Ornithogaea (ôr'nĭthŏjē'ă) *n.* [Gk. *ornis*, bird; *gaia*, earth.] The zoographical region which includes New Zealand and Polynesia.

ornithology (ôr'nĭthŏl'ŏjĭ) *n.* [Gk. *ornis*, bird; *logos*, discourse.] The study of birds.

ornithophilous (ôr'nĭthŏf'ĭlŭs) *a.* [Gk. *ornis*, bird; *philein*, to love.] Bird-loving; *appl.* flowers pollinated through agency of birds.

oroanal (ō'rŏā'năl) *a.* [L. *os*, mouth; *anus*, anus.] Serving as mouth and anus.

oronasal (ō'rŏnā'zăl) *a.* [L. *os*, mouth; *nasus*, nose.] *Pert.* or designating groove connecting mouth and nose.

oropharynx (ō'rŏfăr'ĭngks) *n.* [L. *os*, mouth; *pharyngx*, gullet.] The cavity of the mouth and pharynx; the space between the glossopalatine and pharyngopalatine arches or anterior and posterior pillars of the fauces. *Opp.* nasopharynx.

orrhoid (ŏr'oid) *a.* [Gk. *orrhos*, serum; *eidos*, form.] Serous.

ortet (ôr'tĕt) *n.* [L. *ortus*, origin.] The original single ancestor of a clone; *cf.* ramet.

orthal (ôr'thăl) *a.* [Gk. *orthos*, straight.] Straight up and down; *appl.* jaw movement. *Cf.* palinal, proral.

orthaxial (ôrth'ăksĭăl) *a.* [Gk. *orthos*, straight; L. *axis*, axle.] With a straight axis, or vertebral axis; *appl.* caudal fin.

orthochromatic (ôr'thŏkrōmăt'ĭk) *a.* [Gk. *orthos*, straight; *chroma*, colour.] *Appl.* large oval erythrocytes with nuclear strands passing out to nuclear membrane.

orthodentine (ôr'thŏdĕn'tĭn) *n.* [Gk. *orthos*, straight; L. *dens*, tooth.] Dentine pierced by numerous more or less parallel dentinal tubules; inner layer of circumpulpar dentine and outer layer of pallial dentine; *cf.* osteodentine.

orthoenteric (ôr'thöĕntĕr'ĭk) *a.* [Gk. *orthos*, straight; *enteron*, intestine.] Having alimentary canal along internal ventral body surface; *appl.* certain Tunicata.

orthogamy,—autogamy.

orthogenesis (ôr'thöjĕn'ësĭs) *n.* [Gk. *orthos*, straight; *genesis*, descent.] Evolution in a definite direction; determinate evolution, through variations which, irrespective of natural selection or external forces, gradually produce a new and distinct type.

orthokinesis (ôr'thökĭnē'sĭs) *n.* [Gk. *orthos*, straight; *kinesis*, movement.] Variation in velocity causing dispersal or aggregation of animals as a result of different stimuli; variation in linear velocity.

orthophyte (ôr'thöfīt) *n.* [Gk. *orthos*, straight; *phyton*, plant.] The plant in the interval between megaspore and megaspore production; sporophyte and gametophyte.

orthoploid (ôr'thöploid) *a.* [Gk. *orthos*, straight; *haploos*, onefold; *eidos*, form.] With even chromosome number; polyploid with complete and balanced genomes.

orthopterous (ôrthŏp'tërŭs) *a.* [Gk. *orthos*, straight; *pteron*, wing.] Having straight folded posterior wings, as grasshoppers.

orthoradial (ôr'thörā'dĭăl) *a.* [Gk. *orthos*, straight; L. *radius*, ray.] *Appl.* cleavage where divisions are symmetrically disposed round egg-axis.

orthoselection (ôr'thösēlĕk'shŭn) *n.* [Gk. *orthos*, straight; L. *selectio*, choice.] Selection conducive to advance in adaptation.

orthosomatic (ôr'thösōmăt'ĭk) *a.* [Gk. *orthos*, straight; *somatikos*, of the body.] Having a straight body; *appl.* certain larval insects.

orthospermous (ôr'thöspĕr'mŭs) *a.* [Gk. *orthos*, straight; *sperma*, seed.] With straight seeds.

orthospiral (ôr'thöspī'răl) *a.* [Gk. *orthos*, straight; *speira*, coil.] *Appl.* coiling of parallel chromatids, interlocked at each twist; plectonemic. *Opp.* anorthospiral, paranemic.

orthostichous (ôrthŏs'tĭkŭs) *a.* [Gk. *orthos*, straight; *stichos*, row.] Arranged in a vertical row, *appl.* leaves; *appl.* fin skeleton when peripheral somactids are parallel.

orthostichy (ôrthŏs'tĭkĭ) *n.* [Gk. *orthos*, straight; *stichos*, row.] Vertical line on which a row of leaves or scales is found; arrangement of leaves or scales in this row.

orthotriaene (ôr'thötrī'ēn) *n.* [Gk. *orthos*, straight; *triaina*, trident.] A triaene with cladi directed outwards at right angles to shaft.

orthotropal,—orthotropous.

orthotropic (ôr'thötrŏp'ĭk) *a.* [Gk. *orthos*, straight; *trope*, turn.] Tending to be orientated in line of action of stimulus; growing vertically, as stem or root. *Opp.* plagiotropic.

orthotropism (ôrthŏt'röpĭzm) *n.* [Gk. *orthos*, straight; *trope*, turn.] Growth in a vertical line; condition of an orthotropic plant organ.

orthotropous (ôrthŏt'röpŭs) *a.* [Gk. *orthos*, straight; *trope*, turn.] Having chalaza, hilum, and micropyle in a straight line; *appl.* ovules; atropous.

orthotype (ôr'thötīp) *n.* [Gk. *orthos*, straight; *typos*, pattern.] Genotype originally designated.

oryctics (ŏrĭk'tĭks) *n.* [Gk. *oryktos*, dug out.] The study of fossils; oryctology, palaeontology.

os (ōs) *n.*, **ora** (ō'ră) *plu.* [L. *os*, mouth.] A mouth; mouths.

os (ŏs) *n.*, **ossa** (ŏs'a) *plu.* [L. *os*, bone.] A bone; bones.

oscitate (ŏs'sĭtāt) *v.* [L. *oscitare*, to yawn.] To yawn; to gape.

oscula,—*plu.* of osculum.

osculant (ŏs'kūlănt) *a.* [L. *osculans*, kissing.] Closely adherent; intermediate in character between two groups, genera, or species.

oscular (ŏs'kūlăr) *a.* [L. *osculum*, small mouth.] *Pert.* an osculum.

osculate (ŏs'kūlāt) *v.* [L. *osculare*, to kiss.] To have characters intermediate between two groups.

oscule,—osculum.

osculiferous (ŏs'kūlĭf'ërŭs) *a.* [L. *osculum*, small mouth; *ferre*, to bear.] Having oscula.

osculum (ŏs'kūlŭm) *n.* [L. *osculum*, small mouth.] An excurrent opening in a sponge.

osmeterium (ŏs'mētē'rĭŭm) *n.* [Gk. *osme*, smell; *terein*, to keep.] A forked protrusible organ borne on first thoracic segment of larva of some butterflies, emitting a smell.

osmics (ŏs'mĭks) *n.* [Gk. *osme*, smell.] The study of olfactory organs and the sense of smell, and of odoriferous organs and substances.

osmiophil (ŏs'mĭöfĭl) *a.* [*Osmium*, from Gk. *osme*, smell; *philein*, to love.] Staining readily with osmic acid, as olein in tissues, and as externum of Golgi bodies; osmiophilic.

osmoreceptors (ŏs'mörēsĕp'tŏrz) *n. plu.* [Gk. *osmos*, impulse; L. *recipere*, to receive.] Cells reacting to osmotic changes in blood, and, via parasympathetic fibres innervating the posterior lobe of pituitary gland, controlling secretion of the antidiuretic hormone.

osmosis (ŏsmō'sĭs) *n.* [Gk. *osmos*, impulse.] A diffusion which takes place between two miscible fluids through a permeable membrane.

osmosium (ŏsmō'sĭŭm) *n.* [Gk. *osmos*, impulse.] The part of nematode intestine connecting with demanian vessels.

osmotaxis (ŏs'mötăk'sĭs) *n.* [Gk. *osmos*, impulse; *taxis*, arrangement.] Locomotory response to changes in osmotic pressure; tonotaxis.

osmotic (ŏsmŏt'ĭk) *a.* [Gk. *osmos*, impulse.] *Pert.* osmosis.

osmyl (ŏs'mĭl) *n.* [Gk. *osme*, smell; *hyle*, matter.] Any odorous substance.

osphradium (ŏsfrā'dĭŭm) *n.* [Gk. *osphradion*, strong scent.] A chemical sense organ associated with visceral ganglia in molluscs.

osphresiology (ŏs'frēsĭŏl'öjĭ) *n.* [Gk. *osphresis*, sense of smell; *logos*, discourse.] The study of the sense of smell.

osphresis (ŏs'frēsĭs) *n.* [Gk. *osphresis*, sense of smell.] The sense of smell.

ossa,—bones, *plu.* of os.

ossa triquetra,—Wormian bones.

ossein (ŏs'ëĭn) *n.* [L. *osseus*, bony.] The most abundant organic constituent of bone; bone collagen.

osseous (ŏs'ëŭs) *a.* [L. *osseus*, bony.] Composed of or resembling bone.

osseous labyrinth,—vestibule, semicircular canals, and cochlea, in petrous part of temporal bone and containing the membranous labyrinth.

ossicle (ŏs'ĭkl) *n.* [*Dim.* of L. *os*, bone.] Any small bone; one of those in ear, or in sclerotic; one of those in gastric mill of Crustacea; a plate of skeleton of echinoderms.

ossicone (ŏs'ĭkōn) *n.* [L. *os*, bone; *conus*, cone.] The os cornu or horn core of ruminants.

ossicular (ŏsĭk'ūlăr) *a.* [*Dim.* of L. *os*, bone.] *Pert.* ossicles.

ossiculate,—having ossicles.

ossiculum (ŏsĭk'ūlŭm) *n.* [*Dim.* of L. *os*, bone.] An ossicle; a lithodesma; a partly calcified byssus; a pyrene.

ossification (ŏs'ĭfĭkā'shŭn) *n.* [L. *os*, bone; *facere*, to make.] The formation of bone; replacement of cartilage by bone.

ossify (ŏs'ĭfī) *v.* [L. *os*, bone; *fieri*, to become.] To change to bone.

osteoblast (ŏs'tëöblăst) *n.* [Gk. *osteon*, bone; *blastos*, bud.] A bone-forming cell.

osteochondral (ŏs'tëökôn'dral) *a.* [Gk. *osteon*, bone; *chondros*, cartilage.] *Pert.* bone and cartilage; osteochondrous, consisting of bone and cartilage.

osteoclast (ŏs'tëöklăst) *n.* [Gk. *osteon*, bone; *klan*, to break.]

A cell which absorbs or breaks up bony tissue or cartilage matrix.

osteocomma (ŏs′tēŏkŏm′ă) *n.* [Gk. *osteon*, bone; *komma*, piece.] A segment of the vertebral skeleton; osteomere.

osteocranium (ŏs′tēŏkrā′nĭŭm) *n.* [Gk. *osteon*, bone; *kranion*, skull.] Bony skull as distinguished from cartilaginous or chondrocranium.

osteocyte (ŏs′tēŏsīt) *n.* [Gk. *osteon*, bone; *kytos*, hollow.] A bone cell, developed from osteoblast.

osteodentine (ŏs′tēŏdĕn′tĭn) *n.* [Gk. *osteon*, bone; L. *dens*, tooth.] A variety of dentine which closely approaches bone in structure.

osteodermis (ŏs′tēŏdĕr′mĭs) *n.* [Gk. *osteon*, bone; *derma*, skin.] A dermis which is more or less ossified; a bony dermal plate.

osteogen (ŏs′tēŏjĕn′) *n.* [Gk. *osteon*, bone; *gennaein*, to produce.] The tissue which alters and forms bone.

osteogenesis (ŏs′tēŏjĕn′ĕsĭs) *n.* [Gk. *osteon*, bone; *genesis*, descent.] Bone formation.

osteogenetic (ŏs′tēŏjĕnĕt′ĭk), **osteogenic** (ŏs′tēŏjĕn′ĭk) *a.* [Gk. *osteon*, bone; *genesis*, descent.] *Pert.* or causing formation of bone.

osteoid (ŏs′tēoid) *a.* [Gk. *osteon*, bone; *eidos*, form.] Bone-like.

osteology (ŏs′tēŏl′ŏjĭ) *n.* [Gk. *osteon*, bone; *logos*, discourse.] That part of zoology dealing with structure, nature, and development of bones.

osteomere (ŏs′tēŏmēr) *n.* [Gk. *osteon*, bone; *meros*, part.] A segment of the vertebral skeleton; osteocomma.

osteone,—Haversian system, *q.v.*

osteoplastic (ŏs′tēŏplăs′tĭk) *a.* [Gk. *osteon*, bone; *plastos*, moulded.] Producing bone; *appl.* certain cells.

osteosclereid (ŏs′tēŏsklē′rēĭd) *n.* [Gk. *osteon*, bone; *skleros*, hard; *eidos*, shape.] A sclereid with both ends knobbed.

osteoscute (ŏs′tēŏskūt) *n.* [Gk. *osteon*, bone; L. *scutum*, shield.] A bony external scale or plate, as in labyrinthodonts and armadillos.

ostia,—*plu.* of ostium.

ostial,—of or *pert.* ostia or an ostium.

ostiate (ŏs′tĭăt) *a.* [L. *ostium*, door.] Furnished with ostia.

ostiolar (ŏs′tĭŏlăr) *a.* [L. *ostiolum*, little door.] *Pert.* an ostiole.

ostiolate (ŏs′tĭŏlāt) *a.* [L. *ostiolum*, little door.] Provided with ostioles.

ostiole (ŏs′tĭōl) *n.* [L. *ostiolum*, little door.] A small opening, as of conceptacle, perithecium, stoma, anther sac, etc.; inhalant aperture of sponge.

ostium (ŏs′tĭŭm) *n.* [L. *ostium*, door.] Any mouth-like opening; opening of Fallopian tube; opening between atria of foetal heart; opening in arthropod heart by which blood enters from pericardium; opening from flagellate canal into paragastric cavity in sponges. *Plu.* ostia.

otic (ō′tĭk) *a.* [Gk. *ous*, ear.] *Pert.* ear; *pert.* region of auditory capsule; *appl.* ganglion on mandibular nerve.

otidium (ōtĭd′ĭŭm) *n.* [Gk. *ous*, ear; *idion*, *dim.*] The otocyst of a mollusc.

otoconium (ō′tŏkō′nĭŭm) *n.* [Gk. *ous*, ear; *konia*, sand.] One of minute crystals of calcium carbonate found in membranous labyrinth of inner ear; ear dust; otoconite.

otocrypt (ō′tŏkrĭpt) *n.* [Gk. *ous*, ear; *kryptos*, hidden.] An open invagination of integument of foot in certain molluscs.

otocyst (ō′tŏsĭst) *n.* [Gk. *ous*, ear; *kystis*, bladder.] A sac containing fluid and otoliths, supposed to be auditory; embryonic auditory vesicle.

otolith (ō′tŏlĭth) *n.* [Gk. *ous*, ear; *lithos*, stone.] Calcareous particle or plate-like structure found in auditory organ of many animals.

oto-occipital (ō′tŏŏksĭp′ĭtăl) *n.* [Gk. *ous*, ear; L. *occiput*, back of head.] Bone formed by fusion of opisthotic with exoccipital.

otoporpae (ō′tŏpŏr′pē) *n. plu.* [Gk. *ous*, ear; *porpe*, brooch.] Stripes of cnidoblasts on exumbrella of Hydromedusae.

otosalpinx (ōʹtösălʹpĭngks) *n.* [Gk. *ous*, ear; *salpingx*, trumpet.] Tuba auditiva or Eustachian tube.

otostapes (ōʹtöstāʹpēz) *n.* [Gk. *ous*, ear; L.L. *stapes*, stirrup.] Otic portion of columellar primordium which in adult may give rise to stapes and part of columella

otosteon (ōtŏsʹtēŏn) *n.* [Gk. *ous*, ear; *osteon*, bone.] An auditory ossicle.

ova,—*plu.* of ovum.

oval (ōʹvăl) *a.* [L. *ovum*, egg.] Egg-shaped; *pert.* an egg.

ovalbumin (ōʹvălbūʹmĭn) *n.* [L. *ovum*, egg; *albumen*, white of egg.] The chief protein constituent of white of egg.

ovarian (ōvāʹrĭăn) *a.* [L. *ovarium*, ovary.] *Pert.* an ovary.

ovariole (ōvāʹrĭōl) *n.* [L. *ovarium*, ovary.] Egg tube of insect ovary.

ovariotestis (ōvărʹĭötĕsʹtĭs) *n.* [L. *ovarium*, ovary; *testis*, testicle.] Generative organ when both male and female elements are formed, as in case of sex reversal; *cf.* ovotestis.

ovarium (ōvăʹrĭŭm) *n.* [L. *ovarium*, ovary.] An ovary.

ovary (ōʹvărĭ) *n.* [L. *ovarium*, ovary.] The essential female reproductive gland; an enlarged portion of pistil or gynoecium, containing ovules.

ovate (ōʹvāt) *a.* [L. *ovum*, egg.] Egg-shaped; and attached by the broader end, *appl.* leaves.

ovate-acuminate,—*appl.* an ovate lamina with very sharp point; *appl.* leaves.

ovate-ellipsoidal,—ovate, approaching ellipsoid; *appl.* leaves.

ovate-lanceolate,—having a form of lamina intermediate between ovate and lanceolate.

ovate-oblong,—having an oblong lamina with one end narrower.

ovejector (ōʹvējĕkʹtŏr) *n.* [L. *ovum*, egg; *ejectum*, thrown out.] The muscular terminal part of female genital tract considered as a functional unit, in nematodes.

ovenchyma (ōvĕngʹkĭmă) *n.* [L. *ovum*, egg; Gk. *engchyma*, infusion.] A connective tissue with ovoid cells.

ovicapsule (ōʹvĭkăpʹsūl) *n.* [L. *ovum*, egg; *capsula*, small box.] An egg-case; ootheca.

ovicell (ōʹvĭsĕl) *n.* [L. *ovum*, egg; *cella*, cell.] A dilatation of an ooecium, serving as a brood pouch.

oviducal (ōʹvĭdūkăl) *a.* [L. *ovum*, egg; *ducere*, to lead.] *Pert.* oviduct.

oviduct (ōʹvĭdŭkt) *n.* [L. *ovum*, egg; *ducere*, to lead.] The tube which carries eggs from ovary to exterior; Müllerian duct.

oviferous (ōvĭfʹĕrŭs) *a.* [L. *ovum*, egg; *ferre*, to carry.] Serving to carry eggs; ovigerous.

oviform (ōʹvĭfôrm) *a.* [L. *ovum*, egg; *forma*, shape.] Egg-shaped; oval.

oviger (ōʹvĭjĕr) *n.* [L. *ovum*, egg; *gerere*, to bear.] Egg-carrying leg of Pycnogonida.

ogerous,—oviferous.

oviparity (ōʹvĭpărʹĭtĭ) *n.* [L. *ovum*, egg; *parere*, to bring forth.] Condition of being oviparous.

oviparous (ōvĭpʹărŭs) *a.* [L. *ovum*, egg; *parere*, to bring forth.] Producing eggs; egg-laying; *cf.* viviparous; ovoviviparous.

oviposit (ōʹvĭpŏzʹĭt) *v.* [L. *ovum*, egg; *ponere*, to place.] To lay eggs; *appl.* insects.

ovipositor (ōʹvĭpŏzʹĭtŏr) *n.* [L. *ovum*, egg; *ponere*, to place.] A specialised structure in insects for placing eggs in a suitable place; a tubular extension of genital orifice in fishes.

ovisac (ōʹvĭsăk) *n.* [L. *ovum*, egg; *saccus*, bag.] An egg-capsule or receptacle.

oviscapte (ōʹvĭskăpt) *n.* [L. *ovum*, egg; F. *capter*, from L. *captare*, to conduct.] Ovipositor.

ovism (ōʹvĭzm) *n.* [L. *ovum*, egg.] Theory held by ovists that the egg contained the germ with germs of all future generations within it.

ovocentre (ōʹvösĕnʹtĕr) *n.* [L. *ovum*, egg; *centrum*, centre.] The egg-centrosome during fertilisation.

ovocyst, ovocyte, ovogenesis, — oocyst, oocyte, oogenesis, *q.v.*

ovoid (ōʹvoid) *a.* [L. *ovum*, egg; Gk. *eidos*, form.] Somewhat egg-shaped.

ovomucoid (ō'vōmū'koid) *n.* [L. *ovum*, egg; *mucus*, mucus; Gk. *eidos*, form.] A mucoid of eggs.

ovoplasm,—ooplasm.

ovotestis (ō'vōtĕs'tĭs) *n.* [L. *ovum*, egg; *testis*, testicle.] The hermaphrodite reproductive gland of certain gastropods.

ovoviviparous (ō'vōvĭvĭp'ărŭs) *a.* [L. *ovum*, egg; *vivus*, living; *parere*, to bring forth.] *Pert.* forms which produce an egg with definite shell, which hatches in maternal body; *cf.* oviparous, viviparous.

ovular (ŏv'ūlăr) *a.* [*Dim.* of L. *ovum*, egg.] Like or *pert.* an ovule.

ovulate (ŏv'ūlāt) *a.* [L. *ovum*, egg.] Containing an egg or ovule. *v.* To emit egg or eggs from ovary or ovarian follicles.

ovulation (ŏvūlā'shŭn) *n.* [L. *ovum*, egg; *latum*, borne away.] The emission of the egg or eggs from the ovary.

ovulatory (ŏv'ūlătŏrĭ) *a.* [L. *ovum*, egg; *latum*, borne away.] *Pert.* ovulation.

ovule (ō'vūl) *n.* [L. *ovum*, egg.] The megasporangium of seed-plant; a small egg or egg-like structure.

ovuliferous (ō'vūlĭf'ĕrŭs) *a.* [L. *ovum*, egg; *ferre*, to carry.] Ovule-producing; containing ovules; *appl.* scales, each bearing one or more ovules, developed on bract scales, as in Coniferae.

ovulophore,—a gynoecium bearing ovules.

ovum (ō'vŭm) *n.* [L. *ovum*, egg.] A female germ cell; mature egg-cell. *Plu.* ova.

oxalates (ŏk'sălāts) *n. plu.* [Gk. *oxys*, sharp.] Salts of oxalic acid, occurring as metabolic by-products in various plant tissues and in urine; also found in mantle of certain bivalves.

oxea (ŏksē'ă) *n.* [Gk. *oxys*, sharp.] A sponge spicule, rod-shaped and sharp at both ends.

oxeote (ŏk'sēŏt) *a.* [Gk. *oxys*, sharp.] Like an oxea; in form of a simple rod; *appl.* sponge spicules.

oxidase (ŏk'sĭdās) *n.* [Gk. *oxys*, sharp.] An enzyme which promotes oxidation; an oxidising enzyme.

oxidise (ŏk'sĭdīz) *v.* [Gk. *oxys*, sharp.] To combine with oxygen; to increase oxygen content.

oxidoreductase,—a hydrogen-transferring enzyme, *i.e.*, an oxidase, a dehydrogenase, or a reductase.

oxyaster (ŏk'sĭăs'tĕr) *n.* [Gk. *oxys*, sharp; *aster*, star.] Stellate sponge spicule with sharp-pointed rays.

oxybiotic (ŏk'sĭbīŏt'ĭk) *a.* [Gk. *oxys*, sharp; *biotos*, means of life.] Living in presence of oxygen; aerobic.

oxychlorocruorin (ŏk'sĭklō'rŏkroo'ŏrĭn) *n.* [Gk. *oxys*, sharp; *chloros*, green; L. *cruor*, blood.] Chlorocruorin combined with oxygen, as in aerated blood of worms.

oxychromatin (ŏk'sĭkrō'mătĭn) *n.* [Gk. *oxys*, sharp; *chroma*, colour.] Linin.

oxydactyl (ŏk'sĭdăk'tĭl) *a.* [Gk. *oxys*, sharp; *daktylos*, finger.] Having slender tapering digits.

oxydiact (ŏk'sĭdī'ăkt) *a.* [Gk. *oxys*, sharp; *di-*, two; *aktis*, ray.] Having three rays with two fully developed; *appl.* sponge spicules.

oxygnathous (ŏksĭg'năthŭs) *a.* [Gk. *oxys*, sharp; *gnathos*, jaw.] Having more or less sharp jaws.

oxyhaemocyanin (ŏk'sĭhē'mŏsī'ănĭn) *n.* [Gk. *oxys*, sharp; *haima*, blood; *kyanos*, blue.] Haemocyanin combined with oxygen as in aerated blood of Mollusca and Crustacea.

oxyhaemoglobin (ŏk'sĭhē'mŏglō'bĭn) *n.* [Gk. *oxys*, sharp; *haima*, blood; L. *globus*, globe.] Haemoglobin combined with oxygen, as found in arterial blood; HbO_2.

oxyhexactine (ŏk'sĭhĕksăk'tĭn) *n.* [Gk. *oxys*, sharp; *hex*, six; *aktis*, ray.] A hexactine with rays ending in sharp points.

oxyhexaster (ŏk'sĭhĕksăs'tĕr) *n.* [Gk. *oxys*, sharp; *hex*, six; *aster*, star.] A hexaster with rays ending in sharp points.

oxyluciferin (ŏk'sĭloosĭf'ĕrĭn) *n.* [Gk. *oxys*, sharp; L. *lux*, light; *ferre*, to carry.] The substance formed by action of luciferase on luciferin, emitting light in photogenic organs.

oxyntic (ŏk'sĭn'tĭk) *a.* [Gk. *oxynein*, to sharpen.] Secreting acid; *appl.* parietal cells and fundus glands of stomach.

oxyphil (ŏk'sĭfĭl) *a.* [Gk. *oxys*, sharp; *philein*, to love.] Having strong affinity for acidic stains; oxyphilic. *n.* Oxyphil cell or tissue element.

oxyphilous (ŏksĭf'ĭlŭs) *a.* [Gk. *oxys*, sharp; *philein*, to love.] Tolerating only acid soils or substrates.

oxyphobe (ŏk'sĭfōb) *a.* [Gk. *oxys*, sharp; *phobos*, flight.] Unable to tolerate soil acidity.

oxyphyte (ŏk'sĭfīt) *n.* [Gk. *oxys*, sharp; *phyton*, plant.] A plant thriving on acid soil; a calcifuge.

oxytocic (ŏk'sĭtŏs'ĭk) *a.* [Gk. *oxys*, sharp; *tokos*, birth.] Accelerating parturition; *appl.* pituitary hormone inducing contraction of uterus.

oxytocin (ŏk'sĭtŏs'ĭn) *n.* [Gk. *oxys*, sharp; *tokos*, birth.] Hormone secreted by posterior lobe of pituitary gland, which induces contraction of smooth muscle, particularly of uterine muscle; α-hypophamine; pitocin.

oxytophyte,—oxyphyte.

oxytropism (ŏksĭt'rŏpĭzm) *n.* [Gk. *oxys*, sharp; *trope*, turn.] Tendency of organisms to be attracted by oxygen.

oxytylote (ŏk'sĭtĭlōt') *n.* [Gk. *oxys*, sharp; *tylos*, knob.] A slender, straight sponge spicule, sharp at one end, knobbed at the other.

ozonium (ŏzō'nĭŭm) *n.* [Gk. *ozos*, twig.] Barren mycelium; a dense mycelium, as at base of a stipe.

P

P_1,—denoting first parental generation, P_2 the grandparents, etc., in law of Mendel; *cf.* F_1.

Pacchionian bodies [*A. Pacchioni*, Italian anatomist]. Arachnoideal granulations, eminences of subarachnoid tissue covered by arachnoid membrane and pressing into dura mater.

pace-maker,—a part or region determining rate of activity in other parts of the body; the sinu-auricular node, which initiates the normal heart-beat.

pachydermatous (păk'ĭdĕr'mătŭs) *a.* [Gk. *pachys*, thick; *derma*, skin.] With thick skin or covering.

pachymeninx (păk'ĭmēn'ĭngks) *n.* [Gk. *pachys*, thick; *meningx*, membrane.] The dura mater.

pachynema (păk'ĭnē'mă) *n.* [Gk. *pachys*, thick; *nema*, thread.] Chromosome thread at the pachytene stage.

pachynesis (păkĭn'ēsĭs) *n.* [Gk. *pachynesis*, thickening.] Thickening, as of mitochondria.

pachynosis (păkĭn'ōsĭs) *n.* [Gk. *pachynesis*, thickening.] Growth in thickness, as of plants.

pachytene (păk'ĭtēn) *a.* [Gk. *pachys*, thick; *tainia*, band.] *Appl.* prophase stage in meiosis during which homologous chromosomes are associated as bivalents.

Pacinian bodies or **corpuscles** [*F. Pacini*, Italian anatomist]. Distal nerve-endings, consisting of lamellated connective-tissue capsule with core of nucleated protoplasmic cells containing ramifications of a medullated nerve-fibre; corpusculum lamellosum.

paedogamy (pēdŏg'ămĭ) *n.* [Gk. *pais*, child; *gamos*, marriage.] Type of autogamy in protozoa where gametes are formed after multiple division of nucleus.

paedogenesis (pē'dōjĕn'ēsĭs) *n.* [Gk. *pais*, child; *genesis*, descent.] Reproduction in young or larval stages, as axolotl, certain Diptera.

paedomesoblast (pē'dōmĕs'ōblăst) *n.* [Gk. *pais*, child; *mesos*, middle; *blastos*, bud.] Portions of primitive mesoblast destined to form transitory larval structures.

paedomorphic (pē'dōmôr'fĭk) *a.* [Gk. *pais*, child; *morphe*, form.] *Appl.* or *pert.* primitive or embryonic structures appearing in recent or in adult animals.

paired bodies,—small bodies lying close to sympathetic chain in Elasmobranchii, representing the adrenal medulla.

paired fins,—pectoral and pelvic fins of fishes.

pairing,—process of attraction between homologous chromosomes during zygotene.

palaearctic (pălēârk′tĭk) *a.* [Gk. *palaios*, ancient; *Arktos*, Great Bear.] *Appl.* or *pert.* a zoogeographical region, or sub-region of the holarctic region, including Europe, North Africa, Western Asia, Siberia, northern China, and Japan.

palaeobiology (păl′ēöbīŏl′öjĭ) *n.* [Gk. *palaios*, ancient; *bios*, life; *logos*, discourse.] Biology of extinct plants and animals.

palaeobotany (pălēöbŏt′ănĭ) *n.* [Gk. *palaios*, ancient; *botane*, pasture.] Botany of fossil plants and plant impressions; palaeophytology.

Palaeocene (păl′ēösēn) *a.* [Gk. *palaios*, ancient; *kainos*, recent.] *Appl.* and *pert.* earliest epoch of the Caenozoic era.

palaeocerebellum (păl′ēösĕr′ēbĕl′ŭm) *n.* [Gk. *palaios*, ancient; L. *dim.* of *cerebrum*, brain.] Phylogenetically older region of cerebellum, receiving spinal and vestibular afferent fibres. *Opp.* neocerebellum.

palaeocranium (păl′ēökrā′nĭŭm) *n.* [Gk. *palaios*, ancient; *kranion*, skull.] Type of skull or stage in development extending no further back than vagus nerve.

palaeodendrology (păl′ēödĕndrŏl′öjĭ) *n.* [Gk. *palaios*, ancient; *dendron*, tree; *logos*, discourse.] Botany of fossil trees and tree impressions.

palaeo-ecology (păl′ēöēkŏl′öjĭ) *n.* [Gk. *palaios*, ancient; *oikos*, household; *logos*, discourse.] The study of the relationship between extinct organisms and their life-time environment.

palaeo-encephalon (păl′ēöĕnkĕf′ălŏn, -sĕf-) *n.* [Gk. *palaios*, ancient; *engkephalos*, brain.] The segmental or primitive vertebrate brain.

Palaeogene (păl′ēöjēn) *a.* [Gk. *palaios*, ancient; *genos*, an age.] *Pert.* or *appl.* the early Tertiary period, Eocene and Oligocene.

palaeogenetic (păl′ēöjĕnĕt′ĭk) *a.* [Gk. *palaios*, ancient; *genesis*, descent.] *Appl.* atavistic features fully developed, which are usually characteristically embryonic.

palaeogenetics (păl′ēöjĕnĕt′ĭks) *n.* [Gk. *palaios*, ancient; *genesis*, descent.] Genetics as applied to palaeontology; genetic interpretation of fossil structures or species.

Palaeolaurentian (păl′ēölôrĕn′shĭăn) *a.* [Gk. *palaios*, ancient; River *St Lawrence*.] *Pert.* or *appl.* Archaeozoic era.

Palaeolithic (păl′ēölĭth′ĭk) *a.* [Gk. *palaios*, ancient; *lithos*, stone.] *Appl.* or *pert.* the older or chipped stone age.

palaeontology (păl′ēöntŏl′öjĭ) *n.* [Gk. *palaios*, ancient; *on*, being; *logos*, discourse.] The science of past organic life, based on fossils and fossil impressions.

palaeophytology,—palaeobotany.

palaeotropical (păl′ēötrŏp′ĭkăl) *a.* [Gk. *palaios*, ancient; *tropikos*, *pert.* tropics.] *Appl.* or *pert.* floristic region including African, Indo-Malaysian, and Polynesian sub-regions.

palaeovirus (păl′ēövī′rŭs) *n.* [Gk. *palaios*, ancient; L. *virus*, poison.] A virus evolved from a more or less remote viroid ancestor. *Opp.* neovirus.

Palaeozoic (păl′ēözō′ĭk) *a.* [Gk. *palaios*, ancient; *zoon*, animal.] *Appl.* era comprising the Proterozoic and Deuterozoic faunal epochs, preceding the Mesozoic era; Cambrian to Permian periods; the age of fishes and amphibians; Primary era.

palaeozoology (păl′ēözōŏl′öjĭ) *n.* [Gk. *palaios*, ancient; *zoon*, animal; *logos*, discourse.] Zoology of fossil animals and animal impressions.

palama (păl′ămă) *n.* [Gk. *palame*, the palm.] Foot-webbing of aquatic birds.

palatal (păl′ătăl) *a.* [L. *palatum*, palate.] *Pert.* palate; palatine; *appl.* bone, sinus, etc.

palate (păl′ăt) *n.* [L. *palatum*, palate.] Roof of mouth; insect epipharynx; projection of lower lip of personate corolla.

palatine (păl′ătĭn) *a.* [L. *palatum*, palate.] *Pert.* or in region of palate; *appl.* artery, bone, foramen.

palatoglossal (păl′ătöglŏs′ăl) *a.* [L. *palatum*, palate; Gk. *glossa*, tongue.] *Pert.* palate and tongue; *appl.* a muscle; glossopalatine.

palatonasal (păl′ătönā′zăl) *a.* [L. *palatum*, palate; *nasus*, nose.] *Pert.* palate and nose.

palatopharyngeal (păl′ătöfărĭn′jēăl) *a.* [L. *palatum*, palate; Gk. *pharyngx*, pharynx.] In region of palate and pharynx; pharyngopalatine; *appl.* a muscle.

palatopterygoid (păl′ătötĕr′ĭgoid) *a.* [L. *palatum*, palate; Gk. *pterygion*, little wing; *eidos*, form.] *Pert.* palate and pterygoid.

palatoquadrate (păl′ătökwôd′rāt) *a.* [L. *palatum*, palate; *quadratus*, squared.] Connecting palatine and quadrate; *appl.* dorsal cartilage of mandibular arch.

palea (pā′lēă) *n.* [L. *palea*, chaff.] A small bract on floret of Compositae; an inner chaffy bracteole, valvule or upper palea, of grasses; lower palea or lemma; ramentum or scaly growth of epidermis in ferns.

paleaceous (pālēā′shŭs) *a.* [L. *palea*, chaff.] Chaffy; *appl.* a capitulum furnished with small scaly bracts or paleae.

paleo-,—palaeo-.

palet,—palea, of grasses.

palette (păl′ĕt) *n* [*F. palette* from L. *pala*, spade.] The modified cupule-bearing tarsus of anterior leg, in male beetles.

pali (pā′lī) *n. plu.* [L. *palus*, stake.] A series of small pillars projecting upwards from the theca-base towards stomodaeum of madrepore corals.

paliform (pā′lĭfôrm) *a.* [L. *palus*, stake; *forma*, shape.] Like an upright stake.

palinal (păl′ĭnăl) *a.* [Gk. *palin*, reversely.] From behind forwards; *appl.* jaw movement, as in elephants. *Opp.* proral.

palingenesis (păl′ĭnjĕn′ĕsĭs) *n.* [Gk. *palin*, anew; *genesis*, descent.] Abrupt metamorphosis; rebirth of ancestral characters; recapitulation.

palingenetic (păl′ĭnjĕnĕt′ĭk) *a.* [Gk. *palin*, anew; *genesis*, descent.] Of remote or ancient origin; *pert.* palingenesis.

palisade (pălĭsād′) *n.* [F. *palissade*, from L. *palus*, stake.] Arrangement of apposed elongated cellular structures; *appl.* fungi, the Basidiomycetes; *appl.* cells, of ends of cortical hyphae in lichens; *appl.* tissue, the layer or layers of photosynthetic cells beneath the epidermis of many foliage leaves; *appl.* nerve fibrils in inner surface of electric layer in ray-fish; *appl.* tissue derived from neurolemma at neuromuscular junction in end-plates.

pallaesthesia (păl′ēsthē′zĭă) *n.* [Gk. *pallein*, to quiver; *aisthesis*, sensation.] Vibratory sensation; bone sensibility.

pallet (păl′ĕt) *n.* [L. *pala*, spade.] A shelly plate on a bivalve siphon.

pallial (păl′ĭăl) *a.* [L. *pallium*, mantle.] *Pert.* molluscan pallium or mantle; *appl.* line, groove, sinus, muscles, ganglion.

palliate (păl′ĭāt) *a.* [L. *pallium*, mantle.] Having a mantle or similar structure.

pallidum (păl′ĭdŭm) *n.* [L. *pallidus*, pale.] The medial parts or globus pallidus of lentiform nucleus.

palliopedal (pălĭŏp′ĕdăl) *a.* [L. *pallium*, mantle; *pes*, foot.] *Pert.* molluscan mantle and foot.

pallium (păl′ĭŭm) *n.* [L. *pallium*, mantle.] A mollusc or brachiopod mantle; portion of cerebral wall.

palmar (păl′măr) *a.* [L. *palma*, palm of hand.] *Pert.* palm of hand; *appl.* aponeurosis, nerve, muscle, reflex.

palmaria (pălmā′rĭă) *n. plu.* [L. *palmaris*, *pert.* palm.] The third brachials of Crinoidea.

palmate (păl′māt) *a.* [L. *palma*, palm.] *Appl.* leaves divided into lobes arising from a common centre; *appl.* hand-like tuber, as in certain orchids; *appl.* folds of cervix uteri; having anterior toes webbed, as in most aquatic birds.

palmatifid (pălmăt′ĭfĭd) *a.* [L. *palma*, palm; *findere*, to cleave.] *Appl.* leaves divided into lobes to about the middle, at acute angles to each other.

palmatilobate (pălmăt′ĭlō′bāt) *a.* [L. *palma*, palm; *lobus*, lobe.] Palmate with rounded lobes and divisions half-way to base.

palmatipartite (pălmăt′ĭpâr′tīt) *a.* [L. *palma*, palm; *partitus*, divided.] Palmate with divisions more than half-way to base.

palmatisect (pălmăt′ĭsĕkt) *a.* [L. *palma*, palm; *sectus*, cut.] Palmate with divisions nearly to base.

palmella (pălmĕl′ă) *n.* [Gk. *palmos*, quivering.] A sedentary stage of certain algae, the cells dividing within a jelly-like mass and producing motile gametes.

palmigrade,—plantigrade.

palmiped (păl′mĭpĕd) *a.* [L. *palma*, palm; *pes*, foot.] Web-footed. *n.* A web-footed bird.

palmitin (păl′mĭtĭn) *n.* [Gk. *palma*, palm-tree.] A fat occurring in adipose tissue, milk, and palm-oil; $(C_{15}H_{31}COO)_3C_3H_5$.

palmula (păl′mūlă) *n.* [L. *palma*, palm.] Terminal lobe or process between paired claws of insect feet.

palp,—palpus, *q.v.*

palpacle (păl′păkl) *n.* [L. *palpare*, to touch softly.] The tentacle of a dactylozooid or palpon of Siphonophora.

palpal (păl′păl) *a.* [L. *palpare*, to stroke.] *Pert.* a palpus.

palpate (păl′pāt) *a.* [L. *palpare*, to stroke.] Provided with palpus or palpi. *v.* To examine by touch.

palpebra (păl′pĕbră) *n.* [L. *palpebra*, eyelid.] An eyelid. *Plu.* palpebrae.

palpebral (păl′pĕbrăl) *a.* [L. *palpebra*, eyelid.] *Pert.* eyelids; *appl.* arteries, ligament, nerves, etc.; *appl.* a lobe on which the eye of trilobites rests.

palpi,—*plu.* of palpus.

palpifer (păl′pĭfĕr), **palpiger** (păl′pĭjĕr) *n.* [L. *palpare*, to stroke; *ferre*, *gerere*, to carry.] A maxilla lobe or lobe of prementum bearing palpus of insects.

palpiform (păl′pĭfôrm) *a.* [L. *palpare*, to stroke; *forma*, shape.] Resembling a palpus or insect feeler.

palpimacula (păl′pĭmăk′ūlă) *n.* [L. *palpare*, to stroke; *macula*, spot.] Sensory area on labial palps of certain insects.

palpocil (păl′pösĭl) *n.* [L. *palpare*, to touch; *cilium*, eyelash.] A stiff sensory filament attached to sense cells of Hydromedusae.

palpon (păl′pŏn) *n.* [L. *palpare*, to stroke.] A hydrocyst or dactylozooid of Siphonophora.

palpulus (păl′pūlŭs) *n.* [L. *palpare*, to stroke.] A small palpus or feeler.

palpus (păl′pŭs) *n.*, **palpi** (păl′pī) *plu.* [L. *palpare*, to stroke.] Labial feelers of Insecta; sensory appendages on prostomium of Polychaeta, on mandibles of Crustacea; pedipalpus, *q.v.*

paludal (pălū′dăl) *a.* [L. *palus*, marsh.] Marshy; *pert.*, or growing in, marshes or swamps; paludine, paludinous, paludose, palustral, palustrine.

paludicole (pălū′dĭkōl) *a.* [L. *palus*, marsh; *colere*, to inhabit.] Living in marshes; paludal, palustral.

palule (păl′ūl) *n.* [L. *palus*, stake.] An unattached calcareous process of corals; a small palus.

palus (pā′lŭs) *n.* [L. *palus*, stake.] A stake-like structure. *Plu.* pali, *q.v.*

palustral,—paludal, paludicole.

palynology (pălĭnŏl′öjĭ) *n.* [Gk. *palynein*, to scatter (*pale*, pollen); *logos*, discourse.] The study of pollen and of its distribution; pollen analysis; the study of spores.

pampiniform (pămpĭn′ĭfôrm) *a.* [L. *pampinus*, tendril; *forma*, shape.] Tendril-like; *appl.* a convoluted vein plexus of spermatic cord; *appl.* body, the parovarium.

pamprodactylous (păm′prōdăk′tĭlŭs) *a.* [Gk. *pan*, all; *pro*, in front; *daktylos*, digit.] With all toes pointing forward.

pancreas (păn′krēăs) *n.* [Gk. *pan*, all; *kreas*, flesh.] A compound racemose gland, with exocrine and endocrine functions, of most vertebrates.

pancreatic (pănkrēăt′ĭk) *a.* [Gk. *pan*, all; *kreas*, flesh.] *Pert.* pancreas; *appl.* artery, duct, vein, enzymes, hormones, juice.

pancreaticoduodenal,—*pert.* pancreas and duodenum; *appl.* arteries, veins.

pancreatin,—extract of pancreas containing several enzymes, as amylase, lipase, trypsin.

pancreatrophic (păn′krēătrŏf′ĭk) *a.* [Gk. *pan*, all; *kreas*, flesh; *trophe*, nourishment.] *Appl.* prepituitary hormone or principle causing increase in secretion of insulin.

pancreozymin (păn′krēōzī′mĭn) *n.* [Gk. *pan*, all; *kreas*, flesh; *zyme*, leaven.] Duodenal secretion or hormone which stimulates production of pancreatic enzymes.

pandemic (păndĕm′ĭk) *a.* [Gk. *pandemos*, common.] Epidemic everywhere; very widely distributed; cosmopolitan, *appl.* plants.

panduriform (păndū′rĭfôrm) *a.* [Gk. *pandoura*, lute; L. *forma*, shape.] Fiddle-shaped; *appl.* leaves.

Paneth cells [*J. Paneth*, Austrian physician]. Enzyme-producing cells at base of crypts of Lieberkühn.

pangamic (păngăm′ĭk) *a.* [Gk. *pan*, all; *gamos*, marriage.] *Appl.* indiscriminate mating.

pangamy (păn′gămĭ) *n.* [Gk. *pan*, all; *gamos*, marriage.] Random mating.

pangen (păn′jĕn) *n.* [Gk. *pan*, all; *genos*, offspring.] A hypothetical unit, *q.v.*

pangenesis (pănjĕn′ĕsĭs) *n.* [Gk. *pan*, all; *genesis*, descent.] The gemmule theory, that hereditary characteristics are carried by germs from individual body cells.

panicle (păn′ĭkl) *n.* [L. *panicula*, tuft.] A tuft or bunch of flowers or seeds, close or scattered; a compound raceme.

paniculate (pănĭk′ūlāt) *a.* [L. *panicula*, tuft.] Having flowers arranged in panicles.

panmeristic (păn′mĕrĭs′tĭk) *a.* [Gk. *pan*, all; *meros*, part.] *Appl.* an ultimate protoplasmic structure of independent units.

panmictic (pănmĭk′tĭk) *a.* [Gk. *pan*, all; *miktos*, mixed.] Characterised by, or resulting from, random matings; *pert.* panmixia.

panmixia (pănmĭk′sĭă) *n.* [Gk. *pan*, all; *mixis*, mixing.] Indiscriminate interbreeding consequent on suspension of influence of natural selection.

panniculus (pănĭk′ūlŭs) *n.* [L. *dim.* of *pannus*, cloth.] A layer of tissue, as superficial fascia.

pannose (păn′ōs) *a.* [L. *pannosus*, from *pannus*, cloth.] Like cloth.

panoistic (pănōĭs′tĭk) *a.* [Gk. *pan*, all; *oon*, egg.] *Appl.* ovariole in which nutritive cells are absent, egg-yolk being formed by epithelium of follicle. *Opp.* meroistic.

panphotometric (păn′fōtōmĕt′rĭk) *a.* [Gk. *pan*, all; *phos*, light; *metron*, measure.] *Appl.* leaves oriented to avoid maximum direct sunlight; *cf.* euphotometric.

pansporoblast (pănspō′rōblăst) *n.* [Gk. *pan*, all; *sporos*, seed; *blastos*, bud.] A cell-complex, of Neosporidia, producing sporoblasts and spores; an archespore.

panthalassic (păn′thălăs′ĭk) *a.* [Gk. *pan*, all; *thalassa*, sea.] Living both in coastal and offshore waters; neritic and oceanic.

pantothenic (păntōthĕn′ĭk) *a.* [Gk. *pantothen*, from everywhere.] *Appl.* acid occurring in tissues and foods, the rat anti-grey hair and chick antidermatitis factor of vitamin B complex: vitamin B_3; $C_9H_{17}O_5N$.

pantropic (pantrŏp′ĭk) *a.* [Gk. *pan*, all; *tropikos*, turning.] Turning to any direction; invading many different tissues, *appl.* viruses; polytropic.

pantropical,—distributed throughout the tropics ; *appl.* species.

papilionaceous (păpĭl'ĭŏnā'shŭs) *a.* [L. *papilio*, butterfly.] Resembling a butterfly ; *appl.* a corolla of five petals, one enlarged posterior standard or vexillum, two united anterior forming a keel or carina, and two lateral, the wings or alae.

papilla (păpĭl'ă) *n.* [L. *papilla*, nipple.] A glandular hair with one secreting cell above the epidermis level ; an accessory adhesive organ with retractile tip, of some trematodes ; a conical dermal structure on birds, the beginning of a feather ; one of various small projections of corium of tongue, and eminences on skin ; a conical structure, as nipple, apex of renal pyramid, lacrimal papilla, etc.

papillary (păp'ĭlărĭ) *a.* [L. *papilla*, nipple.] *Pert.* or with papillae ; *appl.* a dermal layer ; *appl.* a process of caudate lobe of liver ; *appl.* muscles between walls of ventricles of heart and chordae tendineae.

papillate (păp'ĭlāt) *a.* [L. *papilla*, nipple.] Covered by papillae ; papillose ; like a papilla ; *appl.* petals with external cells projecting slightly above surface.

papilliform (păpĭl'ĭfôrm) *a.* [L. *papilla*, nipple ; *forma*, shape.] Like a papilla in shape.

papillose,—papillate.

pappiferous (păpĭf'ĕrŭs) *a.* [L. *pappus*, down ; *ferre*, to carry.] Pappus-bearing.

pappose (păpōs') *a.* [L. *pappus*, down.] Having limb of calyx developed as a tuft of hairs or bristles ; downy, or covered with feathery processes ; pappous.

pappus (păp'ŭs) *n.* [L. *pappus*, down.] A circle or tuft of bristles, hairs, or feathery processes in place of limb of a calyx.

papulae (păp'ūlē) *n. plu.* [L. *papula*, pimple.] Dermal gills ; hollow contractile skin processes of Asteroidea, with respiratory function ; pimples ; pustules.

papyraceous (păpĭrā'sēŭs) *a.* [L. *papyrus*, papyrus-rush.] Of papery texture ; papyritious.

para-aortic (păr'ăāôr'tĭk) *a.* [Gk. *para*, beside ; *aorte*, great artery.] *Appl.* chromaffin bodies or paraganglia alongside the abdominal aorta.

parabasal (părăbā'săl) *a.* [Gk. *para*, beside ; *basis*, base.] *Appl.* a striated apparatus surrounding the calyx of certain protozoa ; *appl.* granule, or kinetonucleus, a cell-body of flagellates.

parabasalia (păr'ăbăsā'lĭă) *n. plu.* [Gk. *para*, beside ; *basis*, base.] The basalia of crinoids when a circlet of perradial infrabasalia occurs beneath them.

parabiosis (păr'ăbīō'sĭs) *n.* [Gk. *para*, beside ; *biosis*, manner of life.] The condition of being conjoined, either from birth, as Siamese twins, or experimentally, as laboratory animals ; phylacobiosis, *q.v.*

parabiotic (păr'ăbīŏt'ĭk) *a.* [Gk. *para*, beside ; *bios*, life.] Conjoined to greater or less extent ; tutelary or phylacobiotic, in ants ; living amicably in compound nest, as ants of different species or genera.

parablast (păr'ăblăst) *n.* [Gk. *para*, beside ; *blastos*, bud.] The yolk of meroblastic eggs ; large nuclei of cells laden with yolk-granules, in development of higher mammals.

parabranchia (părăbrăng'kĭă) *n.* [Gk. *para*, beside ; *brangchia*, gills.] A much plumed mollusc osphradium or chemoreceptor.

parabronchi (părăbrŏng'kī) *n. plu.* [Gk. *para*, beside ; *brongchos*, windpipe.] The tertiary lung tubes of birds, their terminations being embedded in lung mesenchyme.

paracardial (părăkâr'dĭăl) *a.* [Gk. *para*, beside ; *kardia*, stomach.] Near, or surrounding, cardia or neck of stomach ; *appl.* lymph-glands.

paracasein,—*see* casein.

paracele,—paracoel.

paracentral (părăsĕn'trăl) *a.* [Gk. *para*, beside; L. *centrum*, centre.] Situated at or near the centre; *appl.* lobule, gyrus, fissure.

paracentric (păr'ăsĕn'trĭk) *a.* [Gk. *para*, beside; *kentron*, centre.] On same side of centromere; *appl.* rearrangements in same chromosome arm; *appl.* inversions not including the centromere, *opp.* pericentric; homobrachial.

parachordal (părăkôr'dăl) *a.* [Gk. *para*, beside; *chorde*, cord.] On either side of notochord; *appl.* paired horizontal cartilage plates on sides of chondrocranium.

parachromatin (părăkrō'mătĭn) *n.* [Gk. *para*, beside; *chroma*, colour.] Achromatic nuclear substance giving rise to spindle-fibres.

parachrosis (păr'ăkrō'sis, părăk'rōsis) *n.* [Gk. *para*, proceeding from; *chros*, colour; *parachroos*, changing colour.] Process or condition of changing colour; discoloration; fading.

parachute (păr'ăshoot) *n.* [F. *parer* from L. *parare*, to prepare; F. *chute*, fall.] A special structure of seeds as aril, caruncle, pappus, wing, which assists dispersal.

paracme (părăk'mē) *n.* [Gk. *parakme*, decadence.] The decline of a species or race after reaching highest point of development.

paracoel (păr'ăsēl) *n.* [Gk. *para*, beside; *koilos*, hollow.] Lateral ventricle or cavity of cerebral hemisphere.

paracondyloid (părăkŏn'dĭloid) *a.* [Gk. *para*, beside; *kondylos*, knuckle; *eidos*, form.] *Appl.* process of occipital occurring beside condyles of some mammals.

paracone (păr'ăkōn) *n.* [Gk. *para*, beside; *konos*, cone.] Antero-external cusp of upper molar.

paraconid (părăkō'nĭd) *n.* [Gk. *para*, beside; *konos*, cone.] Antero-internal cusp of lower molar.

paracorolla (păr'ăkörŏl'ă) *n.* [Gk. *para*, beside; L. *corolla*, small crown.] A corolla appendage.

paracutis (părăkū'tĭs) *n.* [Gk. *para*, beside; L. *cutis*, skin.] A fungal cutis consisting of more or less isodiametric cells.

paracymbium (păr'ăsĭmbĭ'ŭm) *n.* [Gk. *para*, beside; *kymbion*, small boat.] Accessory part of cymbium, between tibia and tarsus, in some spiders.

paracyst (păr'ăsĭst) *n.* [Gk. *para*, beside; *kystis*, bladder.] The antheridium of Pyronema.

paracyte (păr'ăsīt) *n.* [Gk. *para*, beside; *kytos*, hollow.] A modified cell extruded from embryonic tissue into yolk, as in some insects.

paracytoids (părăsī'toidz) *n. plu.* [Gk. *para*, beside; *kytos*, hollow; *eidos*, shape.] Coherent minute chromatin pieces cast out from nuclei of embryonic tissue cells, with cytoplasmic envelope, into the blood, as in certain insects.

parademe (păr'ădēm) *n.* [Gk. *para*, beside; *demas*, body.] A secondary apodeme arising from edge of a sclerite.

paraderm (păr'ădĕrm) *n.* [Gk. *para*, beside; *derma*, skin.] A derm composed of isodiametric hyphae; the delicate limiting membrane of a pronymph.

paradesmus (păr'ădĕs'mŭs) *n.* [Gk. *para*, beside; *desmos*, bond.] Secondary connection between centrioles outside nucleus in mitosis of flagellates; also paradesmose, paradesm.

paradidymis (părădĭd'ĭmĭs) *n.* [Gk. *para*, beside; *didymos*, testicle.] A body of convoluted tubules anterior to lower part of spermatic cord, representing posterior part of embryonic mesonephros; organ of Giraldès.

para-esophageal, — para-oesophageal.

parafacialia (păr'ăfāsĭā'lĭă) *n. plu.* [Gk. *para*, beside; L. *facies*, face.] Narrow parts of head capsule between frontal suture and eyes, as in certain Diptera.

parafibula (părăfĭb'ūlă) *n.* [Gk. *para*, beside; L. *fibula*, buckle.] An accessory element outside fibula at proximal end, seen in some Lacertilia and young marsupials.

paraflagellum (păr'ăflăjĕl'ŭm) *n.* [Gk. *para*, beside; L. *flagellum*, whip.] A subsidiary flagellum.

paraflocculus (păr'ăflŏk'ūlŭs) *n.* [Gk. *para*, beside; L. *floccus*, lock of wool.] Cerebellar lobule lateral to flocculus.

parafrons (păr'ăfrŏns) *n.* [Gk. *para*, beside; L. *frons*, forehead.] Area between eyes and frontal suture in certain insects.

parafrontals (păr'ăfrŭn'tălz) *n. plu.* [Gk. *para*, beside; L. *frons*, forehead.] The continuation of genae between eyes and frontal suture in insects; genavertical plates.

paraganglia (păr'ăgăng'glĭă) *n. plu.* [Gk. *para*, beside; *ganglion*, swelling.] Scattered cell clusters along aorta and in other parts of body, considered to secrete adrenaline; chromophil or phaeochrome cells.

paragaster (părăgăs'tĕr) *n.* [Gk. *para*, beside; *gaster*, stomach.] A central cavity of sponges into which gastric ostia open.

paragastric (părăgăs'trĭk) *a.* [Gk. *para*, beside; *gaster*, stomach.] *Pert.* a paragaster; *appl.* passages or cavities in branches of sponge; *appl.* paired blind canals from infundibulum to oral cone of ctenophores.

paragastrula (părăgăs'troolă) *n.* [Gk. *para*, beside; *gaster*, stomach.] Stage of amphiblastula of sponge when flagellated cells are invaginated into dome of rounded cells.

paragenesis (părăjĕn'ĕsĭs) *n.* [Gk. *para*, beside; *genesis*, descent.] Hybrids' fertility with parent species but not *inter se*; a subsidiary mode of reproduction.

paraglenal (părăglē'năl) *a.* [Gk. *para*, beyond; *glene*, socket.] Hypercoracoid.

paraglobulin (păr'ăglŏb'ūlĭn) *n.* [Gk. *para*, beside; L. *globus*, globe.] Globulin of blood serum.

paraglossa (părăglŏs'ă) *n.* [Gk. *para*, beside; *glossa*, tongue.] A process on each side of ligula of insects; hypopharynx; a paired cartilage of chondrocranium.

paraglycogen (părăglī'kŏjĕn) *n.* [Gk. *para*, beside; *glykys*, sweet; *genos*, birth.] Reserve food-material stored in protoplasm-grains of Gregarinida.

paragnatha (părăg'năthă) *n. plu.* [Gk. *para*, beside; *gnathos*, jaw.] Paired, delicate, unjointed processes of maxilla of certain arthropods.

paragnathous (părăg'năthŭs) *a.* [Gk. *para*, beside; *gnathos*, jaw.] With mandibles of equal length; *appl.* birds.

para-Golgi apparatus,—small constituents of cell, in spaces between parts of Golgi apparatus.

paragula (părăgū'lă) *n.* [Gk. *para*, beside; L. *gula*, gullet.] A region beside gula on insect head.

paragynous (păraj'ĭnŭs) *a.* [Gk. *para*, beside; *gyne*, female.] *Appl.* antheridia lateral to oogonium, as in some Peronosporales.

paraheliode (păr'ăhē'lĭōd) *n.* [Gk. *para*, against; *helios*, sun.] A special arrangement of spines in certain Cactaceae; parasol.

paraheliotropism (păr'ăhēlĭŏt'rŏpĭzm) *n.* [Gk. *para*, against; *helios*, sun; *trope*, turn.] Tendency of plants to turn edges of leaves towards intense illumination, thus protecting surfaces.

parahormone (păr'ăhôr'mōn) *n.* [Gk. *para*, beside; *hormaein*, to arouse.] A substance which acts like a hormone but is a product of ordinary metabolism of cells.

parahypophysis (păr'ăhīpŏf'ĭsĭs) *n.* [Gk. *para*, beside; *hypo*, under; *phyein*, to grow.] Vestigial structure below pituitary gland.

paralectotype (păr'ălĕk'tŏtīp) *n.* [Gk. *para*, beside; *lektos*, chosen; *typos*, pattern.] A specimen, of a series used to designate a species, which is later designated as a paratype.

paralimnic (părălĭm'nĭk) *a.* [Gk. *para*, beside; *limne*, lake.] *Pert.* or inhabiting shore of lakes.

paralinin (părălī′nĭn) *n.* [Gk. *para*, beside; *linon*, linen thread.] Nuclear ground-substance.

parallelinervate, parallelodrome, —*appl.* leaves with veins or nerves parallel.

parallelotropic,—orthotropic.

paralutein (părălū′tēĭn, -loo′tēĭn) *n.* [Gk. *para*, beside; L. *luteus*, golden-yellow.] *Appl.* epithelioid luteal cells of theca interna, *opp.* epithelial follicular luteal cells.

paramastigote (părămăs′tĭgōt) *a.* [Gk. *para*, beside; *mastix*, whip.] Having one long principal flagellum and a short accessory one, as certain Mastigophora.

paramastoid (părămăs′toid) *a.* [Gk. *para*, beside; *mastos*, breast; *eidos*, form.] Beside the mastoid; *appl.* two paroccipital processes of exoccipitals; *appl.* a process projecting from the jugular process.

paramere (păr′ămēr) *n.* [Gk. *para*, beside; *meros*, part.] Half of a bilaterally symmetrical structure; one of paired lobes exterior to penis in some insects.

paramesonephric (păr′ămĕs′ōnĕf′rĭk, -mēz-) *a.* [Gk. *para*, beside; *mesos*, middle; *nephros*, kidney.] *Appl.* ducts on lateral sides of mesonephric ducts and giving rise to oviducts; Müllerian ducts.

parametrium (părămĕt′rĭŭm) *n.* [Gk. *para*, beside; *metra*, womb.] Fibrous tissue partly surrounding uterus.

paramitome (păr′ămĭtōm) *n.* [Gk. *para*, beside; *mitos*, thread.] Interfilar substance of protoplasm.

paramitosis (păr′ămĭtō′sĭs) *n.* [Gk. *para*, beside; *mitos*, thread.] Nuclear division, as in protozoa, in which the chromosomes are not regularly arranged on equator of spindle and tend to cohere at one end when separating.

paramorph (păr′ămôrf) *n.* [Gk. *para*, beside; *morphe*, form.] Any variant form or variety; a form induced by environmental factors without genetically produced changes; *cf.* phenocopy.

paramylon (părăm′ĭlŏn) *n.* [Gk. *para*, beside; *amylon*, starch.] A substance allied to starch, occurring in certain algae and flagellates; paramylum.

paranasal (părănā′zăl) *a.* [Gk. *para*, beside; L. *nasus*, nose.] *Appl.* air-sinuses in maxilla, frontal, ethmoid, sphenoid, and palatine bones.

paranema (păr′ănē′mă) *n.* [Gk. *para*, beside; *nema*, thread.] Paraphysis of cryptogams.

paranemic (părănē′mĭk) *a.* [Gk. *para*, beside; *nema*, thread.] Having spirals not interlocked, as in sister chromatids; anorthospiral. *Opp.* plectonemic, orthospiral.

paranephric (părănĕf′rĭk) *a.* [Gk. *para*, beside; *nephros*, kidney.] Beside the kidney; *appl.* a fatty body behind renal fascia.

paranephrocyte,—*see* athrocyte.

paranephros (părănĕf′rŏs) *n.* [Gk. *para*, beside; *nephros*, kidney.] An adrenal body.

paranota (părănō′tă) *n. plu.* [Gk. *para*, beside; *noton*, back.] Lateral expansions of arthropod notum or tergum, believed to have developed into wings during evolution of insects.

paranuclein (părănū′klēĭn) *n.* [Gk. *para*, beside; L. *nucleus*, kernel.] The substance of a true nucleolus; pyrenin.

paranucleus (părănū′klēŭs) *n.* [Gk. *para*, beside; L. *nucleus*, kernel.] A micronucleus; a spherical mass of mitochondria; formerly nebenkern; an aggregation of mitochondria in the spermatid destined to form axial filament envelope.

para-oesophageal (păr′ăēsŏfăj′ēăl) *a.* [Gk. *para*, beside; *oisophagos*, gullet.] *Appl.* nerves connecting tritocerebrum with suboesophageal ganglion; para-esophageal.

parapet (păr′ăpĕt) *n.* [It. *parare*, to guard; *petto*, breast.] A circular fold of body wall below margin of disc in sea-anemones.

paraphototropism, — Paraheliotropism, *q.v.*

paraphyll (păr′ăfĭl) *n.* [Gk. *para*, beside; *phyllon*, leaf.] One of the branching chlorophyll-containing outgrowths arising between leaves or from their bases, in mosses.

paraphysis (părăf′ĭsĭs) *n.* [Gk. *para*, beside; *physis*, growth.] A slender filamentous epidermal outgrowth occurring among sporogenous organs; a protective or nutritive interascal hypha; a non-sexual hypha; a basidiolum; one of the marginal projections of the pygidium in Coccidae; a non-nervous outgrowth on top of brain of nearly all vertebrates.

parapineal (părăpĭn′ēăl) *a.* [Gk. *para*, beside; L. *pinea*, pine-cone.] *Appl.* parietal organ of epiphysis, eye-like in cyclostomes and some reptiles, pineal body of other vertebrates.

paraplasm (păr′ăplăzm) *n.* [Gk. *para*, beside; *plasma*, mould.] Vegetative or less active part of cell substance; originally, ectoplasm; *cf.* metaplasm.

parapleuron (păr′ăploor′ŏn) *n.* [Gk. *para*, beside; *pleuron*, side.] Episternum of metathorax, or of mesothorax and metathorax, in insects; parapteron of insects; parapleurum.

parapodium (părăpō′dĭŭm) *n.* [Gk. *para*, beside; *pous*, foot.] A paired lateral locomotory structure on body-segments of polychaetes; lateral extension of foot, for propulsion, as in Pteropoda and certain Nudibranchiata.

parapolar (părăpō′lăr) *a.* [Gk. *para*, beside; *polos*, pivot.] Beside the pole; *appl.* first two trunk cells in development of Rhombozoa.

parapophysis (păr′ăpŏf′ĭsĭs) *n.* [Gk. *para*, beside; *apo*, from; *physis*, growth.] A transverse process arising from a vertebral centrum.

parapostgenal (păr′ăpōstjē′năl) *a.* [Gk. *para*, beside; L. *post*, after; *gena*, cheek.] *Appl.* thickened portion of occiput in insects.

paraproct (păr′ăprŏkt) *n.* [Gk. *para*, beside; *proktos*, anus.] A plate situated on each side of anus in Diplopoda and some insects; podical plate.

paraprostate (păr′ăprŏs′tāt) *n.* [Gk. *para*, beside; L. *pro*, before; *stare*, to stand.] Anterior bulbo-urethral glands; superior Cowper's glands of Leydolph.

parapsid (părăp′sĭd) *a.* [Gk. *para*, beside; *hapsis*, arch.] *Appl.* skull with single vacuity, bounded by parietal, postorbital and squamosal.

parapsidal,—*pert.* parapsis; *appl.* furrows or sutures between dorsal portion of mesonotum and the parapsides in Hymenoptera.

parapsides,—*plu.* of parapsis.

parapsis (părăp′sĭs) *n.* [Gk. *para*, beside; *hapsis*, arch.] Lateral portion of mesonotum, as in ants.

parapteron (părăp′tërŏn) *n.* [Gk. *para*, beside; *pteron*, wing.] Tegula, shoulder-lappet, or scapula of insect mesothorax; pennae humerales of birds; parapterum.

parapyles (părăp′ĭlēz) *n. plu.* [Gk. *para*, beside; *pylis*, little gate.] Two accessory openings in certain developing Radiolaria.

paraquadrate (părăkwôd′rāt) *n.* [Gk. *para*, beside; L. *quadratus*, squared.] The squamosal, a hammer-shaped investing bone supporting the suspensorium externally.

pararectal (părărĕk′tăl) *a.* [Gk. *para*, beside; L. *rectus*, straight.] Beside rectum; *appl.* fossa, lymph glands.

parasematic (păr′ăsēmăt′ĭk) *a.* [Gk. *para*, beside; *sema*, sign.] *Appl.* markings, structures, or behaviour tending to mislead or deflect attack by an enemy.

paraseme (păr′ăsēm) *n.* [Gk. *para*, beside; *sema*, sign.] Misleading appearance or marking, as an ocellus near tail of fishes.

paraseptal (părăsĕp′tăl) *a.* [Gk. *para*, beside; L. *septum*, partition.] *Appl.* cartilage more or less enclosing vomeronasal organ.

parasexual (păr′ăsĕk′sūăl) *a.* [Gk. *para*, compared with; L. *sexus*, sex.] *Appl.* or *pert.* the operation of genetic recombination other than by means of the alternation of karyogamy and meiosis characteristic of sexual reproduction.

parasite (păr'ăsīt) *n.* [Gk. *parasitos*, from *para*, beside; *sitos*, food.] An organism living with or within another to its own advantage in food or shelter.

parasitic (părăsĭt'ĭk) *a.* [Gk. *parasitos*, parasite.] *Appl.* an organism living at expense of another, and in or on it.

parasitic castration, — castration caused by presence of a parasite, as in male crabs infested by Sacculina.

parasitism (păr'ăsĭtĭzm) *n.* [Gk. *parasitos*, parasite.] A form of symbiosis in which one symbiont, or parasite, receives advantage to detriment of other, or host.

parasitoid (păr'ăsĭtoid) *n.* [Gk. *parasitos*, parasite; *eidos*, form.] An organism alternately parasitic and free-living.

parasitology (păr'ăsĭtŏl'öjĭ) *n.* [Gk. *parasitos*, parasite; *logos*, discourse.] The science treating of plant and animal parasites.

parasphenoid (părăsfē'noid) *n.* [Gk. *para*, beside; *sphen*, wedge; *eidos*, form.] Membrane bone formingfloor of cranium in certain vertebrates.

paraspore (păr'ăspōr) *n.* [Gk. *para*, beside; *sporos*, seed.] A spore formed from a cortical cell, in certain algae.

parastemon (părăstē'mŏn) *n.* [Gk. *para*, beside; *stemon*, thread.] A sterile stamen; parastamen; staminodium, *q.v.*

parasternalia (părăstĕrnā'lĭă) *n. plu.* [Gk. *para*, beside; *sternon*, breast.] Abdominal ribs or gastralia.

parasternum (părăstĕr'nŭm) *n.* [Gk. *para*, beside; L. *sternum*, breastbone.] The sum-total of abdominal ribs in certain reptiles, also in Stegocephali and Archaeopteryx.

parastichy (părăs'tĭkĭ) *n.* [Gk. *para*, beside; *stichos*, row.] A secondary spiral in phyllotaxis.

parastipes (păr'ăstī'pēz) *n.* [Gk. *para*, beside; L. *stipes*, stalk.] Subgalea or inner sclerite of insect stipes.

parasympathetic (păr'ăsĭmpăthĕt'ĭk) *a.* [Gk. *para*, beside; *sympathes*, of like feelings.] Enteral; *appl.* the craniosacral portion of the autonomic nervous system.

parasynapsis,—parasyndesis, *q.v.*

parasyndesis (păr'ăsĭn'dēsĭs) *n.* [Gk. *para*, beside; *syndesis*, binding together.] Syndesis where homologous chromosomes conjugate lengthwise.

parately (părăt'ēlĭ) *n.* [Gk *para*, beside; *telos*, end.] Evolution from material unrelated to that of type, but resulting in superficial resemblance.

paraterminal (păr'ătĕr'mĭnăl) *a.* [Gk. *para*, beside; L. *terminus*, boundary.] *Appl.* bodies constituting part of anterior median wall of lateral ventricles, in amphibians and reptiles.

paratestis (păr'ătĕs'tĭs) *n.* [Gk. *para*, beside; L. *testis*, testicle.] Small reddish-yellow fatty body in male tritons,—produces autacoids regulating appearance of nuptial apparel.

parathecium (păr'ăthē'sĭŭm) *n.* [Gk. *para*, beside; *theke*, box.] Peripheral layer of apothecium, as in cup fungi; peripheral hyphal layer in lichens.

parathormone,—parathyrin.

parathyreoid,—parathyroid.

parathyrin (păr'ăthī'rĭn) *n.* [Gk. *para*, beside; *thyreos*, shield.] Principle of internal secretion of parathyroids, which regulates calcium and phosphorus metabolism; parathormone.

parathyroid (părăthī'roid) *n.* [Gk. *para*, beside; *thyreos*, shield; *eidos*, form.] One of four small brownish-red endocrine glands near the thyroid.

paratoid (păr'ătoid) *a.* [Gk. *parateinein*, to extend along.] *Appl.* a double row of poison glands extending along back of certain amphibians, as of Salamandra.

paratomy (părăt'ömĭ) *n.* [Gk. *para*, beside; *tome*, cutting.] Reproduction by fission with antecedent regeneration, in certain annelids. *Opp.* architomy.

paratonic (părătŏn′ĭk) *a.* [Gk. *para*, beside; *tonos*, strain.] Stimulating or retarding; *appl.* movements induced by external stimuli, as tropisms and nastic movements, *opp.* autonomic.

paratracheal (păr′ătrăkē′ăl) *a.* [Gk. *para*, beside; L.L. *trachia*, windpipe.] With xylem parenchyma cells around or close to vascular tissue.

paratrophic (păr′ătrŏf′ĭk) *a.* [Gk. *para*, beside; *trephein*, to nourish.] *Appl.* method of nutrition of obligatory parasites.

paratype (păr′ătīp) *n.* [Gk. *para*, beside; *typos*, pattern.] Specimen described at same time as the one regarded as type of a new genus or species; aggregate of external factors affecting manifestation of a genetic character; abnormal type of a species, as of bacterial colony.

para-urethral (părăūrē′thrăl) *a.* [Gk. *para*, beside, *ourethra*, from *ouron*, urine.] *Appl.* racemose glands of the urethra, Littré's glands, Skene's glands.

paravertebral (păr′ăvĕr′tĕbrăl) *a.* [Gk. *para*, beside; L. *vertebra*, vertebra.] Alongside the spinal column; *appl.* sympathetic nerve trunk.

paravesical (părăvĕs′ĭkăl) *a.* [Gk. *para*, beside; L. *vesica*, bladder.] Beside the bladder; *appl.* a fossa or depression of peritoneum.

paraxial (părăk′sĭăl) *a.* [Gk. *para*, beside; L. *axis*, axle.] Alongside the axis; *appl.* a medial column of mesoderm.

paraxon (părăk′sŏn) *n.* [Gk. *para*, beside; *axon*, axle.] A lateral branch of the axis-cylinder process of a nerve cell.

paraxonic (păr′ăksŏn′ĭk) *a.* [Gk. *para*, beside; *axon*, axle.] *Pert.* or having an axis outwith the usual axis; with axis of foot between third and fourth digits, as in Artiodactyla.

parazoon (păr′ăzō′ŏn) *n.* [Gk. *para*, beside; *zoon*, animal.] Any of the Porifera or sponges.

parencephalon (păr′ĕnkĕf′ălŏn, -sĕf-) *n.* [Gk. *para*, beside; *engkephalos*, brain.] One of paired cerebral hemispheres.

parenchyma (părĕng′kĭmă) *n.* [Gk. *para*, beside; *engchyma*, infusion.] Plant-tissue, generally soft and of thin-walled relatively undifferentiated cells, which may vary in structure and function, as pith, of mesophyll, etc.; ground-work tissue of organs.

parenchymalia (părĕng′kĭmā′lĭă) *n. plu.* [Gk. *para*, beside; *engchyma*, infusion.] Spicules of parenchyma of Hexactinellida.

parenchymatous (părĕngkĭm′ătŭs) *a.* [Gk. *para*, beside; *engchyma*, infusion.] *Pert.* or found in parenchyma; *appl.* a kind of cell.

parenchymula (părĕngkĭm′ūlă) *n.* [Gk. *para*, beside; *engchyma*, infusion.] A flagellate sponge larva with cavity filled with gelatinous connective tissue.

parental generation,—*see* P_1.

parenteral (părĕn′tĕrăl) *a.* [Gk. *para*, beside; *enteron*, gut.] *Appl.* injections administered otherwise than by way of alimentary canal.

parhomology (păr′hōmŏl′ŏjĭ) *n.* [Gk. *para*, beside; *homos*, alike; *logos*, discourse.] Apparent similarity of structure.

parichnos (părĭk′nŏs) *n.* [Gk. *para*, beside; *ichnos*, trace.] Two lateral scars at sides of vascular bundle trace in certain extinct ferns.

paries (păr′ĭēz) *n.* [L. *paries*, wall.] The central division of a compartment of Cirripedia; wall of a hollow structure, as of tympanum, or of honey-comb.

parietal (părī′ĕtăl) *a.* [L. *paries*, wall.] *Pert.* or forming part of wall of a structure; *appl.* cells, membrane, layer, lobe, placentation, area between frons and occiput in insects, etc.

parietal bone,—a paired bone of roof of skull.

parietal organ,—epiphyseal photoreceptor in lower vertebrates; parapineal organ.

parietal region,—pineal region of brain.

parietal vesicle,—dilated distal part of pineal stalk.

parietes (părī′ĕtēz) *n. plu.* [L. *parietes*, walls.] *Plu.* of paries; walls or sides of structures.

parietobasilar (părī′ĕtöbăz′ĭlăr) *a.* [L. *paries*, wall; *basis*, base.] *Appl.* muscles between pedal disc and lower part of body-wall in sea-anemones.

parietofrontal (părī′ĕtöfrŭn′tăl) *a.* [L. *paries*, wall; *frons*, forehead.] *Appl.* a skull bone, in place of parietals and frontals, as in Dipnoi.

parietomastoid (părī′ĕtömăs′toid) *a.* [L. *paries*, wall; Gk. *mastos*, breast; *eidos*, form.] Connecting mastoid with parietal; *appl.* a suture.

parieto-occipital (părī′ĕtö-ŏksĭp′ĭtăl) *a.* [L. *paries*, wall; *occiput*, back of head.] *Appl.* fissure between parietal and occipital lobes of cerebrum.

parietotemporal (părī′ĕtötĕm′pörăl) *a.* [L. *paries*, wall; *tempora*, the temples.] *Pert.* parietal and temporal regions; *appl.* a branch of the middle cerebral artery.

parietovaginal (părī′ĕtövăj′ĭnăl) *a.* [L. *paries*, wall; *vagina*, sheath.] *Appl.* paired muscle for retracting introvert and tentacles in Bryozoa.

paripinnate (păr′ĭpĭn′āt) *a.* [L. *par*, equal; *pinna*, wing.] Pinnate without a terminal leaflet.

parivincular (păr′ĭvĭnk′ūlăr) *a.* [L. *par*, equal; *vinculum*, bond.] *Appl.* bivalve hinge ligament attached to nymphae; *cf.* opisthodetic.

paroccipital (părŏksĭp′ĭtăl) *a.* [Gk. *para*, beside; L. *occiput*, back of head.] *Appl.* ventrally-directed processes of exoccipitals.

paroccipu t (pârŏk′sĭpŭt) *n.* [Gk. *para*, beside; L. *occiput*, back of head.] In insects, a thickening of the occiput for articulation of neck sclerites.

paroecious (părē′sĭŭs) *a.* [Gk. *para*, beside; *oikia*, house.] With antheridium and archegonium close to one another; paroicous.

parolfactory (păr′ôlfăk′törĭ) *a.* [Gk. *para*, beside; L. *olfactorius*, olfactory.] *Appl.* an area and sulcus adjoining olfactory trigone of rhinencephalon.

paronychia (păr′önĭk′ĭă) *n. plu.* [Gk. *para*, beside; *onyx*, nail.] Bristles on pulvillus of insect foot; whitlow.

paroophoron (păr′ōŏf′örŏn) *n.* [Gk. *para*, beside; *oon*, egg; *pherein*, to bear.] A few scattered rudimentary tubules, remnants of Wolffian body in female, in broad ligament between uterus and epoophoron.

parosteal (părŏs′tēăl) *a.* [Gk. *para*, beside; *osteon*, bone.] *Appl.* abnormal bone formations.

parosteosis (păr′ŏstēō′sĭs) *n.* [Gk. *para*, beside; *osteon*, bone.] Bone formation in tracts normally fibrous.

parotic (părŏt′ĭk) *n.* [Gk. *para*, beside; *ous*, ear.] A process formed by fusion of exoccipital and opisthotic in adult lizards.

parotid glands, — paired salivary glands opening into mouth cavity of mammals.

parotoid glands,—in some amphibians, large swellings on side of head, formed of aggregated cutaneous glands, sometimes poisonous.

parovarium (păr′ōvā′rĭŭm) *n.* [Gk. *para*, beside; L. *ovarium*, ovary.] A small collection of tubules anterior to ovary, the remnant in adult of embryonic mesonephros; pampiniform body; epoophoron, *q.v.*

pars (pârz) *n.* [L. *pars*, part.] A part of an organ, as pars glandularis, nervosa, intermedia, tuberalis, of pituitary gland. *Plu.* partes.

parthenapogamy (pâr′thĕnăpŏg′ămĭ) *n.* [Gk. *parthenos*, virgin; *apo*, away; *gamos*, marriage.] Diploid or somatic parthenogenesis; ooapogamy.

parthenita (pârthĕn′ĭtă) *n.* [Gk. *parthenos*, virgin.] Unisexual stage of trematodes in intermediate host.

parthenocarpy (pâr′thĕnökâr′pĭ) *n.* [Gk. *parthenos*, virgin; *karpos*, fruit.] Condition of producing fruit without seeds, or of having parthenocarpic fruits.

parthenocaryogamy, — parthenokaryogamy.

parthenogamy (pâr′thĕnŏg′ămĭ) *n.* [Gk. *parthenos*, virgin; *gamos*, marriage.] Parthenomixis, *q.v.*

parthenogenesis (pâr′thĕnöjĕn′ësĭs) *n.* [Gk. *parthenos*, virgin; *genesis*, descent.] Reproduction without fertilisation by a male element.

parthenogenetic (pâr′thĕnöjĕnĕt′ĭk) *a.* [Gk. *parthenos*, virgin; *genesis*, descent.] *Appl.* plants or animals developed from seed or ovum without fertilisation by pollen or spermatozoon; *appl.* reagents which can activate ovum. *Opp.* zyogenetic.

parthenogonidia (pâr′thĕnögŏnĭd′ĭă) *n. plu.* [Gk. *parthenos*, virgin; *gonos*, offspring; *idion*, *dim.*] Zooids of a protozoan colony, with function of asexual reproduction.

parthenokaryogamy (pâr′thĕnökăr′ĭŏg′ămĭ) *n.* [Gk. *parthenos*, virgin; *karyon*, nucleus; *gamos*, marriage.] The fusion of two female haploid nuclei.

parthenomixis (pâr′thĕnömĭk′sĭs) *n.* [Gk. *parthenos*, virgin; *mixis*, mingling.] The mingling of two nuclei produced within one gamete or gametangium; parthenogamy.

parthenosperm (pâr′thĕnöspĕrm) *n.* [Gk. *parthenos*, virgin; *sperma*, seed.] A sperm produced without fertilisation, but resembling a zygote.

parthenospore (pâr′thĕnöspōr) *n.* [Gk. *parthenos*, virgin; *sporos*, seed.] Azygospore, *q.v.*

parthenote (pâr′thĕnōt) *n.* [Gk. *parthenos*, virgin.] A parthenogenetically produced haploid organism.

partial veil,—inner veil of certain fungi, growing from stipe towards edge of pileus and becoming separated to constitute the cortina or superior annulus.

particulate inheritance, — inheritance in one organism of distinctive paternal and maternal characteristics.

partite (pâr′tīt) *a.* [L. *partitus*, divided.] Divided nearly to base.

parturition (pârtūrĭsh′ŭn) *n.* [L. *parturire*, to bring forth.] The act or process of birth.

parumbilical (păr′ŭmbĭl′ĭkăl) *a.* [Gk. *para*, beside; L. *umbilicus*, navel.] Beside the navel; *appl.* small veins from anterior abdominal wall to portal and iliac veins.

pascual (păs′kūăl) *a.* [L. *pascuum*, pasture.] *Pert.* pastures or ground for grazing; *appl.* flora.

passage-cells, — thin-walled endodermal or exodermal cells of root, which permit passage of solutions.

patagial (pătăj′ĭăl) *a.* [L. *patagium*, border.] Of or *pert.* a patagium.

patagiate (pătăj′ĭăt) *a.* [L. *patagium*, border.] Furnished with a patagium.

patagium (pătăj′ĭŭm) *n.* [L. *patagium*, border.] Membranous expansion between fore and hind limbs of bats, and flying squirrels and foxes; similar expansion in lizards and on bird's wing; tegula, or dorsal process of prothorax in certain Lepidoptera; anterior pronotum in Diptera.

patella (pătĕl′ă) *n.* [L. *patella*, small pan.] The knee-cap or elbow-cap; segment between femur and tibia in Pycnogonida; fourth segment or carpodite of spider's leg; a limpet; a rounded apothecium of lichens.

patellar (pătĕl′ăr) *a.* [L. *patella*, small pan.] *Pert.* a patella.

patelliform (pătĕl′ĭfôrm) *a.* [L. *patella*, small pan; *forma*, shape.] Shaped like a patella; pan-shaped; like a bordered disc; patellaroid.

patent (păt′ënt) *a.* [L. *patens*, lying open.] Open; spreading widely, *opp.* fastigiate; expanded.

pateriform (păt′ërĭfôrm) *a.* [L. *patera*, flat dish; *forma*, shape.] Saucer-shaped.

pathetic (păthĕt′ĭk) *a.* [Gk. *pathos*, feeling.] *Appl.* trochlear nerve and superior oblique muscle of eye.

pathogen (păth′öjĕn) *n.* [Gk. *pathos*, suffering; *-genes*, producing.] Any disease-producing micro-organism.

pathogenic (păth′öjĕn′ĭk) *a.* [Gk. *pathos*, suffering; *-genes*, producing.] Disease-producing; *appl.* a parasite in relation to a particular host.

pathology (păthŏl′öjĭ) *n.* [Gk. *pathos*, suffering; *logos*, discourse.] Science dealing with disease and with morbid structures and functions.

patina (păt′ĭnă) *n.* [L. *patina*, dish.] Circles of plates round calyx of crinoids.

patriclinous (păt′rĭklī′nŭs) *a.* [L. *pater*, father; Gk. *klinein*, to incline.] With hereditary characteristics more paternal than maternal; patroclinic, patroclinal.

patulent (păt′ūlĕnt), **patulous** (păt′ūlŭs) *a.* [L. *patulus*, standing open.] Spreading open; expanding.

paturon (pătū′rŏn) *n.* [Gk. *patein*, to trample on; *oura*, after part.] Basal joint of arachnid chelicerae, used for crushing and expressing fluids of insects.

paucilocular (pô′sĭlŏk′ūlăr) *a.* [L. *pauci*, few; *loculus*, compartment.] Containing, or composed of, few small cavities or loculi.

paucispiral (pô′sĭspī′răl) *a.* [L. *pauci*, few; *spira*, coil.] With few coils or whorls.

paulospore (pôl′öspōr) *n.* [Gk. *paula*, rest; *sporos*, seed.] A resting stage in development, as a cyst; chlamydospore, *q.v.*

paunch (pônsh) *n.* [L. *pantex*, paunch.] The rumen, an expansion of oesophagus, first stomach of ruminants.

paurometabolism (pô′römĕtăbölĭzm) *n.* [Gk. *pauros*, brief; *metabole*, change.] Incomplete metamorphosis in which the nymph resembles the adult.

pavement (pāv′mĕnt) *n.* [L. *pavimentum*, from *pavire*, to ram down.] A flat structure of compact units; *appl.* epithelium of flat, nucleated scales in mosaic pattern, simple squamous epithelium; *appl.* teeth, as in certain sharks. *a.* Pavimental.

paxilla (păksĭl′ă) *a.* [L. *paxillus*, peg.] Thick plate supporting calcareous pillars, summit of each covered by group of small spines, in certain Stelleroids; paxillus.

paxillar (păksĭl′ăr) *a.* [L. *paxillus*, peg.] *Pert.* a paxilla.

paxillate,—having paxillae; paxilliferous, paxillose.

paxilliform (păksĭl′ĭfôrm) *a.* [L. *paxillus*, peg; *forma*, shape.] Shaped like a paxilla.

paxillus,—paxilla, *q.v.*; a genus of agarics.

pearl (pĕrl) *n.* [F. *perle*, pearl.] In shells of some Mollusca, an abnormal growth formed with a grain of foreign matter or a minute organism for nucleus and many thin layers of nacre surrounding it.

pectase (pĕk′tās) *n.* [Gk. *pektos*, congealed.] An enzyme of plants which forms vegetable jelly.

pecten (pĕk′tĕn) *n.* [L. *pecten*, comb.] Any comb-like structure; a process of inner retinal surface in reptiles, expanded into a folded quadrangular plate in birds; a ridge of superior ramus of os pubis; a part of stridulating organ of certain spiders; sensory abdominal appendage of scorpions; the scallop; a sterigma.

pectic (pĕk′tĭk) *a.* [Gk. *pektos*, congealed.] *Appl.* substances in cell-walls and cell-sap of plants, including pectic acid and its salts, pectin, and pectose; *appl.* enzymes: pectosinase, pectase, and pectinase, which hydrolyse pectic substances.

pectinal (pĕk′tĭnăl) *a.* [L. *pecten*, comb.] *Pert.* a pecten.

pectinate (pĕk′tĭnāt) *a.* [L. *pecten*, comb.] Comb-like; pectiniform; *appl.* leaves, arrangement of sporangia, a ligament of iris, certain gills, pedicellariae of Asteroidea, a septum between corpora cavernosa, fibres, etc.

pectineal (pĕktĭn′ëăl) *a.* [L. *pecten*, comb.] *Appl.* process of pubis of birds; *appl.* a ridge-line on femur and attached muscle.

pectinellae (pĕk′tĭnĕl′ē) *n. plu.* [L. *pectinella*, small comb.] Transverse, comb-like membranellae constituting adoral ciliary spiral of some infusoria.

pectines (pĕk′tĭnēz) *n. plu.* [L. *pecten*, comb.] *Plu.* of pecten, *q.v.*

pectineus,—a flat muscle between pecten pubis and upper medial part of femur.

pectiniform,—pectinate.

pectinirhomb (pĕk'tĭnĭrŏmb') *n.* [L. *pecten*, comb ; Gk. *rhombos*, wheel.] A type of stereom-folding in Cystidea.

pectocellulose (pĕk'tösĕl'ūlōs) *n.* [Gk. *pektos*, congealed ; L. *cellula*, small cell.] Cellulose mixed with pectose, as in fleshy roots and fruits.

pectoral (pĕk'törăl) *a.* [L. *pectus*, breast.] *Pert.* chest ; in chest region ; *appl.* arch, girdle, fins, etc.

pectoralis major and **minor,**—outer and inner chest muscles connecting ventral chest wall with shoulder and humerus.

pectose (pĕk'tōs) *n.* [Gk. *pektos*, congealed.] A carbohydrate constituent of plant cell-walls, converted into pectin and cellulose by action of pectosinase.

pectus (pĕk'tŭs) *n.* [L. *pectus*, breast.] The chest or breast region; fused pleuron and sternum of arthropods.

pedal (pĕd'ăl) *a.* [L. *pes*, foot.] *Pert.* foot or feet; *appl.* cords, ganglia, glands, etc.

pedalfer (pĕdăl'fĕr) *n.* [*ped*on ; *al*umen ; *fer*rum.] Any of a group of soils, in humid regions, usually characterised by the presence of aluminium and iron compounds, and by the absence of carbonates.

pedate (pĕd'āt) *a.* [L. *pes*, foot.] Pedatipartite ; with toe-like parts.

pedatipartite (pĕdăt'ĭpâr'tīt) *a.* [L. *pes*, foot ; *partitus*, divided.] *Appl.* a variety of palmate leaf with cymose branching of third order.

pedatisect (pĕdăt'ĭsĕkt) *a.* [L. *pes*, foot ; *sectus*, cut.] In pedate arrangement, and with divisions nearly to midrib.

pedicel (pĕd'ĭsĕl) *n.* [L. *pediculus*, small foot.] A small, short foot-stalk of leaf, flower, fruit, or sporangium ; foot-stalk or stem of stationary or fixed organism, or of organ, as optic ; second segment of insect antenna ; pedicellus.

pedicellariae (pĕd'ĭsĕlăr'ĭē) *n. plu.* [L. *pediculus*, small foot.] Minute pincer-like structures studding the surface of certain echinoderms.

pedicellate (pĕd'ĭsĕlāt) *a.* [L. *pediculus*, small foot.] Supported by a pedicel or petiole ; *appl.* Hymenoptera with stalked abdomen ; *cf.* pseudosessile.

pedicellus (pĕd'ĭsĕl'ŭs) *n.* [L. *pediculus*, small foot.] A short foot-stalk ; second joint of insect antennae ; pedicel.

pedicle (pĕd'ĭkl) *n.* [L. *pediculus*, small foot.] A short stem ; backward-projecting vertebral process ; narrow stalk uniting cephalothorax with abdomen in arachnids.

pedipalpus (pĕd'ĭpăl'pŭs) *n.* [L. *pes*, foot ; *palpare*, to feel.] In Arachnoidea, second cephalothoracic paired appendage, variously a pincer-like claw, a simple or leg-like appendage, a chelate structure.

pedocal (pĕd'ökăl) *n.* [*ped*on ; *cal*cium.] Any of a group of soils, of semi-arid and arid regions, characterised by the presence of carbonate of lime.

pedogamy (pēdŏg'ămĭ) *n.* [Gk. *pais*, child ; *gamos*, union.] Paedogamy, *q.v.*

pedogenesis,—paedogenesis, *q.v.*

pedogenic (pĕdöjĕn'ĭk) *a.* [Gk. *pedon*, soil ; *gennaein*, to produce.] *Pert.* the formation of soil.

pedology (pĕdŏl'öjĭ) *n.* [Gk. *pedon*, soil ; *logos*, discourse.] Soil science ; *cf.* edaphology.

pedonic (pĕdŏn'ĭk) *a.* [Gk. *pedon*, ground.] *Appl.* organisms of fresh-water lake-bottom.

peduncle (pĕ̄dŭng'kl) *n.* [L.L. *pedunculus*, small foot.] A stem or stalk, supporting flower or fruit ; a band of white fibres joining different parts of brain ; stalk of crinoids, brachiopods and barnacles ; link between thorax and abdomen in arthropods ; stalk of sedentary protozoa.

pedunculate (pĕdŭng'kūlāt) *a.* [L. L. *pedunculus*, small foot.] Growing on or having a peduncle ; *appl.*

bodies, groups of association cells and fibres of protocerebrum in insects, highly developed in Hymenoptera ; *appl.* hydatid or appendix of epididymis ; pediferous.

pelage (pĕl'ăj) *n.* [F. *pelage*, fur.] The hairy, furry, or woolly coat of mammals.

pelagic (pĕlăj'ĭk) *a.* [Gk. *pelagos*, sea.] Ocean-inhabiting.

pelasgic (pĕlăs'jĭk) *a.* [Gk. *Pelasgikos*, *pert.* Pelasgians.] Moving from place to place.

pellagra-preventive factor,—niacin.

pellicle (pĕl'ĭkl) *n.* [L. *pellicula*, small skin.] The delicate protective investment of protozoa ; any filmy protective covering ; pellicula.

pelliculate (pĕlĭk'ūlāt) *a.* [L. *pellicula*, small skin.] Having a pellicle on external surface.

pellions (pĕl'ĭŏnz) *n. plu.* [Gk. *pella*, cup ; *dim.*] Ring of plates supporting suckers of echinoids ; rosettes.

pelma (pĕl'mă) *n.* [Gk. *pelma*, sole.] The sole of foot ; planta.

pelophilous (pēlŏf'ĭlŭs) *a.* [Gk. *pelos*, clay ; *philein*, to love.] Growing on clay.

peloria (pĕlō'rĭă) *n.* [Gk. *pelorios*, monstrous.] Condition of abnormal regularity ; a modification of structure from irregularity to regularity.

peloric (pĕlŏr'ĭk) *a.* [Gk. *pelorios*, monstrous.] *Appl.* a flower which, normally irregular, becomes regular.

peloton (pĕl'ötŏng) *n.* [F. *peloton*, ball of thread.] A knot or skein of hyphae, as in a mycorrhiza.

pelta (pĕl'tă) *n.* [Gk. *pelte*, shield.] The shield-like apothecium of certain lichens.

peltate (pĕl'tāt) *a.* [Gk. *pelte*, shield.] Shield-shaped ; fastened to stalk at a point within margin, as a leaf.

peltinervate (pĕl'tĭnĕr'vāt) *a.* [Gk. *pelte*, shield ; L. *nervus*, nerve.] Having veins radiating from near the centre, as of a peltate leaf.

pelvic (pĕl'vĭk) *a.* [L. *pelvis*, basin.] *Pert.* or situated at or near pelvis ; *appl.* girdle, cavity, fin, limbs, plexus, etc.

pelvis (pĕl'vĭs) *n.* [L. *pelvis*, basin.] The bony cavity formed by pelvic girdle along with coccyx and sacrum ; expansion of ureter at its junction with kidney ; basal portion of cup of crinoids.

pelvisternum (pĕl'vĭstĕr'nŭm) *n.* [L. *pelvis*, basin ; L. *sternum*, breastbone.] Epipubis separate from pubis.

pen (pĕn) *n.* [L. *penna*, feather.] A leaf midrib ; gladius of certain Cephalopoda.

pendent (pĕn'dënt) *a.* [L. *pendens*, hanging down.] Hanging down, as certain lichens, leaves, flowers, etc.

pendulous (pĕn'dūlŭs) *a.* [L. *pendere*, to hang.] Bending downwards from point of origin ; overhanging ; *appl.* ovules, branches, flowers, etc.

penes,—*plu.* of penis.

penetrance (pĕn'ëtrăns) *n.* [L. *penetrare*, to penetrate.] The frequency, measured as a percentage, with which a gene shows any effect.

penial (pē'nĭăl) *a.* [L. *penis*, penis.] Of or *pert.* penis.

penial setae, — paired needle-like chitinoid bodies at nematode anus ; setae near aperture of vas deferens in earthworms.

penicillate (pĕn'ĭsĭl'āt) *a.* [L. *penicillum*, painter's brush.] Penicilliform ; pencil-shaped ; tipped with hairs ; having a structure like a camel-hair or bottle brush.

penicillus (pĕn'ĭsĭl'ŭs) *n.* [L. *penicillus*, painter's brush.] A brush-shaped structure, as certain type of nematocyst ; tuft of hairs of tegumen ; a tuft of arterioles, in spleen ; a tuft of conidiophores. *Plu.* penicilli.

penis (pē'nĭs) *n.* [L. *penis*, penis.] The male copulatory organ.

pennaceous (pĕnā'shŭs) *a.* [L. *penna*, feather.] Penniform ; like a plume or feather ; *appl.* feathers with hamuli on barbules, *opp.* plumose.

pennate,—pinnate.

Pennsylvanian (pĕn′sĭlvā′nĭăn) *a.* [*Pennsylvania.*] *Appl.* and *pert.* an epoch of the Carboniferous era; *appl.* fossils in North American coalmeasures.

pensile (pēn′sīl) *a.* [L. *pensilis*, hanging down.] Pendent; hanging down; *appl.* some bird's-nests.

pentacapsular (pĕn′tăkăp′sūlăr) *a.* [Gk. *pente*, five; L. *capsula*, capsule.] With five capsules.

pentacarpellary (pĕn′tăkâr′pĕlărĭ) *a.* [Gk. *pente*, five; *karpos*, fruit.] With five carpels.

pentachenium (pĕn′tăkē′nĭŭm) *n.* [Gk. *pente*, five; *a*, not; *chainein*, to gape.] A form of schizocarp with five carpels.

pentacoccous (pĕn′tăkŏk′ŭs) *a.* [Gk. *pente*, five; *kokkos*, kernel.] With five seeds or carpels.

pentacrinoid (pĕn′tăkrĭnoid′) *a.* [Gk. *pente*, five; *krinon*, lily; *eidos*, form.] Resembling a Pentacrinus; *appl.* larval stage of feather-stars.

pentactinal (pĕntăk′tĭnăl) *a.* [Gk. *pente*, five; *aktis*, ray.] Five-rayed; five-branched.

pentacula (pĕntăkū′lă) *n.* [Gk. *pente*, five; L. *aculeus*, prickle.] In life-history of echinoderms, the stage with five tentacles.

pentacyclic (pĕn′tăsĭ̄k′lĭk) *a.* [Gk. *pente*, five; *kyklos*, circle.] Arranged in five whorls.

pentadactyl (pĕn′tădăk′tĭl) *a.* [Gk. *pente*, five; *daktylos*, finger.] Having all four limbs normally terminating in five digits.

pentadelphous (pĕn′tădĕl′fŭs) *a.* [Gk. *pente*, five; *adelphos*, brother.] Having five clusters of more or less united filaments.

pentafid (pĕn′tăfĭd) *a.* [Gk. *pente*, five; L. *findere*, to cleave.] In five divisions or lobes.

pentagonal (pĕntăg′ŏnăl) *a.* [Gk. *pente*, five; *gonia*, angle.] *Appl.* symmetry of a pentamerous flower; quinary; having five angles.

pentagynous (pĕntăj′ĭnŭs) *a.* [Gk. *pente*, five; *gyne*, woman.] Having five styles.

pentamerous (pĕntăm′ĕrŭs) *a.* [Gk. *pente*, five; *meros*, part.] Composed of five parts; in whorls of five or a multiple of five.

pentandrous (pĕntăn′drŭs) *a.* [Gk. *pente*, five; *aner*, male.] Having five stamens.

pentapetalous (pĕn′tăpĕt′ălŭs) *a.* [Gk. *pente*, five; *petalon*, leaf.] Having five petals.

pentaploid (pĕnt′ăploid) *a.* [Gk. *pente*, five; *haploos*, simple; *eidos*, form.] With five sets of chromosomes; having five times the monoploid chromosome number.

pentapterous (pĕntăp′tĕrŭs) *a.* [Gk. *pente*, five; *pteron*, wing.] With five wings, as some fruits.

pentarch (pĕnt′ârk) *a.* [Gk. *pente*, five; *arche*, beginning.] With five alternating xylem and phloem groups.

pentasepalous (pĕn′tăsĕp′ălŭs) *a.* [Gk. *pente*, five; F. *sépale*, sepal.] Having five sepals.

pentasternum (pĕn′tăstĕr′nŭm) *n.* [Gk. *pente*, five; *sternon*, chest.] Sternite of fifth segment of prosoma or third segment of podosoma in Acarina.

pentastichous (pĕntăs′tĭkŭs) *a.* [Gk. *pente*, five; *stichos*, row.] Arranged in five vertical rows.

pepo (pĕ̄p′ö) *n.* [Gk. *pepon*, melon.] An inferior one-celled, many-seeded pulpy fruit, as of Cucurbitaceae.

pepsin (pĕp′sĭn) *n.* [Gk. *pepsis*, digestion.] An enzyme secreted by stomach, acting, with hydrochloric acid, on proteins; also secreted by some insectivorous plants.

peptic (pĕp′tĭk) *a.* [Gk. *peptein*, to digest.] Relating to or promoting digestion; *appl.* pepsin-secreting glands of stomach.

peptonephridia (pĕp′tönĕfrĭd′ĭă) *n. plu.* [Gk. *pepsis*, digestion; *nephros*, kidney.] The anterior nephridia which function as digestive glands, of some Oligochaeta.

peraeopods,—pereiopods.

percnosome (pĕrk′nösōm) *n.* [Gk. *perknos* dark; *soma*, body.]

Deeply-staining granule of an androcyte, possibly a chromatoid accessory body.

percurrent (pěrkŭr'ĕnt) *a.* [L. *percurrens*, running through.] Extending throughout length, or from base to apex.

pereion (pĕrī'ŏn) *n.* [Gk. *peraioun*, to convey.] The thorax of Crustacea.

pereiopods (pĕrī'öpŏdz) *n. plu.* [Gk. *peraioun*, to convey; *pous*, foot.] The locomotory thoracic limbs of Malacostraca; trunk-legs.

perennation (pĕr'ĕnā'shŭn) *n.* [L. *per*, through; *annus*, year.] Condition of living for a number of years.

perennial (pĕrĕn'ĭăl) *a.* [L. *per*, through; *annus*, year.] Persisting through the year, or for a number of years.

perennibranchiate (pĕrĕn'ĭbrăng'kĭāt) *a.* [L. *per*, through; *annus*, year; *branchiae*, gills.] Having gills persisting throughout life, as certain amphibians.

perfect (pĕr'fĕkt) *a.* [L. *perfectus*, finished.] Complete; *appl.* flower with both stamens and pistil; *appl.* fungi producing sexual spores.

perfoliate (pĕrfō'lĭāt) *a.* [L. *per*, through; *folium*, leaf.] *Appl.* a leaf with basal lobes so united as to appear as if stem ran through it.

perforate (pĕr'förāt) *a.* [L. *perforare*, to bore through.] Having pores, as corals, foraminifera, some leaves; *appl.* certain areas of brain perforated by small blood-vessels.

perforation plate,—perforate septum or area of contact between cells or elements of wood-vessels.

perforator (pĕr'förā'tŏr) *n.* [L. *perforare*, to bore through.] A barbed spear-like head and process of some spermatozoa, as of salamander.

perforatorium (pĕr'förătō'rĭŭm) *n.* [L. *perforare*, to bore through.] The acrosome, *q.v.*; acrosome with galea capitis.

perhydridase (pĕrhī'drĭdās) *n.* [L. *per*, through; Gk. *hydor*, water.] An enzyme which causes activation of perhydride hydrogen.

perianth (pĕr'ĭănth) *n.* [Gk. *peri*, around; *anthos*, flower.] A floral envelope; external floral whorls, including calyx and corolla; cover or ring of cells surrounding archegonium in Marchantiales.

periblast (pĕr'ĭblăst) *n.* [Gk. *peri*, around; *blastos*, bud.] The outside layer, epiblast, or blastoderm of an insect embryo.

periblastesis (pĕr'ĭblăs'tēsĭs) *n.* [Gk. *peri*, around; *blaste*, growth.] Envelopment by surrounding tissue, as of lichen gonidia.

periblastic (pĕrĭblăs'tĭk) *a.* [Gk. *peri*, around; *blastos*, bud.] *Pert.* periblast; superficial, as *appl.* segmentation.

periblastula (pĕr'ĭblăs'tūlă) *n.* [Gk. *peri*; around; *blastos*, bud.] A blastula resulting from periblastic segmentation.

periblem (pĕr'ĭblĕm) *n.* [Gk. *peri*, around; *blema*, coverlet.] Layers of ground or fundamental tissue between dermatogen and plerome of growing points.

peribranchial (pĕr'ĭbrăng'kĭăl) *a.* [Gk. *peri*, around; *brangchia*, gills.] Around gills; *appl.* type of gemmation in ascidians; *appl.* atrial cavity in ascidians and lancelet; *appl.* circular spaces surrounding basal parts of papulae of Asteroidea.

peribulbar (pĕr'ĭbŭl'băr) *a.* [Gk. *peri*, around; L. *bulbus*, bulb.] Surrounding the eye-ball; perigemmal, *q.v.*

pericapillary (pĕr'ĭkăpĭl'ărĭ) *a.* [Gk. *peri*, around; L. *capillus*, hair.] *Appl.* cells in contact with outer surface of wall of capillaries, as fibroblasts, histiocytes, pericytes, Rouget cells.

pericardiac,—pericardial.

pericardial (pĕr'ĭkâr'dĭăl) *a.* [Gk. *peri*, around; *kardia*, heart.] *Pert.* pericardium; surrounding heart; *appl.* cavity, septum; *appl.* paired excretory glands in lamellibranchs; *appl.* cells: cords of nephrocytes in certain insects.

pericardium (pĕr′ĭkâr′dĭŭm) *n.* [Gk. *peri*, around ; *kardia*, heart.] The cavity containing heart ; membrane enveloping heart.

pericarp (pĕr′ĭkârp) *n.* [Gk. *peri*, around ; *karpos*, fruit.] The ovary walls of fruits ; a fruit covering.

pericellular (pĕr′ĭsĕl′ūlăr) *a.* [Gk. *peri*, around ; L. *cellula*, small cell.] Surrounding a cell ; *appl.* net of glial origin surrounding a neurocyton.

pericemental,—periodontal.

pericentral (pĕr′ĭsĕn′trăl) *a.* [Gk. *peri*, around ; L. *centrum*, centre.] Around or near centre ; *appl.* auxiliary cells, as in certain algae.

pericentric (pĕr′ĭsĕn′trĭk) *a.* [Gk. *peri*, around ; *kentron*, centre.] *Appl.* breaks in arms of a chromosome on either side of centromere ; *appl.* inversions including the centromere, *opp.* paracentric ; heterobrachial.

perichaetial (pĕr′ĭkē′shĭăl, -tĭăl) *a.* [Gk. *peri*, around ; *chaite*, hair.] *Pert.* perichaetium ; *appl.* leaves.

perichaetine (pĕr′ĭkē′tĭn) *a.* [Gk. *peri*, around ; *chaite*, hair.] Having a ring of chaetae or setae encircling the body.

perichaetium (pĕr′ĭkē′shĭŭm, -tĭŭm) *n.* [Gk. *peri*, around ; *chaite*, hair.] One of membranes or leaves enveloping archegonia or antheridia of bryophytes.

perichondral (pĕr′ĭkôn′drăl) *a.* [Gk. *peri*, around ; *chondros*, cartilage.] *Appl.* ossification in cartilage from without inwards ; *cf.* endochondral.

perichondrium (pĕr′ĭkôn′drĭŭm) *n.* [Gk. *peri*, around ; *chondros*, cartilage.] A fibrous membrane that covers cartilages.

perichordal (pĕr′ĭkôr′dăl) *a.* [Gk. *peri*, around ; *chorde*, cord.] Enveloping or near the notochord.

perichoroidal (pĕr′ĭkōroid′ăl) *a.* [Gk. *peri*, around ; *chorion*, skin ; *eidos*, form.] Surrounding the choroid ; *appl.* lymph-space ; perichorioidal.

perichrome (pĕr′ĭkrōm) *a.* [Gk. *peri*, around ; *chroma*, colour.] Having Nissl bodies arranged near periphery of nerve cell body, as in molecular layer of cerebellar cortex.

perichylous (pĕr′ĭkī′lŭs) *a.* [Gk. *peri*, around ; *chylos*, juice.] With water-storage cells outside chlorenchyma.

pericladium (pĕr′ĭklā′dĭŭm) *n.* [Gk. *peri*, around ; *klados*, branch.] The lowermost clasping portion of a sheathing petiole.

periclinal (pĕr′ĭklī′năl) *a.* [Gk. *peri*, around ; *klinein*, to bend.] *Appl.* system of cells parallel to surface of apex of a growing point ; *appl.* graft hybrids or chimaerae with inner tissue of one species surrounded by epidermis of the other.

periclinium (pĕr′ĭklĭn′ĭŭm) *n.* [Gk. *peri*, round ; *kline*, bed.] The involucre of a composite flower.

pericranium (pĕr′ĭkrā′nĭŭm) *n.* [Gk. *peri*, around ; *kranion*, skull.] Fibrous membrane investing skull ; periosteum of skull.

pericycle (pĕr′ĭsī′kl) *n.* [Gk. *peri*, around ; *kyklos*, circle.] The external layer of stele, the layer between endodermis and conducting tissues.

pericyte (pĕr′ĭsīt) *n.* [Gk. *peri*, around ; *kytos*, hollow.] A macrophage in adventitia of small blood vessels ; a pericapillary cell ; Rouget cell.

pericytial (pĕr′ĭsĭt′ĭal) *a.* [Gk. *peri*, around ; *kytos*, hollow vessel.] Surrounding a cell ; pericellular.

peridental (pĕr′ĭdĕn′tăl) *a.* [Gk. *peri*, around ; L. *dens*, tooth.] Periodontal ; investing a tooth.

periderm (pĕr′ĭdĕrm) *n.* [Gk. *peri*, around ; *derma*, skin.] The outer layer of bark ; phellogen, phellem, and phelloderm collectively ; epiphloem ; external cuticular layer of Hydrozoa ; cell layer of epidermis shed later ; epitrichium of mammals.

peridesm (pĕr′ĭdĕzm) *n.* [Gk. *peri*, around ; *desme*, bundle.] Tissue surrounding a vascular bundle.

peridesmium (pĕr′ĭdĕs′mĭŭm) *n.* [Gk. *peri*, around ; *desmos*, band.] Tissue surrounding a ligament.

peridial (pērĭd'ĭăl) *a.* [Gk. *peridion*, small wallet.] *Pert.* a peridium.

perididymis (pĕr'ĭdĭd'ĭmĭs) *n.* [Gk. *peri*, around; *didymos*, testicle.] The tunica albuginea or fibrous covering of testis.

peridiolum (pērĭd'ĭōlŭm) *n.* [*Dim.* of Gk. *peridion*, small wallet.] A small peridium or collection of spores enclosed within peridial covering; peridiole.

peridium (pērĭd'ĭŭm) *n.* [Gk. *peridion*, small wallet.] The coat investing the sporophore of fungi, outer covering of a sporangium; cortex of sterile hyphae.

peridural (pĕr'ĭdū'răl) *a.* [Gk. *peri*, around; L. *durus*, hard.] *Appl.* perimeningeal space at later stage of development.

perienteric (pĕr'ĭĕntĕr'ĭk) *a.* [Gk. *peri*, around; *enteron*, gut.] Surrounding the enteron.

perienteron (pĕr'ĭĕn'tĕrŏn) *n.* [Gk. *peri*, around; *enteron*, gut.] A cavity surrounding the enteron; visceral cavity in embryo.

perifoliary (pĕr'ĭfō'lĭărĭ) *a.* [Gk. *peri*, around; L. *folium*, leaf.] Round a leaf margin.

perigamium,—perichaetium.

periganglionic (pĕr'ĭgăng'glĭŏn'ĭk) *a.* [Gk. *peri*, around; *gangglion*, little tumour.] Surrounding a ganglion; *appl.* glands or calcareous bodies, or glands of Swammerdam, paired outgrowths of prolonged saccus endolymphaticus, on each side of vertebral column, as in frog.

perigastric (pĕr'ĭgăs'trĭk) *a.* [Gk. *peri*, around; *gaster*, stomach.] Surrounding the viscera; *appl.* abdominal cavity.

perigastrium (pĕr'ĭgăs'trĭŭm) *n.* [Gk. *peri*, round; *gaster*, stomach.] The body cavity or coelom.

perigastrula (pĕr'ĭgăs'troolă) *n.* [Gk. *peri*, round; *gaster*, stomach.] The gastrula resulting after superficial segmentation.

perigemmal (pĕr'ĭjĕm'ăl) *a.* [Gk. *peri*, around; L. *gemma*, bud.] Surrounding a taste-bud; *appl.* nerve fibres, spaces.

perigenous (pĕrĭj'ĕnŭs) *a.* [Gk. *peri*, around; *-genes*, producing.] Borne or growing on all sides of an organism or structure; amphigenous, *q.v.*

perigonadial (pĕr'ĭgŏnăd'ĭăl) *a.* [Gk. *peri*, around; *gone*, seed.] Surrounding the gonads; *appl.* cavity: the gonocoel.

perigonium (pĕr'ĭgō'nĭŭm) *n.* [Gk. *peri*, around; *gone*, seed.] A floral envelope or perianth; involucre round antheridium of mosses; a gonotheca; perigone.

perigynium (pĕr'ĭjĭn'ĭŭm) *n.* [Gk. *peri*, around; *gyne*, female.] Membranous envelope or marsupium of archegonium in liverworts; involucre in mosses; fruit-investing utricle of Carex.

perigynous (pĕrĭj'ĭnŭs) *a.* [Gk. *peri*, around; *gyne*, female.] Having sepals, petals, stamens round the gynoecium.

perigyny (pĕrĭj'ĭnĭ) *n.* [Gk. *peri*, around; *gyne*, female.] Arrangement in a perigynous manner.

perihaemal (pĕr'ĭhē'măl) *a.* [Gk. *peri*, around; *haima*, blood.] *Appl.* blood-vascular system of canals and spaces of Echinoderma; *appl.* dorsal outgrowths of third body-cavity of Enteropneusta.

perikaryon (pĕr'ĭkăr'ĭŏn) *n.* [Gk. *peri*, around; *karyon*, nucleus.] Protoplasm surrounding nucleus in nerve cell body; *cf.* cyton.

perilymph (pĕr'ĭlĭmf) *n.* [Gk. *peri*, round; L. *lympha*, water.] A fluid separating membranous from osseous labyrinth of ear.

perimedullary (pĕr'ĭmĕdŭl'ărĭ) *a.* [Gk. *peri*, around; L. *medulla*, marrow.] Surrounding the pith of a stem; *appl.* a zone.

perimeningeal (pĕr'ĭmĕnĭn'jĕăl) *a.* [Gk. *peri*, around; *meningx*, membrane.] *Appl.* a space between endorhachis and meninx primitiva or spinal cord envelope.

perimetrium (pĕr'ĭmē'trĭŭm) *n.* [Gk. *peri*, around; *metra*, womb.] The peritoneal covering of the uterus.

perimysium (pĕr′ĭmĭz′ĭŭm) *n.* [Gk. *peri*, around ; *mys*, muscle.] Connective tissue binding numbers of fibres into bundles and muscles, and continuing into tendons ; alternatively, *appl.* only to fasciculi envelopes ; *cf.* epimysium.

perinaeal (pĕr′ĭnē′ăl) *a.* [Gk. *perinaion*, part between anus and scrotum.] *Pert.* perinaeum ; *appl.* artery, body, nerve, gland ; perineal.

perinaeum (pĕr′ĭnē′ŭm) *n.* [Gk. *perinaion*, part between anus and scrotum.] A surface of body limited by scrotum or vulva in front, anus behind, and laterally by medial side of thigh ; perineum.

perine,—perinium.

perinephrium (pĕr′ĭnĕf′rĭŭm) *n.* [Gk. *peri*, around ; *nephros*, kidney.] The enveloping tissue of kidney.

perineural (pĕr′ĭnū′răl) *a.* [Gk. *peri*, around ; *neuron*, nerve.] Surrounding a nerve or nerve-cord ; *appl.* a ventral sinus in some insects.

perineurium (pĕr′ĭnū′rĭŭm) *n.* [Gk. *peri*, around ; *neuron*, nerve.] The tubular sheath of a small bundle of nerve fibres.

perineuronal (pĕr′ĭnū′rŏnăl) *a.* [Gk. *peri*, around ; *neuron*, nerve.] Surrounding a nerve cell or nerve cells.

perinium (pĕrĭn′ĭŭm) *n.* [Gk. *peri*, around ; *is*, fibre.] An epispore, or outer microspore-coating of certain Pteridophyta.

periodicity (pē′rĭŏdĭs′ĭtĭ) *n.* [Gk. *periodos*, circuit.] The fulfilment of functions at regular periods or intervals ; rhythm.

periodontal (pĕr′ĭŏdŏn′tăl) *a.* [Gk. *peri*, around ; *odous*, tooth.] Covering or surrounding a tooth ; *appl.* membrane, etc.

perioesophageal (pĕr′ĭē′sŏfăj′ĕăl) *a.* [Gk. *peri*, around ; *oisophagos*, gullet.] Surrounding oesophagus ; *appl.* a nerve ring.

periople (pĕrĭŏp′lē) *n.* [Gk. *peri*, round ; *ople*, hoof.] Thin outer layer of the hoof of equines.

periopticon (pĕr′ĭŏp′tĭkŏn) *n.* [Gk. *peri*, round ; *opsis*, sight.] In insects, the zone of optic lobes nearest the eye.

periosteum (pĕr′ĭŏs′tēŭm) *n.* [Gk. *peri*, around ; *osteon*, bone.] The fibrous membrane investing the surface of bones.

periostracum (pĕr′ĭŏs′trăkŭm) *n.* [Gk. *peri*, around ; *ostrakon*, shell.] The chitinous external layer of most mollusc and brachiopid shells.

periotic (pĕr′ĭōt′ĭk) *n.* [Gk. *peri*, around ; *ous*, ear.] A cranial bone enclosing parts of membranous labyrinth of internal ear.

peripetalous (pĕr′ĭpĕt′ălŭs) *a.* [Gk. *peri*, around ; *petalon*, leaf.] Surrounding petals or petaloid structure.

peripharyngeal (pĕr′ĭfărĭn′jēăl) *a.* [Gk. *peri*, around ; *pharyngx*, gullet.] Encircling or surrounding pharynx ; *appl.* cilia of ascidians and lancelet.

peripheral (pĕrĭf′ĕrăl) *a.* [Gk. *peripherein*, to move round.] Distant from centre ; near circumference ; *appl.* end-organs of nerves, nervous system.

peripherical (pĕr′ĭfĕr′ĭkăl) *a.* [Gk. *peripherein*, to move round.] *Appl.* an embryo more or less completely surrounding endosperm in seed.

periphloem (pĕrĭflō′ĕm) *n.* [Gk. *peri*, around ; *phloios*, smooth bark.] Phloem - sheath ; pericambium.

periphloic (pĕrĭflō′ĭk) *a.* [Gk. *peri*, around ; *phloios*, inner bark.] *Pert.* periphloem ; having phloem outside centric xylem, *appl.* bundles ; amphiphloic. *Opp.* perixylic.

periphoranthium (pĕr′ĭfŏrăn′thĭŭm) *a.* [Gk. *peri*, around ; *pherein*, to bear ; *anthos*, flower.] Involucre of Compositae.

periphorium (pĕrĭfō′rĭŭm) *n.* [Gk. *peri*, around ; *pherein*, to bear.] Fleshy structure supporting ovary, and to which stamens and corolla are attached.

periphyllum,—lodicule.

periphysis (pĕrĭf′ĭsĭs) *n.* [Gk. *peri*, around ; *physis*, growth.] In certain fungi, a filament branching from an hymenium without asci.

periphyton (pĕr′ĭfī′tŏn) *n.* [Gk. *peri*, around; *phyton*, plant.] The plants and animals adhering to parts of rooted aquatic plants.

peripileic (pĕr′ĭpĭl′ëĭk) *a.* [Gk. *peri*, around; L. *pileus*.] *Pert.* or arising from the marginal region of a pileus.

periplasm (pĕr′ĭplăzm) *n.* [Gk. *peri*, around; *plasma*, mould.] The region of an oogonium outside the oosphere, in fungi; centroplasm or zone around the aster; cytoplasm surrounding yolk of centrolecithal ova.

periplasmodium (pĕr′ĭplăzmō′dĭŭm) *n.* [Gk. *peri*, around; *plasma*, model, *eidos*, form.] Protoplasmic mass, derived from tapetal cells and enclosing developing spores.

periplast (pĕr′ĭplăst) *n.* [Gk. *peri*, around; *plastos*, moulded.] Centrosome; attraction-sphere; ectoplasm of flagellates; pellicle covering ectoplasm; inter-cellular substance or stroma of tissues.

peripneustic (pĕr′ĭnū′stĭk, -pnū-) *a.* [Gk. *peri*, around; *pneustikos*, *pert.* breathing.] Having stigmata arranged along sides of body, normal in insect larvae.

peripodial (pĕr′ĭpō′dĭăl) *a.* [Gk. *peri*, around; *pous*, foot.] *Appl.* membrane covering wing-bud of insects.

periportal (pĕr′ĭpôr′tăl) *a.* [Gk. *peri*, around; L. *porta*, gate.] *Pert.* transverse fissure of the liver; *appl.* connective tissue partially separating lobules and forming part of the hepatobiliary capsule of Glisson.

periproct (pĕr′ĭprŏkt) *n.* [Gk. *peri*, round; *proktos*, anus.] The surface immediately surrounding anus of echinoids.

perisarc (pĕr′ĭsârk) *n.* [Gk. *peri*, around; *sarx*, flesh.] The tough outer membrane of Hydrozoa.

periscleral (pĕr′ĭsklē′răl) *a.* [Gk. *peri*, around; *skleros*, hard.] *Appl.* lymph-space external to sclera of eye.

perisome (pĕr′ĭsōm) *n.* [Gk. *peri*, around; *soma*, body.] A body-wall; integument of echinoderms.

perisperm (pĕr′ĭspërm) *n.* [Gk. *peri*, around; *sperma*, seed.] The remains of nucellus of ovule when it is not all absorbed during development of embryo; pericarp of a seed.

perisphere (pĕr′ĭsfēr) *n.* [Gk. *peri*, around; *sphaira*, ball.] Outer region of centrosphere.

perispiracular (pĕr′ĭspīrăk′ūlăr) *a.* [Gk. *peri*, around; L. *spiraculum*, air-hole.] Surrounding a spiracle; *appl.* glands with oily secretion, in certain aquatic insect larvae; peristigmatic.

perisporangium (pĕr′ĭspörăn′jĭŭm) *n.* [Gk. *peri*, around; *sporos*, seed; *anggeion*, vessel.] Membrane covering a sorus; indusium of ferns.

perispore (pĕr′ĭspōr) *n.* [Gk. *peri*, around; *sporos*, seed.] Spore-covering; transient outer membrane enveloping a spore; perisporium; mother cell in algal spores.

perissodactyl (përĭs′ödăk′tĭl) *a.* [Gk. *perissos*, odd; *daktylos*, finger.] With uneven number of digits.

peristalsis (pĕr′ĭstăl′sĭs) *n.* [Gk. *peri*, around; *stellein*, to draw in.] Movement of muscular tubes, as of digestive tract, by means of successive contractions in a definite, usually anteroposterior, direction.

peristaltic (pĕr′ĭstăl′tĭk) *a.* [Gk. *peri*, around; *stellein*, to draw in.] *Appl.* movement by means of successive contractions of muscular walls of tubular structures.

peristasis (pĕrĭs′tăsĭs) *n.* [Gk. *peri*, around; *stasis*, standing.] Environment, including physiological action within the organism, vital to development of a particular genotype.

peristatic (pĕr′ĭstăt′ĭk) *a.* [Gk. *peri*, around; *stasis*, standing.] *Pert.* or influenced by peristasis.

peristethium (pĕr′ĭstē′thĭŭm) *n.* [Gk. *peri*, round; *stethos*, chest.] An insect mesosternum.

peristigmatic,—perispiracular, *q.v.*

peristome (pĕr'ĭstōm) *n.* [Gk. *peri*, around; *stoma*, mouth.] The region surrounding mouth; used in connection with mosses, Vorticella, Actinozoa, annulates, insects.

perisystole (pĕr'ĭsĭs'tölē) *n.* [Gk. *peri*, around; *systole*, drawing together.] The interval elapsing between diastole and systole of heart.

perithecium (pĕr'ĭthē'sĭŭm) *n.* [Gk. *peri*, around; *theke*, case.] A flask-shaped ascocarp with a terminal ostiole; pyrenocarp.

perithelium (pĕr'ĭthē'lĭŭm) *n.* [Gk. *peri*, around; *thele*, nipple.] Connective tissue associated with capillaries.

peritoneal (pĕr'ĭtönē'ăl) *a.* [Gk. *periteinein*, to stretch round.] *Pert.* peritoneum; *appl.* cavity, fossa, membrane, etc.; *appl.* funnel: coelostome of archinephros.

peritoneum (pĕr'ĭtönē'ŭm) *n.* [Gk. *periteinein*, to stretch round.] A serous membrane partly applied to abdominal walls, partly reflected over contained viscera.

peritreme (pĕr'ĭtrēm) *n.* [Gk. *peri*, around; *trema*, hole.] Margin of a shell-opening; small plate perforated by spiracle-opening in ticks and insects; peritrema.

peritrichous (pĕrĭt'rĭkŭs) *a.* [Gk. *peri*, around; *thrix*, hair.] Having adoral band of cilia arranged in a spiral as in Vorticella; having several flagella attached laterally, as in certain bacteria; surrounding a hair follicle, *appl.* nerve endings; peritrichal, peritrichic.

peritrochium (pĕr'ĭtrŏk'ĭŭm) *n.* [Gk. *peri*, round; *trochos*, wheel.] A ciliary band; a circularly ciliated larva.

peritrophic (pĕr'ĭtrŏf'ĭk) *a.* [Gk. *peri*, round; *trophe*, food.] *Appl.* a fold of membrane in mid-gut of insects and to space between it and gut lining; *appl.* mycorrhiza with special fungal populations on root surfaces.

perittogamy (pĕrĭtŏg'ămĭ) *n.* [Gk. *perittos*, extraordinary; *gamos*, marriage.] Random plasmogamy of undifferentiated cells in gametophytes.

periurethral (pĕr'ĭūrē'thrăl) *a.* [Gk. *peri*, round; *ourethra*, from *ouron*, urine.] Surrounding the urethra; *appl.* glands, homologues of prostate.

perivascular (pĕr'ĭvăs'kūlăr) *a.* [Gk. *peri*, around; L. *vasculum*, small vessel.] Surrounding the vascular cylinder; *appl.* fibres; surrounding the blood-vessels; *appl.* lymph channels.

perivisceral (pĕr'ĭvĭs'ĕrăl) *a.* [Gk. *peri*, around; L. *viscera*, bowels.] Surrounding the viscera; *appl.* body cavity.

perivitelline (pĕr'ĭvĭtĕl'ĭn) *a.* [Gk. *peri*, around; L. *vitellus*, yolk of egg.] Surrounding the yolk of an egg; *appl.* space between ovum and zona pellucida.

perixylic (pĕrĭzī'lĭk) *a.* [Gk. *peri*, around; *xylon*, wood.] Having xylem outside centric phloem, *appl.* bundles; amphixylic. *Opp.* periphloic.

perizonium (pĕr'ĭzōn'ĭŭm) *n.* [Gk. *peri*, around; *zone*, girdle.] The membrane or siliceous wall enveloping the auxospore or zygote in diatoms.

permanent cartilage,—cartilage which remains unossified throughout life, *opp.* temporary.

permanent teeth,—set of teeth developed after milk or deciduous dentition; second set of most, third set of some, first set of other mammals.

permanent tissue,—tissue consisting of cells which have completed their period of growth and subsequently change little until they lose their protoplasm and die.

permeants (pĕr'mĕănts) *n. plu.* [L. *permeare*, to pass through.] Animals which move freely from one community or habitat to another.

Permian (pĕr'mĭăn) *a.* [*Perm*, E. Russia.] *Pert.* late period of Palaeozoic era, following the Carboniferous.

peronate (pĕr'ōnāt) *a.* [L. *peronatus*, hide-booted.] Covered with woolly hairs; surrounded by volva, *appl.* stipe; powdery or mealy externally.

peroneal (pĕrōnē'ăl) *a.* [Gk. *perone*, fibula.] *Pert.*, or lying near, the fibula; *appl.* artery, nerve, retinacula, tubercle.

peroneotibial (pĕrōnē'ōtĭb'ĭăl) *a.* [Gk. *perone*, fibula; L. *tibia*, tibia.] In region of fibula and tibia; *appl.* certain muscles

peroneus (pĕrōnē'ŭs) *n.* [Gk. *perone*, fibula.] Two lateral muscles of the leg, longus and brevis, and an anterior muscle, tertius; peronaeus.

peronium (pĕrō'nĭŭm) *n.* [Gk. *perone*, fibula.] In Trachomedusae, one of the mantle-rivets, or cartilaginous processes ascending from disc margin towards centre.

peropod (pē'röpŏd) *a.* [Gk. *peros*, defective; *pous*, foot.] With rudimentary limbs.

peroral (pĕrō'răl) *a.* [L. *per*, through; *os*, mouth.] *Appl.* a membrane formed by concrescence of rows of cilia, in infusoria.

peroxidase (pĕrŏk'sĭdās) *n.* [L. *per*, through; Gk. *oxys*, sharp.] An enzyme which causes activation of peroxide oxygen.

perradius (pĕr'rā'dĭŭs) *n.* [L. *per*, through; *radius*, radius.] One of four primary radii of coelenterates.

perseveration (pĕr'sĕvĕrā'shŭn) *n.* [L. *perseverare*, to persist.] Tendency of a set of neurones to remain in a state of excitation; persistent response after cessation of original stimulus.

persistent (pĕrsĭs'tĕnt) *a.* [L. *persistere*, to persevere.] Remaining attached till maturation, as a corolla; *appl.* teeth with continuous growth; *appl.* organs or parts in adult which normally disappear with larval stage or youth, as gills.

person (pĕr'sŏn) *n.* [L. *persona*, person.] An individual or zooid of a colony.

personate (pĕr'sŏnāt) *a.* [L. *personatus*, masked.] Masked; *appl.* a corolla of two lips, closely approximated and with a projection of the lower closing the throat of the corolla.

perspiration (pĕr'spĭrā'shŭn) *n.* [L. *per*, through; *spirare*, to breathe.] Exudation or excretion through pores of skin.

perthophyte (pĕr'thöfīt) *n.* [Gk. *perthai*, to destroy; *phyton*, plant.] A parasitic fungus that obtains nourishment from host tissues after having killed them by a poisonous secretion.

pertusate (pĕrtū'sāt) *a.* [L. *pertusus*, thrust through.] Pierced at apex.

perula (pēr'ūlă) *n.* [L. *perula*, little wallet.] A leaf-bud scale.

pervalvar (pĕrvăl'văr) *a.* [L. *per*, through; *valvae*, folding-doors.] Dividing a valve longitudinally.

pervious (pĕr'vĭŭs) *a.* [L. *pervius*, passable.] Perforated; permeable; *appl.* nostrils with no septum between nasal cavities.

pes (pĕz) *n.* [L. *pes*, foot.] A foot, base, or foot-like structure, as certain parts of brain, branches of facial nerve.

pessulus (pĕs'ūlŭs) *n.* [L. *pessulus*, bolt.] An internal skeletal element in syrinx of some birds.

petal (pĕt'ăl) *n.* [Gk. *petalon*, leaf.] One of the parts of a corolla; expanded part of ambulacral areas of certain Echinoidea.

petaliform (pĕt'ălĭfôrm) *a.* [Gk. *petalon*, leaf; L. *forma*, shape.] Petal-shaped; petal-like, petaloid, petaline.

petalled (pĕt'ăld) *a.* [Gk. *petalon*, leaf.] With petals; petaliferous, *opp.* apetalous.

petalody (pĕtălō'dĭ) *n.* [Gk. *petalon*, leaf; *eidos*, form.] Conversion of other parts of a flower into petals.

petaloid (pĕt'ăloid) *a.* [Gk. *petalon*, leaf; *eidos*, form.] Like a petal; *appl.* perianth; *appl.* pileus; *appl.* ambulacral areas of certain echinoderms.

petaloideous (pĕt'ăloid'ēŭs) *a.* [Gk. *petalon*, leaf; *eidos*, form.] Petaloid; *appl.* monocotyledons with coloured perianth.

petasma (pĕt′ăsmă) *n.* [Gk. *petasma*, anything spread out.] A complicated membranous plate on inner side of peduncle with interlocking coupling hooks, an apparatus of certain Crustacea.

petiolar (pĕt′ĭōlăr) *a.* [L. *petiolus*, small foot.] *Pert.*, having, or growing on, a small stalk.

petiolate (pĕt′ĭōlāt) *a.* [L. *petiolus*, small foot.] Growing on, or provided with, a petiole; having thorax and abdomen connected by a petiole.

petiole (pĕt′ĭōl) *n.* [L. *petiolus*, small foot.] The foot-stalk of a leaf; a slender stalk connecting thorax and abdomen in insects; a small sclerite at base of palpal organ in spiders; flattened and modified barb base in feathers.

petiolule (pĕt′ĭōlūl) *n.* [*Dim.* of L. *petiolus*, small foot.] The foot-stalk of a leaflet of a compound leaf.

Petit's canal,—spatia zonularia, *q.v.*

petrifaction (pĕt′rĭfăk′shŭn) *n.* [L. *petra*, rock; *facere*, to make.] Fossilisation through saturation by mineral matter in solution, subsequently turned to solid form.

petrohyoid (pĕt′röhī′oid) *a.* [Gk. *petros*, stone; *hyoeides*, *Y*-shaped.] *Pert.* hyoid and petrous part of temporal.

petromastoid (pĕt′römăs′toid) *a.* [Gk. *petros*, stone; *mastos*, breast; *eidos*, form.] *Pert.* mastoid process and petrous portion of temporal.

petro-occipital (pĕt′rö-ŏksĭp′ĭtăl) *a.* [Gk. *petros*, stone; L. *occiput*, back of head.] *Pert.* occipital and petrous part of temporal; *appl.* a fissure.

petrophyte (pĕt′röfīt) *n.* [Gk. *petros*, stone; *phyton*, plant.] A rock-plant.

petrosal (pĕtrō′săl) *a.* [Gk. *petros*, stone.] Of compact bone; *appl.* otic bones of fishes; *appl.* a sphenoidal process, to a ganglion of glossopharyngeal, to nerves and sinus in region of petrous portion of temporal bone; *appl.* bone, the periotic.

petrosphenoidal (pĕt′rösfēnoid′ăl) *a.* [Gk. *petros*, stone; *sphen*, wedge; *eidos*, form.] *Pert.* sphenoid and petrous part of temporal; *appl.* a fissure.

petrosquamosal (pĕt′röskwāmō′săl) *a.* [Gk. *petros*, stone; L. *squama*, scale.] *Pert.* squamosal and petrous part of temporal; *appl.* sinus and suture; petrosquamous.

petrotympanic (pĕt′rötĭmpăn′ĭk) *a.* [Gk. *petros*, stone; *tympanon*, drum.] *Pert.* tympanum and petrous portion of temporal; *appl.* a fissure.

petrous (pĕt′rŭs) *a.* [Gk. *petros*, stone.] Very hard or stony; *appl.* a pyramidal portion of temporal bone between sphenoid and occipital; *appl.* a ganglion on its lower border; petrosal.

Peyer's glands or **patches** [*J. C. Peyer*, Swiss anatomist]. Agminated glands, roundish patches of aggregated lymphatic nodules on intestine walls.

Pflüger's cords [*E. F. W. Pflüger*, German physiologist]. Cell columns growing from the germinal epithelium into the stroma, and which give rise to gonads.

***p*H,**—the negative value of the power to which 10 is raised in order to obtain the concentration of hydrogen ions in gram-molecules per litre, *p*H of a neutral solution being 7; *p*H of acid solutions is smaller than 7, *p*H of alkaline solutions being greater than 7.

phacea (făs′ēă) *n.* [Gk. *phakos*, lentil.] The crystalline lens of the eye.

phacella (făsĕl′ă) *n.* [Gk. *phakelos*, bundle of faggots.] A delicate filament with mesogloea core, and supplied with stinging capsules, occurring in rows in stomach of certain coelenterates; gastric filament.

phacocyst (făk′ösĭst) *n.* [Gk. *phakos*, lentil, lens; *kystis*, bladder.] Transparent sac enclosing lens of eye; capsule of the lens, capsula lentis.

phacoid (făk′oid) *a.* [Gk. *phakos*, lentil; *eidos*, form.] Lentil-shaped.

phaeic,—phaeochrous, *q.v.*

phaeism (fē′ĭzm) *n.* [Gk. *phaios*, dusky.] Duskiness; *appl.* colouring of butterflies; incomplete melanism

phaenantherous (fēnăn'thërŭs) *a.* [Gk. *phainein*, to show; *antheros*, flowering.] With anthers exserted; with stamens exserted.

phaeno-,—*also* pheno-.

phaenogam (fēn'ögăm) *n.* [Gk. *phainein*, to show; *gamos*, marriage.] Phanerogam.

phaeochrome (fē'ökrōm) *n.* [Gk. *phaios*, dusky; *chroma*, colour.] Chromophil; chromaffin.

phaeochromoblast (fē'ökrō'möblăst) *n.* [Gk. *phaios*, dusky; *chroma*, colour; *blastos*, bud.] Cell which develops into a phaeochromocyte or chromaffin cell.

phaeochrous (fē'ökrō'ŭs) *a.* [Gk. *phaios*, dusky; *chros*, colour.] Of dusky colour; phaeic.

phaeodium (fēō'dĭŭm) *n.* [Gk. *phaios*, dusky; *eidos*, form.] In certain Radiolaria, an aggregation of food and excretory substances forming a mass round the central capsule aperture.

phaeomelanin (fē'ömĕl'ănĭn) *n.* [Gk. *phaios*, dusky; *melas*, black.] A brownish melanin; *cf.* eumelanin.

phaeophore,—phaeoplast.

phaeophyll (fē'öfĭl) *n.* [Gk. *phaios*, dusky; *phyllon*, leaf.] The colouring matter of brown algae, a mixture of fucoxanthin, xanthophyll, chlorophyll, and carotene.

phaeophytin (fē'öfī'tĭn) *n.* [Gk. *phaios*, dusky; *phyton*, plant.] Either of two blue-black pigments derived from chlorophylls *a* and *b* by removing magnesium.

phaeoplast (fē'öplăst) *n.* [Gk. *phaios*, dusky; *plastos*, formed.] Chromoplast of brown seaweeds or Phaeophyceae.

phaeospore (fē'öspōr) *n.* [Gk. *phaios*, dusky; *sporos*, seed.] A spore containing phaeoplasts.

phage (fāj) *n.* [Gk. *phagein*, to eat.] An agent causing destruction or lysis of micro-organisms; bacteriophage.

phagocytable (făg'ösī'tăbl) *a.* [Gk. *phagein*, to eat; *kytos*, hollow.] *Appl.* bacteria rendered more easily ingested by leucocytes.

phagocyte (făg'ösīt) *n.* [Gk. *phagein*, to eat; *kytos*, hollow.] A colourless blood-corpuscle which tends to ingest foreign particles; a root cell, with lobed nucleus, capable of digesting endotrophic fungal filaments.

phagocytic,—*pert.* phagocytes; *pert.* or effecting phagocytosis.

phagocytosis (făg'ösītō'sĭs) *n.* [Gk. *phagein*, to eat; *kytos*, hollow.] The ingestion and destruction of microparasites by phagocytes.

phagolysis (făgŏl'ĭsĭs) *n.* [Gk. *phagein*, to eat; *lysis*, loosing.] Dissolution of phagocytes.

phagozoite (făg'özō'īt) *n.* [Gk. *phagein*, to eat; *zoon*, animal.] An animal which feeds on disintegrating or dead tissue.

phalange (făl'ănj) *n.* [Gk. *phalangx*, line of battle.] A phalanx.

phalangeal (fălăn'jëăl) *a.* [Gk. *phalangx*, line of battle.] *Pert.*, or resembling, phalanges; *appl.* bones, cells attached in rows to Corti's rods, etc.

phalanx (făl'ăngks) *n.*, **phalanges** (făl'ănjēz) *plu.* [Gk. *phalangx*, line of battle.] Segments of digits of vertebrates; bundle of stamens united by filaments.

phallic (făl'ĭk) *a.* [Gk. *phallos*, penis.] *Pert.* phallus; *appl.* gland secreting substance for spermatophores, as in certain insects.

phallomere (făl'ömēr) *n.* [Gk. *phallos*, penis; *meros*, part.] Penis valve, in insects.

phallosome (făl'ösōm) *n.* [Gk. *phallos*, penis; *soma*, body.] A structure of tissue from inner surface of basistyles and penis valves, in Culicidae; mesosome.

phallus (făl'ŭs) *n.* [Gk. *phallos*, penis.] The embryonic structure which becomes penis or clitoris; external genitalia of male insect; a genus of Basidiomycetes.

phanerocodonic (făn'ërökōdŏn'ĭk) *a.* [Gk. *phaneros*, manifest; *kodon*, bell.] *Appl.* detached and free-swimming zooids of a hydroid colony. *Opp.* adelocodonic.

phanerogam (făn'ërögăm) *n.* [Gk. *phaneros*, manifest; *gamos*, marriage.] A plant with conspicuous flowers; anthophyte, phaenogam, spermatophyte. *Opp.* cryptogam.

phanerogamous (fănërög'ămŭs) *a.* [Gk. *phaneros*, manifest; *gamos*, marriage.] *Appl.* plants with flowers containing pistils and stamens; phanerogamic.

phanerophyte (făn'ëröfīt) *n.* [Gk. *phaneros*, manifest; *phyton*, plant.] Tree or shrub with aerial dormant buds; plant whose size is not appreciably less during cold or dry season.

phaoplankton (fā'öplăngk'tŏn) *n.* [Gk. *phaos*, light; *plangktos*, wandering.] Surface plankton, living at depths to which light penetrates.

phaosome (fā'ösōm) *n.* [Gk. *phaos*, light; *soma*, body.] An optic organelle in certain epidermal cells of annelids.

pharate (fā'rāt) *a.* [Gk. *pharos*, loose mantle.] *Appl.* instar within previous cuticle prior to ecdysis.

pharmacodynamics (fâr'măködĭnăm'ĭks) *n.* [Gk. *pharmakon*, drug; *dynamis*, power.] The science of the action of drugs.

pharyngeal (fărĭn'jëăl) *a.* [Gk. *pharyngx*, gullet.] *Pert.* pharynx; *appl.* artery, membrane, nerve, tonsil, tubercle, veins, etc.; *appl.* nephridia, in certain worms.

pharyngobranchial (fărĭng'göbrăng'kĭăl) *a.* [Gk. *pharyngx*, gullet; *brangchia*, gills.] *Pert.* pharynx and gills; *appl.* certain bones of fishes.

pharyngopalatine (fărĭng'göpăl'ătĭn) *a.* [Gk. *pharyngx*, gullet; L. *palatum*, palate.] *Pert.* pharynx and palate; *appl.* arch and muscle; palatopharyngeal.

pharyngotympanic (fărĭng'götĭmpăn'ĭk) *a.* [Gk. *pharyngx*, gullet; *tympanon*, drum.] *Appl.* tube connecting pharynx and tympanic cavity, the auditory or Eustachian tube.

pharynx (făr'ĭngks) *n.* [Gk. *pharyngx*, gullet.] A musculomembranous tube extending from under surface of skull to level of sixth cervical vertebra; gullet or anterior part of alimentary canal following buccal cavity.

phasmids (făs'mĭdz) *n. plu.* [Gk. *phasma*, apparition; *dim.*] Caudal papillae in Nematoda, bearing pores connecting with glandular pouch.

phatne (făt'nē) *n.* [Gk. *phatne*, manger.] Tooth socket or alveolus dentis; odontobothrion.

phellema (fĕlē'mă) *n.* [Gk. *phellos*, cork.] Cork; cork and non-suberised layers forming external zone of periderm; phellem.

phelloderm (fĕl'ödĕrm) *n.* [Gk. *phellos* cork; *derma*, skin.] The secondary parenchymatous suberous cortex of trees, formed on inner side of cork-cambium.

phellogen (fĕl'öjĕn) *n.* [Gk. *phellos*, cork; *gennaein*, to generate.] The cork-cambium of tree stems, arising as a secondary meristem and giving rise to cork and phelloderm.

phelloid (fĕl'oid) *a.* [Gk. *phellos*, cork; *eidos*, form.] Cork-like. *n.* Non-suberised cell-layer in outer periderm.

phengophil (fĕng'göfĭl) *a.* [Gk. *phenggos*, light; *philos*, friend.] Preferring light, *appl.* animals.

phengophobe (fĕng'göfōb) *a.* [Gk. *phenggos*, light; *phobos*, fear.] Shunning light, *appl.* animals.

phenocontour,—isophane, *q.v.*

phenocopy (fē'nökŏp'ĭ) *n.* [Gk. *phainein*, to appear; F. *copie*, copy, from L.L. *copia*, transcript.] A modification induced by environmental factors which parallels genetically produced changes; paramorph.

phenogam,—phanerogam, *q.v.*

phenological (fēnölŏj'ĭkăl) *a.* [Gk. *phainein*, to appear; *logos*, discourse.] *Pert.* phenology; *appl.* isolation of species owing to differences in flowering or breeding season.

phenology (fēnŏl'öjĭ) *n.* [Gk. *phainein*, to appear; *logos*, discourse.] Recording and study of periodic biotic events, as of flowering, breeding, migration, etc., in relation to climatic and other factors; phenomenology.

phenotype (fēn'ötīp) *n.* [Gk. *phainein*, to appear; *typos*, image.] The characters of an organism due to the response of genotypic characters to the environment; a group of individuals exhibiting the same phenotypic characters.

phenotypic (fēn'ötĭp'ĭk) *a.* [Gk. *phainein*, to show; *typos*, image.] *Pert.* phenotype, *appl.* characters arising from reaction to environmental stimulus.

pheo-,—*see* phaeo-.

pheron (fĕr'ŏn) *n.* [Gk. *pherein*, to bear.] The colloidal bearer of the active principle of an enzyme; *cf.* agon, symplex.

phialide (fī'ălīd) *n.* [Gk. *phiale*, bowl; *eidos*, form.] A flask-shaped outgrowth of spore-bearing hypha, in certain fungi; a sterigma; *cf.* metula.

phialiform (fĭăl'ĭfôrm) *a.* [L. *phiala*, shallow cup; *forma*, form.] Cup-shaped; saucer-shaped; phialaeform.

phialophore (fĭă'löfōr) *n.* [Gk. *phiale*, bowl; *pherein*, to bear.] A hypha which bears a phialide.

phialopore (fĭăl'öpōr) *n.* [Gk. *phiale*, bowl; *poros*, channel.] The opening in the hollow daughter colony or gonidium of Volvox.

phialospore (fĭăl'ōspōr) *n.* [Gk. *phiale*, bowl; *sporos*, seed.] A spore or conidium borne at tip of a phialide.

philotherm (fĭl'öthĕrm] *n.* [Gk. *philos*, loving; *therme*, heat.] A plant which completes life-cycle only in a warm environment. *Cf.* thermophil, thermophyte, therophyte.

philtrum (fĭl'trŭm) *n.* [Gk. *philtron*, philtre.] The depression on upper lip beneath septum of nose.

phlebenterism (flĕbĕn'tĕrĭzm) *n.* [Gk. *phleps*, vein; *enteron*, intestine.] Condition of having branches of the intestine extending into other organs, as arms or legs.

phleboedesis (flĕbē'dēsĭs) *n.* [Gk. *phleps*, vein; *oidein*, to swell.] Condition of having circulatory system cavity so distended and insinuated as to diminish the coelom, especially so in molluscs.

phlobaphenes (flō'băfēnz) *n. plu.* [Gk. *phloios*, inner bark; *baphe*, dye.] Compounds producing dark brown colour in fern roots.

phloem (flō'ĕm) *n.* [Gk. *phloios*, inner bark.] Bast-tissue; the soft bast of vascular bundles, consisting of sieve-tube tissue.

phloem parenchyma, — thin-walled parenchyma associated with sieve-tubes of phloem.

phloem sheath,—pericycle, together with inner layer of a bundle sheath where latter consists of two layers.

phloeodic flēŏd'ĭk) *a.* [Gk. *phloios*, inner bark; *eidos*, form.] Having the appearance of bark.

phloeoterma (flē'ötĕr'mă) *n.* [Gk. *phloios*, inner bark; *terma*, boundary.] Endodermis; innermost layer of cortex.

phloic (flō'ĭk) *a.* [Gk. *phloios*, inner bark.] *Pert.* phloem; *appl.* procambium that gives rise to phloem.

phobotaxis (fō'bötăk'sĭs) *n.* [Gk. *phobos*, manifest fear; *taxis*, arrangement.] Avoiding reaction; trial-and-error reaction.

pholadophyte (fōlăd'öfīt) *n.* [Gk. *pholas*, lurking; *phyton*, plant.] A plant living in hollows, shunning bright light.

pholidosis (fŏl'ĭdō'sĭs) *n.* [Gk. *pholis*, scale.] Scale arrangement of scaled animals.

phonation (fōnā'shŭn) *n.* [Gk. *phone*, sound.] Production of sounds, *e.g.* by insects.

phonoreceptor (fō'nörēsĕp'tŏr) *n.* [Gk. *phone*, sound; L. *receptor*, receiver.] A receptor of sound waves, as ear, certain sensillae.

phoranthium (fŏrăn'thĭŭm) *n.* [Gk. *pherein*, to bear; *anthos*, flower.] The receptacle of composite plants.

phoresia (fŏrē'sĭă) *n.* [Gk. *pherein*, to bear.] The carrying of one organism by another, without parasitism; *appl.* insects.

phoront (fŏrŏnt') *n.* [Gk. *phora*, producing; *on*, being.] Encysted stage produced by tomite and leading to formation of trophont in life cycle of Holotricha.

phorozooid (fŏr'ŏzō'oid) *n.* [Gk. *pherein*, to bear; *zoon*, animal; *eidos*, form.] Foster forms of Doliolum buds, never sexually mature but set free with gonozooids attached to a ventral outgrowth.

phorozoon (fŏrŏzō'ŏn) *n.* [Gk. *pherein*, to bear; *zoon*, animal.] An asexual organism or larval stage preceding the sexual.

phosphagen,—creatine phosphate in vertebrate muscle, splitting into creatine and phosphoric acid during contraction, and reformed during recovery; arginine phosphate in muscle of certain invertebrates.

phosphene (fŏs'fēn) *n.* [Gk. *phos*, light, *phainein*, to show.] A light impression on retina due to stimulus other than rays of light.

phosphoproteins (fŏs'fŏprō'tēĭnz) *n. plu.* [Gk. *phosphoros*, bringing light; *proteion*, first.] Proteins linked with phosphoric acid, *e.g.* casein, vitellin.

phosphorescence (fŏs'fŏrĕs'ĕns) *n.* [Gk. *phosphoros*, bringing light.] The state of being luminous without sensible heat, common in marine protozoa, some copepods, and the majority of deep-sea animals; bioluminescence.

photic (fō'tĭk) *a.* [Gk. *phos*, light.] *Pert.* light; *appl.* zone, the surface waters penetrated by sunlight; *appl.* euphotic and dysphotic zones, *opp.* aphotic.

photoceptor,—photoreceptor, *q.v.*

photochromatic (fō'tŏkrōmăt'ĭk) *a.* [Gk. *phos*, light; *chroma*, colour.] *Appl.* interval between achromatic and chromatic thresholds.

photodinesis (fō'tŏdīnē'sĭs) *n.* [Gk. *phos*, light; *dine*, eddy.] Protoplasmic streaming induced by light.

photodynamics (fō'tŏdĭnăm'ĭks) *n.* [Gk. *phos*, light; *dynamis*, strength.] The study of the effects of light-stimulation on plants.

photogen (fō'tŏjĕn) *n.* [Gk. *phos*, light; *-genes*, producing.] A light-producing organ, or substance.

photogenesis,—*see* biophotogenesis.

photogenic (fō'tŏjĕn'ĭk) *a.* [Gk. *phos*, light; *-genes*, producing.] Light-producing; luminescent.

photogenin,—luciferase, *q.v.*

photokinesis (fō'tŏkĭnē'sĭs) *n.* [Gk. *phos*, light; *kinesis*, movement.] Aggregation of organisms in response to stimulation by certain regions of the visual spectrum.

photonasty (fō'tŏnăs'tĭ) *n.* [Gk. *phos*, light; *nastos*, close pressed.] Response to diffuse light stimuli, or variations in illumination.

photopathy (fōtŏp'ăthĭ) *n.* [Gk. *phos*, light; *pathos*, feeling.] Aggregation without individual axial orientation in response to light stimulus; reaction to differential illumination of parts of an organism.

photoperiod (fō'tŏpē'rĭŏd) *n.* [Gk. *phos*, light; *periodos*, circuit.] Duration of daily exposure to light; length of day favouring optimum functioning of an organism.

photoperiodism (fō'tŏpē'rĭŏdĭzm) *n.* [Gk. *phos*, light; *periodos*, circuit.] Response of an organism to the relative duration of day and night.

photophase (fō'tŏfāz) *n.* [Gk. *phos*, light; *phainein*, to appear.] Developmental stage during which the plant, after thermophase, shows definite requirements as to duration and intensity of light and temperature.

photophelein (fō'tŏfē'lēĭn) *n.* [Gk. *phos*, light; *phelos*, deceiving.] A substance in plant and animal cells which may produce luciferin; or luciferin, *q.v.*

photophilous (fōtŏf'ĭlŭs) *a.* [Gk. *phos*, light; *philos*, loving.] Seeking, and thriving in, strong light.

photophobic (fō'tōfŏb'ĭk) *a.* [Gk. *phos*, light; *phobos*, fear.] Not tolerating light; shunning light.

photophore (fō'tōfōr) *n.* [Gk. *phos*, light; *pherein*, to bear.] A luminous organ of certain crustaceans and fishes.

photophygous (fōtŏf'ĭgŭs) *a.* [Gk. *phos*, light; *phyge*, flight.] Avoiding strong light.

photopia (fōtō'pĭă) *n.* [Gk. *phos*, light; *ops*, eye.] Adaptation of the eye to light, *opp.* scotopia.

photopic (fōtō'pĭk) *a.* [Gk. *phos*, light; *ops*, eye.] Having or *pert.* light-adapted eye, *opp.* scotopic.

photopsin (fōtŏp'sĭn) *n.* [Gk. *phos*, light; *opsis*, sight.] The protein component of the violet retinal cone pigment iodopsin.

photoreceptor (fō'tōrēsĕp'tŏr) *n.* [Gk. *phos*, light; L. *receptus*, received.] Terminal organ receiving light stimuli; photoceptor.

photospheres (fō'tŏsfērz) *n. plu.* [Gk. *phos*, light; *sphaira*, globe.] Luminous organs of Crustacea.

photosynthesis (fō'tōsĭn'thēsĭs) *n.* [Gk. *phos*, light; *synthesis*, putting together.] Carbon assimilation, requiring presence of chloroplasts and light, and consisting in synthesis of carbohydrates from carbon dioxide and water.

photosynthetic (fō'tōsĭnthĕt'ĭk) *a.* [Gk. *phos*, light; *synthesis*, putting together.] *Appl.* nutrition by carbon assimilation; feeding like a green plant.

photosynthetic quotient—the ratio between the volume of oxygen produced and the volume of carbon dioxide used. *Opp.* respiratory quotient.

photosynthetic zone,—of sea, between surface and compensation point, *q.v.*

phototaxis (fō'tōtăk'sĭs) *n.* [Gk. *phos*, light; *taxis*, arrangement.] Response to stimulus of light.

phototonus (fō'tōtō'nŭs, fōtŏt'ōnŭs) *n.* [Gk. *phos*, light; *tonos*, tension.] Sensitiveness to light; condition of a plant or plant organ induced by light.

phototrophic (fō'tōtrŏf'ĭk) *a.* [Gk. *phos*, light; *trophe*, nourishment.] Requiring light as a source of energy in nutrition; holophytic.

phototropism (fōtŏt'rōpĭzm) *n.* [Gk. *phos*, light; *trope*, turn.] The tendency shown by most plants to turn their aerial growing parts towards the greater light.

phragma (frăg'mă) *n.* [Gk. *phragma*, fence.] A spurious dissepiment; a septum; an endotergite or dorsal apodeme of thorax and abdomen in Diplopoda and insects. *Plu.* phragmata.

phragmocone (frăg'mōkōn) *n.* [Gk. *phragmos*, fence; *konos*, cone.] In belemnites and other molluscs, a cone divided internally by a series of septa perforated by a siphuncle.

phragmocyttarous (frăg'mōsĭt'ărŭs) *a.* [Gk. *phragmos*, fence; *kyttaros*, honey-comb cell.] Building, or *pert.*, combs attached to supporting surface, as of certain wasps; *cf.* stelocyttarous.

phragmoplast (frăg'mōplăst) *n.* [Gk. *phragmos*, fence; *plastos*, moulded.] Barrel-shaped stage of spindle in mitosis.

phragmosome (frăg'mōsōm) *n.* [Gk. *phragmos*, fence; *soma*, body.] A disc, derived from ectoplasm, in equatorial plane of cell and in which the cell plate is formed.

phragmospore (frăg'mōspōr) *n.* [Gk. *phragmos*, fence; *sporos*, seed.] A septate spore.

phratry (frā'trĭ) *n.* [Gk. *phratre*, a subdivision of a tribe.] A sub-tribe or clan.

phreatophyte (frēăt'ōfīt) *n.* [Gk. *phreatia*, tank.] Plant with very long roots reaching water-table.

phrenic (frĕn'ĭk) *a.* [Gk. *phren*, diaphragm, mind.] *Pert.* or in region of diaphragm; *appl.* artery, ganglion, nerve, plexus, vein. *Pert.* mind.

phrenicocolic (frĕn'ĭkōkŏl'ĭk) *a.* [Gk. *phren*, diaphragm; *kolon*, lower part of intestine.] *Appl.* a ligament or a fold of peritoneum from left colic flexure to diaphragm.

phrenicocostal (frĕn′ĭkŏkŏs′tăl) *a.* [Gk. *phren*, diaphragm ; L. *costa*, rib.] *Appl.* a narrow slit or sinus between costal and diaphragmatic pleurae.

phrenicolienal (frĕn′ĭkŏlīē′năl) *a.* [Gk. *phren*, diaphragm ; L. *lien*, spleen.] *Appl.* ligament forming part of peritoneum reflected over spleen and extending to diaphragm ; lienorenal.

phrenicopericardiac (frĕn′ĭkŏpĕr′ĭkâr′dĭăk) *a.* [Gk. *phren*, diaphragm ; *peri*, around ; *kardia*, heart.] *Appl.* a ligament extending from diaphragm to pericardium.

phthisaner (thĭs′ănĕr) *n.* [Gk. *phthisis*, wasting ; *aner*, male.] Pupal male ant parasitised by an Orasema larva.

phthisergate (thĭs′ĕrgāt) *n.* [Gk. *phthisis*, wasting ; *ergates*, worker.] Pupal worker ant parasitised by an Orasema larva ; infra-ergatoid.

phthisogyne (thĭsŏj′ĭnē) *n.* [Gk. *phthisis*, wasting ; *gyne*, female.] Pupal female ant parasitised by an Orasema larva.

phyad (fī′ăd) *n.* [Gk. *phya*, nature.] An inherited form, *opp*. oecad.

phycobilins (fī′kōbī′lĭnz) *n.plu.* [Gk. *phykos*, seaweed ; L. *bilis*, bile.] Chromoproteins of seaweeds, as phycocyanin and phycoerythrin.

phycochrome (fī′kōkrōm) *n.* [Gk. *phykos*, seaweed ; *chroma*, colour.] A pigment of blue-green algae.

phycochrysin (fī′kōkrĭs′ĭn) *n.* [Gk. *phykos*, seaweed ; *chrysos*, gold.] An accessory pigment of orange-yellow algae.

phycocyanin (fī′kōsī′ănĭn) *n.* [Gk. *phykos*, seaweed ; *kyanos*, dark blue.] A pigment of blue-green algae.

phycoerythrin (fī′kōĕrĭth′rĭn) *n.* [Gk. *phykos*, seaweed ; *erythros*, red.] The colouring matter of red algae.

phycology (fīkŏl′ōjĭ) *n.* [Gk. *phykos*, seaweed ; *logos*, discourse.] That part of botany dealing with algae.

phycophaein (fī′kōfē′ĭn) *n.* [Gk. *phykos*, seaweed ; *phaios*, dusky.] The pigment of brown algae.

phycoxanthin (fī′kōzăn′thĭn) *n.* [Gk. *phykos*, seaweed ; *xanthos*, yellow.] Buff colouring matter of diatoms and brown algae.

phyla (fī′lă) *n. plu.* [Gk. *phylon*, tribe.] *Plu.* of phylum, *q.v.*

phylacobiosis (fĭl′ăkōbīō′sĭs) *n.* [Gk. *phylax*, guard ; *biosis*, manner of living.] Mutual or unilateral protective behaviour, as of certain ants.

phylactocarp (fĭlăk′tōkârp) *n.* [Gk. *phylaktikos*, guarding ; *karpos*, fruit.] A modification of hydrocladium in Hydromedusae, for protection of gonophore.

phylembryo (fĭl′ĕmbrĭō) *n.* [Gk. *phylon*, race ; *embryon*, embryo.] Stage in development of Brachiopoda, at completion of protegulum.

phylephebic (fī′lēfē′bĭk) *a.* [Gk. *phylon*, race ; *ephebeia*, manhood.] *Appl.* adult stage in race history.

phyletic (fīlĕt′ĭk) *a.* [Gk. *phylon*, race.] *Pert.* a phylum or race.

phyllade (fĭlād′) *n.* [Gk. *phyllas*, foliage.] A reduced scale-like leaf.

phyllary (fĭl′ărĭ) *n.* [Gk. *phyllon*, leaf.] A bract of the involucre of Compositae.

phyllidium (fĭlĭd′ĭŭm) *n.* [Gk. *phyllidion*, little leaf.] An outgrowth from side of scolex of Cestoidea ; bothridium.

phyllobranchia (fĭl′ōbrăng′kĭă) *n.* [Gk. *phyllon*, leaf ; *brangchia*, gills.] A gill consisting of numbers of lamellae or thin plates.

phyllocaline (fĭl′ōkălēn) *n.* [Gk. *phyllon*, leaf ; *kalein*, to summon.] A complex of substances, or hormone, which stimulates growth of mesophyll.

phylloclade (fĭl′ōklād′) *n.* [Gk. *phyllon*, leaf ; *klados*, sprout.] An assimilative branch of a fruticose thallus in lichens ; a green flattened or rounded stem functioning as a leaf, as in Cactus ; flattened axillary bud as in Ruscus ; phyllocladium, cladode, cladophyll.

phyllocyst (fĭl'ösĭst) *n.* [Gk. *phyllon*, leaf; *kystis*, bladder.] The rudimentary cavity of a hydrophyllium or protective medusoid.

phyllode (fĭl'ōd) *n.* [Gk. *phyllon*, leaf; *eidos*, form.] Winged petiole with flattened surfaces placed laterally to stem, functioning as leaf.

phyllody (fĭl'ödĭ) *n.* [Gk. *phyllon*, leaf; *eidos*, form.] Metamorphosis of an organ into a foliage leaf.

phylloerythrin (fĭl'öĕrĭth'rĭn) *n.* [Gk. *phyllon*, leaf; *erythros*, red.] A red pigment derived from chlorophyll and occurring in bile of herbivorous mammals; bilipurpurin, cholohaematin.

phyllogenetic (fĭl'öjĕnĕt'ĭk) *a.* [Gk. *phyllon*, leaf; *genesis*, descent.] Producing or developing leaves.

phylloid (fĭl'oid) *a.* [Gk. *phyllon*, leaf; *eidos*, form.] Leaf-like. *n.* The leaf regarded as a flattened branch, or as a telome.

phyllomania (fĭl'ömā'nĭă) *n.* [Gk. *phyllon*, leaf; *mania*, madness.] Abnormal leaf-production.

phyllome (fĭl'ōm) *n.* [Gk. *phyllon*, leaf.] The leaf structures of a plant as a whole.

phyllomorphosis (fĭl'ömôr'fōsĭs) *n.* [Gk. *phyllon*, leaf; *morphosis*, form.] Phyllody; variation of leaves at different seasons.

phyllophagous (fĭlŏf'ăgŭs) *a.* [Gk. *phyllon*, leaf; *phagein*, to eat.] Feeding on leaves.

phyllophore (fĭl'öfōr) *n.* [Gk. *phyllophoros*, leaf-bearing.] Terminal bud or growing point of palms.

phyllophorous (fĭlŏf'örŭs) *a.* [Gk. *phyllophoros*, leaf-bearing.] Bearing or producing leaves.

phyllopode (fĭl'öpōd) *n.* [Gk. *phyllon*, leaf; *pous*, foot.] A sheathing leaf-base of Isoëtes.

phyllopodium (fĭl'öpō'dĭŭm) *n.* [Gk. *phyllon*, leaf; *pous*, foot.] The axis of a leaf; the stem regarded as pseudo-axis formed of fused leaf-bases.

phyllopodous (fĭlŏp'ödŭs) *a.* [Gk. *phyllon*, leaf; *pous*, foot.] Having leaf-like swimming-feet, as in Branchiopoda.

phylloptosis (fĭlötō'sĭs, -ptō-) *n.* [Gk. *phyllon*, leaf; *ptosis*, falling.] The fall of the leaf.

phyllorhiza (fĭl'örī'ză) *n.* [Gk. *phyllon*, leaf; *rhiza*, root.] A young leaf with a root.

phyllosiphonic (fĭl'ösīfŏn'ĭk) *a.* [Gk. *phyllon*, leaf; *siphon*, tube.] With insertion of leaf-trace disturbing axial stele tissue. *Opp.* cladosiphonic.

phyllosperm (fĭl'öspĕrm) *n.* [Gk. *phyllon*, leaf; *sperma*, seed.] Seed borne on leaves, as in pteridophytes and cycads.

phyllospondylous (fĭl'öspŏn'dĭlŭs) *a.* [Gk. *phyllon*, leaf; *sphondylos*, vertebra.] *Appl.* vertebrae consisting of hypocentrum and neural arch, both contributing to hollow transverse process, as in Stegocephali.

phyllosporous (fĭlŏs'pörŭs) *a.* [Gk. *phyllon*, leaf; *sporos*, seed.] With sporophylls like foliage-leaves, as Lycopodium; *cf.* stachyosporous.

phyllotactic (fĭl'ötăk'tĭk) *a.* [Gk. *phyllon*, leaf; *taktikos*, fit for arrangement.] *Pert.* phyllotaxis; *appl.* fraction of circumference of stem between successive leaves, representing the angle of their divergence.

phyllotaxis (fĭl'ötăk'sĭs) *n.* [Gk. *phyllon*, leaf; *taxis*, arrangement.] The arrangement of leaves on an axis or stem.

phylloxanthin,—xanthophyll, *q.v.*

phyllozooid (fĭl'özō'oid) *n.* [Gk. *phyllon*, leaf; *zoon*, animal; *eidos*, form.] A shield-shaped medusoid of protective function; a hydrophyllium of Hydromedusae.

phylobiology (fī'löbīŏl'öji) *n.* [Gk. *phylon*, race; *bios*, life; *logos*, discourse.] The study of reactions or behaviour of organisms in relation to their racial history.

phyloephebic,—phylephebic, *q.v.*

phylogenesis (fī'löjĕn'ĕsĭs), **phylogeny** (fīlŏj'ĕnĭ) *n.* [Gk. *phylon*, race; *genesis*, descent.] History of development of species or race; *cf.* ontogeny.

phylogenetic (fī'lŏjĕnĕt'ĭk) *a.* [Gk. *phylon*, race; *genesis*, descent.] *Pert.* race-history; *appl.* reproductive cells, *opp.* autogenetic or body cells.

phylogerontic (fī'lŏjĕrŏn'tĭk) *a.* [Gk. *phylon*, race; *geron*, old man.] *Appl.* decadent stage in race-history.

phylon,—phylum, *q.v.*

phyloneanic (fī'lŏnēā'nĭk) *a.* [Gk. *phylon*, race; *neanikos*, youthful.] *Appl.* youthful stage in race-history.

phylonepionic (fī'lŏnēpĭŏn'ĭk) *a.* [Gk. *phylon*, race; *nepios*, infant.] *Appl.* post-embryonic stage in race-history.

phylum (fī'lŭm) *n.* [Gk. *phylon*, race or tribe.] A group of animals or plants constructed on a similar general plan, a primary division in classification.

phyma (fī'mă) *n.* [Gk. *phyma*, tumour.] An excrescence not containing gonidia, on podetium of lichens.

phyone (fī'ōn) *n.* [Gk. *phyein*, to make to grow.] A prepituitary principle controlling growth; growth hormone; phyon, tethelin.

physa (fī'să) *n.* [Gk. *physa*, bellows.] The modified rounded base of burrowing sea-anemones.

physicist (fĭz'ĭsĭst) *n.* [Gk. *physikos*, physical.] From biological standpoint, an upholder of theory that vital phenomena are explicable on a physico-chemical basis.

physiogenesis (fĭz'ĭŏjĕn'ĕsĭs) *n.* [Gk. *physis*, nature; *genesis*, descent.] The development of vital activities; ontogenesis in its physiological aspect; physiogeny.

physiogenic (fĭz'ĭŏjĕn'ĭk) *a.* [Gk. *physis*, nature; *-genes*, producing.] Caused by functioning of an organ or part; *pert.* physiogenesis.

physiogeny,—physiogenesis, *q.v.*

physiology (fĭzĭŏl'ŏjĭ) *n.* [Gk. *physis*, nature; *logos*, discourse.] That part of biology dealing with functions and activities of organisms.

physoclistous (fī'sŏklĭs'tŭs) *a.* [Gk. *physa*, bladder; *kleiein*, to close.] Having no channel connecting swim-bladder and digestive tract, as in most teleosts.

physodes (fī'sōdz) *n. plu.* [Gk. *physa*, bubble.] Spindles of phloroglucin contained in plasmodium of certain Sarcodina.

physogastry (fīsŏgăs'trĭ) *n.* [Gk. *physan*, to blow up; *gaster*, belly.] Excessive fat-body and enlargement of abdomen in insects.

physostomous (fīsŏs'tŏmŭs) *a.* [Gk. *physa*, bladder; *stoma*, mouth.] Having swim-bladder and digestive tract connected throughout life by pneumatic duct, as in ganoids.

phytobiology (fī'tŏbīŏl'ŏji) *n.* [Gk. *phyton*, plant; *bios*, life; *logos*, discourse.] Plant biology; the life-history of plants.

phytobiotic (fī'tŏbīŏt'ĭk) *a.* [Gk. *phyton*, plant; *bios*, life.] Living within plants; *appl.* some protozoa.

phytochemistry (fī'tŏkĕm'ĭstrĭ) *n.* [Gk. *phyton*, plant; *chemeia*, transmutation.] The chemistry of plants.

phytochromes (fī'tŏkrōmz) *n. plu.* [Gk. *phyton*, plant; *chroma*, colour.] Chromoproteins of plants, as certain seaweed pigments.

phytocoenosis (fī'tŏsēnō'sĭs) *n.* [Gk. *phyton*, plant; *koinos*, common.] The assemblage of plants living in a particular locality.

phytogenesis (fī'tŏjĕn'ĕsĭs) *n.* [Gk. *phyton*, plant; *genesis*, descent.] Evolution, or development, of plants.

phytogenetics (fī'tŏjĕnĕt'ĭks) *n.* [Gk. *phyton*, plant; *genesis*, descent.] Plant genetics.

phytogenous (fītŏj'ĕnŭs) *a.* [Gk. *phyton*, plant; *genos*, generation.] Of vegetable origin; produced by plants.

phytogeny,—phytogenesis.

phytogeography (fī'tŏjēŏg'răfĭ) *n.* [Gk. *phyton*, plant; *ge*, earth; *graphein*, to write.] Study of the geographical distribution of plants; geobotany.

phytography (fītŏg′răfĭ) *n.* [Gk. *phyton*, plant; *graphein*, to write.] Descriptive botany.

phytohormones (fī′tōhôr′mōnz) *n. plu.* [Gk. *phyton*, plant; *hormaein*, to excite.] Internal secretions of plants, as auxins and traumatins; plant hormones.

phytoid (fī′toid) *a.* [Gk. *phyton*, plant; *eidos*, form.] Plant-like. *n.* An individual in a plant colony; *cf.* zooid.

phytolith (fī′tölĭth) *n.* [Gk. *phyton*, plant; *lithos*, stone.] Mineral particle, as hydrate of silica, in plant tissue, particularly of herbage.

phytology (fītŏl′öjĭ) *n.* [Gk. *phyton*, plant; *logos*, discourse.] Botany.

phytoma (fītō′mă) *n.* [Gk. *phyton*, plant.] Vegetative plant-substance.

phytome (fī′tōm) *n.* [Gk. *phyton*, plant.] Plants considered as an ecological unit; vegetation.

phytomer (fī′tömĕr) *n.* [Gk. *phyton*, plant; *meros*, part.] A structural unit of a plant; a bud-bearing node.

phytomorphic (fī′tömôr′fĭk) *a.* [Gk. *phyton*, plant; *morphe*, form.] With plant-like structure.

phyton (fī′tŏn) *n.* [Gk. *phyton*, plant.] A rudimentary plant; propagation unit, smallest detached part which can form another plant; a phytomer, *q.v.*

phytonomy (fītŏn′ömĭ) *n.* [Gk. *phyton*, plant; *nomos*, law.] The laws of origin and development of plants.

phytoparasite (fī′töpăr′ăsīt) *n.* [Gk. *phyton*, plant; *parasitos*, parasite.] Any parasitic plant organism.

phytopathology (fī′töpăthŏl′öjĭ) *n.* [Gk. *phyton*, plant; *pathos*, suffering; *logos*, discourse.] The study of abnormalities of formation and function in plants; study of plant diseases.

phytophagous (fītŏf′ăgŭs), *a.* [Gk. *phyton*, plant; *phagein*, to eat.] Feeding on plants; *cf.* herbivorous.

phytophilous,—phytophagous.

phytophysiology (fī′töfĭzĭŏl′öjĭ) *n.* [Gk. *phyton*, plant; *physis*, nature; *logos*, discourse.] Plant physiology.

phytoplankton (fī′töplăngk′tŏn) *n.* [Gk. *phyton*, plant; *plangkton*, wandering.] Plant plankton.

phytoplasm (fī′töplăzm) *n.* [Gk. *phyton*, plant; *plasma*, mould.] Plant protoplasm.

phytosis (fītō′sĭs) *n.* [Gk. *phyton*, plant.] Production of disease by vegetable parasites, as by fungi; any disease so caused.

phytosociology (fī′tösōsĭŏl′öji) *n.* [Gk. *phyton*, plant; L. *socius*, companion; Gk. *logos*, discourse.] The branch of botany comprising ecology, chorology, and genetics of plant associations.

phytosterols (fītöstĕr′ŏlz) *n. plu.* [Gk. *phyton*, plant; *stereos*, solid; L. *oleum*, oil.] Plant sterols; sterols from phanerogams, as sitosterol, stigmasterol, etc.; *cf.* mycosterols.

phytotomy (fītŏt′ömĭ) *n.* [Gk. *phyton*, plant; *tome*, cutting.] The dissection of plants; plant anatomy.

phytotoxin (fī′tötŏk′sĭn) *n.* [Gk. *phyton*, plant; *toxikon*, poison.] Any toxin originating in plants.

phytotrophic (fī′tötrŏf′ĭk) *a.* [Gk. *phyton*, plant; *trephein*, to nourish.] Autotrophic; holophytic, *q.v.*

phytotype (fī′tötīp) *n.* [Gk. *phyton*, plant; *typos*, pattern.] Representative type of plant.

pia mater (pī′ă mā′tĕr) *n.* [L. *pia mater*, tender mother.] A delicate vascular membrane investing brain and spinal cord.

pigment (pĭg′mĕnt) *n.* [L. *pingere*, to paint.] Colouring matter in plants and animals.

pigment cell,—a chromatophore or chromocyte.

pigmentation (pĭg′mĕntā′shŭn) *n.* [L. *pingere*, to paint.] Disposition of colouring matter in an organ or organism.

pilea,—*plu.* of pileum.

pileate (pĭl′ëāt) *a.* [L. *pileatus*, wearing a cap.] Having a pileus.

pileated,—crested; *appl.* birds.

pileocystidium (pĭl'ëösĭstĭd'ĭŭm) *n.* [L. *pileus*, cap; Gk. *kystis*, bag; *idion*, *dim.*] One of the cystidium-like structures on pileus of certain Basidiomycetes.

pileolated (pĭlē'ölātĕd) *a.* [L. *pileolus*, small cap.] Furnished with a small cap or caps.

pileolus (pĭlē'ölŭs) *n.* [L. *pileolus*, small cap.] A small pileus.

pileorhiza (pĭl'ëörī'ză) *n.* [L. *pileus*, cap; Gk. *rhiza*, root.] A root-covering; a root-cap.

pileum (pĭl'ëŭm) *n.* [L. *pileum*, cap.] Top of head region of bird.

pileus (pĭl'ëŭs) *n.* [L. *pileus*, cap.] Umbrella-shaped structure of mushroom, or of jelly-fish.

pilidium (pīlĭd'ĭŭm) *n.* [Gk. *pilidion*, small cap.] The characteristic helmet-shaped larva of Nemertea; a hemispherical apothecium of certain lichens.

pilifer (pĭl'ĭfĕr) *n.* [L. *pilus*, hair; *ferre*, to carry.] Part of labrum of Lepidoptera.

piliferous (pĭlĭf'ërŭs) *a.* [L. *pilus*, hair; *ferre*, to carry.] Bearing or producing hair; *appl.* outermost layer of root or epiblema which gives rise to root-hairs; piligerous.

pilocystidium,—pileocystidium.

pilomotor (pĭl'ömō'tŏr) *a.* [L. *pilus*, hair; *movere*, to move.] *Appl.* non-myelinated fibres innervating muscles of hair follicles.

pilose (pĭl'ōs) *a.* [L. *pilosus*, hairy.] Hairy, downy.

pilotrichome,—pileocystidium.

pilus (pĭl'ŭs) *n.* [L. *pilus*, hair.] One of slender hair-like structures covering some plants.

pinacocytes (pĭn'ăkösīts) *n. plu.* [Gk. *pinax*, tablet; *kytos*, hollow.] The flattened plate-like cells of dermal epithelium of sponges.

pincers,—prehensile claws, as of lobster; chelae of insects; chelicerae of arachnids.

pineal gland or **body**,—the epiphysis cerebri, a median outgrowth from first cerebral vesicle, first tubular then branched, believed to have endocrine functions, and distally connected with the parietal organ, homologous with a median eye.

pineal region,—portion of brain giving rise to pineal and parapineal organs.

pineal sac,—end vesicle of epiphysis, as in Sphenodon.

pineal system,—the parietal organ and associated structures, as pineal sac, stalk, and nerves, parapineal organ, epiphysis.

pin-eyed,—having stigma at mouth of tubular corolla, with shorter stamens. *Opp.* thrum-eyed.

pinna (pĭn'ă) *n.* [L. *pinna*, feather.] A leaflet of a pinnate leaf; auricula or outer ear; a bird's feather or wing; a fish-fin.

pinnaglobulin,—a brown respiratory pigment containing manganese, in certain bivalves.

pinnate (pĭn'āt) *a.* [L. *pinnatus*, feathered.] Divided in a feathery manner; with lateral processes; of a compound leaf, having leaflets on each side of an axis or midrib.

pinnatifid (pĭnăt'ĭfĭd) *a.* [L. *pinna*, feather; *findere*, to cleave.] *Appl.* leaves lobed half-way to midrib.

pinnatilobate (pĭnăt'ĭlō'bāt) *a.* [L. *pinna*, feather; *lobus*, lobe.] With leaves pinnately lobed.

pinnation (pĭnā'shŭn) *n.* [L. *pinna*, feather.] Pinnate condition.

pinnatipartite (pĭnăt'ĭpâr'tīt) *a.* [L. *pinna*, feather; *partitus*, divided.] With leaves lobed three-quarters of way to midrib.

pinnatiped (pĭnăt'ĭpĕd) *a.* [L. *pinna*, feather; *pes*, foot.] Having lobed toes, as certain birds.

pinnatisect (pĭnăt'ĭsĕkt) *a.* [L. *pinna*, feather; *sectus*, cut.] With leaves lobed almost to base or midrib.

pinnatodentate (pĭnăt'ödĕn'tāt) *a.* [L. *pinna*, feather; *dens*, tooth.] Pinnate, with toothed lobes.

pinnatopectinate (pĭnăt'öpĕk'tĭnāt) *a.* [L. *pinna*, feather; *pecten*, comb.] Pinnate, with pectinate lobes.

pinniform (pĭn'ĭfôrm) *a.* [L. *pinna*, feather; *forma*, shape.] Feather-shaped, or fin-shaped.

pinninervate (pĭn'ĭnĕr'vāt) *a.* [L. *pinna*, feather; *nervus*, sinew.] With veins disposed like parts of feather.

pinnulary (pĭn'ūlărĭ) *n.* [L. *pinnula*, *dim.* of *pinna*, feather.] Any of the ossicles of a pinnule of Crinoidea.

pinnule (pĭn'ūl) *n.* [L. *pinnula, dim.* of *pinna*, feather.] A secondary leaflet of a bipinnate or of a pinnately compound leaf; in Crinoidea, one of side-branches, two rows of which fringe arms.

pinocytosis (pi'nösĭtō'sĭs) *n.* [Gk. *piein*, to drink; *kytos*, hollow.] The ingestion of droplets by cells.

pinulus (pĭn'ūlŭs) *n.* [L. *pinulus*, small fir.] A spicule resembling a fir-tree owing to development of small spines from one ray.

piriform (pĭr'ĭfôrm) *a.* [L. *pirum*, pear; *forma*, shape.] Pear-shaped; *appl.* a muscle of gluteal region, musculus piriformis; pyriform, *q.v.*

piscicolous (pĭsĭk'ölŭs) *a.* [L. *piscis*, fish; *colere*, to inhabit.] Living within fishes, as certain parasites.

pisciform (pĭs'ĭfôrm) *a.* [L. *piscis*, fish; *forma*, shape.] Shaped like a fish.

piscivorous (pĭsĭv'örŭs) *a.* [L. *piscis*, fish; *vorare*, to devour.] Fish-eating.

pisiform (pī'sĭfôrm) *a.* [L. *pisum*, pea; *forma*, shape.] Pea-shaped; *appl.* a carpal bone, os pisiforme.

pisohamate (pī'söhăm'āt) *a.* [L. *pisum*, pea; *hamus*, hook.] *Appl.* a ligament connecting pisiform and hamate bones.

pisometacarpal (pī'sömĕtăkâr'păl) *a.* [L. *pisum*, pea; Gk. *meta*, beyond; L. *carpus*, wrist.] *Appl.* a ligament connecting pisiform bone with fifth metacarpal.

pistil (pĭs'tĭl) *n.* [L. *pistillum*, pestle.] Seed-bearing organ of flower, consisting of ovary, style, and stigma; gynoecium.

pistillate (pĭs'tĭlāt) *a.* [L. *pistillum*, pestle.] Bearing pistils or female reproductive organs.

pistillidium (pĭstĭlĭd'ĭŭm) *n.* [L. *pistillum*, pestle; Gk. *idion*, *dim.*] The female sexual organ of bryophytes, pteridophytes and gymnosperms.

pistillody (pĭstĭl'ödĭ) *n.* [L. *pistillum*, pestle; Gk. *eidos*, form.] The conversion of any organ of a flower into carpels.

pistillum (pĭstĭl'ŭm) *n.* [L. *pistillum*, pestle.] A mass of muscle in a chitinous tube in aurophore of a medusoid colony.

pit (pĭt) *n.* [A.S. *pyt*, pit.] A depression formed in course of cell-wall thickening in plant tissue; embryonic olfactory depression.

pit-chamber,—the cavity of a bordered pit below the overarching border.

pitcher (pĭt'shër) *n.* [L.L. *picarium*, beaker.] A modification of a leaf for insect-catching purposes, as pitcher-shaped leaf of Nepenthes.

pit-fields,—areas of depressions in primary cell-walls.

pith (pĭth) *n.* [A.S. *pitha*, pith.] The medulla or central region of a dicotyledonous stem; stelar parenchyma.

pit-lines,—superficial grooves on dermal bones of primitive fishes, formed by latero-sensory system.

pit-membrane,—middle lamella of plant cell-wall forming floor of pits of adjacent cells.

pitocin,—a hormone of the posterior lobe of the pituitary gland, causing contraction of uterine muscle; *a* hypophamine; oxytocin.

pitressin,—a hormone of the posterior lobe of the pituitary gland, inducing increase in blood pressure; *β* hypophamine; vasopressin.

pituicyte (pĭtū'ĭsīt) *n.* [L. *pituita*, phlegm; Gk. *kytos*, hollow.] A glial cell in pars nervosa of pituitary gland.

pituitary (pĭtū'ĭtărĭ) *a.* [L. *pituita*, phlegm.] *Appl.* a body or hypophysis of hypothalamus of brain. *n.* Hypophysis, an endocrine gland, including anterior and posterior lobes and neural stalk or infundibulum.

pituitrin (pĭtū′ĭtrĭn) *n.* [L. *pituita*, phlegm.] An extract from posterior pituitary lobe ; infundin, infundibulin, hypophysin.

pivot-joint,—a trochoid joint, or one in which movement is limited to rotation.

placenta (plăsĕn′tă) *n.* [L. *placenta*, flat cake.] Ovule-bearing part of carpel ; a sporangium-bearing area ; in eutherian mammals, a double vascular spongy structure formed by interlocking of foetal and maternal tissue in uterus, and in which maternal and foetal blood vessels are in close proximity, allowing nutritive and respiratory exchange by osmosis.

placental (plăsĕn′tăl) *a.* [L. *placenta*, flat cake.] *Pert.* a placenta or similar structure ; *appl.* mammals which develop a placenta ; secreted by placenta, *appl.* anterior-pituitary-like hormone.

placentate (plăsĕn′tāt) *a.* [L. *placenta*, flat cake.] Having a placenta developed ; placentiferous, placentigerous.

placentation (plăs′ĕntā′shŭn) *n.* [L. *placenta*, flat cake.] The manner in which seeds are attached to pericarp, or embryos to uterus ; formation, or structural type, of placenta.

placochromatic (plăk′ŏkrōmăt′ĭk) *a.* [Gk. *plax*, plate ; *chroma*, colour.] With plate-arrangement of chromatophores.

placode (plăk′ōd) *n.* [Gk. *plax*, plate ; *eidos*, form.] A localised thickening of ectoderm forming a neural primordium ; a plate-like structure.

placoid (plăk′oid) *a.* [Gk. *plax*, plate ; *eidos*, form.] Plate-like ; *appl.* hard scales or dermal teeth on external surfaces of elasmobranchs ; *appl.* a sensilla, possibly reacting to differences in air pressure, in insects.

placula (plăk′ūlă) *n.* [Gk. *plax*, plate.] A flattened blastula with small segmentation cavity, an embryonic stage of Urochorda ; a stage in Volvox.

plagioclimax (plā̆′jĭŏklī′măks) *n* [Gk. *plagios*, athwart ; *klimax*, ladder.] Climax of a plagiosere.

plagiosere (plā̆′jĭŏsēr) *n.* [Gk. *plagios*, athwart ; L. *serere*, to put in a row.] Plant succession deviating from its course owing to external intervention, as by human activity ; a deflected sere.

plagiotropic (plā̆′jĭŏtrŏp′ĭk) *a.* [Gk. *plagios*, oblique ; *trope*, turn.] Obliquely inclined ; *appl.* roots and branches. *Opp.* orthotropic.

plagiotropism (plā̆′jĭŏt′rŏpĭzm) *n.* [Gk. *plagios*, oblique ; *trope*, turn.] Tendency to incline from the vertical line to oblique or horizontal.

plagiotropous (plā̆′jĭŏt′rŏpŭs) *a.* [Gk. *plagios*, oblique ; *trope*, turn.] Obliquely inclined ; *appl.* the asymmetrical polar cap of Rhombozoa.

plagula (plăg′ūlă) *n.* [L. *plagula*, curtain.] Ventral plate protecting the pedicle in spiders.

plain muscle,—unstriped or involuntary muscle.

plakea (plăkē′ă) *n.* [Gk. *plakoeis*, flat cake.] Plate-like early stage in formation of a coenobium.

planea,—blastaea, *q.v.*

planetism (plăn′ĕtĭzm) *n.* [Gk. *planetes*, wanderer.] The character of having motile or swarm stages.

planidium (plănĭd′ĭŭm) *n.* [Gk. *planos*, wandering ; *idion*, *dim.*] Active migratory larva of certain insects.

planiform (plăn′ĭfôrm) *a.* [L. *planus*, level ; *forma*, shape.] With nearly flat surface ; *appl.* certain articulation surfaces.

plankton (plăng′ktŏn) *n.* [Gk. *plangktos*, wandering.] The marine or fresh-water plants and animals drifting with the surrounding water, including animals with weak locomotory power.

planoblast (plăn′ŏblăst) *n.* [Gk. *planos*, wandering ; *blastos*, bud.] A free-swimming hydroid individual.

planoconidium (plăn′ŏkŏnĭd′ĭŭm) *n.* [Gk. *planos*, wandering ; *konis*, dust ; *idion*, *dim.*] Zoospore of fungi.

planocyte (plăn'ösīt) *n.* [Gk. *planos*, wandering; *kytos*, hollow.] A wandering cell; a planospore; swarm cell of certain fungi.

planogamete (plăn'ögămēt') *n.* [Gk. *planos*, wandering; *gametes*, spouse.] A ciliated motile protoplast of some algae; motile gamete in certain fungi; microzoospore; zoogamete.

planont (plăn'ŏnt) *n.* [Gk. *planos*, wandering; *on*, being.] Any motile spore, gamete, or zygote; the initial amoebula-stage of Neosporidia; a swarm-spore produced in thick-walled or resting sporangia of certain Phycomycetes.

planosome (plăn'ösōm) *n.* [Gk. *planos*, wandering; *soma*, body.] A supernumerary chromosome due to non-disjunction of mates in meiosis.

planospore (plăn'öspōr) *n.* [Gk. *planos*, wandering; *sporos*, seed.] A motile spore; zoospore. *Opp.* aplanospore.

planozygote (plăn'özĭgōt') *n.* [Gk. *planos*, wandering; *zygotos*, yoked.] A motile zygote.

planta (plăn'tă) *n.* [L. *planta*, sole of foot.] The sole of foot; first tarsal joint of insects; apex of proleg.

plantar (plăn'tăr) *a.* [L. *planta*, sole of foot.] *Pert.* sole of foot; *appl.* arteries, ligaments, muscles, nerves, veins, etc.

plantigrade (plăn'tĭgrād) *a.* [L. *planta*, sole of foot; *gradus*, step.] Walking with whole sole of foot touching the ground.

plantula (plăn'tūlă) *n.* [L. *plantula*, small sole.] A pulvillus-like adhesive pad on tarsal joints of some insects.

planula (plăn'ūlă) *n.* [L. *planus*, flat.] The ovoid young free-swimming larva of coelenterates.

planum (plā'nŭm) *n.* [L. *planus*, flat.] A plane or area; *appl.* certain cranial bone surfaces.

plaque (plăk) *n.* [F. *plaque*, plate.] Area cleared by a phage in a bacterial growth; tâche vierge.

2 D

plasma (plăz'mă) *n.* [Gk. *plasma*, form.] The 'liquid tissue' of body fluids; protoplasm generally.

plasmagene (plăz'măjēn) *n.* [Gk. *plasma*, form; *genos*, descent.] A heritable protein unit or molecule in cytoplasm, influencing or interacting with other plasmagenes; cytoplasmic determiner; blastogene, cytogene.

plasmalemma (plăz'mălĕm'ă) *n.* [Gk. *plasma*, form; *lemma*, skin.] The thin cytoplasmic membrane covering ectoplasm or adjoining cell-wall; vitelline membrane.

plasmaspore (plăz'măspōr) *n.* [Gk. *plasma*, form; *sporos*, seed.] An adhesive spore in a sporangium.

plasmatic (plăzmăt'ĭk) *a.* [Gk. *plasma*, form.] *Pert.* plasma; protoplasmic.

plasmatogamy,—plasmogamy, *q.v.*

plasmatoönkosis (plăz'mătöŏng'kōsĭs) *n.* [Gk. *plasma*, form; *ongkos*, bulk.] A thickened storage organ or toruloid structure of zoosporangium, as in Peronosporales.

plasmatoparous (plăz'mătŏp'ărŭs) *a.* [Gk. *plasma*, form; L. *parere*, to beget.] Developing a mycelium directly upon germination instead of zoospores, as grape mildew and other Plasmopara.

plasmocyte (plăz'mösīt) *n.* [Gk. *plasma*, form; *kytos*, hollow.] A leucocyte.

plasmodesma (plăz'mödĕs'mă) *n.* [Gk. *plasma*, form; *desma*, bond.] Cytoplasmic threads penetrating cell wall and forming intercellular bridge; plasmodesm, plasmodesmid. *Plu.* plasmodesmata.

plasmodial (plăzmō'dĭăl) *a.* [Gk. *plasma*, form; *eidos*, form.] *Pert.* a plasmodium.

plasmodiocarp (plăzmō'dĭökărp') *n.* [Gk. *plasma*, form; *eidos*, form; *karpos*, fruit.] A modification of a plasmodium in some slime moulds.

plasmoditrophoblast, — syntrophoblast, *q.v.*

plasmodium (plăzmō'dĭŭm) *n.* [Gk. *plasma*, form; *eidos*, form.] A collection of amoeboid masses without nuclear fusion; a multinucleate mass of protoplasm without cell-wall, of Myxomycetes; syncytium.

plasmogamy (plăzmŏg'ămĭ) *n.* [Gk. *plasma*, form; *gamos*, marriage.] In Protozoa, fusion of several individuals into a multinucleate mass; fusion of cytoplasmic substance without nuclear fusion.

plasmolysis (plăzmŏl'ĭsĭs) *n.* [Gk. *plasma*, form; *lysis*, loosing.] The withdrawal of water from plant cell, causing contraction of cell-walls and of protoplasm.

plasmomites (plăz'mŏmīts) *n. plu.* [Gk. *plasma*, form; *mitos*, thread.] Minute fibrillae forming with plasmosomes the intergranular substance of a cell.

plasmon (plăz'mŏn) *n.* [Gk. *plasma*, form; *on*, being.] Hypothetical system of cytoplasmic hereditary units, *opp.* gene system in the chromosomes.

plasmonema (plăzmŏnē'mă) *n.* [Gk. *plasma*, form; *nema*, thread.] Protoplasmic thread in connection with plastids. *Plu.* plasmonemata.

plasmophore (plăz'mŏfōr) *n.* [Gk. *plasma*, form; *phora*, carrying.] Telophragma; Z-disc, *q.v.*

plasmoptysis (plăzmŏp'tĭsĭs) *n.* [Gk. *plasma*, form; *ptysis*, expectoration.] Emission of cytoplasm from tips of hyphae in host cells, in certain endotrophic mycorrhizae; *cf.* ptyosome.

plasmosome (plăz'mŏsōm) *n.* [Gk. *plasma*, form; *soma*, body.] The true nucleolus; *cf.* karyosome; a minute cytoplasmic granule.

plasmotomy (plăzmŏt'ŏmĭ) *n.* [Gk. *plasma*, form; *tome*, cutting.] Division of plasmodium by cleavage into multinucleate parts.

plasome (plăs'ōm) *n.* [Gk. *plasma*, form; *soma*, body.] A hypothetical unit, *q.v.*

plasson (plăs'ŏn) *n.* [Gk. *plassein*, to form.] The formative substance which may give rise to cellular elements; undifferentiated protoplasm.

plastic (plăs'tĭk) *a.* [Gk. *plastos*, formed.] Formative; *appl.* substances used in forming or building up tissues or organs; *appl.* force which gives matter definite form.

plastid (plăs'tĭd) *n.* [Gk. *plastos*, formed; *idion*, *dim.*] A cell-body other than nucleus or centrosome.

plastidogen organ,—the axial organ of echinoderms.

plastidome (plăs'tĭdōm) *n.* [Gk. *plastos*, formed; *idion*, *dim*; *domos*, chamber.] In a cell, the plastids as a whole; cytoplasmic inclusions which give rise to plastids.

plastidule (plăs'tĭdūl) *n.* [Gk. *plastos*, formed; *idion*, *dim.*] A hypothetical unit, *q.v.*

plastin (plăs'tĭn) *n.* [Gk. *plastos*, formed.] A substance found in reticulum of cells.

plastochondria,—mitochondria, *q.v.*

plastochrone (plăs'tŏkrōn) *n.* [Gk. *plastos*, formed; *chronos*, time.] Time interval between successive stages in development, as between appearance of successive primordia in spiral systems of phyllotaxis.

plastocont,—chondriocont, *q.v.*

plastodynamia (plăs'tŏdĭnăm'ĭă) *n.* [Gk. *plastos*, formed; *dynamis*, power.] Plastic or formative force.

plastogamy (plăstŏg'ămĭ) *n.* [Gk. *plastos*, formed; *gamos*, marriage.] Union of distinct unicellular individuals with fusion of cytoplasm but not of nuclei.

plastogenes (plăs'tŏjēnz) *n. plu.* [Gk. *plastos*, formed; *gennaein*, to produce.] Cytoplasmic factors, controlled by or interacting with nucleus, which determine differentiation of plastids.

plastokont,—chondriocont, *q.v.*

plastomere (plăs'tŏmēr) *n.* [Gk. *plastos*, formed; *meros*, part.] Chondriomere; the chondriosome content of a sperm; a cytomere.

plastosome,—chondriosome, *q.v.*

plastral (plăs'trăl) *a.* [F. *plastron*, breast-plate.] *Pert.* a plastron.

plastron (plăs'trŏn) *n.* [F. *plastron*, breast-plate.] Ventral bony shield of tortoises and turtles; other corresponding structure; film of gas, or layer of gas bubbles retained by hairs, covering epicuticle of aquatic insects.

plate (plāt) *n.* [F. *plat*, Gk. *platys*, flat.] A flat, broad, plate-like structure or surface; a lamina, scale, disc, etc.

platybasic (plăt'ĭbā'sĭk) *a.* [Gk. *platys*, flat; *basis*, base.] *Appl.* the primitive chondrocranium with wide hypophysial fenestra; *cf.* tropibasic.

platydactyl (plăt'ĭdăk'tĭl) *a.* [Gk. *platys*, flat; *daktylos*, finger.] With flattened-out fingers and toes, as certain tailless amphibians.

platyhieric (plăt'ĭhī'ĕrĭk) *a.* [Gk. *platys*, flat; *hieros*, sacred.] Having sacral index above 100; *cf.* dolichohieric.

platysma (plătĭz'mă) *n.* [Gk. *platysma*, flat piece.] Broad sheet of muscle beneath superficial fascia of neck.

platyspermic (plăt'ĭspĕr'mĭk) *a.* [Gk. *platys*, flat; *sperma*, seed.] With seed bilaterally symmetrical.

plectenchyma (plĕktĕng'kĭmă) *n.* [Gk. *plektos*, twisted; *engchyma*, infusion.] A tissue of cell filaments or tubular cells in algae and fungi.

plectoderm (plĕk'tödĕrm) *n.* [Gk. *plektos*, plaited; *derma*, skin.] Outer tissue of a fruit-body, when composed of densely interwoven branched hyphae.

plectonemic (plĕk'tönēm'ĭk) *a.* [Gk. *plektos*, twisted; *nema*, thread.] Having orthospirals interlocked at each twist, as of sister chromatids; paranemic.

plectonephridia (plĕk'tönĕfrĭd'ĭă) *n. plu.* [Gk. *plektos*, twisted; *nephros*, kidney.] Nephridia of diffuse type formed of networks of fine excretory tubules lying on body-wall and septa of certain oligochaetes; plectonephria, nephridia.

plectron (plĕk'trŏn) *n.* [Gk. *plektron*, instrument to strike with.] Hammer-like form of certain bacilli during sporulation.

plectrum (plĕk'trŭm) *n.* [L. *plectrum*, instrument to strike with.] Styloid process of temporal bone; malleus; uvula.

plegetropism (plējĕt'röpĭzm) *n.* [Gk. *plege*, shock; *trope*, turn.] A movement of an organ, resulting from redistribution of particles in protoplasm, in response to change in velocity.

pleioblastic (plī'öblăs'tĭk) *a.* [Gk. *pleion*, more; *blastos*, bud.] Having several buds; germinating at several points, as spores of certain lichens; pleioblastous.

pleiochasium (plī'ökā'zĭŭm) *n.* [Gk. *pleion*, more; *chasis*, division.] Axis of a cymose inflorescence bearing more than two lateral branches.

pleiocotyl (plī'ökŏt'ĭl) *n.* [Gk. *pleion*, more; *kotyle*, cup.] A plant having more than two cotyledons.

pleiocotyledony (plī'ökŏtĭlē'dönĭ) *n.* [Gk. *pleion*, more; *kotyledon*, cup-shaped hollow.] The condition of having more than two seed-leaves or cotyledons.

pleiocyclic (plī'ösĭk'lĭk) *a.* [Gk. *pleion*, more; *kyklos*, circle.] Living through more than one cycle of activity, as a perennial plant.

pleiomerous (plīŏm'ĕrŭs) *a.* [Gk. *pleion*, more; *meros*, part.] Having more than normal number of parts, as of petals or sepals.

pleiomery (plīŏm'ĕrĭ) *n.* [Gk. *pleion*, more; *meros*, part.] Condition of having more than the normal number of parts, as in a whorl.

pleiomorphous,—pleomorphic.

pleiopetalous (plī'öpĕt'ălŭs) *a.* [Gk. *pleion*, more; *petalon*, leaf.] Having more than the normal number of petals; having double flowers.

pleiophyllous (plī'öfĭl'ŭs) *a.* [Gk. *pleion*, more; *phyllon*, leaf.] Having more than normal number of leaves or leaflets.

pleiosporous,—polysporous.

pleiotaxy (plī'ötăk'sĭ) *n.* [Gk. *pleion*, more; *taxis*, arrangement.] A multiplication of whorls, as in double flowers; pleiotaxis.

pleiotropic (plīötrŏp'ĭk) *a*. [Gk. *pleion*, more; *trope*, turn.] Influencing more than one character; *appl*. effects of a gene; *pert*. pleiotropy.

pleiotropy (plī'ŏt'röpĭ) *n*. [Gk. *pleion*, more; *trope*, turn.] Multiple effects of a single genetic factor; pleiotropism.

pleioxenous (plīöks'ënŭs) *a*. [Gk. *pleion*, more; *xenos*, host.] Parasitic on or in several species of hosts; heteroxenous. *n*. Pleioxeny.

Pleistocene (plīs'tösēn) *a*. [Gk. *pleistos*, most; *kainos*, recent.] *Pert*. or *appl*. glacial and post-glacial epoch following the Tertiary period, and merging into the Psychozoic. *n*. The great Ice Age, with four glacial and three interglacial phases.

pleochroic (plē'ökrō'ĭk) *a*. [Gk. *pleon*, more; *chros*, colour.] With various colours.

pleochromatic (plē'ökrōmăt'ĭk) *a*. [Gk. *pleon*, more; *chroma*, colour.] Exhibiting different colours under different environmental or physiological conditions.

pleogamy (plēŏg'ămĭ) *n*. [Gk. *pleon*, more; *gamos*, marriage.] Maturation, therefore pollination, at different times, as of flowers of one plant.

pleometrosis (plēömē'trösĭs) *n*. [Gk. *pleon*, more; *meter*, mother.] Colony foundation by more than one female, as in some social Hymenoptera. *Opp*. haplometrosis, monometrosis. *a*. pleometrotic.

pleomorphic (plē'ömôr'fĭk) *a*. [Gk. *pleon*, more; *morphe*, form.] Having two or more distinct forms occurring in one life-cycle; having several shapes; polymorphous, pleomorphous, pleiomorphous.

pleon (plē'ŏn) *n*. [Gk. *plein*, to swim.] The abdominal region of Crustacea.

pleophyletic (plē'öfīlĕt'ĭk) *a*. [Gk. *pleon*, more; *phylon*, race.] Originating from several lines of descent; polyphyletic.

pleopod (plē'öpŏd) *n*. [Gk. *plein*, to swim; *pous*, foot.] An abdominal appendage or swimming-leg of Crustacea.

plerergate (plēr'ĕrgāt) *n*. [Gk. *pleros*, full; *ergates*, worker.] A replete worker ant having gaster distended with food.

plerocercoid (plē'rösër'koid) *n*. [Gk. *pleros*, full; *kerkos*, tail; *eidos*, form.] The elongated worm-like larval form of certain cestodes in second intermediate host.

plerocestoid (plē'rösĕs'toid) *n*. [Gk. *pleros*, full; *kestos*, girdle; *eidos*, form.] A metacestode, or sexless encysted stage of a cestoid worm; also plerocercoid.

plerome (plē'rōm) *n*. [Gk. *pleroma*, a filling.] The core or central part of an apical meristem.

plerotic (plērŏt'ĭk) *a*. [Gk. *pleroun*, to fill.] Completely filling a space; *appl*. oospore filling oogonium. *Opp*. aplerotic.

plesiobiotic (plē'sĭöbīŏt'ĭk) *a*. [Gk. *plesios*, near; *biosis*, a living.] Living in close proximity; *appl*. colonies of ants of different species; or of building contiguous nests, *appl*. ants and termites.

plesiometacarpal (plē'sĭömĕtăkâr'-păl) *a*. [Gk. *plesios*, near; *meta*, after; *karpos*, wrist.] *Appl*. condition of retaining proximal elements of metacarpals, as in many Cervidae; *opp*. telemetacarpal.

plesiomorphous (plē'sĭömôr'fŭs) *a*. [Gk. *plesios*, near; *morphe*, form.] Having a similar form.

plesiotype (plē'siötīp) *n*. [Gk. *plesios*, near; *typos*, pattern.] A species related to a genotype found in a different region or geological formation; hypotype, *q.v.*

pleura (ploor'ă) *n*. [Gk. *pleura*, side.] A serous membrane lining thoracic cavity and investing lung; *plu*. of pleuron, *q.v.* *Plu*. pleurae.

pleural (ploor'ăl) *a*. [Gk. *pleura*, side.] *Pert*. a pleura or pleuron, as pleural ganglia; *appl*. costal plates of chelonian carapace.

pleuralia (ploorā'lĭă) *n*. *plu*. [Gk. *pleura*, side.] Defensive spicules scattered over general body surface.

pleuranthous (ploorăn'thŭs) *a.* [Gk. *pleura*, side; *anthos*, flower.] Having inflorescences on lateral axes, not on main axis.

pleurapophysis (ploor'ăpŏf'ĭsĭs) *n.* [Gk. *pleura*, side; *apo*, from; *physis*, growth.] A lateral vertebral process or true rib.

pleurethmoid (plooreth'moid) *n.* [Gk. *pleura*, side; *ethmos*, sieve; *eidos*, form.] The compound ectethmoid and prefrontal of some fishes.

pleurite (ploor'īt) *n.* [Gk. *pleura*, side.] A sclerite of the pleuron.

pleuroblastic (ploor'ŏblăs'tĭk) *a.* [Gk. *pleura*, side; *blastos*, bud.] Producing, having, or *pert.* lateral buds or outgrowths; *appl.* haustoria of Peronosporaceae.

pleurobranchiae (ploor'ŏbrăng'kĭē) *n. plu.* [Gk. *pleura*, side; *brangchia*, gills.] Pleurobranchs, or gills springing from lateral walls of thorax of certain Arthropoda.

pleurocarpic (ploor'ŏkâr'pĭk) *a.* [Gk. *pleura*, side; *karpos*, fruit.] *Appl.* mosses with fructification on lateral branches, *opp.* acrocarpic; pleurocarpous.

pleuroccipital,—exoccipital, *q.v.*

pleurocentrum (ploor'ŏsĕn'trŭm) *n.* [Gk. *pleura*, side; L. *centrum*, centre.] A lateral element of centrum of many fishes and fossil amphibians.

pleurocerebral (ploor'ŏsĕr'ēbrăl) *a.* [Gk. *pleura*, side; L. *cerebrum*, brain.] *Pert.* pleural and cerebral ganglia, in molluscs.

pleurocystidium (ploor'ŏsĭstĭd'ĭŭm) *n.* [Gk. *pleura*, side; *kystis*, bag; *idion*, *dim.*] A cystidium in hymenium of surface of lamella; *cf.* cheilocystidium.

pleurodont (ploor'ŏdŏnt) *a.* [Gk. *pleura*, side; *odous*, tooth.] Having teeth fixed by sides to lateral surface of jaw ridge, as in some lizards.

pleuron (ploor'ŏn) *n.* [Gk. *pleuron*, side.] One of the external lateral pieces of body segments of arthropods; a lateral extension of crustacean shells. *Plu.* pleura.

pleuropedal (ploor'ŏpĕd'ăl) *a.* [Gk. *pleura*, side; L. *pes*, foot.] *Pert.* pleural and pedal ganglia of molluscs.

pleuroperitoneum (ploor'ŏpĕr'-ĭtŏnē'ŭm) *n.* [Gk. *pleura*, side; *periteinein*, to stretch round.] Pleura and peritoneum combined, body-lining membrane of animals without diaphragm.

pleuropodium (ploor'ŏpō'dĭŭm) *n.* [Gk. *pleura*, side; *pous*, foot.] A lateral glandular process of abdomen of some insect embryos.

pleurosphenoid,—sphenolateral, *q.v.*

pleurospore (ploor'ŏspōr) *n.* [Gk. *pleura*, side; *sporos*, seed.] Spore formed on sides of a basidium.

pleurosteon (plooros'tēŏn) *n.* [Gk. *pleura*, side; *osteon*, bone.] Lateral process of sternum in young birds, afterwards costal process.

pleurosternal (ploor'ŏstĕr'năl) *a.* [Gk. *pleuron*, side; *sternon*, chest.] Connecting or *pert.* pleuron and sternum; *appl.* thoracic muscles in insects.

pleurotribe (ploor'ŏtrīb) *a.* [Gk. *pleura*, side; *tribein*, to rub.] *Appl.* flowers whose anthers and stigma are so placed as to rub sides of insects entering,—a device for securing cross-pollination.

pleurotrichome,—pleurocystidium.

pleurovisceral (ploor'ŏvĭs'ĕrăl) *a.* [Gk. *pleura*, side; L. *viscera*, intestines.] *Pert.* pleural and visceral ganglia, of molluscs.

pleurum,—pleuron.

pleuston (ploo'stŏn) *n.* [Gk. *pleustikos*, ready for sailing.] Free-floating plants.

plexiform (plĕk'sĭfôrm) *a.* [L. *plexus*, interwoven; *forma*, shape.] Entangled or complicated; like a network; *appl.* layers of retina; *appl.* peripheral layer of grey matter of cerebral cortex.

plexiform gland,—the axial organ of echinoderms.

plexus (plĕk'sŭs) *n.* [L. *plexus*, interwoven.] A network of interlacing vessels, nerves, or fibres.

plexus myentericus,—Auerbach's plexus, *q.v.*

plica (plī'kă) *n.* [L. *plicare*, to fold.] A fold of skin, membrane, or lamella.

plicate (plī'kāt) *a.* [L. *plicare*, to fold.] Folded like a fan, as a leaf; folded or ridged.

pliciform (plĭs'ĭfôrm) *a.* [L. *plicare*, to fold; *forma*, shape.] Resembling a fold; disposed in folds.

Pliocene (plī'ösēn) *n.* [Gk. *pleion*, more; *kainos*, recent.] The latest epoch of the Tertiary period.

plotophyte (plō'töfīt) *n.* [Gk. *plotos*, floating; *phyton*, plant.] A plant adapted for floating.

ploughshare bone,—pygostyle, *q.v.*; vomer, *q.v.*

pluma (ploom'ă) *n.* [L. *pluma*, feather.] A contour feather of birds.

plumate (ploom'āt) *a.* [L. *pluma*, feather.] Plume-like.

plume (ploom) *n.* [L. *pluma*, feather.] A feather, or feather-like structure.

plumicome (ploom'ĭkōm) *n.* [L. *pluma*, feather; *coma*, hair.] A spicule with plume-like tufts.

plumicorn (ploom'ĭkôrn) *n.* [L. *pluma*, feather; *cornu*, horn.] Horn-like tuft of feathers on bird's head.

plumigerous (ploomĭj'ërŭs) *a.* [L. *pluma*, feather; *gerere*, to carry.] Feathered.

plumiped (ploom'ĭpĕd) *n.* [L. *pluma*, feather; *pes*, foot.] A bird with feathered feet.

plumose (ploom'ōs) *a.* [L. *pluma*, feather.] Feathery; having feathers; feather-like; *appl.* a type arrangement of skeletal fibre in sponges; *appl.* feathers without hamuli on barbules, *opp.* pennaceous.

plumula (ploom'ūlă) *n.* [L. *plumula*, small feather.] An adult down feather, succeeding preplumula; a plumule, *q.v.*

plumular (ploom'ūlăr) *a.* [L. *plumula*, small feather.] *Pert.* a plumule.

plumulate (ploom'ūlāt) *a.* [L. *plumula*, small feather.] Downy; with a downy covering; plumulaceous.

plumule (ploom'ūl) *n.* [L. *plumula*, small feather.] A primary bud on epicotyl, which develops primary axis of a stem; androconia of numerous butterflies; a plumula, *q.v.*

pluriascal (plooriăs'kăl) *a.* [L. *plus*, more; Gk. *askos*, bag.] *Pert.* or containing several asci.

pluriaxial (ploor'ĭăk'sĭăl) *a.* [L. *plus*, more; *axis*, axle.] Having flowers developed on secondary shoots.

plurilocular (ploor'ĭlŏk'ūlăr) *a.* [L. *plus*, more; *loculus*, little place.] Having two or more loculi; multilocular, pluriloculate.

plurinuclear (ploor'ĭnū'klëăr) *a.* [L. *plus*, more; *nucleus*, kernel.] Having several nuclei.

pluripartite (ploor'ĭpâr'tīt) *a.* [L. *plus*, more; *partitus*, divided.] With many lobes or partitions.

pluripolar (ploor'ĭpō'lăr) *a.* [L. *plus*, more; *polus*, axis-end.] Having several poles; *appl.* ganglion cells, etc.; multipolar.

pluriseptate (ploor'ĭsĕp'tāt) *a.* [L. *plus*, more; *septum*, partition.] With multiple septa.

pluriserial (ploor'ĭsē'rĭăl) *a.* [L. *plus*, more; *series*, row.] Arranged in two or more rows.

plurivalent (plooriv'ălënt, ploor'ĭvā'lënt) *a.* [L. *plus*, more; *valere*, to be worth.] *Appl.* a chromatin-rod with more than one chromosome.

plurivorous (plooriv'örŭs) *a.* [L. *plus*, more; *vorare*, to devour.] Feeding on several substrates or hosts.

pluteal (ploot'ëăl) *a.* [L. *pluteus*, shed.] *Pert.* a pluteus.

pluteus (ploot'ëŭs) *n.* [L. *pluteus*, shed.] The free-swimming larva of echinoids and ophiuroids.

pneumathode (nū'măthōd, pn-) *n.* [Gk. *pneuma*, breath; *hodos*, way.] An aerial or respiratory root.

pneumatic (nūmăt'ĭk, pn-) *a.* [Gk. *pneuma*, air.] *Appl.* bones penetrated by canals connected with respiratory system, in birds; *appl.* duct between swim-bladder and alimentary tract, in physostomous fishes.

pneumaticity (nūmătĭs'ĭtĭ, pn-) *n.* [Gk. *pneuma*, air.] State of having air cavities, as bones of flying birds.

pneumatised (nū'mătīzd, pn-) *a.* [Gk. *pneuma*, air.] Furnished with air cavities.

pneumatocyst (nū'mătösĭst, pn-) *n.* [Gk. *pneuma*, air ; *kystis*, bladder.] The air-bladder or swim-bladder of fishes ; air cavity used as float ; air-bladder of bladder-wrack.

pneumatophore (nū'mătöfōr, pn-) *n.* [Gk. *pneuma*, air ; *pherein*, to bear.] The air-sac or float of siphonophores ; an air-bladder of marsh- or shore-plants ; aerating outgrowth in certain ferns ; an aerating root.

pneumatopyle (nū'mătöpīl, pn-) *n.* [Gk. *pneuma*, air ; *pyle*, gate.] A pore of a pneumatophore, opening above to exterior in certain Siphonophora.

pneumatotaxis,—pneumotaxis.

pneumogastric (nū'mögăs'trĭk, pn-) *a.* [Gk. *pneuma*, air ; *gaster*, stomach.] *Appl.* tenth cranial or vagus nerve, supplying pharynx, larynx, heart, lungs, and viscera.

pneumostome (nū'möstōm, pn-) *n.* [Gk. *pneuma*, breath ; *stoma*, mouth.] The pulmonary aperture, through which air passes to and from respiratory mantle cavity in terrestrial gasteropods.

pneumotaxis (nū'mötăk'sĭs, pn-) *n.* [Gk. *pneuma*, air ; *taxis*, arrangement.] Reaction to stimulation by carbon dioxide in solution.

poculiform (pō'kūlĭfôrm) *a.* [L. *poculum*, cup ; *forma*, shape.] Cup-shaped ; goblet-shaped.

pod (pŏd) *n.* [M.E. *pod*, bag.] A superior, one-celled, one- or many-seeded fruit of two valves ; legume ; a husk.

podal (pō'dăl) *a.* [Gk. *pous*, foot.] *Pert.* feet ; pedal ; *pert.* parapodia, *appl.* membrane.

podeon (pŏd'ëŏn) *n.* [Gk. *pous*, foot.] The podeum or slender middle part of abdomen of Hymenoptera, uniting propodeon and metapodeon.

podetiiform (pödē'tĭĭfôrm) *a.* [Gk. *pous*, foot ; L. *forma*, shape.] Resembling a podetium.

podetium (pödē'shĭŭm) *n.* [Gk. *pous*, foot.] A stalk-like elevation ; outgrowth of thallus bearing apothecium in certain lichens.

podex (pō'dĕks) *n.* [L. *podex*, rump.] The region about the anus ; pygidium, *q.v.*

podical (pŏd'ĭkăl) *a.* [L. *podex*, rump.] In anal region ; adanal ; *appl.* a pair of small hard plates or paraprocts beside anus of arthropods.

podite (pŏd'īt) *n.* [Gk. *pous*, foot.] A crustacean walking leg.

podium (pō'dĭŭm) *n.* [Gk. *pous*, foot.] A foot or footlike structure ; a stem axis.

podobranchiae (pŏd'öbrăng'kĭē) *n. plu.* [Gk. *pous*, foot ; *brangchia*, gills.] Podobranchs or foot-gills, springing from coxopodites of thoracic appendages of certain Arthropoda.

podocephalous (pŏd'ökĕf'ălŭs, -sĕf-) *a.* [Gk. *pous*, foot ; *kephale*, head.] Having head of flowers on long stalk.

podoconus (pŏd'ökō'nŭs) *n.* [Gk. *pous*, foot ; *konos*, cone.] A conical mass of endoplasm connecting the central capsule with the disc of Sarcodina.

podocyst (pŏd'ösĭst) *n.* [Gk. *pous*, foot ; *kystis*, bladder.] A pedal sinus or caudal vesicle in certain Gasteropoda.

podocyte (pŏd'ösīt) *n.* [Gk. *pous*, foot ; *kytos*, hollow.] A flat blood-cell with a few pointed outgrowths, in insects.

pododerm (pŏd'öděrm) *n.* [Gk. *pous*, foot ; *derma*, skin.] Dermal layer of a hoof, within horny layer.

podogynium (pŏd'öjĭn'ĭŭm) *n.* [Gk. *pous*, foot ; *gyne*, female.] A stalk supporting the gynoecium ; basigynium.

podomere (pŏd'ömēr) *n.* [Gk. *pous*, foot ; *meros*, part.] A limb segment of arthropods.

podophthalmite (pŏd′ŏfthăl′mīt) *n.* [Gk. *pous*, foot; *ophthalmos*, eye.] In crustaceans, eye-stalk segment farthest from head.

podosoma (pŏd′ösōmă) *n.* [Gk. *pous*, foot; *soma*, body.] The body region in Arachnoidea which bears the four pairs of walking legs.

podotheca (pŏd′ŏthē′kă) *n.* [Gk. *pous*, foot; *theke*, box.] A foot covering, as of birds or reptiles; pupal leg sheath.

podzol (pŏdzŏl) *n.* [Russ. *pod*, under; *zolit'*, to leach.] Grey forest soil; soil type of cold temperate regions, and formed on heath lands and under coniferous forest.

poecilo-,—poikilo-.

pogonion (pōgō′nĭŏn) *n.* [Gk. *pogonion*, little beard.] Most prominent point of chin as represented on mandible.

poikilocyte (poik′ĭlösīt) *n.* [Gk. *poikilos*, various; *kytos*, cell.] A distorted form of erythrocyte present in certain pathological conditions.

poikilogony (poik′ĭlŏg′önĭ) *n.* [Gk. *poikilos*, various; *gone*, generation.] Intraspecific variation in duration of embryological processes, due to environmental factors.

poikilothermal (poik′ĭlöthĕr′măl) *a.* [Gk. *poikilos*, various; *therme*, heat.] *Appl.* cold-blooded animals, or those whose temperature varies with that of surrounding medium; poikilothermous; *Opp.* homoiothermal.

point mutation,—a mutation proper, heritable change occurring at a single gene locus; genovariation, micromutation, transgenation.

pointer cell,—eurycyst, *q.v.*

poison canal,—duct between stylet and lancets of sting of Hymenoptera, conveying secretion of poison glands from poison sac outwards.

polar (pō′lăr) *a.* [Gk. *polos*, pivot.] In region of end of an axis; at, or *pert.*, a pole.

polar body,—one of two cells divided off from ovum during maturation, before germ-nuclei fuse; polocyte.

polar capsules,—of spores containing coiled extrusible filaments, in Cnidosporidia.

polar cartilage,—posterior portion of trabecula, or independent cartilage in that region.

polar corpuscle,—centrosome.

polar globule,—polar body.

polar granule,—centromere, *q.v.*

polar nuclei,—nuclei at each end of angiosperm embryo, which later form secondary nucleus.

polar plates,—two narrow ciliated areas produced in transverse plane, part of equilibrium apparatus of certain Coelenterata.

polar rays,—astral rays, *opp.* spindle-fibres.

polar rings,—two ring-shaped cytoplasmic masses near ovum poles formed after union of germ-nuclei.

polarilocular (pōlăr′ĭlŏk′ūlăr) *n.* [L. *polaris*, polar; *loculus*, compartment.] *Appl.* a cask-shaped spore with two cells separated by a partition having a perforation, of certain lichens; polaribilocular.

polarity (pölăr′ĭtĭ) *n.* [Gk. *polos*, pivot.] The tendency of plants to develop from the poles, roots downwards, stems upwards; the tendency of an ovum to place itself with axis corresponding to that of mother.

pole-capsule,—a cell resembling a nematocyst in Cnidosporidia.

pole-cell,—teloblast of annelids and molluscs.

pole-plates,—end-plates or achromatic masses at spindle poles in protozoan mitosis.

Polian vesicles [*G. S. Poli*, Italian naturalist]. Interradial vesicles opening into ring-vessel of ambulacral system of most Asteroidea and Holothuroidea.

polioplasm (pŏl′ĭöplăzm) *n.* [Gk. *polios*, gray; *plasma*, form.] Spongioplasm; granular protoplasm.

pollakanthic (pŏl′ăkăn′thĭk) *a.* [Gk. *pollakis*, many times; *anthos*, flower.] Having several flowering periods. *Opp.* hapaxanthic.

pollen (pŏl'ĕn) *n.* [L. *pollen*, fine flour.] The male fertilising element or haploid microspore of seed-plants.

pollen analysis,—qualitative and quantitative determination of the occurrence of pollen in deposits, as in peat; palynology, *q.v.*

pollen basket,—the pollen-transporting hairs at back of tibia of worker bees; corbicula.

pollen-chamber,—pit formed at apex of nucellus below micropyle.

pollen-flower,—a flower without nectar attracting pollen-feeding insects.

pollen profile,—the vertical distribution of pollen grains in a deposit.

pollen sac,—loculus of anther; microsporangium of seed-plants.

pollen spectrum,—the relative numerical distribution or percentage of pollen grains of different species in a sample of deposit.

pollen tube,—a tubular process developed from pollen grains after attachment to stigma, and growing towards ovule, represents male gametophyte.

pollex (pŏl'ĕks) *n.* [L. *pollex*, thumb.] The thumb, or innermost digit of the normal five in anterior limb.

pollinarium (pŏlĭnā'rĭŭm) *n.* [L. *pollen*, fine flour.] The pollinium with its caudicle and adhesive disc.

pollination (pŏl'ĭnā'shŭn) *n.* [L. *pollen*, fine flour.] Fertilisation in flowers; transference of pollen from anther to stigma, or from stigma to ovule.

pollination - drop, — mucilaginous drop exuded from micropyle and which detains pollen grains, as in gymnosperms.

polliniferous (pŏl'ĭnĭf'ĕrŭs) *a.* [L. *pollen*, fine flour; *ferre*, to carry.] Pollen-bearing; adapted for transferring pollen; pollinigerous.

pollinium (pŏlĭn'ĭŭm) *n.* [L. *pollen*, fine flour.] An agglutinated pollen mass in orchids and other plants.

pollinodium (pŏl'ĭnō'dĭŭm) *n.* [L. *pollen*, fine flour; Gk. *hodos*, way.] An antheridium of certain algae and fungi.

pollinoid (pŏl'ĭnoid) *n.* [L. *pollen*, fine flour; Gk. *eidos*, form.] A male gamete, or spermatium.

polocytes (pŏl'ŏsīts) *n. plu.* [Gk. *polos*, axis; *kytos*, hollow.] Polar bodies, *q.v.*

polster (pŏl'stĕr) *n.* [Ger. *Polster*, pad.] A low compact perennial or cushion plant.

polyadelphous (pŏl'ĭădĕl'fŭs) *a.* [Gk. *polys*, many; *adelphos*, brother.] Having stamens united by filaments into more than two bundles.

polyandrous (pŏl'ĭăn'drŭs) *a.* [Gk. *polys*, many; *aner*, male.] Having twenty or more stamens; mating with more than one male.

polyandry (pŏl'ĭăn'drĭ) *n.* [Gk. *polys*, many; *aner*, male.] Condition of a female consorting with several males.

polyanisomere (pŏl'ĭăn'īsŏmēr) *n.* [Gk. *polys*, many; *anisos*, unequal; *meros*, part.] A structural unit composed of polyisomeres and anisomeres, *q.v.*, as vertebral column.

polyarch (pŏl'ĭârk) *a.* [Gk. *polys*, many; *arche*, beginning.] Having many protoxylem bundles; *appl.* multipolar spindle in higher plants.

polyaxon (pŏl'ĭăk'sŏn) *n.* [Gk. *polys*, many; *axis*, axle.] Type of spicule laid down along numerous axes.

polyblast (pŏl'ĭblăst) *n.* [Gk. *polys*, many; *blastos*, bud.] A histiocyte; tissue macrophage.

polyblastic (pŏl'ĭblăs'tĭk) *a.* [Gk. *polys*, many; *blastos*, bud.] Having spores divided by a number of septa; *appl.* lichens; polyblastous.

polycarp (pŏl'ĭkârp) *n.* [Gk. *polys*, many; *karpos*, fruit.] A gonad of some ascidians, on inner surface of mantle.

polycarpellary (pŏl'ĭkâr'pĕlărĭ) *a.* [Gk. *polys*, many; *karpos*, fruit.] With compound gynoecium.

polycarpic (pŏl'ĭkâr'pĭk), **polycarpous** (pŏl'ĭkâr'pŭs) *a.* [Gk. *polys*, many; *karpos*, fruit.] With numerous carpels; producing seed season after season, *appl.* perennials.

polycaryo-,—polykaryo-.

polycentric (pŏl′isĕn′trĭk) *a.* [Gk. *polys*, many; *kentron*, centre.] With several growth centres; *opp.* monocentric; with several centromeres, *appl.* chromosome. *n.* A polycentric chromosome.

polycercous (pŏl′isĕr′kŭs) *a.* [Gk. *polys*, many; *kerkos*, tail.] *Appl.* bladderworms developing several cysts, each with head.

polychasium (pŏl′ĭkā′zĭŭm) *n.* [Gk. *polys*, many; *chasis*, division.] A cymose branch system when more than two branches arise about the same point.

polychromasy, -ie (pŏl′ĭkrō′măsĭ) *n.* [Gk. *polys*, many; *chroma*, colour.] Multiple and differential tinting with one staining mixture.

polychromatic (pŏl′ĭkrōmăt′ĭk) *a.* [Gk. *polys*, many; *chroma*, colour.] With several colours, as pigment areas; *appl.* two forms of erythrocytes with well-defined chromatin.

polychromatocyte (pŏl′ikrō′mătŏsīt) *n.* [Gk. *polys*, many; *chroma*, colour; *kytos*, hollow.] A blood cell developed from a normoblast and which becomes a normocyte or mature erythrocyte; polychromatophil erythrocyte or rubricyte.

polychromatophil (pŏlĭkrō′mătŏfĭl) *a.* [Gk. *polys*, many; *chroma*, colour; *philein*, to love.] Having a staining reaction characterised by varying colours; *appl.* erythroblasts with small haemoglobin content.

polycotyledon (pŏl′ĭkŏtĭlē′dŏn) *n.* [Gk. *polys*, many; *kotyledon*, hollow vessel.] A plant with more than two seed-leaves.

polycotyledonary (pŏl′ĭkŏtĭlē′dŏnărĭ) *a.* [Gk. *polys*, many; *kotyledon*, hollow vessel.] Having placenta in many divisions.

polycotyledonous (pŏl′ĭkŏtĭlē′dŏnŭs) *a.* [Gk. *polys*, many; *kotyledon*, hollow vessel.] Having more than two cotyledons or seed lobes, as fir embryo.

polycotyledony (pŏl′ĭkŏtĭlē′dŏnĭ) *n.* [Gk. *polys*, many; *kotyledon*, hollow vessel.] A great increase in number of cotyledons.

polycrotism (pŏlĭk′rŏtĭzm) *n.* [Gk. *polys*, many; *krotos*, beating.] Condition of having several secondary elevations in pulse curve.

polycyclic (pŏl′isĭk′lĭk) *a.* [Gk. *polys*, many; *kyklos*, circle.] Having many whorls or ring structures.

polycystid (pŏl′isĭs′tĭd) *a.* [Gk. *polys*, many; *kystis*, bladder.] Septate; partitioned off.

polydactyly (pŏl′ĭdăk′tĭlĭ) *n.* [Gk. *polys*, many; *daktylos*, finger.] Condition of having an excessive number of fingers or toes; polydactylism.

polydesmic (pŏlĭdĕs′mĭk, -dĕz-) *a.* *Appl.* cyclomorial scales made up of monodesmic scales; *cf.* synpolydesmic, deuteropolydesmic.

polyembryony (pŏl′ĭĕm′brĭŏnĭ) *n.* [Gk. *polys*, many; *embryon*, foetus.] Formation of several embryos in one ovule; instance of a zygote giving rise to more than one embryo, *e.g.* identical twins, offspring of armadillos, certain insects, etc.

polyenergid (pŏl′ĭĕn′ĕrjĭd) *a.* [Gk. *polys*, many; *energos*, active.] *Appl.* nuclei with more than one centriole.

polygamous (pŏlĭg′ămŭs) *a.* [Gk. *polys*, many; *gamos*, marriage.] Bearing male, female, and hermaphrodite flowers; consorting with more than one mate.

polygamy (pŏlĭg′ămĭ) *n.* [Gk. *polys*, many; *gamos*, marriage.] Condition of having staminate, pistillate, and hermaphrodite flowers on same individual; condition of having more than one mate at a time.

polygene (pŏl′ĭjēn) *n.* [Gk. *polys*, many; *genos*, descent.] A gene or minor mutant controlling quantitative characters; buffering gene. *Opp.* oligogene.

polygenesis (pŏlĭjĕn′ĕsĭs) *n.* [Gk. *polys*, many; *genesis*, descent.] Derivation from more than one source; origin of a new type at more than one place or time. *Opp.* monogenesis.

polygenetic (pŏl′ĭjĕnĕt′ĭk) *a.* [Gk. *polys*, many; *genesis*, descent.] Derived from more than one source; polyphyletic.

polygenic (pŏl′ĭjē′nĭk) *a.* [Gk. *polys*, many; *-genes*, producing.] Controlled by a number of genes; *pert.* polygenes; polygenetic, *q.v.*

polygerm (pŏl′ĭjĕrm) *n.* [Gk. *polys*, many; L. *germen*, bud.] An isolated group of morulae.

polygoneutic (pŏl′ĭgōnū′tĭk) *a.* [Gk. *polys*, many; *goneuein*, to beget.] Rearing more than one brood in a season.

polygynoecial (pŏl′ĭjĭnē′sĭăl) *a.* [Gk. *polys*, many; *gyne*, woman; *oikos*, house.] Having multiple fruits formed by united gynoecia.

polygynous (pŏlĭj′ĭnŭs) *a.* [Gk. *polys*, many; *gyne*, female.] Consorting with more than one female at a time; with many styles.

polyhybrid (pŏl′ĭhī′brĭd) *n.* [Gk. *polys*, many; L. *hybrida*, mongrel.] A hybrid heterozygous for many genes.

polyisomeres (pŏl′ĭī′sōmērz) *n. plu.* [Gk. *polys*, many; *isos*, equal; *meros*, part.] Parts all homologous with each other, as leaves of plants of the same species; *cf.* anisomeres, polyanisomere.

polykaric (pŏl′ĭkăr′ĭk) *a.* [Gk. *polys*, many; *karyon*, nut.] Multinucleate.

polykaryocyte (pŏlĭkăr′ĭōsīt) *n.* [Gk. *polys*, many; *karyon*, nut; *kytos*, hollow.] A multinucleate cell, of bone marrow.

polykaryon (pŏl′ĭkăr′ĭŏn) *n.* [Gk. *polys*, many; *karyon*, nut.] A polyenergid nucleus; a nucleus with more than one centriole.

polykont (pŏl′ĭkŏnt) *a.* [Gk. *polys*, many; *kontos*, pole.] Multiflagellate.

polylecithal (pŏl′ĭlĕs′ĭthal) *a.* [Gk. *polys*, many; *lekithos*, yolk.] Containing relatively much yolk, as centrolecithal eggs; *cf.* megalolecithal, mesolecithal, meiolecithal.

polylepidous (pŏl′ĭlĕp′ĭdŭs) *a.* [Gk. *polys*, many; *lepis*, scale.] Having many scales.

polymastigote (pŏl′ĭmăstī′gōt) *a.* [Gk. *polys*, many; *mastix*, whip.] Having flagella arranged in a tuft.

polymastism (pŏl′ĭmăs′tĭzm) *n.* [Gk. *polys*, many; *mastos*, breast.] Occurrence of more than normal number of mammae; polymastia.

polymegaly (pŏl′ĭmĕg′ălĭ) *n.* [Gk. *polys*, many; *megalos*, greatly.] Occurrence of more than two sizes of sperm in one animal.

polymeniscous (pŏl′ĭmēnĭs′kŭs) *a.* [Gk. *polys*, many; *meniskos*, small moon.] Having many lenses, as compound eye.

polymerous (pŏlĭm′ĕrŭs) *a.* [Gk. *polys*, many; *meros*, part.] Consisting of many parts or members.

polymorph (pŏl′ĭmôrf) *n.* [Gk. *polys*, many; *morphe*, form.] A polymorphonuclear leucocyte.

polymorphic,—polymorphous, *q.v.*

polymorphism (pŏl′ĭmôr′fĭzm) *n.* [Gk. *polys*, many; *morphe*, form.] Occurrence of different forms of individuals in same species; occurrence of different forms, or different forms of organs, in same individual at different periods of life.

polymorphonuclear (pŏl′ĭmôr′fōnū′klēăr) *a.* [Gk. *polys*, many; *morphe*, form; L. *nucleus*, kernel.] *Appl.* amoeboid leucocytes with multipartite nuclei connected by fine threads of chromatin.

polymorphous (pŏl′ĭmôr′fŭs) *a.* [Gk. *polys*, many; *morphe*, form.] Showing a marked degree of variation in body form, during the life history, or within the species; *pert.* or containing variously shaped units; *appl.* layer, the inner cell-lamina of cerebral cortex; polymorphic, pleomorphic; *cf.* monomorphic.

polynucleate (pŏl′ĭnūklēăt) *a.* [Gk. *polys*, many; L. *nucleus*, kernel.] Polykaric; multinucleate.

polyoestrous (pŏl′ĭē′strŭs) *a.* [Gk. *polys*, many; *oistros*, gadfly.] Having a succession of oestrous periods in one sexual season; *cf.* monoestrous.

polyp (pŏl′ĭp) *n.* [L. *polypus*, polyp.] A simple Actinozoon, or a separate zooid of a colony.

polyparium (pŏl′ĭpā′rĭŭm) *n.* [L. *polypus*, polyp.] The common base and connecting tissue of a colony of polyps; polypary.

polypetalous (pŏl'ĭpĕt'ălŭs) *a.* [Gk. *polys*, many; *petalon*, leaf.] Having separate, free, or distinct petals.

polyphagous (pŏlĭf'ăgŭs) *a.* [Gk. *polys*, many; *phagein*, to eat.] Eating various kinds of food; of insects, using many different food plants; *cf.* monophagous, oligophagous, stenophagous; of Sporozoa, passing different phases of life-history in different cells.

polyphyletic (pŏl'ĭfīlĕt'ĭk) *a.* [Gk. *polys*, many; *phylon*, race.] Convergent, as *appl.* a group; combining characteristics of more than one ancestral type through independent acquisition; having origin from several lines of descent; *cf.* oligophyletic, monophyletic.

polyphyllous (pŏl'ĭfĭl'ŭs) *a.* [Gk. *polys*, many; *phyllon*, leaf.] Many-leaved.

polyphyodont (pŏl'ĭfī'ödŏnt) *a.* [Gk. *polyphyes*, manifold; *odous*, tooth.] Having many successive sets of teeth.

polypide (pŏl'ĭpīd) *n.* [L. *polypus*, polyp.] An individual or person of a zooid colony; polypite.

polyplanetic (pŏl'ĭplănĕt'ĭk) *a.* [Gk. *polys*, many; *planetes*, wanderer.] Having several motile phases with intervening resting stages.

polyplastic (pŏl'ĭplăs'tĭk) *a.* [Gk. *polys*, many; *plastos*, formed.] Capable of assuming many forms.

polyploid (pŏl'ĭploid) *a.* [Gk. *polys*, many; *aploos*, onefold; *eidos*, form.] With a reduplication of the chromosome number, as triploid, tetraploid, etc., having three, four, etc., times the normal haploid or gametic number; exhibiting polyploidy. *n.* An organism with more than two chromosome sets.

polypneustic (pŏl'ĭnū'stĭk, -pnū-) *a.* [Gk. *polys*, many; *pnein*, to breathe.] *Appl.* lateral lobes bearing multiple spiracle pores, in certain insects.

polypod (pŏl'ĭpŏd) *a.* [Gk. *polys*, many; *pous*, foot.] Furnished with many feet or legs; *appl.* larva, as of Lepidoptera; polypodous.

polypoid (pŏl'ĭpoid) *a.* [L. *polypus*, polyp; Gk. *eidos*, form.] Polyp-like.

polyprotodont (pŏl'ĭprō'tödŏnt) *a.* [Gk. *polys*, many; *protos*, first; *odous*, tooth.] With four or five incisors on each side of upper jaw, and one or two fewer on lower.

polyrhizal (pŏl'ĭrī'zăl) *a.* [Gk. *polys*, many; *rhiza*, root.] With many roots or rootlets; polyrhizous.

polysaccharides (pŏl'ĭsăk'ărīdz) *n. plu.* [Gk. *polys*, many; L. *saccharum*, sugar.] Polymers of sugars, having large molecules, *e.g.* vegetable gums, starches, cellulose, hemicelluloses, etc.

polysepalous (pŏl'ĭsĕp'ălŭs) *a.* [Gk. *polys*, many; F. *sépale*, sepal.] Having free or distinct sepals.

polysiphonic (pŏl'ĭsīfŏn'ĭk) *a.* [Gk. *polys*, many; *siphon*, tube.] *Appl.* a hydromedusa stem consisting of several hydrocauli bound together.

polysomic (pŏl'ĭsō'mĭk) *a.* [Gk. *polys*, many; *soma*, body.] Having one or more chromosomes, not the entire set, in the polyploid state; *pert.* a number of homologous genes.

polysomitic (pŏl'ĭsömĭt'ĭk) *a.* [Gk. *polys*, many; *soma*, body; *temnein*, to cut.] Having many body-segments; formed from fusion of primitive body segments.

polysomy (pŏlĭsō'mĭ) *n.* [Gk. *polys*, many; *soma*, body.] The polysomic condition.

polyspermous (pŏl'ĭspĕr'mŭs) *a.* [Gk. *polys*, many; *sperma*, seed.] Having many seeds.

polyspermy (pŏl'ĭspĕr'mĭ) *n.* [Gk. *polys*, many; *sperma*, seed.] Entry of several sperms into one ovum.

polyspondyly (pŏl'ĭspŏn'dĭlĭ) *n.* [Gk. *polys*, many; *sphondylos*, vertebra.] Condition of having vertebral parts multiple where myotome has been lost; *cf.* diplospondyly.

polysporic,—polysporous.

polysporocystid (pŏl'ĭspōrösĭs'tĭd) *n.* [Gk. *polys*, many; *sporos*, seed; *kystis*, bladder; *eidos*, form.] *Appl.* oocyst of Sporozoa when more than four sporocysts are present.

polysporous (pŏl'ĭspō'rŭs) *a.* [Gk. *polys*, many; *sporos*, seed.] Many-seeded; many-spored.

polystachyous (pŏl′ĭstăk′ĭŭs) *a.* [Gk. *polys*, many; *stachys*, ear of corn.] With numerous spikes.

polystelic (pŏl′ĭstēl′ĭk) *a.* [Gk. *polys*, many; *stele*, post.] With several steles.

polystely (pŏl′ĭstē′lĭ) *n.* [Gk. *polys*, many; *stele*, post.] Arrangement of axial vascular tissue in several steles, each containing more than one vascular bundle.

polystemonous (pŏl′ĭstēm′ŏnŭs) *a.* [Gk. *polys*, many; *stemon*, warp.] Having stamens more than double the number of petals or sepals.

polystichous (pŏlĭs′tĭkŭs) *a.* [Gk. *polys*, many; *stichos*, row.] Arranged in numerous rows or series.

polystomatous (pŏl′ĭstŏm′ătŭs) *a.* [Gk. *polys*, many; *stoma*, mouth.] Having many pores, mouths, openings, or suckers; many-mouthed, as Discomedusae and sponges.

polystomium (pŏl′ĭstō′mĭŭm) *n.* [Gk. *polys*, many; *stoma*, mouth.] A suctorial mouth of Discomedusae.

polystylar (pŏl′ĭstī′lăr) *a.* [Gk. *polys*, many; *stylos*, pillar.] Many-styled.

polysymmetrical (pŏl′ĭsĭmĕt′rĭkăl) *a.* [Gk. *polys*, many; *symmetria*, due proportion.] Divisible through several planes into bilaterally symmetrical portions.

polytene (pŏl′ĭtēn) *a.* [Gk. *polys*, many; *tainia*, band.] *Appl.* chromosome resulting from close association of products of paired multiple chromosomes; *appl.* theory of origin of giant chromosomes, by multiplication of chromonemata.

polythalamous (pŏl′ĭthăl′ămŭs) *a.* [Gk. *polys*, many; *thalamos*, chamber.] Aggregate or collective, as *appl.* fruits; *appl.* galls; *appl.* shells made up of many chambers formed successively.

polythelia (pŏl′ĭthē′lĭă) *n.* [Gk. *polys*, many; *thele*, nipple.] The occurrence of supernumerary nipples.

polythermic (pŏl′ĭthĕr′mĭk) *a.* [Gk. *polys*, much; *therme*, heat.] Tolerating relatively high temperatures.

polytocous (pŏlĭt′ŏkŭs) *a.* [Gk. *polys*, many; *tokos*, offspring.] Prolific; producing several young at a birth; fruiting repeatedly; caulocarpous.

polytomous (pŏlĭt′ŏmŭs) *a.* [Gk. *polys*, many; *tome*, cutting.] Having more than two secondary branches.

polytopic (pŏl′ĭtŏp′ĭk) *a.* [Gk. *polys*, many; *topos*, place.] Occurring or originating in several places.

polytrichous (pŏlĭt′rĭkŭs) *a.* [Gk. *polys*, many; *thrix*, hair.] Having the body covered with an even coat of cilia, as certain infusorians; having many hair-like outgrowths.

polytrochal (pŏlĭt′rŏkăl) *a.* [Gk. *polys*, many; *trochos*, wheel.] Having several circlets of cilia between mouth and posterior end, as in certain annulates; polytrochous.

polytrophic (pŏl′ĭtrŏf′ĭk) *a.* [Gk. *polys*, many; *trophe*, nourishment.] *Appl.* ovariole in which nutritive cells are enclosed in oocyte follicles; nourished by more than one organism or substance; obtaining food from many sources.

polytropic (pŏl′ĭtrŏp′ĭk) *a.* [Gk. *polys*, many; *tropikos*, turning.] Turning in many directions; infecting many kinds of tissue, *appl.* viruses; pantropic.

polytypic (pŏl′ĭtĭp′ĭk) *a.* [Gk. *polys*, many; *typos*, type.] Having or *pert.* many types; *appl.* species having geographical subspecies; *appl.* genus having several species; *opp.* monotypic.

polyvoltine (pŏl′ĭvŏl′tĭn) *a.* [Gk. *polys*, many; It. *volta*, time.] Producing several broods in one season, *appl.* certain silkworms.

polyxylic (pŏlĭzī′lĭk) *a.* [Gk. *polys*, many; *xylon*, wood.] Having many xylem strands and several concentric vascular rings; *appl.* stem, as in Cycadales.

polyzoarium (pŏl′ĭzōā′rĭŭm) *n.* [Gk. *polys*, many; *zoon*, animal.] The skeletal system of a polyzoan colony; the colony itself.

polyzoic (pŏl'ĭzō'ĭk) *a.* [Gk. *polys*, many; *zoon*, animal.] *Appl.* a colony of many zooids; *appl.* a spore containing many sporozoites.

polyzooid (pŏl'ĭzō'oid) *n.* [Gk. *polys*, many; *zoon*, animal; *eidos*, form.] An individual in a polyzoan colony.

pome (pōm) *n.* [L. *pomum*, apple.] An inferior, indehiscent, two or more celled fleshy fruit.

pompetta (pŏmpĕt'ă) *n.* [It. *pompetta*, little pump.] An organ forcing spermatozoa into penis, as in Phlebotomus; sperm pump.

pomum Adami,—laryngeal prominence, ridge of thyroid cartilage in front of neck, more pronounced in males.

ponogen (pŏn'öjĕn) *n.* [Gk. *ponos*, toil; *gennaein*, to produce.] Waste matter produced by exertion; fatigue poison.

pons (pŏnz) *n.* [L. *pons*, bridge.] A structure connecting two parts; pons Varolii, *q.v.*

pons Varolii (pŏnz vărō'lĭī) *n.* [L. *pons*, bridge; *C. Varolio* or *Varolius*, Italian anatomist.] Broad band of white fibres connecting cerebrum, cerebellum and medulla oblongata, and including the pontine nuclei of grey matter.

pontal, pontic, pontile, pontine,—*pert.* a pons or the pons Varolii.

ponticulus (pŏntĭk'ūlŭs) *n.* [L. *ponticulus*, small bridge.] A vertical ridge on auricular cartilage; propons, *q.v.*

popliteal (pŏplĭt'ëăl, pŏp'lĭtē'ăl) *a.* [L. *poples*, ham.] *Pert.* region behind and above knee-joint; *appl.* artery, glands, vein, muscle, etc.

popliteal nerve,—internal or medial, the tibial nerve; external or lateral, the common peroneal nerve.

porcellanous (pôr'sĕlănŭs) *a.* [F. *porcelaine*, from It. *porcellana*, Venus shell.] Resembling porcelain, white and opaque; *appl.* calcareous shells, as of Foraminifera, certain Mollusca, etc.

pore (pōr) *n.* [Gk. *poros*, channel.] A minute opening or interstice, as of the skin, sieve-plates, stomata, etc.

pore-canals,—minute spiral tubules passing through the cuticle, but not the epicuticle, of insects.

pore-organ,—structure surrounding canal for excretion of mucilage through pores, in desmids.

pore-rhombs,—canals grouped in half rhombs on each of two adjoining plates of calyx in Cystidea.

poricidal (pō'rĭsī'dăl) *a.* [Gk. *poros*, channel; L. *caedere*, to cut.] Dehiscing by valves or pores, as fruit of poppy, stamens of ling.

poriferous (pörĭf'ërŭs) *a.* [Gk. *poros*, channel; L. *ferre*, to bear.] Furnished with numerous openings.

poriform (pō'rĭfôrm) *a.* [Gk. *poros*, channel; L. *forma*, shape.] Resembling a pore.

porocyte (pō'rösīt) *n.* [Gk. *poros*, channel; *kytos*, hollow.] A perforated cell of Porifera.

porogam (pō'rögăm) *n.* [Gk. *poros*, channel; *gamos*, marriage.] A plant whose pollen-tube enters ovule by micropyle, *opp.* chalazogam.

porogamy (pörŏg'ămĭ) *n.* [Gk. *poros*, channel; *gamos*, marriage.] Entrance of a pollen-tube into ovule by micropyle to secure fertilisation *opp.* aporogamy.

poroids (pō'roidz) *n. plu.* [Gk. *poros*, channel; *eidos*, shape.] Minute depressions in theca of dinoflagellates and diatoms.

porophyllous (pō'röfĭl'ŭs) *a.* [Gk. *poros*, channel; *phyllon*, leaf.] Having, or *appl.*, leaves with numerous transparent spots.

porphyrins (pôr'fĭrĭnz) *n. plu.* [Gk. *porphyra*, purple.] Certain coloured organic compounds which combine with metals to form respiratory pigments and catalysts.

porphyrophore (pôr'fĭröfōr') *n.* [Gk. *porphyra*, purple; *pherein*, to bear.] A reddish-purple pigment-bearing cell.

porphyropsin (pôrfĭrŏp'sĭn) *n.* [Gk. *porphyra*, purple; *opsis*, sight.] Visual purple, a retinal pigment in fishes.

porrect (pŏrĕkt′) *a.* [L. *porrectus*, stretched out.] Extended outwards.

porta (pôr′tă) *n.* [L. *porta*, gate.] A gate-like structure, as transverse fissure of liver; hilum.

portal (pôr′tăl) *a.* [L. *porta*, gate.] *Appl.* a system of veins draining alimentary canal, spleen, and pancreas to the liver; also a system to kidney in lower vertebrates.

portio (pôr′tĭō, pôr′shĭō) *n.* [L. *portio*, portion.] A part or portion of a nerve, blood-vessel, etc.

position-effect, — effect due to relative position of a gene or genes within the chromosome.

positive tropism,—tendency to move towards a source of stimulus.

postabdomen (pōst′ăbdō′mĕn) *n.* [L. *post*, after; *abdomen*, belly.] In scorpions, metasoma or posterior narrower five segments of abdomen; anal tubercle in spiders.

postanal (pōstā′năl) *a.* [L. *post*, after; *anus*, vent.] Situated behind anus.

postantennal (pōstăntĕn′ăl) *a.* [L. *post*, after; *antenna*, sail-yard.] Situated behind antennae; *appl.* a sensory organ in Myriopoda and Collembola, organ of Tömösvary.

postaxial (pōstăk′sĭăl) *a.* [L. *post*, after; *axis*, axle.] On posterior side of axis; as on fibular side of leg.

postbacillary (pōst′băsĭl′ărĭ) *a.* [L. *post*, after; *bacillum*, small staff.] Having nuclei behind sensory zone of retinal cells; *appl.* ocellus, inverted eye, as of spiders. *Opp.* prebacillary.

postbranchial (pōstbrăng′kĭăl) *a.* [L. *post*, after; *branchiae*, gills.] Behind gill-clefts; *appl.* a structure arising in pharynx; *appl.* bodies: the ultimobranchial bodies.

postcardinal (pōstkâr′dĭnăl) *a.* [L. *post*, after; Gk. *kardia*, heart.] Behind region of heart; *appl.* a dorsal vein.

postcava (pōstkā′vă) *n.* [L. *post*, after; *cavus*, hollow.] The inferior or posterior vena cava of vertebrates above fishes; postcaval vein.

postcentral (pōstsĕn′trăl) *a.* [L. *post*, after; *centrum*, centre.] Behind central region; *appl.* a cerebral sulcus, part of intraparietal sulcus.

postcentrum (pōstsĕn′trŭm) *n.* [L. *post*, after; *centrum*, centre.] The posterior part of vertebral centrum of certain vertebrates.

postcerebral (pōstsĕr′ĕbrăl) *a.* [L. *post*, after; *cerebrum*, brain.] Posterior to the brain; *appl.* cephalic salivary glands, as in Hymenoptera.

postclavicle (pōstklăv′ĭkl) *n.* [L. *post*, after; *clavicula*, small key.] A membrane bone occurring in shoulder girdle of some higher ganoids and teleosts; also postcleithrum.

postclitellian (pōst′klĭtĕl′ĭăn) *a.* [L. *post*, after; *clitellae*, pack-saddle.] Situated behind clitellum.

postclival (pōstklī′văl) *a.* [L. *post*, after; *clivus*, hill.] *Appl.* fissure behind clivus of cerebellum.

postclypeus (pōstklĭp′ĕŭs) *n.* [L. *post*, after; *clypeus*, shield.] The posterior part of clypeus of an insect; *cf.* anteclypeus.

postcolon (pōst′kōlŏn) *n.* [L. *post*, after; *colon*, colon.] Part of gut between colon and rectum in certain mites.

postcornual (pōstkôr′nŭăl) *a.* [L. *post*, after; *cornu*, horn.] *Appl.* glands situated behind horns, as in chamois.

postcranial (pōstkrā′nĭăl) *a.* [L. *post*, after; *cranium*, skull.] *Appl.* area of posterior head region.

postdicrotic (pōst′dīkrŏt′ĭk) *a.* [L. *post*, after; Gk. *dis*, twice; *krotein*, to beat.] *Appl.* a secondary wave of a pulse, or that succeeding the dicrotic.

postembryonic (pōst′ĕmbrĭŏn′ĭk) *a.* [L. *post*, after; Gk. *embryon*, foetus.] *Pert.* the age or stages succeeding the embryonic.

posterior (pŏstē′rĭŏr) *a.* [L. *posterior*, latter.] Situated behind or dorsally; behind the axis; superior, or next the axis.

posterolateral (pŏs′tĕrōlăt′ĕrăl) *a*. [L. *posterus*, following; *latus*, side.] Placed posteriorly and towards the side; *appl*. arteries.

posteromedial (pŏs′tĕrōmē′dĭăl) *a*. [L. *posterus*, following; *medius*, middle.] Placed posteriorly and medianly; *appl*. arteries.

postesophageal,—postoesophageal.

postflagellate (pōstflăj′ĕlāt) *a*. [L. *post*, after; *flagellum*, lash.] *Appl*. forms of trypanosome intermediate between flagellates and cyst.

postfrons (pōstfrŏns) *n*. [L. *post*, after; *frons*, forehead.] Portion of frons posterior to antennary base line in insects.

postfrontal (pōstfrŭn′tăl) *a*. [L. *post*, after; *frons*, forehead.] *Appl*. a bone occurring behind orbit of some vertebrates.

postfurca (pōstfŭr′kă) *n*. [L. *post*, after; *furca*, fork.] A posterior sternal furca of an insect.

postganglionic (pōstgăng′glĭŏn′ĭk) *a*. [L. *post*, after; Gk. *ganglion*, tumour.] *Appl*. autonomic nerve-fibres issuing from ganglia; *cf*. preganglionic.

postgena (pōstjĕn′ă) *n*. [L. *post*, after; *gena*, cheek.] Posterior portion of insect gena.

postglenoid (pōstglē′noid) *a*. [L. *post*, after; Gk. *glene*, socket.] Behind the glenoid fossa; *appl*. a process or tubercle.

posthepatic (pōst′hēpăt′ĭk) *a*. [L. *post*, after; Gk. *hepar*, liver.] *Appl*. latter part of alimentary canal, that from liver to end.

postheterokinesis (pōsthĕt′ĕrōkĭnē′sĭs) *n*. [L. *post*, after; Gk. *heteros*, other; *kinesis*, movement.] Case of meiosis in which the sex-chromosome passes undivided to one pole in the second spermatocyte division.

posticous (pŏstī′kŭs, pŏs′tĭkŭs) *a*. [L. *posticus*, behind.] On outer or posterior surface; extrorse; postical.

postischium (pōstĭs′kĭŭm) *n*. [L. *post*, after; Gk. *ischion*, hip.] A lateral process on hinder side of ischium of some reptiles.

postlabrum (pōstlā′brŭm) *n*. [L. *post*, after; *labrum*, lip.] Posterior portion of insect labrum, where differentiated.

postmentum (pōst′mĕntŭm) *n*. [L. *post*, after; *mentum*, chin.] The united cardines constituting the base of labium of insects.

postminimus (pōstmĭn′ĭmŭs) *n*. [L. *post*, after; *minimus*, smallest.] A rudimentary additional digit occurring occasionally in amphibians and mammals.

postmitotic (pōstmĭtŏt′ĭk) *n*. [L. *post*, after; Gk. *mitos*, thread.] A cell with individual life originating in mitosis and ending at death; *cf*. intermitotic.

postneural (pōstnū′răl) *a*. [L. *post*, after; Gk. *neuron*, nerve.] Pygal, *appl*. plates of chelonian carapace.

postnodular (pōstnŏd′ūlăr) *a*. [L. *post*, after; *nodulus*, small knot.] *Appl*. a cerebellar fissure between nodule and uvula.

postnotum (pōstnō′tŭm) *n*. [L. *post*, after; Gk. *noton*, back.] Postscutellum.

postoesophageal (pōst′ēsŏfăj′ēal) *a*. [L. *post*, after; Gk. *oisophagos*, gullet.] *Appl*. commissure connecting ganglia of tritocerebrum; postesophageal.

postoral (pōst′ōrăl) *a*. [L. *post*, after; *os*, mouth.] Behind the mouth; *appl*. appendages of arthropods. *Opp*. preoral.

postorbital (pōstôr′bĭtăl) *a*. [L. *post*, after; *orbis*, circle.] Behind the orbit; *appl*. bone forming part of posterior wall of orbit; *appl*. luminescent organ in certain fishes.

postotic (pōstō′tĭk) *a*. [L. *post*, after; Gk. *ous*, ear.] Behind the ear; *appl*. a system of nerves.

postparietal (pōst′părī′ĕtăl) *a*. [L. *post*, after; *paries*, wall.] *Appl*. paired bones sometimes occurring between parietal and interparietal.

postpatagium (pōst′pătăj′ĭŭm) *n*. [L. *post*, after; *patagium*, border.] In birds, small fold of skin extending between upper arm and trunk.

postpermanent (pōstpĕr'mănĕnt) *a.* [L. *post*, after; *permanens*, remaining.] *Appl.* traces of a dentition succeeding the permanent.

postphragma (pōstfrăg'mă) *n.* [L. *post*, after; *phragma*, fence.] A phragma developed in relation with a postnotum in insects.

postpituitary (pōst'pĭtū'ĭtărĭ) *a.* [L. *post*, after; *pituita*, phlegm.] *Pert.* or secreted by posterior lobe of the hypophysis or pituitary gland.

postpubic (pōstpū'bĭk) *a.* [L. *post*, after; *pubes*, adult.] At posterior end of pubis; *appl.* processes of pubis parallel to ischium.

postpubis (pōstpū'bĭs) *n.* [L. *post*, after; *pubes*, adult.] A ventral process or bone of pelvic girdle in some Sauropsida.

postpyramidal (pōst'pĭrăm'ĭdăl) *a.* [L. *post*, after; *pyramis*, pyramid.] Behind the pyramid; *appl.* a cerebellar fissure.

postretinal (pōstrĕt'ĭnăl) *a.* [L. *post*, after; *retina*, from *rete*, net.] Situated behind the retina; *appl.* nerve fibres connecting periopticon and inner ends of ommatidia.

postscutellum (pōst'skūtĕl'ŭm) *n.* [L. *post*, after; *scutellum*, small shield.] A projection under mesoscutellar lobe of insects, the base of mesophragma; sclerite behind scutellum; postnotum, pseudonotum.

postsegmental (pōst'sĕgmĕn'tăl) *a.* [L. *post*, after; *segmentum*, piece.] Posterior to body segments or somites, *opp.* presegmental.

postsphenoid (pōstsfē'noid) *n.* [L. *post*, after; Gk. *sphen*, wedge; *eidos*, form.] The posterior part of sphenoid.

poststernellum (pōst'stërnĕl'ŭm) *n.* [L. *post*, after; *sternum*, breastbone.] Most posterior portion of an insect sternite.

poststernite (pōststĕr'nīt) *n.* [L. *post*, after; *sternum*, breast-bone.] Posterior sternal sclerite of insects; sternellum.

post-temporal (pōst-tĕm'pŏrăl) *a.* [L. *post*, after; *tempora*, temples.] Behind temporal bone; *appl.* bone and fossa.

post-trematic (pōst-trēmăt'ĭk) *a.* [L. *post*, after; Gk. *trema*, hole.] Post-branchial; *appl.* nerves running in posterior wall of first gill cleft to pharynx.

postzygapophysis (pōst'zĭgăpŏf'ĭsĭs) *n.* [L. *post*, after; Gk. *zygon*, yoke; *apo*, from; *physis*, growth.] An articular process on posterior face of neural arch for articulation with following vertebra.

potamoplankton (pŏt'ămöplăngk'tŏn) *n.* [Gk. *potamos*, river; *plangktos*, wandering.] The plankton of streams and their backwaters.

potential (pötĕn'shăl) *a.* [L. *potens*, powerful.] Latent, as *appl.* characteristics.

pouch (powch) *n.* [O.F. *poche*, bag.] A bag-like structure; a sac or bladder, as pharyngeal pouches, marsupial pouch; a pod.

Poupart's ligament [*F. Poupart*, French anatomist]. The inguinal ligament.

powder - down feathers, — those which do not develop beyond the early stage, and in which the tips of barbs disintegrate into powder.

prae-,—*also* pre-.

praeabdomen (prē'ăbdō'mĕn) *n.* [L. *prae*, before; *abdomen*, belly.] The anterior, broader part of abdomen of scorpions; mesosoma.

prae-auricular (prē'ôrĭk'ūlăr) *a.* [L. *prae*, before; *auricula*, small ear.] *Appl.* a sulcus at anterior part of auricular surface of hip-bone.

praeaxial (prēăk'sĭăl) *a.* [L. *prae*, before; *axis*, axle.] On anterior border or surface.

praecentrum (prēsĕn'trŭm) *n.* [L. *prae*, before; *centrum*, centre.] The anterior part of the vertebral centrum of certain lower vertebrates.

praecoces (prēkō'sēz) *n. plu.* [L. *prae*, before; *coquere*, to cook.] Newly-hatched birds able to take care of themselves; *cf.* altrices.

praecostal (prēkŏs'tăl) *a.* [L. *prae*, before; *costa*, rib.] *Appl.* short spurs on basal portion of hind wing of Lepidoptera.

praecoxa (prēkŏk'să) *n.* [L. *prae*, before; *coxa*, hip.] Subcoxa.

praecrural (prēkroor'ăl) *a.* [L. *prae*, before; *crus*, leg.] On anterior side of leg or thigh.

praecuneus (prēkū'nëŭs) *n.* [L. *prae*, before; *cuneus*, wedge.] The medial surface of parietal lobe, or quadrate lobe of cerebrum.

praemorse (prēmôrs') *a.* [L. *praemorsus*, bitten off.] With irregular and abrupt termination, as if end were bitten off; premorse.

praeoccipital (prē'ŏksĭp'ĭtăl) *a.* [L. *prae*, before; *occiput*, back of head.] *Appl.* an indentation or notch in front of posterior end of cerebral hemispheres; pre-occipital.

praeoral (prēō'răl) *a.* [L. *prae*, before; *os*, mouth.] *Pert.* part of body of a larva anterior to mouth; *appl.* process, loop, lobe, ciliated rings; preoral.

praepubic (prēpū'bĭk) *a.* [L. *prae*, before; *pubes*, mature.] On anterior part of pubis; *appl.* elongated processes of pubis of certain vertebrates.

praeputial (prēpū'shĭăl) *a.* [L. *praeputium*, foreskin.] *Pert.* the praepuce; *appl.* glands, sac; preputial.

praeputium (prēpū'shĭŭm) *n.* [L. *praeputium*, foreskin.] Foreskin; part of integument of penis which leaves surface at neck and is folded upon itself; prepuce; fold of labia minora over glans clitoridis.

praescutum (prēskū'tŭm) *n.* [L. *prae*, before; *scutum*, shield.] The anterior part of notum of an insect thoracic ring.

praesphenoid (prēsfē'noid) *n.* [L. *prae*, before; Gk. *sphen*, wedge.] The anterior part of sphenoid.

praesternal (prēstĕr'năl) *a.* [L. *prae*, before; *sternum*, breast-bone.] *Appl.* jugular notch, on superior border of sternum.

praetarsus (prētâr'sŭs) *n.* [L. *prae*, before; *tarsus*, ankle.] Terminal outgrowth on tarsus of insects and spiders.

pratal (prā'tăl) *a.* [L. *pratum*, meadow.] *Pert.* meadows; *appl.* flora of rich humid grass-lands.

pre-,—*also* prae-.

preadaptation (prē'ădăptā'shŭn) *n.* [L. *prae*, before; *ad*, to; *aptare*, to fit.] Constitutional predisposition of an organism to fit into a different environment; adaptation of a mutant to particular conditions.

pre-anal (prēā'năl) *a.* [L. *prae*, before; L. *anus*, anus.] Anterior to anus; *appl.* commissures, in Nematoda.

preantenna (prē'ăntĕn'ă) *n.* [L. *prae*, before; *antenna*, sail-yard.] One of the pair of feelers on the first segment in Onychophora.

pre-axial (prēăk'sĭăl) *a.* [L. *prae*, before; *axis*, axle.] In front of the axis.

prebacillary (prē'băsĭl'ărĭ) *a.* [L. *prae*, before; *bacillum*, small staff.] Having nuclei distal to sensory zone of retinal cells; *appl.* ocellus, converted or erect eye, as of spiders. *Opp.* postbacillary.

prebasilare (prē'băzĭlā'rē) *n.* [L. *prae*, before; *basis*, base.] Transverse sclerite between mentum of gnathochilarium and first body sternite, in certain Diplopoda.

precapillary (prē-kăpĭl'ărĭ) *a.* [L. *prae*, before; *capillus*, hair.] *Appl.* arterioles having an incomplete muscular layer.

precartilage (prē'kârtĭ'lĕj) *n.* [L. *prae*, before; *cartilago*, gristle.] Type of cartilage preceding formation of other kinds, or persisting as in fin rays of certain fishes.

precava (prēkā'vă) *n.* [L. *prae*, before; *cavus*, hollow.] The superior or anterior vena cava; precaval vein.

precentral (prēsĕn'trăl) *a.* [L. *prae*, before; *centrum*, centre.] Anteriorly to centre; *appl.* a sulcus parallel to central sulcus of cerebrum; *appl.* gyrus.

precheliceral (prē'kēlĭs'ĕral) *a* [L., *prae*, before; *chele*, claw; *keras*. horn.] Anterior to chelicerae; *appl*. segment of mouth region or gnathosoma in Arachnoidea.

prechordal (prēkôr'dăl) *a*. [L. *prae*, before; Gk. *chorde*, cord.] Anteriorly to notochord or spinal cord; *appl*. part of base of skull.

precipitins, — specific antibodies in immune serum which form precipitates with their respective antigens; *e.g*. bacterio-, haemato-, lacto-, myco-, phyto-, zooprecipitin.

preclavia (prēklā'vĭă) *n*. [L. *prae*, before; *clavis*, key.] An element of pectoral girdle.

preclimax (prēklī'măks) *n*. [L. *prae*, before; Gk. *klimax*, ladder.] The plant community immediately preceding the climax community; *cf*. proclimax.

preclival (prēklī'văl) *a*. [L. *prae*, before; *clivus*, hill.] *Appl*. fissure in front of clivus of cerebellum.

precoracoid (prēkŏr'ăkoid) *n*. [L. *prae*, before; Gk. *korax*, crow.] An anterior ventral bone of pectoral girdle.

precoxa,—subcoxa, *q.v*.

precursor (prēkŭr'sŏr) *n*. [L. *praecursor*, forerunner.] The substance which precedes the formation of a compound.

precystic (prēsĭs'tĭk) *a*. [L. *prae*, before; Gk. *kystis*, bladder.] *Appl*. small forms appearing before the encystment stage in some protozoa.

predelineation (prē'dēlĭnēā'shŭn) *n*. [L. *prae*, before; *de*, down; *linea*, line.] Formation and individualisation of various physiological molecules in definite areas and substances of undeveloped egg,—theory of germinal localisation.

predentary (prēdĕn'tărĭ) *n*. [L. *prae*, before; *dens*, tooth.] A bone at tip of jaw of many dinosaurs.

predentin (prēdĕn'tĭn) *n*. [L. *prae*, before; *dens*, tooth.] Substance of fibrils or Korff's fibres which changes into dentin.

predigital (prēdĭj'ĭtăl) *n*. [L. *prae*, before; *digitus*, finger.] A primary wing-quill connected with distal phalanx of second digit.

pre-epistome (prēĕp'ĭstōm) *n*. [L. *prae*, before; Gk. *epi*, upon; *stoma*, mouth.] A plate covering basal portion of epistome of certain Arachnoidea.

prefemur (prē'fēmŭr) *n*. [L. *prae*, before; *femur*, thigh.] Second trochanter, as in walking legs of Pycnogonida.

preflagellate (prēflăj'ĕlāt) *a*. [L. *prae*, before; *flagellum*, lash.] *Appl*. forms of trypanosomes intermediate between cyst and elongate flagellates.

prefloration (prē'flōrā'shŭn) *n*. [L. *prae*, before; *flos*, flower.] The form and arrangement of floral leaves in the flower-bud; ptyxis and aestivation.

prefoliation (prē'fōlĭā'shŭn) *n*. [L. *prae*, before; *folium*, leaf.] The form and arrangement of foliage leaves in the bud; ptyxis and vernation.

preformation theory,—theory according to which it was supposed that each ovum of an animal contained a miniature adult, and that nourishment only was required to develop it into the perfect forms.

prefrontal (prēfrŭn'tăl) *a*. [L. *prae*, before; *frons*, forehead.] *Appl*. a bone anterior to frontal of certain vertebrates; *appl*. paired plates or scales anterior to frontal scale in some reptiles.

pregammation (prē'gămā'shŭn) *n*. [L. *prae*, before; *gammation*, *dim*. of Γ.] A bar in front of the gammation in Palaeospondylus.

preganglionic (prēgăng'glĭŏn'ĭk) *a*. [L. *prae*, before; Gk. *ganglion*, tumour.] *Appl*. medullated fibres from spinal cord, ending in synapses around sympathetic ganglion cells.

pregenital (prējĕn'ĭtăl) *a*. [L. *prae*, before; *genitalis*, *pert*. generation.] Situated anterior to genital opening; *appl*. segment behind fourth pair of walking legs in Arachnoidea.

preglobulin (prēglŏb'ūlĭn) *n.* [L. *prae*, before ; *globulus*, small globe.] A compound proteid of white blood corpuscles.

pregnancy cells,—modified oxyphil cells of anterior lobe of hypophysis, multiplying during pregnancy.

prehallux (prēhăl'ŭks) *n.* [L. *prae*, before ; *hallux*, great toe.] A rudimentary additional digit on hind limb.

prehalteres (prēhăl'tērēz) *n. plu.* [L. *prae*, before ; Gk. *halter*, weight.] The squamae of Diptera.

prehaustorium (prē'hôstō'rĭŭm) *n.* [L. *prae*, before ; *haurire*, to drink.] A rudimentary root-like sucker.

prehensile (prēhĕn'sīl) *a.* [L. *prehendere*, to seize.] Adapted for holding, as a suctorial tentacle.

prehepatic (prē'hēpăt'ĭk) *a.* [L. *prae*, before; Gk. *hepar*, liver.] *Appl.* part of digestive tract anterior to liver.

preheterokinesis (prēhĕt'ĕrŏkĭnē'sĭs) *n.* [L. *prae*, before ; Gk. *heteros*, other ; *kinesis*, movement.] Case of meiosis in which the sex-chromosome passes undivided to one pole in the first spermatocyte division.

prehyoid (prēhī'oid) *a.* [L. *prae*, before ; Gk. *hyoeides*, Υ-shaped.] Mandibulo-hyoid ; *appl.* cleft between mandible and ventral parts of hyoid arch.

preinterparietal (prēĭn'tĕrpărī'ĕtăl) *n.* [L. *prae*, before ; *inter*, between ; *paries*, wall.] One of two small upper membranous centres of formation of supraoccipital.

prelacteal (prēlăk'tēăl) *a.* [L. *prae*, before ; *lac*, milk.] *Pert.* a dentition which may occur previous to the milk dentition.

prelocalisation (prēlō'kălīzā'shŭn) *n.* [L. *prae*, before ; *locus*, place.] The theory that certain portions of ovum are predestined to develop into certain organs or parts.

premandibular (prē'măndĭb'ūlăr) *a.* [L. *prae*, before ; *mandibulum*, jaw.] Anterior to mandible ; *appl.* somites of Amphioxus ; *appl.* a bone of certain reptiles.

premaxilla (prē'măksĭl'ă) *n.* [L. *prae*, before ; *maxilla*, jaw.] A paired bone anterior to maxilla in most vertebrates ; os incisivum.

premaxillary (prē'măksĭl'ărĭ) *a.* [L. *prae*, before ; *maxilla*, jaw.] Anterior to maxilla ; *pert.* premaxilla.

premedian (prēmē'dĭăn) *a.* [L. *prae*, before ; *medius*, middle.] Anterior to middle of body or part ; *appl.* a head-plate in certain primitive fishes ; *appl.* vein in front of median vein of certain insect wings.

prementum (prē'mĕntŭm) *n.* [L. *prae*, before ; *mentum*, chin.] The united stipites bearing ligula and labial palps of insects.

premolar (prēmō'lăr) *a.* [L. *prae*, before ; *mola*, mill.] *Appl.* teeth developed between canines and molars, bicuspid teeth.

premorse,—praemorse.

prenasal (prēnā'zăl) *a.* [L. *prae*, before ; *nasus*, nose.] *Appl.* a bone developed in septum in front of mesethmoid in certain skulls ; rostral.

preocular (prēŏk'ūlăr) *a.* [L. *prae*, before ; *oculus*, eye.] Anterior to the eye, as antennae, scales.

preopercular (prē'ŏpĕr'kūlăr) *a.* [L. *prae*, before ; *operculum*, cover.] Anterior to gill-cover ; *appl.* luminescent organ in certain fishes ; *appl.* bone : the preoperculum.

preoperculum (prē'ŏpĕr'kūlŭm) *n.* [L. *prae*, before ; *operculum*, cover.] Anterior membrane bone of operculum or gill-cover ; preopercle.

preoptic nerve,—nervus terminalis or terminal nerve, *q.v.*

preoral (prēō'răl) *a.* [L. *prae*, before ; *os*, mouth.] Situated in front of mouth ; *appl.* cilia, etc. ; *appl.* food cavity, the anterior part of the 'buccal cavity,' between labrum, prementum and mandibles, in insects.

preorbital (prēôr'bĭtăl) *a.* [L. *prae*, before ; *orbis*, circle.] Anterior to orbit ; *appl.* a membrane bone of teleosts ; *appl.* glands in ruminants.

preparietal (prēpărī'ĕtăl) *n.* [L. *prae*, before; *paries*, wall.] A bone in front of parietals in some extinct reptiles.

prepatagium (prēpătăj'ĭŭm) *n.* [L. *prae*, before; *patagium*, border.] The alar membrane, or fold of skin extending between upper arm and forearm of birds.

prepatellar (prē'pătĕl'ăr) *a.* [L. *prae*, before; *patella*, knee-pan.] *Appl.* bursa between lower part of patella and the skin.

prepenna (prēpĕn'ă) *n.* [L. *prae*, before; *penna*, feather.] A nestling down feather which is succeeded by adult contour feather; protoptile and mesoptile.

prepharynx (prēfăr'ĭngks) *n.* [L. *prae*, before; Gk. *pharyngx*, gullet.] Narrow thin-walled structure connecting oral sucker and pharynx, in trematodes.

prephragma (prēfrăg'mă) *n.* [L. *prae*, before; Gk. *phragma*, fence.] A phragma developed in relation with the notum of insects.

prepituitary (prē'pĭtū'ĭtărĭ) *n.* [L. *prae*, before; *pituita*, phlegm.] Anterior lobe of the pituitary gland; prehypophysis.

preplacental (prē'plăsĕn'tăl) *a.* [L. *prae*, before; *placenta*, flat cake.] Occurring before placenta formation or development.

preplumula (prēploom'ūlă) *n.* [L. *prae*, before; *plumula*, small feather.] A nestling down feather which is succeeded by adult down feather.

prepollex (prēpŏl'ĕks) *n.* [L. *prae*, before; *pollex*, thumb.] A rudimentary additional digit occurring sometimes preaxially to thumb of certain amphibians and mammals.

prepotency (prēpō'tĕnsĭ) *n.* [L. *prae*, before; *potens*, powerful.] The fertilisation of a flower by pollen from another flower in preference to pollen from its own stamens, when both are offered simultaneously; capacity of one parent to transmit more characteristics to offspring than the other parent.

prepotent (prēpō'tĕnt) *a.* [L. *prae*, before; *potens*, powerful.] Transmitting the majority of characteristics; *appl.* a flower exhibiting a preference for cross-pollination.

prepuberal (prēpū'bĕrăl) *a.* [L. *prae*, before; *pubes*, mature.] Anterior to pubis; prepubertal, *q.v.*

prepubertal (prēpū'bĕrtăl) *a.* [L. *prae*, before; *pubertas*, adult state.] *Pert.* age or state before puberty.

prepubic (prēpū'bĭk) *a.* [L. *prae*, before; *pubes*, mature.] *Pert.* prepubis; *appl.* processes of pelvic arch, in certain fishes.

prepubis (prēpū'bĭs) *n.* [L. *prae*, before; *pubes*, mature.] Part of pelvic girdle of certain reptiles, anterior to os pubis.

prepuce,—praeputium, *q.v.*

prepupa (prēpū'pă) *n.* [L. *prae*, before; *pupa*, puppet.] A quiescent stage preceding the pupal in some insects.

preputial,—praeputial, *q.v.*

prepyloric (prē'pīlŏr'ĭk) *a.* [L. *prae*, before; *pyloros*, gate-keeper.] *Appl.* ossicle hinged to pyloric ossicle in gastric mill of Crustacea.

prepyramidal (prē'pĭrăm'ĭdăl) *a.* [L. *prae*, before; *pyramis*, pyramid.] In front of pyramid; *appl.* a cerebellar fissure; *appl.* tract, the rubrospinal fasciculus.

prescutum (prēskū'tŭm) *n.* [L. *prae*, before; *scutum*, shield.] Anterior sclerite of insect notum.

presegmental (prē'sĕgmĕn'tăl) *a.* [L. *prae*, before; *segmentum*, piece.] Anterior to body segments or somites, *opp.* postsegmental.

presentation-time,—minimum duration of continuous stimulation necessary for production of a response.

prespermatid (prēspĕr'mătĭd) *n.* [L. *prae*, before; Gk. *sperma*, seed.] Secondary spermatocyte.

presphenoid (prēsfē'noid) *n.* [L. *prae*, before; Gk. *sphen*, wedge.] In many vertebrates, a cranial bone anterior to the basisphenoid.

pressor (prĕs'ŏr) *a.* [L. *pressare*, to press.] Causing a rise of arterial pressure ; *appl.* stimuli, nervefibres.

pressure (prĕsh'ŭr) *n.* [L. *pressare*, to press.] Tension in plant tissue caused by turgidity of cells.

presternal (prēstĕr'năl) *a.* [L. *prae*, before ; *sternum*, breast-bone.] Situated in front of sternum or breast-bone ; *pert.* anterior part of sternum.

presternum (prēstĕr'nŭm) *n.* [L. *prae*, before ; *sternum*, breast-bone.] The manubrium or anterior part of sternum ; anterior sclerite of insect sternum.

presynaptic (prē'sĭnăp'tĭk) *a.* [L. *prae*, before ; Gk. *synapsis*, union.] *Appl.* vesicles liberating acetylcholine in terminal arborisation of an axon.

pretarsus (prētâr'sŭs) *n.* [L. *prae*, before ; Gk. *tarsos*, sole of foot.] Terminal part of leg, or claws, of insects and spiders.

pretrematic (prē'trēmăt'ĭk) *a.* [L. *prae*, before ; Gk. *trema*, hole.] Pre-branchial ; prespiracular ; *appl.* nerves running in anterior wall of first gill cleft to pharynx.

pretrochantin (prētrōkăn'tĭn) *n.* [L. *prae*, before ; Gk. *trochanter*, runner.] Subcoxa.

prevernal (prē'vĕrnăl) *a.* [L. *prae*, before ; *vernus*, spring.] *Pert.*, or appearing in, early spring.

prevertebral (prēvĕr'tēbrăl) *a.* [L. *prae*, before ; *vertebra*, vertebra.] *Pert.* or situated in region in front of vertebral column ; *appl.* portion of base of skull ; *appl.* ganglia of sympathetic system.

previtamin (prē'vītămĭn) *n.* [L. *prae*, before ; *vita*, life ; *Ammon.*] Precursor of a vitamin ; provitamin.

prevomer (prēvō'mĕr) *n.* [L. *prae*, before ; *vomer*, ploughshare.] A bone anterior to pterygoid in some vertebrates ; vomer of non-mammalian vertebrates ; in Monotremata, a membrane bone in floor of nasal cavities, the dumb-bell or paradoxical bone.

prezygapophysis (prēzĭg'ăpŏf'ĭsĭs) *n.* [L. *prae*, before ; Gk. *zygon*, yoke.] *apo*, from ; *physis*, growth.] A process on anterior face of neural arch, for articulation with vertebra in front.

prickle (prĭkl) *n.* [A.S. *pricu*, point.] A pointed process arising through epidermal tissue, as of bramble ; a modified trichome.

prickle-cells,—cells of deeper layers of stratified squamous epithelium, have short, fine, marginal connecting fibrils, prickle-like when broken.

primary (prī'mărĭ) *a.* [L. *primus*, first.] First ; principal ; original ; *appl.* axis, feathers, meristem, root, wood, etc. ; Palaeozoic.

primary centre,—part of central nervous system directly linked by nerve fibres with a peripheral organ.

primary meristem,—ground meristem, procambium, and protoderm ; *cf.* promeristem.

primary root,—radicle.

primaxil (prīmăk'sĭl) *n.* [L. *primus*, first ; *axilla*, armpit.] The first axillary arm of a crinoid.

primibrachs (prī'mĭbrăks) *n. plu.* [L. *primus*, first ; *brachia*, arms.] In crinoids, all brachials up to and including the first axillary.

primine (prī'mĭn) *n.* [L. *primus*, first.] The external integument of an ovule ; occasionally *appl.* first-formed or internal coat.

primite (prĭm'īt) *n.* [L. *primus*, first.] The first of any pair of individuals of a catenoid colony in pseudo-conjugation of Gregarinida, in which protomerite of one (the satellite) becomes attached to deutomerite of another (the primite).

primitive (prĭm'ĭtĭv) *a.* [L. *primitivus*, original.] Of earliest origin ; *appl.* groove, knot, streak, etc. ; *appl.* sheath, *i.e.* neurolemma.

primitive node,—area of proliferating cells in which the primitive streak begins, thickened anterior wall of primitive pit ; Hensen's node.

primitive pit,—enclosure at anterior end of the confluent primitive folds.

primitive plate,—floor of the primitive groove.

primitive streak,—two primary embryonic folds, between which lies the primitive groove.

primordial (prīmôr'dĭăl) *a.* [L. *primordium*, beginning.] Primitive; original; first commenced; first formed; *appl.* ova, cell, utricle, veil, etc.

primordium (prīmôr'dĭŭm) *n.* [L. *primordium*, beginning.] Original form; a structure when first indicating assumption of form; anlage.

priodont (prī'ödŏnt) *a.* [Gk. *prion*, saw; *odous*, tooth.] Saw-toothed; *appl.* stag-beetles with smallest development of mandible projections.

prisere (prī'sēr) *n.* [L. *primus*, first; *serere*, to put in a row.] Plant succession on area previously without vegetation; primary sere.

prismatic (prĭzmăt'ĭk) *a.* [L. *prisma*, prism.] Like a prism; *appl.* cells, leaves; consisting of prisms, as prismatic layer of shells.

pro-acrosome (prōăk'rösōm) *n.* [Gk. *pro*, before; *akros*, tip; *soma*, body.] Structure in spermatid, which develops into acrosome.

proamnion (prōăm'nĭŏn) *n.* [Gk. *pro*, before; *amnion*, foetal membrane.] An area of blastoderm in front of head of early embryos of higher vertebrates.

proandry (prōăn'drĭ) *n.* [Gk. *pro*, before; *aner*, male.] Meroandry with retention of anterior pair of testes only. *Opp.* metandry.

proangiosperm (prōăn'jĭöspërm) *n.* [Gk. *pro*, before; *anggeion*, vessel; *sperma*, seed.] A fossil type of angiosperm.

proatlas (prōăt'lăs) *n.* [Gk. *pro*, before; *Atlas*.] A median bone intercalated between atlas and skull in certain reptiles.

probasidium (prō'băsĭd'ĭŭm) *n.* [Gk. *pro*, before; *basis*, base; *idion*, *dim.*] A thick-walled resting spore, as of Uredinales, Ustilaginales, Auriculariales; the cell which gives rise to a heterobasidium; an immature basidium, before forming sterigmata or basidiospores.

proboscidiform (prōbŏs'-sĭd'ĭfôrm) *a.* [Gk. *proboskis*, trunk; L. *forma*, shape.] Proboscis-like; *appl.* infusorians with tentacles on a proboscis-like process.

proboscis (prōbŏs'sĭs) *n.* [Gk. *proboskis*, trunk.] A trunk-like process of head, as of insects, annelids, nemerteans, elephants.

probud,—a larval bud from the stolon in Doliolidae, which moves by pseudopodia to the cadophore and there divides to produce definitive buds.

procambial strand,—a longitudinal strand of elongated cells near periphery of plerome of a vascular bundle; desmogen strand.

procambium (prōkăm'bĭŭm) *n.* [L. *pro*, before; L.L. *cambium*, nutriment.] The tissue from which vascular bundles are developed.

procarp (prō'kârp) *n.* [Gk. *pro*, before *karpos*, fruit.] The female organ of red seaweeds, a one or more celled structure, consisting of the carpogonium, trichogyne, and auxiliary cells.

procartilage (prōkâr'tĭlēj) *n.* [L. *pro*, before; *cartilago*, gristle.] The early stage of cartilage.

procercoid (prōsĕr'koid] *n.* [Gk. *pro*, before; *kerkos*, tail; *eidos*. form.] Early larval form of certain cestodes in first intermediate host.

procerebrum (prōsĕr'ēbrŭm) *n.* [L. *pro*, before; *cerebrum*, brain.] The fore-brain, developed in preantennary region of insects.

procerus (prō'sērŭs) *n.* [Gk. *pro*, before; *keras*, horn.] Pyramidal muscle of the nose.

prochorion (prōkō'rĭŏn) *n.* [Gk. *pro*, before; *chorion*, skin.] An enveloping structure of blastodermic vesicle preceding formation of chorion.

prochromatin (prōkrō'mătĭn) *n.* [Gk. *pro*, before; *chroma*, colour.] Plasmosome substance; paranuclein, pyrenin, pseudochromatin.

prochromosome (prōkrō′mōsōm) *n.* [Gk. *pro*, before; *chroma*, colour; *soma*, body.] A discrete mass of basichromatin, primordium of the future chromosome.

proclimax (prō′klīmăks) *n.* [Gk. *pro*, before; *klimax*, ladder.] Stage in a sere appearing instead of usual climatic climax; *cf.* preclimax.

procoelous (prōsē′lŭs) *a.* [Gk. *pro*, before; *koilos*, hollow.] With concave anterior face, as vertebral centra.

procoracoid (prōkŏr′ăkoid) *n.* [Gk. *pro*, before; *korax*, crow; *eidos*, form.] An anteriorly directed process from glenoid fossa of urodeles.

procruscula (prōkrŭs′kūlă) *n. plu.* [L. *pro*, for; *dim.* of *crus*, leg.] A pair of blunt locomotory outgrowths on posterior half of a redia.

procrypsis (prōkrĭp′sĭs) *n.* [Gk. *pro*, for; *krypsis*, concealment.] Shape, pattern, colour, or behaviour tending to make animals less conspicuous in their normal environment; camouflage.

procryptic (prōkrĭp′tĭk) *a.* [Gk. *pro*, for; *kryptos*, hidden.] With coloration or pattern adapted for concealment.

proctal (prŏk′tăl) *a.* [Gk. *proktos*, anus.] Anal; *appl.* fish fins.

proctiger (prŏk′tĭjĕr) *n.* [Gk. *proktos*, anus; L. *gerere*, to bear.] Anal portion of terminalia in Diptera; anal lobe.

proctodaeum (prŏk′tōdē′ŭm) *n.* [Gk. *proktos*, anus; *hodos*, way.] The latter part of embryonic alimentary canal, formed by anal invagination; a similar ectoderm-lined part in certain invertebrates.

procumbent (prōkŭm′bĕnt) *a.* [L. *pro*, forward; *cumbens*, lying down.] Prostrate; trailing on the ground; *appl.* stems.

prodeltidium (prōdĕltĭd′ĭŭm) *n.* [Gk. *pro*, before; Δ, delta; *idion*, *dim.*] A plate which develops into a pseudodeltidium.

prodentine (prōdĕn′tĭn) *n.* [L. *pro*, before; *dens*, tooth.] A layer of uncalcified matrix capping tooth cusps before formation of dentine.

proembryo (prō′ĕm′brĭō) *n.* [Gk. *pro*, before; *embryon*, foetus.] An embryonic structure preceding true embryo; first results of spore segmentation.

proenzyme (prōĕn′zīm) *n.* [Gk. *pro*, before; *en*, in; *zyme*, leaven.] Zymogen.

proepimeron (prō′ĕpĭmē′rŏn) *n.* [Gk. *pro*, before; *epi*, upon; *meros*, upper thigh.] A sclerite posterior to propleura; posterior pronotal lobe of Diptera.

proerythrocyte (prō′ĕrĭth′rōsīt) *n.* [Gk. *pro*, before; *erythros*, red; *kytos*, hollow.] An immature red blood corpuscle; pronormocyte, reticulocyte.

proeusternum (prō′ūstĕr′nŭm) *n.* [Gk. *pro*, before; *eu*, well; *sternon*, breastplate.] Sclerite between propleura, forming ventral part of prothorax in Diptera.

profunda (prŏfŭn′dă) *a.* [L. *profundus*, deep.] Deep-seated, *appl.* a branch of brachial, femoral, or costocervical artery, to the ranine artery, terminal part of lingual artery, and to a vein of femur. *n.* A deep artery or vein.

profundal,—*appl.* or *pert.* zone of deep water and bottom below compensation depth in lakes.

progamete (prō′gămēt) *n.* [Gk. *pro*, before; *gamos*, marriage.] A structure giving rise to gametes by abstriction, in certain fungi.

progamic (prōgăm′ĭk) *a.* [Gk. *pro*, before; *gamos*, marriage.] *Appl.* brood-division for gamete production.

progastrin (prōgăs′trĭn) *n.* [Gk. *pro*, before; *gaster*, stomach.] Precursor of gastric secretion in mucous membrane of stomach.

progenesis (prōjĕn′ēsĭs) *n.* [Gk. *pro*, before; *genesis*, origin.] The maturation of gametes before completion of body growth; *cf.* neoteny.

progeotropism (prōʹjēŏtʹrŏpĭzm) *n.* [Gk. *pro*, for; *ge*, earth; *trope*, turn.] Positive geotropism.

progestational (prōjĕstāʹshŏnăl) *a.* [L. *pro*, before; *gestare*, to bear.] *Appl.* phase of oestrous cycle during luteal and endometrial activity; *appl.* hormones controlling uterine cycle and preparing uterus for nidation.

progesterone (prōjĕsʹtĕrōn) *n.* [L. *pro*, before; *gestare*, to bear.] A crystalline steroid, $C_{21}H_{30}O_2$, pure progestational corpus luteum hormone or corporin, lutin, progestin, progestone.

progestin (prōjĕsʹtĭn) *n.* [L. *pro*, for; *gestare*, to bear.] Progestational hormone of corpus luteum containing progesterone; a brand of progesterone.

proglottides (prōglŏtʹĭdēz) *n. plu.* [Gk. *pro*, for; *glotta*, tongue.] The propagative body-segments of a tape-worm, formed by strobilisation from neck. *Sing.* proglottis.

prognathous (prŏgʹnăthŭs) *a.* [Gk. *pro*, forth; *gnathos*, jaw.] Having prominent or projecting jaws; with mouth-parts anterior, *opp.* hypognathous, *appl.* insects; with projecting anthers; prognathic.

progonal (prōgōʹnăl) *a.* [Gk. *pro*, before; *gonos*, begetting.] *Appl.* sterile anterior portion of genital ridge.

progoneate (prōgŏnʹēāt) *a.* [Gk. *pro*, before; *gone*, generation.] Having the genital aperture anteriorly, as on third segment behind head of Diplopoda. *Opp.* opisthogoneate.

prohaemocyte (prōhēʹmŏsīt) *n.* [Gk. *pro*, before; *haima*, blood; *kytos*, hollow.] A cell that develops into a haemocyte; a proleucocyte, *q.v.*

prohydrotropism (prōʹhīdrŏtʹrŏpĭzm) *n.* [Gk. *pro*, for; *hydor*, water; *trope*, turn.] Positive hydrotropism.

proiospory (prōĭŏsʹpŏrĭ) *n.* [Gk. *proios*, early; *sporos*, seed.] Premature development of spores; prospory.

projectile (prŏjĕkʹtĭl) *a.* [L. *pro*, forth; *jacere*, to throw.] Protrusible; that can be thrust forward.

projection (prŏjĕkʹshŭn) *n.* [L. *pro*, forth; *jacere*, to throw.] The referring of stimulations to end-organs of sense by means of connecting projection nerve-fibres; the throwing forth by a plant of pollen, spores, or seeds.

projicient (prŏjĭshʹĕnt) *a.* [L. *projiciens*, projecting.] *Appl.* sense organs reacting to distant stimuli, as light, sound.

prokaryocyte (prōkărʹĭŏsīt) *n.* [Gk. *pro*, before; *karyon*, nucleus; *kytos*, hollow.] A prorubricyte.

prolabium (prōlāʹbĭŭm) *n.* [L. *pro*, in front of; *labium*, lip.] Middle part of upper lip; *cf.* philtrum.

prolactin (prōlăkʹtĭn) *n.* [L. *pro*, for; *lac*, milk.] The lactogenic prepituitary hormone; luteotrophic hormone.

prolamines,—a class of proteins present in seeds of cereals.

prolan, — gonadotropic hormones occurring in various tissues and body-fluids during pregnancy in some mammals; prolan A stimulating ovarian follicles and male germ cells, prolan B being the luteinising hormone.

proleg (prōʹlĕg) *n.* [L. *pro*, for; M.E. *leg*, leg.] An unjointed abdominal appendage of arthropod larvae; propes.

proleucocyte (prōlūʹkŏsīt, -loo-) *n.* [Gk. *pro*, before; *leukos*, white; *kytos*, hollow.] A small leucocyte with basophil cytoplasm and large nuclei, and developing into macronucleocyte, in insects; leucoblast.

proliferate (prōlĭfʹĕrāt) *v.* [L. *proles*, offspring; *ferre*, to bear.] To reproduce repeatedly; to resume growth, of reproductive shoots.

proliferation (prōlĭfʹĕrāʹshŭn) *n.* [L. *proles*, offspring; *ferre*, to bear.] Prolification; increase by frequent and repeated reproduction.

proliferous (prŏlĭfʹĕrŭs) *a.* [L. *proles*, offspring; *ferre*, to bear.] Multiplying quickly; *appl.* bud-bearing leaves; developing supernumerary parts abnormally.

proline,—an amino acid convertible into ornithine, also a metabolic product of ornithine; $C_5H_9NO_2$.

proloculus (prōlŏk'ūlŭs) *n.* [L. *pro*, before; *loculus*, compartment.] First chamber, microspheric when formed by conjugation of swarm spores, megalospheric when formed asexually by fission, in polythalamous foraminifera.

promegaloblast (prōmĕg'ălōblăst) *n.* [Gk. *pro*, before; *megalos*, large; *blastos*, bud.] A cell which develops into a megaloblast; rubriblast.

promeristem (prōmĕr'ĭstĕm) *n.* [Gk. *pro*, before; *meristes*, divider.] Meristem of growing point, and primary meristems.

prometaphase (prō'mĕt'ăfāz) *n.* [Gk. *pro*, before; *meta*, after; *phasis*, appearance.] Stage between prophase and metaphase in mitosis and meiosis.

promitosis (prō'mĭtō'sĭs) *n.* [Gk. *pro*, before; *mitos*, thread.] A simple type of mitosis, exemplified in nuclei of protokaryon type; protomitosis, *q.v.*

promonocyte (prōmŏn'ösīt) *n.* [Gk. *pro*, before; *monos*, single; *kytos*, hollow.] A cell developed from a monoblast and developing into a monocyte.

promontory (prŏm'ŏntörĭ) *n.* [L. *pro*, forth; *mons*, mountain.] Prominence or projection, as of cochlea and sacrum.

promorphology (prō'môrfŏl'öjĭ) *n.* [Gk. *pro*, before; *morphe*, form; *logos*, discourse.] Morphology from the geometrical standpoint.

promotor (prōmō'tŏr) *n.* [L. *promovere*, to move forwards.] A protractor muscle, *opp.* remotor.

promuscis (prōmŭs'sĭs) *n.* [L. *promuscis*, proboscis.] The proboscis of Hemiptera.

promycelium (prō'mīsē'lĭŭm) *n.* [Gk. *pro*, before; *mykes*, mushroom.] Mycelium developing from a zygospore, itself giving rise to a sporangium or to sporidia; a protobasidium.

promyelocyte (prōmī'ëlösīt) *n.* [Gk. *pro*, before; *myelos*, marrow; *kytos*, hollow.] Amoeboid marrow cell which develops into a myelocyte or granulocyte.

pronate (prō'nāt) *a.* [L. *pronare*, to bend forward.] Prone; inclined.

pronation (prōnā'shŭn) *n.* [L. *pronare*, to bend forward.] Act by which palm of hand is turned downwards by means of pronator muscles; *cf.* supination.

pronephric (prōnĕf'rĭk) *n.* [Gk. *pro*, before; *nephros*, kidney.] *Pert.* or in region of pronephros; *appl.* duct, tubules.

pronephros (prōnĕf'rŏs) *n.* [Gk. *pro*, before; *nephros*, kidney.] The fore kidney of embryonic or larval life.

pronormocyte (prōnôr'mösīt) *n.* [Gk. *pro*, before; L. *norma*, rule; Gk. *kytos*, hollow.] An immature red blood corpuscle; proerythrocyte, reticulocyte.

pronotum (prōnō'tŭm) *n.* [Gk. *pro*, before; *noton*, back.] The dorsal part of prothorax of insects.

pronucleus (prōnū'klëŭs) *n.* [L. *pro*, before; *nucleus*, kernel.] Egg or sperm nucleus after maturation.

pronymph (prō'nĭmf) *n.* [L. *pro*, before; *nympha*, maiden.] The stage in metamorphosis of Diptera preceding nymph stage.

pro-oestrus (prō'ēstrŭs) *n.* [Gk. *pro*, before; *oistros*, gadfly.] Period of preparation for pregnancy; phase before oestrus or heat; pro-oestrum.

pro-ostracum (prōŏs'trăkŭm) *n.* [Gk. *pro*, before; *ostrakon*, shell.] The horny pen of a decapod dibranchiate shell or belemnite; anterior phragmocone.

prootic (prō'ōtĭk) *n.* [Gk. *pro*, before; *ous*, ear.] The anterior bone of otic capsule in vertebrates. *a. Pert.* a centre of ossification of petromastoid part of temporal bone.

propagative (prŏp'ăgātĭv) *a.* [L. *propagare*, to propagate.] Reproductive; *appl.* a cell, a phase, an individual of a colony.

propagulum (prŏpăg′ūlŭm) *n.* [L. *propagare*, to propagate.] A bud or shoot capable of developing into an adult; propagule.

propatagium,—prepatagium, *q.v.*

properithecium (prō′pĕrĭthē′sĭŭm) *n.* [Gk. *pro*, before; *peri*, around; *theke*, case.] A young perithecium which contains a single zygote giving rise ultimately to ascospores.

propes (prōpēs) *n.* [L. *pro*, before; *pes*, foot.] Proleg, *q.v.*

prophase (prō′fāz) *n.* [Gk. *pro*, before; *phasis*, appearance.] The preparatory changes, the first stage in mitosis, or in meiosis.

prophialide (prōfī′ălīd) *n.* [Gk. *pro*, before; *phiale*, bowl; *eidos*, form.] A hyphal structure or sporocladium giving rise to phialides.

prophloem,—protophloem, *q.v.*

prophototropism (prō′fōtŏt′rŏpĭzm) *n.* [Gk. *pro*, for; *phos*, light; *trope*, turn.] Positive phototropism.

prophyllum (prōfĭl′ŭm) *n.* [Gk. *pro*, before; *phyllon*, leaf.] A small bract or bracteole; first foliage leaf, at base of branch; prophyll.

proplastid (prōplăs′tĭd) *n.* [Gk. *pro*, before; *plastos*, formed; *idion*, *dim.*] An immature plastid, as in meristematic cells.

propleuron (prōploor′ŏn) *n.* [Gk. *pro*, before; *pleura*, side.] A lateral plate of prothorax of insects.

propneustic (prōnū′stĭk, -pnū-) *a.* [Gk. *pro*, before; *pnein*, to breathe.] With only prothoracic spiracles open for respiration.

propodeon (prōpō′dēŏn) *n.* [Gk. *pro*, before; *pous*, foot.] An abdominal segment in front of petiole or podeon, of Hymenoptera; otherwise the median segment, Latreille's segment, epinotum, propodeum.

propodite (prŏ′pŏdīt) *n.* [Gk. *pro*, before; *pous*, foot.] Foot segment sixth from body, in Malacostraca; tibia in spiders.

propodium (prōpō′dĭŭm) *n.* [Gk. *pro*, before; *pous*, foot.] The small anterior part of a molluscan foot.

propodosoma (prō′pŏdŏsō′mă) *n* [Gk. *pro*, before; *pous*, foot; *soma*, body.] Body region bearing first and second legs in Acarina.

propolis (prŏ′pŏlĭs) *n.* [Gk. *pro*, for; *polis*, city.] Resinous substance from buds or leaf axils of certain trees, utilised by worker bees to fasten comb portions and fill up crevices; bee-glue.

propons (prō′pŏnz) *n.* [L. *pro*, before; *pons*, bridge.] Alae pontis, delicate bands of white matter crossing anterior end of pyramid below pons Varolii; ponticulus.

proprioception (prō′prĭŏsĕp′shŭn) *n.* [L. *proprius*, one's own; *capere*, to take.] The reception of stimuli originating within the organism.

proprioceptor (prō′prĭŏsĕp′tŏr) *n.* [L. *proprius*, one's own; *capere*, to take.] A receptor in muscle, tendon, vestibule of internal ear, etc.

propriogenic (prō′prĭŏjĕn′ĭk) *a.* [L. *proprius*, one's own; *genus*, kind.] *Appl.* effectors other than muscle, or organs which are both receptors and effectors; *cf.* myogenic.

propriospinal (prō′prĭŏspī′năl) *a.* [L. *proprius*, one's own; *spina*, spine.] *Pert.* wholly to the spinal cord; *appl.* fibres, etc.

prop-roots,—adventitious aerial roots growing downwards from stem, as in mangrove and maize.

propterygium (prō′tĕrĭj′ĭŭm, prŏ′-ptĕrĭj′ĭŭm) *n.* [Gk. *pro*, before; *pterygion*, little wing.] The foremost of three basal cartilages supporting pectoral fin of elasmobranchs.

propulsive pseudopodium, — in some Neosporidia, a pseudopodium developed posteriorly which by its elongation pushes the body forward.

propupa (prōpū′pă) *n.* [L. *pro*, before; *pupa*, puppet.] Stage in insect metamorphosis preceding pupa stage; prepupa.

propygidium (prō′pījĭd′ĭŭm) *n.* [Gk. *pro*, before; *pygidion*, small rump.] The dorsal plate anterior to pygidium in Coleoptera.

prorachis (prōrā′kĭs) *n.* [Gk. *pro*, before; *rhachis*, spine.] The face of Pennatulacea which is sterile and coincides with asulcar aspect of terminal zooid.

proral (prō′răl) *a.* [Gk. *prora*, prow.] From front backwards; *appl.* jaw movement, as in rodents. *Opp.* palinal.

prorsad (prŏr′săd) *adv.* [L. *prorsus*, forwards; *ad*, to.] Anteriorly; forward.

prorsal (prŏr′săl) *a.* [L. *prorsus*, forwards.] Anterior.

prorubricyte (prōroob′rĭsīt) *n.* [L. *pro*, before; *ruber*, red; Gk. *kytos*, hollow vessel.] A basophil erythroblast.

proscapula (prōskăp′ūlă) *n.* [L. *pro*, before; *scapula*, shoulder-blade.] The clavicle.

proscolex (prōskō′lěks) *n.* [Gk. *pro*, before; *skolex*, worm.] A rounded cyst with fluid-filled cavity, a stage in development of tapeworm.

prosecretin (prō′sēkrē′tĭn) *n.* [L. *pro*, before; *secretus*, separated.] The precursor of secretin; prosecretine.

prosencephalisation (prŏs′ěnkěf′ălīzā′shŭn,-sěf-) *n.* [Gk. *pros*, before; *engkephalos*, brain.] The progressive shifting of controlling centres towards the fore-brain and the increasing complexity of cerebral cortex in the course of evolution.

prosencephalon (prŏs′ěnkěf′ălŏn, -sěf-) *n.* [Gk. *pros*, before; *engkephalos*, brain.] The fore-brain, comprising telencephalon and diencephalon; the first primary brain-vesicle.

prosenchyma (prŏsěng′kĭmă) *n.* [Gk. *pros*, near; *engchyma*, infusion.] Tissue of prosenchymatous cells.

prosenchymatous (prŏs′ěngkĭm′ătŭs) *a.* [Gk. *pros*, near; *engchyma*, infusion.] *Appl.* elongated pointed cells, with thin or thick cell-walls, as in mechanical and vascular tissues of plants. *Opp.* parenchymatous.

prosethmoid (prŏsěth′moid) *n.* [Gk. *pros*, near; *ethmos*, sieve; *eidos*, form.] An anterior cranial bone of teleosts.

prosicula (prōsĭk′ūlă) *n.* [L. *pro*, before; *sicula*, small dagger.] Distal part of sicula, bearing the nema in graptolites.

prosiphon (prōsī′fŏn) *n.* [Gk. *pro*, for; *siphon*, tube.] A spout-like prolongation of edges of mantle-flaps of certain molluscs; endosiphuncle.

prosocoel (prŏs′ŏsēl) *n.* [Gk. *proso*, forward; *koilos*, hollow.] A narrow cavity in epistome of Molluscoidea, the first main part of coelom; median cavity between third and lateral ventricles of brain; interventricular foramen.

prosodetic (prŏs′ŏdět′ĭk) *a.* [Gk. *prosodos*, advance.] Anterior to beak; *appl.* certain bivalve ligaments.

prosodus (prŏs′ŏdŭs) *n.* [Gk. *prosodos*, advance.] A delicate canalicule between chamber and incurrent canal in some sponges.

prosoma (prōsō′mă) *n.* [Gk. *pro*, before; *soma*, body.] The anterior part of body; a cephalothorax.

prosopyle (prŏs′ŏpīl) *n.* [Gk. *proso*, forward; *pyle*, gate.] The aperture of communication between adjacent incurrent and flagellate canals in some sponges.

prosorus (prō′sōrŭs) *n.* [Gk. *pro*, before; *soros*, heap.] The cell from which a sorus or group of sporangia is derived.

prospory (prō′spŏrĭ) *n.* [Gk. *pro*, before; *sporos*, seed.] Precocious development of sporangia; seed production in plants that are not fully developed.

prostalia (prŏstā′lĭă) *n. plu.* [L. *pro*, forth; *stare*, to stand.] Projecting spicules of Hexactinellida.

prostate (prŏs′tāt) *a.* [L. *pro*, before; *stare*, to stand.] *Appl.* a muscular and glandular organ around commencement of male urethra in pelvic cavity. *n.* The prostate gland; the spermiducal gland in annelids.

prostatic (prŏstăt'ĭk) *a.* [L. *pro*, before; *stare*, to stand.] *Pert.* prostate gland; *appl.* duct, nerve, sinus, utricle, hormone, etc.

prostemmate (prōstĕm'āt) *a.* [Gk. *pro*, before; *stemma*, wreath.] *Appl.* an ante-ocular structure or organ of some Collembola, of doubtful function; prostemmatic.

prosternum (prōstĕr'nŭm) *n.* [L. *pro*, before; *sternum*, breast-bone.] Ventral part of prothorax of insects; presternum, *q.v.*; ventral part of cheliceral segment in Arachnoidea.

prostheca (prŏsthē'kă) *n.* [Gk. *prostheke*, appendage.] Movable inner lobe of mandibles in certain beetle larvae.

prosthetic (prŏsthĕt'ĭk) *a.* [Gk. *prosthetos*, added.] *Appl.* non-protein constituent of a conjugated or compound protein.

prosthion (prŏs'thĭŏn) *n.* [Gk. *prosthios*, foremost.] The alveolar point, middle point of the upper alveolar arch.

prosthomere (prŏs'thŏmēr) *n.* [Gk. *prosthen*, forward; *meros*, part.] Most anterior or preoral somite.

prostomiate (prōstŏm'ĭāt) *a.* [Gk. *pro*, before; *stoma*, mouth.] Having a portion of head in front of mouth.

prostomium (prōstō'mĭŭm) *n.* [Gk. *pro*, before; *stoma*, mouth.] In worms and molluscs, part of head anterior to mouth.

prostrate (prŏs'trāt) *a.* [L. *prostratus*, thrown down.] Procumbent; trailing on the ground.

protamines,—simple basic proteins occurring in fish testes.

protandrism (prōtăn'drĭzm) *n.* [Gk. *protos*, first; *aner*, male.] Protandry, sometimes exclusively in zoological application.

protandrous (prōtăn'drŭs) *a.* [Gk. *protos*, first; *aner*, male.] Exhibiting protandry; proterandrous.

protandry (prōtăn'drĭ) *n.* [Gk. *protos*, first; *aner*, male.] Condition of hermaphrodite plants and animals where male elements mature and are shed before female elements mature; proterandry.

protaspis (prōtăs'pĭs) *n.* [Gk. *protos*, first; *aspis*, shield.] Developmental stage of trilobites.

protaxis (prōt'ăksĭs) *n.* [Gk. *protos*, first; L. *axis*, axle.] Primordial filament or axis in evolution of plant stem.

protaxon (prōt'ăksŏn) *n.* [Gk. *protos*, first; *axon*, axle.] Axon-base.

protease (prō'tēās) *n.* [Gk. *proteion*, first.] Any proteolytic enzyme.

protegulum (prōtĕg'ūlŭm) *n.* [L. *pro*, before; *tegulum*, covering.] The semicircular or semielliptical embryonic shell of brachiopods.

proteid (prō'tēĭd) *n.* [Gk. *proteion*, first; *eidos*, form.] The nitrogenous material of plant cells; albuminous substance; a term subject to varying restrictions by different authors; protein, *q.v.*

protein (prō'tēĭn) *n.* [Gk. *proteion*, first.] Albuminous substance; a nitrogenous compound of cell protoplasm; a complex substance characteristic of living matter and consisting of aggregates of amino-acids, and generally containing sulphur.

proteism (prō'tēĭzm) *n.* [L. *Proteus*, a sea-god.] The capacity to change shape, as of amoeba and some other Protista.

protembryo (prōt'ĕmbriŏ) *n.* [Gk. *protos*, first; *embryon*, embryo.] The fertilised ovum and its cleavage stages preceding formation of blastula.

protenchyma (prōtĕng'kĭma) *n.* [Gk. *protos*, first; *engchyma*, infusion.] Zone of primordial tissue of a carpophore below origin of the universal veil.

protentomon (prōt'ĕntŏmŏn) *n.* [Gk. *protos*, first; *entomon*, insect.] The hypothetical archetype of insects.

proteoclastic (prō'tēŏklăs'tĭk) *a.* [Gk. *proteion*, first; *klan*, to break.] *Appl.* enzymes or ferments which break down proteins; proteolytic.

proteolysis (prō′tëŏl′ĭsĭs) *n.* [Gk. *proteion*, first; *lysis*, loosing.] The disintegration of proteins, as by proteolytic enzymes.

proteolytic (prō′tëölĭt′ĭk) *a.* [Gk. *proteion*, first; *lysis*, loosing.] *Appl.* enzymes which change proteins into proteoses, peptones, polypeptides, and eventually into amino acids.

proteose (prō′tëōs) *n.* [Gk. *proteion*, first.] The first cleavage product of action of hydrolysis on a protein molecule.

proterandrous (prŏt′ërăn′drŭs) *a.* [Gk. *proteros*, earlier; *aner*, male.] Protandrous, *q.v.*; proterandric.

proteranthous (prŏt′ërăn′thŭs) *a.* [Gk. *proteros*, earlier; *anthos*, flower.] Flowering before foliage leaves appear.

proterogenesis (prŏt′ëröjĕn′ësĭs) *n.* [Gk. *proteros*, forward; *genesis*, descent.] Foreshadowing of adult or later forms by youthful or earlier forms. *Opp.* palingenesis.

proteroglyph (prŏt′ëröglĭf) *a.* [Gk. *proteros*, in front; *glyphein*, to carve.] With specialised fang teeth in anterior upper jaw region.

proterogynous (prŏtërŏj′ĭnŭs) *a.* [Gk. *proteros*, earlier; *gyne*, woman.] Protogynous.

proterosoma (prŏt′ërösō′mă) *n.* [Gk. *proteros*, forward; *soma*, body.] Body region comprising gnathosoma and propodosoma, in Acarina.

proterotype (prŏt′ërötīp) *n.* [Gk. *proteros*, earlier; *typos*, pattern.] Original or primary type, as holotype, paratypes, syntypes.

Proterozoic (prŏt′ërözō′ĭk) *a.* [Gk. *proteros*, earlier; *zoon*, animal.] *Pert.* or *appl.* the older Palaeozoic faunal epoch, the age of primitive invertebrates.

prothallial (prōthăl′ĭăl) *a.* [Gk. *pro*, before; *thallos*, young shoot.] *Pert.* a prothallus; *appl.* cell in pollen grain of gymnosperms, considered as vestige of a thallus.

prothallium,—prothallus, *q.v.*

prothalloid (prōthăl′oid) *a.* [Gk. *pro*, before; *thallos*, young shoot; *eidos*, form.] Like a prothallus.

prothallus (prōthăl′ŭs) *n.* [Gk. *pro*, before; *thallos*, young shoot.] The hyphae of lichens during the initial growth stages; a small, thin structure, the gametophyte or haploid sexual generation of pteridophytes, developed from spores; protothallus.

protheca (prōthē′kă) *n.* [Gk. *pro*, before; *theke*, box.] The rudiment of coral formation; basal part of coral calicle.

prothecium (prōthē′sĭŭm) *n.* [Gk. *pro*, before; *theke*, box.] A primary perithecium of certain fungi.

prothetely (prōthĕt′ëlĭ) *n.* [Gk. *protheein*, to run before; *telos*, completion.] The development or manifestation of pupal or of imaginal characters in insect larva. *Opp.* hysterotely.

prothoracic (prō′thōrăs′ĭk) *a.* [Gk. *pro*, before; *thorax*, chest.] *Pert.* prothorax; *appl.* glands secreting ecdysone or moulting hormone.

prothorax (prōthō′răks) *n.* [Gk. *pro*, before; *thorax*, chest]. Anterior thoracic segment of Arthropoda.

prothrombin (prōthrŏm′bĭn) *n.* [Gk. *pro*, before; *thrombos*, clot.] Thrombogen, after activation by thromboplastin and calcium, forming thrombin; thrombogen.

prothyalosome (prōt′hī′ălösōm) *n.* [Gk. *protos*, first; *hyalos*, glass; *soma*, body.] The area surrounding germinal spot in germinal vesicle.

protista (prōtĭs′tă) *n. plu.* [Gk. *protistos*, first of all.] The primitive organisms from which animals and plants arose; protobionta; protophyta and protozoa.

protistology (prō′tĭstŏl′öjĭ) *n.* [Gk. *protistos*, first of all; *logos*, discourse.] The science dealing with primitive forms of life.

proto-aecidium (prō′töēsĭd′ĭŭm) *n.* [Gk. *protos*, first; *oikidion*, small house.] A cell-mass surrounded by hyphal layers, containing cells eventually producing aecidiospores and disjunctor cells; protoaecium, aecial primordium, primordial aecidium.

protobasidium (prō'töbăsĭd'ĭŭm) *n.* [Gk. *protos*, first ; *basidion*, small pedestal.] A basidium producing a mycelium of four cells from each of which a sporidium is developed by abstriction ; promycelium.

protobiology (prō'töbīŏl'öjĭ) *n.* [Gk. *protos*, first ; *bios*, life ; *logos*, discourse.] The study of ultramicroscopic organisms.

protobiont (prō'töbī'ŏnt) *n.* [Gk. *protos*, first ; *bion*, living.] A protist ; protophyton or protozoon.

protobios,— ultramicroscopic life ; ultraviruses.

protoblast (prō'töblăst) *n.* [Gk. *protos*, first ; *blastos*, bud.] A naked cell, devoid of membrane ; first or single-cell stage of an embryo ; a blastomere which develops into a definite organ or part ; internal-bud stage in life-history of Neosporidia.

protoblema (prō'töblē'mă) *n.* [Gk. *protos*, first ; *blema*, coverlet.] A layer of flaky tissue covering the teleoblema and constituting the primary or primordial veil of certain fungi ; protoblem.

protobroch (prō'töbrŏk) *a.* [Gk. *protos*, first ; *brochos*, mesh.] *Appl.* nuclei of gonia in resting stage ; *cf.* deutobroch.

protocephalic (prō'tökĕfăl'ĭk, -sĕf-) *a.* [Gk. *protos*, first ; *kephale*, head.] *Appl.* or *pert.* primary head region of insect embryo ; *pert.* protocephalon.

protocephalon (prō'tökĕf'ălŏn, -sĕf-) *n.* [Gk. *protos*, first ; *kephale*, head.] Head-part of cephalothorax in Malacostraca ; first of six segments composing insect head.

protocercal (prō'tösĕr'kăl) *a.* [Gk. *protos*, first ; *kerkos*, tail.] Having caudal fin divided into two equal lobes ; diphycercal, the primitive form of caudal fin.

protocerebrum (prō'tösĕr'ĕbrŭm) *n.* [Gk. *protos*, first ; L. *cerebrum*, brain.] Anterior pair of ganglionic centres of crustaceans ; anterior part of insect brain, formed by fused ganglia of optic segment of head ; protocerebron.

protochlorophyll (prō'töklō'röfĭl) *n.* [Gk. *protos*, first ; *chloros*, green ; *phyllon*, leaf.] A substance which is converted to chlorophyll by agency of light ; etiolin.

protocnemes (prō'töknēmz) *n. plu.* [Gk. *protos*, first ; *kneme*, wheel-spoke.] The six primary pairs of mesenteries of Zoantharia.

protoconch (prō'tökŏngk) *n.* [Gk. *protos*, first ; *kongche*, shell.] The larval shell of molluscs, indicated by cicatrix on adult shell.

protocone (prō'tökōn) *n.* [Gk. *protos*, first ; *konos*, cone.] Inner cusp of upper molar.

protoconid (prō'tökō'nĭd) *n.* [Gk. *protos*, first ; *konos*, cone ; *eidos*, form.] External cusp of lower molar.

protoconidium (prō'tökŏnĭd'ĭŭm) *n.* [Gk. *protos*, first ; *konis*, dust ; *idion*, *dim.*] A rounded or club-shaped cell or hemispore at the tip of a filament, giving rise to deuteroconidia, as in dermatophytes.

protoconule (prō'tökō'nūl) *n.* [Gk. *protos*, first ; *konos*, cone.] Anterior intermediate cusp of upper molar.

protocorm (prō'tökôrm) *n.* [Gk. *protos*, first ; *kormos*, trunk.] Swelling of rhizophore, preceding root formation, as in certain club-mosses ; undifferentiated cell-mass of archegonium in Gingkoales.

protocormic (prō'tökôr'mĭk) *a.* [Gk. *protos*, first ; *kormos*, trunk.] *Appl.* or *pert.* primary trunk region of insect embryo.

protocranium prō'tökrā'nĭŭm) *n.* [Gk. *protos*, first ; *kranion*, skull.] Posterior part of insect epicranium.

protoderm (prō'tödĕrm) *n.* [Gk. *protos*, first ; *derma*, skin.] The outer cell layer of apical meristem ; primordial epidermis of plants ; superficial dermatogen.

protoepiphyte (prō'töĕp'ĭfīt) *n.* [Gk. *protos*, first ; *epi*, upon ; *phyton*, plant.] A plant growing upon another and getting all its nourishment from that other.

protofibrils (prō′tōfī′brĭlz) *n. plu.* [Gk. *protos*, first; L. *fibrilla*, small fibre.] Minute threads seen in ground substance between submicroscopic fibrils, in connective tissue.

protogene (prō′tōjēn) *n.* [Gk. *protos*, first; *genos*, descent.] A dominant allelomorph, *opp.* allogene.

protogenesis (prō′tōjĕn′ĕsĭs) *n.* [Gk. *protos*, first; *genesis*, origin.] First embryonic stage, including development of archenteron; *cf.* deuterogenesis.

protogenic (prō′tōjĕn′ĭk) *a.* [Gk. *protos*, first; *genos*, offspring.] Persistent from beginning of development.

protogynous (prōtŏj′ĭnŭs) *a.* [Gk. *protos*, first; *gyne*, woman.] Having female elements mature before male; proterogynous.

protogyny (prōtŏj′ĭnĭ) *n.* [Gk. *protos*, first; *gyne*, woman.] Condition of hermaphrodite plants and animals in which female elements mature and are spent before maturation of male elements; proterogyny.

protohaem (prō′tōhēm) *n.* [Gk. *protos*, first; *haima*, blood.] Haematin.

protokaryon (prō′tōkăr′ĭŏn) *n.* [Gk. *protos*, first; *karyon*, nut.] A simple or primitive nucleus consisting of a mass of chromatin suspended in nuclear sap.

protoloph (prō′tōlŏf) *n.* [Gk. *protos*, first; *lophos*, crest.] Anterior transverse crest of upper molars.

protomala (prō′tōmā′lă) *n.* [Gk. *protos*, first; L. *mala*, cheek.] A mandible of myriopods.

protomerite (prō′tōmĕrīt) *n.* [Gk. *protos*, first; *meros*, part.] Anterior part of medullary protoplasm of adult gregarines; *cf.* primite.

protomite (prōtŏm′īt) *n.* [Gk. *pro*, early; *tome*, cutting; *mitos*, thread.] Stage between tomont and tomite in life cycle of Holotricha.

protomitosis (prō′tōmĭtō′sĭs) *n.* [Gk. *protos*, first; *mitos*, thread.] Primitive mitosis; cruciform division, as in slime fungi; promitosis.

protomonostelic (prō′tōmŏn′ŏstēl′ĭk) *a.* [Gk. *protos*, first; *monos*, alone; *stele*, column.] *Appl.* stem or root with protostele or central cylinder.

protomont (prō′tŏmŏnt′) *n.* [Gk. *pro*, early; *tome*, cutting; *onta*, beings.] Transitory stage, between trophont and tomont, with condensed central nucleus, in life cycle of Holotricha.

protomorphic (prō′tōmôr′fĭk) *a.* [Gk. *protos*, first; *morphe*, form.] First-formed; primordial.

protonema (prō′tōnē′mă) *n.* [Gk. *protos*, first; *nema*, thread.] The filamentous thallus of mosses from which the moss plant buds; early filamentous stage in development of certain algae.

protonematoid (prō′tōnē′mătoid) *a.* [Gk. *protos*, first; *nema*, thread; *eidos*, form.] Like a protonema.

protonephridial (prō′tōnĕfrĭd′ĭăl) *a.* [Gk. *protos*, first; *nephros*, kidney.] *Appl.* excretory water-vascular system of flat-worms.

protonephridium (prō′tōnĕfrĭd′ĭŭm) *n.* [Gk. *protos*, first; *nephros*, kidney; *idion*, *dim.*] The primitive excretory tube, with coelomic opening or protonephridiostome.

protoneurone (prō′tōnū′rōn) *n.* [Gk. *protos*, first; *neuron*, nerve.] The primitive intermediary cell connecting receptor with effector; cellular unit of nerve net; a unipolar ganglion cell.

protopathic (prō′tōpăth′ĭk) *a.* [Gk. *protos*, first; *pathos*, feeling.] *Appl.* stimuli and nerve systems concerned with sensation of pain and of marked variations in temperature.

protopepsia (prō′tōpĕp′sĭă) *n.* [Gk. *protos*, first; *pepsis*, digestion.] Solution and alteration of food-material accomplished in stomach.

protoperithecium (prō′tōpĕr′ĭthē′sĭŭm) *n.* [Gk. *protos*, first; *peri*, around; *theke*, case.] Primary haploid perithecium, as in certain Pyrenomycetes.

protophloem (prō'töflō'ëm) *n.* [Gk. *protos*, first; *phloios*, inner bark.] The first phloem elements of a vascular bundle.

protophyte (prō'töfīt) *n.* [Gk. *protos*, first; *phyton*, plant.] A unicellular vegetable organism or primitive plant; protophyton; the gametophyte in the antithetic alternation of generations, *opp.* antiphyte.

protoplasm (prō'töplăzm) *n.* [Gk. *protos*, first; *plasma*, form.] Living cell substance; cytoplasm and karyoplasm.

protoplasmic (prō'töplăz'mĭk) *a.* [Gk. *protos*, first; *plasma*, form.] *Pert.* or consisting of protoplasm.

protoplasmic bead,—structure on anterior part of middle piece of mammalian spermatozoon.

protoplast (prō'töplăst) *n.* [Gk. *protos*, first; *plastos*, formed.] An energid; a living uninucleate primitive protoplasmic unit; protoplasm of one cell.

protopod (prō'töpŏd) *a.* [Gk. *protos*, first; *pous*, foot.] With feet or legs on anterior segments.

protopodite (prō'töpödīt) *n.* [Gk. *protos*, first; *pous*, foot.] Basal segment of arthropod limb.

protoptile (prō'tötīl, -ptīl) *n.* [Gk. *protos*, first; *ptilon*, feather.] The primary prepenna, succeeded by mesoptile.

protoscolex,—proscolex, *q.v.*

protospore (prō'töspōr) *n.* [Gk. *protos*, first; *sporos*, seed.] A spore of first generation; a mycelium-producing spore.

protostele (prō'töstēlē) *n.* [Gk. *protos*, first; *stele*, column.] Concentric bundle or pithless central cylinder of vascular tissue of most roots and some stems.

protosternum (prō'töstĕr'nŭm) *n.* [Gk. *protos*, first; *sternon*, chest.] Sternite of cheliceral segment of prosoma in Acarina.

protostigmata (prō'töstĭg'mătă) *n.* *plu.* [Gk. *protos*, first; *stigma*, pricked mark.] Two primary gill slits of embryo.

protostoma (prō'tŏst'ömă) *n.* [Gk. *protos*, first; *stoma*, mouth.] Original mouth of gastrula; blastopore.

protostylic (prō'töstĭl'ĭk) *a.* [Gk. *protos*, first; *stylos*, column.] Exhibiting protostyly, or having lower jaw connected with cranium by original dorsal end of arch.

protothallus (prō'töthăl'ŭs) *n.* [Gk. *protos*, first; *thallos*, young shoot.] First-formed structure which develops into a thallus, as of a lichen.

prototheca (prō'töthē'kă) *n.* [Gk. *protos*, first; *theke*, box.] A skeletal cup-shaped plate at aboral end of coral embryo, the first skeletal formation.

prototherian (prō'töthē'rĭăn) *a.* [Gk. *protos*, first; *therion*, small animal.] *Appl.* egg-laying mammals without placenta.

prototroch (prō'tötrŏk) *n.* [Gk. *protos*, first; *trochos*, wheel.] A pre-oral circlet of cilia of a trochosphere or trochelminth larva.

prototrophic (prō'tötrŏf'ĭk) *a.* [Gk. *protos*, first; *trophe*, nourishment.] Nourished from one supply or in one manner only; feeding on inorganic matter, *appl.* iron, sulphur, and nitrifying bacteria; *appl.* plants.

prototype (prō'tötīp) *n.* [Gk. *protos*, first; *typos*, model.] An original type species or example; an ancestral form.

protovertebrae (prō'tövĕr'tēbrē) *n.* *plu.* [Gk. *protos*, first; L. *vertebra*, vertebra.] A series of primitive mesodermal segments in a vertebrate embryo.

protoxylem (prō'tözī'lĕm) *n.* [Gk. *protos*, first; *xylon*, wood.] Primary xylem lying next pith of stems.

protozoa,—*plu.* of protozoon.

protozoaea (prō'tözōē'ă) *n.* [Gk. *protos*, first; *zoon*, animal.] Stage in life-history of certain arthropods, succeeding free-swimming nauplius.

protozoology (prō'tözōŏl'öjĭ) *n.* [Gk. *protos*, first; *zoon*, animal; *logos*, discourse.] The branch of zoology dealing with protozoa.

protozoon (prō′tözō′ŏn) *n.* [Gk. *protos*, first; *zoon*, animal.] A unicellular or non-cellular animal organism. *Plu.* protozoa.

protozygote (prō′tözī′gōt) *n.* [Gk. *protos*, first; *zygon*, yoke.] A homozygote having dominant characters, *opp.* allozygote.

protractor (prōtrăk′tŏr) *n.* [L. *pro*, forth; *tractus*, drawn out.] A muscle which draws out or extends a part. *Opp.* retractor.

protriaene (prō′trīēn) *n.* [Gk. *pro*, before; *triaina*, trident.] A triaene with anteriorly-directed branches.

protrophic,—prototrophic.

provascular tissue,—procambium.

proventriculus (prō′vĕntrĭk′ūlŭs) *n.* [L. *pro*, before; *ventriculus*, small stomach.] In decapod crustaceans, the so-called stomach containing gastric mill; in insects, the digestive chamber anterior to stomach; in worms, that anterior to gizzard; in birds, the glandular stomach anterior to gizzard.

provinculum (prōvĭng′kūlŭm) *n.* [L. *pro*, before; *vinculum*, bond.] A primitive hinge of young stages of certain Lamellibranchia.

provitamin (prōvī′tămĭn) *n.* [L. *pro*, before; *vita*, life; *ammoniacum*, resinous gum.] Precursor of a vitamin; previtamin.

proximal (prŏk′sĭmăl) *a.* [L. *proximus*, next.] Nearest body or centre or base of attachment; *opp.* distal.

prozonite (prōzō′nīt) *n.* [Gk. *pro*, before; *zone*, girdle.] The anterior ring of a diplosomite. *Opp.* metazonite.

prozymogen (prōzī′mŏjĕn) *n.* [Gk. *pro*, before; *zyme*, leaven; *-genes*, producing.] Precursor of zymogen, activated by secretin.

pruinose (proo′ĭnōs) *a.* [L. *pruina*, hoar-frost.] Covered with whitish particles or globules; covered by bloom.

psalterium (sôltē′rĭŭm, psôl-) *n.* [L. *psalterium*, psalter.] The third stomach of ruminants, the omasum or manyplies; the lyra, a thin triangular lamina joining lateral portions of fornix.

psammophilous (sămŏf′ĭlŭs, psăm-) *a.* [Gk. *psammos*, sand; *philos*, loving.] Thriving in sandy places.

psammophore (săm′öfōr, psăm-) *n.* [Gk. *psammos*, sand; *phora*, carrying.] One of rows of hairs under mandibles and sides of head in desert ants, used for removal of sand grains.

psammophyte (săm′öfīt, psăm-) *n.* [Gk. *psammos*, sand; *phyton*, plant.] A plant growing in sandy or gravelly ground.

psammosere (săm′ösēr, psăm-) *n.* [Gk. *psammos*, sand; L. *serere*, to put in a row.] A plant succession originating in a sandy area, as on dunes.

pseudambulacrum (sū′dămbūlā′-krŭm, psū-) *n.* [Gk. *pseudes*, false; L. *ambulare*, to walk.] The lancet-plate with adhering side-plates and covering plates, of Blastoidea.

pseudannual (sūdăn′ūăl, psū-) *n.* [Gk. *pseudes*, false; L. *annus*, year.] A plant which completes its growth in one year but provides a bulb or other means of surviving winter.

pseudapogamy (sū′dăpŏg′ămĭ, psū-) *n.* [Gk. *pseudes*, false; *apo*, away; *gamos*, marriage.] Fusion of pair of vegetative nuclei, as in certain fungi and in fern prothallus.

pseudaposematic (sūdăp′ösēmăt′ĭk, psū-) *a.* [Gk. *pseudes*, false; *apo*, from; *sema*, sign.] Imitating warning coloration or other protective features of hurtful animals.

pseudaposporv (sū′dăpŏs′pörĭ, psū-) *n.* [Gk. *pseudes*, false; *apo*, away; *sporos*, seed.] Spore formation without haplosis, the gametophyte originating from a diploid spore.

pseudaxis (sūdăk′sĭs, psū-) *n.* [Gk. *pseudes*, false; *axis*, axle.] An apparent main axis; sympodium.

pseudepisematic (sūdĕp′ĭsēmăt′ĭk, psū-) *a.* [Gk. *pseudes*, false; *epi*, upon; *sema*, sign.] Having or displaying alluring coloration or markings.

pseudhaemal (sūdhē′măl, psū-) *a.* [Gk. *pseudes*, false; *haima*, blood.] *Appl.* the vascular system of certain worms and echinoderms.

pseudholoptic (sū'dhölŏp'tĭk, psū-) *a.* [Gk. *pseudes*, false; *holos*, whole; *optikos*, relating to sight.] Intermediate between holoptic and dichoptic, conditions in eyes of Diptera.

pseudimago (sū'dĭmā'gō, psū-) *n.* [Gk. *pseudes*, false; L. *imago*, image.] Stage between pupa and imago in metamorphosis of certain insects; subimago.

pseudoacrorhagus (sū'döăk'rörā'gŭs, psū-) *n.* [Gk. *pseudes*, false; *akros*, summit; *rhax*, grape.] A structure resembling an acrohagus, but containing ordinary ectodermal nematocysts, in certain Actiniaria.

pseudo-aethalium (sū'döēthā'lĭŭm, psū-) *n.* [Gk. *pseudes*, false; *aithalos*, soot.] A dense aggregation of distinct sporangia, as in Myxomycetes. *Cf.* aethalium.

pseudoalveolar (sū'döăl'vēölăr, psū-) *a.* [Gk. *pseudes*, false; L. *alveus*, hollow.] *Appl.* a structure of cytoplasm containing starch grains or deutoplasm spheres.

pseudoangiocarpic (sū'döăn'jiökâr'pĭk, psū-) *a.* [Gk. *pseudes*, false; *anggeion*, vessel; *karpos*, fruit.] With an exposed hymenium temporarily enclosed by incurved edge of pileus or by a secondary pseudovelum.

pseudoaposematic,—*see* pseudaposematic.

pseudoaquatic (sū'döăkwăt'ĭk, psū-) *a.* [Gk. *pseudes*, false; L. *aqua*, water.] Thriving in moist ground.

pseudoarticulation (sū'döâr'tĭkūlā'shŭn, psū-) *n.* [Gk. *pseudes*, false; L. *articulus*, joint.] Incomplete subdivision of a segment, or groove having the appearance of a joint, as in limbs of arthropods.

pseudobasidium (sū'döbăsĭd'ĭŭm, psū-) *n.* [Gk. *pseudes*, false; *basis*, base; *idion*, *dim.*] A large basidium with thickened wall, constituting a resting spore.

pseudoblepharoplast (sū'döblĕf'ărö-plăst, psū-) *n.* [Gk. *pseudes*, false; *blepharis*, eyelash; *plastos*, formed.] Temporary concentration of chromatin near centriole in sperm-formation of certain insects.

pseudobrachium (sū'döbrăk'ĭŭm, psū-) *n.* [Gk. *pseudes*, false; *brachion*, arm.] Appendage for locomotion on a substratum, formed from elongated pterygials of pectoral fin of Pediculates.

pseudobranch (sū'döbrăngk', psū-) *n.* [Gk. *pseudes*, false; *brangchia*, gills.] An accessory gill of some fishes, not respiratory in function; spiracular or vestigial hyoidean gill.

pseudobulb (sū'döbŭlb, psū-) *n.* [Gk. *pseudes*, false; L. *bulbus*, bulb.] A thickened internode of orchids, for storage of water and reserves.

pseudobulbil (sū'döbŭl'bĭl, psū-) *n.* [Gk. *pseudes*, false; L. *bulbus*, bulb.] An outgrowth of some ferns, a substitute for sporangia.

pseudobulbous (sū'döbŭl'bŭs, psū-) *a.* [Gk. *pseudes*, false; L. *bulbus*, bulb.] Adapted to xerophytic conditions through development of pseudobulbs.

pseudocarp (sū'dökârp, psū-) *n.* [Gk. *pseudes*, false; *karpos*, fruit.] A false fruit, one in which other parts than ovary assist in formation.

pseudocellus (sū'dösĕl'ŭs, psū-) *n.* [Gk. *pseudes*, false; L. *ocellus*, little eye.] One of scattered sense organs of unknown function in certain insects.

pseudocentrous (sū'dösĕn'trŭs, psū-) *a.* [Gk. *pseudes*, false; L. *centrum*, centre.] *Appl.* vertebrae composed of two pairs of arcualia meeting and forming a suture laterally.

pseudochromatin,—prochromatin.

pseudocilia (sū'dösĭl'ĭă, psū-) *n. plu.* [Gk. *pseudes*, false; L. *cilium*, eyelid.] Protoplasmic threads projecting from cell through surrounding sheath of mucilage, as in Tetrasporaceae.

pseudocoel (sū'dösēl, psū-) *n.* [Gk. *pseudes*, false; *koilos*, hollow.] The narrow cavity between the two laminae of septum lucidum; so-called fifth ventricle of brain; space between mesodermal tissue of the body wall and gastrodermis, derived from blastocoel, as in Trochelminthes and Nemathelminthes.

pseudoconch (sū'dŏkŏngk, psū-) *n.* [Gk. *pseudes*, false ; *kongche*, shell.] A structure developed above and behind the true concha in crocodiles.

pseudocone (sū'dŏkōn, psū-) *a.* [Gk. *pseudes*, false ; *konos*, cone.] *Appl.* insect compound eye having cone cells filled with transparent gelatinous material.

pseudoconidium (sū'dŏkŏnĭd'ĭŭm, psū-) *n.* [Gk. *pseudes*, false ; *konis*, dust ; *idion*, *dim.*] One of the spores formed on lateral projections of pseudomycelium of certain yeasts.

pseudoconjugation (sū'dŏkŏnjoogā'shŭn, psū-) *n.* [Gk. *pseudes*, false ; L. *cum*, with ; *jugum*, yoke.] Conjugation of Sporozoa in which two individuals, temporarily and without true fusion, join end to end, protomerite to deutomerite, or side to side.

pseudocostate (sū'dŏkŏs'tāt, psū-) *a.* [Gk. *pseudes*, false ; L. *costa*, rib.] False-veined, having a marginal vein uniting all others.

pseudoculus (sū'dŏk'ūlŭs) *n.* [Gk. *pseudes*, false ; L. *oculus*, eye.] An oval area on each side of head of Pauropoda, possibly a receptor for mechanical vibrations.

pseudocyst (sū'dŏsĭst, psū-) *n.* [Gk. *pseudes*, false ; *kystis*, bladder.] A residual protoplasmic mass which swells and ruptures, liberating spores of Sporozoa.

pseudodeltidium (sū'dŏdĕltĭd'ĭŭm, psū-) *n.* [Gk. *pseudes*, false ; Δ, delta ; *idion*, *dim.*] A plate partly or entirely closing deltidial fissure in ventral valve of certain Testicardines.

pseudoderm (sū'dŏdĕrm, psū-) *n.* [Gk. *pseudes*, false ; *derma*, skin.] A kind of covering or skin of certain compact sponges, formed also towards pseudogastric cavity.

pseudodont (sū'dŏdŏnt, psū-) *a.* [Gk. *pseudes*, false ; *odous*, tooth.] Having false or horny teeth, as monotremes.

pseudo-elater (sū'dŏĕl'ătĕr) *n.* [Gk. *pseudes*, false ; *elater*, driver.] One of the chains of cells in sporogonium of liverworts.

pseudofoliaceous (sū'dŏfōlĭā'shŭs, psū-) *a.* [Gk. *pseudes*, false ; L. *folium*, leaf.] With expansions resembling leaves.

pseudogamy (sū'dŏg'ămĭ, psū-) *n.* [Gk. *pseudes*, false ; *gamos*, marriage.] Union of hyphae from different thalli ; activation of ovum by a spermatozoon which plays no part thereafter ; pseudomixis.

pseudogaster (sū'dŏgăs'tĕr, psū-) *n.* [Gk. *pseudes*, false ; *gaster*, stomach.] An apparent gastral cavity of certain sponges, opening to exterior by pseudo-osculum and having true oscula opening into itself.

pseudogastrula (sū'dŏgăs'troolă, psū-) *n.* [Gk. *pseudes*, false ; *gaster*, stomach.] The stage of Sycon development when archaeocytes become completely enclosed by flagellate cells.

pseudogyne (sū'dŏjĭnē, psū-) *n.* [Gk. *pseudes*, false ; *gyne*, female.] A worker ant with female thoracic characters.

pseudoheart, — the axial organ of echinoderms ; one of the contractile vessels pumping blood from dorsal to ventral vessel in annelids.

pseudoidium (sū'dŏĭd'ĭŭm, psū-) *n.* [Gk. *pseudes*, false ; *oon*, egg ; *idion*, *dim.*] A separate hyphal cell which may germinate. *Plu.* pseudoidia.

pseudolamina (sū'dŏlăm'ĭnă, psū-) *n.* [Gk. *pseudes*, false ; L. *lamina*, plate.] Expanded apical portion of a phyllode.

pseudomanubrium (sū'dŏmănū'brĭŭm, psū-) *n.* [Gk. *pseudes*, false ; L. *manubrium*, handle.] The manubrium considered as a process of subumbrella where the former contains the gastric cavity, in certain Trachylinae.

pseudometamerism (sū'dömĕt'ămĕrĭzm, psū-) *n.* [Gk. *pseudes*, false ; *meta*, after ; *meros*, part.] Apparent serial segmentation ; an approximation to metamerism, as in certain flat-worms.

pseudomitotic (sū'dömĭtŏt'ĭk, psū-) *a.* [Gk. *pseudes*, false ; *mitos*, thread.] Diaschistic, *q.v.*

pseudomixis (sū'dömĭk'sĭs, psū-) *n.* [Gk. *pseudes*, false ; *mixis*, mingling.] A form of nuclear fusion, not regularly sexual, leading to embryo formation ; pseudogamy ; somatogamy.

pseudomonocarpous (sū'dömŏnökâr'pŭs, psū-) *a.* [Gk. *pseudes*, false ; *monos*, alone ; *karpos*, fruit.] With seeds retained in leaf-bases until liberated, as in cycads.

pseudomonocotyledonous (sū'dömŏn'ökŏtĭlē'dönŭs, psū-) *a.* [Gk. *pseudes*, false ; *monos*, alone ; *kotyledon*, cup-like hollow.] With two cotyledons coalescing to appear as one.

pseudomonocyclic (sū'dömŏn'ösĭk'lĭk, psū-) *a.* [Gk. *pseudes*, false ; *monos*, alone ; *kyklos*, circle.] *Appl.* crinoids with infrabasals absent in adults but present in young or in near ancestors.

pseudomycelium (sū'dömīsē'lĭŭm, psū-) *n.* [Gk. *pseudes*, false ; *mykes*, fungus.] An assemblage of chains or groups of adherent cells, of yeasts ; sprout mycelium.

pseudomycorrhiza (sū'dömī'körī'ză) *n.* [Gk. *pseudes*, false ; *mykes*, fungus ; *rhiza*, root.] Association of short roots of conifers with parasitic fungi in the absence of mycorrhizal fungi.

pseudonavicella (sū'dönăvĭsĕl'ă psū-) *n.* [Gk. *pseudes*, false ; L. *navicella*, small boat.] A small boat-shaped spore containing sporozoites, in Sporozoa.

pseudonotum (sū'dönō'tŭm, psū-) *n.* [Gk. *pseudes*, false ; *noton*, back.] Postnotum or postscutellum.

pseudonuclein,—paranuclein, *q.v.*

pseudonucleoli (sū'dönūklē'ölī, psū-) *n. plu.* [Gk. *pseudes*, false ; L. *nucleus*, kernel.] Knots or granules in nuclear reticulum not true nucleoli.

pseudonychium (sū'dŏnĭk'ĭŭm, psū-) *n.* [Gk. *pseudes*, false ; *onyx*, claw.] A lobe or process between claws of insects.

pseudo-osculum (sū'döŏs'kūlŭm, psū-) *n.* [Gk. *pseudes*, false ; L. *osculum*, small mouth.] The exterior opening of a pseudogaster.

pseudo-ostiolum (sū'döŏs'tĭölŭm, psū-) *n.* [Gk. *pseudes*, false ; L. *ostiolum*, small door.] A small opening formed by breaking down of cell-walls or tissues, in certain fungi without perithecia ; pseudo-ostiole, pseudostiole.

pseudoparaphysis (sū'döpărăf'ĭsĭs, psū-) *n.* [Gk. *pseudes*, false ; *para*, beside ; *phyein*, to grow.] Basidiolum, *q.v.* ; a paraphysoid, *q.v.*

pseudoparenchyma (sū'döpărĕng'kĭmă, psū-) *n.* [Gk. *pseudes*, false ; *para*, beside ; *engchyma*, infusion.] A tissue-like collection of hyphae which resembles parenchyma.

pseudopenis (sū'döpē'nĭs, psū-) *n.* [Gk. *pseudes*, false ; L. *penis*, penis.] The protruded evaginated portion of male deferent duct, in certain Oligochaeta ; copulatory structure in Orthoptera.

pseudoperculum (sū'döpĕr'kūlŭm, psū-) *n.* [Gk. *pseudes*, false ; L. *operculum*, lid.] A structure resembling an operculum or closing membrane.

pseudoperianth (sū'döpĕr'ĭănth, psū-) *n.* [Gk. *pseudes*, false ; *peri*, round ; *anthos*, flower.] An archegonium-investing envelope of certain liverworts.

pseudoperidium (sū'döpērĭd'ĭŭm, psū-) *n.* [Gk. *pseudes*, false ; *peridion*, small wallet.] The aecidiospore envelope of certain fungi.

pseudoplasmodium (sūdöplăzmō'dĭŭm, psū-) *n.* [Gk. *pseudes*, false ; *plasma*, form.] An aggregation of amoebulae without fusion of their protoplasm.

pseudopod (sū′dŏpŏd, psū-) *n.* [Gk. *pseudes*, false; *pous*, foot.] A foot-like body-wall process of certain larvae; a pseudopodium, *q.v.*

pseudopodiospore (sūdŏpō′dĭŏ-spōr, psū-) *n.* [Gk. *pseudes*, false; *pous*, foot; *sporos*, seed.] An amoebula or amoeboid swarm-spore which moves by means of pseudo-podia.

pseudopodium (sū′dŏpō′dĭŭm, psū-) *n.* [Gk. *pseudes*, false; *pous*, foot; *eidos*, form.] A blunt protrusion of ectoplasm serving for locomotion and prehension in protozoa; in certain mosses, the sporogonium-supporting pedicel; pseudopod.

pseudopore (sū′dŏpōr, psū-) *n.* [Gk. *pseudes*, false; *poros*, channel.] A small orifice between outermost tube and intercanal system of certain sponges.

pseudopregnancy (sū′dŏprĕg′nănsĭ, psū-) *n.* [Gk. *pseudes*, false; L. *prae*, before; *gignere*, to beget.] Condition of development of accessory reproductive organs simulating true pregnancy, although fertilisation has not taken place.

pseudopupa (sū′dŏpū′pă, psū-) *n.* [Gk. *pseudes*, false; L. *pupa*, puppet.] The semi-pupa or coarctate stage of certain insect larvae.

pseudoramose (sū′dŏrā′mōs, psū-) *a.* [Gk. *pseudes*, false; L. *ramus*, branch.] Having false branches.

pseudoramulus (sū′dŏrăm′ūlŭs, psū-) *n.* [Gk. *pseudes*, false; L. *ramulus*, small branch.] A spurious branch of certain algae.

pseudoraphe (sūdŏrā′fē, psū-) *n.* [Gk. *pseudes*, false; *rhaphe*, seam.] A smooth axial area in some diatoms.

pseudo-reduction,—the preliminary division of chromatin-rods preceding formation of tetrads and actual reduction in maturation.

pseudorhabdites (sū′dŏrăb′dīts, psū-) *n. plu.* [Gk. *pseudes*, false; *rhabdos*, rod.] Granular masses of formed secretion produced by gland-cells of Rhabdocoelida.

pseudorhiza (sū′dŏrīză) *n.* [Gk. *pseudes*, false; *rhiza*, root.] A root-like structure connecting mycelium in the soil with the fruit-body of a fungus; storage trunk. *Plu.* pseudorhizae.

pseudosacral (sū′dŏsā′krăl, psū-) *a.* [Gk. *pseudes*, false; L. *sacer*, sacred.] *Appl.* sacral vertebra attached to pelvis by transverse process and not by sacral rib.

pseudoscolex (sū′dŏskō′lĕks, psū-) *n.* [Gk. *pseudes*, false; *skolex*, worm.] Modified anterior proglottides of certain cestodes where true scolex is absent.

pseudosematic (sū′dŏsēmăt′ĭk, psū-) *a.* [Gk. *pseudes*, false; *sema*, sign.] Having false coloration or markings, as in protective mimicry, or for alluring or aggressive purposes.

pseudoseptate (sū′dŏsĕp′tāt, psū-) *a.* [Gk. *pseudes*, false; L. *septum*, division.] Apparently, but not morphologically, septate.

pseudoseptum (sū′dŏsĕp′tŭm, psū-) *n.* [Gk. *pseudes*, false; L. *septum*, partition.] A perforated or incomplete septum; septum with pores, as in certain fungi.

pseudosessile (sū′dŏsĕs′ĭl, psū-) *a.* [Gk. *pseudes*, false; L. *sedere*, to sit.] *Appl.* abdomen of petiolate insects when petiole is so short that abdomen is close to thorax.

pseudosperm (sū′dŏspërm, psū-) *n.* [Gk. *pseudes*, false; *sperma*, seed.] A false seed or carpel.

pseudospore (sū′dŏspōr, psū-) *n.* [Gk. *pseudes*, false; *sporos*, seed.] An encysted resting myxamoeba; formerly, a basidiospore.

pseudostele (sū′dŏstēlē, psū-) *n.* [Gk. *pseudes*, false; *stele*, pillar.] An apparently stelar structure, as midrib of leaf.

pseudostigma (sū′dŏstĭg′mă) *n.* [Gk. *pseudes*, false; *stigma*, mark.] A cup-like pit of integument, as the socket of a sensory seta in Acarina.

pseudostiole,—pseudo-ostiolum.

pseudostipe (sū′dŏstīp, psū-) *n.* [Gk. *pseudes*, false; L. *stipes*, stalk.] A stem-like structure formed by presumptive spore-producing tissue, as in Gasteromycetes.

pseudostipula (sū'dŏstĭp'ūlă, psū-) *n.* [Gk. *pseudes*, false; L. *stipula*, small stalk.] Part of lamina at base of leaf-stalk, which resembles a stipule.

pseudostoma (sū'dŏs'tŏmă, psū-) *n.* [Gk. *pseudes*, false; *stoma*, mouth.] A temporary mouth or mouth-like opening; a pseudo-osculum.

pseudostroma (sū'dŏstrō'mă, psū-) *n.* [Gk. *pseudes*, false; *stroma*, bedding.] A mass of mixed fungous and host cells.

pseudothecium (sū'dŏthē'sĭŭm, psū-) *n.* [Gk. *pseudes*, false; *theke*, case.] A spherical fruit-body resembling a perithecium.

pseudotrachea (sū'dŏtrā'kēă, psū-) *n.* [Gk. *pseudes*, false; L. *trachia*, windpipe.] A trachea-like structure; one of the trachea-like food-channels of labellum, as in Diptera.

pseudo-unipolar (sū'dŏūnĭpō'lăr, psū-) *a.* [Gk. *pseudes*, false; L. *unus*, one; *polus*, pole.] *Appl.* unipolar nerve cells with a T-shaped or Y-shaped axon, formed by partial fusion of axons of originally bipolar cells.

pseudovarium (sū'dōvā'rĭŭm, psū-) *n.* [Gk. *pseudes*, false; L. *ovarium*, ovary.] Ovary producing pseudova.

pseudovelum (sū'dŏvē'lŭm, psū-) *n.* [Gk. *pseudes*, false; *velum*, covering, veil.] Velum without muscular and nervous cells, in Scyphozoa; pseudoveil of fungi, formed by union of contemporaneous outgrowths from pileus and stipe, protecting the immature hymenium.

pseudovitellus (sū'dŏvĭtĕl'ŭs, psū-) *n.* [Gk. *pseudes*, false; L. *vitellus*, egg-yolk.] A cellular double-string structure of Aphididae, a supposed substitute for Malpighian tubes.

pseudovum (sūdō'vŭm, psū-) *n.* [Gk. *pseudes*, false; L. *ovum*, egg.] An ovum that can develop without fertilisation; a parthenogenetic ovum; the earlier condition of viviparously-produced Aphididae.

pseudozoaea (sū'dŏzŏē'ă, psū-) *n.* [Gk. *pseudes*, false; *zoon*, animal.] A larval stage of stomatopods, so-called from its resemblance to zoaea stage of decapods.

psilophyte (sī'lŏfīt) *n.* [Gk. *psilos*, without trees; *phyton*, plant.] Any plant of savanna.

psoas (sō'ăs, psō'ăs) *n.* [Gk. *psoa*, loins.] Name of two loin muscles, major and minor, formerly magnus and parvus.

psorosperms (sō'rŏspĕrmz, psō'-) *n. plu.* [Gk. *psora*, itch; *sperma*, seed.] The resistant encysted stages of Sporozoa; minute parasitic organisms generally.

psychogenetic (sī'kŏjĕnĕt'ĭk) *a.* [Gk. *psyche*, soul; *genesis*, descent.] *Pert.* mental development; caused by the mind; of mental origin; psychogenic.

psychon (sī'kŏn, psī'-) *n.* [Gk. *psyche*, mind.] Synapse during passage of impulse from one nerve cell to the next.

psychophysics (sī'kŏfĭz'ĭks) *n.* [Gk. *psyche*, mind; *physikos*, physical.] The study of qualitative and quantitative relations between physical stimuli and sensations.

psychophysiology (sī'kŏfĭzĭŏl'ŏjĭ) *n.* [Gk. *psyche*, mind; *physis* nature; *logos*, discourse.] Physiology in relation to mental processes.

psychosomatic (sī'kŏsōmăt'ĭk) *a.* [Gk. *psyche*, mind; *soma*, body.] *Pert.* relationship between mind and body; *pert.* or having body reactions to mental stimuli.

Psychozoic (sī'kŏzō'ĭk) *a.* [Gk. *psyche*, mind; *zoon*, animal.] *Pert.* or *appl.* geological era in which Man predominates; anthropozoic.

psychrophil (sī'krŏfĭl, psī-) *a.* [Gk. *psychros*, cold; *philein*, to love.] Thriving at relatively low temperatures, at below 20° C., *appl.* certain bacteria; psychrophilic. *n.* Psychrophile.

psychrophyte (sī'krŏfīt, psī-) *n.* [Gk. *psychros*, cold; *phyton*, plant.] A plant which grows on a cold substratum.

pteralia (tĕrā'lĭă, ptĕr-) *n. plu.* [Gk. *pteron*, wing.] Axillary sclerites forming articulation of wing in insects.

pterate,—pterote.

pterergate (tĕrĕr'gāt, ptĕr-) *n.* [Gk. *pteron*, wing; *ergates*, worker.] A worker or a soldier ant with vestigial wings.

pteridine (tĕr'ĭdĭn, ptĕr-) *n.* [Gk. *pteron*, wing.] A yellow pigment, first isolated from wings of butterflies, a constituent of folic acid.

pteridology (tĕr'ĭdŏl'ōjĭ, ptĕr-) *n.* [Gk. *pteris*, fern; *logos*, discourse.] The branch of botany dealing with ferns.

pteridophyte (tĕr'ĭdōfīt, ptĕr-) *n.* [Gk. *pteris*, fern; *phyton*, plant.] A vascular cryptogam, any of the ferns, club-mosses, or horse-tails.

pterins (tĕr'ĭnz, ptĕr-) *n. plu.* [Gk. *pteron*, wing.] Wing pigments of certain butterflies, related chemically to uric acid.

pterion (tĕr'ĭŏn, ptĕr-) *n.* [Gk. *pteron*, wing.] The point of junction of parietal, frontal, and great wing of sphenoid; *appl.* ossicle, a sutural bone.

pterocardiac (tĕr'ōkâr'dĭăk, ptĕr-) *a.* [Gk. *pteron*, wing; *kardia*, stomach.] *Appl.* ossicles with curved ends in gastric mill of Crustacea.

pterocarpous (tĕr'ōkâr'pŭs, ptĕr-) *a.* [Gk. *pteron*, wing; *karpos*, fruit.] With winged fruit.

pterodium (tĕrō'dĭŭm, ptĕr-) *n.* [Gk. *pteron*, wing.] A winged fruit or samara.

pteroid (tĕr'oid, ptĕr-) *a.* [Gk. *pteron*, wing; *pteris*, fern; *eidos*, form.] Resembling a wing; like a fern.

pteromorphae (tĕr'ōmôr'fē, ptĕr-) *n. plu.* [Gk. *pteron*, wing; *morphe*, shape.] Outgrowths from notogaster which cover sides of podosoma and third and fourth pair of legs in certain Acarina.

pteropaedes (tĕr'ōpē'dēz, ptĕr-) *n. plu.* [Gk. *pteron*, wing; *pais*, child.] Birds able to fly when newly hatched.

pteropegum (tĕr'ōpē'gŭm, ptĕr-) *n.* [Gk. *pteron*, wing; *pege*, source.] An insect's wing socket.

pteropleurite (tĕr'ōploo'rīt, ptĕr-) *n.* [Gk. *pteron*, wing; *pleura*, side.] Thoracic sclerite between wing insertion and mesopleurite, in Diptera.

pteropodial (tĕr'ōpō'dĭăl, ptĕr-) *a.* [Gk. *pteron*, wing; *pous*, foot.] *Appl.* wing-like lobes of mid-foot of Pteropoda or sea-butterflies.

pteropodium (tĕr'ōpō'dĭŭm, ptĕr-) *n.* [Gk. *pteron*, wing; *pous*, foot.] A winged foot, as of certain bats.

pterospermous (tĕr'ōspĕr'mŭs, ptĕr-) *a.* [Gk. *pteron*, wing; *sperma*, seed.] With winged seeds.

pterostigma (tĕr'ōstĭg'mă, ptĕr-) *n.* [Gk. *pteron*, wing; *stigma*, mark.] An opaque cell on insect wings.

pterote (tĕrōt, ptĕr'ōt) *a.* [Gk. *pterotos*, winged.] Winged; having wing-like outgrowths; alate.

pterotheca (tĕr'ōthē'kă, ptĕr-) *n.* [Gk. *pteron*, wing; *theke*, case.] The wing-case of pupae.

pterotic (tĕrō'tĭk, ptĕr-) *n.* [Gk. *pteron*, wing; *ous*, ear.] A cranial bone overlying horizontal semicircular canal of ear *a. Appl.* bone between prootic and epiotic.

pteroylglutamic acid,—vitamin M or folic acid, *q.v.*

pterygial (tĕrĭj'ĭăl, ptĕr-) *a.* [Gk. *pteryx*, wing.] *Pert.* a wing or fin; *appl.* a bone supporting a fin-ray; *pert.* a pterygium.

pterygiophore (tĕrĭj'ĭōfōr, ptĕr-) *n.* [Gk. *pterygion*, little wing; *pherein*, to bear.] One of the cartilaginous fin-rays; an actinost, *q.v.*

pterygium (tĕrĭj'ĭŭm, ptĕr-) *n.* [Gk. *pterygion*, little wing.] A prothoracic process of weevils; a small lobe on base of under-wings in Lepidoptera; a vertebrate limb.

pterygobranchiate (tĕr'ĭgōbrăng'-kĭāt, ptĕr-) *a.* [Gk. *pteryx*, wing; *brangchia*, gills.] Having spreading or feathery gills, as certain Crustacea.

pterygoda (tĕr′ĭgōdă, ptĕr-) *n. plu.* [Gk. *pteryx*, wing; *eidos*, form.] The tegulae of an insect.

pterygoid (tĕr′ĭgoid, ptĕr-) *n.* [Gk. *pteryx*, wing; *eidos*, form.] A cranial bone. *a.* Wing-like; *appl.* wing-like processes of sphenoid, canal, fissure, fossa, plexus, muscles.

pterygoideus,—externus and internus, muscles causing protrusion and raising of mandible.

pterygomandibular (tĕr′ĭgömăndĭb′ūlăr, ptĕr-) *a.* [Gk. *pteryx*, wing; L. *mandibulum*, jaw.] *Pert.* pterygoid and mandible; *appl.* a tendinous band or raphe of buccopharyngeal muscle.

pterygomaxillary (tĕr′ĭgömăksĭl′ărĭ, ptĕr-) *a.* [Gk. *pteryx*, wing; L. *maxilla*, jaw.] *Appl.* a fissure between maxilla and pterygoid process of sphenoid.

pterygopalatine (tĕr′ĭgöpăl′ătĭn, ptĕr-) *a.* [Gk. *pteryx*, wing; L. *palatus*, palate.] *Pert.* region of pterygoid and palatal cranial bones; *appl.* canal, fossa, groove, ganglion; pterygopalatal.

pterygophore,—pterygiophore, *q.v.*

pterygopodial (tĕr′ĭgöpō′dĭăl, ptĕr-) *a.* [Gk. *pteryx*, wing; *pous*, foot.] *Appl.* mucous glands associated with claspers, in elasmobranchs.

pterygoquadrate (tĕr′ĭgökwôd′rāt, ptĕr-) *a.* [Gk. *pteryx*, wing; L. *quadratus*, squared.] *Appl.* a cartilage constituting dorsal half of mandibular arch of certain fishes.

pterygospinous (tĕr′ĭgöspī′nŭs, ptĕr-) *a.* [Gk. *pteryx*, wing; L. *spina*, spine.] *Appl.* a ligament between lateral pterygoid plate and spinous process of sphenoid.

pterylae (tĕr′ĭlē, ptĕr-) *n. plu.* [Gk. *pteron*, feather; *hyle*, a wood.] A bird's feather-tracts, skin areas on which feathers grow; *opp.* apteria.

pterylosis (tĕrĭlō′sĭs, ptĕr-) *n.* [Gk. *pteron*, feather; *hyle*, a wood.] Arrangement of pterylae and apteria in birds.

ptilinum (tĭlī′nŭm, ptĭl-) *n.* [Gk. *ptilon*, feather.] A head-vesicle or bladder-like expansion of head of a fly emerging from pupa.

ptilopaedic (tĭlöpē′dĭk, ptĭl-) *a.* [Gk. *ptilon*, feather; *pais*, child.] Covered with down when hatched.

ptilosis,—pterylosis.

ptyalin (tī′ălĭn, ptī-) *n.* [Gk. *ptyalon*, saliva.] The starch-digesting enzyme of saliva; salivary amylase.

ptyophagous (tīŏf′ăgŭs, ptī-) *a.* [Gk. *ptyein* to spit; *phagein*, to eat.] Digesting, by host cells, the cytoplasm emitted by tips of hyphae, *appl.* a type of mycorrhiza; *cf.* plasmoptysis.

ptyosome (tī′ösōm, ptī-) *n.* [Gk. *ptyein*, to spit; *soma*, body.] Cytoplasmic mass formed by plasmoptysis, *q.v.*, in ptyophagous mycorrhiza.

ptyxis (tĭk′sĭs, ptĭk′sĭs) *n.* [Gk. *ptyxis*, fold.] The form in which young leaves are folded or rolled on themselves in the bud.

puberty (pū′bĕrtĭ) *n.* [L. *pubertas*, adult state.] Beginning of sexual maturity.

puberulent (pūbĕr′ūlĕnt) *a.* [L. *pubes*, adult.] Covered with down or fine hair.

pubes (pūbēz) *n.* [L. *pubes*, adult.] The pubic region.

pubescence (pū′bĕs′ĕnt) *n.* [L. *pubescere*, to become mature.] Downy or hairy covering on some plants and certain insects.

pubescent (pūbĕs′ĕnt) *a.* [L. *pubescere*, to become mature.] Covered with soft hair or down.

pubic (pū′bĭk) *a.* [L. *pubes*, mature.] In region of pubes; *appl.* arch, ligament, symphysis, tubercle, vein.

pubis (pū′bĭs) *n.* [L. *pubes*, mature.] Anterior part of hip-bone, consisting of body and rami; antero-ventral portion of pelvic girdle; os pubis.

pudendal (pūdĕn′dăl) *a.* [L. *pudere*, to be ashamed.] In region of pudendum; *appl.* artery, cleft, nerve, veins; pudic.

pudendum (pūdĕn′dŭm) *n.* [L. *pudere*, to be ashamed.] Vulva, or external female genitalia.

pudic,—pudendal.

puffing,—ejection of a cloud of spores from ripe ascocarp or apothecium.

pullulation (pŭl'ūlā'shŭn) *n.* [L. *pullulare*, to sprout.] Gemmation; reproduction by vegetative budding, as in yeast cells.

pulmobranchia (pŭl'mōbrăng'kĭă) *n.* [L. *pulmo*, lung; Gk. *brangchia*, gills.] A gill-like organ adapted to air-breathing conditions; a lung book, as of spiders.

pulmogastric (pŭl'mōgăs'trĭk) *a.* [L. *pulmo*, lung; Gk. *gaster*, stomach.] *Pert.* lungs and stomach.

pulmonary (pŭl'mŏnărĭ) *a.* [L. *pulmo*, lung.] *Pert.* lungs; *appl.* artery, ligament, valves, veins, pleura, etc.

pulmonary cavity or **sac,**—the mantle-cavity of molluscs without ctenidia.

pulmones (pŭlmō'nēz) *n. plu.* [L. *pulmo*, lung.] Lungs.

pulp (pŭlp) *n.* [L. *pulpa*, fruit-pulp.] Soft, fleshy part of fruit; the dental papilla; soft mass of splenic tissue; mesodermal core of feather cylinder.

pulsating vacuole,—contractile vacuole.

pulse (pŭls) *n.* [L. *pulsus*, driven.] The beat or throb observable in arteries, due to action of heart. [O.F. *pols*, from L. *puls*, pottage.] A legume; a leguminous plant.

pulse wave,—a wave of increased pressure over arterial system, started by ventricular systole.

pulsellum (pŭlsĕl'ŭm) *n.* [L. *pulsare*, to beat.] A flagellum situated at posterior end of protozoan body.

pulverulent (pŭlvĕr'ūlĕnt) *a.* [L. *pulverulentus*, dusty.] Powdery; powdered.

pulvillar (pŭlvĭl'ăr) *a.* [L. *pulvillus*, small cushion.] *Pert.* or at a pulvillus.

pulvilliform (pŭlvĭl'ĭfôrm) *a.* [L. *pulvillus*, small cushion; *forma*, shape.] Like a small cushion.

pulvillus (pŭlvĭl'ŭs) *n.* [L. *pulvillus*, small cushion.] Pad, process, or membrane on foot or between claws, sometimes serving as an adhesive organ, in insects; lobe beneath each claw.

pulvinar (pŭlvī'năr) *n.* [L. *pulvinar*, couch.] An angular prominence on thalamus. [L. *pulvinus*.] *a.* Cushion-like; *pert.* a pulvinus.

pulvinate (pŭl'vĭnāt) *a.* [L. *pulvinus*, cushion.] Cushion-like; *appl.* a repugnatorial gland in ants; having a pulvinus.

pulvinoid (pŭlvī'noid) *a.* [L. *pulvinus*, cushion; Gk. *eidos*, form.] Resembling a pulvinus; *appl.* modified petiole.

pulvinulus (pŭlvĭn'ūlŭs) *n.* [L. *pulvinus*, cushion.] A pulvillus *q.v.*; a branched outgrowth of thallus of certain lichens.

pulvinus (pŭlvī'nŭs) *n.* [L. *pulvinus*, cushion.] A cellular swelling at junction of axis and leaf-stalk.

pulviplume (pŭl'vĭploom) *n.* [L. *pulvis*, powder; *pluma*, feather.] A powder-down feather.

punctate (pŭng'ktāt) *a.* [L. *punctum*, point.] Dotted; having surface covered with small holes or dots; having a dot-like appearance.

punctulate (pŭng'ktūlāt) *a.* [L. *dim.* of *punctum*, point.] Covered with very small dots or holes.

punctum (pŭng'ktŭm) *n.* [L. *punctum*, point.] A minute dot, point, or orifice, as puncta lacrimalia, puncta vasculosa; apex of a growing point, punctum vegetationis.

puncture (pŭng'ktūr) *n.* [L. *punctura*, prick.] A small round surface depression.

pupa (pū'pă) *n.* [L. *pupa*, puppet.] The third or chrysalis stage of insect life; insect enclosed in a case, during stage in metamorphosis preceding imago; embryo with series of transverse rings of cilia, in Holothuria.

pupal (pū'păl) *a.* [L. *pupa*, puppet.] *Pert.* pupa.

puparium (pūpā'rĭŭm) *n.* [L. *pupa*, puppet.] The casing of a pupa; a coarctate pupa; pupal instar, exemplified in blow-fly.
pupate (pūpāt') *v.* [L. *pupa*, puppet.] To pass into the pupal stage.
pupiform (pū'pĭfôrm) *a.* [L. *pupa*, puppet; *forma*, shape.] Pupa-shaped; pupa-like.
pupigerous (pūpĭj'ërŭs) *a.* [L. *pupa*, puppet; *gerere*, to bear.] Containing a pupa.
pupil (pū'pĭl) *n.* [L. *pupilla*, pupil of eye.] Aperture of iris through which rays pass to retina; central spot of an ocellus.
pupillary (pū'pĭlărĭ, pūpĭl'ărĭ) *a.* [L. *pupilla*, pupil of eye.] *Pert.* pupil of eye; *appl.* a membrane.
pupiparous (pūpĭp'ărŭs) *a.* [L. *pupa*, puppet; *parere*, to beget.] Bringing forth young already developed to the pupa stage, as certain parasitic insects.
purines (pū'rĭnz) *n. plu.* [Gk. *pyren*, nucleus.] Basic substances containing carbon, hydrogen, and nitrogen, as adenine and guanine, occurring during metabolism.
Purkinje cells [*J. E. Purkinje*, Bohemian physiologist]. An incomplete stratum of flask-shaped cells between the molecular and nuclear layers of cerebellar cortex.
Purkinje fibres,—muscle fibres in atrioventricular bundle and its terminal strands, differing from typical cardiac fibres especially in a higher rate of conduction of the contractile impulse.
pustule (pŭs'tūl) *n.* [L. *pustula*, blister.] A blister-like prominence.
pusule (pū'sūl) *n.* [L. *pusula*, blister.] Non-contractile vacuole containing watery fluid, filling or emptying by duct, found in many Dinoflagellata; a contractile vacuole in some protophytes; pusula.
putamen (pūtā'mĕn) *n.* [L. *putamen*, nut-shell.] The hard endocarp or stone of some fruits; lateral part of lentiform nucleus of cerebrum; shell membrane of bird's egg.
putrefaction (pū'trĕfăk'shŭn) *n.* [L. *putrefacere*, to make rotten.] The decomposition of proteins by anaerobic micro-organisms.
pycnial,—pycnidial.
pycnic (pĭk'nĭk) *a.* [Gk. *pyknos*, thick.] Thick-set; *appl.* type of body-build, short, stocky, with broad face and head; pyknic.
pycnid,—pycnidium.
pycnidia,—*plu.* of pycnidium.
pycnidial,—*pert.* pycnidia; *appl.* drops: fungal nectar; pycnial.
pycnidiophore (pĭknĭd'ĭöfōr) *n.* [Gk. *pyknos*, dense; *idion*, *dim.*; *pherein*, to bear.] A conidiophore producing pycnidia.
pycnidiospore (pĭknĭd'ĭöspōr) *n.* [Gk. *pyknos*, dense; *idion*, *dim.*; *sporos*, seed.] The spore produced by pycnidia; pycnidial conidium.
pycnidium (pĭknĭd'ĭŭm) *n.* [Gk. *pyknos*, dense; *idion*, *dim.*] A small flask-shaped organ or spermogonium containing slender filaments which form pycnidiospores or spermatia by abstriction, in life-history of wheat rust; receptacle for stylospores in fungi and lichens; pycnium.
pycnoconidangium, — spermogonium.
pycnoconidium, pycnogonidium, —pycnidiospore, *q.v.*
pycnoplasson (pĭk'nöplăs'ŏn) *n.* [Gk. *pyknos*, dense; *plassein*, to mould.] An unexpanded form of plasson.
pycnosis (pĭknō'sĭs) *n.* [Gk. *pyknosis*, condensation.] Cell-degeneration; nuclear condensation; formation of intensely staining clump of chromosomes; thickening of thallus, as in certain Ascomycetes; also pyknosis.
pycnospore,—pycnidiospore, *q.v.*
pycnotic (pĭknŏt'ĭk) *a.* [Gk. *pyknosis*, condensation.] Characterised by, or *pert.* pycnosis; *appl.* small irregular nucleus of degenerated cells; also pyknotic.
pycnoxylic (pĭknözī'lĭk) *a.* [Gk. *pyknos*, dense; *xylon*, wood.] Having compact wood. *Opp.* manoxylic.

pygal (pī'găl) *a.* [Gk. *pyge*, rump.] Situated at or *pert.* posterior end of back; *appl.* certain plates of chelonian carapace.

pygidial (pī'jĭd'ĭăl) *a.* [Gk. *pygidion*, narrow rump.] *Pert.* pygidium; *appl.* paired repugnatorial glands in certain beetles.

pygidium (pījĭd'ĭŭm) *n.* [Gk. *pygidion*, narrow rump.] A caudal shield covering abdomen of certain arthropods; terminal uncovered abdominal segment of a beetle; compound terminal segment of a scale insect; sensory dorsal plate of ninth abdominal segment of fleas; anal segment of annelids.

pygochord (pī'gōkôrd) *n.* [Gk. *pyge*, rump; *chorde*, cord.] A ventral median ridge-like outgrowth of intestinal epithelium in certain Enteropneusta.

pygostyle (pī'gōstīl) *n.* [Gk. *pyge*, rump; *stylos*, column.] An upturned compressed bone at end of vertebral column of birds, formed by fusion of hindmost vertebrae.

pykn-,—*see* pycn-.

pylangium (pĭlăn'jĭŭm) *n.* [Gk. *pyle*, gate; *anggeion*, vessel.] Proximal portion of a truncus arteriosus.

pylocyte (pī'lōsīt) *n.* [Gk. *pylos*, gateway; *kytos*, hollow.] A pore-cell at inner end of small funnel-shaped depression, the porocyte of certain sponges.

pylome (pī'lōm) *n.* [Gk. *pyloma*, gate.] In certain Sarcodina, an aperture for emission of pseudopodia and reception of food.

pyloric (pīlŏr'ĭk) *a.* [Gk. *pyloros*, gate-keeper.] *Pert.* or in region of pylorus; *appl.* artery, antrum, glands, orifice, valve, vein; *appl.* posterior region of gizzard in decapod crustaceans, and to ossicle in gastric mill; *appl.* sphincter between mid-gut and hind-gut, in insects.

pylorus (pīlō'rŭs) *n.* [Gk. *pyloros*, gate-keeper.] Lower orifice of stomach, communicating with duodenum.

pyogenic (pīōjĕn'ĭk) *a.* [Gk. *pyon*, pus; *gennaein*, to produce.] Pus-forming; *appl.* bacteria; pyogenetic.

pyramid (pĭr'ămĭd) *n.* [L. *pyramis*, pyramid.] A conical structure, protuberance, eminence, as of cerebellum, medulla oblongata, temporal bone, vestibule, kidney; pyramidal cell of cerebral cortex; a piece of the dental apparatus of echinoids.

pyramidal (pĭrăm'ĭdăl) *a.* [L. *pyramis*, pyramid.] Conical; like a pyramid; *appl.* leaves, a carpal bone, brain cells, tract, lobes, processes, muscles.

pyrene (pī'rēn) *n.* [Gk. *pyren*, fruit-stone.] A fruit-stone or kernel; putamen.

pyrenin (pīrē'nĭn) *n.* [Gk. *pyren*, fruit-stone.] The substance of a true nucleolus, paranuclein.

pyrenocarp (pīrē'nōkârp) *n.* [Gk. *pyren*, fruit-stone; *karpos*, fruit.] An ascocarp with a small terminal opening; a perithecium; a fleshy fruit with stone or hard kernel; drupaceous fruit.

pyrenoid (pīrē'noid) *n.* [Gk. *pyren*, fruit-stone; *eidos*, form.] A colourless plastid of lower plants, a centre of starch formation. *a.* Nucleiform.

pyrenophore (pīrē'nōfōr) *n.* [Gk. *pyren*, fruit-stone; *pherein*, to bear.] Part of cytoplasm which contains the nucleus.

pyretic (pīrĕt'ĭk) *a.* [Gk. *pyretos*, fever.] Increasing heat production; causing rise in body temperature.

pyridoxine,—vitamin B_6, rat anti-dermatitis factor or adermin; $C_8H_{11}NO_3$.

pyriform (pĭr'ĭfôrm) *a.* [L. *pyrum*, pear; *forma*, shape.] Pear-shaped; *appl.* cells, spores, etc.; *appl.* a muscle, a larval sensory organ in Bryozoa, an organ of larval molluscs, vestigial left vesicula seminalis of nautilus, a type of silk gland in spiders, etc.; piriform, *q.v.*

pyxidiate (pĭksĭd'ĭāt) *a.* [Gk. *pyxis*, box; *idion*, *dim.*] Opening like a box by transverse dehiscence; *pert.*, or like, a pyxidium or a pyxis.

pyxidium (pĭksĭd′ĭŭm) *n.* [Gk. *pyxis*, box; *idion*, *dim.*] A pyxis, or a capsular fruit which dehisces transversely.

pyxis (pĭk′sĭs) *n.* [Gk. *pyxis*, box.] A dilatation of podetium in lichens.

Q

Q-disc,—anisotropic or A-disc, *q.v.*

quadrangular (kwŏdrăng′gūlăr) *a.* [L. *quadrangulus.*] *Appl.* lobes or lobules of cerebellar hemispheres, connected by monticulus.

quadrant (kwŏd′rănt) *n.* [L. *quadrans*, fourth part.] All the cells derived by divisions from one of the first four cleavage cells or blastomeres.

quadrat (kwŏd′răt) *n.* [L. *quadratus*, squared.] A small square or rectangular area delimited on ground selected for botanical or other biological studies.

quadrate (kwŏd′rāt) *n.* [L. *quadratus*, squared.] The bone with which lower jaw articulates in birds, reptiles, amphibians, and fishes; ligament extending from annular ligament to neck of radius; one of lobes of liver; lobe of cerebrum, the praecuneus. *a. Appl.* plates: paired sclerites at base of sting in Hymenoptera.

quadratojugal (kwŏdrā′töjoo′găl) *n.* [L. *quadratus*, squared; *jugum*, yoke.] Membranous bone connecting quadrate and jugal bones; quadratomaxillary.

quadratomandibular (kwŏdrā′tömăndĭb′ūlăr) *a.* [L. *quadratus*, squared; *mandibulum*, jaw.] *Pert.* quadrate and mandibulum.

quadratomaxillary,—quadratojugal.

quadratus (kwŏdrā′tŭs) *n.* [L. *quadratus*, squared.] Name of several muscles: quadratus femoris, labii, lumborum, plantae.

quadricarpellary (kwŏd′rĭkâr′pĕlărĭ) *a.* [L. *quattuor*, four; Gk. *karpos*, fruit.] Containing four carpels.

quadriceps (kwŏd′rĭsĕps) *n.* [L. *quattuor*, four; *caput*, head.] Muscle in front of thigh, extending lower leg and divided into four portions at upper end.

quadrifarious (kwŏdrĭfā′rĭŭs) *a.* [L. *quadrifariam*, four-fold.] In four rows; *appl.* leaves.

quadrifid (kwŏd′rĭfĭd) *a.* [L. *quattuor*, four; *findere*, to cleave.] Deeply cleft into four parts.

quadrifoliate (kwŏd′rĭfō′lĭāt) *a.* [L. *quattuor*, four; *folium*, leaf.] Four-leaved; *appl.* compound palmate leaf, with four leaflets arising at a common point.

quadrigeminal bodies, — corpora quadrigemina, *q.v.*

quadrijugate (kwŏd′rĭjoo′gāt) *a.* [L. *quattuor*, four; *jugum*, yoke.] *Appl.* pinnate leaf having four pairs of leaflets.

quadrilobate (kwŏd′rĭlō′bāt) *a.* [L. *quattuor*, four; *lobus*, lobe.] Four-lobed.

quadrilocular (kwŏd′rĭlŏk′ūlăr) *a.* [L. *quattuor*, four; *loculus*, compartment.] Having four loculi or chambers, as ovary, or anthers, of certain plants.

quadrimaculate (kwŏd′rĭmăk′ūlāt) *a.* [L. *quattuor*, four; *macula*, spot.] Having four spots.

quadrinate,—quadrifoliate, *q.v.*

quadripennate (kwŏd′rĭpĕn′āt) *a.* [L. *quattuor*, four; *penna*, wing.] With four wings.

quadriserial (kwŏd′rĭsē′rĭăl) *a.* [L. *quattuor*, four; *series*, row.] Arranged in four rows or series; quadriseriate.

quadritubercular (kwŏd′rĭtūbĕr′kūlăr) *a.* [L. *quattuor*, four; *tuberculum*, small hump.] *Appl.* teeth with four tubercles.

quadrivalent (kwôdrĭv′ălĕnt) *n.* [L. *quattuor*, four; *valere*, to be strong.] Association of four chromosomes held together by chiasmata between diplotene and metaphase of first division in meiosis.

quadrivoltine (kwŏd′rĭvŏl′tĭn) *a.* [L. *quattuor*, four; It. *volta*, time.] Having four broods in a year; *appl.* certain silkworms.

quadrumanous (kwŏdroo′mănŭs) *a.* [L. *quattuor*, four; *manus*, hand.] Having hind-feet, as well as front feet, constructed like hands, as most Primates except man.

quadrupedal (kwŏdroo′pĕdăl) *a.* [L. *quadrupes*, four-footed.] Having, or walking on, four feet; *pert.* four-footed animals.

quadruplex (kwŏd′rooplĕks) *a.* [L. *quadruplex*, four-fold.] Having four dominant genes, in polyploidy.

quartet (kwôrtĕt′) *n.* [L. *quartus*, fourth.] A group of four nuclei or cells resulting from the two meiotic mitoses; *cf.* tetrad; four cells derived from a sporocyte, or resulting from meridional and horizontal cleavage.

quaternary (kwŏtĕr′nărĭ) *a.* [L. *quaterni*, four each.] *Appl.* flower symmetry when there are four parts in a whorl.

Quaternary,—*appl.* or *pert.* period comprising Pleistocene and Holocene epochs.

quaternate (kwŏtĕr′nāt) *a.* [L. *quaterni*, four each.] In sets of four; *appl.* leaves growing in fours from one point.

queen (kwēn) *n.* [A.S. *cwen*, woman.] The reproductive female in colonies of social Hymenoptera.

quiescence (kwīĕs′ĕns) *n.* [L. *quiescere*, to become still.] Temporary cessation of development, or of other activity, owing to unfavourable environment; *cf.* diapause.

quill (kwĭl) *n.* [M.E. *quille*, feather.] The calamus or barrel of a feather; the calamus and rachis; a hollow spine, as of porcupine.

quill feathers,—feathers of wings (remiges) and tail (rectrices) of bird.

quill-knobs,—tubercles or exostoses on ulna of birds, for attachment of fibrous ligaments connecting with quill follicle.

quinary (kwī′nărĭ) *a.* [L. *quini*, five each.] *Appl.* flower symmetry when there are five parts in a whorl.

quinate (kwī′nāt) *a.* [L. *quini*, five each.] *Appl.* five leaflets growing from one point; quinquefoliolate.

quincuncial (kwĭnkŭn′sĭăl) *a.* [L. *quinque*, five; *uncia*, twelfth part.] Arranged in quincunx.

quincunx (kwĭn′kŭngks) *n.* [L. *quinque*, five; *uncia*, twelfth part.] Arrangement of five structures of which four are at corners of a square and one at centre; arrangement of five petals or leaves, of which two are exterior, two interior, and the fifth partly exterior, partly interior.

quinquecostate (kwĭn′kwĕkŏs′tāt) *a.* [L. *quinque*, five; *costa*, rib.] Having five ribs on the leaf.

quinquefarious (kwĭn′kwĕfā′rĭŭs) *a.* [L. *quinque*, five; *fariam*, in rows.] In five directions, rows, or parts.

quinquefid (kwĭn′kwĕfĭd) *a.* [L. *quinque*, five; *findere*, to cleave.] Cleft into five parts.

quinquefoliate (kwĭn′kwĕfō′lĭāt) *a.* [L. *quinque*, five; *folium*, leaf.] With five leaves.

quinquefoliolate,—quinate, *q.v.*

quinquelobate (kwĭn′kwĕlō′bāt) *a.* [L. *quinque*, five; L.L. *lobus*, lobe.] With five lobes.

quinquepartite (kwĭn′kwĕpâr′tīt) *a.* [L. *quinque*, five; *partitus*, divided.] Divided into five parts.

quinquetubercular (kwĭn′kwĕtūbĕr′kūlăr) *a.* [L. *quinque*, five; *tuberculum*, small hump.] *Appl.* molar teeth with five tubercles.

R

race (rās) *n.* [F. *race*, race, family.] A permanent variety; a particular breed; a microspecies.

racemation (răs′ĕmā′shŭn) *n.* [L. *racemus*, bunch.] A cluster, as of grapes.

raceme (răsēm′) *n.* [L. *racemus*, bunch.] Inflorescence having a common axis and stalked flowers in acropetal succession, as hyacinth.

racemiferous (răsĕmĭf′ĕrŭs) *a.* [L. *racemus*, bunch; *ferre*, to carry.] Bearing racemes.

racemiform (răsē′mĭfôrm) *a.* [L. *racemus*, bunch; *forma*, shape.] In the form of a raceme.

racemose (răs'ēmōs) *a.* [L. *racemus*, bunch.] Bearing flowers in clusters; *appl.* inflorescence with monopodial branching, as racemes, spikes; *appl.* glands with many branches whose shape suggests a raceme.

racemule (răs'ēmūl) *n.* [L. *racemulus*, small bunch.] A small raceme.

racemulose (răsĕm'ūlōs) *a.* [L. *racemulus*, small bunch.] In small clusters.

rachial (rā'kĭăl) *a.* [Gk. *rhachis*, spine.] *Pert.* a rachis; rhachial.

rachidial (răkĭd'ĭăl) *a.* [Gk. *rhachis*, spine.] *Pert.* a rachis.

rachidian (răkĭd'ĭăn) *a.* [Gk. *rhachis*, spine.] Placed at or near a rachis; *appl.* median tooth in row of teeth of radula.

rachiform (rā'kĭfôrm) *a.* [Gk. *rhachis*, spine; L. *forma*, shape.] In the form of a rachis.

rachiglossate (rā'kĭglŏs'āt) *a.* [Gk. *rhachis*, spine; *glossa*, tongue.] Having a radula with pointed teeth, as whelks.

rachilla (răkĭl'ă) *n.* [Gk. *rhachis*, spine.] A small rachis; axis of spikelet, as in grasses.

rachiodont (răk'ĭŏdŏnt) *a.* [Gk. *rhachis*, spine; *odous*, tooth.] *Appl.* egg-eating snakes with well-developed hypophyses of anterior thoracic vertebræ, which function as teeth.

rachiostichous (răk'ĭŏs'tĭkŭs) *a.* [Gk. *rhachis*, spine; *stichos*, row.] Having a succession of somactids as axis of fin skeleton, as in dipnoans.

rachis (rā'kĭs) *n.* [Gk. *rhachis*, spine.] The spinal column; the stalk or axis; the shaft of a feather; median dorsal elevation of opisthosoma in trilobites; rhachis.

rachitomous (răkĭt'ŏmŭs) *a.* [Gk. *rhachis*, spine; *tomos*, cut.] Temnospondylous, *q.v.*

racket cells,—*see* raquet mycelium.

radial (rā'dĭăl) *a.* [L. *radius*, ray.] *Pert.* radius; *pert.* ray of an echinoderm; *appl.* plates supporting oral disc of crinoids; *appl.* fibres supporting retina; *appl.* leaves or flowers growing out like rays from a centre. *n.* An endoskeletal support of fin in fishes; cross-vein of wing in insects.

radial notch,—lesser sigmoid cavity of coronoid process of ulna.

radial symmetry,—arrangement of similar parts round a median vertical axis, as in jellyfish.

radiale (rādĭā'lē) *n.* [L. *radius*, ray.] A carpal bone in line with radius.

radiant (rā'dĭănt) *a.* [L. *radians*, radiating.] Emitting rays; radiating; *pert.* radiants; *pert.* radiation. *n.* An organism or group of organisms dispersed from an original geographical location.

radiate (rā'dĭāt) *a.* [L. *radius*, ray.] Radially symmetrical; radiating, *appl.* sternocostal ligaments; stellate, *appl.* ligament connecting head of rib with two vertebrae and their intervertebral disc.

radiate-veined,—veined in a palmate manner.

radiatiform (rā'dĭā'tĭfôrm) *a.* [L. *radius*, ray; *forma*, shape.] With radiating marginal florets.

radical (răd'ĭkăl) *a.* [L. *radix*, root.] Arising from root close to ground, as basal leaves and peduncles. *n.* A group of atoms that does not exist in the free state but as a unit in a compound, as OH, NH_4, C_6H_5, etc.

radicant (răd'ĭkănt) *a.* [L. *radicari*, to take root.] With roots developing from stem; rooting.

radicate (răd'ĭkāt) *a.* [L. *radicatus*, rooted.] Rooted; possessing root-like structures; fixed to substrate as if rooted.

radicel (răd'ĭsĕl) *n.* [*Dim.* of L. *radix*, root.] A small root; rootlet.

radicicolous,—radicolous.

radiciflorous (rădĭsĭflō'rŭs) *a.* [L. *radix*, root; *flos*, flower.] With flowers arising at extreme base of stem; rhizanthous.

radiciform (rădĭs'ĭfôrm) *a.* [L. *radix*, root; *forma*, shape.] Resembling a root; radicine.

radicivorous (răd'ĭsĭv'ŏrŭs) *a.* [L. *radix*, root; *vorare*, to devour.] Root-eating.

radicle (răd′ĭkl) *n.* [L. *radix*, root.] A small root; primary root; lower part of tigellum.

radicolous (rădĭk′ölŭs) *a.* [L. *radix*, root; *colere*, to inhabit.] Inhabiting roots; radicicolous.

radicose (răd′ĭkōs) *a.* [L. *radix*, root.] With large root.

radicular (rădĭk′ūlăr) *a.* [L. *radix*, root.] *Pert.* a radicule or radicle.

radicule (răd′ĭkūl) *n.* [L. *radix*, root.] A rootlet.

radiculose (rădĭk′ūlōs) *a.* [L. *radix*, root.] Having many rootlets.

radiobiology (rā′dĭöbīŏl′öjĭ) *n.* [L. *radius*, ray; Gk. *bios*, life; *logos*, discourse.] The study of the effects of radioactivity on living cells and organisms.

radiocarbon (rā′dĭökâr′bŏn) *n.* [L. *radius*, ray; *carbo*, charcoal.] A radioactive isotope of carbon, C^{14}, used in chronological and physiological research.

radiocarpal (rā′dĭökâr′păl) *a.* [L. *radius*, ray; L.L. *carpus*, wrist.] *Pert.* radius and wrist.

radioecology (rā′dĭöēkŏl′öjĭ) *n.* [L. *radius*, ray; Gk. *oikos*, household; *logos*, discourse.] The study of radiation as affecting the relationship between living organisms and environment, and of the ecological effects and destination of radioisotopes; radiation ecology.

radioiodine (rā′dĭöī′ödĭn) *n.* [L. *radius*, ray; Gk. *io-eides*, violet-coloured.] A radioactive isotope of iodine, I^{131}, used in studying the thyroid gland.

radiole (rā′dĭōl) *n.* [L. *radiolus*, small shuttle.] A spine of sea-urchins.

radiomedial (rā′dĭömē′dĭăl) *n.* [L. *radius*, ray; *medius*, middle.] A cross-vein between radius and medius of insect wing.

radiophosphorus (rā′dĭöfŏs′förŭs) *n.* [L. *radius*, ray; Gk. *phosphoros*, bringing light.] A radioactive isotope of phosphorus, P^{32}, used in physiological research and therapeutics.

radioreceptor (rā′dĭörēsĕp′tŏr) *n.* [L. *radius*, ray; *receptor*, receiver.] A terminal organ for receiving light, or temperature, stimuli.

radiosymmetrical (rā′dĭösĭmĕt′rĭkăl) *a.* [L. *radius*, ray; Gk. *syn*, with; *metron*, measure.] Having similar parts similarly arranged round a central axis.

radioulna (rā′dĭöŭl′nă) *n.* [L. *radius*, ray; *ulna*, elbow.] Radius and ulna combined as a single bone.

radioulnar (rā′dĭöŭl′năr) *a.* [L. *radius*, ray; *ulna*, elbow.] *Pert.* radius and ulna.

radius (rā′dĭŭs) *n.* [L. *radius*, ray.] A bone of arm or fore-limb between humerus and carpals, in some vertebrates fused with ulna; barbule, of feather; one of radial depressions or markings on fish scales; a plate of Aristotle's lantern; an insect wing-vein; radial area of disc in sea-anemones; ray of composite flower.

radix (rā′dĭks) *n.* [L. *radix*, root.] A root; point of origin of a structure, as of aorta.

radula (răd′ūlă) *n.* [L. *radere*, to scrape.] A short and broad strip of membrane with longitudinal rows of chitinous teeth in mouth of most gastropods; *cf.* odontophore; a hyphal structure with numerous short lateral sterigmata bearing radula spores; a genus of liverworts.

radulate (răd′ūlāt) *a.* [L. *radere*, to scrape.] Having a radula or rasping organ; raduliferous.

raduliform (răd′ūlĭfôrm) *a.* [L. *radere*, to scrape; *forma*, shape.] Like a radula or flexible file.

Rainey's corpuscles [*G. Rainey*, English morphologist]. Spores of Sarcocystis, an elongated sporozoan found in voluntary muscle fibres.

Rainey's tubes, — elongated sacs found in substance of voluntary muscle, which are adult stages of Dolichosporidia; Miescher's tubes.

ramal (rā′măl) *a.* [L. *ramus*, branch.] Belonging to branches; originating on a branch.

ramate (rā'māt) *a.* [L. *ramus*, branch.] Branched.
ramellose (răm'ĕlōs) *a.* [L. *ramus*, branch.] Having small branches.
rament, ramenta,—*see* ramentum.
ramentaceous (rā'mĕntā'shŭs) *a.* [L. *ramenta*, shavings.] Like a ramentum; covered by ramenta.
ramentiferous (rā'mĕntĭf'ĕrŭs) *a.* [L. *ramenta*, shavings; *ferre*, to carry.] Bearing ramenta.
ramentum (rāmĕn'tŭm) *n.* [L. *ramenta*, shavings.] One of brown scale-like structures found on fern leaves; *plu.* ramenta, elongated membranous hairs, epidermal outgrowths.
rameous (rā'mĕŭs) *a.* [L. *rameus*, *pert.* branches.] Branched; *pert.* a branch.
ramet (rā'mĕt) *n.* [L. *ramus*, branch.] An individual member of a clone; *cf.* ortet.
rami,—*plu.* of ramus.
rami communicantes,—nerve fibres connecting sympathetic ganglia and spinal nerves.
ramicorn (rā'mĭkôrn) *a.* [L. *ramus*, branch; *cornu*, horn.] Having branched antennae, as some insects.
ramiferous (rămĭf'ĕrŭs) *a.* [L. *ramus*, branch; *ferre*, to bear.] Branched.
ramification (răm'ĭfĭkā'shŭn) *n.* [L. *ramus*, branch; *facere*, to make.] Branching; a branch of a tree, nerve, artery, etc.
ramiflorous (răm'ĭflō'rŭs) *a.* [L. *ramus*, branch; *flos*, flower.] Having flowers on branches.
ramiform (răm'ĭfôrm) *a.* [L. *ramus*, branch; *forma*, shape.] Branch-like.
ramigenous,—ramiparous.
ramigerous (rămĭj'ĕrŭs) *a.* [L. *ramus*, branch; *gerere*, to carry.] Bearing branches.
ramiparous (rămĭp'ărŭs) *a.* [L. *ramus*, branch; *parere*, to beget.] Producing branches.
ramoconidium (rā'mōkŏnĭd'ĭŭm) *n.* [L. *ramus*, branch; Gk. *konis*, dust; *idion*, *dim.*] A fungal spore produced from a portion of a conidiophore.
ramose (rā'mōs) *a.* [L. *ramosus*, branching.] Much branched.
ramule (răm'ūl) *n.* [L. *ramulus*, twig.] A small branch; ramulus.
ramuliferous (răm'ūlĭf'ĕrŭs) *a.* [L. *ramulus*, twig; *ferre*, to bear.] Bearing small branches.
ramulose (răm'ūlōs), **ramulous**, (răm'ūlŭs) *a.* [L. *ramulus*, twig.] With many small branches.
ramulus (răm'ūlŭs), **ramuscule** (rămŭs'kūl) *n.* [L. *ramulus*, twig.] A small branch.
ramus (rā'mŭs) *n.* [L. *ramus*, branch.] Any branch-like structure; part of chewing apparatus of rotifers; barb of feathers; mandible, or its proximal part, of vertebrates; branch of a spinal nerve. *Plu.* rami.
ranine (rā'nīn) *a.* [L. *rana*, frog.] *Pert.* under surface of tongue; *appl.* artery and vein.
ranivorous (rănĭv'ōrŭs) *a.* [L. *rana*, frog; *vorare*, to devour.] Feeding on frogs.
Ranvier's nodes [*L.-A. Ranvier*, French histologist]. Constrictions or interruptions of medullary sheath of a nerve fibre.
raphe (rā'fē) *n.* [Gk. *rhaphe*, seam.] A seam-like suture, as junction line of some fruits; line of fusion of funicle and anatropous ovule; a slit-like line in diatom valves; line, or ridge, of perineum, scrotum, hard palate, medulla oblongata, etc.
raphides (răf'ĭdēz) *n. plu.* [Gk. *rhaphis*, needle.] Minute crystals, frequently of calcium oxalate, formed as metabolic by-products in plant cells.
raphidiferous (răf'ĭdĭf'ĕrŭs) *a.* [Gk. *rhaphis*, needle; L. *ferre*, to carry.] Containing raphides.
raptatory (răp'tătōrĭ) *a.* [L. *raptare*, to rob.] Preying.
raptorial (răptō'rĭăl) *a.* [L. *raptor*, robber.] *Appl.* birds of prey.
raquet mycelium,—hyphae enlarged at one end of each segment, small and large ends alternating; racquet or racket mycelium.

rasorial (răsō'rĭăl) *a.* [L. *radere*, to scratch.] Adapted for scratching or scraping, as fowls.

rassenkreis (râs'ĕnkrīs) *n.* [Ger. *Rasse*, race; *Kreis*, circle.] Polytypic species.

rastellus (răstĕl'ŭs) *n.* [L. *rastellus*, rake.] A group of teeth in arachnid chelicera.

rate-gene,—a gene which influences the rate of a developmental process; rate-factor.

Rathke's pouch [*M. H. Rathke*, German anatomist]. Diverticulum of buccal ectoderm in vertebrates, the commencement of prepituitary gland formation; craniobuccal or neurobuccal pouch.

ratite (răt'īt) *a.* [L. *ratis*, raft.] Having an unkeeled sternum. *Opp.* carinate.

rattle (rătl) *n.* [M.E. *ratelen*, to clatter.] The sound-producing series of horny joints at end of rattlesnake's tail; crepitaculum.

Rauber's layer [*A. Rauber*, Estonian anatomist]. Covering layer of cells formed by part of trophoblast on embryonic ectoderm.

Ravian process [*J. J. Rau* or *Ravius*, Dutch anatomist]. Folian process, *q.v.*

ray (rā) *n.* [L. *radius*, ray.] A parenchymatous band penetrating from cortex towards centre of stem; one of bony spines supporting fins; division of a radiate animal, as arm of asteroid; one of straight uriniferous tubules passing from medulla through cortex of kidney (medullary rays).

ray florets,—the outermost florets of a composite flower.

reaction time, — time interval between stimulus and response.

reaction type,—phenotype.

read,—the abomasum or fourth stomach of ruminants.

recapitulation theory,—theory that ontogeny tends to recapitulate phylogeny, that individual life-history reproduces certain stages in life-history of race; biogenetic law; Haeckel's law.

receptacle (rēsĕp'tăkl) *n.* [L. *recipere*, to receive.] An organ used as a repository; peduncle of a racemose inflorescence; torus or thalamus of a flower; modified end of thallus branch containing conceptacles in algae, or soredia in lichens; a pycnidium; a sporophore; terminal disc of mosses.

receptacular (rēsĕptăk'ūlăr) *a.* [L. *recipere*, to receive.] *Pert.* a receptacle of any kind; largely composed of the receptacle, as certain fruits.

receptaculum (rēsĕptăk'ūlŭm) *n.* [L. *receptaculum*, reservoir.] A receptacle of any kind.

receptaculum chyli,—the cavity in lower part of thoracic duct; cisterna chyli.

receptaculum ovorum,—an internal sac in which ova are collected in earthworm.

receptaculum seminis,—female organ for reception of spermatozoa; spermatheca.

receptive spot,—small mucilaginous area adjacent to aperture in an ovum at which sperm enters; point of sperm entry into ovum; antheridial wall at point of contact with oogonium and of penetration of oosphere by fertilisation tube.

receptor (rēsĕp'tŏr) *n.* [L. *receptor*, receiver.] Part of cell which functions as an antibody in combining with outside molecules or haptophores; specialised tissue or cell sensitive to a specific stimulus; sense organ.

recess (rēsĕs') *n.* [L. *recessus*, withdrawn.] A fossa, sinus, cleft, or hollow space, as omental, optic, pineal recess; recessus.

recessive (rēsĕs'ĭv) *a.* [L. *recessus*, withdrawn.] *Appl.* character possessed by one parent which in a hybrid is masked by the corresponding alternative or dominant character derived from the other parent; the allele which is not manifest in the F_1 heterozygote.

reciprocal hybrids,—two hybrids, one descended from male of one species and female of another, the other from a female of first and a male of second.

reclinate (rĕk'lĭnāt) *a.* [L. *reclinare*, to lean.] Curved downwards from apex to base; *appl.* an ovule suspended from a funiculus.

reclining (rēklī'nĭng) *a.* [L. *reclinare*, to lean.] Leaning over; not perpendicular.

recrudescence (rēkroodĕs'ĕns) *n.* [L. *re*, again; *crudescere*, to become violent.] State of breaking out into renewed activity; fresh growth from ripe part; a relapse.

recruitment (rēkroot'mĕnt) *n.* [O.F. *recruter* from L. *recrescere*, to grow again.] Activation of additional motor neurones, causing increased reflex when stimulus of same intensity is continued; facilitation.

rectal (rĕk'tăl) *a.* [L. *rectus*, straight.] *Pert.* rectum; *appl.* gland: a small vascular sac of unknown significance near end of gut in fishes; *appl.* columns: longitudinal folds of mucous membrane of anal canal; anal columns, columns of Morgagni.

rectigradation (rĕk'tĭgrădā'shŭn) *n.* [L. *rectus*, straight; *gradatio*, flight of steps.] Adaptive evolutionary tendency; a structure exhibiting an adaptive trend or sequence in evolution.

rectinerved (rĕk'tĭnĕrvd) *a.* [L. *rectus*, straight; *nervus*, nerve.] With veins or nerves straight.

rectipetality (rĕk'tĭpĕtăl'ĭtĭ) *n.* [L. *rectus*, straight; *petere*, to seek.] Tendency to rectilinear growth; autotropism, *q.v.*

rectirostral (rĕk'tĭrŏs'trăl) *a.* [L. *rectus*, straight; *rostrum*, beak.] Straight-beaked.

rectiserial (rĕk'tĭsē'rĭăl) *a.* [L. *rectus*, straight; *series*, row.] Arranged in straight or vertical rows.

rectivenous (rĕk'tĭvē'nŭs) *a.* [L. *rectus*, straight; *vena*, vein.] With straight veins.

rectogenital (rĕk'töjĕn'ĭtăl) *a.* [L. *rectus*, straight; *genitalia*, genitals.] *Pert.* rectum and genital organs.

recto-uterine (rĕk'töū'tĕrĭn) *a.* [L. *rectus*, straight; *uterus*, womb.] *Appl.* posterior ligaments of uterus.

rectovesical (rĕk'tövĕs'ĭkăl) *a.* [L. *rectus*, straight; *vesica*, bladder.] *Pert.* rectum and bladder.

rectrices (rĕk'trĭsēz) *plu.* [L. *regere*, to rule.] The stiff tail feathers of a bird, used in steering. *Sing.* rectrix.

rectricial (rĕktrĭs'ĭăl) *a.* [L. *regere*, to rule.] *Pert.* rectrices.

rectum (rĕk'tŭm) *n.* [L. *rectus*, straight.] The posterior terminal part of alimentary canal.

rectus (rĕk'tŭs) *n.* [L. *rectus*, straight.] A name for a rectilinear muscle, as rectus femoris, rectus abdominis, etc.

recurrent (rēkŭr'ĕnt) *a.* [L. *re*, back; *currere*, to run.] Returning or re-ascending towards origin.

recurrent sensibility, — sensibility shown by motor roots of spinal cord due to sensory fibres of sensory roots.

recurved (rēkŭrvd') *a.* [L. *recurvus*, bent back.] Bent backwards; recurvate, retrocurved.

recurvirostral (rēkŭr'vĭrŏs'trăl) *a.* [L. *recurvus*, bent back; *rostrum*, beak.] With beak bent upwards.

recutite (rĕk'ūtīt) *a.* [L. *recutitus*, skinned.] Seemingly devoid of epidermis.

red body,—rete mirabile, *q.v.*

red corpuscle,—a coloured blood corpuscle of vertebrates, containing haemoglobin; erythrocyte.

red glands,—rete mirabile, *q.v.*

red nucleus,—collection of nerve cells in tegmentum of midbrain.

redia (rē'dĭă) *n.* [*F. Redi*, Italian scientist]. A larval stage of certain Trematoda.

redintegration (rĕd'ĭntĕgrā'shŭn) *n.* [L. *redintegrare*, to make whole again.] Restoration or regeneration of an injured or lost part.

redox (rēdŏks) *a.* [*red*uction-*ox*idation.] *Pert.* mutual reduction and oxidation.

reduction (rēdŭk'shŭn) *n.* [L. *reductus*, reduced.] Halving of number of chromosomes at meiosis ; structural and functional development less complex than that of ancestry, *opp.* amplification ; decrease in size, as in old age ; decreasing the oxygen content or increasing the proportion of hydrogen in a chemical compound.

reduplicate (rēdū'plĭkāt) *a.* [L. *re*, again ; *duplicare*, to repeat.] *Appl.* aestivation in which margins of bud sepals or petals turn outwards at points of contact.

reduviid (rĕdū'vĭĭd) *a.* [L. *reduvia*, hangnail.] *Appl.* eggs of certain insects, protected by micropyle apparatus with porches.

reflected (rēflĕk'tĕd) *a.* [L. *reflectere*, to turn back.] Turned or folded back on itself.

reflector layer,—layer of cells on inner surface of photogenic tissue, as in fire-flies.

reflex (rē'flĕks) *a.* [L. *reflectere*, to turn back.] Reflected ; involuntary, *appl.* reaction to stimulus. *n.* Function of reflex arc or arcs, being unit reaction or reaction pattern.

reflex action,—simplest expression of principles according to which nervous system acts, involuntary action on activation of reflex arc.

reflex arc,—the unit mechanism of nervous system, consisting of organ whence reaction starts, nervous path, and gland cells or muscle cells ; receptor, conductor, and effector.

reflex chain,—*see* chain behaviour.

reflexed (rēflĕksd') *a.* [L. *reflectere*, to turn back.] Curved or turned backwards.

refracted (rēfrăk'tĕd) *a.* [L. *re*, back ; *frangere*, to break.] Bent backwards at an acute angle.

refractory (rēfrăk'tŏrĭ) *a.* [L. *refractarius*, obstinate.] Unresponsive ; *appl.* period after excitation during which repetition of stimulus fails to induce a response.

regeneration (rējĕn'ĕrā'shŭn) *n.* [L. *re*, again ; *generare*, to beget.] Renewal of a portion of body which has been injured or lost.

regma (rĕg'mă) *n.* [Gk. *rhegma*, fracture.] A seed-vessel whose valves open by elastic movement.

regular (rĕg'ūlăr) *a.* [L. *regula*, rule.] Radially symmetrical or actinomorphic ; *appl.* flower.

Reil, island of,—*see* insula.

Reissner's membrane [*E. Reissner*, German physiologist]. The membrana vestibularis, stretching from lamina spiralis ossea to outer cochlear wall of ear.

rejuvenescence (rē'joovĕnĕs'ĕns) *n.* [L. *re*, again ; *juvenescere*, to grow young.] A renewal of youth ; in cells, renewed life and vigour following on conjugation and interchange and fusion of nuclear and protoplasmic material ; rejuvenation.

relational spiral,—plectonemic coiling round one another of two chromosomes or chromatids ; orthospiral.

relaxation-time,—the period during which excitation subsides after removal of stimulus.

relaxin (rēlăk'sĭn) *n.* [L. *relaxare*, to loosen.] A luteal hormone which produces relaxation of pelvic ligaments during pregnancy.

relay cell,—interneurone or internuncial cell, *q.v.*

relic spiral,—surviving coil of chromosome at telophase and prophase.

relict (rĕl'ĭkt) *a.* [L. *relictus*, abandoned.] Not functional but originally adaptive, *appl.* structures ; surviving in an area isolated from main distribution area, owing to intervention of environmental events, *e.g.* of glaciation ; *appl.* species.

Remak's fibres [*R. Remak*, German anatomist]. Grey or gelatinous nerve fibres ; amyelinate or non-medullated fibres.

Remak's plexus,—Meissner's plexus, *q.v.*

remex (rē′mĕks) *n.*, **remiges** (rĕm′ĭjēz) *plu.* [L. *remex*, rower.] The large feathers or quills of a bird's wing, comprising primaries and secondaries.

remiped (rĕm′ĭpĕd) *n.* [L. *remus*, oar; *pes*, foot.] Having feet adapted for rowing motion.

remotor (rēmō′tŏr) *n.* [L. *removere*, to draw back.] A retractor muscle, *opp.* promotor.

renal (rē′năl) *a.* [L. *ren*, kidney.] *Pert.* kidneys or renes; nephric.

renal columns,—cortical tissue between medullary pyramids of kidney; columns of Bertini.

renal portal,—*appl.* a system of circulation in which some returning blood passes through kidneys.

rendzina (rĕnjē′nă) *n.* [Polish.] Any of a group of rich, dark greyish-brown, limey soils of humid or subhumid grass-lands, having a brown upper layer and yellowish-grey lower layers.

renes (rē′nēz) *n. plu.* [L. *ren*, kidney.] Kidneys.

renette,—a glandular excretory cell in nematodes.

reniculus (rĕnĭk′ūlŭs) *n.* [*Dim.* of L. *ren*, kidney.] Kidney lobe, comprising papillæ, pyramid, and surrounding part of cortex.

reniform (rĕn′ĭfôrm) *a.* [L. *ren*, kidney; *forma*, shape.] Shaped like a kidney.

renin (rē′nĭn) *n.* [L. *ren*, kidney.] A kidney protein, with vasopressor and diuretic effects.

reniportal,—*see* renal portal.

rennin (rĕn′ĭn) *n.* [A.S. *rennan*, to cause to run.] Milk-curdling enzyme of gastric juice, converts caseinogen into casein; also secreted by glandular hairs of insectivorous plants; chymosin.

renopericardial (rē′nōpĕrĭkâr′dĭăl) *a.* [L. *ren*, kidney; Gk. *peri*, round; *kardia*, heart.] *Appl.* a ciliated canal connecting kidney and pericardium in higher molluscs.

repand (rēpănd′) *a.* [L. *repandus*, bent backwards.] With undulated margin; *appl.* leaf; wrinkled; *appl.* colony of bacteria.

repandodentate (rēpăn′dōdĕn′tāt) *a.* [L. *repandus*, bent backwards; *dens*, tooth.] Varying between undulated and toothed.

reparative (rĕpăr′ătĭv) *a.* [L. *reparare*, to mend.] Restoring; *appl.* buds developing after injury to leaf.

repeat (rĕpēt′) *n.* [L. *repetere*, to fetch back.] Duplication or further repetition of a chromosome segment owing to unequal crossing-over.

repent (rē′pĕnt) *a.* [L. *repens*, crawling.] Creeping along the ground.

repletes (rĕplēts′) *n. plu.* [L. *repletus*, filled up.] Workers with distensible crops for storing and regurgitating honey-dew and nectar, and constituting a physiological caste of honey ants.

replicate (rĕp′lĭkāt) *a.* [L. *replicare*, to fold back.] Doubled over on itself.

replicatile (rĕp′lĭkātĭl) *a.* [L. *replicare*, to fold back.] *Appl.* wings folded back on themselves when at rest.

replum (rĕp′lŭm) *n.* [L. *replum*, bolt.] The longitudinal division between valves of some pericarps; a placental dissepiment.

reproduction (rē′prōdŭk′shŭn) *n.* [L. *re*, again; *producere*, to lead forth.] Continuation of species or race, sexually or through cell-rupture, cell-division, budding, spore-formation, conjugation, or parthenogenesis.

reptiloid (rĕp′tĭloid) *a.* [L. *repere*, to crawl; Gk. *eidos*, form.] With characteristics of a reptile.

repugnatorial (rēpŭg′nătō′rĭăl) *a.* [L. *repugnare*, to resist.] Defensive or offensive; *appl.* glands and other structures.

reservoir (rĕz′ërvwâr) *n.* [F. from L. *reservare*, to keep back.] A non-contractile space discharging into gullet of Mastigophora.

residual air,—volume of air remaining in lungs after strongest possible breathing out.

residual meristem,—meristematic ring, *q.v.*

resilifer (rēzĭl'ĭfĕr) *n.* [L. *resilire*, to leap back; *ferre*, to carry.] Projection of valve carrying the resilium; resiliophore.

resilium (rēzĭl'ĭŭm) *n.* [L. *resilire*, to leap back.] The horny flexible hinge of a bivalve.

resin (rĕz'ĭn) *n.* [L. *resina*, resin.] An acidic excretion product of certain plants, either as an amorphous vitreous solid, or, in solution in an essential oil, as a balsam.

resin canals,—ducts in bark, wood, mesophyll, etc., particularly of conifers, lined with glandular epithelium excreting essential oils, *e.g.* terpenes, forming oxidation products, such as resin.

respiration (rĕs'pĭrā'shŭn) *n.* [L. *respiratio*, breathing.] Gaseous interchange between an organism and its surrounding medium.

respiratory enzymes,—enzymes involved in physiological oxidation-reduction processes, *e.g.*, oxidases, dehydrogenases, hydrases, peroxidases, catalases.

respiratory heart,—a name given to auricle and ventricle of right side of heart where there is no direct communication between right and left sides. *Opp.* systemic heart.

respiratory pigments, — pigments concerned with oxidation-reduction processes in living organisms, as haemoglobin, haemocyanin, chlorocruorin, etc., and catalysts, as cytochrome.

respiratory quotient,—the ratio between the volume of carbon dioxide produced and the volume of oxygen used.

restibrachium (rĕstĭbrā'kĭŭm) *n.* [L. *restis*, rope; *brachium*, arm.] Restiform body or inferior peduncle of cerebellum.

restiform (rĕs'tĭfôrm) *a.* [L. *restis*, rope; *forma*, shape.] Having appearance of a rope; *appl.* two bodies of nerve fibres on medulla oblongata, the inferior cerebellar peduncles.

restitution (rĕs'tĭtū'shŭn) *n.* [L. *restitutio*, restoration.] The formation of a single body by union of separate pieces of tissue; the union of separated cells or blastomeres, or at chromosome breaks; regeneration; *appl.* nucleus resulting from failure of first meiotic division.

resupinate (rēsū'pĭnāt) *a.* [L. *resupinare*, to bend back.] So twisted that parts are upside down.

resupination (rēsū'pĭnā'shŭn) *n.* [L. *resupinare*, to bend back.] Inversion.

rete (rē'tē) *n.* [L. *rete*, net.] A net or network; a plexus.

rete Malpighii,—Malpighian layer or deeper portion of epidermis, from stratum granulosum inwards; stratum germinativum.

rete mirabile,—network of blood-vessels, chiefly arterial, in wall of swim-bladder of fishes; and in certain mammals, also called red body, glands, spots, vasoganglion.

rete mucosum,—Malpighian layer.

retecious (rētē'sĭŭs) *a.* [L. *rete*, net.] In form of a network.

reteform,—retiform.

retentate (rētĕn'tāt) *n.* [L. *retentare*, to hold back.] Any substance retained by a semipermeable membrane during dialysis. *Opp.* diffusate or dialysate.

retial (rē'tĭăl, rē'shĭăl) *a.* [L. *rete*, net.] *Pert.* a rete.

retiary (rē'shĭărĭ) *a.* [L. *rete*, net.] Making, or having, a net-like structure; constructing a web; net-like, retecious, retiform.

reticle (rĕt'ĭkl) *n.* [L. *reticulum*, small net.] A reticulum; reticule.

reticular (rētĭk'ūlăr) *a.* [L. *reticulum*, small net.] Having interstices like network; *pert.* a reticulum; *appl.* tissue.

reticular cells,—mesenchymal cells of bone-marrow, lymph glands, and spleen, giving rise to granulocytes, lymphocytes and monocytes.

reticulate (rētĭk'ūlāt) *a.* [L. *reticulatus*, latticed.] Like network; *appl.* nervation of leaf or insect wing; *appl.* thickening of cell-wall; *appl.*

species formation due to intercrossing between several lines.

reticulin (rētĭk′ūlĭn) *n.* [L. *reticulum*, small net.] A scleroprotein resembling collagen, occurring in fibres of reticular tissue.

reticulocyte (rētĭk′ūlōsīt) *n.* [L. *reticulum*, small net; *kytos*, hollow.] An immature erythrocyte, of reticular appearance when stained; proerythrocyte.

reticulo-endothelial (rētĭk′ūlōĕn′dōthē′lĭăl) *a.* [L. *reticulum*, small net; Gk. *endon*, within; *thele*, nipple.] *Appl.* cells, or stationary histiocytes of various organs, and functioning as phagocytes in the production of antibodies, or in destroying erythrocytes; *appl.* system, or metabolic apparatus, consisting of reticulum and endothelial cells and of wandering histiocytes.

reticulose (rētĭk′ūlōs) *a.* [L. *reticulum*, small net.] Of network formation.

reticulospinal (rētĭk′ūlōspī′năl) *a.* [L. *reticulum*, small net; *spina*, spine.] Connecting reticular formation of the brain with spinal cord; *appl.* nerve fibres.

reticulum (rētĭk-ūlŭm) *n.* [L. *reticulum*, small net.] Delicate network of cell protoplasm; cross-fibres about base of petioles in palms; the honey-comb bag or second stomach of a ruminant; the framework of reticular tissue in many organs.

retiform (rē′tĭfôrm) *a.* [L. *rete*, net; *forma*, shape.] In form of a network; also reteform.

retina (rĕt′ĭnă) *n.* [L. *rete*, net.] The inner, nervous membrane of eye which receives images.

retinaculum (rĕt′ĭnăk′ūlŭm) *n.* [L. *retinaculum*, tether.] A small glandular mass to which an orchid pollinium adheres at dehiscence; a fibrous band which holds parts closely together; a minute hooked prominence holding egg-sac in position in cirripedes; a structure linking together fore and hind wings of some insects; appendages modified to hold furcula beneath abdomen in spring-tails. *Plu.* retinacula.

retinaculum tendinum,—annular ligament of wrist or ankle.

retinal (rĕt′ĭnăl) *a.* [L. *rete*, net.] *Pert.* the retina.

retinella (rĕtĭnĕl′ă) *n.* [*Dim.* of L. *rete*, net.] Neurofibrillar network of phaosome.

retinene [rĕt′ĭnēn) *n.* [L. *retina*, retina.] A carotenoid retinal pigment formed from visual yellow in dark-adapted eye; vitamin A aldehyde.

retinerved (rē′tĭnĕrvd) *a.* [L. *rete*, net; *nervus*, sinew.] Having reticulate veins or nerves.

retinoblasts (rĕt′ĭnōblăsts) *n. plu.* [L. *rete*, net; Gk. *blastos*, bud.] Retinal epithelial cells which give rise to neuroblasts and spongioblasts.

retinophore (rĕt′ĭnōfōr) *n.* [L. *rete*, net; Gk. *pherein*, to bear.] A crystal cell in ommatidium of Arthropoda.

retinula (rĕtĭn′ūlă) *n.* [L. *rete*, net.] Group of elongated pigmented cells, innermost element of an ommatidium.

retisolution (rē′tĭsōlū′shŭn) *n.* [L. *rete*, net; *solutio*, solution.] Dissolution of the Golgi apparatus.

retispersion (rētĭspĕr′shŭn) *n.* [L. *rete*, net; *dispersio*, dispersion.] Peripheral distribution of Golgi apparatus in a cell.

retort-shaped organs,—glandular tissue at proximal ends of maxillary stylets, in Hemiptera.

retractile (rētrăk′tĭl) *a.* [L. *retractus*, withdrawn.] *Appl.* a part or organ that may be drawn inwards, as feelers, claws, etc.

retractor (rētrăk′tŏr) *n.* [L. *retrahere*, to draw back.] A muscle which by contraction withdraws the part attached to it. *Opp.* protractor.

retrahens (rē′trăhĕnz) *n.* [L. *retrahere*, to draw back.] A muscle which draws a part backwards, as the auricularis posterior.

retral (rĕt′ral) *a.* [L. *retro*, backwards.] Backward; posterior.
retrobulbar (rĕt′röbŭl′băr) *a.* [L. *retro*, backwards; *bulbus*, bulb.] Posterior to eyeball.
retrocaecal (rĕt′rösē′kăl) *a.* [L. *retro*, backwards; *caecus*, blind.] Behind caecum; *appl.* fossae.
retrocerebral (rĕt′rösĕr′ĕbrăl) *a.* [L. *retro*, behind; *cerebrum*, brain.] Situated behind the cerebral ganglion; *appl.* glands in Rotifera.
retrocurved (rĕt′rökŭrvd′) *a.* [L. *retro*, backwards; *curvus*, bent.] Bent backwards; recurved.
retrofract (rĕt′röfrăkt) *a.* [L. *retro*, backwards; *fractus*, broken.] Bent backwards at an angle.
retrogression (rĕt′rögrĕsh′ŭn) *n.* [L. *retrogressus*, going back.] A step from superior to inferior type in individual or race; degeneration.
retrogressive (rĕt′rögrĕs′ĭv) *a.* [L. *retrogressus*, going back.] Degenerating; assuming characteristics of a lower type.
retrolingual (rĕt′rölĭng′gwăl) *a.* [L. *retro*, backwards; *lingua*, tongue.] Behind the tongue; *appl.* a gland.
retromorphosis (rĕt′römôr′fōsĭs) *n.* [L. *retro*, backwards; Gk. *morphe*, form.] Development with degenerating tendency.
retroperitoneal (rĕt′röpĕr′ĭtönē′ăl) *a.* [L. *retro*, backwards; Gk. *peri*, round; *teinein*, to stretch.] Behind peritoneum; *appl.* space between peritoneum and spinal column.
retropharyngeal (rĕt′röfărĭn′jēăl) *a.* [L. *retro*, backwards; Gk. *pharyngx*, pharynx.] Behind the pharynx; *appl.* a space, lymph glands.
retropubic (rĕt′röpū′bĭk) *a.* [L. *retro*, backwards; *pubes*, mature.] *Appl.* a pad or mass of fatty tissue behind pubic symphysis.
retrorse (rētrôrs′) *a.* [L. *retrorsum*, backwards.] Turned or directed backwards. *Opp.* antrorse.
retroserrate (rĕt′rösĕr′āt) *a.* [L. *retro*, backwards; *serra*, saw.] Toothed, with teeth directed backwards; runcinate.
retroserrulate (rĕt′rösĕr′ūlāt) *a.* [L. *retro*, backwards; *serrula*, small saw.] With small retrorse teeth.
retro-uterine (rĕt′röū′tĕrīn) *a.* [L. *retro*, backwards; *uterus*, womb.] Behind the uterus.
retroverse (rĕt′rövĕrs′) *a.* [L. *retroversus*, turned backwards.] Retrorse.
retroversion (rĕt′rövĕr′shŭn) *n.* [L. *retroversus*, turned backwards.] State of being reversed or turned backwards.
retuse (rētūs′) *a.* [L. *retusus*, blunted.] Obtuse with a broad shallow notch in middle; *appl.* leaves, molluscan shells.
revehent (rĕv′ĕhĕnt) *a.* [L. *revehens*, carrying back.] In renal portal system, *appl.* vessels carrying blood back from excretory organs.
reverse mutation,—mutation of a mutant gene back to its original state; back mutation.
reversed (rēvĕr′sd) *a.* [L. *reversus*, turned back.] Inverted; *appl.* a spiral shell whose turns are directed sinistrally; *appl.* barbs united to rhachis by their apices.
reversion (rēvĕr′shŭn) *n.* [L. *reversio*, turning back.] Atavism; a return in a greater or less degree to some ancestral type; a return from cultivation or domestication to the wild state; a reverse mutation.
reversionary (rēvĕr′shŏnărĭ) *a.* [L. *reversio*, turning back.] *Appl.* atavistic characteristics.
revert (rēvĕrt′) *v.* [L. *revertere*, to turn back.] To exhibit ancestral features; to hark back.
revolute (rĕv′ölūt) *a.* [L. *revolvere*, to roll back.] Rolled backwards from margin upon under surface, as some leaves.
rhabdi,—*plu.* of rhabdus.
rhabdite (răb′dīt) *n.* [Gk. *rhabdos*, rod.] One of short rod-like bodies in epidermal cells in Turbellaria and Temnocephaloidea; a gonapophysis.
rhabditiform (răbdĭt′ĭfôrm) *a.* [Gk. *rhabdos*, rod; L. *forma*, shape.] *Appl.* larvae of roundworms with short straight oesophagus, with double bulb.

rhabditis (răbdī'tĭs) *n.* [Gk. *rhabdos*, rod.] Larva of certain nematodes.

rhabdocrepid (răb'dökrē'pĭd) *a.* [Gk. *rhabdos*, rod ; *krepis*, foundation.] *Appl.* a desma with uniaxial crepis, in sponge spicules.

rhabdoid (răb'doid) *a.* [Gk. *rhabdos*, rod ; *eidos*, form.] Rod-like. *n.* Any rod-shaped body.

rhabdolith (răb'dölĭth) *n.* [Gk. *rhabdos*, rod ; *lithos*, stone.] A calcareous rod found in some protozoa, strengthening the walls.

rhabdome (răb'dōm) *n.* [Gk. *rhabdos*, rod.] A refractive rod composed of rhabdomeres enclosed by retinula cells of ommatidium.

rhabdomere (răb'dömēr) *n.* [Gk. *rhabdos*, rod ; *meros*, part.] The refracting element in a retinula.

rhabdopod (răb'döpŏd) *n.* [Gk. *rhabdos*, rod ; *pous*, foot.] An element of clasper of some male insects.

rhabdosphere (răb'dösfēr) *n.* [Gk. *rhabdos*, rod ; *sphaira*, globe.] Aggregated rhabdoliths found in deep-sea calcareous oozes.

rhabdus (răb'dŭs) *n.* [Gk. *rhabdos*, rod.] A rod-like spicule.

rhachi-,—rachi-.

Rhaetic (rē'tĭk) *a.* [L. *Rhaetia*, Grisons and Tirol.] *Appl.* fossils found in marls, shales, and limestone between Trias and Lias.

rhagiocrine (rā'jĭökrĭn) *a.* [Gk. *rhax*, grape ; *krinein*, to separate.] *Appl.* cells : histiocytes.

rhagon (rā'gŏn) *n.* [Gk. *rhax*, grape.] A bun-shaped type of sponge with apical osculum and large gastral cavity.

rhamphoid (răm'foid) *a.* [Gk. *rhamphos*, beak ; *eidos*, form.] Beak-shaped.

rhamphotheca (rămfōthē'kă) *n.* [Gk. *rhamphos*, beak ; *theke*, case.] The horny sheath of a bird's beak.

rheobase (rē'öbās) *n.* [Gk. *rhein*, to flow ; *basis*, ground.] The minimal or liminal electric stimulus that will produce a response ; rheobasis.

rheogameon (rē'ögămē'ŏn) *n.* [Gk. *rhein*, to flow ; *gamos*, marriage ; *on*, being.] A polytypic species ; rassenkreis.

rheoplankton (rē'öplăngk'tŏn) *n.* [Gk. *rhein*, to flow ; *plangktos*, wandering.] The plankton of running waters.

rheoreceptors (rē'örēsĕp'tŏrz) *n. plu.* [Gk. *rhein*, to flow ; L. *recipere*, to receive.] Cutaneous sense organs of fishes and certain amphibians, receiving stimulus of water current, as pit organs, lateral line organs, ampullæ of Lorenzini, vesicles of Savi.

rheotaxis (rē'ötăk'sĭs) *n.* [Gk. *rhein*, to flow ; *taxis*, arrangement.] Locomotor response to stimulus of a current, usually of water current.

rheotropic (rē'ötrŏp'ĭk) *a.* [Gk. *rhein*, to flow ; *trope*, turn.] Responding to current stimulus ; rheotactic.

rheotropism (rēŏt'röpĭzm) *n.* [Gk. *rhein*, to flow ; *trope*, turn.] Curvature or growth response to influence of a water or air current.

rhesus factor,—Rh factor, antigen in blood of rhesus monkey and man, and agglutinated by an (rh) antibody in individuals lacking the factor, which is inherited as a Mendelian dominant.

rhexigenous (rĕksĭj'ënŭs) *a.* [Gk. *rhexis*, a breaking ; *-genes*, born.] Resulting from rupture or tearing ; rhexogenous.

rhexilysis (rĕksĭl'ĭsĭs) *n.* [Gk. *rhexis*, a breaking ; *lysis*, loosing.] The separation of parts, or production of openings or cavities, by rupture of tissues ; rhexolysis.

rhexis (rĕks'ĭs) *n.* [Gk. *rhexis*, a breaking.] Fragmentation of chromosomes, caused by physical or chemical agents.

rhigosis (rīgō'sĭs) *n.* [Gk. *rhigos*, cold.] Sensation of cold.

rhinal (rī'năl) *a.* [Gk. *rhis*, nose.] Of or *pert.* the nose ; *appl.* fissure separating rhinencephalon, or olfactory lobe and tract, and cerebral hemisphere.

rhinarium (rīnā'rĭŭm) *n.* [Gk. *rhis*, nose.] The muzzle or external nasal area of mammals; nostril area; part of nasus of some insects.

rhinencephalon (rī′nĕnkĕf′ălŏn, -sĕf-) *n.* [Gk. *rhis*, nose; *engkephalos*, brain.] The part of the fore-brain forming most of the hemispheres in fishes, amphibians and reptiles, and comprising in man the olfactory lobe, uncus, the supracallosal, subcallosal and dentate gyri, fornix, and hippocampus.

rhinion (rĭn′ĭŏn) *n.* [Gk. *rhis*, nose.] Most prominent point at which nasal bones touch.

rhinocaul (rī′nökôl) *n.* [Gk. *rhis*, nose; *kaulos*, stalk.] Narrowed portion of brain which bears the olfactory lobe; olfactory peduncle.

rhinocoel (rī′nösēl) *n.* [Gk. *rhis*, nose; *koilos*, hollow.] Cavity in olfactory lobe of brain.

rhinopharynx,—nasopharynx, *q.v.*

rhinophore (rī′nöfōr) *n.* [Gk. *rhis*, nose; *pherein*, to bear.] A process on aboral side of eye of certain molluscs, with supposed olfactory function.

rhinotheca (rī′nöthē′kă) *n.* [Gk. *rhis*, nose; *theke*, case.] The sheath of upper jaw of a bird.

rhipidate (rĭp′ĭdāt) *a.* [Gk. *rhipis*, fan.] Fan-shaped; flabelliform.

rhipidium (rīpĭd′ĭŭm) *n.* [Gk. *rhipis*, fan; *idion*, *dim.*] A fan-shaped cymose inflorescence; a fan-shaped colony of zooids.

rhipidoglossate (rĭp′ĭdöglŏs′āt) *a.* [Gk. *rhipis*, fan; *glossa*, tongue.] Having a radula with numerous teeth in a fan-like arrangement, as ear-shells.

rhipidostichous (rĭp′ĭdŏs′tĭkŭs) *a.* [Gk. *rhipis*, fan; *stichos*, row.] *Appl.* fan-shaped fins.

rhizanthous (rīzăn′thŭs) *a.* [Gk. *rhiza*, root; *anthos*, flower.] Producing a root, and a flower apparently straight from it.

rhizautoicous (rī′zôtoik′ŭs) *a.* [Gk. *rhiza*, root; *autos*, self; *oikos*, house.] With antheridial and archegonial branches coherent.

rhizine (rī′zĭn) *n.* [Gk. *rhiza*, root.] A rhizoid, as of most lichens.

rhizobia (rīzō′bĭă) *n. plu.* [G. *rhiza*, root; *bios*, life.] Bacteria of root-nodules of leguminous plants. *Sing.* rhizobium.

rhizoblasts,—rhizoplasts.

rhizocaline (rī′zökălēn′) *n.* [Gk. *rhiza*, root; *kalein*, to summon.] A substance promoting root growth, present in pollen and leaves of some plants, also found in urine.

rhizocarp (rī′zökârp) *n.* [Gk. *rhiza*, root; *karpos*, fruit.] A perennial herb.

rhizocarpous (rī′zökâr′pŭs) *a.* [Gk. *rhiza*, root; *karpos*, fruit.] Having perennial roots and annual stems.

rhizocaul (rī′zökôl) *n.* [Gk. *rhiza*, root; *kaulos*, stem.] The root-like horizontal portion of a zoophyte; hydrorhiza.

rhizocorm (rī′zökôrm) *n.* [Gk. *rhiza*, root; *kormos*, log.] An underground stem like a single-jointed rhizome, popularly a bulb.

rhizodermis (rīzödĕr′mĭs) *n.* [Gk. *rhiza*, root; *derma*, skin.] Outermost layer of root tissue; epiblema, piliferous layer.

rhizogenic (rī′zöjĕn′ĭk) *a.* [Gk. *rhiza*, root; *genos*, descent.] Root-producing; arising from endodermic cells, not developed from pericycle; *pert.*, or stimulating, root formation.

rhizogenous,—rhizogenic.

rhizoid (rī′zoid) *n.* [Gk. *rhiza*, root; *eidos*, form.] A root-like outgrowth of thallus, *e.g.* of algae, liverworts, mosses, ferns; unicellular hairs on lower side of prothallus; a hypha functioning within a substrate. *a.* Rootlike; *appl.* form of bacterial colony.

rhizomatous (rīzō′mătŭs) *a.* [Gk. *rhizoma*, root.] Like a rhizome; *appl.* mycelium within a substratum or host, *opp.* stoloniferous.

rhizome (rī′zōm) *n.* [Gk. *rhizoma*, root.] A thick horizontal stem partly along and partly under ground, sending out shoots above and roots below.

rhizomorph (rī′zömôrf) *n.* [Gk. *rhiza*, root; *morphe*, form.] A root-like strand of hyphae in certain fungi.

rhizomorphoid (rī′zömôr′foid) *a.* [Gk. *rhiza*, root; *morphe*, form; *eidos*, particular kind.] Resembling a rhizomorph; branching like a root.

rhizomorphous (rī′zömôr′fŭs) *a.* [Gk. *rhiza*, root; *morphe*, form.] In form of a root; root-like; rhizomorphic.

rhizomycelium (rī′zömīsē′lĭŭm) *n.* [Gk. *rhiza*, root; *mykes*, fungus.] A rhizoid mycelium connecting reproductive bodies in certain Phycomycetes.

rhizophagous (rīzŏf′ăgŭs) *a.* [Gk. *rhiza*, root; *phagein*, to eat.] Root-eating.

rhizophore (rī′zöfōr) *n.* [Gk. *rhiza*, root; *pherein*, to bear.] A naked branch which grows down into soil and develops roots from apex, as in club-mosses.

rhizophorous (rīzŏf′örŭs) *a.* [Gk. *rhiza*, root; *pherein*, to bear.] Root-bearing.

rhizopin (rī′zöpĭn) *n.* [*Rhizopus*, a genus of Mucoraceae.] A plant growth-promoting substance extracted from substrate of Rhizopus and probably identical with heteroauxin.

rhizoplasts (rī′zöplăsts) *n.plu.* [Gk. *rhiza*, root; *plastos*, moulded.] Fibrillae connecting parabasal body or blepharoplast and nucleus in Flagellata; intracytoplasmic portions of axonemes.

rhizopodium (rī′zöpō′dĭŭm) *n.* [Gk. *rhiza*, root; *pous*, foot.] A branching and anastomosing filamentous pseudopodium.

rhizosphere (rī′zösfēr) *n.* [Gk. *rhiza*, root; *sphaira*, ball.] The soil immediately surrounding the root system of a plant.

rhizotaxis (rī′zötăk′sĭs) *n.* [Gk. *rhiza*, root; *taxis*, arrangement.] Root arrangement.

rhodocyte,—erythrocyte,

rhodogenesis (rō′döjĕn′ĕsĭs) *n.* [Gk. *rhodon*, rose; *genesis*, origin.] Formation, or reconstitution after bleaching, of rhodopsin.

rhodophane (rō′döfān) *n.* [Gk. *rhodon*, rose; *phainein*, to appear.] A red chromophane in retinal cones of fishes and birds.

rhodophyll (rō′döfĭl) *n.* [Gk. *rhodon*, rose; *phyllon*, leaf.] The red colouring matter of red algae.

rhodopin (rō′döpĭn) *n.* [Gk. *rhodon*, rose; *piein*, to absorb.] A carotenoid pigment of certain bacteria.

rhodoplast (rō′döplăst) *n.* [Gk. *rhodon*, rose; *plastos*, formed.] A reddish plastid or chromatophore, in red algae.

rhodopsin (rōdŏp′sĭn) *n.* [Gk. *rhodon*, rose; *opsis*, sight.] A temporary reddish-purple pigment in retinal rods; visual purple.

rhodoxanthin (rō′dözăn′thĭn) *n.* [Gk. *rhodon*, rose; *xanthos*, yellow.] A carotenoid pigment, found in aril of yew; $C_{40}H_{50}O_2$.

rhombencephalon (rômb′ĕnkĕf′ălŏn, -sĕf-) *n.* [Gk. *rhombos*, rhomb; *engkephalos*, brain.] Hind-brain, consisting of the isthmus rhombencephali, metencephalon, and myelencephalon: the third primary vesicle.

rhombic (rôm′bĭk) *a.* [Gk. *rhombos*, rhomb.] *Appl.* lip and grooves of brain at rhomboid fossa.

rhombocoele (rŏm′bösēl) *n.* [Gk. *rhombos*, rhombus; *koilos*, hollow.] Dilatation of the central canal of the medulla spinalis near its posterior end, the terminal ventricle.

rhombogene (rôm′böjēn) *n.* [Gk. *rhombos*, rhomb; *-genes*, producing.] Phase of parent form in life cycle of some Mesozoa, involving production of infusoriform embryos, or males. *Cf.* nematogene.

rhomboid (rôm′boid) *a.* [Gk. *rhombos*, rhombus; *eidos*, form.] Rhombus-shaped; *appl.* fossa, sinus, ligament, scales.

rhomboideum,—the rhomboid or costoclavicular ligament.

rhomboideus, major and **minor**,—parallel muscles connecting scapula with thoracic vertebrae.

rhomboid-ovate,—between rhomboid and oval in shape.

rhopalium (rōpăl'ĭŭm) *n.* [Gk. *rhopalon*, club.] A marginal sense organ of Discomedusae.

rhynchocoel (rĭng'kösēl) *n.* [Gk. *rhyngchos*, snout; *koilos*, hollow.] In Nemertea, tubular cavity with muscular walls serving to evert proboscis.

rhynchodaeum (rĭng'ködē'ŭm) *n.* [Gk. *rhyngchos*, snout; *hodaios*, *pert.* a way.] The precerebral region of a nemertine.

rhynchodont (rĭng'ködŏnt) *a.* [Gk. *rhyngchos*, snout; *odous*, tooth.] With a toothed beak.

rhynchophorous (rĭngkŏf'örŭs) *a.* [Gk. *rhyngchos*, beak; *pherein*, to bear.] Beaked.

rhynchostome (rĭng'köstōm) *n.* [Gk. *rhyngchos*, snout; *stoma*, mouth.] Anterior terminal pore through which proboscis is everted, in Nemertea.

rhythm (rĭthm) *n.* [Gk. *rhythmos*, measured motion.] Regularity of movement, as seen in heart pulsation, or in movement of telegraph plant leaves; periodic occurrence; seasonal variation.

rhytidome (rĭt'ĭdōm) *n.* [Gk. *rhytis*, wrinkle; *domos*, layer.] The outer bark.

rib (rĭb) *n.* [A.S. *ribb*, rib.] A curved bone of thorax articulating with spine and either free at other end or connected with sternum; primary or central vein of a leaf; costa.

Ribaga's organ,—abdominal opening leading to Berlese's organ, *q.v.*

riboflavin (rīböflā'vĭn) *n* [L. *ribes*, currant; *flavus*, yellow.] Vitamin B_2 or growth factor G, important in oxidation processes; agon of yellow enzyme; lactoflavin; $C_{17}H_{20}O_6N_4$.

rictal (rĭk'tăl) *a.* [L. *rictus*, mouth aperture.] *Pert.* mouth gape of birds.

rigor (rĭg'ŏr) *n.* [L. *rigor*, stiffness.] The rigid state of plants when not sensitive to stimuli; contraction and loss of irritability of muscle on heating, due to coagulation of proteins.

rigor mortis,—stiffening of body after death, due to myosin-formation, and lasting till commencement of decomposition.

rima (rī'mă) *n.* [L. *rima*, cleft.] A cleft or fissure, *e.g.* glottidis, palpebrarum, pudendi; orifice of mouth.

rimate (rī'māt) *a.* [L. *rima*, cleft.] Having fissures.

rimiform (rī'mĭfôrm) *a.* [L. *rima*, cleft; *forma*, shape.] In shape of a narrow fissure.

rimose (rī'mōs) *a.* [L. *rima*, cleft.] Having many clefts or fissures.

rimulose (rĭm'ūlōs) *a.* [L.L. *rimula*, small cleft.] Having many small clefts.

rind (rīnd) *n.* [A.S. *rinde*, bark.] The outer layer, tissue or cortex.

ring-bark,—bark of a tree where formations of phellogen are cylindrical; *cf.* scale-bark.

ring-canal,—a circular canal running close to and parallel with umbrella margin in Hydrozoa; circular vessel around gullet in Echinoidea.

ring cell,—a thick-walled cell of sporangium annulus of ferns.

ring centriole,—disc at end of body or middle portion of spermatozoon, perforated for axial filament; end ring, terminal disc.

ring-chromosomes,—chromosomes with no ends, in mitosis; chromosomes attached end to end, in meiosis.

ring gland,—glandular structure around aorta, with elements representing corpus allatum, corpus cardiacum, pericardial gland, and hypocerebral ganglion, secreting the metamorphosis-producing hormone in Diptera; Weismann's gland.

ring-porous,—*appl.* wood in which the vessels tend to be larger and have thinner walls than those in diffuse-porous wood.

ring-vessel,—a structure in head of cestodes, which unites the four longitudinal excretory trunks.

ringent (rĭn'jĕnt) *a.* [L. *ringi*, to open mouth.] Having lips, as of a corolla, or valves, separated by a distinct gap; with upper lip arched; gaping.

ringless,—*appl.* ferns without an annulus.

riparian (rīpā'rĭăn) *a.* [L. *ripa*, river bank.] Riparial, riparious; frequenting, growing on, or living on the banks of streams or rivers; *pert.* ripa or line of ependymal fold over a plexus or a tela.

risorius (rĭsō'rĭŭs) *n.* [L. *risus*, laughter.] A cheek muscle stretching from over masseter muscle to corner of mouth.

rivinian (rĭvĭn'ĭăn) *a.* [*A. Q. Rivinus*, German anatomist.] *Appl.* sublingual glands and ducts; *appl.* notch in ring of bone surrounding tympanic membrane.

rivose (rī'vōs) *a.* [L. *rivus*, stream.] Marked with irregularly winding furrows or channels.

rivulose (rĭv'ūlōs) *a.* [L. *rivulus*, rivulet.] Marked with sinuate narrow lines or furrows.

rod-epithelium,—epithelium consisting of apparently striated cells.

rod fibre,—fibre with which a rod of retina is connected internally.

rod fructification,—fructification occurring in Basidiomycetes by means of rod-like gonidia from a hyphal branch.

rod granule,—nucleus of rod fibre.

rodent (rō'dĕnt) *n.* [L. *rodere*, to gnaw.] An animal with a habit of gnawing or nibbling, as a rabbit.

roding (rō'dĭng) *n.* [A.S. *rode*, raid.] Patrolling flight of birds defending territory.

rods and cones, — nerve-epithelium layer of retina.

rolandic (rŏlăn'dĭk) *a.* [*L. Rolando*, Italian anatomist]. *Appl.* fissure or central sulcus of cerebral hemispheres; *appl.* tubercle or tuberculum cinereum of posterior region of medulla oblongata, and gelatinous substance of dorsal horn of spinal medulla.

root (root) *n.* [A.S. *wyrt*, root.] Descending portion of plant, fixing it in soil, and absorbing moisture and nutrients; radix, *q.v.*; embedded part of hair, nail, tooth, or other structure; pulmonary veins and artery, bronchus, and bronchial vessels joining lung to heart and trachea; pedicle of vertebra; efferent and afferent fibres of a spinal nerve, leaving or entering the spinal cord.

root-borer,—a larval form or insect which bores into roots of plants.

root-cap,—a protective cap of tissue at apex of root.

root-cell,—clear colourless base of an alga, attaching thallus to substratum.

root-climber,—a plant which climbs by roots developed from stem.

root-hairs,—unicellular epidermal outgrowths from roots, of protective and absorbent function.

rootlet,—an ultimate branch of a root.

root-nodules,—small swellings on roots of leguminous plants and containing nitrogen-fixing bacteria.

root-parasitism, — a condition exhibited by semi-parasitic plants, roots of which penetrate roots of neighbouring plants and draw from them elaborated food material.

root-pocket,—a sheath containing a root, especially of aquatic plants.

root-pressure,—the force by which water is made to rise in axial stele of a plant, a main factor in transport of water through plant.

root-process,—a branched structure fixing an algal thallus to substratum.

root-sheath,—a coleorhiza; an orchid velamen; that part of a hair follicle continuous with epidermis.

root-stalk,—a root-stock or rhizome; root-like horizontal portion of Hydrozoa.

root-stock,—more or less erect underground part of stem; a rhizome, *q.v.*

root-tubercles,—root nodules, *q.v.*

root-tubers,—swollen roots of certain plants, as of Ficaria.

roridous (rō'rĭdŭs) *a.* [L. *ros*, dew.] Like dew; covered with droplets.

rosaceous (rōzā'shŭs) *a.* [L. *rosa*, rose.] With five petals arranged in a circle; resembling a rose.

rosellate (rōzĕl'āt) *a.* [L. *rosa*, rose.] Arranged like rosettes; rosulate.

Rosenmüller's organ [*J. C. Rosenmüller*, German anatomist]. Epoophoron, *q.v.*

rosette (rōzĕt′) *n.* [F. from L. *rosa*, rose.] A cluster of leaves arising in close circles from a central axis; a group of cells between embryo and proembryonic remains, also arrangement of embryos, as in Pinus; a plant disease due to deficiency of boron or of zinc; a cluster of crystals, as in certain plant cells; a swirl or vortex of hair in pelage; a small cluster of blood cells; group of spiracular channels in exocuticle of some aquatic insects; a thin plate formed by coalescence of interradial basals of larval crinoid; a large ciliated funnel leading out of anterior sperm reservoir of earthworm; two circles of ciliated cells forming excretory organ in Ctenophora.

rosette organ,—in certain ascidians, ventral complex stolon from which buds are constricted off.

rostel (rŏs′tĕl) *n.* [L. *rostellum*, *dim.* of *rostrum*, beak.] A rostellum.

rostellar (rŏstĕl′ăr) *a.* [L. *rostellum*, small beak.] *Pert.* a rostellum.

rostellate (rŏs′tĕlāt) *a.* [L. *rostellum*, small beak.] Furnished with a rostellum.

rostelliform (rŏstĕl′ĭfôrm) *a.* [L. *rostellum*, small beak; *forma*, shape.] Shaped like a small beak.

rostellum (rŏstĕl′ŭm) *n.* [L. *rostellum*, small beak.] A small rostrum; projecting structure developed from a stigmatic surface of orchid flower; rounded prominence, furnished with hooks, on scolex of tape-worm; tubular mouth-parts of certain apterous insects; beaked-shaped process.

rostral (rŏs′trăl) *a.* [L. *rostrum*, beak.] *Pert.* a rostrum.

rostral gland,—premaxillary part of labial gland, as in snakes; labral gland of spiders.

rostrate (rŏs′trāt) *a.* [L. *rostrum*, beak.] Beaked.

rostriform (rŏs′trĭfôrm), **rostroid** (rŏs′troid) *a.* [L. *rostrum*, beak; *forma*, shape; Gk. *eidos*, form.] Beak-shaped.

rostrulate (rŏs′troolāt) *a.* [L.L. *rostrulum*, small beak.] With, or like, a rostrulum.

rostrulum (rŏs′troolŭm) *n.* [L.L. *rostrulum*, small beak.] A small rostrum.

rostrum (rŏs′trŭm) *n.* [L. *rostrum*, beak.] Beak or beak-like process; process projecting between eyes of crayfish; a median ventral plate at base of capitulum of Cirripedia; labrum of spiders; prominence or mucro at posterior end of sepion; anterior end of gregarine, which forms epimerite; pre-nasal region; anterior continuation of basisphenoid; backward prolongation of anterior end of corpus callosum.

rosular (rŏz′ūlăr), **rosulate** (rŏz′ūlāt) *a.* [L. *rosa*, rose.] Arranged in rosettes.

rot (rŏt) *n.* [A.S. *rotian*, to rot.] Decay; decomposition; disease caused by fungi or bacteria; a parasitic disease causing emaciation.

rotate (rō′tāt) *a.* [L. *rota*, wheel.] Shaped like a wheel; rotiform.

rotation (rōtā′shŭn) *n.* [L. *rota*, wheel.] Turning as on a pivot, as limbs; circulation, as of cell sap.

rotator (rōtā′tŏr) *n.* [L. *rota*, wheel.] A muscle which allows of circular motion.

rotatores spinae,—paired muscles, one on either side of thoracic vertebrae, each arising from transverse process and inserted into vertebra next above.

rotiform (rō′tĭfôrm) *a.* [L. *rota*, wheel; *forma*, shape.] Wheel-shaped; circular.

rotula (rŏt′ūlă) *n.* [L. *rotula*, small wheel.] One of five radially-directed bars bounding circular aperture of oesophagus of a sea-urchin; patella or knee-cap.

rotular (rŏt′ūlăr) *a.* [L. *rotula*, small wheel.] *Pert.* the rotula.

rotuliform (rŏt′ūlĭfôrm) *a.* [L. *rotula*, small wheel; *forma*, shape.] Shaped like a small wheel.

rotundifolious (rötŭn'dĭfō'lĭŭs) *a.* [L. *rotundus*, round; *folium*, leaf.] With rounded leaves.

Rouget cells [*A. D. Rouget*, French physiologist]. Contractile branched cells external to walls of capillaries, associated with alteration of lumen; pericapillary cells; pericytes.

rouleaux (roolō', rool'ōz) *n. plu.* [F. *rouleau*, roll.] Formations like piles of coins into which red blood corpuscles tend to aggregate.

rubiginose (roobĭj'ĭnōs), **rubiginous** (roobĭj'ĭnŭs) *a.* [L. *rubigo*, rust.] Of a brownish-red tint; rust-coloured; affected by rust parasites.

rubriblast (roob'rĭblăst) *n.* [L. *ruber*, red; Gk. *blastos*, bud.] Immature proerythrocyte; proerythroblast.

rubricyte (roob'rĭsīt) *n.* [L. *ruber*, red; Gk. *kytos*, hollow vessel.] A polychromatophil erythrocyte.

rubrospinal (roob'röspī'năl) *a.* [L. *ruber*, red; *spina*, spine.] *Appl.* descending tract or fasciculus of axons of red nucleus, in ventrolateral column of spinal cord.

ruderal (rood'ĕrăl) *a.* [L. *rudus*, debris.] Growing among rubbish or debris.

rudimentary (rood'ĭmĕn'tărĭ) *a.* [L. *rudimentum*, first attempt.] In an imperfectly developed condition; at an early stage of development; arrested at an early stage; vestigial (certain authors).

ruff (rŭf) *n.* [A.S. *ruh*, rough.] A neck fringe of hair or feathers.

Ruffini's organs [*A. Ruffini*, Italian anatomist]. Cylindrical end-bulbs containing interlaced branches of nerve endings, in subcutaneous tissue of finger; corpuscles of Ruffini.

rufine (roo'fēn) *n.* [L. *rufus*, reddish.] A red pigment in mucous glands of slugs.

rufinism (roo'fĭnĭzm) *n.* [L. *rufus*, reddish.] Red pigmentation due to inhibition of formation of dark pigment.

ruga (roog'ă) *n.* [L. *ruga*, wrinkle.] A fold or wrinkle, as of skin, or of mucous membrane of certain organs.

rugate (roog'āt) *a.* [L. *rugare*, to wrinkle.] Wrinkled; ridged.

rugose,—with many wrinkles or ridges; rugous.

rugulose (roog'ūlōs) *a.* [L. *ruga*, wrinkle.] Finely wrinkled.

rumen (room'ĕn) *n.* [L. *rumen*, cud.] The paunch or first cavity of ruminant's stomach.

ruminant (room'ĭnănt) *n.* [L. *ruminare*, to chew the cud.] An animal which returns and re-chews what has been swallowed.

ruminate (room'ĭnāt) *a.* [L. *ruminare*, to chew the cud.] Appearing as if chewed; *appl.* endosperm with infolding of testa or of perisperm, appearing mottled in section; *appl.* seeds having such endosperm, as betel-nut and nutmeg. *v.* To chew the cud.

rumination (room'ĭnāshŭn) *n.* [L. *ruminatio*, chewing of cud.] The act of ruminant animals in returning food from first stomach to mouth in small quantities for thorough mastication and insalivation.

runcinate (rŭn'sĭnāt) *a.* [L. *runcina*, plane.] *Appl.* a pinnatifid leaf when divisions point towards base, as in dandelion.

runner (rŭn'ĕr) *n.* [A.S. *rinnan*, to run.] Slender prostrate stem which roots at nodes, as of strawberry; stolon.

rupestrine (roopĕs'trĭn), **rupicoline** (roopĭk'ölĭn), **rupicolous** (roopĭk'ölŭs) *a.* [L. *rupes*, rock; *colere*, to inhabit.] Growing or living on rocks.

ruptile (rŭp'tĭl) *a.* [L. *rumpere*, to break.] Bursting in an irregular manner.

rust (rŭst) *n.* [A.S. *rust*, redness.] A disease of grasses and other plants caused by Uredinales; parasitic fungi which produce uredospores in summer, teleutospores in winter.

rut (rŭt) *n.* [M.E. *rutien*, to rut.] Period of heat in male animals; *cf.* oestrus.

rutilism (root'ĭlĭzm) *n.* [L. *rutilus*, red.] Rufinism.

S

sabuline (săb'ūlĭn) *a.* [L. *sabulum*, sand.] Sandy; sabulose, sabulous; growing in coarse sand.

sac (săk) *n.* [L. *saccus*, sack.] A sack, bag, or pouch.

saccate (săk'āt) *a.* [L. *saccus*, sack.] Pouched; *appl.* a calyx of which two lateral sepals are expanded into little sacs or pouches; gibbous.

saccharose (săk'ărōs) *n.* [Gk. *sakchar*, sugar.] Cane sugar; sucrose.

sacciferous (săksĭf'ĕrŭs) *a.* [L. *saccus*, sack; *ferre*, to bear.] Furnished with a sac.

sacciform (săk'sĭfôrm) *a.* [L. *saccus*, sack; *forma*, shape.] Like a sac or pouch; saccular.

sacculate (săk'ūlāt) *a.* [L. *sacculus*, small bag.] Provided with sacculi.

sacculus (săk'ūlŭs) *n.* [L. *sacculus*, small bag.] A saccule or small sac; a peridium; lower part of vestibule of ear; appendix of laryngeal ventricle; lower portion of harpe.

saccus (săk'ŭs) *n.* [L. *saccus*, sack.] A sac-like structure, — as saccus vasculosus, saccus endolymphaticus; saccus lacrimalis; ninth abdominal sternite of certain male insects; median invagination of vinculum in Lepidoptera.

sacral (sā'krăl) *a.* [L. *sacer*, sacred.] *Pert.* the sacrum.

sacral index,—one hundred times the breadth of sacrum at base, divided by anterior length.

sacral ribs,—elements of sacrum joining true sacral vertebrae to pelvis.

sacrocaudal (sā'krōkôd'ăl) *a.* [L. *sacer*, sacred; *cauda*, tail.] *Pert.* sacrum and tail region.

sacrococcygeal (sā'krōkŏksĭj'ēăl) *a.* [L. *sacer*, sacred; Gk. *kokkyx*, cuckoo.] *Pert.* sacrum and coccyx.

sacro-iliac (sā'krōĭl'ĭăk) *a.* [L. *sacer*, sacred; *ilia*, flanks.] *Pert.* sacrum and ilium; *appl.* joint, ligaments.

sacrolumbar (sā'krōlŭm'băr) *a.* [L. *sacer*, sacred; *lumbus*, loin.] *Pert.* sacral and lumbar regions.

sacrospinal (sā'krōspī'năl) *a.* [L. *sacer*, sacred; *spina*, spine.] *Pert.* sacral region and spine; *appl.* muscle; erector spinae.

sacrovertebral (sā'krōvĕr'tēbrăl) *a.* [L. *sacer*, sacred; *vertebra*, joint.] *Pert.* sacrum and vertebrae.

sacrum (sā'krŭm) *n.* [L. *sacer*, sacred.] The os sacrum or bone forming termination of vertebral column, usually of several fused vertebrae; vertebra or vertebrae to which pelvic girdle is attached.

sagitta (săjĭt'ă) *n.* [L. *sagitta*, arrow.] An elongated otolith in sacculus of teleosts; a genus of arrow-worms.

sagittae (săjĭt'ē) *n. plu.* [L. *sagitta*, arrow.] The inner genital valves in Hymenoptera.

sagittal (săjĭt'ăl) *a.* [L. *sagitta*, arrow.] *Appl.* the suture between parietals; *appl.* section or division in median longitudinal plane.

sagittate (săj'ĭtāt) *a.* [L. *sagitta*, arrow.] Shaped like head of an arrow; *appl.* leaf.

sagittocyst (săjĭt'ōsĭst) *n.* [L. *sagitta*, arrow; Gk. *kystis*, bladder.] A cyst or capsule, in turbellarians, containing a single spindle.

saliva (sălī'vă) *n.* [L. *saliva*, spittle.] A fluid containing ptyalin, secreted by buccal glands.

salivarium (sălĭvā'rĭŭm) *n.* [L. *saliva*, spittle.] Recess of preoral food cavity, with opening of the salivary duct, in insects.

salivary (săl'ĭvărĭ) *a.* [L. *saliva*, spittle.] *Pert.* saliva; *appl.* glands, ducts, etc.; *appl.* chromosomes conspicuous in salivary gland cells of Diptera; *appl.* amylase.

salivation (săl'ĭvā'shŭn) *n.* [L. *saliva*, spittle.] Flow of saliva into mouth.

salpingian (sălpĭn'jĭăn) *a.* [Gk. *salpingx*, trumpet.] *Pert.* Eustachian or Fallopian tube.

salpingopalatine,—*pert.* Eustachian tubes and palate.

salpinx (săl'pĭngks) *n.* [Gk. *salpingx*, trumpet.] Eustachian tube; Fallopian tube.

salsuginous (sălsū'jĭnŭs) *a.* [L. *salsugo*, saltness.] Growing in soil impregnated with salts.

saltation,—mutation, *q.v.*
saltatorial (săltătō'rĭăl) *a.* [L. *saltare*, to leap.] Adapted for, or used in, leaping; *appl.* limbs of jumping insects; saltatory.
salted animals,—those which have survived certain diseases but remain infective and provide a source of material for preventive inoculation.
saltigrade (săl'tĭgrād) *a.* [L. *saltare*, to leap; *gradus*, step.] Moving by leaps, as some insects and spiders.
samara (săm'ără) *n.* [L. *samara*, seed of elm.] A winged indehiscent fruit, as of elm, ash, maple.
samaroid (săm'ăroid) *a.* [L. *samara*, seed of elm; Gk. *eidos*, form.] Samariform; resembling a samara.
sanguicolous (sănggwĭk'ōlŭs) *a.* [L. *sanguis*, blood; *colere*, to inhabit.] Living in blood of animals.
sanguiferous (sănggwĭf'ërŭs) *a.* [L. *sanguis*, blood; *ferre*, to carry.] Conveying blood, as arteries, veins.
sanguimotor (săng'gwĭmō'tŏr) *a.* [L. *sanguis*, blood; *movere*, to move.] *Pert* circulation of blood.
sanguivorous (sănggwĭv'ŏrŭs) *a.* [L. *sanguis*, blood; *vorare*, to devour.] Living on blood.
sanidaster (săn'ĭdăs'tër) *n.* [Gk. *sanidion*, panel; *aster*, star.] A slender rod-like spicule with spines at intervals.
Santorini's cartilages [*G. D. Santorini*, Italian anatomist]. The corniculate cartilages of the larynx.
Santorini's duct,—the accessory pancreatic duct.
Santorini's muscle,—risorius, *q.v.*
saphena (săfē'nă) *n.* [Gk. *saphenes*, clear.] A conspicuous vein of leg, extending from foot to femoral vein.
saphenous (săfē'nŭs) *a.* [Gk. *saphenes*, clear.] *Pert.* internal or external saphena; *appl.* a branch of femoral nerve.
sap-hypha,—a laticiferous hypha.
saprobic (săprŏb'ĭk) *a.* [Gk. *sapros*, rotten; *bios*, life.] Living on decaying organic matter; *appl.* certain Protista.
saprobiont (săprŏbī'ŏnt) *n.* [Gk. *sapros*, rotten; *bion*, living.] A saprophyte, or a saprozoite; a saprophagic organism.
saprogenic (săp'rōjĕn'ĭk) *a.* [Gk. *sapros*, rotten; *-genes*, producing.] Causing decay; resulting from decay.
sapropelic (săp'rōpēl'ĭk) *a.* [Gk. *sapros*, rotten; *pelos*, mud.] Living among debris of bottom ooze.
saprophage (săp'rōfāj) *n.* [Gk. *sapros*, rotten; *phagein*, to eat.] An organism which feeds on decaying organic matter; a saprophagic organism; saprobiont.
saprophyte (săp'rōfīt) *n.* [Gk. *sapros*, rotten; *phyton*, plant.] A plant which lives on dead and decaying organic matter; a saprophytic organism; *cf.* autophyte.
saprotrophic (săp'rōtrŏf'ĭk) *a.* [Gk. *sapros*, rotten; *trophe*, nourishment.] Feeding on dead or decaying organic matter, *appl.* bacteria and fungi.
saprozoic (săp'rōzō'ĭk) *a.* [Gk. *sapros*, rotten; *zoon*, animal.] Living on dead or decaying organic matter, *appl.* animals.
saprozoite (săprōzō'īt) *n.* [Gk. *sapros*, rotten; *zoon*, animal.] An animal which lives on dead or decaying organic matter; a saprozoic organism.
sap-wood,—the more superficial, paler, softer wood of trees; alburnum.
sarcenchyma (sârsĕng'kĭmă) *n.* [Gk. *sarx*, flesh; *engchyma*, infusion.] Parenchyma whose ground-substance is granular and not abundant.
sarcinaeform (sârsī'nĭfôrm) *a.* [L. *sarcina*, package; *forma*, shape.] Arranged in more or less cubical clumps; sarciniform; *appl.* cocci.
sarcocarp (sâr'kōkârp) *n.* [Gk. *sarx*, flesh; *karpos*, fruit.] The fleshy or pulpy part of a fruit.
sarcocystin (sâr'kōsĭs'tĭn) *n.* [Gk. *sarx*, flesh; *kystis*, bladder.] A toxin derived from Sarcosporidia.
sarcocyte (sâr'kōsīt) *n.* [Gk. *sarx*, flesh; *kytos*, hollow.] The middle layer of ectoplasm in Gregarinina.

sarcode (sâr'kōd) *n.* [Gk. *sarx*, flesh.] The body protoplasm of Protista.

sarcoderm (sâr'kōdĕrm) *n.* [Gk. *sarx*, flesh; *derma*, skin.] The fleshy layer between a seed and external covering.

sarcodic (sârkŏd'ĭk) *a.* [Gk. *sarx*, flesh.] *Pert.* or resembling protoplasm.

sarcodictyum (sâr'kōdĭk'tĭŭm) *n.* [Gk. *sarx*, flesh; *diktyon*, net.] The second or network protoplasmic zone of Radiolaria.

sarcogenic (sâr'kōjĕn'ĭk) *a.* [Gk. *sarx*, flesh; *-genes*, producing.] Flesh-producing.

sarcoid (sâr'koid) *a.* [Gk. *sarx*, flesh; *eidos*, form.] Fleshy, as sponge tissue.

sarcolemma (sâr'kōlĕm'ă) *n.* [Gk. *sarx*, flesh; *lemma*, skin.] The tubular sheath of a muscle fibre.

sarcolyte (sâr'kōlīt) *n.* [Gk. *sarx*, flesh; *lyterios*, loosing.] A non-nucleated muscle fragment undergoing phagocytosis in development of insects; a transient striated cell in thymus; a myoid cell.

sarcoma (sârkō'mă) *n.* [Gk. *sarx*, flesh.] A fleshy excrescence or tumour, usually malignant.

sarcomatrix (sârkōmā'trĭks) *n.* [Gk. *sarx*, flesh; L. *matrix*, womb.] The fourth protoplasmic zone of a radiolarian, the seat of digestion and assimilation.

sarcomere (sâr'kōmēr) *n.* [Gk. *sarx*, flesh; *meros*, part.] A transverse portion of a sarcostyle, between telophragmata; inocomma, comma.

sarcophagous (sârkŏf'ăgŭs) *a.* [Gk. *sarx*, flesh; *phagein*, to eat.] Subsisting on flesh.

sarcoplasm (sâr'kōplăzm) *n.* [Gk. *sarx*, flesh; *plasma*, mould.] The longitudinal interstitial substance between fibrils of muscular tissue.

sarcosoma (sâr'kōsō'mă) *n.* [Gk. *sarx*, flesh; *soma*, body.] The fleshy, *opp.* skeletal, portion of body.

sarcosomes,—mitochondria in muscle cells.

sarcosperm (sâr'kōspĕrm) *n.* [Gk. *sarx*, flesh; *sperma*, seed.] Sarcoderm.

sarcostyle (sâr'kōstīl) *n.* [Gk. *sarx*, flesh; *stylos*, pillar.] A fibril or muscle column of muscular tissue; a dactylozooid column.

sarcotesta (sâr'kōtĕs'tă) *n.* [Gk. *sarx*, flesh; L. *testa*, shell.] Softer fleshy outer portion of a testa.

sarcotheca (sâr'kōthē'kă) *n.* [Gk. *sarx*, flesh; *theke*, box.] The sheath of a hydrozoan sarcostyle.

sarcous (sâr'kŭs) *a.* [Gk. *sarx*, flesh.] *Pert.* flesh or muscle tissue.

sarcous disc,—anisotropic or A-disc in myofibrillae.

sarmentaceous (sârmĕntā'shŭs) *a.* [L. *sarmentum*, twig.] Having slender prostrate stems or runners; sarmentose, sarmentous.

sarmentum (sârmĕn'tŭm) *n.* [L. *sarmentum*, twig.] The slender stem of a climber or runner.

sarothrum (sârō'thrŭm) *n.* [Gk. *sarothron*, broom.] Enlarged hairy tarsal joint of bee, pollen-brush.

sartorius (sârtō'rĭŭs) *n.* [L. *sartor*, tailor.] A thigh muscle which enables legs to be moved inwards.

satellite (săt'ĕlīt) *n.* [L. *satelles*, attendant.] The second of any pair of individuals of a catenoid colony in pseudoconjugation of Gregarinida; *cf.* primite; a short segment constricted from the rest of a chromosome; *appl.* cells closely applied to others, as Schwann's sheath to medullary sheath; *appl.* a minute body adjacent to nucleolus and containing desoxyribonucleic acid, as in nerve cells.

saurian (sôr'ĭăn) *a.* [Gk. *sauros*, lizard.] *Pert.* or resembling a lizard.

saurognathous (sôrŏg'năthŭs) *a.* [Gk. *sauros*, lizard; *gnathos*, jaw.] With a saurian arrangement of jaw-bones.

sauroid (sôr'oid) *a.* [Gk. *sauros*, lizard; *eidos*, form.] Resembling a saurian or part of a saurian; *appl.* cells: normoblasts, *q.v.*

savanna (săvăn'ă) *n.* [Sp. *sabana.*] Subtropical or tropical grassland with xerophilous vegetation and scattered trees; transitional zone between grasslands and tropical rain forests.

saxicavous (săksĭk'ăvŭs) *a.* [L. *saxum*, rock; *cavus*, hollow.] *Appl.* rock-borers, as some molluscs; lithophagous.

saxicoline (săksĭk'ölĭn) *a.* [L. *saxum*, rock; *colere*, to inhabit.] Living or growing among rocks; saxicolous.

scaberulous (skăbĕr'ūlŭs) *a.* [L. *scaber*, rough.] Somewhat rough.

scabrate (skăb'rāt) *a.* [L. *scaber*, rough.] Rough with a covering of stiff hairs, scales, or points; scabrous.

scala (skā'lă) *n.* [L. *scala*, ladder.] Any of three canals in cochlea of ear.

scalariform (skălā'rĭfôrm) *a.* [L. *scala*, ladder; *forma*, shape.] Ladder-shaped; *appl.* vessels or tissues having bars like a ladder; *appl.* series of pits in cell-walls; *appl.* conjugation between parallel filaments, as in Spyrogyra.

scale (skāl) *n.* [A.S. *sceala*, shell, husk.] A flat, small, plate-like external structure, dermal or epidermal; a bony, horny, or chitinous outgrowth; bract of a catkin; ligule of certain flowers; modification of a stellate hair on certain leaves.

scale-bark,—bark in irregular sheets or patches, due to irregular or dipping formation of phellogen; *cf.* ring-bark.

scale leaf,—a bud-protecting cataphyllary leaf.

scalene (skălēn') *a.* [Gk. *skalenos*, uneven.] *Pert.* scalene muscles; *appl.* tubercle on first rib, for attachment of scalenus anticus or anterior.

scalenus (skălē'nŭs) *n.* [Gk. *skalenos*, uneven.] One of three neck muscles —scalenus posticus, medius, anticus.

scaliform (skā'lĭfôrm) *a.* [L. *scala*, ladder; *forma*, shape.] Ladder-shaped; scalariform, *q.v.*

scalp (skălp) *n.* [M.E. *scalp.*] The skin and subcutaneous tissues of surface of head where hair grows.

scalpella (skălpĕl'ă) *n. plu.* [L. *scalpellum*, small knife.] Paired pointed processes, parts of maxillae of Diptera.

scalpriform (skăl'prĭfôrm) *a.* [L. *scalprum*, chisel; *forma*, shape.] Chisel-shaped; *appl.* incisors of rodents.

scalprum (skăl'prŭm) *n.* [L. *scalprum*, chisel.] The cutting edge of an incisor.

scandent (skăn'dĕnt) *a.* [L. *scandere*, to climb.] Climbing by stem-roots or tendrils; trailing, as grasses over shrubs.

scansorial (skănsō'rĭăl) *a.* [L. *scandere*, to climb.] Formed or adapted for climbing; habitually climbing.

scape (skāp) *n.* [Gk. *skapos*. stalk.] A flower-stalk arising at or under ground; a radical peduncle, as cowslip; a structure formed by two basal segments of antennae of Diptera; an epigynal structure protecting vulva in spiders; scapus, *q.v.*

scapha (skăf'ă) *n.* [L. *scapha*, boat.] Narrow curved groove between helix and antihelix of ear.

scaphium (skăf'ĭŭm) *n.* [Gk. *skaphe*, boat.] Process of ninth (copulatory) segment of male Lepidoptera; anterior Weberian ossicle; keel of leguminous flower.

scaphocephalic (skăf'ökĕfăl'ĭk, -sĕf-) *a.* [Gk. *skaphe*, boat; *kephale*, head.] With narrow, elongated skull.

scaphocerite (skăf'ösĕrīt) *n.* [Gk. *skaphe*, boat; *keras*, horn.] Scale-like exopodite of second antenna of Decapoda.

scaphognathite (skăfögnăth'īt) *n.* [Gk. *skaphe*, boat; *gnathos*, jaw.] Epipodite of second maxilla of Decapoda, regulating flow of water through respiratory chamber; baler.

scaphoid (skăf'oid) *a.* [Gk. *skaphe*, boat; *eidos*, form.] Shaped like a boat; *appl.* carpal and tarsal bones; *appl.* fossa above pterygoid fossa. *n.* Os naviculare.

scapholunar (skăf'ölū'năr, -loo'-) *a.* [Gk. *skaphe*, boat; L. *luna*, moon.] *Pert.* scaphoid and lunar carpal bones, or those bones fused; scapholunatum.

scapiform (skā'pĭfôrm) *a.* [Gk. *skapos*, stalk; L. *forma*, shape.] Scapoid; resembling a scape.

scapose (skā'pōs) *a.* [Gk. *skapos*, stalk.] Consisting of, or in form of, a scape.

scapula (skăp'ūlă) *n.* [L. *scapula*, shoulder-blade.] The shoulder-blade; name given to various structures suggestive of a shoulder-blade, as tegula, patagium, mesothoracic pleuron, fore-leg trochanter of certain insects; in Crinoidea, proximal plate of ray that has an articular facet for arms.

scapular (skăp'ūlăr) *a.* [L. *scapula*, shoulder-blade.] *Pert.* scapula. *n.* A feather growing from shoulder and lying laterally along back.

scapulus (skăp'ūlŭs) *n.* [L. *dim.* of *scapus*, stem.] Modified sub-marginal region in certain sea-anemones.

scapus (skā'pŭs) *n.* [L. *scapus*, stem, stalk.] A scape; stem of feather; hair shaft; part of column below, and including, parapet in sea-anemones.

scarabaeiform (skăr'ăbē'ĭfôrm) *a.* [L. *Scarabaeus*, a genus of beetles; *forma*, form.] *Appl.* a C-shaped larval type of certain beetles.

scarfskin (skârf'skĭn) *n.* [A.S. *sceorfa*, scurf.] The cuticle or epidermis.

scarious (skā'rĭŭs) *a.* [F. *scarieux*, membranous.] Thin, dry, membranous; scaly or scurfy.

schindylesis (skĭn'dĭlē'sĭs) *n.* [Gk. *schindylesis*, fissure.] Articulation in which a thin plate of bone fits into a cleft or fissure, as that between vomer and palatines.

schistocytes (skĭs'tösīts) *n. plu.* [Gk. *schizein*, to cleave; *kytos*, hollow.] Fragments of erythrocytes; blood corpuscles undergoing fragmentation; microcytes; poikilocytes.

schizocarp (skĭz'ökârp) *n.* [Gk. *schizein*, to cleave; *karpos*, fruit.] A dry seed-vessel which splits into two or more one-seeded carpels or mericarps.

schizocarpic,—*appl.* dry fruits which split into two or more mericarps, as carcerulus, cremocarp, lomentum, regma, compound samara.

schizochroal (skĭzökrō'ăl) *a.* [Gk. *schizein*, to cleave; *chros*, body-surface.] With lenses separate and cornea not continuous; *appl.* certain trilobite eyes.

schizocoel (skĭz'ösēl) *n.* [Gk. *schizein*, to cleave; *koilos*, hollow.] Coelom formed by splitting of mesoblast into layers.

schizogamy (skĭzŏg'ămĭ) *n.* [Gk. *schizein*, to cleave; *gamos*, marriage.] Fission into a sexual and a non-sexual zooid in some Polychaeta.

schizogenesis (skĭz'öjĕn'ësĭs) *n.* [Gk. *schizein*, to cleave; *genesis*, descent.] Reproduction by fission.

schizogenetic (skĭz'öjënĕt'ĭk) *a.* [Gk. *schizein*, to cleave; *genesis*, descent.] Reproducing or formed by fission; *appl.* resin ducts; *appl.* spaces formed by delamination of adjacent cell-walls; schizogenous.

schizognathous (skĭzŏg'năthŭs) *a.* [Gk. *schizein*, to cleave; *gnathos*, jaw.] Having vomer small and pointed in front and maxillopalatines not united with each other and vomer; *appl.* a type of palate found in some Carinatae, *e.g.* in pigeon.

schizogony (skĭzŏg'önĭ) *n.* [Gk. *schizein*, to cleave; *gonos*, offspring.] Cleavage multiplication in protozoa.

schizokinete (skĭz'ökĭnēt') *n.* [Gk. *schizein*, to cleave; *kinetos*, movable.] Motile vermicule stage in life-history of Haemosporidia.

schizolysigenous (skĭzölĭsĭj'ënŭs) *a.* [Gk. *schizein*, to cleave; *lysis*, loosing; *gennaein*, to produce.] Formed schizogenously and enlarged lysigenously, *appl.* glands, cavities, as in pericarp of Citrus.

schizolysis (skĭzŏl′ĭsĭs) *n.* [Gk. *schizein*, to cleave; *lysis*, loosing.] Fragmentation; disjunction at septa, as of hyphae.

schizont (skĭzŏnt′) *n.* [Gk. *schizein*, to cleave; *onta*, beings.] A stage following trophozoite stage of parasitic Sporozoa, reproducing in host by multiple fission.

schizontoblast (skĭzŏn′töblăst) *n.* [Gk. *schizein*, to cleave; *onta*, beings; *blastos*, bud.] A cytomere of Caryotropha.

schizontocytes (skĭzŏn′tösīts) *n. plu.* [Gk. *schizein*, to cleave; *on*, being; *kytos*, hollow.] Cytomeres into which a schizont divides, and which themselves divide into clusters of merozoites.

schizopelmous (skĭz′öpĕl′mŭs) *a.* [Gk. *schizein*, to cleave; *pelma*, sole of foot.] With two separate flexor tendons connected with toes, as some birds.

schizophyte (skĭz′öfīt) *n.* [Gk. *schizein*, to cleave; *phyton*, plant.] A plant which reproduces solely by fission, as bacteria, yeasts, blue-green algae.

schizopod stage,—that stage in development of a decapod crustacean larva when it resembles an adult Mysis in having exopodite and endopodite to all thoracic limbs.

schizorhinal (skĭz′örī′năl) *a.* [Gk. *schizein*, to cleave; *rhis*, nose.] Having external narial opening elongated, and posterior border angular or slit-like; *opp.* holorhinal.

schizostele (skĭz′östē′lē) *n.* [Gk. *schizein*, to cleave; *stele*, post.] One of a number of strands formed by division of plerome of stem.

schizostely (skĭz′östē′lĭ) *n.* [Gk. *schizein*, to cleave; *stele*, a post.] Condition of stem in which plerome gives rise to a number of strands, each composed of one vascular bundle; astely.

schizothecal (skĭz′öthē′kăl) *a.* [Gk. *schizein*, to cleave; *theke*, case.] Having scale-like horny tarsal plates.

schizozoite (skĭz′özō′īt) *n.* [Gk. *schizein*, to cleave; *zoon*, animal.] A merozoite formed from each segment of a dividing schizont.

Schlemm, canal of [*F. S. Schlemm*, German anatomist]. Sinus venosus sclerae, circular canal near sclero-corneal junction and joining with anterior chamber of eye and anterior ciliary veins.

Schwann's sheath [*Th. Schwann*, German anatomist]. Primitive sheath or neurolemma, *q.v.*

sciaphyte,—skiaphyte, *q.v.*

sciatic (sīăt′ĭk) *a.* [Gk. *ischion*, hip-joint.] *Pert.* hip region; *appl.* artery, nerve, veins, etc.

scion (sī′ŏn) *n.* [F. *scion*, shoot.] A branch or shoot for grafting purposes; cion (U.S.A.).

sciophilous,—skiophilous, *q.v.*

sciophyll,—skiophyll, *q.v.*

scissile (sĭs′ĭl) *a.* [L. *scissilis*, cleavable] Cleavable; splitting, as into layers.

scissiparity (sĭs′ĭpăr′ĭtĭ) *n.* [L. *scissio*, cleaving; *parere*, to beget.] Schizogenesis.

sclera (sklē′ră) *n.* [Gk. *skleros*, hard.] The tough, opaque, fibrous tunic of the eyeball; sclerotic coat, sclerotica.

scleratogenous layer, — strand of the fused sclerotomes formed along the neural tube, later surrounding the notochord.

sclere (sklēr) *n.* [Gk. *skleros*, hard.] A small skeletal structure; sponge spicule.

sclereid (sklē′rēĭd) *n.* [Gk. *skleros*, hard; *eidos*, form.] Any cell with a thick lignified wall; a sclerenchymatous cell; a stone cell.

sclerenchyma (sklĕrĕng′kĭmă) *n.* [Gk. *skleros*, hard; *engchyma*, infusion.] Hard tissue of coral; plant tissue of thickened and of hard cells of vessels.

sclerid,—sclereid.

sclerins,—scleroproteins, *q.v.*

sclerite (sklē′rīt) *n.* [Gk. *skleros*, hard.] Calcareous plate or spicule; chitinous plate; part of exoskeleton.

sclerobase (sklē′röbās) *n.* [Gk. *skleros*, hard; *basis*, base.] The calcareous axis of Alcyonaria.

sclerobasidium (sklē'röbăsĭd'ĭŭm) *n.* [Gk. *skleros*, hard; *basis*, base; *idion*, *dim.*] A thick-walled resting body or encysted probasidium of rust and smut fungi; hypnobasidium.

scleroblast (sklē'röblăst) *n.* [Gk. *skleros* hard; *blastos*, bud.] A sponge cell from which a sclere develops; an immature sclereid.

scleroblastema (sklē'röblăst'ēmă) *n.* [Gk. *skleros*, hard; *blastema*, bud.] Embryonic tissue involved in development of skeleton.

scleroblastic (sklĕr'öblăs'tĭk) *a.* [Gk. *skleros*, hard; *blastos*, bud.] *Appl.* skeletal-forming tissue.

sclerocarp (sklēr'ökârp) *n.* [Gk. *skleros*, hard; *karpos*, fruit.] The hard seed coat or stone, usually the endocarp, of succulent fruit.

sclerocauly (sklĕr'ökôl'ĭ) *n.* [Gk. *skleros*, hard; *kaulos*, stalk.] Condition of excessive skeletal structure in a stem.

sclerocorneal (sklĕr'ökôr'nëăl) *a.* [Gk. *skleros*, hard; L. *cornea*, cornea.] *Pert.* cornea and sclera.

scleroderm (sklē'rödĕrm) *n.* [Gk. *skleros*, hard; *derma*, skin.] An indurating integument; skeletal part of corals.

sclerodermatous (sklĕr'ödĕr'mătŭs) *a.* [Gk. *skleros*, hard; *derma*, skin.] With an external skeletal structure.

sclerodermite (sklĕr'ödĕr'mīt) *n.* [Gk. *skleros*, hard; *derma*, skin.] The hard outer covering of an arthropod segment.

sclerogen (sklēr'öjĕn) *n.* [Gk. *skleros*, hard; *-genes*, producing.] Woody tissue in plant cells.

sclerogenic (sklĕr'öjĕn'ĭk), **sclerogenous** (sklĕröj'ënŭs) *a.* [Gk. *skleros*, hard; *-genes*, producing.] Producing lignin.

scleroid (sklē'roid) *a.* [Gk. *skleros*, hard; *eidos*, form.] Hard; skeletal.

scleromeninx (sklē'römē'nĭngks) *n.* [Gk. *skleros*, hard; *meningx*, membrane.] The dura mater.

sclerophyll (sklē'röfĭl) *n.* [Gk. *skleros*, hard; *phyllon*, leaf.] A plant with hard leaves; a sclerophyllous plant.

sclerophyllous (sklĕr'öfĭl'ŭs) *a.* [Gk. *skleros*, hard; *phyllon*, leaf.] *Appl.* leaves resistant to drought through having much sclerenchymatous tissue and reduced intercellular spaces; hard-leaved.

sclerophylly (sklē'röfĭl'ĭ) *n.* [Gk. *skleros*, hard; *phyllon*, leaf.] Condition of excessive skeletal structure in leaves.

scleroproteins (sklē'röprō'tëĭnz) *n. plu.* [Gk. *skleros*, hard; *proteion*, first.] Albuminoids; group of proteins occurring in connective, skeletal and epidermal tissues, as ossein, collagen, gelatin, chondrin, elastin, keratin, etc.

scleroseptum (sklēr'ösĕp'tŭm) *n.* [Gk. *skleros*, hard; L. *septum*, division.] A radial vertical wall of calcium carbonate in madrepore corals.

sclerosis (sklĕrō'sĭs) *n.* [Gk. *skleros*, hard.] Hardening by increase of connective tissue or of lignin.

sclerotal (sklĕrō'tăl) *a.* [Gk. *skleros*, hard.] Sclerotic.

sclerotesta (sklēr'ötĕs'tă) *n.* [Gk. *skleros*, hard; L. *testa*, shell.] The hard lignified inner layer of a testa.

sclerotic (sklērŏt'ĭk) *n.* [Gk. *skleros*, hard.] The sclera. *a.* Indurated; containing lignin; *pert.* sclerosis; *pert.* sclera.

sclerotic ossicles, — ring of small bones round sclera of birds.

sclerotica,—sclera.

sclerotioid (sklērŏt'ĭoid) *a.* [Gk. *skleros*, hard; *eidos*, form.] Like, or *pert.* a sclerotium.

sclerotium (sklērō'tĭŭm, -shĭŭm) *n.* [Gk. *skleros*, hard.] Resting, dormant, or winter stage of some fungi when they become a mass of hardened mycelium or of waxy protoplasm.

sclerotome (sklēr'ötōm) *n.* [Gk. *skleros*, hard; *tome*, cutting.] A partition of connective tissue between two myomeres; mesenchymatous tissue destined to form a vertebra.

sclerous (sklē'rŭs) *a.* [Gk. *skleros*, hard.] Sclerotal; scleroid.
scobiculate (sköbĭk'ūlāt) *a.* [*Dim.* of L. *scobis*, sawdust.] Granulated; scobicular.
scobiform (skŏb'ĭfôrm) *a.* [L. *scobis*, sawdust; *forma*, shape.] Resembling sawdust.
scobina (sköbī'nă) *n.* [L. *scobina*, file.] Pedicel of a spikelet of grasses.
scobinate (sköbī'nāt) *a.* [L. *scobina*, file.] Having a rasp-like surface.
scolecid (skōlĕs'ĭd) *a.* [Gk. *skolex*, worm.] *Pert.* a scolex; scolecoid.
scoleciform (skōlĕs'ĭfôrm) *a.* [Gk. *skolex*, worm; L. *forma*, shape.] Like a scolex, scolecoid.
scolecite (skō'lēsīt) *n.* [Gk. *skolex*, worm.] Vermiform body branching from mycelium of Discomycetes; Woronin hypha.
scolecospore (skō'lēköspōr) *n.* [Gk. *skolex*, worm; *sporos*, seed.] A worm-like or thread-like spore.
scolex (skō'lĕks) *n.* [Gk. *skolex*, worm.] The head or anterior end of a tape-worm.
scolite (skō'līt) *n.* [Gk. *skolex*, worm; *lithos*, stone.] A fossil worm burrow.
scolopale (skō'löpālē) *n.* [Gk. *skolos*, stake; *pale*, struggle.] Vibratile central peg-like portion of a scolophore.
scolophore (skō'löfōr) *n.* [Gk. *skolos*, stake; *pherein*, to bear.] Chordotonal sensilla or nerve end organ of auditory apparatus of insects.
scolopidium (skŏlöpĭd'ĭŭm) *n.* [Gk. *skolops*, stake; *idion*, *dim.*] A chordotonal sensilla in insects.
scolus (skō'lŭs) *n.* [Gk. *skolos*, thorn.] A thorny process of some insect larvae.
scopa (skō'pă) *n.* [L. *scopa*, brush.] A pollen-brush of bees.
scopate (skō'pāt) *a.* [L. *scopa*, brush.] Having a tuft of hairs like a brush; scopiferous.
scopiform (skō'pĭfôrm) *a.* [L. *scopa*, brush; *forma*, shape.] Brush-like.
scopula (skŏp'ūlă) *n.* [L. *scopula*, small brush.] A small tuft of hairs; brush-like adhesive organ formed by cilia in certain peritrichous ciliates; a needle-like sponge spicule with brush-like head; in climbing spiders an adhesive tuft of club-like hairs on each foot, replacing third claw.
scopulate (skŏp'ūlāt) *a.* [L. *scopula*, small brush.] Like a brush.
scopuliferous (skŏp'ūlĭf'ërŭs) *a.* [L. *scopula*, small brush; *ferre*, to carry.] Having a small brush-like structure.
scopuliform (skŏp'ūlĭfôrm) *a.* [L. *scopula*, small brush; *forma*, shape.] Resembling a small brush.
scorpioid (skôr'pĭoid) *a.* [Gk. *skorpios*, scorpion; *eidos*, form.] Circinate, *appl.* inflorescence; resembling a scorpion.
scorpioid cyme,—a uniparous cymose inflorescence in which daughter-axes are developed right and left alternately.
scorteal (skôr'tëăl) *a.* [L. *scorteus*, leathern.] *Appl.* or *pert.* a tough cortex, as of certain fungi.
scotoma (skötō'ma) *n.* [Gk. *skotos*, darkness.] A spot where vision is absent within the visual field; blind spot.
scotopia (skötō'pĭă) *n.* [Gk. *skotos*, darkness; *ops*, eye.] Adaptation of the eye to darkness, *opp.* photopia.
scotopic (skötŏp'ĭk) *a.* [Gk. *skotos*, darkness; *ops*, eye.] Having or *pert.* dark-adapted eye; *opp.* photopic.
scotopsin (skötŏp'sĭn) *n.* [Gk. *skotos*, darkness; *opsis*, sight.] The protein component of rhodopsin or visual purple.
scrobe (skrōb) *n.* [L. *scrobis*, ditch.] A groove on either side of beetle rostrum.
scrobicula (skröbĭk'ūlă) *n.* [L.L. *dim.* of *scrobis*, ditch.] The smooth area round boss of echinoid test.
scrobicular (skröbĭk'ūlăr) *a.* [L.L. *dim.* of *scrobis*, ditch.] In region of scrobicula.
scrobiculate (skröbĭk'ūlāt) *a.* [L.L. *dim.* of *scrobis*, ditch.] Marked with little pits or depressions.

scrobicule,—scrobicula, or scrobiculus.

scrobiculus (skrŏbĭk'ūlŭs) *n.* [L.L. *dim.* of *scrobis*, ditch.] A pit or depression.

scrobiculus cordis,—pit of stomach.

scrotal (skrō'tăl) *a.* [L. *scrotum.*] *Pert.* or in region of scrotum.

scrotum (skrō'tŭm) *n.* [L. *scrotum.*] External sac or sacs containing testicles, in mammals; covering of testis in insects.

scurf (skŭrf) *n.* [A.S. *scurf.*] Scaly skin; dried outer skin peeling off in scales; scaly epidermal covering of some leaves.

scuta,—*plu.* of scutum, *q.v.*

scutal (skū'tăl) *a.* [L. *scutum*, shield.] *Pert.* a scutum.

scutate (skū'tāt) *a.* [L. *scutum*, shield.] Protected by large scales or horny plates.

scute (skūt) *n.* [L. *scutum*, shield.] An external scale, as of reptile, fish, or scaly insect; a scale-like structure; bony plate separating sinuses of mastoid bone from tympanic cavity.

scutella (skūtĕl'ă) *n.* [L. *scutellum*, small shield.] A scutellum or shield-like structure; *plu.* of scutellum.

scutellar (skū'tĕlăr) *a.* [L. *scutellum*, small shield.] *Pert.* a scutellum.

scutellate (skū'tĕlat, skūtĕl'āt) *a.* [L. *scutellum*, small shield.] Shaped like a small shield; scutelliform.

scutellation (skū'tĕlā'shŭn) *n.* [L. *scutellum*, small shield.] Arrangement of scales, as on tarsus of bird.

scutelliform,—scutellate.

scutelligerous (skū'tĕlĭj'ĕrŭs) *a.* [L. *scutellum*, small shield; *gerere*, to bear.] Furnished with scutella or a scutellum.

scutelliplantar (skūtĕl'ĭplăn'tăr) *a.* [L. *scutellum*, small shield; *planta*, sole of foot.] Having tarsus covered with small plates or scutella.

scutellum (skūtĕl'ŭm) *n.* [L. *scutellum*, small shield.] A tarsal scale of birds; posterior part of insect notum; the single massive cotyledon lying next starchy endosperm in seed of maize; development of part of cotyledon which separates embryo from endosperm in seed of grasses.

scutiferous,—scutigerous.

scutiform (skū'tĭfôrm) *a.* [L. *scutum*, shield; *forma*, shape.] Shaped like a shield; *appl.* floating leaf of Salvinia.

scutigerous (skūtĭj'ĕrŭs) *a.* [L. *scutum*, shield; *gerere*, to bear.] Bearing a shield-like structure; scutiferous.

scutiped (skū'tĭpĕd) *a.* [L. *scutum*, shield; *pes*, foot.] Having foot or part of it covered by scutella.

scutum (skū'tŭm) *n.* [L. *scutum*, shield.] Broad apex of style, as in Asclepiadeae; one of eight plates surrounding antheridium of Chara; a shield-like plate, horny, bony, or chitinous, developed in integument; fornix or modified spine overhanging aperture in some Cheilostomata; middle sclerite of insect notum; dorsal shield of ticks.

scyphi,—*plu.* of scyphus.

scyphiferous (sĭfĭf'ĕrŭs) *a.* [L. *scyphus*, cup; *ferre*, to bear.] Bearing scyphi, as some lichens.

scyphiform (sĭf'ĭfôrm) *a.* [L. *scyphus*, cup; *forma*, shape.] Shaped like a cup; scyphoid.

scyphistoma (sĭfĭs'tŏmă) *n.* [Gk. *skyphos*, cup; *stoma*, mouth.] A scyphula, the scyphozoon polyp stage in development of Aurelia; hydra-tuba.

scyphoid (sĭf'oid) *a.* [Gk. *skyphos*, cup; *eidos*, form.] Cup-shaped; scyphiform.

scyphose (sĭf'ōs) *a.* [L. *scyphus*, cup.] Having scyphi; scyphiform.

scyphula (sĭf'ūlă) *n.* [L.L. *dim.* of *scyphus*, cup.] A scyphistoma.

scyphulus (sĭf'ūlŭs) *n.* [*Dim.* of L. *scyphus*, cup.] A small cup-shaped structure.

scyphus (sī'fŭs) *n.* [L. *scyphus*, Gk. *skyphos*, cup.] Cup of narcissus; funnel-shaped corolla; cup-shaped expansion of podetium in some lichens.

sebaceous (sēbā'shŭs) *a.* [L. *sebum*, tallow.] Containing or secreting fatty matter; *appl.* glands.

sebiferous (sēbĭf'ĕrŭs) *a.* [L. *sebum*, tallow; *ferre*, to carry.] Conveying fatty matter.

sebific (sēbĭf'ĭk) *a.* [L. *sebum*, tallow; *facere*, to make.] Sebiparous; colleterial, *q.v.*, *appl.* glands in insects.

sebiparous (sēbĭp'ărŭs) *a.* [L. *sebum*, tallow; *parere*, to beget.] Secreting fatty matter.

sebum (sē'bŭm) *n.* [L. *sebum*, tallow.] The secretion of sebaceous glands, consisting of fat and isocholesterin.

secodont (sĕk'ödŏnt) *a.* [L. *secare*, to cut; Gk. *odous*, tooth.] Furnished with teeth adapted for cutting.

secondary (sĕk'öndărĭ) *a.* [L. *secundus*, second.] Second in importance or in position; arising, not from growing point, but from other tissue; Mesozoic. *n.* A forearm quill-feather of bird's wing; an insect hind-wing.

secondary bud,—an axillary bud, accessory to normal one.

secondary capitula,—six small cells rising from each capitulum of Chara.

secondary growth,—development of secondary meristem or cambium producing new tissue on both sides, as in woody dicotyledons.

secondary meristem,—phellogen.

secondary prothallium, — a tissue produced in megaspore of Selaginella after true prothallium is formed.

secondary roots, — branches of primary root, arising within its tissue, and in turn giving rise to tertiary roots; roots arising at other than normal points of origin.

secondary spore,—a small or abjointed spore; a mycelial spore.

secondary tissue, — tissue formed through phellogen, externally cork, and internally phelloderm.

secondary wood, — wood formed from cambium.

secreta (sēkrē'tă) *n. plu.* [L. *secretum*, separated.] Any products of a secretory process; all the secretions.

secretin (sēkrē'tĭn) *n.* [L. *secernere*, to separate.] A chemical substance or hormone produced in intestinal mucous membrane and which stimulates secretion of pancreatic juice.

secretion (sēkrē'shŭn) *n.* [L. *secretio*, separation.] Substance or fluid which is separated and elaborated by cells or glands; process of such separation.

secretitious (sē'krētĭsh'ŭs) *a.* [L. *secernere*, to separate.] Produced by secretion, *appl.* substance or fluid.

secretory (sēkrē'törĭ) *a.* [L. *secernere*, to separate.] Effecting or *pert.* the secretion; secreting.

sectile (sĕk'tĭl) *a.* [L. *secare*, to cut.] Cut into small partitions or compartments.

sectorial (sĕktō'rĭăl) *a.* [L. *sector*, cutter.] Formed or adapted for cutting, as certain teeth; *appl.* chimaera when two different tissues extend from centre to periphery, a wedge of one tissue inserted in the other.

secund (sĕk'ŭnd) *a.* [L. *secundus*, following.] Arranged on one side; *appl.* flowers or leaves on stem.

secundiflorous (sĕkŭnd'ĭflō'rŭs) *a.* [L. *secundus*, following; *flos*, flower.] Having flowers on one side of stem only.

secundine (sĕk'ŭndĭn) *n.* [L. *secundus*, following.] The second coat of ovule, lying within primine.

secundines,—foetal membranes collectively; placenta and membranes expelled after birth; afterbirth.

secundly (sĕk'ŭndlĭ) *adv.* [L. *secundus*, following.] On one side of a stem or axis.

sedentary (sĕd'ĕntărĭ) *a.* [L. *sedere*, to sit.] Not free-living; *appl.* animals attached by a base to some substratum; not migratory.

seed (sēd) *n.* [A.S. *saed*, seed.] A mature fruit containing an embryo ready for germination under suitable conditions; semen. *v.* To introduce micro-organisms into a culture medium.

seed-bud,—an ovule.

seed-coat,—the testa.

seed-leaf,—seed-lobe or cotyledon.

seed-plant,—a seed-bearing plant.

seed-stalk,—the funicle.

seed-vessel,—a structure containing seed, as a pod.

Seessel's pouch [*A. Seessel*, American embryologist]. A dorsal endodermal diverticulum from anterior end of fore-gut, behind buccopharyngeal membrane.

segment (sĕg′mĕnt) *n.* [L. *segmentum*, piece.] A division formed by cleavage of an ovum; part of an animal or of a jointed appendage; metamere; division of leaf if cleft nearly to base; portion of a chromosome.

segmental (sĕgmĕn′tăl) *a.* [L. *segmentum*, piece.] Of the nature of a segment; *pert.* a segment.

segmental arteries, — diverticula from dorsal aortae arising in spaces between successive somites.

segmental duct,—an embryonic nephridial duct which gives rise to Wolffian or Müllerian duct.

segmental interchange,—exchange of non-homologous segments as between two chromosomes; mutual translocation.

segmental organ, — an embryonic excretory organ; a nephridium.

segmental papillae, — conspicuous pigment spots by which true segments may be recognised in leeches.

segmentation (sĕg′mĕntā′shŭn) *n.* [L. *segmentum*, piece.] The division or splitting into segments or portions; cleavage of an ovum.

segmentation cavity,—blastocoel or central cavity formed at an early state of egg cleavage.

segmentation nucleus, — body formed by union of male and female pronuclei in fertilisation of ovum.

segregation (sĕg′rĕgā′shŭn) *n.* [L. *segregare*, to separate.] Separation of parental chromosomes at meiosis and dissociation of paternal and maternal characters; separation of genes.

seiospore (sī′ŏspōr) *n.* [Gk. *seiein*, to shake; *sporos*, seed.] A spore shaken from a sporophore and becoming air-borne.

seiroderm (sī′rödĕrm) *n.* [Gk. *seira*, chain; *derma*, skin.] Dense outer tissue composed of parallel chains of hyphal cells, in certain fungi.

seirospore (sī′röspōr) *n.* [Gk. *seira*, chain; *sporos*, seed.] One of spores arranged like a chain; formerly, a catenulate spore of certain red algae.

seismaesthesia (sīs′mĕsthē′zĭă) *n.* [Gk. *seismos*, a shaking; *aisthesis*, perception.] Perception of mechanical vibrations.

seismonastic (sīs′mönăs′tĭk) *a.* [Gk. *seismos*, a shaking; *nastos*, pressed close.] Resulting from, or *pert.*, stimulus of mechanical shock or vibrations; *appl.* plant movements.

sejugous (sĕj′oogŭs, sējoog′ŭs) *a.* [L. *sex*, six; *jugum*, yoke.] With six pairs of leaflets; sejugate.

selachine (sĕl′ăkĭn) *n.* [Gk. *selachos*, shark.] A neurohumor of selachians which induces blanching of skin.

selenodont (sĕlē′nödŏnt) *a.* [Gk. *selene*, moon; *odous*, tooth.] *Appl.* molars lengthened out anteroposteriorly and curved.

selenoid (sĕlē′noid) *a.* [Gk. *selene*, moon; *eidos*, form.] Crescentic.

selenotropism (sĕlēnŏt′röpĭzm) *n.* [Gk. *selene*, moon; *trope*, turn.] Tendency to turn towards moon's rays.

self-fertile, self-sterile,—capable, —incapable,—of being fertilised by its own male elements; *appl.* hermaphrodite plants and animals.

self-pollination, — transference of pollen-grains from anthers to stigma of same flower; selfing.

sella turcica (sĕl′ă tŭr′sĭkă) *n.* [L. *sella*, saddle; *turcicus*, Turkish.] Deep depression on superior surface of sphenoidal bone behind tuberculum sellae, the deepest part, fossa hypophyseos, lodging the pituitary body; transverse bar formed by union of apodemes of posterior somites of certain Decapoda.

sellaeform (sĕl′ēfôrm) *a.* [L. *sella*, saddle ; *forma*, shape.] Saddle-shaped.

sellar (sĕl′ăr) *a.* [L. *sella*, saddle.] *Pert.* pituitary fossa or sella turcica.

selliform,—sellaeform.

selva (sĕl′vă) *n.* [Sp. *selva*, from L. *silva*, forest.] Tropical rain-forest.

sematic (sēmăt′ĭk) *a.* [Gk. *sema*, sign.] Functioning as a danger signal, as warning colours or odours ; *appl.* warning and recognition markings ; *cf.* aposematic, episematic, parasematic.

semeiography (sēmīŏg′răfĭ) *n.* [Gk. *semeion*, sign ; *graphein*, to write.] A description of symptoms.

semen (sē′mĕn) *n.* [L. *semen*, seed.] Fluid composed of secretions of testes and accessory glands, and containing spermatozoa.

semiamplexicaul (sĕm′ĭămplĕk′sĭkôl) *a.* [L. *semi*, half ; *amplecti*, to embrace ; *caulis*, stem.] Partially surrounding stem.

semianatropous (sĕm′ĭănăt′röpŭs) *a.* [L. *semi*, half ; Gk. *ana*, up ; *trope*, turn.] With half-inverted ovule.

semicaudate (sĕm′ĭkô′dāt) *a.* [L. *semi*, half ; *cauda*, tail.] With tail rudimentary.

semicells,—the two halves of a cell, which are interconnected by an isthmus, as in certain green algae.

semicircular (sĕm′ĭsër′kūlăr) *a.* [L. *semi*, half ; *circulus*, circle.] Describing a half-circle ; *appl.* canals and ducts of ear labyrinth.

semiclasp (sĕm′ĭklăsp) *n.* [L. *semi*, half ; M.E. *claspen*, to hold.] One of two apophyses which may combine to form the clasper in certain male insects.

semicomplete (sĕm′ĭkŏmplēt′) *a.* [L. *semi*, half ; *completus*, filled.] Incomplete ; *appl.* metamorphosis.

semicylindrical (sĕm′ĭsĭlĭn′drĭkăl) *a.* [L. *semi*, half ; *cylindrus*, cylinder.] Round on one side, flat on the other; *appl.* leaves.

semifloret (sĕm′ĭflō′rĕt) *n.* [L. *semi*, half ; *flos*, flower.] A semi-floscule or ray of composite flowers.

semiflosculous (sĕm′ĭflŏs′kūlŭs) *a.* [L. *semi*, half ; *flosculus*, small flower.] Having ligulate florets.

semigamy,—hemigamy, *q.v.*

semilethal (sĕm′ĭlē′thăl) *a.* [L. *semi*, half ; *lethalis*, deadly.] Not wholly lethal ; *appl.* genes causing a mortality of more than fifty per cent, or permitting survival until reproduction has been effected ; *cf.* subvital.

semiligneous (sĕm′ĭlĭg′nëŭs) *a.* [L. *semi*, half ; *ligneus*, wooden.] Partially lignified ; with stem woody only near base.

semilocular (sĕm′ĭlŏk′ūlăr) *a.* [L. *semi*, half ; *loculus*, compartment.] *Appl.* ovary with incomplete loculi.

semilunar (sĕm′ĭlū′năr, -loo-) *a.* [L. *semi*, half ; *luna*, moon.] Half-moon shaped ; *appl.* branches of internal carotid artery, fibro-cartilages of knee, ganglia, fascia, lobules of cerebellum, valves ; *appl.* notch, greater sigmoid cavity between olecranon and coronoid process of ulna. *n.* A carpal bone, os lunatum.

semimembranosus (sĕm′ĭmĕm′brănō′sŭs) *n.* [L. *semi*, half ; *membranosus*, membranous.] A thigh muscle with flat membrane-like tendon at upper extremity.

semimetamorphosis (sĕm′ĭmĕtămôr′fōsĭs) *n.* [L. *semi*, half ; Gk. *metamorphosis*, transformation.] Partial, or semicomplete metamorphosis.

seminal (sĕm′ĭnăl) *a.* [L. *semen*, seed.] *Pert.* semen ; *appl.* fluid, duct, vesicle ; *appl.* cotyledons, first roots of grasses.

seminal receptacle,—spermatheca, *q.v.*

semination (sĕm′ĭnā′shŭn) *n.* [L. *seminatio*, sowing.] Dispersal of seeds ; discharge of spermatozoa ; *cf.* insemination.

seminiferous (sĕmĭnĭf′ërŭs) *a.* [L. *semen*, seed ; *ferre*, to carry.] Secreting or conveying seed or seminal fluid ; bearing seed.

seminude (sĕm′ĭnūd) *a.* [L. *semi*, half; *nudus*, naked.] With ovules or seeds exposed.

seminymph (sĕm′ĭnĭmf) *n.* [L. *semi*, half; *nympha*, nymph.] Stage in development of insects approaching complete metamorphosis.

semiorbicular (sĕm′ĭôrbĭk′ūlăr) *a.* [L. *semi*, half; *orbis*, orb.] Half rounded; hemispherical.

semiovate (sĕm′ĭō′vāt) *a.* [L. *semi*, half; *ovum*, egg.] Half-oval; somewhat oval.

semioviparous (sĕm′ĭōvĭp′ărŭs) *a.* [L. *semi*, half; *ovum*, egg; *parere*, to beget.] Between oviparous and viviparous, as a marsupial whose young are imperfectly developed when born.

semiovoid (sĕm′ĭō′void) *a.* [L. *semi*, half; *ovum*, egg; Gk. *eidos*, form.] Somewhat ovoid in shape.

semipalmate (sĕm′ĭpăl′māt) *a.* [L. *semi*, half; *palma*, palm of hand.] Having toes webbed halfway down.

semiparasite (sĕm′ĭpăr′ăsīt) *n.* [L. *semi*, half; Gk. *parasitos*, eating beside another.] A partial parasite, as a plant which derives part only of its nutriment from its host.

semipenniform (sĕm′ĭpĕn′ĭfôrm) *a.* [L. *semi*, half; *penna*, feather; *forma*, shape.] *Appl.* certain muscles bearing some resemblance to plume or feather.

semipermeable (sĕm′ĭpĕr′mëăbl) *a.* [L. *semi*, half; *per*, through; *meare*, to pass.] *Appl.* membrane which permits some dissolved substances to pass but not others, although permeable to a solvent, such as water.

semiplacenta (sĕm′ĭplăsĕn′tă) *n.* [L. *semi*, half; *placenta*, flat cake.] A non-deciduate placenta.

semiplume (sĕm′ĭploom) *n.* [L. *semi*, half; *pluma*, feather.] A feather with ordinary shaft but downy web.

semipupa (sĕm′ĭpū′pă) *n.* [L. *semi*, half; *pupa*, puppet.] Larval stage in development of certain insects.

semirecondite (sĕm′ĭrĕkŏn′dīt) *a.* [L. *semi*, half; *recondere*, to conceal.] Half-concealed, as insect head by thorax.

semisagittate (sĕm′ĭsăj′ĭtāt) *a.* [L. *semi*, half; *sagitta*, arrow.] Shaped like a half arrow-head.

semisaprophyte (sĕm′ĭsăp′röfīt) *n.* [L. *semi*, half; Gk. *sapros*, rotten; *phyton*, plant.] A plant partially saprophytic.

semispecies (sĕm′ĭspē′shēz) *n.* [L. *semi*, half; *species*, particular kind.] A species differentiated from another species as a result of geographical isolation.

semispinalis (sĕm′ĭspĭnā′lĭs) *n.* [L. *semi*, half; *spinalis*, spinal.] A muscle of back, also of neck, on each side of spinal column, arising from transverse and inserted into spinous processes.

semistreptostylic, — between monimostylic and streptostylic; with slightly movable quadrate.

semitendinosus (sĕm′ĭtĕn′dĭnōsŭs) *n.* [L. *semi*, half; *tendo*, sinew.] A dorsal muscle of thigh stretching from tuber ischii to tibia.

semitendinous (sĕm′ĭtĕn′dĭnŭs) *a.* [L. *semi*, half; *tendere*, to stretch.] Half tendinous.

semituberous (sĕm′ĭtūbërŭs) *a.* [L. *semi*, half; *tuber*, hump.] Having somewhat tuberous roots.

senescence (sĕnĕs′ĕns) *n.* [L. *senescere*, to grow old.] Advancing age; ageing; *appl.* condition of protozoa after many bipartitions.

senility (sĕnĭl′ĭtĭ) *n.* (L. *senilis*, senile.] Senile derangement; vital exhaustion of protozoa.

sense organ,—an organ functional in receiving external stimulation; receptor.

sensiferous (sĕnsĭf′ërŭs) *a.* [L. *sensus*, sense; *ferre*, to carry.] Receiving or conveying sense impressions; sensigerous.

sensile (sĕn′sĭl) *a.* [L. *sensilis*, sensitive.] Capable of affecting a sense.

sensilla (sĕnsĭl′ă) *n.* [L. *sensus*, sense.] A small sense organ.

sensitive (sĕn'sĭtĭv) *a.* [L. *sensus*, sense.] Capable of receiving impressions from external objects; reacting to a stimulus; *appl.* plants, as Mimosa.

sensorial (sĕnsō'rĭăl) *a.* [L. *sensus*, sense.] *Pert.* the sensorium.

sensorium (sĕnsō'rĭŭm) *n.* [L. *sensus*, sense.] Seat of sensation or consciousness; entire nervous system with sense organs; the sensory, neuromuscular, and glandular system.

sensory (sĕn'sŏrĭ) *a.* [L. *sensus*, sense.] Having direct connection with any part of sensorium.

sentient (sĕn'shĭĕnt) *a.* [L. *sentire*, to feel.] *Appl.* cells which are sensitive and perceptive.

sepal (sĕp'ăl) *n.* [F. *sépale*; L. *separare*, to separate.] A leaf-like division of calyx.

sepaled (sĕp'ăld) *a.* [L. *separare*, to separate.] Having sepals; sepalous.

sepaline (sĕp'ălĭn) *a.* [L. *separare*, to separate.] Like a sepal; sepaloid.

sepalody (sĕpăl'ŏdĭ) *n.* [L. *separare*, to separate; Gk. *eidos*, form.] Conversion of petals or other parts of a flower into sepals.

sepaloid (sĕp'ăloid) *a.* [L. *separare*, to separate; Gk. *eidos*, form.] Like a sepal; sepaline.

sepicolous (sēpĭk'ŏlŭs) *a.* [L. *sepes*, hedge; *colere*, to inhabit.] Living in hedges.

sepiment (sĕp'ĭmĕnt) *n.* [L. *sepimentum*, fence.] A partition; a dissepiment, *q.v.*

sepion (sēp'ĭŏn) *n.* [Gk. *sepion*, cuttle-bone.] Cuttle-bone, or sepiabone, sepiost, sepiostaire, sepium.

septa,—*plu.* of septum.

septal (sĕp'tăl) *a.* [L. *septum*, partition.] *Pert.* a septum; *pert.* hedgerows, *appl.* flora.

septal fossula,—a small primary septum which appears to lie in a pit in some fossil corals.

septal neck,—in nautilus, a shelly tube continuous for some distance beyond each septum as support to siphuncle.

septate (sĕp'tāt) *a.* [L. *septum*, partition.] Divided by partitions.

septempartite (sĕp'tĕmpâr'tīt) *a.* [L. *septem*, seven; *pars*, part.] *Appl.* leaf with seven divisions extending nearly to base.

septenate (sĕp'tĕnāt) *a.* [L. *septeni*, seven each.] With parts in sevens; *appl.* seven leaflets of a leaf.

septicidal (sĕp'tĭsī'dăl) *a.* [L. *septum*, division; *caedere*, to cut.] Dividing through middle of ovary septa; dehiscing at septum.

septiferous (sĕptĭf'ĕrŭs) *a.* [L. *septum*, partition; *ferre*, to bear.] Having septa.

septifolious (sĕp'tĭfō'lĭŭs) *a.* [L. *septem*, seven; *folium*, leaf.] With seven leaves or leaflets.

septiform (sĕp'tĭfôrm) *a.* [L. *septum*, partition; *forma*, shape.] In form of a septum.

septifragal (sĕptĭf'răgăl) *a.* [L. *septum*, partition; *frangere*, to break.] With slits as in septicidal dehiscence, but with septa broken and placentae and seeds left in middle.

septomaxillary (sĕp'tŏmăksĭl'ărĭ) *a.* [L. *septum*, partition; *maxilla*, jaw.] *Pert.* maxilla and nasal septum; *appl.* a small bone in many amphibians and reptiles and in certain birds.

septonasal (sĕp'tŏnā'zăl) *a.* [L. *septum*, partition; *nasus*, nose.] *Pert.* nasal, or internarial, septum.

septulate (sĕp'tūlāt) *a.* [L. *septulum*, small septum.] Having spurious, or secondary septa.

septulum (sĕp'tūlŭm) *n.* [L. *septulum*, small septum.] A small or secondary septum.

septum (sĕp'tŭm) *n.* [L. *septum*, partition.] A partition separating two cavities or masses of tissue, as in fruits, chambered shells, corals, heart, nose, tongue, etc.

septum lucidum,—thin inner walls of cerebral hemispheres, between corpus callosum and fornix; septum pellucidum.

septum narium,—partition between nostrils; septum mobile nasi.

septum transversum, — foetal diaphragm; ridge within ampulla of semicircular canal.

sera,—*plu.* of serum.

seral (sĕr'ăl) *a.* [L. *serere*, to put in a row.] *Pert.* a sere; *appl.* a plant community before reaching equilibrium or climax.

sere (sēr) *n.* [L. *serere*, to put in a row.] A successional series of plant communities, as from prisere to climax; a stage in a succession.

seriate (sē'rĭāt) *a.* [L. *serere*, to put in a row.] Arranged in a row or series.

sericate (sĕr'ĭkāt), **sericeous** (sĕrĭsh'ŭs) *a.* [L. *sericus*, silken.] Covered with fine close-pressed silky hairs; silky.

serific (sĕrĭf'ĭk) *a.* [L. *sericum*, silk; *facere*, to make.] Silk-producing.

serology (sērŏl'ŏjĭ) *n.* [L. *serum*, whey; Gk. *logos*, discourse.] The study of sera.

serosa (sērō'să) *n.* [L. *serum*, whey.] Any serous membrane, or tunica serosa; visceral peritoneum; false amnion or outer layer of amniotic fold; outer larval membrane of insects.

serosity (sērŏs'ĭtĭ) *n.* (L. *serum*, whey.] Watery part of animal fluid; condition of being serous.

serotinous (sērŏt'ĭnŭs) *a.* [L. *serus*, late.] Appearing or blooming late in the season; flying late in the evening, as bats.

serotonin (sērŏt'ŏnĭn) *n.* [L. *serum*, whey; Gk. *tonos*, tightening.] A vasoconstrictor compound in blood platelets, also in brain cells, which causes contraction of smooth muscle; 5 hydroxytryptamine.

serous (sē'rŭs) *a.* [L. *serum*, serum.] Watery; *pert.* serum; *appl.* fluid, cells, tissue, glands.

serous alveoli,—alveoli which secrete a watery non-viscid saliva, *opp.* mucous alveoli.

serous membrane,—a thin membrane of connective tissue, lining some closed cavity of body, and reflected over viscera, as mesentery.

serozyme (sē'rŏzīm) *n.* [L. *serum*, serum; Gk. *zyme*, leaven.] Thrombinogen; prothrombin, *q.v.*

serozymogenic (sē'rŏzī'mŏjĕn'ĭk) *a.* [L. *serum*, serum; Gk. *zyme*, leaven; *gennaein*, to produce.] *Appl.* cells of serous alveoli when containing zymogen granules.

serpulite (sĕr'pūlīt) *n.* [L. *serpula*, small snake; Gk. *lithos*, stone.] The fossil tube of a polychaete; *appl.* grit containing fossil worm-tubes.

serra (sĕr'ă) *n.* [L. *serra*, saw.] Any saw-like structure.

serrate (sĕr'āt) *a.* [L. *serra*, saw.] Notched on edge like a saw; *appl.* leaves and other structures.

serrate-ciliate,—with hairs fringing toothed edges.

serrate-dentate,—with serrate edges themselves toothed.

serratiform (sĕrā'tĭfôrm) *a.* [L. *serra*, saw; *forma*, shape.] Like a saw.

serration (sĕrā'shŭn) *n.* [L. *serra*, saw.] Saw-like formation.

serratirostral (sĕrăt'ĭrŏs'trăl) *a.* [L. *serra*, saw; *rostrum*, beak.] With serrate bill; *appl.* birds.

serratodenticulate (sĕrăt'ŏdĕntĭk'ūlāt) *a.* [L. *serra*, saw; *dens*, tooth.] With many-toothed serrations.

serratulate,—serrulate.

serrature (sĕr'ătūr) *n.* [L. *serra*, saw.] A saw-like notch; a serration.

serratus magnus,—or anterior, a muscle stretching from upper ribs to scapula.

serriferous (sĕrĭf'ĕrŭs) *a.* [L. *serra*, saw; *ferre*, to carry.] Furnished with a saw-like organ or part.

serriform (sĕr'ĭfôrm) *a.* [L. *serra*, saw; *forma*, shape.] Like a saw.

serriped (sĕr'ĭpĕd) *a.* [L. *serra*, saw; *pes*, foot.] With notched feet.

serrula (sĕr'ūlă) *n.* [L. *serrula*, small saw.] A comb-like ridge on chelicerae of some Arachnida.

serrulate (sĕr'ūlāt) *a.* [L. *serrula*, small saw.] Finely-notched.

serrulation (sĕr'ūlā'shŭn) *n.* [L. *serrula*, small saw.] Small notch; condition of being finely notched.

Sertoli cells [*E. Sertoli*, Italian histologist]. Enlarged lining epithelium-cells connected with groups of developing spermatozoa in testes; supporting cells.

serule (sĕr′ūl) *n.* [L. *serere*, to put in a row; *dim.*] A minor sere; succession of minor life forms.

serum (sē′rŭm) *n.* [L. *serum*, whey.] Watery fluid which separates from blood on coagulation; the secretion of a serous membrane; whey.

serum albumin, serum globulin,—two of proteins of serum.

sesamoid (sĕs′ămoid) *a.* [Gk. *sesamon*, sesame; *eidos*, form.] *Appl.* a bone developed within a tendon and near a joint, as patella, radial or ulnar sesamoid, fabella. *n.* A sesamoid bone.

sesamoidal (sĕs′ămoidăl) *a.* [L. *sesamon*, sesame; *eidos*, form.] *Pert.* a sesamoid bone.

sessile (sĕs′ĭl) *a.* [L. *sedere*, to sit.] Sitting directly on base without support, stalk, pedicel, or peduncle; attached or stationary, *opp.* free-living or motile.

seston (sĕs′tŏn) *n.* [Gk. *sesis*, sifting.] Microplankton; all bodies, living and non-living, floating or swimming in water; *cf.* nekton, neuston, plankton, tripton.

seta (sē′tă) *n.* [L. *seta*, bristle.] Any bristle-like structure; sporophore of liverworts and mosses; chaeta of Chaetopoda.

setaceous (sētā′shŭs) *a.* [L. *seta*, bristle.] Bristle-like; set with bristles.

setiform (sē′tĭfŏrm) *a.* [L. *seta*, bristle; *forma*, shape.] Bristle-shaped; *appl.* teeth when very fine and closely set.

setigerous (sētĭj′ĕrŭs) *a.* [L. *seta*, bristle; *gerere*, to bear.] Bristle-bearing; setiferous; setiparous.

setigerous sac,—a sac, in which is lodged a bundle of setae, formed by invagination of epidermis in parapodium of Chaetopoda.

setirostral (sē′tĭrŏs′trăl) *a.* [L. *seta*, bristle; *rostrum*, beak.] *Appl.* birds with beak bristles.

setobranchia (sē′tŏbrăng′kĭă) *n.* [L. *seta*, bristle; Gk. *brangchia*, gills.] A tuft of setae attached to gills of certain decapods; coxopoditic setae.

setose (sētōs′) *a.* [L. *seta*, bristle.] Set with bristles; bristly.

setula (sĕt′ūlă) *n.* [*Dim.* from L. *seta*, bristle.] A setule: a thread-like or hair-like bristle.

setuliform (sĕt′ūlĭfôrm) *a.* [*Dim.* from L. *seta*, bristle; *forma*, shape.] Thread-like; like a setula or fine bristle.

setulose (sĕt′ūlōs) *a.* [*Dim.* from L. *seta*, bristle.] Set with small bristles.

sex (sĕks) *n.* [L. *sexus*, sex.] The sum of characteristics, structures, functions, by which an animal or plant is classed as male or female.

sex-chromosome,—the chromosome whose presence, absence, or particular form may determine sex; X, Y, or W chromosome; also monosome, idiochromosome, heterochromosome, special or odd chromosome, etc.

sex differentiation,—differentiation of gametes; differentiation of organisms into kinds with different sexual organs.

sexdigitate (sĕksdĭj′ĭtāt) *a.* [L. *sex*, six; *digitus*, finger.] With six fingers or toes.

sexfid (sĕks′fĭd) *a.* [L. *sex*, six; *findere*, to cleave.] Cleft into six, as a calyx.

sexfoil (sĕks′foil) *n.* [L. *sex*, six; *folium*, leaf.] A group of six leaves or leaflets round one axis.

sex hormones,—gonad hormones and gonadotropic hormones.

sex-limited inheritance,—inheritance of characters whose factors have effect in one sex only.

sex-linked inheritance,—transmission of characters whose factors are borne by the sex-chromosome.

sex mosaic,—an intersex, *q.v.*; gynandromorph, *q.v.*

sex ratio,—number of males per hundred females, or, per hundred births; percentage of males in a population.

sex-reversal,—sex-transformation, a change-over from one sex to the other, natural, pathological, or artificially induced.

sexual (sĕk′sūăl) *a.* [L. *sexus*, sex.] *Pert.* sex; *appl.* reproduction, etc.

sexual cell,—ovum or sperm.

sexual dimorphism,—marked differences, in shape, size, structure, colour, etc., between male and female of the same species.

sexuparous (sĕk'sū'părŭs) *a.* [L. *sexus*, sex; *parere*, to bear.] Producing sexual offspring, as after bearing parthenogenetic females in Pterygota.

shaft (shâft) *n.* [A.S. *sceaft*, spear-shaft.] A rachis; distal part of stem of feather; stem of hair; scapus; straight cylindrical part of long bone.

Sharpey's fibres [*W. Sharpey*, Scottish surgeon]. Calcified bundles of white fibres and elastic fibres perforating and holding together periosteal lamellae; perforating fibres.

sheath (shēth) *n.* [A.S. *sceth*, shell or pod.] A protective covering; theca; investing petiole; insect wing-cover.

shell (shĕl) *n.* [A.S. *scell*, shell.] The hard outer covering of animal or fruit; a calcareous, siliceous, bony, horny, or chitinous covering.

shell gland, shell sac,—organ in whose walls material for forming a shell is secreted.

shield (shēld) *n.* [A.S. *scyld*, shield.] Carapace, *q.v.*; clypeus, *q.v.*; scutellum, *q.v.*; scutum, *q.v.*; disc-like ascocarp or apothecium borne on thallus of lichens.

shift (shĭft) *n.* [A.S. *sciftan*, to divide.] *Appl.* translocation in which the portion between two breaks is transferred to a gap left by a third break in the same chromosome; *cf.* insertional.

short-day,—*appl.* plants in which the flowering period is hastened by a relatively short photoperiod, ordinarily less than 12 hours.

shoulder girdle,—pectoral girdle, typically comprising scapula, coracoid, precoracoid, and clavicle.

Shrapnell's membrane [*H. J. Shrapnell*, English anatomist]. Small, flaccid part of the tympanic membrane above malleolar folds; pars flaccida, *opp.* pars tensa.

sialaden (sīăl'ădĕn) *n.* [Gk. *sialon*, saliva; *aden*, gland.] A salivary gland.

sialic (sī'ălĭk) *a.* [Gk. *sialon*, saliva.] *Pert.* saliva.

sialoid (sī'ăloid) *a.* [Gk. *sialon*, saliva; *eidos*, form.] Like saliva.

siblings (sĭb'lĭngz) *n. plu.* [A.S. *sibb*, kin.] Offspring of same parents, but not at same birth.

siccous (sĭk'ŭs) *a.* [L. *siccus*, dry.] Dry; with little or no juice.

sicula (sĭk'ūlă) *n.* [L. *sicula*, small dagger.] A small dagger-shaped body at end of a graptolite, supposed to be skeleton of primary zooid of colony.

sicyoid (sĭs'ĭoid, sĭk'-) *a.* [Gk. *sikyos*, gourd; *eidos*, form.] Gourd-shaped.

side-chain theory,—Ehrlich's theory of phenomena of immunity, *i.e.*, that toxins unite with living protoplasm by possessing the same property as that by which nutritive proteins are normally assimilated.

siderocyte (sĭd'ērösīt) *n.* [Gk. *sideros*, iron; *kytos*, hollow.] An erythrocyte containing free iron not utilised in haemoglobin formation.

siderophil (sĭd'ēröfĭl') *a.* [Gk. *sideros*, iron; *philos*, loving.] Staining deeply with iron-coating stains; tending to absorb iron; siderophilous. *n.* An organism which thrives in the presence of iron.

sierozem (syĕr'özĕm) *n.* [Russ. *seryi*, grey; *zemlya*, soil.] Grey soil, containing little humus, of middle-latitude continental desert regions.

sieve area,—perforated area of cell-wall of sieve elements, with groups of pores surrounded by callose.

sieve cell,—a phloem cell having perforated areas of cell-wall; a cell of sieve tubes.

sieve disc,—sieve plate, in phloem cells.

sieve elements,—the conducting parts of phloem, sieve cells and sieve-tube cells.

sieve pit,—a primary pit giving rise to a sieve pore.

sieve plate,—part of the wall of a sieve cell, containing simple or compound sieve areas; the perforated and thickened end of a sieve-tube cell; area of coxal lobe of pedipalp, with openings of salivary ducts, in spiders.

sieve pore,—one of the perforations in a sieve area or sieve plate.

sieve tissue, — essential tissue of phloem of vascular bundles.

sieve tubes,—phloem vessels, long slender structures consisting of elongated cells placed end to end, forming lines of conduction.

sight (sīt) *n.* [A.S. *siht*, sight.] The visual faculty; impressions of outward things conveyed to brain by retina and optic nerves.

sigillate (sĭj'ĭlāt) *a.* [L. *sigillum*, seal.] Having seal-like markings, as certain rhizomes and roots.

sigma (sĭg'mă) *n.* [Gk. Σ, sigma.] A C-shaped sponge spicule.

sigmaspire (sĭg'măspīr) *n.* [Gk, Σ, sigma; L. *spira*, coil.] A sigma with an additional twist.

sigmoid (sĭg'moid) *a.* [Gk. Σ, sigma; *eidos*, form.] Curved like a sigma; curved in two directions; *appl.* arteries, cavities, valves.

sigmoid flexure, — an S-shaped double curve as in a bird's neck; S-shaped curve of colon.

silicle (sĭl'ĭkl) *n.* [L. *silicula*, little pod.] A silicula, or short flat form of siliqua.

silicole (sĭl'ĭkōl) *n.* [L. *silex*, flint; *colere*, to inhabit.] A plant thriving in markedly siliceous soil; *cf.* calcifuge.

silicula,—*see* silicle.

silicular (sĭlĭk'ūlăr) *a.* [L. *silicula*, little pod.] Siliculose; siliculous; like, *pert.*, or having a silicle.

siliqua (sĭl'ĭkwă) *n.* [L. *siliqua*, pod.] A long cylindrical fruit divided in two by a false septum, characteristic of Cruciferae; silique; superficial funicles surrounding olive, *q.v.*

siliquiform (sĭl'ĭkwĭfôrm) *a.* [L. *siliqua*, pod; *forma*, shape.] Formed like a silique or siliqua.

siliquose (sĭl'ĭkwōs) *a.* [L. *siliqua*, pod.] Siliquous; bearing siliques.

Silurian (sĭlū'rĭăn) *a.* [L. *Silures*, a people of South Wales.] *Pert.* or *appl.* period of Palaeozoic era, between Ordovician and Devonian.

silva,—selva, *q.v.*; sylva, *q.v.*

silvicolous (sĭlvĭk'ölŭs) *a.* [L. *silvicola*, forest inhabitant.] Inhabiting or growing in woodlands; *appl.* plant formations.

simblospore (sĭm'blöspōr) *n.* [Gk. *simblos*, beehive; *sporos*, seed.] Swarm spore or zoospore.

simian (sĭm'ĭăn) *a.* [L. *simia*, ape.] Possessing characteristics of, or *pert.*, anthropoid apes.

simple eyes,—ocelli which occur with or without compound eyes in adults of many insects; usually the only eyes possessed by larvae; eyes with only one lens.

simplex (sĭm'plĕks) *a.* [L. *simplex*, simple.] Having one dominant gene, in polyploidy.

simulation (sĭm'ūlā'shŭn) *n.* [L. *simulare*, to simulate.] Assumption of features or structures intended to deceive enemies, as forms of leaf and stick insects, and all varieties of protective coloration.

sincipital (sĭnsĭp'ĭtăl) *a.* [L. *semi*, half; *caput*, head.] *Pert.* the sinciput.

sinciput (sĭn'sĭpŭt) *n.* [L. *semi*, half; *caput*, head.] Upper or fore part of head.

sinistral (sĭn'ĭstrăl) *a.* [L. *sinister*, left.] On the left; *appl.* a shell whose spiral turns in opposite direction to dextral.

sinistrorse (sĭn'ĭstrôrs) *a.* [L. *sinister*, left; *vertere*, to turn.] *Appl.* a spiral twining towards the left, *opp.* dextrorse.

sinuate (sĭn'ūāt) *a.* [L. *sinus*, curve.] Winding; tortuous; having a wavy indented margin, as leaves; sinuous.

sinu-auricular (sĭn'ūôrĭk'ūlăr) *a.* [L. *sinus*, gulf; *auricula*, small ear.] *Appl.* node, a group of cells of the auricle near opening of anterior vena cava and where heart-beat is initiated; *cf.* pace-maker; *appl.*

valves between sinus venosus and atrium; sinuatrial.

sinupalliate (sĭn'ūpăl'ĭăt) *a.* [L. *sinus*, curve; *pallium*, mantle.] In molluscs, having well-developed siphon, and so an indented pallial line. *Opp.* integripalliate.

sinus (sī'nŭs) *n.* [L. *sinus*, curve, or gulf.] A cavity, depression, recess, or dilatation; a groove or indentation.

sinus glands,—endocrine glands in eye-stalks of decapod crustaceans.

sinus pocularis,—uterus masculinus.

sinus rhomboidalis,—in vertebrate embryos, posterior incompletely-closed part of medullary canal; later, a dilatation of canal in sacral region, formed from it.

sinus venosus,—posterior chamber of tubular heart of embryo; in lower vertebrates, a corresponding structure receiving venous blood and opening into auricle; cavity of auricle.

sinuses of Valsalva [*A. M. Valsalva*, Italian anatomist]. Dilatations of pulmonary artery and of aorta, opposite pulmonary and aortic semilunar valves of heart.

sinusoid (sī'nŭsoid) *n.* [L. *sinus*, curve; Gk. *eidos*, form.] A minute blood space in organ tissue formed from intercrescence of endodermal cells and vascular endothelium, as in liver; blood space with irregular lumen connecting arterial and venous capillaries.

siphon (sī'fŏn) *n.* [Gk. *siphon*, reed or tube.] A tubular or siphon-like structure of various organisms, subserving various purposes.

siphonate (sī'fŏnāt) *a.* [Gk. *siphon*, tube.] Furnished with a siphon or siphons.

siphonet (sī'fŏnĕt) *n.* [Gk. *siphon*, tube.] The honeydew tube of an aphid.

siphonial (sīfō'nĭăl) *a.* [Gk. *siphon*, tube.] *Pert.* a siphonium.

siphonium (sīfō'nĭŭm) *n.* [Gk. *siphon*, tube.] Membranous tube connecting air-passages of quadrate with air-space in mandible; also siphoneum.

siphonogamic (sī'fŏnŏgăm'ĭk) *a.* [Gk. *siphon*, tube; *gamos*, marriage.] Securing fertilisation through a pollen tube; siphonogamous.

siphonogamy (sī'fŏnŏg'ămĭ) *n.* [Gk. *siphon*, tube; *gamos*, marriage.] Fertilisation by means of a pollen tube.

siphonoglyph (sī'fŏnöglĭf') *n.* [Gk. *siphon*, tube; *glyphein*, to engrave.] One of two longitudinal grooves or sulci of gullet of sea-anemones.

siphonoplax (sī'fŏnöplăks') *n.* [Gk. *siphon*, tube; *plax*, tablet.] A calcareous plate connected with siphon of certain molluscs.

siphonostele (sī'fŏnöstē'lē) *n.* [Gk. *siphon*, tube; *stele*, post.] The hollow vascular cylinder of a stem, which may contain pith.

siphonostelic (sī'fŏnöstēl'ĭk) *a.* [Gk. *siphon*, tube; *stele*, post.] *Appl.* hollow cylindrical stems, chiefly of ferns.

siphonostomatous (sī'fŏnöstŏm'ătŭs) *a.* [Gk. *siphon*, tube; *stoma*, mouth.] With tubular mouth; having front margin of shell notched for emission of siphon.

siphonozooid (sī'fŏnözō'oid) *n.* [Gk. *siphon*, tube; *zoon*, animal; *eidos*, form.] Small modified polyp without tentacles and serving to propel water through canal system of certain Alcyonarian colonies.

siphorhinal (sī'förī'năl) *a.* [Gk. *siphon*, tube; *rhines*, nostrils.] With tubular nostrils.

siphuncle (sī'fŭngkl) *n.* [L. *siphunculus*, small tube.] A siphonet; a median tube of skin, partly calcareous, connecting up all compartments of a nautilus shell.

siphunculate (sĭfŭng'kūlāt) *a.* [L. *siphunculus*, small tube.] Having a siphuncle; having mouth-parts modified for sucking, as certain lice.

siro-,—*see* seiro-.

sitology (sītŏl'ŏjĭ) *n.* [Gk. *sitos*, food; *logos*, discourse.] Science of food, diet, and nutrition.

sitophore (sī'tŏfōr) *n.* [Gk. *sitos*, food; *pherein*, to bear.] Trough of hypopharynx between arms of suspensorium.

sitotoxin (sīt′ŏtŏk′sĭn) *n.* [Gk. *sitos*, food; *toxikon*, poison.] Food poison.

sitotropism (sītŏt′rŏpĭzm) *n.* [Gk. *sitos*, food; *trope*, turn.] Tendency to turn in direction of food; reaction towards stimulating influences of food.

skeletal (skĕl′ĕtăl) *a.* [Gk. *skeletos*, dried.] *Pert.* the skeleton.

skeletogenous (skĕl′ĕtŏj′ĕnŭs) *a.* [Gk. *skeletos*, hard; *gennaein*, to produce.] *Appl.* embryonic structures or parts which later become parts of skeleton.

skeleton (skĕl′ĕtŏn) *n.* [Gk. *skeletos*, dried, hard.] Hard framework, internal or external, which supports and protects softer parts of plant or animal; bones in their natural arrangement.

skeletoplasm (skĕl′ĕtŏplăzm) *n.* [Gk. *skeletos*, hard; *plasma*, mould.] Formative material destined to form supporting structures.

Skene's glands [*A. J. C. Skene*, Scottish gynaecologist]. Mucous glands of the female urethra; para-urethral glands.

skiaphyte (skī′ăfīt) *n.* [Gk. *skia*, shade; *phyton*, plant.] A plant growing in the shade, as algae under rocks; skiarophyte.

skin (skĭn) *n.* [A.S. *scinn*, skin.] The external covering of an animal, plant, fruit, or seed.

skin-gills, — transparent contractile outgrowths from skin of Asteroidea, with respiratory function.

skin-rings, — annular markings on body of worms.

skiophilous (skĭŏf′ĭlŭs) *a.* [Gk. *skia*, shade; *philein*, to love.] Shade-loving; skiophil, heliophobous.

skiophyll (skī′ŏfĭl) *n.* [Gk. *skia*, shade; *phyllon*, leaf.] A plant having dorsiventral leaves. *Opp.* heliophyll.

skotoplankton (skŏt′ŏplăngk′tŏn) *n.* [Gk. *skotos*, darkness; *plangktos*, wandering.] Plankton living at depths below 500 metres.

skototaxis (skŏt′ŏtăk′sĭs) *n.* [Gk. *skotos*, darkness; *taxis*, arrangement.] Positive orientation towards darkness, not negative phototaxis.

skull (skŭl) *n.* [M.E. *skulle*, cranium.] Cranium or hard and bony part of head of vertebrate, containing brain.

sliding growth,—of cells, when new part of cell-wall slides over walls of cells with which it comes in contact; gliding growth. *Opp.* interpositional or intrusive growth.

slime bodies,—cytoplasmic bodies elaborating a viscid proteid, as in sieve-tube cells.

slime layer,—carbohydrate sheath of certain bacterial cells, capsule when thickened.

slime spore,—myxospore, *q.v.*

slough (slŭf) *n.* [M.E. *slouh*, skin of snake.] The dead outer skin cast off periodically by snakes.

smegma (smĕg′mă) *n.* [Gk. *smegma*, unguent.] Secretion of praeputial glands, or of clitoris glands; sebum praeputiale.

smell (smĕl) *n.* [M.E. *smel*, odour.] Sensation and perception induced by stimulation of the olfactory cells by odorous molecules; an odour.

smut (smŭt) *n.* [A. S. *smitta*, spot.] A disease of grasses and other plants, caused by Ustilaginales, fungi producing numerous black spores; any smut fungus.

soboles (sŏb′ŏlēz) *n.* [L. *soboles*, offshoot.] A sucker or underground creeping stem.

soboliferous (sŏbŏlĭf′ĕrŭs) *a.* [L. *soboles*, offshoot; *ferre*, to carry.] Having shoots or running stems.

sociation (sŏsĭā′shŭn) *n.* [L. *sociare*, to associate.] A minor unit of vegetation; micro-association.

society (sŏsī′ĕtĭ) *n.* [L. *societas*, company.] A number of organisms forming a community; a community of plants other than dominants within an association or consociation.

soft-rayed,—having jointed fin-rays.

soft-shelled, —*appl.* eggs; *appl.* turtles with soft leathery skin.

sola,—*plu.* of solum.

solaeus,—soleus, *q.v.*

solar (sō'lăr) *a* [L. *sol*, sun.] Having branches or filaments like rays of sun; dextrorse, *q.v.*

solar plexus,—a network of sympathetic nerves with some ganglia, situated behind stomach and supplying abdominal viscera; coeliac plexus.

solarisation (sō'lărīzā'shŭn) *n.* [L. *solaris*, solar.] Retardation or inhibition of photosynthesis due to prolonged exposure to intense light.

soleaform (sŏl'ëăfôrm) *a.* [L. *solea*, sandal; *forma*, shape.] Slipper-shaped.

solenia (sōlē'nĭă) *n. plu.* [Gk. *solen*, channel.] Endoderm-lined canals, diverticula from coelentera of zooid colony.

solenidion (sōlēnĭd'ĭŏn) *n.* [Gk. *solen*, pipe; *idion*, *dim.*] A modified blunt seta associated with a sensory cell, on legs of Acarina. *Plu.* solenidia.

solenocytes (sōlē'nösīts) *n. plu.* [Gk. *solen*, channel; *kytos*, hollow.] Slender club-shaped tubular flagellated cells connected with nephridia of some Polychaeta, Trochelminthes and of Amphioxus.

solenostele (sōlē'nöstē'lē) *n.* [Gk. *solen*, channel; *stele*, column.] A stage after the siphonostele in fern-stem development.

soleus (sŏlē'ŭs) *n.* [L. *solea*, sole of foot.] A flat calf muscle beneath gastrocnemius.

soliped (sŏl'ĭpĕd) *a.* [L. *solus*, single; *pes*, foot.] Single-hoofed, as horse; solidungulate.

solitary glands or follicles,—lymphoid nodules occurring singly on intestines, and constituting Peyer's patches when aggregated.

solonchak (sŏlŏnchâk') *n.* [Russ. *solonchak*, salt-marsh.] Any of a group of pale saline soils typical of certain poorly drained semi-arid regions.

solonets (sŏlŏnyĕts') [Russ. *solonet'*, to become salty.] Any of a group of dark alkaline soils formed from solonchak by leaching.

solum (sŏlŭm) *n.* [L. *solum*, ground, soil.] Floor, as of a cavity; soil between source material and top-soil.

soma (sō'mă) *n.* [Gk. *soma*, body.] The animal or plant body as a whole with exception of germinal cells.

somactids (sōmăk'tĭdz) *n. plu.* [Gk. *soma*, body; *aktis*, ray.] Endoskeletal supports of dermal fin-rays; radials.

somacule (sō'măkūl) *n.* [Gk. *soma*, body.] A hypothetical unit, *q.v.*

somaesthesis (sōmēsthē'sĭs) *n.* [Gk. *soma*, body; *aisthesis*, sensation.] Sensation due to stimuli from skin, muscle, or internal organs.

somaesthetic (sō'mēsthĕt'ĭk) *a.* [Gk. *soma*, body; *aisthesis*, sensation.] *Appl.* sense of pressure, cold, warmth, pain, hunger, vertigo, etc.

somatic (sōmăt'ĭk) *a.* [Gk. *soma*, body.] *Pert.* purely bodily part of animal or plant; *opp.* germinal; *appl.* mutation occurring in a body cell.

somatoblast (sō'mătöblăst) *n.* [Gk. *soma*, body; *blastos*, bud.] A cell which gives rise to somatic cells; a specialised micromere in oosperm division of Annulates.

somatocyst (sō'mătösĭst) *n.* [Gk. *soma*, body; *kystis*, bladder.] An air cavity in pneumatophore of Siphonophores.

somatoderm (sō'mătödĕrm) *n.* [Gk. *soma*, body; *derma*, skin.] The outer cells in Mesozoa.

somatogamy (sōm'ătŏg'ămĭ) *n.* [Gk. *soma*, body; *gamos*, marriage.] Pseudogamy; pseudomixis.

somatogenic (sō'mătöjĕn'ĭk) *a.* [Gk. *soma*, body; *gennaein*, to produce.] Developing from somatic cells; somatogenetic; *appl.* variation or adaptations arising from external stimuli.

somatome (sō'mătōm) *n.* [Gk. *soma*, body; *tome*, cutting.] A somite or body segment.

somatophyte (sō'mătöfīt) *n.* [Gk. *soma*, body; *phyton*, plant.] A plant whose cells develop mainly into adult body tissue.

somatoplasm (sō'mătöplăzm) *n.* [Gk. *soma*, body; *plasma*, mould.] The substance of a somatic cell.

somatopleural (sō'mătöploor'ăl) *a.* [Gk. *soma*, body; *pleura*, side.] *Pert.* the somatopleure.

somatopleure (sō'mătöploor) *n.* [Gk. *soma*, body; *pleura*, side.] The body-wall formed by somatic layer of mesoblast becoming closely connected with surface epiblast.

somatotrophic (sō'mătötrŏf'ĭk) *a.* [Gk. *soma*, body; *trephein*, to increase.] Stimulating nutrition and growth; *appl.* a hormone of the anterior lobe of the pituitary gland.

somatotrophin,—growth hormone or somatotrophic hormone, STH.

somatotype (sō'mătötīp) *n.* [Gk. *soma*, body; *typos*, pattern.] Body type or conformation as rated by measurements.

somatropic (sō'mătrŏp'ĭk) *a.* [Gk. *soma*, body; *tropikos*, turning.] Influencing or stimulating growth; somatotrophic, *q.v.*

somite (sō'mīt) *n.* [Gk. *soma*, body.] A mesoblastic segment or compartment; a body segment of an articulate animal.

sonic (sŏn'ĭk) *a.* [L. *sonare*, to sound.] *Pert.* or produced by sound.

Sonoran (sŏnō'răn) *a.* [*Sonora*, Mexican State.] *Appl.* or *pert.* zoogeographical region of southern North America, including northern Mexico, between nearctic and neotropical regions; Medio-Columbian.

soral (sō'răl) *a.* [Gk. *soros*, heap.] *Pert.* a sorus.

soralium (sōrā'lĭŭm) *n.* [Gk. *soros*, heap.] A well-defined group of soredia.

sorede,—soredium.

soredia,—*plu.* of soredium.

soredial (sōrē'dĭăl) *a.* [Gk. *soros*, heap.] *Pert.* or resembling a soredium.

sorediate (sōrē'dĭăt) *a.* [Gk. *soros*, heap.] Bearing soredia.

soredium (sōrē'dĭŭm) *n.* [Gk. *soros*, heap.] A scale-like or globular body consisting of fungal hyphae with some algal cells, on thallus of some lichens, and serving for propagation.

soreuma,—soredium.

soriferous (sōrĭf'ërŭs) *a.* [Gk. *soros*, heap; L. *ferre*, to carry.] Bearing sori.

sorocarp (sō'rökârp) *n.* [Gk. *soros*, heap; *karpos*, fruit.] The unenclosed, simple fruit-body of certain Myxomycetes.

sorogen (sō'röjĕn) *n.* [Gk. *soros*, heap; *gennaein*, to produce.] The cell or tissue that develops into a sorus.

sorophore (sō'röfōr) *n.* [Gk. *soros*, heap; *pherein*, to bear.] Base or stalk bearing a sorus or sorocarp.

sorosis (sōrō'sĭs) *n.* [Gk. *soros*, heap.] A composite fruit formed by fusion of fleshy axis and flowers, as pineapple.

sorption (sôrp'shŭn) *n.* [L. *sorbere*, to suck in.] Retention of material at a surface, by absorption or by adsorption.

sorus (sō'rŭs) *n.* [Gk. *soros*, heap.] A collection of small stalked sporangia on under surface of fern pinnule; group of antheridia on frond of seaweeds; clusters of spores in some Sarcodina.

spadiceous (spădĭsh'ŭs) *a.* [L. *spadix*, palm-branch.] Arranged like a spadix; spadicifloral.

spadiciform (spădĭ'sĭfôrm) *a.* [L. *spadix*, palm-branch; *forma*, shape.] Resembling a spadix.

spadicose (spăd'ĭkōs) *a.* [L. *spadix*, a palm-branch.] Like a spadix.

spadix (spā'dĭks) *n.* [L. *spadix*, palm-branch with fruit.] A racemose inflorescence with elongated axis, sessile flowers, and an enveloping spathe; a succulent spike; endodermal rudiment of developing manubrium of certain Coelentera; conoid amalgamation of certain tentacles in Nautilus.

spanandry (spănăn'drĭ) *n.* [Gk. *spanos*, scarce; *aner*, male.] A scarcity of males; progressive decrease in number of males, as in some insects.

spanogamy (spănŏg'ămĭ) *n.* [Gk. *spanos*, scarce; *gamos*, marriage.] Progressive decrease in number of females.

spasm (spăzm) *n.* [Gk. *spasmos*, tension.] Involuntary muscular contraction; spastic or spasmodic contraction of muscle fibres.

spasmoneme (spăz'mönēm) *n.* [Gk. *spasmos*, tension; *nema*, thread.] In certain infusorians, a stalk-muscle formed by union of longitudinal myonemes.

spat (spăt) *n.* [A.S. *spaetan*, to spit.] The spawn or young of bivalve molluscs.

spathaceous (spăthā'shŭs) *a.* [L. *spatha*, broad blade.] Resembling or bearing a spathe; spathal.

spathe (spāth) *n.* [Gk. *spathe*, broad blade.] A large enveloping leaf, green or petaloid, protecting a spadix.

spathed (spāthd) *a.* [Gk. *spathe*, broad blade.] Furnished with a spathe.

spathella (spăthĕl'ă) *n.* [L. *spatha*, broad blade.] Small spathe surrounding division of palm spadix.

spathose (spā'thōs) *a.* [L. *spatha*, broad blade.] With or like a spathe.

spatia zonularia,—canal of Petit, surrounding marginal circumference of lens of eye.

spatula (spăt'ūlă) *n.* [L. *spatula*, spoon.] A breast-bone or anchor process of certain dipterous larvae.

spatulate (spăt'ūlāt) *a.* [L. *spatula*, spoon.] Spoon-shaped; *appl.* a leaf with broad, rounded apex, thence tapering to base.

spawn (spôn) *n.* [O.F. *espandre*, to shed.] Collection of eggs deposited by bivalve molluscs, fishes, frogs, etc.; mycelium of certain fungi. *v.* To deposit eggs, as by fishes, etc.

spay (spā) *v.* [L. *spado*, eunuch.] To deprive of ovaries.

speciation (spēsĭā'shŭn) *n.* [L. *species*, particular kind.] The evolution of species; development of a specific quality; species formation.

species (spē'shēz) *n.* [L. *species*, particular kind.] A group of interbreeding individuals not interbreeding with another such group; a systematic unit including geographic races and varieties, and included in a genus.

specific (spĕsĭf'ĭk) *a.* [L. *species*, particular kind; *facere*, to make.] Peculiar to; *pert.* a species; *appl.* characteristics distinguishing a species; *appl.* name: the second name in binomial nomenclature.

specific dynamic action, — *see* dynamic.

specificity (spĕs'ĭfĭs'ĭtĭ) *n.* [L. *species*, kind; *facere*, to make.] Condition of being specific; being limited to a species; restriction of parasites to particular hosts.

spectrum (spĕk'trŭm) *n.* [L. *spectrum*, appearance.] A statistical survey of the distribution of species for determination and comparison of biogeographical regions.

spelaeology (spē'lēŏl'öjĭ) *n.* [Gk. *spelaion*, cave; *logos*, discourse.] The study of caves and cave life.

sperm (spĕrm) *n.* [Gk. *sperma*, seed.] The male fertilising element; spermatozoid, *q.v.*; spermatozoon, *q.v.* semen, *q.v.*

sperm centrosome, — end-knob of axial filament of spermatozoon, situated on middle piece just at base of head; according to others, the small body at apex of head.

sperm nucleus,—male pronucleus.

sperm pump,—an organ forcing spermatozoa into penis, as in Phlebotomus; pompetta.

spermaduct (spĕr'mădŭkt) *n.* [Gk. *sperma*, seed; L. *ducere*, to lead.] Duct for conveying spermatozoa.

spermagonium, — spermatogonium, *q.v.*; spermogonium, *q.v.*; spermagone.

spermangium (spĕrmăn'jĭŭm) *n.* [Gk. *sperma*, seed; *anggeion*, vessel.] An organ producing male spore-like cells, in Ascomycetes.

spermaphore (spĕr'măfōr) *n.* [Gk. *sperma*, seed; *pherein*, to bear.] Placenta of plants.

spermaphyte (spěr'măfīt) *n.* [Gk. *sperma*, seed ; *phyton*, plant.] Seed-plant ; phanerogram, spermatophyte.

spermary (spěr'mărĭ) *n.* [Gk. *sperma*, seed.] An organ in which spermatozoa or antheridia are produced ; spermarium ; testis.

spermatangium (spěr'mătăn'jĭŭm) *n.* [Gk. *sperma*, seed ; *anggeion*, vessel.] Antheridium of certain algae.

spermateleosis (spěr'mătēlē'ōsĭs) *n.* [Gk. *sperma*, seed ; *teleiosis*, completion.] Development of spermatozoon from spermatid in spermatogenesis, *q.v.*

spermatheca (spěr'măthē'kă) *n.* [Gk. *sperma*, seed ; *theke*, case.] A receptaculum seminis ; a sac, in female or in hermaphroditic invertebrates, for storing spermatozoa.

spermatia,—*plu.* of spermatium.

spermatic (spěrmăt'ĭk) *a.* [Gk. *sperma*, seed.] *Pert.* spermatozoa ; *pert.* testis.

spermatid (spěr'mătĭd) *n.* [Gk. *sperma*, seed.] A haploid cell arising by division of secondary spermatocyte, and becoming a spermatozoon.

spermatiferous (spěrmătĭf'ërŭs) *a.* [Gk. *sperma*, seed ; L. *ferre*, to carry.] Bearing spermatia.

spermatiophore (spěrmā'shĭöfōr) *n.* [Gk. *sperma*, seed ; *pherein*, to bear.] A spermatia - producing sporophore.

spermatise (spěr'mătīz) *v.* [Gk. *sperma*, seed.] To impregnate.

spermatium (spěrmā'shĭŭm) *n.* [Gk. *sperma*, seed.] A non-motile sperm of red algae ; pycnidiospore in rust fungi ; oidium in toadstools and mushrooms ; small conidium in cup fungi.

spermatoblast (spěr'mătöblăst) *n.* [Gk. *sperma*, seed ; *blastos*, bud.] A spermatid ; a Sertoli cell, *q.v.*

spermatoblastic (spěr'mătöblăs'tĭk) *a.* [Gk. *sperma*, seed ; *blastos*, bud.] Sperm-producing.

spermatocyst (spěr'mătösĭst) *n.* [Gk. *sperma*, seed ; *kystis*, bladder.] A seminal sac.

spermatocyte (spěr'mătösīt) *n.* [Gk. *sperma*, seed ; *kytos*, hollow.] A cell arising by growth from a spermatogonium ; a primary spermatocyte divides to form two secondary spermatocytes, each of which gives rise to two spermatids.

spermatocytogenesis (spěr'mătösī'töjěn'ësĭs) *n.* [Gk. *sperma*, seed ; *kytos*, hollow ; *genesis*, descent.] First phase of spermatogenesis, preceding spermiogenesis.

spermatogenesis (spěr'mătöjěn'ësĭs) *n.* [Gk. *sperma*, seed ; *genesis*, origin.] Sperm-formation, from spermatogonium, through primary and secondary spermatocytes, and spermatid, to spermatozoon.

spermatogenetic (spěr'mătöjënět'ĭk) *a.* [Gk. *sperma*, seed ; *genesis*, descent.] *Pert.* sperm-formation ; sperm-producing ; spermatogenic, spermatogenous.

spermatogonial (spěr'mătögō'nĭăl) *a.* [Gk. *sperma*, seed ; *gonos*, offspring.] *Pert.* a spermatogonium.

spermatogonium (spěr'mătögō'nĭŭm) *n.* [Gk. *sperma*, seed ; *gonos*, offspring.] Primordial male germ-cell ; sperm mother-cell ; spermogonium, *q.v.*

spermatoid (spěr'mătoid) *a.* [Gk. *sperma*, seed ; *eidos*, form.] Like a sperm.

spermatomerites (spěr'mătŏm'ërīts) *n. plu.* [Gk. *sperma*, seed ; *meros*, part.] Chromatin granules formed from sperm-nucleus.

spermatophore (spěr'mătöfōr) *n.* [Gk. *sperma*, seed ; *pherein*, to bear.] A capsule of albuminous matter containing a number of sperms ; spermatiophore, *q.v.*

spermatophyte (spěr'mătöfīt) *n.* [Gk. *sperma*, seed ; *phyton*, plant.] A seed-plant ; phanerogam, spermaphyte, spermophyte.

spermatoplasm (spěr'mătöplăzm) *n.* [Gk. *sperma*, seed ; *plasma*, mould.] Protoplasm of sperm cells.

spermatoplast (spěr'mătöplăst) *n.* [Gk. *sperma*, seed ; *plastos*, moulded.] A male sexual cell.

spermatosome (spĕr′mătösōm) *n.* [Gk. *sperma*, seed; *soma*, body.] A spermatozoon.

spermatoxin (spĕr′mătŏk′sĭn) *n.* [Gk. *sperma*, seed; *toxikon*, poison.] Antibodies causing sterility, formed after injection of spermatozoa in serum.

spermatozeugma (spĕr′mătözū′gmă) *n.* [Gk. *sperma*, seed; *zeugma*, bond.] Union by conjugation of two or more spermatozoa, as in vas deferens of some insects.

spermatozoa,—*plu.* of spermatozoon, *q.v.*

spermatozoid (spĕr′mătözō′ĭd) *n.* [Gk. *sperma*, seed; *zoon*, animal; *idion*, *dim.*] An antherozoid; a free-swimming male gamete; spermatozooid.

spermatozoon (spĕr′mătözō′ŏn) *n.* [Gk. *sperma*, seed; *zoon*, animal.] A male reproductive cell, consisting usually of head, middle piece, and locomotory flagellum.

spermiducal (spĕrmĭdū′kăl) *a.* [Gk. *sperma*, seed; L. *ducere*, to lead.] *Appl.* glands into or near which sperm-ducts open, in many vertebrates; *appl.* glands associated with male ducts, or prostates, in Oligochaeta.

spermiduct,—spermaduct, *q.v.*

spermin (spĕr′mĭn) *n.* [Gk. *sperma*, seed.] The hormone of testis.

spermine (spĕr′mēn) *n.* [Gk. *sperma*, seed.] A substance whose phosphate occurs in semen, also found in pancreas and yeast; $C_{10}H_{26}N_4$.

spermiocalyptrotheca (spĕr′mĭökălĭp′tröthē′kă) *n.* [Gk. *sperma*, seed; *kalyptra*, covering; *theke*, case.] The head-cap of a spermatozoon.

spermiogenesis (spĕr′mĭöjĕn′ĕsĭs) *n.* [Gk. *sperma*, seed; *genesis*, origin.] Development of spermatozoon from spermatid; spermioteleosis, spermateleosis; spermatogenesis, *q.v.*

spermism (spĕr′mĭzm) *n.* [Gk. *sperma*, seed.] Theory held by spermists or animalculists that embryo is derived from spermatozoon alone.

spermium (spĕr′mĭŭm) *n.* [Gk. *sperma*, seed.] Spermatozoon.

spermoblast (spĕr′möblăst) *n.* [Gk. *sperma*, seed; *blastos*, bud.] A spermatid; spermatoblast.

spermocarp (spĕr′mökârp) *n.* [Gk. *sperma*, seed; *karpos*, fruit.] An oogonium after fertilisation.

spermocentre (spĕr′mösĕn′tĕr) *n.* [Gk. *sperma*, seed; L. *centrum*, a centre.] The male centrosome during fertilisation.

spermoderm (spĕr′mödĕrm) *n.* [Gk. *sperma*, seed; *derma*, skin.] The seed coat, consisting of inner tegmen and outer testa; episperm.

spermoduct,—spermaduct, *q.v.*

spermogenesis, — spermatogenesis.

spermogoniferous (spĕr′mögönĭf′-ĕrŭs) *a.* [Gk. *sperma*, seed; *gonos*, offspring; L. *ferre*, to carry.] Having spermogonia.

spermogonium (spĕr′mögō′nĭŭm) *n.* [Gk. *sperma*, seed; *gonos*, generation.] A capsule containing spermatia, in certain fungi and lichens.

spermogonous (spĕrmŏg′önŭs) *a.* [Gk. *sperma*, seed; *gonos*, offspring.] Like or *pert.* a spermogonium.

spermology (spĕrmŏl′öjĭ) *n.* [Gk. *sperma*, seed; *logos*, discourse.] The study of seeds.

spermophyte,—spermatophyte.

spermotheca (spĕr′möthē′kă) *n.* [Gk. *sperma*, seed; *theke*, case.] A chamber for storing sperms received in copulation; spermatheca, *q.v.*

spermotype (spĕr′mötīp) *n.* [Gk. *sperma*, seed; *typos*, pattern.] A plant specimen grown from seed of a type plant.

spermozeugma (spĕrmözūg′mă) *n.* [Gk. *sperma*, seed; *zeugma*, bond.] A mass of regularly aggregated spermatozoa, for delivery into a spermatheca.

sphacelate (sfăs′ĕlāt) *a.* [Gk. *sphakelos*, gangrene.] Decayed; withered; mortified.

sphacelia (sfăsē′lĭă) *n.* [Gk. *sphakelos*, gangrene.] Conidial or honeydew stage in development of fungus, producing sclerotium or ergot.

sphaer-,—*also* spher-.
sphaeraphides (sfērăf'ĭdēz) *n. plu.* [Gk. *sphaira*, globe; *rhaphis*, needle.] Conglomerate raphides: globular clusters of minute crystals in plant cells; cluster crystals.
sphaerenchyma (sfērĕng'kĭmă) *n.* [Gk. *sphaira*, globe; *engchyma*, juice.] Tissue of spherical cells.
sphaeridia (sfērĭd'ĭă) *n. plu.* [Gk. *sphaira*, globe; *idion*, *dim.*] Small rounded bodies, probably balancing organs, found on echinoderms.
sphaeroid (sfē'roid) *a.* [Gk. *sphaira*, globe; *eidos*, form.] Globular, ellipsoidal, or cylindrical; *appl.* an aggregate of individual protozoa; *appl.* a dilated hyphal cell containing oil-droplets, in lichens.
sphaeroplast (sfē'röplăst) *n.* [Gk. *sphaira*, globe; *plastos*, formed.] A bioblast; a hypothetical unit, *q.v.*; spheroplast.
sphagnicolous (sfăgnĭk'ölŭs) *a.* [Gk. *sphagnos*, moss; L. *colere*, to inhabit.] Inhabiting peat mosses.
sphagnous (sfăg'nŭs) *a.* [Gk. *sphagnos*, moss.] *Pert.* peat moss.
sphenethmoid (sfēnĕth'moid) *n.* [Gk. *sphen*, wedge; *ethmos*, sieve; *eidos*, form.] Single bone replacing orbitosphenoids in Anura; girdle-bone.
spheno-ethmoidal (sfē'nöĕthmoid'ăl) *a.* [Gk. *sphen*, wedge; *ethmos*, sieve; *eidos*, form.] *Pert.* or in region of sphenoid and ethmoid; *appl.* a recess above superior nasal concha, and a suture.
sphenofrontal (sfē'nöfrŭn'tăl) *a.* [Gk. *sphen*, wedge; L. *frons*, forehead.] *Pert.* sphenoid and frontal bones; *appl.* a suture.
sphenoid (sfē'noid) *n.* [Gk. *sphen*, wedge; *eidos*, form.] A basal compound skull bone of some vertebrates; 'butterfly' bone. *a.* Wedge-shaped; cuneate, cuneiform.
sphenoidal (sfēnoid'ăl) *a.* [Gk. *sphen*, wedge; *eidos*, form.] Wedge-shaped; *pert.* or in region of sphenoid; *appl.* fissure, processes, nostrum, sinus.
sphenolateral (sfēn'ölăt'ĕrăl) *n.* [Gk. *sphen*, wedge; L. *latus*, side.] One of a dorsal pair of cartilages parallel to trabeculae; pleurosphenoid.
sphenomandibular (sfē'nömăndĭb'ūlăr) *a.* [Gk. *sphen*, wedge; L. *mandibulum*, jaw.] *Pert.* sphenoid and mandible; *appl.* ligament.
sphenomaxillary (sfē'nömăksĭl'ărĭ) *a.* [Gk. *sphen*, wedge; *maxilla*, jaw.] *Pert.* sphenoid and maxilla; *appl.* fissure and (pterygopalatine) fossa.
sphenopalatine (sfē'nöpăl'ătīn) *a.* [Gk. *sphen*, wedge; L. *palatus*, palate.] *Pert.* sphenoid and palatine; *appl.* artery, foramen, nerves; *appl.* ganglion: the pterygopalatine ganglion.
sphenoparietal (sfē'nöpărī'ĕtăl) *a.* [Gk. *sphen*, wedge; L. *paries*, wall.] *Pert.* sphenoid and parietal; *appl.* a cranial suture.
sphenopterygoid (sfē'nötĕr'ĭgoid, -ptĕr-) *a.* [Gk. *sphen*, wedge; *pteryx*, wing; *eidos*, form.] *Pert.* sphenoid and pterygoid; *appl.* mucous pharyngeal glands near openings of Eustachian tubes, as in birds.
sphenosquamosal (sfē'nöskwāmō'săl) *a.* [Gk. *sphen*, wedge; L. *squama*, scale.] *Appl.* cranial suture between sphenoid and squamosal.
sphenotic (sfēnŏt'ĭk) *n.* [Gk. *sphen*, wedge; *ous*, ear.] Post-frontal cranial bone of many fishes.
sphenoturbinal (sfē'nötŭr'bĭnăl) *n.* [Gk. *sphen*, wedge; L. *turbo*, whirl.] Laminar process of sphenoid.
sphenozygomatic (sfē'nözĭg'ömătĭk) *a.* [Gk. *sphen*, wedge; *zygoma*, *zygon*, cross-bar.] *Appl.* cranial suture between sphenoid and zygomatic.
spher-,—*also* sphaer-.
spheraster (sfērăs'tĕr) *n.* [Gk. *sphaira*, globe; *aster*, star.] A many-rayed globular spicule.
sphere-crystals,—sphaeraphides.
spheridium (sfērĭd'ĭŭm) *n.* [Gk. *sphaira*, globe; *idion*, *dim.*] A

spherical apothecium or capitulum in certain lichens. *Plu.* spheridia.

spheroidal (sfēroid'ăl) *a.* [Gk. *sphaira*, globe; *eidos*, form.] Globular but not perfectly spherical; *appl.* glandular epithelium.

spheroidocyte (sfēroid'ōsīt) *n.* [Gk. *sphaira*, globe; *eidos*, form; *kytos*, hollow.] A type of blood-cell or haemocyte in insects.

spherome (sfē'rōm) *n.* [Gk. *esphairomen*, made globular.] Cell inclusions producing oil or fat globules; intracellular fatty globules as a whole.

spheromere (sfē'römēr) *n.* [Gk. *sphaira*, globe; *meros*, part.] A segment of a radiate animal.

spheroplasts (sfē'röplăsts) *n. plu.* [Gk. *sphaira*, globe; *plastos*, formed.] Chondriosomes; bioblasts; bodies found among granulations of protoplasm.

spherula (sfĕr'ūlă) *n.* [L. *sphaerula*, small globe.] A spherule or small sphere; a small spherical spicule.

spherulate (sfĕr'ūlāt) *a.* [L. *sphaerula*, small globe.] Covered with small spheres.

sphincter (sfĭng'ktër) *n.* [Gk. *sphinggein*, to bind tight.] A muscle which contracts or closes an orifice, as that of bladder, mouth, anus, vagina, etc.

sphragidal (sfrā'jĭdăl) *a.* [Gk. *sphragis*, seal.] *Appl.* plastic fluid secreted by tubular glands opening into vesiculae seminales in male Lepidoptera and forming a sphragis.

sphragis (sfrā'jĭs) *n.* [Gk. *sphragis*, seal.] A structure sealing bursa copulatrix on female abdomen of certain Lepidoptera after pairing, and consisting of hardened sphragidal fluid.

sphygmic (sfĭg'mĭk) *a.* [Gk. *sphygmos*, pulse.] *Pert.* pulse; *appl.* second phase of systole.

sphygmoid (sfĭg'moid) *a.* [Gk. *sphygmos*, pulse; *eidos*, form.] Pulsating; like a pulse.

sphygmus (sfĭg'mŭs) *n.* [Gk. *sphygmos*, pulse.] The pulse.

spica (spī'kă) *n.* [L. *spica*, spike.] Spike; calcar of birds.

spicate (spī'kāt) *a.* [L. *spica*, spike.] Spiked; arranged in spikes, as an inflorescence; bearing spikes; with spur-like prominence; spiciferous, spiciform, spicigerous.

spicose (spī'kōs) *a.* [L. *spica*, spike.] With spikes or ears, as corn.

spicula (spĭk'ūlă) *n.* [L. *spicula*, small spike.] A small spike; a needle-like body; *plu.* of spiculum.

spicular (spĭk'ūlăr) *a.* [L. *spicula*, small spike.] *Pert.* or like a spicule.

spiculate (spĭk'ūlāt) *a.* [L. *spicula*, small spike.] Set with spicules; divided into small spikes.

spicule (spĭk'ūl) *n.* [L. *spicula*, small spike.] A minute needle-like body, siliceous or calcareous, found in invertebrates; a minute pointed process.

spiculiferous (spĭkūlĭf'ërŭs) *a.* [L. *spicula*, small spike; *ferre*, to carry.] Furnished with or protected by spicules; spiculigenous, spiculigerous, spiculose.

spiculiform (spĭk'ūlĭfôrm) *a.* [L. *spicula*, small spike; *forma*, shape.] Spicule-shaped.

spiculum (spĭk'ūlŭm) *n.* [L. *spiculum*, a dart.] A spicular structure; the dart of a snail.

spider cells,—neuroglia cells with numerous plasmatic and/or fibrillar processes; astrocytes, astroglia, macroglia.

Spigelian (spĭgē'lĭăn) *a.* [*A. van den Spieghel* or *Spigelius*, Flemish anatomist]. *Appl.* a small lobe of liver, originally named lobus exiguus, in mammals; *appl.* caudate lobe.

spigots (spĭg'ōts) *n. plu.* [L. *spica*, spike.] Conical spinning tubes, in spiders.

spike (spīk) *n.* [L. *spica*, spike, ear of corn.] Inflorescence with sessile flowers along axis.

spikelet (spīk'lët) *n.* [L. *spica*, spike.] A secondary spike of grasses, bearing few flowers; locusta.

spina (spī'nă) *n.* [L. *spina*, spine.] A spine; median apodeme behind furca, as in many Orthoptera.

spinal (spī'năl) *a.* [L. *spina*, spine.] *Pert.* backbone, or spinal cord; *appl.* foramen, ganglion, nerves, etc.

spinal canal,—vertebral canal containing spinal cord.

spinal cord,—nervous tissue contained in spinal or vertebral canal; medulla spinalis.

spinalis (spīnā'lĭs) *n.* [L. *spina*, spine.] Name given to muscles connecting vertebrae.

spinasternum (spī'năstĕr'nŭm) *n.* [L. *spina*, thorn; *sternum*, breastbone.] An intersegmental sternal sclerite or poststernellum with an internal spine, in certain insects.

spinate (spī'nāt) *a.* [L. *spina*, thorn.] Spine-shaped; spine-bearing; spiniferous, spinigerous.

spination (spīnā'shŭn) *n.* [L. *spina*, thorn.] The occurrence, development, or arrangement of spines.

spindle (spĭn'dl) *n.* [A.S. *spinnan*, to spin.] A structure resembling a spinning-machine spindle; an elongated peduncle bearing sessile flowers; a structure formed of achromatin fibres during mitosis; a muscle-spindle, *q.v.*; fuseau, *q.v.*

spindle-fibre locus,—centrosome, *q.v.*

spine (spīn) *n.* [L. *spina*, spine.] A sharp-pointed process on leaves, bones, echinoids, porcupines; the backbone or vertebral column; pointed process of vertebra; scapular ridge; fin-ray.

spinescent (spīnĕs'ĕnt) *a.* [L. *spinescere*, to become spiny.] Tapering; tending to become spiny.

spiniferous (spīnĭf'ĕrŭs) *a.* [L. *spina*, spine; *ferre*, to carry.] Spine-bearing; *appl.* pads on ventral side of distal end of leg in Peripatus; spinate, spinigerous.

spiniform (spī'nĭfôrm) *a.* [L. *spina*, spine; *forma*, shape.] Spine-shaped.

spinisternite (spī'nĭstĕr'nīt) *n.* [L. *spina*, spine; *sternum*, breast bone.] A small sternite with spiniform apodema, between thoracic segments of insects.

spinneret (spĭn'ĕrĕt) *n.* [A.S. *spinnan*, to spin.] One of organs perforated by tubes connected with glands secreting liquid silk, in spiders; one of organs preparing material for puparia, as in Coccidae.

spinnerule (spĭn'ĕrūl) *n.* [A.S. *spinnan*, to spin.] A tube discharging silk secretion of spiders.

spinning glands,—glands which secrete material for webs in spiders, and for cocoons in caterpillars.

spino-occipital (spī'nōŏksĭp'ĭtăl) *a.* [L. *spina*, spine; *occiput*, back of head.] *Appl.* nerves arising in trunk somites which later form part of the skull.

spinose (spī'nōs) *a.* [L. *spinosus*, prickly.] Bearing many spines.

spinous (spī'nŭs) *a.* [L. *spina*, spine.] Spiny; spine-like; *appl.* plane of body.

spinous process,—median dorsal spinelike process of vertebra; a process of sphenoid; a process between articular surfaces of proximal end of tibia.

spinulate (spĭn'ūlāt) *a.* [L. *spinula*, small spine.] Covered with small spines.

spinulation (spĭnūlā'shŭn) *n.* [L. *spinula*, small spine.] A defensive spiny covering; state of being spinulate.

spinule (spĭn'ūl) *n.* [L. *spinula*, small spine.] A small spine.

spinulescent (spĭnūlĕs'ĕnt) *a.* [L. *spinula*, small spine.] Tending to be spiny.

spinuliferous (spĭnūlĭf'ĕrŭs) *a.* [L. *spinula*, small spine; *ferre*, to bear.] Bearing small spines; spinulose, spinulous.

spiny-finned,—bearing fins with spiny rays for support.

spiny-rayed,—*appl.* fins supported by spiny rays.

spiracle (spīr'ăkl) *n.* [L. *spiraculum*, air-hole.] First pharyngeal aperture or visceral cleft; branchial passage between mandibular and hyoid arches in fishes; lateral branchial opening in tadpoles; nasal aperture of Cetacea; respiratory aperture behind eye of skates and rays; breathing aperture of insects; aperture of book lungs; any of five openings round mouth of Blastoidea; spiraculum.

spiracular (spīrăk'ūlăr) *a.* [L. *spiraculum*, air-hole.] *Pert.* a spiracle.

spiraculate (spīrăk'ūlāt) *a.* [L. *spiraculum*, air-hole.] Having spiracles; spiraculiferous.

spiraculiform (spīrăk'ūlĭfôrm) *a.* [L. *spiraculum*, air-hole; *forma*, shape.] Spiracle-shaped.

spiraculum,—spiracle, *q.v.*

spiral (spī'răl) *a.* [L. *spira*, coil.] Winding, like a screw; *appl.* leaves alternately placed; *appl.* flower with spirally inserted parts; *appl.* thickening of cell-wall; *appl.* chromatids and chromosomes. *n.* A coiled structure; coil of the chromosome thread in mitosis and meiosis; *cf.* internal, relational, relic spiral.

spiral cleavage,—cleavage into unequal parts, arranged in mosaic fashion and interlocking, upper cells rotating to right to alternate with lower; oblique or alternating cleavage.

spiral valve,—in fishes, except teleosts, a spiral infolding of intestine wall; of Heister, folds of mucous membrane in neck of gall-bladder.

spiral vessels,—first xylem elements of a stele, spiral fibres coiled up inside tubes and so adapted for rapid elongation.

spiralia (spīrā'lĭă) *n. plu.* [L. *spira*, coil.] Coiled structures supported by crura, in certain brachiopods.

spiranthy (spīrăn'thĭ) *n.* [Gk. *speira*, coil; *anthos*, flower.] Displacement of flower parts through twisting.

spiraster (spīrăs'tër) *n.* [L. *spira*, coil; *aster*, star.] A spiral and rayed sponge spicule.

spire (spīr) *n.* [L. *spira*, coil.] Totality of whorls of a spiral shell.

spireme (spī'rēm) *n.* [Gk. *speirema*, coil.] Thread-like appearance of nuclear chromatin during prophase of mitosis.

spiricles (spīr'ĭklz) *n. plu.* [L. *spira*, coil.] Thin, coiled, thread-like outgrowths of some seed-coats.

spiriferous (spīrĭf'ërŭs) *a.* [L. *spira*, coil; *ferre*, to bear.] Having a spiral structure.

spirillar (spīrĭl'ăr) *a.* [L. *spirillum*, small coil.] *Pert.* or resembling a spirillum.

spirillum (spīrĭl'ŭm) *n.* [L. *spirillum*, small coil.] A thread-like curved bacterium; a motile filament in a cryptogam antheridium.

spirivalve (spī'rĭvălv) *n.* [L. *spira*, coil; *valvae*, folding doors.] A gastropod with spiral shell.

spiroid (spī'roid) *a.* [Gk. *speira*, coil; *eidos*, form.] Spirally formed.

spironeme (spī'rŏnēm) *n.* [Gk. *speira*, coil; *nema*, thread.] Coiling thread in infusorian stalk.

spirulate (spĭr'ūlāt) *a.* [L. *spira*, coil.] *Appl.* any spiral structure or coiled arrangement.

splanchnic (splăngk'nĭk) *a.* [Gk. *splangchnon*, entrail.] *Pert.* viscera; *appl.* nerves.

splanchnocoel (splăngk'nŏsēl) *n.* [Gk. *splangchnon*, entrail; *koilos*, hollow.] The cavity of lateral plates of embryo, persisting as visceral cavity of adult.

splanchnocranium, — viscerocranium, *q.v.*

splanchnology (splăngknŏl'ŏjĭ) *n.* [Gk. *splangchnon*, entrail; *logos*, discourse.] The branch of anatomy dealing with viscera.

splanchnopleure (splăngk'nŏploor) *n.* [Gk. *splangchnon*, entrail; *pleura*, side.] Inner layer of mesoblast, applied to viscera.

spleen (splēn) *n.* [Gk. *splen*, spleen.] A vascular organ in which lymphocytes are produced and red blood corpuscles destroyed, in vertebrates; lien.

splenetic (splĕnĕt'ĭk) *a.* [Gk. *splen*, spleen.] *Pert.* the spleen.

splenial (splē'nĭăl) *a.* [L. *splenium*, a patch.] *Pert.* splenius muscle, or splenial bone.

splenial bone,—membrane bone in lower jaw of some vertebrates.

splenic (splĕn'ĭk) *a.* [Gk. *splen*, spleen.] *Pert.* the spleen.

splenic nodules,—splenic corpuscles, Malpighian bodies, *q.v.*

splenium (splē'nĭŭm) *n.* [L. *splenium*, patch.] Posterior border of corpus callosum.

splenius (splē'nĭŭs) *n.* [L. *splenium*, patch.] Muscle of upper dorsal region and back of neck.

splenocyte (splē'nösīt) *n.* [Gk. *splen*, spleen; *kytos*, hollow.] A large monocyte believed to originate in spleen; endothelial leucocyte; a large mononuclear leucocyte.

splenophrenic (splē'nöfrĕn'ĭk) *a.* [Gk. *splen*, spleen; *phren*, midriff.] *Pert.* spleen and diaphragm.

spondyl (spŏn'dĭl) *n.* [Gk. *sphondylos*, vertebra.] A vertebra; spondyle.

spondylous (spŏn'dĭlŭs) *a.* [Gk. *sphondylos*, vertebra.] Vertebral.

spondylus (spŏn'dĭlŭs) *n.* [Gk. *sphondylos*, vertebra.] A spondyl or vertebra.

spongicolous (spŭnjĭk'ölŭs) *a.* [L. *spongia*, sponge; *colere*, to inhabit.] Living in sponges.

spongin (spŭn'jĭn) *n.* [L. *spongia*, sponge.] Material of skeletal fibres of horny sponges.

sponginblast (spŭn'jĭnblăst) *n.* [L. *spongia*, sponge; Gk. *blastos*, bud.] A spongin-producing cell.

spongioblasts (spŭn'jĭöblăsts) *n. plu.* [Gk. *sponggia*, sponge; *blastos*, bud.] Embryonic epithelial cells which give rise to neuroglia cells and fibres radiating to periphery of spinal cord.

spongiocoel (spŭn'jĭösēl) *n.* [Gk. *sponggia*, sponge; *koilos*, hollow.] The cavity, or system of cavities, in sponges.

spongiocyte (spŭn'jĭösīt) *n.* [Gk. *sponggia*, sponge; *kytos*, hollow.] A vacuolated cell of zona fasciculata of adrenal cortex.

spongioplasm (spŭn'jĭöplăzm) *n.* [Gk. *sponggia*, sponge; *plasma*, mould.] Cytoplasmic threadwork of a cell; cytoreticulum; mitomes.

spongiose (spŏn'jĭōs) *a.* [L. *spongia*, sponge.] Of a spongy texture; spongoid; full of small cavities.

spongoblast,—sponginblast, *q.v.*

spongophare (spŏng'göfār) *n.* [Gk. *sponggos*, sponge; *pherein*, to bear.] The upper chamber-bearing part of a sponge; *cf.* hypophare.

spongophyll (spŏng'göfĭl) *n.* [Gk. *sponggos*, sponge; *phyllon*, leaf.] A leaf having spongy parenchyma, without palisade tissue, between upper and lower epidermis, as in certain aquatics.

spongy (spŭn'ji) *a.* [L. *spongia*, sponge.] Of open texture; lacunar; *appl.* parenchyma of mesophyll; *appl.* tissue surrounding embryo sac, as in gymnosperms.

spontaneous generation, — abiogenesis, *q.v.*

spoon,—small sclerite at base of balancers in Diptera; pinion or tegula.

sporabola (spöräb'ölă) *n.* [Gk. *sporos*, seed; *bolos*, a throw.] The trajectory of a spore discharged from a sterigma.

sporadic (spörăd'ĭk) *a.* [Gk. *sporadikos*, scattered.] *Appl.* plants confined to limited localities.

sporadin (spörăd'ĭn) *n.* [Gk. *sporaden*, scattered about.] Trophozoite of gregarines moving about in lumen of gut.

sporange,—sporangium.

sporangia,—*plu.* of sporangium.

sporangial (spörăn'jĭăl) *a.* [Gk. *sporos*, seed; *anggeion*, vessel.] *Pert.* a sporangium.

sporangiferous (spörănjĭf'ërŭs) *n.* [Gk. *sporos*, seed; *anggeion*, vessel; L. *ferre*, to bear.] Sporangia-bearing.

sporangiform (spörăn'jĭfôrm) *a.* [Gk. *sporos*, seed; *anggeion*, vessel; L. *forma*, shape.] Sporangioid; like a sporangium.

sporangiocarp (spörăn'jĭökârp) *n.* [Gk. *sporos*, seed; *anggeion*, vessel; *karpos*, fruit.] An enclosed collection of sporangia; a structure of asci and sterile hyphae surrounded by a peridium; an ascocarp.

sporangiolum (spŏrăn'jĭŏlŭm) *n.* [Gk. *sporos*, seed ; *anggeion*, vessel.] A secondary or small few-spored sporangium ; modified tip in arbusculae ; ptyosome ; sporangiole.

sporangiophore (spŏrăn'jĭŏfōr) *n.* [Gk. *sporos*, seed ; *anggeion*, vessel ; *pherein*, to bear.] A stalk-like structure bearing sporangia.

sporangiosorus (spŏrăn'jĭŏsō'rŭs) *n.* [Gk. *sporos*, seed ; *anggeion*, vessel ; *soros*, heap.] A compact group of sporangia.

sporangiospore (spŏrăn'jĭŏspōr) *n.* [Gk. *sporos*, seed ; *anggeion*, vessel ; *sporos*.] A sporangium spore.

sporangium (spŏrăn'jĭŭm) *n.* [Gk. *sporos*, seed ; *anggeion*, vessel.] A spore-case, capsule, or cell in which spores are produced.

spore (spōr) *n.* [Gk. *sporos*, seed.] A highly specialised reproductive cell of plants ; a resistant dormant form of certain bacteria ; a falciform cell of Sporozoa.

spore formation, — reproduction by encystation followed by division and free-cell liberation ; endogenous multiplication ; sporogony, sporogenesis, sporulation.

spore group,—compound spore or sporodesm.

spore mother-cells,—sixteen cells produced by repeated division of an archesporium, each in turn dividing into four spores ; sporoblasts.

sporetia (spŏrē'tĭă, -shĭă) *n. plu.* [Gk. *sporos*, seed.] Idiochromidia ; chromidia of generative chromatin.

sporidesm,—sporodesm.

sporidiferous (spŏrĭdĭf'ërŭs) *a.* [Gk. *sporos*, seed ; L. *ferre*, to bear.] Sporidia-bearing.

sporidiole (spŏr'ĭdĭōl) *n.* [Gk. *sporos*, seed.] A protobasidium ; a sporidium arising from promycelium, in rusts ; sporidiolum.

sporidium (spŏrĭd'ĭŭm) *n.* [Gk. *sporos*, seed ; *idion*, *dim.*] Conidium developed by abstriction from gonidiophore in fungi ; ascospore ; basidiospore.

sporidochium (spŏr'ĭdŏkī'ŭm) *n.* [Gk. *sporos*, seed ; *docheion*, holder.] Receptacle of certain fungi ; *cf.* sporodochium.

sporiferous (spŏrĭf'ërŭs) *a.* [Gk. *sporos*, seed ; L. *ferre*, to bear.] Spore-bearing.

sporification (spŏr'ĭfĭkā'shŭn) *n.* [Gk. *sporos*, seed ; L. *facere*, to make.] Formation of spores.

sporiparity (spŏr'ĭpăr'ĭtĭ) *n.* [Gk. *sporos*, seed ; L. *parere*, to beget.] Reproduction by spore formation.

sporiparous (spŏrĭp'ărŭs) *a.* [Gk. *sporos*, seed ; L. *parere*, to beget.] Reproducing by spore formation.

sporoblast (spŏr'ŏblăst) *n.* [Gk. *sporos*, seed ; *blastos*, bud.] An archespore ; a stage in spore formation, a sporoblast giving rise to spores, and these to sporozoites.

sporocarp (spŏr'ŏkârp) *n.* [Gk. *sporos*, seed ; *karpos*, fruit.] An ascocarp ; a structure formed from archicarp and investing hyphae, enclosing spored asci ; a sorus covered by indusium.

sporocladium (spŏr'ŏklădē'ŭm, -klā'-dĭŭm) *n.* [Gk. *sporos*, seed ; *kladion*, small young branch.] Branch of a conidiophore, bearing sporangia or conidia.

sporocyst (spŏr'ŏsĭst) *n.* [Gk. *sporos*, seed ; *kystis*, bladder.] A stage in spore formation preceding liberation of spores, or protective envelope of a spore, in protozoa ; encysted embryo stage of trematode after degeneration following entry into intermediate host.

sporocystid (spŏrŏsĭs'tĭd) *a.* [Gk. *sporos*, seed ; *kystis*, bladder ; *eidos*, form.] *Appl.* oocyst of Sporozoa when the zygote forms sporocysts.

sporocyte (spŏr'ŏsīt) *n.* [Gk. *sporos*, seed ; *kytos*, hollow.] A spore mother-cell.

sporodesm (spŏr'ŏdĕzm) *n.* [Gk. *sporos*, seed ; *desmos*, bond.] A compound spore in which each cell can germinate independently ; multilocular or septate or pluricellular spore, spore group, sporidesm.

sporodochium (spŏr′ödökī′ŭm) *n.* [Gk. *sporos*, seed; *docheion*, holder.] A hemispherical aggregate of conidiophores; *cf.* sporidochium.

sporoduct (spŏr′ödŭkt) *n.* [Gk. *sporos*, seed; L. *ducere*, to lead.] A special apparatus for dissemination of spores of Sporozoa and of some Fungi.

sporogenesis,—spore formation, *q.v.*

sporogenous (spöröj′ënŭs) *a.* [Gk. *sporos*, seed; *gennaein*, to produce.] Spore-producing; sporiparous.

sporogonial (spŏrögō′nĭăl) *a.* [Gk. *sporos*, seed; *gonos*, offspring.] *Pert.* a sporogonium.

sporogonium (spŏrögō′nĭŭm) *n.* [Gk. *sporos*, seed; *gonos*, offspring.] A structure developed from a fertilised oosphere of an archegonium, giving rise to asexual spores, in mosses.

sporogony (spörŏg′önĭ) *n.* [Gk. *sporos*, seed; *gonos*, birth.] Spore-formation; sporogenesis.

sporoid (spō′roid) *a.* [Gk. *sporos*, seed; *eidos*, like.] Like a spore.

sporokinete (spŏr′ökĭnēt′) *n.* [Gk. *sporos*, seed; *kinein*, to move.] A motile spore from the oocyst of certain Haemosporidia.

sporont (spŏrŏnt) *n.* [Gk. *sporos*, seed; *on*, being.] Gametocyte stage in life-history of Sporozoa.

sporophore (spŏr′öfōr) *n.* [Gk. *sporos*, seed; *pherein*, to bear.] A spore-bearing structure, in fungi; an inflorescence; process of plasmodium producing spores on free surface, in Mycetozoa.

sporophydium (spŏröfĭd′ĭŭm) *n.* [Gk. *sporos*, seed; *phyas*, shoot; *idion*, *dim.*] The sporangium of certain thallophytes.

sporophyll (spŏr′öfĭl) *n.* [Gk. *sporos*, seed; *phyllon*, leaf.] A sporangium-bearing leaf.

sporophyte (spŏr′öfīt) *n.* [Gk. *sporos*, seed; *phyton*, plant.] A stem covered with sporophylls or leaves, each bearing a sporangium, in ferns; the diploid spore-producing phase in alternation of plant generations. *Opp.* gametophyte.

sporoplasm (spŏr′öplăzm) *n.* [Gk. *sporos*, seed; *plasma*, mould.] Sporozoite, binucleate amoebula, or central part of a spore.

sporosac (spŏr′ösăk) *n.* [Gk. *sporos*, seed; L. *saccus*, sack.] An ovoid pouch-like body, consisting of a gonad, a degraded reproductive zooid of a medusoid colony.

sporotamium (spŏr′ötămī′ŭm) *n.* [Gk. *sporos*, seed; *tamieion*, store.] Cell-layer beneath apothecium, as in lichens.

sporozoid (spŏrözō′ĭd) *n.* [Gk. *sporos*, seed; *zoon*, animal; *eidos*, form.] A motile spore; zoospore.

sporozoite (spŏrözō′īt) *n.* [Gk. *sporos*, seed; *zoon*, animal.] Spore liberated through dissolving of membrane of sporocyst, a phase in life-history of Sporozoa.

sport,—a mutation, *q.v.*

sporulation (spôrūlā′shŭn) *n.* [L. *sporula*, small seed.] Brood-formation by multiple cell-fission; spore-formation; liberation of spores.

spot fruit,—sorus, as of ferns.

spur (spŭr) *n.* [A.S. *spora*, spur.] A calcar; cog-tooth of malleus; rim of sclera outside iridial angle; cuticular outgrowth on legs of certain insects; a process of a petal or of a sepal, functioning as a nectar receptacle; small reproductive shoot; a brachyplast, *q.v.*

spuriae (spū′rĭē) *n. plu.* [L. *spurius*, false.] Feathers of alula or bastard wing.

spurious (spū′rĭŭs) *a.* [L. *spurius*, false.] Seemingly true but morphologically false; *appl.* dissepiment, fruit, teeth, vein, wing.

squama (skwā′mă) *n.* [L. *squama*, scale.] A squame or scale; a part arranged like a scale; vertical part of frontal bone; part of occipital bone above and behind foramen magnum; anterior and upper part of temporal bone; antitegula or calyptron, a scale below wing base, of Diptera; a scale-like body attached to second podomere of antenna of some Crustacea.

squamate (skwā′māt) *a.* [L. *squama*, scale.] Scaly.

squamation (skwămā'shŭn) *n.* [L. *squama*, scale.] Scale arrangement.

squame,—squama, *q.v.*

squamella (skwămĕl'ă) *n.* [*Dim.* of L. *squama*, scale.] A small scale or bract ; a palea.

squamellate (skwămĕl'āt) *a.* [L. *squama*, a scale.] Having small scales or bracts ; squamelliferous.

squamelliform (skwămĕl'ĭfôrm) *a.* [L. *squama*, scale ; *forma*, shape.] Resembling a squamella.

squamiferous (skwămĭf'ërŭs) *a.* [L. *squama*, scale ; *ferre*, to bear.] Bearing scales ; squamigerous.

squamiform (skwā'mĭfôrm) *a.* [L. *squama*, scale ; *forma*, shape.] Scale-like.

squamosal (skwămō'săl) *n.* [L. *squama*, scale.] A membrane bone of vertebrate skull forming part of posterior side wall.

squamose (skwā'mōs) *a.* [L. *squama*, scale.] Covered with scales ; squamous.

squamous (skwā'mŭs) *a.* [L. *squama*, scale.] *Appl.* simple epithelium of flat nucleated cells, scaly or pavement epithelium.

squamula (skwăm'ūlă) *n.* [L. *squama*, scale.] A squamule or small scale ; minute membranous scale, or lodicule, in grasses ; tegula of some insects ; one of small circular areas into which pouch scales of Gymnophiona are divided.

squamulate (skwăm'ūlāt) *a.* [L. *squama*, scale.] Having minute scales ; squamulose.

squamule,—squamula.

squarrose (skwôr'ōs) *a.* [L.L. *squarrosus*, scurfy.] Rough with projecting scales or rigid leaves.

squarrulose (skwôr'ūlōs) *a.* [L.L. *squarrosus*, scurfy.] Tending to become squarrose.

stachyosporous (stăkĭŏs'pörŭs) *a.* [Gk. *stachys*, ear of corn ; *sporos*, seed.] Bearing sporangia on axis, as Selaginella ; *cf.* phyllosporous.

stadium (stā'dĭŭm) *n.* [L. *stare*, to stand.] A stage in development or life-history of plant or animal ; stade ; interval between two successive ecdyses in insects.

stag-horned (stăg'hôrnd) *a.* [Icel. *stiga*, to mount ; A.S. *horn*.] Having large branched mandibles, as a stag-beetle.

stagnicolous (stăgnĭk'ölŭs) *a.* [L. *stagnum*, standing water ; *colere*, to inhabit.] Living or growing in stagnant water.

stalk-cell,—the barren cell of two into which the antheridial cell of gymnosperms divides ; basal cell of crosier in Discomycetes.

stalk-eyed,—having eyes at end of a short stalk, as in some Crustacea, *opp.* sessile-eyed.

stamen (stā'mĕn) *n.* [L. *stamen*, warp.] The male organ of a flower, consisting of stalk or filament with anther containing pollen.

staminal (stăm'ĭnăl) *a.* [L. *stamen*, warp.] *Pert.* a stamen.

staminate (stăm'ĭnāt) *a.* [L. *stamen*, warp.] Producing, or consisting of, stamens.

staminiferous (stămĭnĭf'ërŭs) *a.* [L. *stamen*, warp ; *ferre*, to bear.] Staminigerous ; stamen-bearing.

staminode (stăm'ĭnōd) *n.* (L. *stamen*, warp ; Gk. *eidos*, form.] A foliaceous scale-like body in some flowers, derived from a metamorphosed stamen ; a rudimentary, imperfect, or sterile stamen ; staminodium.

staminody (stăm'ĭnödĭ) *n.* [L. *stamen*, warp ; Gk. *eidos*, form.] Metamorphosis of flower organs into stamens.

standard (stănd'ărd) *n.* [O.F. *estandart*, from L. *stare*, to stand.] The vexillum or upper petal in Papilionaceae ; a tree or shrub not supported by a wall.

stapedius (stăpē'dĭŭs) *n.* [L.L. *stapes*, stirrup.] A muscle pulling the head of the stapes.

stapes (stā'pēz) *n.* [L.L. *stapes*, stirrup.] Stirrup-shaped innermost bone of middle ear ; operculum or internal end of columella auris, fitting into and filling fenestra ovalis in amphibians.

staphyle (stăf'ĭlē) *n.* [Gk. *staphyle*, bunch of grapes.] Uvula.

starch (stârch) *n.* [A.S. *stearc*, stiff.] The common carbohydrate formed by plants and stored in seeds; $(C_6H_{10}O_5)_n$.

starch sheath,—endodermis with starch grains.

stasimorphy (stăs'ĭmôr'fĭ) *n.* [Gk. *stasis*, standing; *morphe*, form.] A deviation in form due to arrested development.

stasis (stā'sĭs) *n.* [Gk. *stasis*, standing.] Stoppage, or retardation, as of growth, or of movement of animal fluids.

stathmokinesis (stăth'mökĭnē'sĭs) *n.* [Gk. *stathmos*, station; *kinesis*, movement.] Inhibition of cell division, as by colchicine or other agent.

static (stăt'ĭk) *a.* [Gk. *statikos*, causing to stand.] *Pert.* system at rest or in equilibrium; *appl.* postural reactions; *opp.* kinetic; *appl.* proprioceptors, as otoliths and semicircular canals.

stato-acoustic (stăt'öăkoo'stĭk) *a.* [Gk. *statos*, standing; *akouein*, to hear.] *Pert.* sense of balance and of hearing; *appl.* eighth cranial or acoustic nerve, dividing into vestibular and cochlear nerves.

statoblast (stăt'öblăst) *n.* [Gk. *statos*, stationary; *blastos*, bud.] A specialised bud or 'winter-egg' of some Polyzoa, developed on funiculus and set free on death of parent organism.

statocone (stăt'ökōn) *n.* [Gk. *statos*, stationary; *konis*, dust.] A minute structure contained in a statocyst.

statocyst (stăt'ösĭst) *n.* [Gk. *statos*, stationary; *kystis*, bladder.] A vesicle of many invertebrates, with function of perception of position of body in space; a statocyte or geoperceptive cell containing statoliths.

statocyte (stăt'ösīt) *n.* [Gk. *statos*, stationary; *kytos*, hollow.] A cell containing statoliths.

statolith (stăt'ölĭth) *n.* [Gk. *statos*, stationary; *lithos*, stone.] A structure of calcium carbonate, sand grain, or secreted substance, contained in a statocyst; a cell inclusion, as oil droplet, starch grain, crystal, which changes its intracellular position under the influence of gravity.

statorhabd (stăt'örăbd) *n.* [Gk. *statos*, stationary; *rhabdos*, rod.] A short tentacular process carrying the statolith in Trachomedusae.

statospore (stăt'öspōr) *n.* [Gk. *statos*, stationary; *sporos*, seed.] A resting spore.

staurophyll (stô'röfĭl) *n.* [Gk. *stauros*, palisade; *phyllon*, leaf.] A leaf having palisade or other compact tissue throughout.

staurospore (stôr'öspōr) *n.* [Gk. *stauros*, cross; *sporos*, seed.] A cross-shaped or a triquetrous spore.

steapsin (stē'ăpsĭn) *n.* [Gk. *stear*, tallow; *pepsis*, digestion.] A lipolytic enzyme of pancreatic juice.

stearin (stē'ărĭn) *n.* [Gk. *stear*, tallow.] The solid part of fat, held dissolved by olein at body temperature; a component of many animal and vegetable fats.

steganopodous (stĕgănŏp'ödŭs) *a.* [Gk. *steganos*, covered; *pous*, foot.] Having feet completely webbed; totipalmate.

stege (stē'jē, stĕg'ē) *n.* [Gk. *stege*, roof.] The inner layer of rods of Corti.

stegocarpous (stĕg'ökâr'pŭs) *a.* [Gk. *stegein*, to cover; *karpos*, fruit.] Having a capsule with operculum and peristome; stegocarpic.

stegocrotaphic (stĕg'ökrŏt'ăfĭk) *a.* [Gk. *stege*, roof; *krotaphos*, the temples.] *Appl.* skull whose only gaps on dorsal surface are nares, orbits, and parietal foramen.

stelar parenchyma,—pith.

stelar system,—of plants, vascular and associated conjunctive tissue.

stele (stēlē) *n.* [Gk. *stele*, pillar.] A bulky strand or cylinder of vascular tissue contained in stem and root of plants, developed from plerome.

stellar,—stellate.

stellate (stĕl′āt) *a.* [L *stella*, star.] Star-shaped; asteroid; radiating; *appl.* leaf, hair, spicule, cells of Kupffer, ganglion of sympathetic system, ligament of rib, veins beneath fibrous tunic of kidney, etc.

stellate reticulum,—enamel pulp of dental germ.

stelliform,—stellate, asteroid.

stelocyttarous (stē′lösĭt′ărŭs) *a.* [Gk. *stele*, pillar; *kyttaros*, honey-comb cell.] Building, or *pert.*, stalked combs, as of certain wasps; *cf.* phragmocyttarous.

stem (stĕm) *n.* [A.S. *stemn*, tree-stem.] Main axis of a plant.

stem body,—equatorial part of the spindle, as between two nuclei at telophase.

stem-cell, — a primordial germ-cell.

stemma (stĕm′ă) *n.* [Gk. *stemma*, garland.] A simple eye or ocellus of arthropods; a lateral ocellus; an ocellus of an ommatidium.

stenobaric (stĕn′öbăr′ĭk) *a.* [Gk. *stenos*, narrow; *baros*, weight.] *Appl.* animals adaptable only to small differences in pressure or altitude; *cf.* eurybaric.

stenobathic (stĕn′öbăth′ik) *a.* [Gk. *stenos*, narrow; *bathys*, deep.] Having a narrow vertical range of distribution, *opp.* eurybathic.

stenobenthic (stĕn′öbĕn′thĭk) *a.* [Gk. *stenos*, narrow; *benthos*, depth of the sea.] *Pert.*, or living within a narrow range of depth of the sea-bottom, *opp.* eurybenthic.

stenochoric (stĕn′ökō′rĭk) *a.* [Gk. *stenos*, narrow; *choros*, place.] Having a narrow range of distribution.

stenocyst (stĕn′ösĭst) *n.* [Gk. *stenos*, narrow; *kystis*, bladder.] One of the auxiliary cells in leaves of certain mosses.

stenoecious (stĕnē′sĭŭs) *a.* [Gk. *stenos*, narrow; *oikos*, abode.] Having a narrow range of habitat selection, *opp.* euryoecious.

stenohaline (stĕn′öhăl′īn) *a.* [Gk. *stenos*, narrow; *halinos*, saline.] *Appl.* organisms adaptable to a narrow range of salinity, *opp.* euryhaline.

stenohygric (stĕn′öhī′grĭk) *a.* [Gk. *stenos*, narrow; *hygros*, wet.] *Appl.* organisms adaptable to a narrow variation in atmospheric humidity.

stenomorphic (stĕn′ömôr′fĭk) *a.* [Gk. *stenos*, narrow; *morphe*, form.] Dwarfed; smaller than typical form, owing to cramped habitat.

stenonian duct,—Stensen's duct.

stenonotal (stĕn′önō′tăl) *a.* [Gk. *stenos*, narrow; *noton*, back.] With very small thorax, as worker insect.

stenopetalous (stĕn′öpĕt′ălŭs) *a.* [Gk. *stenos*, narrow; *petalon*, leaf.] With narrow petals.

stenophagous (stĕnŏf′ăgŭs) *a.* [Gk. *stenos*, narrow; *phagein*, to eat.] Subsisting on a limited variety of food, *opp.* euryphagous; *cf.* monophagous.

stenophyllous (stĕn′öfĭl′ŭs) *a.* [Gk. *stenos*, narrow; *phyllon*, leaf.] Narrow-leaved.

stenopodium (stĕn′öpō′dĭŭm) *n.* [Gk. *stenos*, narrow; *pous*, foot.] A crustacean limb in which the protopodite bears distally both endopodite and exopodite.

stenosepalous (stĕn′ösĕp′ălŭs) *a.* [Gk. *stenos*, narrow; F. *sépale*, sepal.] With narrow sepals.

stenostomatous (stĕn′östŏm′ătŭs) *a.* [Gk. *stenos*, narrow; *stoma*, mouth.] Narrow-mouthed.

stenothermic (stĕn′öthĕr′mĭk) *a.* [Gk. *stenos*, narrow; *therme*, heat.] *Appl.* organisms adaptable only to slight variations in temperature, *opp.* eurythermic.

stenotopic (stĕn′ötŏp′ĭk) *a.* [Gk. *stenos*, narrow; *topos*, place.] Having a restricted range of geographical distribution, *opp.* eurytopic.

stenotropic (stĕn′ötrŏp′ĭk) *a.* [Gk. *stenos*, narrow; *trope*, turn.] Having a very limited adaptation to varied conditions.

Stensen's duct [*N. Stensen*, Danish physiologist]. Duct of the parotid gland.

stephanion (stĕfăn′ĭŏn) *n.* [Gk. *stephanos*, crown.] The point where superior temporal ridge is crossed by coronal suture.

steppe (stĕp) *n.* [Russ. *step'*.] Xerophilous and generally treeless grassland ; short-grass plains.

stercobilin (stĕrkŏbī′lĭn) *n.* [L. *stercus*, dung ; *bilis*, bile.] The brown pigment of faeces ; urobilin ; $C_{33}H_{42}O_6N_4$.

stercomarium (stĕrkŏmā′rĭum) *n.* [L. *stercus*, dung.] The system of stercome - containing tubes of certain Sarcodina.

stercome (stĕr′kōm) *n.* [L. *stercus*, dung.] Faecal matter of Sarcodina, in masses of brown granules.

stercoral (stĕr′kŏrăl) *a.* [L. *stercus*, dung.] *Pert.* faeces ; *appl.* a dorsal pocket or sac of proctodaeum in spiders.

stereid (stĕr′ëĭd) *n.* [Gk. *stereos*, solid ; *eidos*, form.] A lignified parenchyma cell with pit canals ; stone cell, *q.v.*

stereid bundles,—bands or bundles of sclerenchymatous fibres.

stereoblastula (stĕr′ëŏblăs′tūlă) *n.* [Gk. *stereos*, solid ; *blastos*, bud.] Abnormal form of echinoid larva unable to gastrulate.

stereocilia (stĕr′ëŏsĭl′ĭă) *n. plu.* [Gk. *stereos*, rigid ; L. *cilium*, eyelash.] Non-motile secretory projections on epithelium of duct of epididymis.

stereognostic (stĕr′ëŏgnŏs′tĭk) *a.* [Gk. *stereos*, solid ; L. *gnoscere*, to know.] *Appl.* sense which appreciates size, shape, weight.

stereokinesis (stĕr′ëŏkĭnē′sĭs) *n.* [Gk. *stereos*, solid ; *kinesis*, movement.] Movement or inhibition of movement in response to contact stimuli ; thigmotaxis.

stereome (stĕr′ëōm) *n.* [Gk. *stereoma*, solid body.] Sclerenchymatous and collenchymatous masses along with hardened parts of vascular bundles forming supporting tissue in plants ; the thick-walled elongated cells of the central cylinder in mosses.

stereoplasm (stĕr′ëŏplăzm) *n.* [Gk. *stereos*, solid ; *plasma*, mould.] The more solid part of protoplasm, *opp.* hygroplasm ; a vesicular substance filling interseptal spaces of certain corals.

stereospondylous (stĕr′ëŏspŏn′dĭlŭs) *a.* [Gk. *stereos*, solid ; *sphondylos*, vertebra.] Having vertebrae each fused into one piece ; *cf.* temnospondylous.

stereotaxy (stĕr′ëŏtăk′sĭ) *n.* [Gk. *stereos*, solid ; *taxis*, arrangement.] The mechanical reaction to continuous contact with a solid.

stereotropism (stĕrëŏt′rŏpĭzm) *n.* [Gk. *stereos*, solid ; *trope*, turn.] Tendency of organisms to attach themselves to solid objects, or to live in crannies or tunnels, in total contact with solids ; thigmotaxis.

sterigma (stērĭg′mă) *n.* [Gk. *sterigma*, support.] A slender filament arising from basidium or conidiophore, and giving rise to spores by abstriction ; flange- or rib-like part of a decurrent leaf, lying along the stem. *Plu.* sterigmata.

sterile (stĕr′ĭl) *a.* [L. *sterilis*, barren.] Incapable of propagation ; aseptic ; axenic, *q.v.*

sterilise (stĕr′ĭlīz) *v.* [L. *sterilis*, barren.] To render incapable of reproduction, or of conveying infection.

sternal (stĕr′năl) *a.* [Gk. *sternon*, chest.] *Pert.* sternum, or sternite ; *appl.* ribs united to sternum.

sternebrae (stĕr′nëbrē) *n. plu.* [L. *sternum*, breast-bone ; *ebra*, on analogy of vert*ebra*.] Divisions of a segmented sternum or breast-bone.

sternellum (stĕrnĕl′ŭm) *n.* [*Dim.* of L. *sternum*, breast-bone.] A sternal sclerite of insects ; sclerite behind eusternum ; poststernite.

sternite (stĕr′nīt) *n.* [Gk. *sternon*, chest.] A ventral plate of an arthropod segment ; a sternal sclerite.

sternobranchial (stĕr′nŏbrăng′kĭăl) *a.* [L. *sternum*, breast-bone ; *branchiae*, gills.] *Appl.* vessel conveying blood to gills, in certain Crustacea.

sternoclavicular (stĕr′nöklăvĭk′ūlăr) *a.* [L. *sternum*, breast-bone; *claviculum*, small key.] *Appl.* and *pert.* articulation between sternum and clavicle.

sternocostal (stĕr′nökŏs′tăl) *a.* [L. *sternum*, breast-bone; *costa*, rib.] *Pert.* sternum and ribs; *appl.* ligament, surface of heart.

sternokleidomastoid (stĕr′nöklī′dömăs′toid) *a.* [Gk. *sternon*, chest; *kleis*, key; *mastos*, breast; *eidos*, form.] *Appl.* an oblique neck muscle stretching from sternum to mastoid process.

sternopleurite (stĕr′nöploo′rīt) *n.* [Gk. *sternon*, chest; *pleura*, side.] Thoracic sclerite formed by union of episternum and sternum, in insects; sternopleuron.

sternoscapular (stĕr′nöskăp′ūlăr) *a.* [L. *sternum*, breast-bone; *scapula*, shoulder-blade.] *Appl.* a muscle connecting sternum and scapula.

sternotribe (stĕr′nötrīb) *a.* [Gk. *sternon*, chest; *tribein*, to rub.] *Appl.* flowers with fertilising elements so placed as to be brushed by sternites of visiting insects.

sternoxiphoid (stĕr′nözĭf′oid) *a.* [Gk. *sternon*, chest; *xiphos*, sword; *eidos*, form.] *Appl.* plane through junction of sternum and xiphoid cartilage.

sternum (stĕr′nŭm) *n.* [L. *sternum*, breast-bone.] Breast-bone of vertebrates; ventral plate of typical arthropod segment; all the ventral sclerites of a thoracic segment in insects.

sterols (stĕr′ŏlz) *n. plu.* [Gk. *stereos*, solid; L. *oleum*, oil.] Alcohols (of a cyclic structure including the cyclopentenophenanthrene ring) found in plants and animals, and comprising the mycosterols, phytosterols, and zoosterols, *q.v.*

sterraster (stĕrăs′tĕr) *n.* [Gk. *sterros*, solid; *aster*, star.] Aster with actines soldered together by silica.

sterrula (stĕr′ūlă) *n.* [Gk. *sterros*, solid.] Solid free-swimming larva of Alcyonaria, preceding planula.

Stewart's organs,—five vesicles of coelom of lantern protruding into the perivisceral space and acting as internal gills in some Echinoidea.

stichic (stĭk′ĭk) *a.* [Gk. *stichos*, row.] In a row parallel to long axis.

stichidium (stĭkĭd′ĭŭm) *n.* [Gk. *stichos*, row; *idion*, *dim.*] A tetraspore receptacle of some algae.

stichochrome (stĭk′ökrōm) *a.* [Gk. *stichos*, row; *chroma*, colour.] With Nissl granules arranged in rows, as in motor neurones.

stigma (stĭg′mă) *n.* [Gk. *stigma*, mark.] Portion of pistil which receives pollen; eye-spots of some protophyta and protozoa; an arthropod spiracle; apertures connected with tracheae of insects; coloured wing spot of certain butterflies and other insects; thickened area near apex of wing-membrane in dragon-flies; gill-slit of tunicates; spots or stomata formed as artefacts in walls of capillaries.

stigmata,—*plu.* of stigma.

stigmatic (stĭgmăt′ĭk) *a.* [Gk. *stigma*, mark.] *Appl.* lid cell of an archegonium; *pert.* a stigma.

stigmatiferous (stĭgmătĭf′ërŭs) *a.* [Gk. *stigma*, mark; L. *ferre*, to carry.] Stigma-bearing.

stigmatiform (stĭg′mătĭfôrm) *a.* [Gk. *stigma*, mark; L. *forma*, shape.] Resembling a stigma; stigmatoid.

stile(t),—*see* style(t).

stilt-roots,—buttress-roots, *q.v.*

stimulant (stĭm′ūlănt) *n.* [L. *stimulare*, to incite.] A stimulus-producing agent.

stimulation (stĭmūlā′shŭn) *n.* [L. *stimulare*, to incite.] Excitation or irritation of an organism or part by external or internal influences.

stimulose (stĭm′ūlōs) *a.* [L. *stimulare*, to incite.] Furnished with stinging hairs or cells.

stimulus (stĭm′ūlŭs) *n.* [L. *stimulus*, goad.] An agent which causes a reaction or change in an organism or in any of its parts; a stinging hair.

sting (stĭng) *n.* [A.S. *stingan*, to sting.] Stinging hair or cell; spine of sting-ray; offensive and defensive organ for piercing, also for inoculating with poison.

stipe (stīp) *n.* [L. *stipes*, stalk.] The stem bearing pileus in agarics boletes, etc.; stalk of seaweeds; stem or caudex of palms and tree-ferns; stem of fern fronds; a stipes.

stipel (stī'pĕl) *n.* [L. *stipes*, stalk.] An outgrowth of leaflets resembling the stipule of a leaf-base.

stipella (stĭpĕl'ă) *n.* [*Dim.* from L. *stipes*, stalk.] Stipule of a leaflet in a compound leaf.

stipellate (stī'pĕlāt) *a.* [L. *stipes*, stalk.] Bearing stipels.

stipes (stī'pĕz) *n.* [L. *stipes*, stalk.] Peduncle of a stalked eye; distal part of protopodite of first maxilla of insects, itself divided into eustipes and parastipes, and the eustipes further into dististipes, proxistipes and basistipes.

stipiform (stī'pĭfôrm) *a.* [L. *stipes*, stalk; *forma*, shape.] Resembling a stalk or stem.

stipitate (stĭp'ĭtāt) *a.* [L. *stipes*, stalk.] Stalked.

stipites (stĭp'ĭtēz) *n. plu.* [L. *stipes*, stalk.] *Plu.* of stipes; paired part, anterior to mentum, of gnathochilarium.

stipitiform,—stipiform.

stipular (stĭp'ūlăr) *a.* [L. *stipula*, small stalk.] Like, *pert.*, or growing in place of, stipules; stipellar.

stipulate (stĭp'ūlāt) *a.* [L. *stipula*, small stalk.] With stipules; stipuliferous.

stipule (stĭp'ūl) *n.* [L. *stipula*, small stalk.] One of two foliaceous or membranaceous processes developed at base of a leaf petiole, sometimes in tendril or spine form; paraphyll, *q.v.*

stipuliform (stĭp'ūlĭfôrm) *a.* [L. *stipula*, small stalk; *forma*, shape.] In the form of a stipule.

stipuloid (stĭp'ūloid) *n.* [L. *stipula*, small stalk; Gk. *eidos*, form.] A unicellular outgrowth from basal node of branches in Charophyta.

stirps (stĕrps) *n.* [L. *stirps*, stock.] The sum-total of germs or gemmules to be found in a newly fertilised ovum; stirp. *Plu.* stirpes.

stock (stŏk) *n.* [A.S. *stocc*, post.] Stem of tree or bush receiving bud, or scion, in grafting; a gilliflower; an asexual zooid which produces sexual zooids of one sex by gemmation, as in Polychaeta; live-stock.

stolon (stō'lŏn) *n.* [L. *stolo*, shoot.] A creeping stem or runner capable of developing rootlets and stem, and ultimately forming a new individual; a creeping hypha which can form aerial mycelium and rhizoids or haustoria; a cylindrical stem of some Polyzoa from which individuals grow out at intervals; a horizontal tubular branch of some coelenterates from which new zooids arise by budding; the cadophore and bud-forming ventral outgrowth of tunicates.

stolonate (stō'lŏnāt) *a.* [L. *stolo*, shoot.] Having stolons; resembling a stolon; developing from a stolon; *appl.* plants and animals which develop by means of stolons; stoloniferous.

stolotheca (stō'lŏthē'kă) *n.* [L. *stolo*, shoot; *theca*, case.] Theca budded from side of metasicula of graptolites, and producing buds of autotheca, bitheca, and a second stolotheca.

stoma (stŏ'mă) *n.*, **stomata** (stŏm'ătă) *plu.* [Gk. *stoma*, mouth.] A small orifice; minute openings, with guard cells, in epidermis of plants, especially on under surface of leaves, or, the stomatic pores only; apertures in endothelium of serous membranes; part of alimentary canal between mouth opening and oesophagus, in nematodes.

stomach (stŭm'ăk) *n.* [Gk. *stomachos*, throat, gullet.] Ventriculus; sac-like portion of food canal beyond gullet, in vertebrates; corresponding part, or entire digestive cavity, of invertebrates.

stomachic (stŏmăk'ĭk) *a.* [Gk. *stomachos*, gullet.] *Pert.* the stomach.

stomal,—stomatal.

stomata,—*plu.* of stoma.

stomatal (stŏm'ătăl) *a.* [Gk. *stoma*, mouth.] *Pert.* or like a stoma; stomatic.

stomate (stŏm'āt) *a.* [Gk. *stoma*, mouth.] With stoma or stomata.

stomatic (stŏmăt'ĭk) *a.* [Gk. *stoma*, *Pert.*, or like, a stoma; *appl.* pore; stomatal.

stomatiferous (stŏmătĭf'ĕrŭs) *a.* [Gk. *stoma*, mouth; L. *ferre*, to carry.] Bearing stomata.

stomatogastric (stŏm'ătŏgăs'trĭk) *a.* [Gk. *stoma*, mouth; *gaster*, stomach.] *Pert.* mouth and stomach; *appl.* visceral system of nerves supplying anterior part of alimentary canal; *appl.* recurrent nerve from frontal to stomachic ganglion, in insects.

stomatogenesis (stŏm'ătŏjĕn'ĕsĭs) *n.* [Gk. *stoma*, mouth; *genesis*, origin.] The formation of a mouth, as in Ciliata.

stomatose, stomatous,—stomate.

stomidium (stŏmĭd'ĭŭm) *n.* [Gk. *stoma*, mouth; *idion*, *dim.*] Aperture representing terminal pore of degenerated tentacles of Actiniaria.

stomions (stŏm'ĭŏnz) *n. plu.* [Gk. *stomion.* small mouth.] Dermal pores or ostia perforating dermal membrane of developing sponge.

stomium (stō'mĭŭm) *n.* [Gk. *stomion*, small mouth.] Group of thin-walled cells in fern sporangium where rupture of mature capsule takes place; slit of dehiscing anther.

stomocoel (stŏm'ŏsēl) *n.* [Gk. *stoma*, mouth; *koilos*, hollow.] System of cavities in lips.

stomodaeal canal,—in Ctenophora, a canal given off by each per-radial canal, and situate parallel to stomodaeum.

stomodaeum (stŏm'ŏdē'ŭm) *n.* [Gk. *stoma*, mouth; *odaios*, *pert.* way.] Anterior ectoderm-lined portion of alimentary canal; anterior pitted-in portion of embryonic gut.

stone canal,—madreporic canal, an S-shaped cylinder extending from madreporite to near mouth border in echinoderms; hydrophoric canal.

stone cells,—sclerotic cells or rounded sclerenchymatous elements, as found in pear; brachysclereids.

stone fruit,—fruit with a hard endocarp; a drupe.

storage trunk,—root-like part of a fungal stipe; pseudorhiza.

strangulated (străng'gūlātĕd) *a.* [L. *strangulare*, to throttle.] Constricted in places; contracted and expanded irregularly.

strata,—*plu.* of stratum.

stratification (străt'ĭfĭkā'shŭn) *n.* [L. *stratum*, layer; *facere*, to make.] Arrangement in layers; superimposition of layers of epithelium cells; vertical grouping within a community.

stratified epithelium,—epithelium cells arranged in many superimposed layers.

stratiform (străt'ĭfôrm) *a.* [L. *stratum*, layer; *forma*, shape.] *Appl.* fibrocartilage coating osseous grooves, or developed in some tendons.

stratose (strā'tōs) *a.* [L. *stratum*, layer.] Arranged in layers.

stratum (strā'tŭm) *n.* [L. *stratum*, layer.] A layer, as of cells, or of tissue; a group of organisms inhabiting a vertical division of an area; vegetation of similar height in a plant community, as trees, shrubs, herbs, and mosses; a layer of rock. *Plu.* strata.

stratum compactum,—surface layer of decidua vera.

stratum corneum,—horny external layer of epidermis.

stratum cylindricum,—inner ectodermal layer surrounding mesodermal pulp of feather.

stratum fibrosum,—external fibrous tissue of articular capsule.

stratum germinativum,—Malpighian layer or rete Malpighii, *q.v.*

stratum granulosum,—superficial layer of rete mucosum of skin.

stratum lucidum,—layer of cells between stratum corneum and stratum granulosum of skin.

stratum opticum,—layer of nerve-fibres constituting innermost layer of retina ; layer of multipolar nerve cells of anterior corpora quadrigemina, *cf.* stratum zonale.

stratum spinosum,—layer of prickle-cells in epidermis.

stratum spongiosum,—deeper three-fourths of decidua vera.

stratum synoviale,—internal stratum of articular capsule ; synovial membrane, *q.v.*

stratum zonale, cinereum, opticum, lemnisci,—strata of anterior corpora quadrigemina, from surface inwards.

strepsinema (strĕp'sĭnē'mă) *n.* [Gk. *strepsis,* twisting ; *nema,* thread.] Chromosome thread at the strepsitene stage.

strepsitene (strĕp'sĭtēn) *a.* [Gk. *strepsis,* twisting ; *tainia,* band.] *Appl.* stage in meiosis where the diplotene threads appear to be twisted.

streptostylic (strĕp'tōstĭl'ĭk) *a.* [Gk. *streptos,* pliant ; *stylos,* column.] Exhibiting streptostyly, or having quadrate in movable articulation with squamosal ; *cf.* monimostylic.

stria (strī'ă) *n.* [L. *stria,* groove, channel.] A narrow line, streak, band, groove, or channel.

striated (strī'ātĕd) *a.* [L. *striatus,* grooved.] Marked by narrow lines or grooves, usually parallel ; striate.

striated muscle,—voluntary muscle, fibres presenting transverse striations ; bundles of fibres enclosed in a sheath continuous with tendons.

striatum (strīā'tŭm) *a.* [L. *striatus,* grooved.] Corpus striatum, *q.v.*

stridulating organs,—a special apparatus on metathoracic and anterior abdominal segments for producing song of cicadas ; sound-producing organs of various other Arthropoda.

striga (strī'gă) *n.* [L. *striga,* ridge, furrow.] A band of upright, stiff, pointed hairs or bristles ; a bristle-like scale.

strigate (strī'gāt) *a.* [L. *striga,* ridge.] Bearing strigae.

strigilis (strĭj'ĭlĭs) *n.* [L. *strigilis,* curry-comb.] A mechanism for cleaning antennae, at junction of tibia and tarsus on first leg of bees.

strigillose (strĭj'ĭlōs) *a.* [L. *strigilla,* small ridge.] Minutely strigose.

strigose (strī'gōs) *a.* [L. *striga,* ridge.] Covered with stiff hairs ; ridged ; marked by small furrows.

striola (strīō'lă) *n.* [L. *striola,* small channel.] Fine narrow line or streak.

striolate (strī'ōlāt) *a.* [L. *striola,* small channel.] Finely striate.

stripe of Hensen,—*see* Hensen's stripe.

strobila (strŏb'ĭlă) *n.* [Gk. *strobilos,* fir cone.] Stage in development of some Scyphozoa, where from a succession of annular discs embryos take form of a pile of discs separated off in turn ; chain of proglottides of tapeworms.

strobilaceous (strŏb'ĭlā'shŭs) *a.* [Gk. *strobilos,* fir cone.] Cone-shaped ; *pert.* or having strobiles.

strobilation (strŏb'ĭlā'shŭn) *n.* [Gk. *strobilos,* fir cone.] Reproduction by body-segmentation into zooids, as in coelenterates, or into proglottides, as in tape-worms ; strobilisation.

strobile (strŏb'ĭl) *n.* [Gk. *strobilos,* fir cone.] A strobila, or strobilus ; a spike formed of persistent membranous bracts, each having a pistillate flower ; a cone ; an assemblage of sporophylls.

strobiliferous (strŏbĭlĭf'ĕrŭs) *a.* [Gk. *strobilos,* fir cone ; L. *ferre,* to carry.] Producing strobiles.

strobiloid (strŏb'ĭloid) *a.* [Gk. *strobilos,* fir cone ; *eidos,* form.] Strobiliform ; resembling or shaped like a strobilus or cone.

strobilus (strŏb'ĭlŭs) *n.* [Gk. *strobilos,* fir cone.] A strobile ; a cone.

stroma (strō'mă) *n.* [Gk. *stroma,* bedding.] Transparent filmy framework of red blood corpuscles ; protoplasmic body of a plastid ; connective tissue binding and supporting an organ ; in ovary, a soft, vascular, reticular framework in meshes of which ovarian follicles are imbedded; tissue of hyphae, or of fungous cells with host tissue, in or upon which spore-bearing structures may be produced.

stromata,—*plu.* of stroma; short protrusions from a sclerotium, each composed of hyphae, in which perithecia are developed in some thallophytes.

stromate (strō'māt) *a.* [Gk. *stroma*, bedding.] Having, or being within or upon, a stroma; *appl.* fruit-bodies of fungi.

stromatic (strōmăt'ĭk) *a.* [Gk. *stroma*, bedding.] *Pert*, like, in form or nature of, a stroma; stromatiform, stromatous, stromatoid.

stromatolysis (strō'mătŏl'ĭsĭs) *n.* [Gk. *stroma*, bedding; *lysis*, loosing.] Continued action of a haemolysin on cell stroma after haemoglobin has been liberated.

strombuliferous (strŏmbūlĭf'ërŭs) *a.* [*Dim.* of L. *strombus*, spiral shell; *ferre*, to carry.] Having spirally-coiled organs or structures.

strombuliform (strŏm'būlĭfôrm) *a.* [*Dim.* of L. *strombus*, spiral shell; *forma*, shape.] Spirally coiled.

stromoid,—stromatoid, stromatic.

strongyle (strŏn'jĭl), **strongylon** (strŏn'jĭlŏn) *n.* [Gk. *stronggylos*, rounded.] A two-rayed rod sponge spicule rounded at both ends; a nematode.

strophiolate (strŏf'ĭōlāt) *a.* [L. *strophiolum*, small garland.] Having excrescences round hilum.

strophioles (strŏf'ĭōlz) *n. plu.* [L. *strophiolum*, small garland.] Small excrescences arising from various parts of a seed testa, never developed before fertilisation; caruncles.

strophotaxis (strŏfötăk'sĭs) *n.* [Gk. *strophos*, twisted; *taxis*, arrangement.] Twisting movement or tendency, in response to an external stimulus.

struma (stroom'ă) *n.* [L. *struma*, scrofulous tumour.] A swelling on a plant organ.

strumiferous (stroomĭf'ërŭs) *a.* [L. *struma*, tumour; *ferre*, to carry.] Having a struma or strumae.

strumiform (stroom'ĭfôrm) *a.* [L. *struma*, wen; *forma*, shape.] Cushion-like.

strumose (stroomōs'), **strumulose** (stroom'ūlōs) *a.* [L. *struma*, wen.] Having small cushion-like swellings.

strut-roots,—buttress roots, *q.v.*

stupeous (stū'pëŭs), **stupose** (stū'pōs) *a.* [L. *stupa*, tow.] Tow-like; having a tuft of matted filaments.

stupulose (stū'pūlōs) *a.* [L. *stupa*, tow.] Covered with short filaments.

stylar (stī'lăr) *a.* [L. *stylus*, pricker.] *Pert.* a style.

stylate (stī'lāt) *a.* [L. *stylus*, pricker.] Having a style or styles.

style (stīl) *n.* [Gk. *stylos*, pillar; L. *stylus*, pricker.] Slender upper part of pistil, supporting stigma; a rod-like sponge spicule pointed at one end; a calcareous projection from pore tabula in some Millepora; abdominal bristle-like process on male insects; arista, *q.v.*; embolus of spiders; any of the small projections of cingulum of a molar tooth.

stylet (stī'lĕt) *n.* [L. *stylus*, pricker.] Small, pointed bristle-like appendage; unpaired part of terebra or sting, held in position by stylet-sheath; needle-like digit of chelicerae in certain parasitic Acarina.

stylifer (stī'lĭfĕr) *n.* [L. *stylus*, pricker; *ferre*, to carry.] Portion of clasper which carries style.

styliferous (stīlĭf'ërŭs) *a.* [L. *stylus*, pricker; *ferre*, to carry.] Bearing a style; having bristly appendages.

styliform (stī'lĭfôrm) *a.* [L. *stylus*, pricker; *forma*, shape.] Pricker- or bristle-shaped.

styloconic (stī'lökŏn'ĭk) *a.* [Gk. *stylos*, pillar; *konos*, cone.] Having terminal peg on conical base; *appl.* type of olfactory sensilla in insects.

styloglossal (stī'löglŏs'ăl) *a.* [Gk. *stylos*, pillar; *glossa*, tongue.] *Pert.* styloglossus muscle connecting styloid process and tongue.

stylogonidium,—conidium, *q.v.*

stylohyal (stī'lōhī'ăl) *n.* [Gk. *stylos*, pillar; *hyoeides*, *Y*-shaped.] Distal part of styloid process of temporal bone; a small interhyal between hyal and hyomandibular.

stylohyoid (stī'lōhī'oid) *a.* [Gk. *stylos*, pillar; *hyoeides*, *Y*-shaped.] *Appl.* a ligament attached to styloid process and lesser cornu of hyoid; *appl.* a muscle; *appl.* a branch of facial nerve.

styloid (stī'loid) *a.* [Gk. *stylos*, pillar; *eidos*, form.] *Appl.* processes of temporal bone, fibula, radius, ulna.

stylomandibular (stī'lōmăndĭb'ūlăr) *a.* [Gk. *stylos*, pillar; L. *mandibulum*, jaw.] *Appl.* ligamentous band extending from styloid process of temporal bone to angle of lower jaw.

stylomastoid (stī'lōmăs'toid) *a.* [Gk. *stylos*, pillar; *mastos*, breast; *eidos*, like.] *Appl.* foramen between styloid and mastoid processes, also an artery entering that foramen.

stylopharyngeus (stī'lōfărĭn'jēŭs) *n.* [Gk. *stylos*, pillar; *pharyngx*, pharynx.] A muscle extending from the base of styloid process downwards along side of pharynx.

stylopodium (stīlōpō'dĭŭm) *n.* [Gk. *stylos*, pillar; *pous*, foot.] A conical swelling surrounding bases of divaricating styles of Umbelliferae; structure attaching mericarps to carpophore; upper arm, or thigh.

stylospore (stī'lōspōr) *n.* [Gk. *stylos*, pillar; *sporos*, seed.] A stalked spore, as in Coniomycetes; conidium.

stylosporous (stīlŏs'pōrŭs) *a.* [Gk. *stylos*, pillar; *sporos*, seed.] *Pert.* a stylospore or conidium.

stylostegium (stī'lōstē'jĭŭm) *n.* [Gk. *stylos*, pillar; *stege*, roof.] Inner corona of milk-weed plants.

stylostome (stī'lōstōm) *n.* [L. *stylus*, pricker; Gk. *stoma*, mouth.] A tube in skin produced by tissue reaction of host to insertion of chelicerae of a mite.

stylus (stī'lŭs) *n.* [L. *stylus*, pricker.] A style; stylet; simple pointed spicule; molar cusp; pointed process.

subabdominal (sŭb'ăbdŏm'ĭnăl) *a.* [L. *sub.* under; *abdomen*, belly.] Nearly in abdominal region.

subacuminate (sŭb'ăkū'mĭnāt) *a.* [L. *sub*, under; *acumen*, point.] Somewhat tapering.

subaduncate (sŭb'ădŭng'kāt) *a.* [L. *sub*, under; *aduncus*, hooked.] Somewhat crooked.

subaerial (sŭb'āē'rĭăl) *a.* [L. *sub*, under; *aer*, air.] Growing just above surface of ground.

subalpine (sŭbăl'pīn) *a.* [L. *sub*, under; *alpinus*, alpine.] *Appl.* zone below timber line, or to plants or animals growing or living there.

subalternate (sŭb'ăltĕr'nāt, -ôl-) *a.* [L. *sub*, under; *alternus*, one after another.] Tending to change from alternate to opposite.

subanconeus (sŭb'ăngkōnē'ŭs) *n.* [L. *sub*, under; Gk. *angkon*, elbow.] Small muscle extending from triceps to elbow.

subapical (sŭbăp'ĭkăl) *a.* [L. *sub*, under; *apex*, extremity.] Nearly at the apex.

subarachnoid (sŭbărăk'noid) *a.* [L. *sub*, under; Gk. *arachne*, spider's web; *eidos*, form.] *Appl.* a cavity filled with cerebrospinal fluid between arachnoid and pia mater; *appl.* cisternae of brain, and longitudinal septum in region of spinal medulla.

subarborescent (sŭb'ârbŏrĕs'ĕnt) *a.* [L. *sub*, under; *arborescens*, growing into a tree.] Somewhat like a tree.

subarcuate (sŭbâr'kūāt) *a.* [L. *sub*, under; *arcus*, bow.] *Appl.* a blind fossa which extends backwards under superior semicircular canal, in infant skull.

subatrial (sŭbā'trĭăl) *a.* [L. *sub*, under; *atrium*, hall.] Below the atrium; *appl.* longitudinal ridges on inner side of metapleural folds, uniting to form ventral part of atrium, in development of lancelet.

subauricular (sŭb'ôrĭk'ūlăr) *a.* [L. *sub*, under; *auricula*, external ear.] Below the ear.

subaxillary (sŭbăks'ĭlărĭ) *a.* [L. *sub*, under; *axilla*, arm-pit.] *Appl.* outgrowths just beneath the axil.

sub-basal (sŭb-bā'săl) *a.* [L. *sub*, under; Gk. *basis*, foundation.] Situated near the base.

sub-branchial (sŭb-brăng'kĭăl) *a.* [L. *sub*, under; Gk. *brangchia*, gills.] Under the gills.

sub-bronchial (sŭb-brŏng'kĭăl) *a.* [L. *sub*, under; Gk. *brongchos*, windpipe.] Below the bronchials.

subcalcareous (sŭb-kălkā'rēŭs) *a.* [L. *sub*, under; *calx*, lime.] Somewhat limy.

subcalcarine (sŭbkăl'kărĭn) *a.* [L. *sub*, under; *calcar*, spur.] Under the calcarine fissure; *appl.* lingual gyrus of brain.

subcallosal (sŭb'kălō'săl) *a.* [L. *sub*, under; *callus*, hard skin.] *Appl.* a gyrus below corpus callosum.

subcampanulate (sŭb'kămpăn'ūlāt) *a.* [L. *sub*, under; *campanula*, little bell.] Somewhat bell-shaped.

subcapsular (sŭbkăp'sūlăr) *a.* [L. *sub*, under; *capsula*, little chest.] Inside a capsule.

subcardinal (sŭbkâr'dĭnăl) *a.* [L. *sub*, under; *cardo*, hinge.] *Appl.* pair of veins between mesonephroi.

subcarinate (sŭbkăr'ĭnāt) *a.* [L. *sub*, under; *carina*, keel.] Somewhat keel-shaped.

subcartilaginous (sŭb'kârtĭlăj'ĭnŭs) *a.* [L. *sub*, under; *cartilago*, gristle.] Not entirely cartilaginous.

subcaudal (sŭbkôd'ăl) *a.* [L. *sub*, under; *cauda*, tail.] Situate under tail, as a shield or plate.

subcaudate (sŭbkôd'āt) *a.* [L. *sub*, under; *cauda*, tail.] Having a tail-like process.

subcaulescent (sŭb'kôlĕs'ĕnt) *a.* [L. *sub*, under; *caulis*, stalk.] Borne on a very short stem.

subcellular (sŭbsĕl'ūlăr) *a.* [L. *sub*, under; *cellula*, small cell.] *Appl.* functional units within the cell, as chloroplasts, chromosomes, etc.

subcentral (sŭbsĕn'trăl) *a.* [L. *sub*, under; *centrum*, centre.] Nearly central.

subchela (sŭbkē'lă) *n.* [L. *sub*, under; Gk. *chele*, claw.] A prehensile claw of which last joint folds back on preceding, as in Squilla.

subchelate (sŭbkē'lāt) *a.* [L. *sub*, under; Gk. *chele*, claw.] Having subchelae; having imperfect chelae.

subcheliceral (sŭb'kēlĭs'ĕrăl) *a.* [L. *sub*, under; Gk. *chele*, claw; *keras*, horn.] Beneath the chelicerae; *appl.* plate or epistome, for attachment of pharyngeal dilators in certain Acarina.

subchordal (sŭbkôr'dăl) *a.* [L. *sub*, under; *chorda*, cord.] Under the notochord.

subcingulum (sŭbsĭng'gūlŭm) *n.* [L. *sub*, under; *cingulum*, girdle.] The lower lip part of a cingulum or girdle of rotifers.

subclavate (sŭbklā'vāt) *a.* [L. *sub*, under; *clavus*, club.] Somewhat club-shaped.

subclavian (sŭbklā'vĭăn) *a.* [L. *sub*, under; *clavis*, key.] Below clavicle; *appl.* artery, vein, nerve, muscle.

subclimax (sŭbklī'măks) *n.* [L. *sub*, under; Gk. *klimax*, ladder.] Stage in plant succession preceding final stage; proclimax, *q.v.*

subcoracoid (sŭbkôr'ăkoid) *a.* [L. *sub*, under; Gk. *korax*, crow; *eidos*, like.] Below the coracoid.

subcordate (sŭbkôr'dāt) *a.* [L. *sub*, under; *cor*, heart.] Tending to be heart-shaped.

subcorneous (sŭb'kôr'nēŭs) *a.* [L. *sub*, under; *cornu*, horn.] Under a horny layer; slightly horny.

subcortical (sŭbkôr'tĭkăl) *a.* [L. *sub*, under; *cortex*, bark.] Under cortex, or cortical layer; *appl.* cavities under dermal cortex of sponges.

subcosta (sŭbkŏs'tă) *n.* [L. *sub*, under; *costa*, rib.] An auxiliary vein joining costa of insect wing.

subcostal,—below ribs; *appl.* zone, muscles, arteries, plane; *pert.* subcosta.

subcoxa (sŭbkŏk'să) *n.* [L. *sub*, under; *coxa*, hip.] Basal ring, or segment, articulated distally with coxa of arthropod leg; praecoxa, pretrochantin.

subcrenate (sŭbkrē′nāt) *a.* [L. *sub*, under; L.L. *crena*, notch.] Tending to have rounded scallops, as a leaf margin.

subcrureal (sŭbkroor′ēăl) *a.* [L. *sub*, under; *crus*, leg.] *Appl.* subcrureus or articularis genus muscle, extending from lower femur to knee.

subcubical (sŭbkū′bĭkăl) *a.* [L. *sub*, under; *cubus*, cube.] *Appl.* cells not quite so long as broad, as those lining alveoli of thyroid.

subcutaneous (sŭb′kūtā′nēŭs) *a.* [L. *sub*, under; *cutis*, skin.] Under the cutis or skin; *appl.* parasites living just under skin; *appl.* inguinal or external abdominal ring.

subcuticular (sŭb′kūtĭk′ūlăr) *a.* [L. *sub*, under; *cuticula*, cuticle.] Under the cuticle, epidermis, or outer skin.

subcutis (sŭbkū′tĭs) *n.* [L. *sub*, under; *cutis*, skin.] A loose layer of connective tissue between corium and deeper tissues of skin; tela subjunctiva; inner layer of cutis of mushrooms, under the epicutis.

subdentate (sŭbdĕn′tāt) *a.* [L. *sub*, under; *dens*, a tooth.] Slightly toothed or notched.

subdermal (sŭbdĕr′măl) *a.* [L. *sub*, under; Gk. *derma*, skin.] Beneath the skin; beneath derma.

subdorsal (sŭbdôr′săl) *a.* [L. *sub*, under; *dorsum*, back.] Situated almost on dorsal surface.

subdural (sŭbdū′răl) *a.* [L. *sub*, under; *durus*, hard.] *Appl.* the space separating spinal dura mater from arachnoid.

subepicardial (sŭb′ĕpĭkâr′dĭăl) *a.* [L. *sub*, under; Gk. *epi*, upon; *kardia*, heart.] *Appl.* areolar tissue attaching visceral layer of pericardium to muscular wall of heart.

subepiglottic (sŭb′ĕpĭglŏt′ĭk) *a.* [L. *sub*, under; Gk. *epi*, upon; *glotta*, tongue.] Beneath epiglottis.

subepithelial (sŭb′ĕpĭthē′lĭăl) *a.* [L. *sub*, under; Gk. *epi*, upon; *thallein*, to grow.] Below epithelium; *appl.* plexus of cornea; *appl.* endothelium: Débove's membrane, *q.v.*

suber (sū′bĕr) *n.* [L. *suber*, cork-tree.] Cork tissue.

subereous (sūbē′rēŭs) *a.* [L. *suber*, cork-tree.] Of corky texture.

suberic (sūbĕr′ĭk) *a.* [L. *suber*, cork-tree.] *Pert.* or derived from cork.

suberiferous (sūbĕrĭf′ĕrŭs) *a.* [L. *suber*, cork-tree; *ferre*, to bear.] Cork-producing.

suberification (sū′bĕrĭfĭkā′shŭn) *n.* [L. *suber*, cork-tree; *facere*, to make.] Conversion into cork tissue.

suberin (sū′bĕrĭn) *n.* [L. *suber*, cork-tree.] The waxy substance developed in a thickened cell-wall, characteristic of cork tissues.

suberisation (sū′bĕrĭzā′shŭn) *n.* [L. *suber*, cork-tree.] Modification of cell-walls due to suberin formation.

suberose (sū′bĕrōs) *a.* [L. *suber*, cork-tree.] With corky, waterproof texture. (sŭbĕrōs′) *a.* [L. *sub*, under; *erosus*, gnawed.] As if somewhat gnawed.

sub-esophageal,— sub-oesophageal.

subfusiform (sŭbfū′zĭfôrm) *a.* [L. *sub*, under; *fusus*, spindle; *forma*, shape.] Somewhat spindle-shaped; elliptic-fusiform; boletiform.

subgalea (sŭbgā′lēă) *n.* [L. *sub*, under; *galea*, helmet.] Part of maxilla, at base of stipes, of insects.

subgeniculate (sŭb′jĕnĭk′ūlāt) *a.* [L. *sub*, under; *geniculum*, little knee.] Somewhat bent.

subgenital (sŭbjĕn′ĭtăl) *a.* [L. *sub*, under; *genitalis*, genital.] Below reproductive organs; *appl.* shallow pit or pouch beneath gonad in Aurelia; *appl.* portico formed by fusion of subgenital pouches of Discomedusae; *appl.* plate formed by ninth abdominal sternite and coxites, hypandrium of certain insects.

subgerminal (sŭbgĕr′mĭnăl) *a.* [L. *sub*, under; *germen*, bud.] Beneath the germinal disc; *appl.* cavity.

subglenoid (sŭbglē′noid) *a.* [L. *sub*, under; Gk. *glene*, socket; *eidos*, form.] Beneath glenoid cavity.

subglossal (sŭbglŏs′ăl) *a.* [L. *sub*, under; Gk. *glossa*, tongue.] Beneath the tongue.

subharpal (sŭbhâr′păl) *a.* [L. *sub*, under; Gk. *harpe*, sickle.] *Appl.* plate in area below harpe in insects.

subhyaloid (sŭbhī′ăloid) *a.* [L. *sub*, under; Gk. *hyalos*, glass; *eidos*, like.] Beneath hyaloid membrane or fossa of eye.

subhymenium (sŭb′hīmē′nĭŭm) *n.* [L. *sub*, under; Gk. *hymen*, membrane.] Layer of small cells between trama and hymenium in gill of agarics.

subhyoid (sŭbhī′oid) *a.* [L. *sub*, under; Gk. *hyoeides*, Υ-shaped.] Below hyoid at base of tongue.

subicle,—subiculum of fungi.

subiculum (sŭbĭk′ūlŭm) *n.* [L. *subiculum*, under layer.] A mycelial covering of substrate; part of the hippocampus bordering the hippocampal fissure; bony ridge bounding oval opening in interior wall of middle ear.

subimago (sŭb′ĭmā′gō) *n.* [L. *sub*, under; *imago*, likeness.] A stage between pupa and imago in life-history of some insects; pseudimago.

subinguinal (sŭbĭn′gwĭnăl) *a.* [L. *sub*, under; *inguen*, groin.] Situated below a horizontal line at level of great saphenous vein termination; *appl.* lymph-glands.

subjugal (sŭbjoog′ăl) *a.* [L. *sub*, under; *jugum*, yoke.] Below jugal or cheek bone.

subjugular (sŭbjoog′ūlăr, -jŭg′-) *a.* [L. *sub*, under; *jugulum*, collar-bone.] *Appl.* a ventral fish-fin nearly far enough forward to be jugular.

sublanceolate (sŭblăn′sēōlāt) *a.* [L. *sub*, under; *lanceolatus*, speared.] Tending to be narrow and to taper towards both ends.

sublaryngeal (sŭblărĭn′jēăl) *a.* [L. *sub*, under; Gk. *laryngx*, larynx.] Situate below larynx.

sublenticular (sŭblĕntĭk′ūlăr) *a.* [L. *sub*, under; *lenticula*, small lentil.] Somewhat lens-shaped.

subliminal (sŭblĭm′ĭnăl) *a.* [L. *sub*, under; *limen*, threshold.] Inadequate for perceptible response, *appl.* stimuli; *cf.* limen.

sublingua (sŭblĭng′gwă) *n.* [L. *sub*, under; *lingua*, tongue.] A single or double projection or fold beneath tongue, in some mammals.

sublingual (sŭblĭng′gwăl) *a.* [L. *sub*, under; *lingua*, tongue.] Beneath tongue; *appl.* gland, artery, etc.; *appl.* ventral pharyngeal gland, in Hymenoptera.

sublitoral (sŭblĭt′ŏrăl) *a.* [L. *sub*, under; *litus*, sea-shore.] Below litoral; *appl.* shallow water zone to about 100 fathoms; sublittoral.

sublobular (sŭblŏb′ūlăr) *a.* [L. *sub*, under; *lobus*, lobe.] *Appl.* veins at base of lobules of liver.

sublocular (sŭblŏk′ūlăr) *a.* [L. *sub*, under; *loculus*, compartment.] Somewhat locular or cellular.

submalleate (sŭbmăl′ēăt) *a.* [L. *sub*, under; *malleus*, hammer.] Somewhat hammer-shaped; *appl.* trophi of rotifer mastax.

submandibular (sŭb′măndĭb′ūlăr) *a.* [L. *sub*, under; *mandibulum*, jaw.] Beneath lower jaw; *appl.* gland and duct; submaxillary.

submarginal (sŭbmâr′jĭnăl) *a.* [L. *sub*, under; *margo*, margin.] Placed nearly at margin.

submarginate (sŭb′mâr′jĭnāt) *a.* [L. *sub*, under; *margo*, margin.] *Appl.* a bordering structure near a margin.

submaxilla (sŭb′măksĭl′ă) *n.* [L. *sub*, under; *maxilla*, jaw.] Mandible.

submaxillary (sŭb′măksĭl′ărĭ) *a.* [L. *sub*, under; *maxilla*, jaw.] Beneath lower jaw; *appl.* duct, ganglion, gland, triangle; mandibular.

submedian (sŭbmē′dĭăn) *a.* [L. *sub*, under; *medius*, middle.] *Appl.* tooth or vein next median.

submental (sŭbmĕn′tăl) *a.* [L. *sub*, under; *mentum*, chin.] Beneath chin; *appl.* artery, glands, triangle, vibrissae; *pert.* submentum.

submentum (sŭbmĕn′tŭm) *n.* [L. *sub*, under; *mentum*, chin.] Basal part of labium of insects.

submersed (sŭbmĕrsd′) *a.* [L. *submergere*, to submerge.] *Appl.* plants growing entirely under water.

submicron (sŭbmĭk′rŏn) *n.* [L. *sub*, under; Gk. *mikros*, small.] A particle seen as a separate disc only with aid of ultramicroscope; *cf.* amicron.

submucosa (sŭb′mūkō′să) *n.* [L. *sub*, under; *mucosus*, mucous.] Layer of tissue under mucous membrane.

subnasal (sŭbnā′zăl) *a.* [L. *sub*, under; *nasus*, nose.] Beneath the nose.

subneural (sŭbnū′răl) *a.* [L. *sub*, under; Gk. *neuron*, nerve.] *Appl.* blood vessel in annelids; *appl.* gland and ganglion of nervous system of tunicates.

subnotochordal (sŭb′nōtŏkôr′dăl) *a.* [L. *sub*, under; Gk. *noton*, back; *chorde*, cord.] *Appl.* a rod, the hypochord, ventral to true notochord.

suboccipital (sŭb′ŏksĭp′ĭtăl) *a.* [L. *sub*, under; *occiput*, back of head.] *Appl.* muscles, nerve, triangle, under occipitals of skull.

subocular shelf,—ingrowth from suborbitals supporting eyeball of fishes.

suboesophageal (sŭbēsŏfăj′ēăl) *a.* [L. *sub*, under; Gk. *oisophagos*, gullet.] Below the gullet; *appl.* anterior ganglion of ventral nerve cord; subesophageal.

subopercular (sŭb′ŏpĕr′kūlăr) *a.* [L. *sub*, under; *operculum*, cover.] Under operculum of fishes, or shell-lid of molluscs.

suboperculum (sŭb′ŏpĕr′kūlŭm) *n.* [L. *sub*, under; *operculum*, cover.] The subopercle, a membrane bone of operculum of fishes.

suboptic (sŭbŏp′tĭk) *a.* [L. *sub*, under; Gk. *optikos*, relating to sight.] Below the eye.

suboral (sŭbō′răl) *a.* [L. *sub*, under; *os*, mouth.] Below or near mouth.

suborbital (sŭbôr′bĭtăl) *a.* [L. *sub*, under; *orbis*, circle.] *Appl.* structures below orbit.

subovate (sŭbō′vāt) *a.* [L. *sub*, under; *ovum*, egg.] Suboval; subovoid; somewhat oval or egg-shaped.

subpalmate (sŭbpăl′māt) *a.* [L. *sub*, under; *palma* palm.] Tending to become palmate; *appl.* leaves.

subparietal (sŭb′părī′ĕtăl) *a.* [L. *sub*, under; *paries*, wall.] Beneath parietals; *appl.* sulcus which is lower boundary of parietal lobe.

subpectinate (sŭbpĕk′tĭnāt) *a.* [L. *sub*, under; *pecten*, comb.] Tending to be comb-like in structure.

subpedunculate (sŭb′pēdŭng′kūlāt) *a.* [L. *sub*, under; L.L. *pedunculus*, little foot.] Resting on very short stalk.

subpericardial (sŭb′pĕrĭkâr′dĭăl) *a.* [L. *sub*, under; Gk. *peri*, round; *kardia*, heart.] Under pericardium.

subperitoneal (sŭb′pĕrĭtŏnē′ăl) *a.* [L. *sub*, under; Gk. *peritonaion*, something stretched round.] *Appl.* connective tissue under peritoneum.

subpetiolar (sŭbpĕt′ĭŏlăr) *a.* [L. *sub*, under; *petiolus*, little foot.] Within petiole or leaf-stalk.

subpetiolate (sŭbpĕt′ĭŏlāt) *a.* [L. *sub*, under; *petiolus*, small foot.] Almost sessile.

subpharyngeal (sŭb′fărĭn′jēăl) *a.* [L. *sub*, under; Gk. *pharyngx*, pharynx.] Below the throat.

subphrenic (sŭbfrĕn′ĭk) *a.* [L. *sub*, under; Gk. *phren*, midriff.] Below the diaphragm.

subpial (sŭbpī′ăl) *a.* [L. *sub*, under; *pia*, kind.] Under the pia mater.

subpleural (sŭbploor′ăl) *a.* [L. *sub*, under; Gk. *pleura*, side.] Beneath inner lining of thoracic wall.

subpubic (sŭbpū′bĭk) *a.* [L. *sub*, under; *pubes*, adult.] Below the pubic region; *appl.* arcuate ligament.

subpulmonary (sŭbpŭl′mŏnărĭ) *a.* [L. *sub*, under; *pulmo*, lung.] Beneath the lungs.

subradicate (sŭbrăd′ĭkāt) *v.* [L. *sub*, slightly; *radicari*, to take root.] To have a slight downward extension of base, as of stipe.

subradius (sŭbrā′dĭŭs) *n.* [L. *sub*, under; *radius*, ray.] In radiate animals, a radius of fourth order, that between adradius and perradius, or between adradius and interradius.

subradular (sŭbrăd′ūlăr) *a.* [L. *sub*, under; *radere*, to scrape.] *Appl.* organ containing nerve endings, situated at anterior end of odontophore.

subramose (sŭbrā′mōs) *a.* [L. *sub*, under; *ramus*, branch.] Slightly branching.

subreniform (sŭbrĕn′ĭfôrm) *a.* [L. *sub*, under; *renes*, kidneys; *forma*, shape.] Slightly kidney-shaped.

subretinal (sŭbrĕt′ĭnăl) *a.* [L. *sub*, under; *rete*, net.] Beneath retina.

subrostral (sŭbrŏs′trăl) *a.* [L. *sub*, under; *rostrum*, beak.] Below the beak or rostrum; *appl.* a cerebral fissure.

subsacral (sŭbsā′krăl) *a.* [L. *sub*, under; *sacrum*, sacred.] Below the sacrum.

subsartorial (sŭb′sârtō′rĭăl) *a.* [L. *sub*, under; *sartor*, tailor.] *Appl.* plexus under sartorius of thigh.

subscapular (sŭbskăp′ūlăr) *a.* [L. *sub*, under; *scapula*, shoulder-blade.] Beneath the scapula; *appl.* artery, muscles, nerves, etc.

subsclerotic (sŭb′sklērŏt′ĭk) *a.* [L. *sub*, under; Gk. *skleros*, hard.] Beneath sclera; between sclerotic and choroid layers of eye.

subscutal (sŭbskūtăl) *a.* [L. *sub*, under; *scutum*, shield.] Under a scutum; *appl.* cephalic gland or Géné's organ, *q.v.*, in ticks.

subsere (sŭb′sēr) *n.* [L. *sub*, under; *serere*, to put in a row.] Plant succession on denuded area; secondary succession.

subserous (sŭbsē′rŭs) *a.* [L. *sub*, under; *serum*, whey.] Beneath a serous membrane; *appl.* areolar tissue.

subserrate (sŭbsĕr′āt) *a.* [L. *sub*, under; *serra*, saw.] Somewhat notched or saw-toothed.

subsessile (sŭbsĕs′ĭl) *a.* [L. *sub*, under; *sedere*, to sit.] Nearly sessile; with almost no stalk.

subsidiary cells,—additional modified epidermal cells lying outside guard-cells.

subspatulate (sŭbspăt′ūlāt) *a.* [L. *sub*, under; *spatula*, spoon.] Somewhat spoon-shaped.

subspinous (sŭbspī′nŭs) *a.* [L. *sub*, under; *spina*, spine.] Tending to become spiny.

substantia (sŭbstăn′shĭă) *n.* [L. *substantia*, substance.] Substance; matter.

substantia adamantina,—enamel of teeth.

substantia alba,—white matter of brain and spinal cord.

substantia eburnea,—dentine.

substantia gelatinosa,—gelatinous neuroglia, with some nerve cells, in spinal cord.

substantia grisea,—grey matter of brain and spinal cord.

substantia nigra,—a semilunar layer of grey cells of mid-brain.

substantia ossea,—cement of teeth; crusta petrosa.

substantia reticularis, — anterior and lateral reticular formations in medulla oblongata.

substantia spongiosa,—cancellous tissue of bone.

substantive variation,—changes in actual constitution or substance of parts; *cf.* meristic variation.

substernal (sŭbstĕr′năl) *a.* [L. *sub*, under; *sternum*, breast-bone.] Below the sternum.

substipitate (sŭbstĭp′ĭtāt) *a.* [L. *sub*, under; *stipes*, stalk.] Having an extremely short stem.

substomatal,—hypostomatic.

substrate (sŭb′strāt) *n.* [L. *sub*, under; *stratum*, layer.] Inert substance containing or receiving a nutrient solution; the substance upon which an enzyme acts, zymolyte; a substance undergoing oxidation utilised in plant respiration, a respiratory substrate; substratum.

substratose (sŭbstrā'tōs) *a.* [L. *sub*, under; *stratum*, layer.] Slightly or indistinctly stratified.

substratum (sŭbstrā'tŭm) *n.* [L. *sub*, under; *stratum*, layer.] The base to which a stationary animal or a plant is fixed; substrate, *q.v.*

subtectal (sŭbtĕk'tăl) *a.* [L. *sub*, under; *tectum*, roof.] *Pert.* alisphenoid of fish skull.

subtegminal (sŭbtĕg'mĭnăl) *a.* [L. *sub*, under; *tegmen*, covering.] Under the tegmen or inner coat of a seed.

subtentacular canals,—two prolongations of echinoderm coelom.

subthalamus,—hypothalamus, *q.v.*; part of hypothalamus excluding optic chiasma and region of mamillary bodies.

subthoracic (sŭb'thōrăs'ĭk) *a.* [L. *sub*, under; Gk. *thorax*, breast.] Not so far forward as to be called thoracic; *appl.* certain fish-fins.

subtrapezoidal (sŭb'trăpēzoid'ăl) *a.* [L. *sub*, under; Gk. *trapezion*, small table; *eidos*, form.] Somewhat trapezoid-shaped.

subtruncate (sŭbtrŭng'kāt) *a.* [L. *sub*, under; *truncatus*, maimed.] Terminating rather abruptly.

subtypical (sŭbtĭp'ĭkăl) *a.* [L. *sub*, under; *typus*, image.] Deviating slightly from type.

subulate (sū'būlāt) *a.* [L. *subula*, awl.] Awl-shaped; narrow and tapering from base to a fine point; *appl.* leaves, as of onion.

subumbellate (sŭbŭm'bĕlāt) *a.* [L. *sub*, under; *umbella*, small shade.] Tending to an umbellate arrangement with peduncles arising from a common centre.

subumbonal (sŭbŭm'bōnăl) *a.* [L. *sub*, under; *umbo*, boss.] Beneath or anterior to umbo of bivalve shell.

subumbrella (sŭb'ŭmbrĕl'ă) *n.* [L. *sub*, under; *umbra*, shade.] Concave inner surface of medusoid bell.

subuncinate (sŭbŭn'sĭnāt) *a.* [L. *sub*, under; *uncus*, hook.] Having a somewhat hooked process; somewhat hook-shaped.

subungual (sŭbŭng'gwăl) *a.* [L. *sub*, under; *unguis*, nail.] Under a nail, claw, or hoof; hyponychial.

subunguis (sŭbŭng'gwĭs) *n.* [L. *sub*, under; *unguis*, nail.] The ventral scale of a claw.

subuniversal veil,—protoblema.

subvaginal (sŭbvăj'ĭnăl) *a.* [L. *sub*, under; *vagina*, sheath.] Within or under a sheath.

subvertebral (sŭbvĕr'tĕbrăl) *a.* [L. *sub*, under; *vertebra*, turning joint.] Under the spinal column.

subvital (sŭb'vītăl) *a.* [L. *sub*, under; *vitalis*, vital.] Deficient in vitality; *appl.* genes causing a mortality of less than fifty per cent; *cf.* semilethal.

subzonal (sŭbzō'năl) *a.* [L. *sub*, under; *zona*, belt.] *Appl.* layer of cells internal to zona radiata.

subzygomatic (sŭbzī'gōmăt'ĭk) *a.* [L. *sub*, under; Gk. *zygon*, yoke.] Under the cheek-bone.

succate (sŭk'āt) *a.* [L. *succus*, sap.] Containing juice; juicy; succose, succous.

succession (sŭksĕsh'ŏn) *n.* [L. *successio*, succession.] A geological, ecological, or seasonal sequence of species; the development of plant communities; chronological distribution of organisms in a given area; lagging of sex-chromosomes behind euchromosomes in moving to the poles after meiosis.

succiferous (sŭksĭf'ĕrŭs) *a.* [L. *succus*, sap; *ferre*, to carry.] Sap-conveying.

succiput (sŭk'sĭpŭt) *n.* [L. *sub*, under; *caput*, head.] Area below foramen of neck in insects.

succise (sŭksīs') *a.* [L. *succisus*, lopped off.] Abrupt; appearing as if a part were cut off.

succubous (sŭk'ūbŭs) *a.* [L. *sub*, under; *cubare*, to lie down.] With each leaf covering part of that under it.

succulent (sŭk'ūlĕnt) *a.* [L. *succus*, sap.] Full of juice or sap.

succus (sŭk'ŭs) *n.* [L. *succus*, juice, sap.] The juice of a plant; fluid secreted by glands.

sucker (sŭk'ĕr) *n.* [A.S. *sucan*, to suck.] A stem-branch, first subterranean and then aerial, which may ultimately form an independent plant; haustorium, *q.v.*; an organ adapted for creating a vacuum, in some animals for purposes of ingestion, in others to assist in locomotion or attachment.

sucking disc,—a disc assisting in attachment, as at end of echinoderm tube-foot.

sucrose (sū'krōs) *n.* [F. *sucre*, sugar.] Cane sugar, $C_{12}H_{22}O_{11}$.

suctorial (sŭktō'rĭăl) *a.* [L. *sugere*, to suck.] Adapted for sucking; furnished with suckers; *appl.* a pad of fat in relation with buccinator, supposed to assist in sucking.

sudation (sūdā'shŭn) *n.* [L. *sudatio*, perspiration.] Discharge of water and substances in solution, as through pores; sweating.

sudor (sū'dŏr) *n.* [L. *sudor*, sweat.] Perspiration.

sudoriferous (sū'dŏrĭf'ĕrŭs) *a.* [L. *sudor*, sweat; *ferre*, to carry.] Conveying, producing, or secreting sweat; *appl.* glands and their ducts; sudoriparous.

sufflaminal (sŭflă'mĭnăl) *a.* [L. *sufflamen*, blast.] *Appl.* a plate partly forming gill-chamber in certain extinct fishes.

suffrutex (sŭf'rootĕks) *n.* [L. *sub*, under; *frutex*, shrub.] An undershrub.

suffruticose (sŭfroot'ĭkōs) *a.* [L. *sub*, under; *frutex*, shrub.] Somewhat shrubby.

sugent (sū'jĕnt), **sugescent** (sūjĕs'ĕnt) *a.* [L. *sugere*, to suck.] Suctorial.

sulcate (sŭl'kāt) *a.* [L. *sulcus*, furrow.] Furrowed; grooved.

sulcation (sŭlkā'shŭn) *n.* [L. *sulcatio*, ploughing.] Fluting; formation of ridges and furrows, as in elytra.

sulcus (sŭl'kŭs) *n.* [L. *sulcus*, furrow.] A groove; *appl.* cerebral grooves; those of heart, tongue, cornea, bones, etc.; stomodaeal groove of Anthozoa; longitudinal flagellum groove of Dinoflagellata; sulculus.

summation (sŭmā'shŭn) *n.* [L. *summa*, sum total.] Combined action of either simultaneous or successive subliminal stimuli or impulses which produces an excitatory or inhibitory response.

summer egg,—thin-shelled, quickly developing egg of some fresh-water forms, laid in spring or summer; *cf.* winter egg.

supercarpal (sūpĕrkâr'păl, soo-) *a.* [L. *super*, over; *carpus*, wrist.] Upper carpal or above the carpus.

supercilia (sūpĕrsĭl'ĭă, soo-) *n. plu.* [L. *supercilia*, eyebrows.] The eyebrows.

superciliary (sūpĕrsĭl'ĭărĭ, soo-) *a.* [L. *super*, over; *cilia*, eyelids.] *Pert.* eyebrows; above orbit.

superciliary arches,—two arched elevations below frontal eminences.

superficial (sūpĕrfĭsh'ăl, soo-) *a.* [L. *super*, over; *facies*, face.] On, or near, the surface; *appl.* arteries, veins, etc.

superfoetation (sū'pĕrfētā'shŭn) *n.* [L. *super*, over; *foetus*, big with.] Fertilisation of ovary by more than one kind of pollen; successive fertilisation, of two ova of different oestrous periods, in the same uterus; superfetation; hypercyesis.

superglottal (sūpĕrglŏt'ăl, soo-) *a.* [L. *super*, over; Gk. *glotta*, tongue.] Above the glottis.

superior (sūpē'rĭŏr, soo-) *a.* [L. *superior*, upper.] Upper; higher; growing or arising above another organ; anterior.

superlinguae (sū'pĕrlĭng'gwē, soo-) *n. plu.* [L. *super*, over; *lingua*, tongue.] Paired lobes of hypopharynx in certain insects.

superparasite,—hyperparasite, *q.v.*

supersacral (sūpĕrsā'krăl, soo-) *a.* [L. *super*, over; *sacrum*, sacred.] Above the sacrum.

supersonic (sū'pĕrsŏn'ĭk, soo-) *a.* [L. *super*, over; *sonare*, to sound.] *Appl.* sounds of high frequency inaudible by human ear, as emitted by certain animals.

supersphenoidal (sū'pĕrsfēnoid'ăl, soo-) *a.* [L. *super*, over; Gk. *sphen*, wedge; *eidos*, form.] Above sphenoid bone.

supervolute (sūpĕrvŏlūt', soo-) *a.* [L. *super*, over; *volvere*, to roll.] Having a plaited and rolled arrangement in the bud.

supinate (sū'pĭnāt) *a.* [L. *supinus*, bent backwards.] Inclining or leaning backwards.

supination (sūpĭnā'shŭn) *n.* [L. *supinus*, bent backward.] Movement of arm by which palm of hand is turned upwards; *cf.* pronation.

supinator brevis and **longus**,—two arm muscles used in supination.

supplemental air,—volume of air which can be expelled from the lungs after normal breathing out; reserve air.

supplementary type,—hypotype, *q.v.*

suppression (sŭprĕsh'ŭn) *n.* [L. *suppressio*, a keeping back.] Non-development of an organ or part.

suppressor,—*appl.* genes which nullify the phenotypic effect of another gene.

supra-acromial (sū'pră-ăkrō'mĭăl, soo-) *a.* [L. *supra*, above; Gk. *akros*, summit; *omos*, shoulder.] Above the acromion of the shoulder-blade.

supra-anal (sū'pră-ā'năl, soo-) *a.* [L. *supra*, above; *anus*, anus.] Suranal: above anus or anal region.

supra-angular, — surangular, *q.v.*

supra-auricular (sū'pră-ôrĭk'ūlăr, soo-) *a.* [L. *supra*, above; *auris*, ear.] Above the auricle or ear; *appl.* feathers.

suprabranchial (sū'prăbrăng'kĭăl, soo-) *a.* [L. *supra*, above; *branchiae*, gills.] Above the gills.

suprabuccal (sū'prăbŭk'ăl, soo-) *a.* [L. *supra*, above; *bucca*, cheek.] Above cheek and mouth.

suprabulbar (sū'prăbŭl'băr) *a.* [L. *supra*, above; *bulbus*, bulb.] *Appl.* region between hair-bulb and fibrillar region of hair.

supracallosal (sū'prăkălō'săl, soo-) *a.* [L. *supra*, above; *callosus*, hard.] *Appl.* a gyrus on upper surface of corpus callosum of brain.

supracaudal (sū'prăkôd'ăl, soo-) *a.* [L. *supra*, above; *cauda*, tail.] Above the tail or caudal region.

supracellular (sū'prăsĕl'ūlăr, soo-) *a.* [L. *supra*, above; *cellula*, small cell.] *Appl.* structures, fibrous or laminar, originating from many cells.

supracerebral (sūprăsĕr'ēbrăl) *a.* [L. *supra*, above; *cerebrum*, brain.] *Appl.* lateral pharyngeal glands, as in Hymenoptera.

suprachoroid (sū'prăkō'roid, soo-) *a.* [L. *supra*, above; Gk. *chorion*, skin.] Over the choroid; between choroid and sclera; *appl.* lamina; suprachorioid.

supraclavicle (sū'prăklăv'ĭkl, soo-) *n.* [L. *supra*, above; *clavicula*, small key.] Supracleithrum, a bone of shoulder girdle of fishes.

supraclavicular (sū'prăklăvĭk'ūlăr, soo-) *a.* [L. *supra*, above; *clavicula*, small key.] Above or over the clavicle; *appl.* nerves.

supracleithrum (sū'prăklī'thrŭm, soo-) *n.* [L. *supra*, above; Gk. *kleithron*, key.] Supraclavicle.

supracondylar (sū'prăkŏn'dĭlăr, soo-) *a.* [L. *supra*, above; Gk. *kondylos*, knob.] Above a condyle; *appl.* ridge and process.

supracostal (sū'prăkŏs'tăl, soo-) *a.* [L. *supra*, above; *costa*, rib.] Over or externally to the ribs.

supracranial (sū'prăkrā'nĭăl, soo-) *a.* [L. *supra*, above; Gk. *kranion*, skull.] Over or above the skull.

supradorsal (sū'prădôr'săl, soo-) *a.* [L. *supra*, above; *dorsum*, back.] On or over the back; *appl.* small cartilaginous elements in connection with primitive vertebral column.

supra-episternum (sū'pră-ĕp'ĭstĕr-nŭm) *n.* [L. *supra*, above; Gk. *epi*, upon; L. *sternum*, breast-bone.] Upper sclerite of episternum in some insects.

supra-ethmoid (sū'pră-ĕth'moid, soo-) *n.* [L. *supra*, above; Gk. *ethmos*, sieve; *eidos*, form.] Dermethmoid, a bone external to mesethmoid.

supraglenoid (sū'prăglē'noid, soo-) *a.* [L. *supra*, above; Gk. *glene*, socket.] Above the glenoid cavity; *appl.* tuberosity at apex of glenoid cavity.

suprahyoid (sū'prăhī'oid, soo-) *a.* [L. *supra*, above; Gk. *hyoeides*, Υ-shaped.]. Over the hyoid bone; *appl.* aponeurosis, glands, muscles.

supralabial (sū'prălā'bĭăl, soo-) *a.* [L. *supra*, above; *labium*, lip.] On the lip; *appl.* scutes or scales.

supralitoral (sū'prălĭt'ŏrăl, soo-) *a.* [L. *supra*, above; *litus*, seashore.] *Pert.* seashore above high-water-mark, or spray zone; supralittoral.

supraloral (sū'prălō'răl, soo-) *a.* [L. *supra*, above; *lorum*, thong.] Above the loral region, as in birds, snakes.

supramastoid crest,—ridge at upper boundary of mastoid region of temporal bone; temporal line.

supramaxillary (sū'prămăksĭl'ărĭ, soo-) *a.* [L. *supra*, above; *maxilla*, jaw.] *Pert.* upper jaw.

suprameatal (sū'prămēā'tăl, soo-) *a.* [L. *supra*, above; *meatus*, passage.] *Appl.* triangle and spine over external acoustic meatus.

supranasal (sū'prănā'zăl, soo-) *a.* [L. *supra*, above; *nasus*, nose.] Over nasal bone or nose.

supraoccipital (sū'prăŏksĭp'ĭtăl, soo-) *n.* [L. *supra*, above; *occiput*, back of head.] A large median bone of upper occipital region.

supraocular (sū'prăŏk'ūlăr, soo-) *a.* [L. *supra*, above; *oculus*, eye.] Over or above the eye; *appl.* scales.

supraoesophageal (sū'prăēsŏfăj'ëăl, soo-) *a.* [L. *supra*, above; Gk. *oisophagos*, gullet.] Above or over the gullet; supraesophageal.

supraorbital (sū'prăôr'bĭtăl, soo-) *a.* [L. *supra*, above; *orbis*, circle.] Above orbital cavities; *appl.* process, artery, foramen, nerve, vein, etc. *n.* A skull bone in certain fishes.

suprapatellar (sū'prăpătĕl'ăr, soo-) *a.* [L. *supra*, above; *patella*, kneepan.] *Appl.* bursa between upper part of patella and femur.

suprapericardial,—*see* ultimobranchial.

suprapharyngeal (sū'prăfarĭn'jëal, soo-) *a.* [L. *supra*, above; Gk. *pharyngx*, pharynx.] Above or over pharynx.

suprapubic (sū'prăpū'bĭk, soo-) *a.* [L. *supra*, above; *pubes*, adult.] Above the pubic bone.

suprapygal (sū'prăpī'găl, soo-) *a.* [L. *supra*, above; Gk. *pyge*, rump.] Above the pygal bone.

suprarenal (sū'prărē'năl, soo-) *a.* [L. *supra*, above; *renes*, kidneys.] Situated above kidneys; adrenal; *appl.* arteries, glands, veins, plexus.

suprarenal bodies, capsules, or **glands,**—paired endocrine glands situate near, or apposed to, kidneys of vertebrates; adrenals.

suprarenin (sū'prărē'nĭn) *n.* [L. *supra*, above; *renes*, kidneys.] Synthetic adrenaline.

suprarostral (sū'prărŏs'trăl, soo-) *a.* [L. *supra*, above; *rostrum*, beak.] *Appl.* a cartilaginous plate anterior to trabeculae in Amphibia.

suprascapula (sū'prăskăp'ūla, soo-) *n.* [L. *supra*, above; *scapula*, shoulder-blade.] A cartilage of dorsal part of pectoral girdle in rays; an incompletely ossified extension of scapula of amphibians and certain reptiles.

suprascapular (sū'prăskăp'ūlăr, soo-) *a.* [L. *supra*, above; *scapula*, shoulder - blade.] Above the shoulder-blade; *appl.* artery, ligament, nerve.

supraseptal (sū'prăsĕp'tăl, soo-) *a.* [L. *supra*, above; *septum*, partition.] *Appl.* two plates diverging from interorbital septum.

suprasphenoid (sū'prăsfē'noid, soo-) *n.* [L. *supra*, above; Gk. *sphen*, wedge.] Membrane bone dorsal to sphenoid cartilage.

suprasphenoidal (sū'prăsfēnoid'ăl, soo-) *a.* [L. *supra*, above; Gk. *sphen*, wedge.] Above sphenoid bone of skull.

supraspinal (sū'prăspī'năl, soo-) *a.* [L. *supra*, above; *spina*, spine.]

Above or over spinal column ; *appl.* a ligament ; above ventral nerve cord, in insects ; *appl.* a cord of connective tissue and pulsating vessel.

supraspinatous (sū'prăspīnā'tŭs, soo-) *a.* [L. *supra*, above ; *spina*, spine.] *Appl.* scapular fossa and fascia for origin of supraspinatus.

supraspinatus,—shoulder-muscle inserted into proximal part of greater tubercle of humerus.

suprastapedial (sū'prăstăpē'dĭăl, soo-) *n.* [L. *supra*, above ; *stapes*, stirrup.] The part of columella of ear above stapes, homologous with mammalian incus.

suprasternal (sū'prăstĕr'năl, soo-) *a.* [L. *supra*, above ; *sternum*, breastbone.] Over or above breast-bone ; *appl.* a slit-like space in cervical muscle ; *appl.* supernumerary sternal elements in some mammals ; *appl.* body-plane.

suprastigmal (sū'prăstĭg'măl, soo-) *a.* [L. *supra*, above ; *stigma*, mark.] Above a stigma or breathing-pore of insects.

supratemporal (sū'prătĕm'pŏrăl, soo-) *a.* [L. *supra*, above ; *tempora*, temples.] *Pert.* upper temporal region of skull ; *appl.* bone, arch, fossa.

suprathoracic (sū'prăthōrăs'ĭk, soo-) *a.* [L. *supra*, above ; Gk. *thorax*, breast.] Above thoracic region.

supratidal (sū'prătī'dăl) *a.* [L. *supra*, above ; A.S. *tid*, time.] Above high-tide mark ; *appl.* spray zone, or to organisms living there.

supratonsillar (sū'prătŏn'sĭlăr, soo-) *a.* [L. *supra*, above ; *tonsillae*, tonsils.] *Appl.* a small depression in lymphoid mass of palatine tonsil.

supratrochlear (sū'prătrŏk'lēăr, soo-) *a.* [L. *supra*, above ; Gk. *trochlea*, pulley.] Over trochlear surface ; *appl.* nerve, foramen, lymph glands.

supratympanic (sū'prătĭmpăn'ĭk, soo-) *a.* [L. *supra*, above ; *tympanum*, drum.] Above the eardrum.

sural (sū'răl) *a.* [L. *sura*, calf of leg.] *Pert.* calf of leg ; *appl.* arteries and nerves.

suranal,—supra-anal, *q.v.*

surangular (sūrăng'gūlar) *n.* [L. *supra*, above ; *angulus*, angle.] Supra-angular ; a bone of lower jaw of some fishes, reptiles, and birds.

surculose (sŭr'kūlōs) *a.* [L. *surculus*, shoot.] Surculous ; surculigerous ; *appl.* plants producing suckers first underground, thence aerial and forming independent plants ; bearing suckers ; stoloniferous.

surculus (sŭr'kūlŭs) *n.* [L. *surculus*, shoot.] Underground shoot, ultimately aerial and independent ; sucker.

surcurrent (sŭrkŭr'ënt) *a.* [L. *supra*, above ; *currere*, to run.] Proceeding or prolonged up a stem, *opp.* decurrent.

surrenal,—suprarenal.

suscept (sŭs'sĕpt) *n.* [L. *suscipere*, to undergo.] A plant or animal susceptible to disease ; a species harbouring a virus.

suspensor (sŭspĕn'sŏr) *n.* [L. *suspendere*, to hang up.] A modified portion of a hypha from which a gametangium or a zygospore is suspended ; zygosporophore ; a chain of cells developed from hypobasal segment of angiosperm zygote, attaching embryo to embryo sac ; occurring in modified form in other plants ; terminal filament of ovariole.

suspensorium (sŭspĕnsō'rĭŭm) *n.* [L. *suspendere*, to hang up.] The upper part of hyoid arch from which lower jaw is suspended ; suspensory structure of hypopharynx ; the skeletal support of a gonopodium.

suspensory (sŭspĕn'sŏrĭ) *a.* [L. *suspendere*, to hang up.] *Pert.* a suspensorium ; serving for suspension ; *appl.* various ligaments.

sustentacular (sŭstĕntăk'ūlăr) *a.* [L. *sustentaculum*, prop, support.] Supporting ; *appl.* connective tissue acting as a supporting framework for an organ ; *appl.* cells, fibres.

sustentaculum lienis,—fold of peritoneum supporting spleen.

sustentaculum tali,—projection of calcaneus supporting middle articular surface for ankle bone.

sustentator (sŭs'tĕntā'tŏr) *n.* [L. *sustinere*, to sustain.] Sustentor or hooked cremaster of Lepidoptera.

sutural (sū'tūrăl, soo-) *a.* [L. *sutura*, seam.] *Pert.* a suture; *appl.* dehiscence taking place at a suture.

sutural bones,—irregular isolated bones occurring in the course of sutures, especially in lambdoidal suture and posterior fontanelle; ossa suturarum, Wormian bones.

suture (sū'tūr, soo-) *n.* [L. *sutura*, seam.] Line of junction of two parts immovably connected; line of union of shell-wall and edge of septum, as in ammonites; line of junction between sclerites; an immovable articulation of bone as in skull; dehiscence line.

Swammerdam's glands [*J. Swammerdam*, Dutch naturalist]. Periganglionic glands, *q.v.*

Swammerdam's vesicle,—the spermatheca of gastropods.

swarm (swôrm) *n.* [A.S. *swearm*, swarm.] A large number of small motile organisms viewed collectively; departure of a number of bees from one hive to form another.

swarm cell,—a motile isogamete, of certain fungi.

swarm spore,—zoospore, *q.v.*

swimmerets,—paired abdominal appendages of crustaceans, functional partly for swimming.

swimming bells,—nectocalyces of siphonophores, serving to propel the colony.

swimming or **swim bladder,** — air bladder of fishes, developed as a diverticulum of the alimentary canal.

swimming funnel,—tube of Dibranchiata through which water is expelled from mantle cavity, expulsion providing means of propulsion.

swimming ovaries,—groups of ripe ova of Acanthocephala, detached from ovary and floating in body cavity.

swimming-plates,—in Ctenophora, ciliated comb-like plates, arranged in eight equidistant bands or combribs, propellers of the organism.

syconium (sīkō'nĭŭm) *n.* [Gk. *sykon*, fig.] A syconus: a composite, succulent, receptacular fruit.

sylva (sĭl'vă) *n.* [L. *sylva*, forest.] Forest of a region; forest-trees collectively.

sylvestral (sĭlvĕs'trăl) *a.* [L. *sylvestris*, *pert.* forest.] *Appl.* flora of woodlands and forest.

sylvian (sĭl'vĭăn) *a.* [*F. Sylvius* or *de la Boe*, French anatomist]. *Appl.* structures described by Sylvius, as aqueduct (*q.v.*) fissure (lateral cerebral fissure), fossa, veins, etc.

symbiont (sĭm'bĭŏnt) *n.* [Gk. *syn*, with; *bioun*, to live.] One of the partners in symbiosis; symbion, symbiote.

symbiosis (sĭmbĭō'sĭs) *n.* [Gk. *symbioun*, to live together.] A condition in which two animals, two plants, or plant and animal, symbiotes or symbionts, live in mutually beneficial partnership; the living together of organisms belonging to more than one species.

symbiote,—symbiont, *q.v.*

symbiotic (sĭmbĭŏt'ĭk) *a.* [Gk. *symbioun*, to live together.] Living in beneficial partnership; living together, whether in actual contact or not, with mutual benefit or antagonism.

symmetrical (sĭmĕt'rĭkăl) *a.* [Gk. *syn*, with; *metron*, measure.] Regularly shaped; divisible into exactly similar parts.

symmetry (sĭm'ĕtrĭ) *n.* [Gk. *syn*, with; *metron*, measure.] State of divisibility into similar halves; regularity of form; similarity of structure on each side of an axis, central, dorsoventral, or anteroposterior. *See* bilateral and radial symmetry.

sympathetic (sĭmpăthĕt'ĭk) *a.* [Gk. *syn*, with ; *pathos*, feeling.] *Appl.* system of nerves supplying viscera and blood-vessels, and intimately connected with spinal and some cerebral nerves ; *appl.* segmental nerves supplying spiracles in insects ; *appl.* coloration in imitation of surroundings.

sympathin (sĭm'păthĭn) *n.* [Gk. *syn*, with ; *pathos*, feeling.] Substance yielded by sympathetic nerves and having physiological properties of adrenaline.

sympathoblast (sĭm'păthŏblăst) *n.* [Gk. *syn*, with ; *pathos*, feeling ; *blastos*, bud.] A cell which develops into a neurone of sympathetic ganglia.

sympathochromaffin (sĭm'păthŏkrō'-măfĭn) *a.* [Gk. *syn*, with ; *pathos*, feeling ; *chroma*, colour ; L. *affinis* related.] *Appl.* cells forming sympathoblasts and chromaffin bodies.

sympathomimetic (sĭm'păthŏmĭ-mĕt'ĭk) *a.* [Gk. *syn*, with ; *pathos*, feeling ; *mimetikos*, imitating.] *Appl.* substances which produce effects like those produced by sympathetic stimulation.

sympatric (sĭmpăt'rĭk) *a.* [Gk. *syn*, with ; *patra*, native land.] Having the same, or overlapping, areas of geographical distribution. *Opp.* allopatric.

sympetalous (sĭmpĕt'ălŭs) *a.* [Gk. *syn*, with ; *petalon*, leaf.] Having a tubular corolla formed by union of petals ; gamopetalous.

symphily (sĭm'fĭlĭ) *n.* [Gk. *syn*, with ; *philein*, to love.] Commensalism, of symphiles, with mutual liking.

symphoresis (sĭmfŏr'ēsĭs) *n.* [Gk. *symphoresis*, a bringing together.] Conveyance collectively, as movement of spermatid group to a Sertoli cell.

symphyantherous, — synantherous, *q.v.*

symphyllodium (sĭm'fĭlō'dĭŭm) *n.* [Gk. *syn*, with ; *phyllon*, leaf ; *eidos*, form.] A structure formed by coalescence of external coats of two or more ovules ; a compound ovuliferous scale.

symphyllous,—gamophyllous, *q.v.*

symphyogenesis (sĭm'fĭŏjĕn'ēsĭs) *n.* [Gk. *symphyein*, to grow together ; *genesis*, descent.] Development of an organ from union of two others.

symphysial (sĭmfĭz'ĭăl) *a.* [Gk. *symphysis*, a growing together.] Symphyseal ; symphysian ; *pert.* a symphysis.

symphysis (sĭm'fĭsĭs) *n.* [Gk. *symphysis*, a growing together.] The coalescence of parts ; the line of junction of two pieces of bone separate in early life, as pubic symphysis ; slightly movable articulation with bony surfaces connected by fibrocartilage.

symplast (sĭm'plăst) *n.* [Gk. *syn*, with ; *plastos*, formed.] Multinucleate body formed by nuclear fragmentation of a single energid ; coenocyte, *q.v.*

symplastic (sĭmplăs'tĭk) *a.* [Gk. *symplassein*, to mould together.] Being formed with co-ordinated development of parts ; *appl.* growth of contiguous cells without displacement of cell-walls.

symplectic (sĭmplĕk'tĭk) *n.* [Gk. *symplektos*, plaited.] A bone of fish skull between quadrate and hyomandibular.

symplex (sĭm'plĕks) *n.* [Gk. *symplektos*, plaited.] The combination of the active substance and protoplasmic protein which constitutes an enzyme ; *cf.* agon, pheron.

sympodial (sĭmpō'dĭăl) *a.* [Gk. *syn*, with ; *pous*, foot.] *Pert.* or resembling a sympodium in principle ; *appl.* branching, growth of axillary shoots when apical budding has ceased.

sympodite (sĭm'pŏdīt) *n.* [Gk. *syn*, with ; *pous*, foot.] The protopodite of Crustacea.

sympodium (sĭmpō'dĭŭm) *n.* [Gk. *syn*, with ; *pous*, foot.] A primary axis consisting of a line connecting bases of consecutive branchings.

synacme (sĭnăk'mē) *n.* [Gk. *syn*, with ; *akme*, prime.] Condition when stamens and pistils mature simultaneously ; synanthesis ; synacmy.

synaesthesia (sĭnēsthē'zĭă) *n.* [Gk. *syn*, with ; *aisthesis*, sensation.] The accompaniment of a sensation due to stimulation of the appropriate receptor, as sound, by a sensation characteristic of another sense, as colour.

synangium (sĭnăn'jĭŭm) *n.* [Gk. *syn*, with ; *anggeion*, vessel.] A compound sporangium in which sporangia are coherent, as in some ferns ; anterior portion of truncus arteriosus.

synantherous (sĭnăn'thērŭs) *a.* [Gk. *syn*, with ; *antheros*, flowery.] Having anthers united to form a tube.

synanthesis,—synacme, *q.v.*

synanthous (sĭnăn'thŭs) *a.* [Gk. *syn*, with ; *anthos*, flower.] Having flowers and leaves appearing simultaneously ; having flowers united together.

synanthy (sĭnăn'thĭ) *n.* [Gk. *syn*, with ; *anthos*, flower.] Adhesion of flowers usually separate.

synaporium (sĭnăpō'rĭŭm) *n.* [Gk. *syn*, with ; *aporia*, want.] An animal association formed owing to unfavourable environmental conditions or disease.

synaposematic (sĭnăp'ösēmăt'ĭk) *a.* [Gk. *syn*, with ; *apo*, from ; *sema*. sign.] Having warning colours in common ; *appl.* mimicry of a more powerful species as means of defence.

synapse (sĭnăps') *n.* [Gk. *synapsis*, union.] The connection of one nerve cell and another through the medium of terminal branchings of dendrons or axons ; the area of contiguity between two nerve cells ; *cf.* ephapse.

synapsid (sĭnăp'sĭd) *a.* [Gk. *synapsis*, union.] *Appl.* skulls with supra- and infra-temporal fossae united in a single fossa.

synapsis (sĭnăp'sĭs) *n.* [Gk. *synapsis*, union.] Stage or period from contraction of nucleus to segmentation of spireme into chromosomes ; syndesis, *q.v.* ; synapse, *q.v.*

synaptene (sĭnăp'tēn) *a.* [Gk. *synapsis*, union ; *tainia*, band.] *Appl.* zygotene stage in meiosis ; synaptotene.

synaptic membrane,—a membrane intervening between nerve-ending and muscle fibre supplied by it, also between processes of one neurone and those of another.

synapticula (sĭnăptĭk'ūlă) *n.* [Gk. *synaptos*, joined.] One of small rods connecting septa of mushroom-coral, or like structure.

synaptospermous (sĭnăptöspĕr'mŭs) *a.* [Gk. *synaptos*, joined ; *sperma*, seed.] Having seeds germinating close to the parent plant.

synaptospore (sĭnăp'töspōr) *n.* [Gk. *synaptos*, joined ; *sporos*, seed.] Aggregate spore ; clinospores joined together.

synaptychus (sĭnăp'tĭkŭs) *n.* [Gk. *syn*, with ; *a*, together ; *ptyche*, plate.] Aptychus in which paired plates are permanently united.

synarthrosis (sĭn'ârthrō'sĭs) *n.* [Gk. *syn*, with ; *arthron*, joint.] An articulation in which bone surfaces are in almost direct contact, fastened together by connective tissue or hyaline cartilage, with no appreciable motion.

synascus (sĭnăs'kŭs) *n.* [Gk. *syn*, together ; *askos*, bag.] An ascogonium containing a number of asci.

syncarp (sĭn'kârp) *n.* [Gk. *syn*, with ; *karpos*, fruit.] A syncarpium : an aggregate fruit with united carpels.

syncarpous (sĭnkâr'pŭs) *a.* [Gk. *syn*, with ; *karpos*, fruit.] Bearing a collective fruit ; with carpels united.

syncarpy (sĭnkâr'pĭ) *n.* [Gk. *syn*, with ; *karpos*, fruit.] Condition of having carpels united to form a compound ovary.

syncaryo-,—*see* synkaryo-.

syncerebrum (sĭnsĕr'ēbrŭm) *n.* [Gk. *syn*, with ; L. *cerebrum*, brain.] A secondary brain formed by union with brain of one or more of ventral cord ganglia, in some arthropods.

syncheimadia (sĭnkīmăd'ĭă) *n. plu.* [Gk. *syn*, with; *cheimadion*, winter dwelling.] Societies overwintering together.

synchondrosis (sĭn'kŏndrō'sĭs) *n.* [Gk. *syn*, with; *chondros*, cartilage.] A synarthrosis in which the connecting medium is cartilage.

synchorology (sĭn'kōrŏl'öjĭ) *n.* [Gk. *syn*, with; *choros*, place; *logos*, discourse.] Study of the distribution of plant or animal associations; geographical distribution of communities.

synchronic (sĭnkrŏn'ĭk) *a.* [Gk. *syn*, with; *chronos*, time.] Contemporary; existing at the same time, *appl.* species, etc. *Opp.* allochronic.

syncladous (sĭnklā'dŭs) *a.* [Gk. *syn*, together; *klados*, branch.] With offshoots or branchlets in tufts; *appl.* certain mosses.

synconium (sĭnkō'nĭŭm) *n.* [Gk. *syn*, with; *konos*, cone.] Hollow inflorescence axis of fig; synconus; syconium.

syncraniate (sĭnkrā'nĭăt) *a.* [Gk. *syn*, with; *kranion*, skull.] Having vertebral elements fused with skull.

syncranterian (sĭnkrăntē'rĭăn) *a.* [Gk. *syn*, with; *kranteres*, wisdom teeth.] With teeth in a continuous row.

syncryptic (sĭnkrĭp'tĭk) *a.* [Gk. *syn*, with; *kryptos*, hidden.] *Appl.* animals alike, though unrelated, through common protective resemblance to surroundings.

syncytiotrophoblast,—syncytium.

syncytium (sĭnsĭt'ĭŭm) *n.* [Gk. *syn*, with; *kytos*, hollow.] A multinucleated mass of protoplasm without differentiation into cells; outer stratum of trophoblast of mammalian ovum, the syncytiotrophoblast; plasmodium; *cf.* coenocyte.

syndactyl (sĭndăk'tĭl) *a.* [Gk. *syn*, with; *daktylos*, digit.] With fused digits, as in many birds.

syndactylism (sĭndăk'tĭlĭzm) *n.* [Gk. *syn*, with; *daktylos*, digit.] Whole or part fusion of two or more digits.

syndesis (sĭndē'sĭs) *n.* [Gk. *syndesis*, a binding together.] Conjugation or fusion of homologous chromosomes in meiosis; synapsis.

syndesmology (sĭn'dĕsmŏl'öjĭ) *n.* [Gk. *syndesmos*, ligament; *logos*, discourse.] The branch of anatomy dealing with ligaments and articulations.

syndesmosis (sĭn'dĕsmō'sĭs) *n.* [Gk. *syndesmos*, ligament.] A slightly movable articulation, with bony surfaces connected by an interosseous ligament; *cf.* symphysis.

syndrome (sĭn'drōm) *n.* [Gk. *syn*, together; *dromein*, to run.] A group of concomitant symptoms.

synecology (sĭnēkŏl'öji) *n.* [Gk. *syn*, together; *oikos*, household; *logos*, discourse.] Ecology of plant or of animal communities.

synecthry (sĭnĕk'thrĭ) *n.* [Gk. *syn*, with; *echthros*, hatred.] Commensalism of synecthrans with mutual dislike.

synema,—synnema, *q.v.*

synenchyma (sĭnĕng'kĭmă) *n.* [Gk. *syn*, together; *engchyma*, infusion.] Fungous tissue composed of laterally closely joined hyphae.

syneresis (sĭnĕr'ĕsĭs) *n.* [Gk. *syn*, together; *ereidein*, to press.] Contraction of a gel with expression of liquid; contraction of clotting blood and separation of serum.

synergic (sĭnĕr'jĭk) *a.* [Gk. *synergos*, co-operator.] Operating together; synergetic; *appl.* muscles which combine with prime movers and fixation muscles in movement; *appl.* system of muscles and nerves affecting a particular movement; *appl.* certain hormones.

synergid (sĭnĕr'jĭd) *n.*, **sinergidae** (sĭnĕr'jĭdē) *plu.* [Gk. *synergos*, co-operator.] Two help-cells lying beside ovum at micropylar end of embryo-sac of an ovule.

synethogametism (sĭnē'thögămĕt'ĭzm) *n.* [Gk. *synethes*, well suited; *gametes*, spouse.] Ability of gametes to fuse; gametal compatibility. *Opp.* asynethogametism.

syngametic (sĭn'gămĕt'ĭk) *a.* [Gk. *syn*, together; *gametes*, spouse.] *Pert.* union of morphologically similar cells; isogamic.

syngamy (sĭn'gămĭ) *n.* [Gk. *syn*, with; *gamos*, marriage.] Sexual reproduction; fusion of gametes.

syngenesious (sĭn'jĕnē'sĭŭs) *a.* [Gk. *syn*, with; *genesis*, descent.] Having stamens united in cylindrical form by anthers; with anthers united.

syngenesis (sĭnjĕn'ĕsĭs) *n.* [Gk. *syn*, with; *genesis*, descent.] Sexual reproduction; theory that germs of all human beings, past, present, and future, were created simultaneously, and that there are germs within germs *ad infinitum*; coenogenesis, *q.v.*

syngenetic (sĭn'jĕnĕt'ĭk) *a.* [Gk. *syn*, with; *genesis*, descent.] Sexually reproduced; descended from the same ancestors.

syngnaths (sĭn'gnăths) *n. plu.* [Gk. *syn*, with; *gnathos*, jaw.] Paired jaws or mouth-plates of Stelleroids.

syngonic (sĭngŏn'ĭk) *a.* [Gk. *syn*, with; *gone*, seed.] Producing male and female gametes in the same gone.

syngynous,—epigynous, *q.v.*

synhesma (sĭnhĕs'mă) *n.* [Gk. *syn*, with; *hesmos*, a swarm.] A swarm; a swarming society.

synizesis (sĭnĭzē'sĭs) *n.* [Gk. *synizesis*, contraction.] The attraction-figure associated with syndesis; contracted phase of nucleus during synapsis; myosis or contraction of pupil.

synkaryon (sĭnkăr'ĭŏn) *n.* [Gk. *syn*, with; *karyon*, nucleus.] Zygote nucleus resulting from fusion of pronuclei.

synkaryophyte (sĭnkăr'ĭöfīt) *n.* [Gk. *syn*, with; *karyon*, nucleus; *phyton*, plant.] Diploid plant; sporophyte.

synkaryotic (sĭn'kărĭŏt'ĭk) *a.* [Gk. *syn*, with; *karyon*, nucleus.] Diploid, *appl.* nucleus.

synnema (sĭn'nē'mă) *n.* [Gk. *syn*, with; *nema*, thread.] Bundle or column of fused thread-like structures, as of conidiophores or of hyphae; coremium; the united stamen filaments of a monadelphous flower.

synochreate, synocreate (sĭnŏk'-rëăt) *a.* [Gk. *syn*, with; L. *ocrea*, legging.] With stipules united, enclosing stem in a sheath.

synoecious (sĭnē'sĭŭs), **synoicous** (sĭnoik'ŭs) *a.* [Gk. *syn*, with; *oikos*, house.] Having antheridia and archegonia on same receptacle, or stamens and pistils on same flower, or male and female flowers on same capitulum.

synoekete (sĭnēkēt') *n.* [Gk. *syn*, with; *oiketes*, dweller.] A tolerated guest in a colony.

synoikous,—synoecious.

synosteosis (sĭn'ŏstëō'sĭs) *n.* [Gk. *syn*, with; *osteon*, bone.] Ossification from two or more centres in the same bone, as from diaphysis and epiphyses in long bones; anchylosis, *q.v.*

synostosis,—synosteosis.

synotic tectum,—in higher vertebrates, a cartilaginous arch between otic capsules representing cartilaginous roof or tegmen of cranium in lower vertebrates.

synovia (sĭnō'vĭă) *n.* [Gk. *syn*, with; L. *ovum*, egg.] Viscid, glairy secretion of synovial membrane.

synovial membrane,—inner stratum of articular capsule, connective tissue secreting a lubricating fluid for joints.

synoviparous (sĭn'ōvĭp'ărŭs) *a.* [Gk. *syn*, with; L. *ovum*, egg; *parere*, to beget.] Secreting synovia.

synpelmous (sĭnpĕl'mŭs) *a.* [Gk. *syn*, with; *pelma*, sole.] Having two tendons united before they go to separate digits.

synpolydesmic (sĭn'pŏlĭdĕs'mĭk, -dĕz-) *a.* [Gk. *syn*, with; *polys*, many; *desmos*, bond.] *Appl.* cyclomorial scales made up of fused monodesmic scales with continuous dentine layer.

synsacrum (sĭnsā'krŭm) *n.* [Gk. *syn*, with; L. *sacrum*, sacred.] A mass of fused vertebrae supporting the pelvic girdle of birds and of certain extinct saurians.

synsepalous (sĭnsĕp'ălŭs) *a.* [Gk. *syn*, with ; F. *sépale*, sepal.] With calyx composed of fused or united sepals.

synspermous (sĭnspĕr'mŭs) *a.* [Gk. *syn*, with ; *sperma*, seed.] Having several seeds united.

synsporous (sĭnspō'rŭs) *a.* [Gk. *syn*, with ; *sporos*, seed.] Propagating by cell conjugation, as in algae.

syntagmata (sĭntăg'mătă) *n. plu.* [Gk. *syn*, together ; *tagma*, corps.] Groups of units or segments forming well-defined regions, as head, thorax, and abdomen of arthropods ; *cf.* tagmata.

syntechnic (sĭntĕk'nĭk) *n.* [Gk. *syn*, with ; *techne*, skill.] Resemblance in unrelated animals, due to environment ; convergence.

syntelome (sĭntĕl'ōm) *n.* [Gk. *syn*, with ; *telos*, end.] A compound telome.

syntenosis (sĭntĕnō'sĭs) *n.* [Gk. *syn*, with ; *tenon*, sinew.] Tendinous articulation.

syntrophoblast (sĭntrŏf'ōblăst) *n.* [Gk. *syn*, together ; *trephein*, to nourish ; *blastos*, bud.] Trophoblastic syncytium ; plasmoditrophoblast.

syntropic (sĭntrŏp'ĭk) *a* [Gk. *syn*, together ; *trope*, turn.] Turning or arranged in the same direction, as ribs on one side.

syntype (sĭn'tīp) *n.* [Gk. *syn*, with ; *typos*, pattern.] Any one specimen of a series used to designate a species when holotype and paratypes have not been selected ; cotype.

synusia (sĭnoo'sĭă) *n.* [Gk. *synousia*, a living together.] A plant community of relatively uniform composition, living in a particular environment and forming part of a phytocoenosis, *q.v.*

synzoospore (sĭnzō'ŏspōr) *n.* [Gk. *syn*, with ; *zoon*, animal ; *sporos*, seed.] A group of zoospores which do not separate.

syringeal (sĭrĭn'jēăl) *a.* [Gk. *syringx*, pipe.] *Pert.* the syrinx.

syringium (sĭrĭn'jĭŭm) *n.* [Gk. *syringx*, pipe.] A syringe-like organ for ejection of disagreeable fluid of some insects.

syringograde (sĭrĭng'gōgrād) *a.* [Gk. *syringx*, pipe ; L. *gradus*, step.] Jet-propelled, moving by alternate suction and ejection of water through siphons, as Loligo and Salpa.

syrinx (sĭr'ĭngks) *n.* [Gk. *syringx*, pipe.] Vocal organ of birds, at base of trachea.

systaltic (sĭstăl'tĭk) *a.* [Gk. *systellein*, to draw in.] Contractile ; alternately contracting and dilating.

systemic circulation,—course of blood from left ventricle through the body to right atrium, *opp.* pulmonary or lesser circulation.

systemic heart,—heart of invertebrates, and auricle and ventricle of left side of heart of higher vertebrates. *Opp.* respiratory heart.

systilius,—systylius, *q.v.*

systole (sĭs'tōlē) *n.* [Gk. *systole*, drawing together.] Contraction of heart causing circulation of blood ; contraction of any contractile cavity. *Opp.* diastole.

systrophe (sĭs'trōfĭ) *n.* [Gk. *systrophe*, a gathering.] An aggregation of starch grains in chloroplasts, induced by illumination.

systylius (sĭstī'lĭŭs) *n.* [Gk. *syn*, with ; *stylos*, column.] The columella-lid of some mosses.

systylous (sĭstī'lŭs) *a.* [Gk. *syn*, with ; *stylos*, column.] With coherent styles ; with fixed columella-lid, as in mosses.

syzygium (sĭzĭj'ĭŭm) *n.* [Gk. *syn*, with ; *zygon*, yoke.] Group of associated gregarines.

syzygy (sĭz'ĭjĭ) *n.* [Gk. *syn*, with ; *zygon*, yoke.] A close suture of two adjacent arms, found in crinoids ; a number of individuals, two to five, adhering in strings in association of gregarines ; reunion of chromosome fragments at meiosis.

T

tables (tā'blz) *n. plu.* [L. *tabula*, board.] Outer and inner layers of flat compact bones, especially of skull.

tabula (tăb'ūlă) *n.*, **tabulae** (tăb'ūlē) *plu.* [L. *tabula*, table.] Horizontal partitions traversing vertical canals of Hydrocorallina and of tabulate corals.

tabular (tăb'ūlăr) *a.* [L. *tabula*, table.] Arranged in a flat surface or table; flattened, as certain cells.

tabulare (tăb'ūlā'rē) *n.* [L. *tabula*, table.] Skull bone posterior to parietal in some vertebrates.

tachyauxesis (tăk'ĭôksē'sĭs) *n.* [Gk. *tachys*, quick; *auxesis*, growth.] Relatively quick growth; growth of a part at a faster rate than that of the whole. *Opp.* bradyauxesis.

tachygen (tăk'ijĕn) *n.* [Gk. *tachys*, quick; *gennaein*, to produce.] A structure originating abruptly in evolution.

tachygenesis (tăk'ĭjĕn'ësĭs) *n.* [Gk. *tachys*, quick; *genesis*, descent.] Development with omission of certain embryonic stages, as in some crustaceans, or of nymphal stages, as in some insects; accelerated development, in phylogeny. *Opp.* bradygenesis.

tachysporous (tăkĭs'pörŭs) *a.* [Gk. *tachys*, quick; *sporos*, seed.] Dispersing seeds quickly.

tachytelic (tăk'ĭtĕl'ĭk) *a.* [Gk. *tachys*, quick; *telos*, fulfilment.] Evolving at a rate faster than the standard rate, *opp.* bradytelic; *cf.* horotelic.

tactic (tăk'tĭk) *a.* [Gk. *taktos*, arranged.] *Pert.* taxis, *q.v.*; *appl.* movements from place to place in response to stimuli; *appl.* stimuli inducing locomotion.

tactile (tăk'tĭl) *a.* [L. *tactilis*, that may be touched.] Serving the sense of touch, as special end-organs or tangoreceptors; *appl.* cells, cones, corpuscles, discs, hairs, etc.

tactor (tăk'tŏr) *n.* [L. *tactus*, touch.] Tactile end-organ; tangoreceptor.

tactual (tăk'tūăl) *a.* [L. *tactus*, touch.] *Pert.* sense of touch.

taenia (tē'nĭă) *n.* [L. *taenia*, ribbon.] A band, as of nerve or of muscle; ligula, *q.v.*

taeniate (tē'nĭāt) *a.* [L. *taenia*, ribbon.] Ribbon-like; striped.

taenidium (tēnĭd'ĭŭm) *n.*, **taenidia** *plu.* [Gk. *tainia*, ribbon; *idion*, *dim.*] Spiral ridge of cuticle strengthening the chitinous layer of insect tracheae and tracheoles.

taenioid (tē'nĭoid) *a.* [Gk. *tainia*, ribbon; *eidos*, form.] Ribbon-shaped; like a tape-worm.

taenioles (tē'nĭōlz) *n. plu.* [L. *taeniola*, small ribbon.] Four longitudinal gastric ridges of a scyphula.

tagmata (tăg'mătă) *n. plu.* [Gk. *tagma*, corps.] Units; parts; segments; molecular groups; *cf.* syntagmata.

taiga (tīgă) *n.* [Russ.] Northern coniferous forest zone, especially in Siberia.

talocalcaneal (tāl'ökălkā'nëăl) *a.* [L. *talus*, ankle-bone; *calcaneum*, heel.] *Pert.* talus and calcaneus; *appl.* articulation, ligaments.

talocrural (tā'lökroor'ăl) *a.* [L. *talus*, ankle; *crus*, leg.] *Pert.* ankle and shank bones; *appl.* articulation: the ankle joint.

talon (tăl'ŏn) *n.* [F., from L. *talus*, ankle.] Claw of bird of prey; posterior heel of molar tooth.

taloscaphoid (tāl'öskăf'oid) *a.* [L. *talus*, ankle; Gk. *skaphe*, boat; *eidos*, form.] *Pert.* talus and scaphoid bone.

talus (tā'lŭs) *n.* [L. *talus*, ankle.] The ankle-bone or astragalus.

tandem,—*appl.* satellites separated from each other by a constriction.

tangoreceptor (tăng'görësĕp'tŏr) *n.* [L. *tangere*, to touch; *receptor*, receiver.] A receptor sensitive to slight pressure differences.

tapesium (tăpē'zĭŭm) *n.* [Gk. *tapes*, rug.] A dense outer mycelium bearing ascus-producing hyphae.

tapetal (tăpē'tăl) *a.* [L. *tapete*, carpet.] *Pert.* tapetum; *appl.* cells.

tapetum (tăpē'tŭm) *n.* [L. *tapete*, carpet.] Outer and posterior part of choroid; pigment layer of retina; main body of fibres of corpus callosum; special nutritive layer investing sporogenous tissue of sporangium.

taphrophyte (tăf'röfīt) *n.* [Gk. *taphros*, ditch; *phyton*, plant.] Ditch-dwelling plant.

tap-root (tăp'root) *n.* [M.E. *tappe*, short pipe; A.S. *wyrt*, root.] An elongated parent root with secondary roots in acropetal succession; persistent primary root.

tarsal (târ'săl) *a.* [Gk. *tarsos*, sole of foot.] *Pert.* tarsus, of foot and eyelid; *appl.* arteries, bones, glands.

tarsale (tărsā'lē) *n.*, **tarsalia** (tărsā'lĭă) *plu.* [Gk. *tarsos*, sole of foot.] Ankle-bones.

tarsi (târ'sī) *n. plu.* [Gk. *tarsos*, sole of foot.] *Plu.* of tarsus; two thin elongated plates of dense connective tissue helping to support the eyelid.

tarsomeres (târ'sömērz) *n. plu.* [Gk. *tarsos*, sole of foot; *meros*, part.] The two parts of dactylopodite in spiders, basitarsus and telotarsus.

tarsometatarsal (târ'sömĕt'ătâr'săl) *a.* [Gk. *tarsos*, sole of foot; *meta*, beyond.] *Pert.* an articulation of tarsus with metatarsus.

tarsometatarsus (târ'sömĕt'ătâr'sŭs) *n.* [Gk. *tarsos*, sole of foot; *meta*, beyond.] A short straight bone of bird's leg formed by fusion of distal row of tarsals with second to fifth metatarsals.

tarsophalangeal (târ'söfălăn'jëăl) *a.* [Gk. *tarsos*, sole of foot; *phalangx*, line of battle.] *Pert.* tarsus and phalanges.

tarsus (târ'sŭs) *n.* [Gk. *tarsos*, sole of foot.] Ankle-bones, usually consisting of two rows; segment of leg distal to tibia, in insects; telotarsus or second dactylopodite in spiders; fibrous connective tissue plate of eyelid.

tartareous (târtā'rëŭs) *a* [L.L. *tartarum*, an acid salt.] Having a rough and crumbling surface.

tassel (tăsl) *n.* [O.F. *tasel*, clasp.] Male inflorescence of maize plant; appendix colli of goat, sheep, pig, etc.

taste-bud,—an end-organ of taste, consisting of a flask-shaped group of gustatory and supporting cells found on tongue and adjacent parts; a gustatory calyculus.

tauidion (tôĭd'ĭŏn) *n.* [Gk. *tau*, T; *idion*, *dim.*] Part of cranial floor of Palaeospondylus.

tautomeric (tô'tömĕr'ĭk) *a.* [Gk. *tauto*, the same; *meros*, part.] *Pert.* the same part; *appl.* cells, neurones with axis cylinders passing into white matter of same side of spinal cord.

tautonym (tô'tönĭm) *n.* [Gk. *tauto*, the same; *onyma*, name.] The same name given to a genus and one of its species or subspecies.

tautotype (tô'tötīp) *n.* [Gk. *tautos*, the same; *typos*, pattern.] A genotype by virtue of tautonymy.

taxeopodous (tăk'sëŏp'ödŭs) *a.* [Gk. *taxis*, arrangement; *pous*, foot.] Having proximal and distal tarsal bones in straight lines parallel to limb axis.

taxis (tăk'sĭs) *n.* [Gk. *taxis*, arrangement.] A tendency of an organism towards (positive) or away from (negative) a source of stimulus; a directed reaction of a motile animal; *cf.* tropism.

Tawara's node [*S. Tawara*, Japanese pathologist]. The atrioventricular node.

taxon (tăk'sŏn) *n.* [Gk. *taxis*, arrangement.] Any definite unit in classification of plants and animals; taxonomic unit.

taxonomy (tăksŏn'ömĭ) *n.* [Gk. *taxis*, arrangement; *nomos*, law.] The laws of classification as applied to natural history.

taxy,—taxis.

tectal (tĕk'tăl) *a.* [L. *tectum*, roof.] Of or *pert.* tectum.

tectology (tĕktŏl'öjĭ) *n.* [Gk. *tekton*, builder; *logos*, discourse.] Morphology in which an organism is considered as a group of morphological as distinct from physiological units or individuals.

tectorial (tĕktō'rĭăl) *a.* [L. *tectorius*, *pert.* cover.] Covering; *appl.* membrane covering the spiral organ of Corti.

tectorium (tĕktō'rĭŭm) *n.* [L. *tectorium* cover.] Membrane of Corti; the coverts of birds.

tectospondylic (tĕk'tōspŏndĭl'ĭk) *a.* [L. *tectus*, covered; Gk. *sphondylos*, vertebra.] Having vertebrae with several concentric rings of calcification, as in some elasmobranchs; tectospondylous.

tectostracum (tĕktŏs'trăkŭm) *n.* [L. *tectum*, cover; Gk. *ostrakon*, shell.] Thin, waxy outer covering of exoskeleton, as of Acarina.

tectotype (tĕk'tōtīp) *n.* [Gk. *tekton*, builder; *typos*, pattern.] Description of a species, based on microscopical examination of a prepared section; the section used.

tectrices (tĕktrī'sēz, tĕk'trĭsēz) *n. plu.* [L. *tectus*, covered.] Wing-coverts; small feathers covering bases of remiges.

tectum (tĕk'tŭm) *n.* [L. *tectum*, roof.] A roof-like structure, as corpora quadrigemina forming roof of mesencephalon; dorsal wall of capitulum in Acarina.

teeth (tēth) *n. plu.* [A.S. *toth*, tooth.] Hard bony growths on maxillae, premaxillae, and mandibles of mammals; growths of similar, of chitinous, or of horny formation borne on jaws, tongue, or pharynx.

tegmen (tĕg'mĕn) *n.* [L. *tegmen*, covering.] The integument, endopleura, or inner seed-coat; calyx covers of Crinoidea; ninth abdominal tergite of male insects; thin hardened fore-wing of Orthoptera, Phasmida, and Dictyoptera; plate of bone over tympanic antrum.

tegmen cranii,—roof of chondrocranium.

tegmentum (tĕgmĕn'tŭm) *n.* [L. *tegmen*, covering.] A protective bud-scale; dorsal part of cerebral peduncles; a tegmen.

tegmina,—*plu.* of tegmen.

tegula (tĕg'ūlă) *n.* [L. *tegula*, tile.] A small sclerite on mesothorax overhanging articulation of wings in Lepidoptera and Hymenoptera; a small lobe or alula at wing-base of Diptera.

tegular (tĕg'ūlăr) *a.* [L. *tegula*, tile.] *Pert.* a tegula; consisting of a tile-like structure.

tegumen (tĕg'ūmĕn) *n.* [L. *tegumen*, cover.] Tegmen; ninth abdominal tergite, as in Lepidoptera.

tegument,—integument.

tegumental (tĕg'ūmĕn'tăl) *a.* [L. *tegumentum*, covering.] *Pert.* an integument; *appl.* gland cells of epidermis which secrete epicuticle in various arthropods.

tela (tē'lă) *n.* [L. *tela*, web.] A web-like tissue; *appl.* chorioidea, folds of the pia mater forming membranous roof of third and fourth ventricles; *appl.* interlacing fibrilliform or hyphal tissue of fungi, tela contexta.

telamon (tĕl'ămōn) *n.* [Gk. *telamon*, supporting strap.] Chitinised curved plate in lateral wall of cloaca in male nematodes.

telarian (tĕlā'rĭăn) *a.* [L. *tela*, web.] Web-spinning.

teleblem,—teleoblema.

teleceptor (tĕlēsĕp'tŏr) *n.* [Gk. *tele*, far; L. *capere*, to take.] A sense organ which receives stimuli originating at a distance; distance receptor; distoceptor, telereceptor, teloreceptor.

telegamic (tĕlĕgăm'ĭk) *a.* [Gk. *tele*, far; *gamos*, marriage.] Attracting females from a distance, *appl.* scent-apparatus of butterflies.

telegenesis (tĕlĕjĕn'ĕsĭs) *n.* [Gk. *tele*, afar; *genesis*, descent.] Artificial insemination.

telegony (tĕlĕg'ōnĭ) *n.* [Gk. *tele*, far; *gonos*, offspring.] The supposed influence of a male parent on offspring, subsequent to his own, of the same female parent by another sire.

teleianthous (tĕl'īăn'thŭs) *a.* [Gk. *teleios*, complete; *anthos*, flower.

Appl. a flower having both gynoecium and androecium.

teleiochrysalis (tĕl′ĭōkrĭs′ălĭs) *n.* [Gk. *teleios*, complete; *chrysallis*, from *chrysos*, gold.] Nymph during the resting stage preceding the adult form of certain mites.

telemetacarpal (tĕl′ĕmĕtăkâr′păl) *a.* [Gk. *tele*, far; *meta*, after; *karpos*, wrist.] *Appl.* condition of retaining distal elements of metacarpals, as in some Cervidae. *Opp.* plesiometacarpal.

telemorphosis (tĕl′ĕmôr′fōsĭs, -môrfō′sĭs) *n.* [Gk. *tele*, far; *morphosis*, a shaping.] Alteration of form in response to a distant stimulus, as of hypha or zygophore in response to another hypha or zygophore.

telencephalon (tĕl′ĕnkĕf′ălŏn, -sĕf-) *n.* [Gk. *tele*, far; *engkephalos*, brain.] The anterior part of forebrain, including the cerebral hemispheres, lateral ventricles, optic part of hypothalamus, and anterior portion of third ventricle; endbrain.

teleoblema (tĕl′ēöblē′mă) *n.* [Gk. *teleos*, complete; *blema*, coverlet.] Universal veil; volva; teleblem, teleoblem.

teleodont (tĕl′ēödŏnt) *a.* [Gk. *teleos*, complete; *odous*, tooth.] *Appl.* forms of stag-beetles with largest mandible development.

teleology (tĕl′ēŏl′ōji) *n.* [Gk. *teleos*, complete; *logos*, discourse.] The doctrine of adaptation to a definite purpose, and that evolution is purposive.

teleophore (tĕl′ēöfōr) *n.* [Gk. *teleos*, complete; *pherein*, to bear.] A gonotheca, or transparent case enclosing medusae of Hydrozoa.

teleoptile (tĕl′ēötīl, -ptīl) *n.* [Gk. *teleos*, complete; *ptilon*, feather.] A feather of definitive plumage; *cf.* neoptile; neossoptile; a pennaceous feather; *cf.* mesoptile, metaptile.

teleorganic (tĕl′ēôrgăn′ĭk) *a.* [Gk. *telein*, to fulfil; *organon*, instrument.] *Appl.* functions vital to an organism.

teleosis (tĕlē′ōsis) *n.* [Gk. *teleosis*, completion.] Purposive development or evolution.

teleotrocha,—trochosphere, *q.v.*

telereceptor,—teleceptor, *q.v.*

telescopiform (tĕlĕskŏp′ĭfôrm) *a.* [Gk. *tele*, far; *skopein*, to view; L. *forma*, shape.] Having joints that telescope into each other.

telethmoid,—prenasal, *q.v.*

teleutosorus (tĕlū′tösō′rŭs) *n.* [Gk. *teleute*, completion; *soros*, heap.] A group of developing teleutospores; sorus of last summer-stage of certain rust fungi; telium.

teleutospore (tĕlū′töspōr) *n.* [Gk. *teleute*, completion; *sporos*, seed.] In Uredinales, a winter-spore formed in autumn, germinating in following spring; teliospore, teleutobud or winter-bud, teleutogonidium, brand spore.

teleutosporiferous (tĕlū′töspörĭf′ĕrŭs) *a.* [Gk. *teleute*, completion; *sporos*, seed; L. *ferre*, to carry.] *Appl.* rusts bearing teleutospores; teliosporiferous.

telia,—*plu.* of telium.

telial,—*pert.* or having, telia.

telic (tĕl′ĭk) *a.* [Gk. *telos*, end.] Purposive; *pert.* teleosis.

teliosorus,—teleutosorus, *q.v.*

teliospore,—teleutospore, *q.v.*

teliostage (tĕl′ĭöstāj) *n.* [Gk. *telos*, end; F. *étage*, stage, from L. *stare*, to stand.] Last summer-stage of certain fungi in which telia are produced; teleutoform stage.

telium (tĕl′ĭŭm) *n.* [Gk. *telos*, end.] A teleutosorus.

teloblast (tĕl′öblăst) *n.* [Gk. *telos*, end; *blastos*, bud.] A stage derived from tritoblast and dividing into sporoblasts, in Neosporidia; a large cell which buds forth rows of smaller cells, as in annelid and mollusc embryos.

telocentric (tĕl′ösĕn′trĭk) *a.* [Gk. *telos*, end; *kentron*, centre.] With terminal centromere, *appl.* chromosomes; *cf.* acrocentric, metacentric.

telocoele (tĕl′ösēl) *n.* [Gk. *telos*, end; *koilos*, hollow.] First, or second, ventricle of brain; lateral ventricle; telencephalic vesicle.

telodendrion (tĕl′ödĕn′drĭön) *n.* [Gk. *telos*, end; *dendrion*, *dim.* of *dendron*, tree.] The terminal arborisation of an axon.

telofemur (tĕl′öfē′mŭr) *n.* [Gk. *telos*, end; L. *femur*, thigh.] Distal segment of femur, between basifemur and genu, in certain Acarina.

telokinesis (tĕl′ökĭnē′sĭs) *n.* [Gk. *telos*, end; *kinesis*, movement.] Last stage of mitosis when daughter-nuclei are re-formed; changes in cell after telophase.

telolecithal (tĕl′ölĕs′ĭthăl) *a.* [Gk. *telos*, end; *lekithos*, yolk.] Having yolk accumulated in one hemisphere, as in mesolecithal and polylecithal eggs.

telolemma (tĕl′ölĕm′ă) *n.* [Gk. *telos*, end; *lemma*, skin.] A capsule containing a nerve-fibre termination, in neuromuscular spindles; end-sheath.

telome (tĕl′ōm) *n.* [Gk. *telos*, end.] Morphological unit, consisting of stalk and sporangium, in cormophytes; sporophytic unit; terminal part of a mesome.

telomere (tĕl′ömēr) *n.* [Gk. *telos*, end; *meros*, part.] End of each chromosome arm distal to centromere.

telomitic (tĕl′ömĭt′ĭk) *a.* [Gk. *telos*, end; *mitos*, thread.] Having chromosomes attached endwise to spindle-fibres; having centromere terminal.

telophase (tĕl′öfāz) *n.* [Gk. *telos*, end; *phasis*, aspect.] Final phase of mitosis with cytoplasm division.

telophragma (tēl′öfrăg′mă) *n.* [Gk. *telos*, end; *phragma*, fence.] The Z-disc or Krause's membrane separating sarcomeres of muscle fibrils.

telosynapsis,—telosyndesis, *q.v.*

telosyndesis (tĕl′ösĭndē′sĭs) *n.* [Gk. *telos*, end; *syndesis*, binding together.] End to end union of chromosome halves in meiosis.

telotarsus (tĕl′ötâr′sŭs) *n.* [Gk. *telos*, end; *tarsos*, sole of foot.] Distal part or tarsus of dactylopodite of spiders. *Cf.* tarsomeres.

telotaxis (tĕl′ötăk′sĭs) *n.* [Gk. *telos*, end; *taxis*, arrangement.] Movement along line between animal and source of stimulus; goal orientation.

telotroch (tĕl′ötrök) *n.* [Gk. *telos*, end; *trochos*, wheel.] Pre-anal tuft of cilia of trochosphere.

telotrocha,—trochosphere, *q.v.*

telotrophic (tĕl′ötrŏf′ĭk) *a.* [Gk. *telos*, end; *trophe*, nourishment.] Acrotrophic, *appl.* ovarioles.

telson (tĕl′sŏn) *n.* [Gk. *telson*, extremity.] The unpaired terminal abdominal segment of Crustacea and Limulus; curved caudal spine or sting in scorpions; twelfth abdominal segment in Protura and in some insect embryos.

telum (tē′lŭm) *n.* [Gk. *telos*, end.] Last abdominal segment of insect.

temnospondylous (tĕm′nöspŏn′dĭlŭs) *a.* [Gk. *temnein*, to cut; *sphondylos*, vertebra.] With vertebrae not fused but in articulated pieces; *cf.* stereospondylous.

temperature coefficient,—quotient of two growth rates at temperatures differing by 10° C.

temporal (tĕm′pöräl) *a.* [L. *tempora*, temples.] *Pert.*, or in region of, temples.

temporalis,—broad radiating muscle arising from whole of temporal fossa and extending to coronoid process of mandible.

temporomalar (tĕm′pörömā′lăr) *a.* [L. *tempora*, temples; *mala*, cheek.] *Appl.* branch of maxillary nerve supplying temple and cheek, zygomatic nerve.

temporomandibular (tĕm′pörömăndĭb′ūlăr) *a.* [L. *tempora*, temples; *mandibula*, jaw.] *Appl.* articulation: the hinge of the jaws; *appl.* external lateral ligament between zygomatic process of temporal bone and neck of mandible.

temporomaxillary (tĕm′pörömăksĭl′ărĭ) *a.* [L. *tempora*, temples; *maxilla*, jaw.] *Pert.* temporal and maxillary region; *appl.* posterior facial vein.

tenacle,—tenaculum.

tenaculum (tĕnăk'ūlŭm) *n.* [L. *tenax*, holding.] Holdfast of algae; filaments surrounding ostiole of ascus and containing the spore mass in Haerangiomycetes; an ectodermal area modified for adhesion of sand-grains, in certain sea-anemones; in teleosts, fibrous band extending from eye-ball to skull.

tendines,—tendons; *plu.* of tendo.

tendinous (tĕn'dĭnŭs) *a.* [L. *tendere*, to stretch.] Of the nature of a tendon; having tendons.

tendo calcaneus, tendo Achillis,—the tendon of the heel.

tendon (tĕn'dŏn) *n.* [L. *tendo*, tendon, from *tendere*, to stretch.] A white glistening fibrous cord connecting a muscle with a movable structure.

tendon cells,—cells in white fibrous connective tissue, with wing-like processes extending between bundles of fibres.

tendon reflex, — contraction of muscles in a state of slight tension by a tap on their tendons.

tendril (tĕn'drĭl) *n.* [O.F. *tendrillon*, tender sprig.] A specialised twining stem or leaf by which creepers support themselves.

tendril-fibres, — cerebellar fibres with branches adhering to dendrites of Purkinje's cells; clinging fibres; *cf.* basket cells.

tendrillar (tĕn'drĭlăr) *a.* [O.F. *tendrillon*, tender sprig.] Acting as a tendril; twining.

tenent (tĕn'ĕnt) *a.* [L. *tenere*, to hold.] Holding; *appl.* tubular hairs with expanded tips, of arolium; *appl.* hairs secreting an adhesive fluid, on tarsus of spiders.

teneral (tĕn'ĕrăl) *a.* [L. *tener*, tender.] Immature; *appl.* stage on emergence from nymphal integument.

tenia,—taenia, *q.v.*

tenofibrils (tĕn'ōfībrĭlz) *n. plu.* [L. *tenere*, to hold; *fibrilla*, small fibre.] Delicate fibrils connecting epithelial cells and passing through intercellular bridges.

Tenon, capsule of [*J. R. Tenon*, French anatomist]. The fibro-elastic membrane surrounding the eye-ball from optic nerve to ciliary region; fascia bulbi.

tenoreceptor (tĕn'ōrēsĕp'tŏr) *n.* [Gk. *tenon*, tendon; L. *recipere*, to receive.] A proprioceptor in tendon reacting to contraction.

tensor (tĕn'sŏr) *a.* [L. *tendere*, to stretch.] *Appl.* muscles which stretch parts of body.

tentacles (tĕn'tăklz) *n. plu.* [L.L. *tentaculum* feeler.] Slender flexible organs on head of many invertebrate animals, used for feeling, exploration, prehension, or attachment; adhesive structures of insectivorous plants, as of sundew; *cf.* antenna.

tentacular (tĕntăk'ūlăr) *a.* [L.L. *tentaculum*, feeler.] *Pert.* tentacles; *appl.* a canal branching from perradial canal to tentacle base in Ctenophores.

tentaculiferous (tĕntăk'ūlĭf'ĕrŭs) *a.* [L.L. *tentaculum*, feeler; L. *ferre*, to carry.] Bearing tentacles.

tentaculiform (tĕntăk'ūlĭfôrm) *a.* [L.L. *tentaculum*, feeler; L. *forma*, shape.] Like a tentacle in shape or structure.

tentaculocyst (tĕntăk'ūlōsĭst) *n.* [L.L. *tentaculum*, feeler; Gk. *kystis*, bladder.] A sense organ of Trachylinae, a club-shaped body on umbrella margin, containing one or more lithites.

tentaculozooids (tĕntăk'ūlōzō'oidz) *n. plu.* [L.L. *tentaculum*, feeler; Gk. *zoon*, animal; *eidos*, form.] Long slender tentacular individuals at outskirts of hydrozoan colony.

tentaculum (tĕntăk'ūlŭm) *n.* [L.L. *tentaculum*, feeler.] A tentacle or feeler.

tentilla (tĕntĭl'ă), **tentillum** (tĕntĭl'ŭm) *n.* [L. *tentare*, to feel.] A tentacle branch.

tentorium (tĕntō'rĭŭm) *n.* [L. *tentorium*, tent.] A chitinous framework supporting brain of insects; a transverse fold of dura mater, ossified in some mammals, between cerebellum and occipital lobes of brain.

tepal (tĕp'ăl) *n.* [F. *tépale*, from *pétale*.] A perianth segment which is sepaloid or petaloid.

tephrous (tĕf'rŭs) *a.* [Gk. *tephra*, ashes.] Ashy-grey; cinereous.

teratology (tĕr'ătŏl'öjĭ) *n.* [Gk. *teras*, monster; *logos*, discourse.] Science treating of malformations and monstrosities of plants and animals.

tercine (tĕr'sĭn) *n.* [L. *tertius*, third.] The third coat of an ovule or a layer of the second.

terebra (tĕr'ëbră) *n.* [L. *terebra*, borer.] An ovipositor modified for boring, sawing, or stinging, as in certain Hymenoptera.

terebrate (tĕr'ëbrāt) *a.* [L. *terebra*, borer.] Furnished with a boring organ; adapted for boring.

terebrator,—a boring organ; trichogyne, *q.v.*, of lichens.

teres (tē'rēz) *n.* [L. *teres*, rounded.] The round ligament of liver; two muscles, teres major and minor, extending from scapula to humerus.

terete (tërēt'), **teretial** (tërē'shĭăl) *a.* [L. *teres*, rounded.] Nearly cylindrical in section, as stems.

tergal (tĕr'găl) *a.* [L. *tergum*, back.] Situated at back; *pert.* tergum.

tergeminate (tĕrjĕm'ĭnāt) *a.* [L. *ter*, thrice; *gemini*, twins.] Thrice forked with twin leaflets.

tergite (tĕr'jīt) *n.* [L. *tergum*, back.] Dorsal chitinous plate of each segment of most Arthropoda; a tergal sclerite.

tergosternal (tĕr'göstĕr'năl) *a.* [L. *tergum*, back; *sternum*, breastbone.] Connecting tergite and corresponding sternite; *appl.* muscles, in insects.

tergum (tĕr'gŭm) *n.* [L. *tergum*, back.] The back generally; dorsal portion of arthropod somite; notum; dorsal plate of barnacles.

terminal (tĕr'mĭnăl) *a.* [L. *terminus*, end.] *Pert.*, or situated at, the end, as terminal bud at end of twig; *appl.* a cranial nerve ending in nasal mucosa, the nervus terminalis or preoptic nerve; *appl.* filament, slender prolongation of ovariole; *appl.* chiasma at extreme end of chromatid; *appl.* gene at end of telomere.

terminalia (tĕrmĭnā'lĭă) *n. plu.* [L. *terminus*, end.] External genitalia, or hypopygium, in Diptera.

terminalisation (tĕr'mĭnălīzā'shŭn) *n.* [L. *terminus*, end.] Movement of chiasmata towards chromosome ends during diplotene and diakinesis.

termitarium (tĕr'mĭtā'rĭŭm) *n.* [L. *termes*, wood-worm.] An elaborately constructed nest of a termite colony.

termitophil (tĕr'mĭtöfĭl) *a.* [L. *termes*, wood-worm; Gk. *philein*, to love.] Living in termite nest; *appl.* certain fungi and insects.

termones (tĕr'mōnz) *n. plu.* [Gk. *termon*, limit.] Sex-determining substances or hormones, as in certain protozoa.

ternary (tĕr'nărĭ), **ternate** (tĕr'nāt) *a.* [L. *terni*, three each.] Arranged in threes; having three leaflets to a leaf; trifoliolate; trilateral, *appl.* symmetry.

ternatopinnate (tĕr'nātöpĭn'āt) *a.* [L. *terni*, three each; *pinna*, feather.] Having three pinnate leaflets to each compound leaf.

terraneous (tĕrā'nëŭs) *a.* [L. *terra*, earth.] *Appl.* land vegetation.

terrestrial (tërĕs'trĭăl) *a.* [L. *terra*, earth.] *Appl.* organisms living on land; *cf.* aerial, aquatic.

terricolous (tĕrĭk'ölŭs) *a.* [L. *terra*, earth; *colere*, to inhabit.] Inhabiting the soil; terrestrial, *q.v.*

terrigenous (tĕrĭj'ënŭs) *a.* [L. *terra*, earth; *gignere*, to produce.] Derived from land; *appl.* deposits.

territory (tĕr'ĭtörĭ) *n.* [L. *territorium*, domain.] An area defended by a bird shortly before and during the breeding season; an area sufficient for food requirements of an animal or aggregation of animals; foraging area.

tertial (tĕr'shăl) *n.* [L. *tertius*, third.] A scapular or tertiary wing-feather.

tertiary (tĕr'shĭărĭ) *a.* [L. *tertius*, third.] *Appl.* roots produced by secondary roots ; *appl.* inner wall of some wood fibres ; tertial, *appl.* wing feathers of humerus, otherwise scapulars.

Tertiary. *Appl.* era following the Mesozoic and preceding Quaternary ; earlier period of Caenozoic era, Eocene to Pliocene epochs.

tessellated (tĕs'ĕlātĕd) *a.* [L. *tessella*, small stone cube.] Checkered ; *appl.* markings or colours arranged in squares ; *appl.* epithelium.

tesserae (tĕs'ĕrē) *n. plu.* [L. *tessera*, square block.] Prisms of lime, in calcification of cartilage.

test (tĕst) *n.* [L. *testa*, shell.] A shell or hardened outer covering.

testa (tĕs'tă) *n.* [L. *testa*, shell.] Test ; outer coat of seed, or episperm.

testaceous (tĕstā'sēŭs) *a.* [L. *testa*, shell.] Protected by a shell-like outer covering.

testes,—*plu.* of testis.

testicle (tĕs'tĭkl) *n.* [L. *dim.* of *testis*, testicle.] Testis.

testicular (tĕstĭk'ūlăr) *a.* [L. *dim.* of *testis*, testicle.] Having two oblong tubercles, as in some orchids ; testicle-shaped ; testiculate ; *pert.* testis.

testis (tĕs'tĭs) *n.* [L. *testis*, testicle.] Male reproductive gland producing spermatozoa.

testosterone (tĕs'tŏstē'rōn) *n.* [L. *testis*, testicle ; Gk. *stear*, suet.] Testicular hormone ; $C_{19}H_{28}O_2$.

testudinate (tĕstū'dĭnāt) *a.* [L. *testudo*, tortoise.] Having a hard protective shell, as in tortoise.

tetaniform (tĕt'ănĭfôrm) *a.* [Gk. *tetanos*, stretched ; L. *forma*, shape.] Like tetanus ; tetanoid.

tetanise (tĕt'ănīz) *v.* [Gk. *tetanos*, stretched.] To cause a muscle to contract by a series of induction shocks.

tetanus (tĕt'ănŭs) *n.* [Gk. *tetanos*, stretched.] State of a muscle undergoing a continuous fused series of contractions due to electrical stimulation ; a rigid state of plant tissue caused by continued stimulus.

tethelin (tĕth'ēlĭn) *n.* [Gk. *tethelos*, swelling.] Growth-promoting principle isolated from pituitary body.

tetrabranchiate (tĕt'răbrăng'kĭāt) *a.* [Gk. *tetras*, four ; *brangchia*, gills.] Having four gills.

tetracarpellary (tĕt'răkâr'pĕlărĭ) *a.* [Gk. *tetras*, four ; *karpos*, fruit.] Having four carpels.

tetracerous (tĕtrăs'ĕrŭs) *a.* [Gk. *tetras*, four ; *keras*, horn.] Four-horned.

tetrachaenium (tĕtrăkē'nĭŭm) *n.* [Gk. *tetras*, four ; *a*, not ; *chainein*, to gape.] Four adherent achenes, as constituting fruit of Labiatae.

tetrachotomous (tĕt'răkŏt'ŏmŭs) *a.* [Gk. *tetracha*, fourfold ; *tome*, cutting.] Divided up into fours.

tetracoccus (tĕt'răkŏk'ŭs) *n.* [Gk. *tetras*, four ; *kokkos*, kernel.] Any minute organism found in groups of four.

tetracotyledonous (tĕt'răkŏtĭlē'dŏnŭs) *a.* [Gk. *tetras*, four ; *kotyledon*, cup-like hollow.] With four cotyledons.

tetracrepid (tĕt'răkrĕp'ĭd) *a.* [Gk. *tetras*, four ; *krepis*, edge.] *Appl.* a minute caltrop or four-rayed spicule.

tetract (tĕt'răkt) *n.* [Gk. *tetras*, four ; *aktis*, ray.] A four-rayed spicule.

tetractine (tĕtrăk'tĭn) *n.* [Gk. *tetras*, four ; *aktis*, ray.] A spicule of four equal and similar rays meeting at equal angles ; a tetraxon.

tetracyclic (tĕt'răsĭ'klĭk) *a.* [Gk. *tetras*, four ; *kyklos*, circle.] With four whorls.

tetracyte (tĕt'răsīt) *n.* [Gk. *tetras*, four ; *kytos*, hollow.] One of four daughter-cells formed from a mother-cell by meiosis.

tetrad (tĕt'răd) *n.* [Gk. *tetras*, four.] A group of four ; *appl.* four spores formed by first and second meiotic divisions of spore mother-cell ; four-cell stage in development of bryophytes and pteridophytes ; a quadruple group of chromatids at meiosis ; a quadrangular mass or loop of chromosomes in a stage of mitosis ; *cf.* quartet.

tetradactyl (tĕt'rădăk'tĭl) *a.* [Gk. *tetras,* four ; *daktylos,* finger.] Having four digits.

tetradidymous (tĕt'rădĭd'ĭmŭs) *a.* [Gk. *tetras,* four ; *didymos,* double.] Having or *pert.* four pairs.

tetradymous (tĕtrăd'ĭmŭs) *a.* [Gk. *tetradymos,* fourfold.] Having four cells, *appl.* spores.

tetradynamous (tĕt'rădĭn'ămŭs) *a.* [Gk. *tetras,* four ; *dynamis,* power.] Having four long stamens and two short.

tetragenic (tĕt'rajĕnĭk) *a.* [Gk. *tetras,* four ; *genos,* descent.] Controlled by four genes.

tetragonal (tĕtrăg'ŏnăl) *a.* [Gk. *tetras,* four ; *gonia,* angle.] Having four angles ; quaternary.

tetragynous (tĕtrăj'ĭnŭs) *a.* [Gk. *tetras,* four ; *gyne,* female.] With four carpels to a gynoecium.

tetrahedral (tĕt'răhē'drăl) *a.* [Gk. *tetras,* four ; *hedra,* base.] Having four triangular sides ; *appl.* apical cell in plants having a unicellular growing point.

tetralophodont (tĕt'rălŏf'ŏdŏnt) *a.* [Gk. *tetras,* four ; *lophos,* crest ; *odous,* tooth.] *Appl.* molar teeth with four ridges.

tetralophous (tĕt'rălŏf'ŭs) *a.* [Gk. *tetras,* four ; *lophos,* crest.] *Appl.* a spicule with four rays branched or crested.

tetramerous (tĕtrăm'ĕrŭs) *a.* [Gk. *tetras,* four ; *meros,* part.] Composed of four parts ; in multiples of four.

tetramite (tĕt'rămīt) *n.* [Gk. *tetras,* four ; *mitos,* thread.] A tetrad formed by four parallel chromatids prior to diakinesis.

tetramorphic (tĕt'rămôr'fĭk) *a.* [Gk. *tetras,* four ; *morphe,* form.] Having four forms ; of four different lengths, as basidia.

tetrandrous (tĕtrăn'drŭs) *a.* [Gk. *tetras,* four ; *aner,* man.] Having four stamens.

tetrapetalous (tĕt'răpĕt'ălŭs) *a.* [Gk. *tetras,* four ; *petalon,* leaf.] Having four petals.

tetraploid (tĕt'răploid) *a.* [Gk. *tetraple,* fourfold.] With four times the normal haploid number of chromosomes. *n.* An organism with four chromosome sets.

tetrapneumonous (tĕt'rănū'mŏnŭs, -pnū-) *a.* [Gk. *tetras,* four ; *pneumon,* lung.] Having four lung-books, as certain spiders.

tetrapod (tĕt'răpŏd) *n.* [Gk. *tetras,* four ; *pous,* foot.] A four-footed animal ; quadruped.

tetrapterous (tĕtrăp'tĕrŭs) *a.* [Gk. *tetras,* four ; *pteron,* wing.] Having four wings.

tetrapyrenous (tĕt'răpīrē'nŭs) *a.* [Gk. *tetras,* four ; *pyren,* fruit-stone.] Having four fruit-stones ; being a four-stoned fruit.

tetraquetrous (tĕtrăkwĕt'rŭs) *a.* [Gk. *tetras,* four ; L. *quadratus,* squared.] Having four angles, as some stems.

tetrarch (tĕt'rârk) *a.* [Gk. *tetras,* four ; *arche,* beginning.] With four protoxylem bundles.

tetraselenodont (tĕt'răsĕlē'nŏdŏnt) *a.* [Gk. *tetras,* four ; *selene,* moon ; *odous,* tooth.] Having four crescentic ridges on molar teeth.

tetrasepalous (tĕt'răsĕp'ălŭs) *a.* [Gk. *tetras,* four ; F. *sépale,* sepal.] Having four sepals.

tetraseriate,—tetrastichous, quadriserial, quadriseriate.

tetrasome (tĕt'răsōm) *n.* [Gk. *tetras,* four ; soma, body.] Association of four homologous chromosomes in meiosis.

tetrasomic (tĕt'răsō'mĭk) *a.* [Gk. *tetras,* four ; *soma,* body.] *Pert.* or having four homologous chromosomes. *n.* An organism with four chromosomes of one type.

tetraspermous (tĕt'răspĕr'mŭs) *a.* [Gk. *tetras,* four ; *sperma,* seed.] Having four seeds.

tetrasporangium (tĕt'răspŏrăn'jĭŭm) *n.* [Gk. *tetras,* four ; *sporos,* seed ; *anggeion,* vessel.] Sporangium producing tetraspores, as in red algae.

tetraspore (tĕt′răspōr) *n.* [Gk. *tetras*, four ; *sporos*, seed.] One of a group of four non-motile spores produced by sporangium of certain algae ; one of four basidial spores, as in Hymenomycetes.

tetrasporic,—four-spored.

tetrasporocystid (tĕt′răspō′rŏsĭs′tĭd) *a.* [Gk. *tetras*, four ; *sporos*, seed ; *kystis*, bladder.] *Appl.* oocyst of Sporozoa when four sporocysts are present.

tetrasternum (tĕt′răstĕr′nŭm) *n.* [Gk. *tetras*, four ; *sternon*, chest.] Sternite of fourth segment of prosoma or second segment of podosoma in Acarina.

tetrastichous (tĕtrăs′tĭkŭs) *a.* [Gk. *tetras*, four ; *stichos*, row.] Arranged in four rows.

tetrathecal (tĕt′răthē′kăl) *a.* [Gk. *tetras*, four ; *theke*, case.] Having four loculi ; quadrilocular.

tetraxon (tĕtrăk′sŏn) *n.* [Gk. *tetras*, four ; *axon*, axis.] A tetractine.

tetrazoic (tĕt′răzō′ĭk) *a.* [Gk. *tetras*, four ; *zoon*, animal.] Having four sporozoites ; *appl.* spores of Coccidia.

tetrazooid (tĕt′răzō′oid) *n.* [Gk. *tetras*, four ; *zoon*, animal ; *eidos*, form.] Zooid developed from each of four parts constricted from stolon process of embryonic ascidian.

textura (tĕkstū′ră) *n.* [L. *textura*, fabric.] Tissue.

thalamencephalon (thăl′ămĕnkĕf′-ălŏn, -sĕf-) *n.* [Gk. *thalamos*, chamber ; *engkephalos*, brain.] The part of the fore-brain comprising thalamus, corpora geniculata and epithalamus.

thalamomamillary (thăl′ămōmăm′-ĭlărĭ) *a.* [Gk. *thalamos*, chamber ; L. *mamilla*, nipple.] *Appl.* fasciculus or bundle of Vicq-d'Azyr, from corpus mamillare to thalamus.

thalamus (thăl′ămŭs) *n.* [Gk. *thalamos*, chamber.] The receptacle or torus of a flower ; ovoid ganglionic mass on either side of third ventricle of brain.

thalassin (thălăs′ĭn) *n.* [Gk. *thalassa*, sea.] A toxin of sea-anemone tentacles.

thalassoid (thălăs′oid) *a.* [Gk. *thalassa*, sea ; *eidos*, form.] *Pert.* fresh-water organisms resembling, or originally, marine forms ; pseudo-marine ; halolimnic.

thalassophyte (thălăs′ŏfīt) *n.* [Gk. *thalassa*, sea ; *phyton*, plant.] Any marine alga.

thalassoplankton (thălăs′ŏplăngk′-tŏn) *n.* [Gk. *thalassa*, sea ; *plangktos*, wandering.] Marine plankton.

thalliform,—thalloid.

thalline (thăl′īn) *a.* [Gk. *thallos*, young shoot.] Consisting of a thallus ; thalloid.

thallodal,—thalloid.

thallogen,—thallophyte.

thalloid (thăl′oid) *a.* [Gk. *thallos*, young shoot ; *eidos*, form.] Resembling a thallus ; *appl.* exciple formed by thalloid hyphae.

thallome (thăl′ōm) *n.* [Gk. *thallos*, young shoot.] A thallus-like structure ; a thallus.

thallophyte (thăl′ŏfīt) *n.* [Gk. *thallos*, young shoot ; *phyton*, plant.] A plant not differentiated into stem and root, varying widely in form, as algae, fungi, and lichens. *Opp.* cormophyte.

thallose,—thalloid.

thallospore (thăl′ŏspōr) *n.* [Gk. *thallos*, young shoot ; *sporos*, seed.] Spore cell in vegetative part of a fungus.

thallus (thăl′ŭs) *n.* [Gk. *thallos*, young shoot.] A combination of cells presenting no differentiation of leaf and stem, vegetative or assimilative part as in Thallophyta.

thalposis (thăl′pŏsĭs, thălpō′sĭs) *n.* [Gk. *thalpos*, warmth.] Sensation of warmth.

thamniscophagy (thăm′nĭskŏf′ăjĭ) *n.* [Gk. *thamnos*, bush ; *dim.* ; *phagein*, to eat.] Disintegration and absorption of arbusculae and sporangioles in mycorrhiza.

thanatoid (thăn′ătoid) *a.* [Gk. *thanatos*, death ; *eidos*, form.] Deadly ; *appl.* poisonous snakes ; resembling death.

thanatology (thăn'ătŏl'ŏjĭ) *n.* [Gk. *thanatos*, death; *logos*, discourse.] Theories concerning death.

thanatosis (thănătō'sĭs) *n.* [Gk. *thanatos*, death.] Habit or act of feigning death; death of a part.

thebesian (thēbē'zĭăn) *a.* [*A. C. Thebesius*, German anatomist]. *Appl.* valve of coronary sinus.

theca (thē'kă) *n.* [Gk. *theke*, case.] A spore or pollen case; a sporangium; a capsule; a structure serving as protective covering for organ or organism, as of spinal cord, follicle, pupa, proboscis, tube-animal.

thecacyst (thē'kăsĭst) *n.* [Gk. *theke*, case; *kystis*, bladder.] Sperm envelope or spermatophore formed by spermatheca.

thecal (thē'kăl) *a.* [Gk. *theke*, case.] Surrounded by a protective membrane or tissue; *pert.* a theca; *pert.* an ascus.

thecaphore (thē'kăfōr) *n.* [Gk. *theke*, case; *pherein*, to bear.] A structure on which a theca is borne.

thecaspore,—ascospore, *q.v.*

thecasporous (thēkăspō'rŭs) *a.* [Gk. *theke*, case; *sporos*, a seed.] Having spores enclosed.

thecate (thē'kāt) *a.* [Gk. *theke*, case.] Covered or protected by theca; theciferous; thecigerous.

thecial (thē'sĭăl) *a.* [Gk. *theke*, case.] Within or *pert.* a thecium.

thecium (thē'sĭŭm) *n.* [Gk. *theke*, case.] That part of a fungus or lichen containing the sporules.

thecodont (thē'kŏdŏnt) *a.* [Gk. *theke*, case; *odous*, tooth.] Having teeth in sockets.

theelin (thē'lĭn) *n.* [Gk. *thelys*, female.] Follicular hormone; folliculin, oestrin, oestrone; $C_{18}H_{22}O_2$.

theelol (thē'lŏl) *n.* [Gk. *thelys*, female.] Hydrated theelin occurring in female urine; oestriol; $C_{18}H_{24}O_3$.

thelephorous (thēlē'fŏrŭs) *a.* [Gk. *thele*, teat; *pherein*, to bear.] Having nipples or nipple-like projections; with a closely nippled surface.

thelyblast (thē'lĭblăst) *n.* [Gk. *thelys*, female; *blastos*, bud.] A matured female germ cell.

thelygenic (thē'lĭjĕn'ĭk) *a.* [Gk. *thelys*, female; *-genes*, producing.] Producing offspring preponderantly or entirely female; thelytocous.

thelyotoky (thē'lĭŏt'ŏkĭ) *n.* [Gk. *thelys*, female; *tokos*, offspring.] Parthenogenesis in case where females only are produced; thelytoky.

thelyplasm (thē'lĭplăzm) *n.* [Gk. *thelys*, female; *plasma*, mould.] Female plasm, *opp.* arrhenoplasm.

thenal (thē'năl) *a.* [Gk. *thenar*, palm of hand.] *Pert.* or in region of palm of hand.

thenar (thē'năr) *n.* [Gk. *thenar*, palm of hand.] The muscular mass forming ball of thumb.

thermium (thĕrmī'ŭm) *n.* [Gk. *thermai*, hot springs.] Plant community in warm or hot springs.

thermocleistogamy (thĕr'mŏklīstŏg'ămĭ) *n.* [Gk. *therme*, heat; *kleistos*, closed; *gamos*, marriage.] Self-pollination of flowers when unopened owing to unfavourable temperature.

thermocline (thĕr'mŏklīn) *n.* [Gk. *therme*, heat; *klinein*, to swerve.] More or less abrupt change in water temperature in relation to depth; *appl.* layer between upper and deep layers, also to seasonal temperature change within the upper, mixed layer.

thermogenesis (thĕr'mŏjĕn'ĕsĭs) *n.* [Gk. *therme*, heat; *genesis*, production.] Body-heat production by oxidation; heat production by bacteria.

thermolysis (thĕrmŏl'ĭsĭs) *n.* [Gk. *therme*, heat; *lysis*, loosing.] Loss of body heat; chemical dissociation owing to heat.

thermonasty (thĕr'mŏnăs'tĭ) *n.* [Gk. *therme*, heat; *nastos*, close pressed.] Plant movement in response to variations of temperature.

thermoperiodicity (thĕr'mŏpĕr'ĭŏdĭs'ĭtĭ) *n.* [Gk. *therme*, heat;

periodos, period.] Effects of temperature difference between light and dark periods upon plants.

thermophase (thĕr'möfāz) *n.* [Gk. *therme*, heat; *phainein*, to appear.] First developmental stage in some annual and perennial plants, and which can be partly or entirely completed during seed ripening if temperature and humidity are favourable; vernalisation phase.

thermophil (thĕr'möfĭl) *a.* [Gk *therme*, heat; *philos*, loving.] Thriving at relatively high temperatures, above 40° C., *appl.* certain bacteria; thermophilic. *n.* Thermophile.

thermophylactic (thĕr'möfĭlăk'tĭk) *a.* [Gk. *therme*, heat; *phylaktikos*, fit for preserving.] Heat-resistant; tolerating heat, as certain bacteria.

thermophyte (thĕr'möfīt) *n.* [Gk. *therme*, heat; *phyton*, plant.] A heat-tolerant plant; a therophyte, *q.v.*

thermoscopic (thĕr'möskŏp'ĭk) *a.* [Gk. *therme*, heat; *skopein*, to view.] Adapted for recognising changes of temperature, as special sense-organs of certain cephalopods.

thermotactic (thĕr'mötăk'tĭk) *a.* [Gk. *therme*, heat; *taxis*, arrangement.] *Pert.* thermotaxis; *appl.* optimum, the range of temperature preferred by an organism.

thermotaxis (thĕr'mötăk'sĭs) *n.* [Gk. *therme*, heat; *taxis*, arrangement.] Locomotor reaction to temperature stimulus; regulation of body temperature.

thermotropism (thĕrmŏt'röpĭzm) *n.* [Gk. *therme*, heat; *trope*, turn.] Curvature in plants in response to temperature stimulus.

therophyllous (thĕr'öfĭl'ŭs) *a.* [Gk. *theros*, summer; *phyllon*, leaf.] Having leaves in summer; with deciduous leaves.

therophyte (thĕr'öfīt) *n.* [Gk. *theros*, summer; *phyton*, plant.] A plant which completes life-cycle within a single season, being dormant as seed during unfavourable period; an annual.

thesocytes (thē'sösīts) *n. plu.* [Gk. *thesis*, deposit; *kytos*, hollow.] Sponge-cells storing reserve material.

theta (θ) **factor**,—the thyrotropic hormone.

thiamine,—aneurin or vitamin B_1, antineuritic or antiberiberi vitamin, found in rice polishings, cereals, and yeast; $C_{12}H_{18}N_4OSCl_2$.

thigmocyte (thĭg'mösīt) *n.* [Gk. *thigema*, touch; *kytos*, hollow.] A corpuscle which undergoes cytolysis on contact with foreign substance.

thigmomorphosis (thĭg'mömôr'fōsĭs, -môrfō'sĭs) *n.* [Gk. *thigema*, touch; *morphosis*, form.] Structural change due to contact; swelling at ends of contacting zygophores.

thigmotaxis (thĭg'mötăk'sĭs) *n.* [Gk. *thigema*, touch; *taxis*, arrangement.] The tendency of minute organisms to attach themselves to objects on contact; locomotor reaction to touch stimulus.

thigmotropism (thĭgmŏt'röpĭzm) *n.* [Gk. *thigema*, touch; *trope*, turn.] The tendency to respond to mechanical contact by clinging and curving, as in tendrils; response to stimulus of contact.

thinophyte (thī'nöfīt) *n.* [Gk. *this*, sand-heap; *phyton*, plant.] Dune plant.

thiogenic (thīöjĕn'ĭk) *a.* [Gk. *theion*, sulphur; *gennaein*, to produce.] Sulphur-producing; *appl.* bacteria utilising sulphur compounds.

thiophil (thī'öfĭl) *n.* [Gk. *theion*, sulphur; *philein*, to love.] An organism thriving in the presence of sulphur compounds as certain bacteria. *a.* Thiophilic.

thoracic (thōrăs'ĭk) *a.* [Gk. *thorax*, chest.] *Pert.*, or in region of, thorax.

thoracic duct,—vessel conveying lymph and chyle from abdomen to left subclavian vein; *cf.* cisterna chyli.

thoracic index,—one hundred times depth of thorax at nipple level divided by breadth.

thoracolumbar (thōrā'kŏlŭm'băr) *a.* [Gk. *thorax*, chest; L. *lumbus*, loin.] *Pert.* thoracic and lumbar part of spine; *appl.* nerves, the sympathetic system.

thoracopod (thōrā'kŏpŏd) *n.* [Gk. *thorax*, chest; *pous*, foot.] Any thoracic leg of Malacostraca.

thorax (thō'răks) *n.* [Gk. *thorax*, chest.] In higher vertebrates, that part of body between neck and abdomen containing heart, lungs, etc.; body region behind head of other animals.

thread-cells,—stinging cells or cnidoblasts in coelenterates; in skin of myxinoids, cells whose long threads form a network in which mucous secretion of ordinary gland cells is entangled.

thread-press,—the muscular portion of a spinning tube.

three-nerved leaf,—a leaf with three distinct primary veins.

thremmatology (thrĕm'ătŏl'ŏjĭ) *n.* [Gk. *thremma*, nursling; *logos*, discourse.] The science of breeding animals and plants under domestic conditions.

threshold,—limen, *q.v.*

thrombin (thrŏm'bĭn) *n.* [Gk. *thrombos*, clot.] Fibrin-ferment which converts fibrinogen into fibrin.

thrombocytes (thrŏm'bŏsīts) *n. plu.* [Gk. *thrombos*, clot; *kytos*, hollow.] Blood-platelets; in non-mammalian vertebrates, nucleated spindle-shaped cells concerned with clotting of blood.

thrombogen (thrŏm'bŏjĕn) *n.* [Gk. *thrombos*, clot; *-genes*, producing.] Prothrombin.

thrombokinase (thrŏm'bŏkīnās') *n.* [Gk. *thrombos*, clot; *kinein*, to move.] A factor which, with calcium, activates prothrombin to form thrombin, found in tissues and blood-platelets; thromboplastin.

thromboplastid (thrŏm'bŏplăs'tĭd) *n.* [Gk. *thrombos*, clot; *plastos*, moulded.] A blood platelet.

thromboplastin (thrŏm'bŏplăs'tĭn) *n.* [Gk. *thrombos*, clot; *plastos*, moulded.] Thrombokinase or thromboplastic factor; thrombozyme, cytozyme.

thrombosis (thrŏmbō'sĭs) *n.* [Gk. *thrombos*, clot.] Clotting, as of blood.

thrombozyme (thrŏm'bŏzīm) *n.* [Gk. *thrombos*, clot; *zyme*, leaven.] Thrombokinase.

thrum-eyed,—short-styled, with long stamens extending to mouth of tubular corolla. *Opp.* pin-eyed.

thryptophyte (thrĭp'tŏfīt) *n.* [Gk. *thryptein*, to enfeeble; *phyton*, plant.] Any fungus that modifies host tissue without any direct lethal effect.

thyloses (thī'lŏsēz) *n. plu.* [Gk. *thylakos*, pouch.] Masses of parenchyma formed inside wood vessels through pressure in secondary wood; tylosis, *q.v.*

thymic (thī'mĭk) *a.* [Gk. *thymos*, thymus.] *Pert.* the thymus; *appl.* corpuscles: the concentric corpuscles of Hassall.

thymocyte (thī'mŏsīt) *n.* [Gk. *thymos*, thymus; *kytos*, hollow.] A small lymphocyte in cortex of thymus.

thymovidin (thīmō'vĭdĭn) *n.* [Gk. *thymos*, thymus; L. *ovum*, egg.] A thymus hormone of birds, which influences egg albumin and shell formation.

thymus (thī'mŭs) *n.* [Gk. *thymos*, thymus.] An endocrine gland in lower anterior part of neck, or surrounding heart, in man regressing after maximum development at puberty.

thyreo,—*also see* thyro-.

thyreoid (thī'rĕoid) *a.* [Gk. *thyreos*, oblong shield; *eidos*, form.] Shield-shaped; peltate; thyroid. *n.* An endocrine gland, the thyroid, *q.v.*

thyreothecium (thī'rĕŏthē'sĭŭm) *n.* [Gk. *thyreos*, oblong shield; *theke*, case.] A shield-like fruit-body of certain ectoparasitic fungi.

thyridium (thīrĭd'ĭŭm) *n.* [Gk. *thyra*, door; *idion*, *dim.*] Hairless whitish area on certain insect wings.

thyro-arytaenoid (thī'röărĭtē'noid) *n.* [Gk. *thyra*, door ; *arytaina*, pitcher ; *eidos*, form.] A muscle of larynx.

thyroepiglottic (thī'röĕp'ĭglŏt'ĭk) *a.* [Gk. *thyra*, door ; *epi*, upon ; *glotta*, tongue.] *Appl.* ligament connecting epiglottis stem and angle of thyroid cartilage.

thyroglossal (thī'röglŏs'ăl) *a.* [Gk. *thyra*, door ; *glossa*, tongue.] *Pert.* thyroid and tongue ; *appl.* an embryonic duct, the ductus thyreoglossus.

thyrohyals (thī'röhī'ălz) *n. plu.* [Gk. *thyra*, door ; *hyoeides*, *Y*-shaped.] Greater cornua of hyoid bone.

thyrohyoid (thī'röhī'oid) *a.* [Gk. *thyra*, door; *hyoeides*, *Y*-shaped.] *Appl.* muscle extending from thyroid cartilage to hyoid cornu.

thyroid (thī'roid) *a.* [Gk. *thyra*, door ; *eidos*, form.] Shield-shaped ; *appl.* a ductless highly vascular gland at front and sides of neck ; also to arteries, cartilage, and veins. *n.* The thyroid gland.

thyrotrophic (thī'rötrŏf'ĭk) *a.* [Gk. *thyra*, door ; *trophe*, nourishment.] *Appl.* a prepituitary hormone which stimulates growth and function of thyroid gland ; thyrotropic.

thyroxine (thī'rŏksĭn) *n.* [Gk. *thyra*, door ; *oxys*, sharp.] A compound isolated from thyroid gland, with properties resembling those of iodothyroglobulin ; $C_{15}H_{11}O_4NI_4$.

thyrse,—thyrsus.

thyrsoid (thĕr'soid) *a.* [Gk. *thyrsos*, wand ; *eidos*, form.] Resembling a thyrsus in shape.

thyrsus (thĕr'sŭs) *n.* [Gk. *thyrsos*, wand.] A mixed inflorescence with main axis racemose, later axes cymose, with cluster almost double-cone shaped ; hypha-bearing lateral chlamydospores ; penis.

thysanuriform (thĭs'ănū'rĭfôrm) *a.* [Gk. *thysanos*, fringe ; *oura*, tail ; L. *forma*, form.] Campodeiform ; *appl.* a larva resembling Thysanura.

tibia (tĭb'ĭă) *n.* [L. *tibia*, shin.] Shin-bone, inner and larger of leg-bones between knee and ankle ; fourth joint of insect and arachnid leg.

tibial (tĭb'ĭăl) *a.* [L. *tibia*, shin.] *Pert.* or in region of tibia.

tibiale (tĭbĭâ'lē) *n.* [L. *tibia*, shin.] Embryonic structure partly represented by astragalus ; a sesamoid bone in tendon of posterior tibial muscle.

tibiofibula (tĭb'ĭöfĭb'ūlă) *n.* [L. *tibia*, shin ; *fibula*, buckle.] Bone formed of fused tibia and fibula.

tibiofibular (tĭb'ĭöfĭb'ūlăr) *a.* [L. *tibia*, shin ; *fibula*, buckle.] *Pert.* tibia and fibula ; *appl.* articulation, syndesmosis ; *pert.* tibiofibula.

tibiotarsal (tĭb'ĭötâr'săl) *a.* [L. *tibia*, shin ; Gk. *tarsos*, sole of foot.] *Pert.* tibia and tarsus ; *pert.* or in region of tibiotarsus.

tibiotarsus (tĭb'ĭötâr'sŭs) *n.* [L. *tibia*, shin ; Gk. *tarsos*, sole of foot.] Tibial bone to which proximal tarsals are fused, in birds.

tidal (tī'dăl) *a.* [A.S. *tid*, time.] *Pert.* tides ; ebbing and flowing ; *appl.* air, volume of air normally inhaled and exhaled at each breath ; *appl.* wave, main flow of blood during systole.

Tiedemann's vesicles [*F. Tiedemann*, German anatomist]. Small rounded glandular chambered bodies at neck of Polian vesicles ; racemose vesicles of Asteroidea.

tige (tēzh, tĭj) *n.* [F. *tige*, stem.] Paturon, *q.v.* ; stem.

tigellum (tĭjĕl'ŭm) *n.* [F. *tigelle*, *dim.* of *tige*, stem.] The central embryonic axis, consisting of radicle and plumule.

tigroid (tī'groid.) *a.* [Gk. *tigroeides*, spotted.] *Appl.* granules or bodies, chromophil substance or Nissl granules of the neurocyton.

tigrolysis (tĭgrŏl'ĭsĭs) *n.* [Gk. *tigroeides*, spotted ; *lysis*, loosing.] Chromatolysis of tigroid granules.

timbal (tĭm'băl) *n.* [F. *timbale*, kettle-drum.] Sound-producing organ in cicadas.

Timofeev's corpuscles [*D. A. Timofeev*, Russian anatomist]. Specialised sensory nerve endings in submucosa of urethra and in prostatic capsule.

tinctorial (tĭngktō'rĭăl) *a.* [L. *tinctorius, pert.* dyeing.] Producing dye-stuff ; *appl.* certain lichens.

tip cell,—the uninucleate ultimate cell of a hyphal crosier, distal to the dome cell and directed towards the basal cell.

tiphophyte (tĭf'ofīt) *n.* [Gk. *tiphos,* pool ; *phyton,* plant.] Pond plant.

tissue (tĭs'ū, tĭsh'ū) *n.* [F. *tissu,* woven.] The fundamental structure of which animal and plant organs are composed ; an organisation of like cells.

tmema (tmē'mă) *n.* [Gk. *tmetos,* cut.] An intercalary cell which separates aecidiospores of certain rust fungi.

tocopherol (tŏkŏf'ërŏl) *n.* [Gk. *tokos,* birth ; *pherein,* to carry.] *a* tocopherol, vitamin E, present in wheat germ, etc. ; anti-sterility vitamin ; $C_{29}H_{50}O_2$.

tokocytes (tŏk'ösīts) *n. plu.* [Gk. *tokos,* offspring; *kytos,* hollow.] Reproductive cells of sponges.

tokostome (tŏk'östōm) *n.* [Gk. *tokos,* birth ; *stoma,* mouth.] Female genital aperture, as in mites, etc.

tolypophagy (tŏl'ĭpŏf'ăjĭ) *n.* [Gk. *tolype,* clew ; *phagein,* to eat.] Disintegration and absorption of hyphal coils in mycorrhizae.

tomentose (tōmĕn'tōs) *a.* [L. *tomentum,* stuffing.] Covered closely with matted hairs or fibrils.

tomentum (tōmĕn'tŭm) *n.* [L. *tomentum,* stuffing.] The closely matted hair on leaves or stems.

Tomes' fibres [Sir *J. Tomes,* English dentist]. Dentinal fibres, processes of odontoblasts in dentinal tubules.

Tomes' granular layer,—a layer of interglobular spaces in dentine.

tomite (tŏmīt) *n.* [Gk. *tome,* cutting ; *mitos,* thread.] Free-swimming non-feeding stage following protomite stage in life cycle of Holotricha.

tomium (tō'mĭŭm) *n.* [Gk. *tomos,* cutting.] The sharp edge of a bird's beak.

tomont (tŏmŏnt') *n.* [Gk. *tome,* cutting ; *onta,* beings.] Stage in life cycle of Holotricha when body divides, usually in a cyst.

tongue (tŭng) *n.* [A.S. *tunge,* tongue.] An organ on floor of mouth, usually movable and protrusible ; any tongue-like structure, as radula, ligula ; hypopharynx, in some insects ; lingua.

tonicity (tŏnĭs'ĭtĭ) *n.* [Gk. *tonos,* tension.] Normal tone or tension ; tonus.

tonofibrillae (tŏn'öfībrĭl'ē) *n. plu.* [Gk. *tonos,* tension ; L. *fibrilla,* small fibre.] Epitheliofibrillae, *q.v.*, regarded as skeletal or supporting structures rather than as myofibrillae ; supporting fibrils, as of cilia.

tonoplast (tŏn'öplăst) *n.* [Gk. *tonos,* tension ; *plastos,* modelled.] A vacuolar membrane ; a plastid with distinct vacuole walls ; a special form of vacuole-producing plastid.

tonotaxis (tŏnötăk'sĭs) *n.* [Gk. *tonos,* tension ; *taxis,* arrangement.] Response to change in density of surrounding medium.

tonsil (tŏn'sĭl) *n.* [L. *tonsilla,* tonsil.] One of aggregations of lymphoid tissue in pharynx or near tongue base.

tonsilla (tŏnsĭl'ă) *n.* [L. *tonsilla,* tonsil.] A tonsil ; posterior lobule of cerebellar hemisphere, on either side of uvula of inferior vermis.

tonsillar ring,—partial ring of lymphoid tissue formed by the palatine, pharyngeal and lingual tonsils ; Waldeyer's tonsillar ring.

tonus (tŏn'ŭs) *n.* [Gk. *tonos,* tension.] Tonicity, or condition of being slightly stretched, as of muscles.

topaesthesia (tŏp'ĕsthē'sĭa) *n.* [Gk. *topos,* place : *aisthesia,* sensation.] Appreciation of locus of a tactile sensation.

topochemical (tŏp'ökĕm'ĭkăl) *a.* [Gk. *topos,* place ; *chemeia,* transmutation.] *Appl.* sense, the perception of odours in relation to track or place, as in ants.

topodeme (tŏp′ödēm) *n.* [Gk. *topos*, place; *demos*, people.] Deme occupying a particular geographical area.

toponym (tŏp′önĭm) *n.* [Gk. *topos*, place; *onyma*, name.] The name of a place or of a region; a name designating the place of origin of a plant or animal.

topotaxis (tŏp′ötăk′sĭs) *n.* [Gk. *topos*, place; *taxis*, arrangement.] Movement induced by spatial differences in stimulation intensity, and orientation in relation to sources of stimuli, as telotaxis, tropotaxis, menotaxis, mnemotaxis, *q.v.*; tropism.

topotype (tŏp′ötīp) *n.* [Gk. *topos*, place; *typos*, pattern.] A specimen from locality of original type.

toral (tō′răl) *a.* [L. *torus*, a swelling.] Of or *pert.* a torus.

torcular (tôr′kūlăr) *n.* [L. *torcular*, wine-press.] Occipital junction of venous sinuses of dura mater; confluens sinuum, torcular Herophili.

tori,—*plu.* of torus.

torma (tôr′mă) *n.* [Gk. *tormos*, socket.] A thickening at junction of labrum and clypeus.

tormogen (tôr′möjĕn) *n.* [Gk. *tormos*, socket; *-genes*, producing.] A cell secreting the socket of a bristle, in insects.

tornaria (tôrnā′rĭă) *n.* [L. *tornare*, to turn.] The free larval stage in development of Balanoglossida.

tornate (tôr′nāt) *a.* [L. *tornare*, to turn.] With blunt extremities, as a spicule.

torose (tō′rōs) *a.* [L. *torus*, swelling.] Having fleshy swellings; knobbed.

torques (tôr′kwēz) *n.* [L. *torques*, necklace.] A necklace-like arrangement of fur, feathers, or the like.

torsion (tôr′shŭn) *n.* [L. *torquere*, to twist.] Spiral bending; the twisting round of a gastropod body as it develops.

torticone (tôr′tĭkōn) *n.* [L. *torquere*, to twist; *conus*, cone.] A turreted, spirally-twisted shell.

torula condition,—yeast-like isolated cells resulting from growth of blue mould conidia in saccharine solution.

torulaceous,—torulose, monilioid.

toruloid (tôr′ūloid) *a.* [L. *torulus*, small swelling; Gk. *eidos*, form.] *Appl.* a structure, plasmatoönkosis, storage organ of zoosporangium, as in Peronosporales.

torulose (tôr′ūlōs) *a.* [L. *torulus*, small swelling.] With small swellings; beaded; moniliform.

torulus (tôr′ūlŭs) *n.* [L. *torulus*, small swelling.] The insect antenna insertion socket; antennifer, *q.v.*

torus (tō′rŭs) *n.* [L. *torus*, swelling.] Axis bearing floral leaves; receptacle or thalamus; thickened centre of a bordered pit-membrane; firm prominence, or marginal fold or ridge; ridge bearing uncini in Polychaeta; pedicel in Diptera.

totipalmate (tō′tĭpăl′māt) *a.* [L. *totus*, all; *palma*, palm of hand.] Having feet completely webbed; steganopodous.

totipotent (tötĭp′ötĕnt) *a.* [L. *totus*, all; *potens*, powerful.] *Appl.* blastomeres which can develop into complete embryos when separated from aggregate of blastomeres; *appl.* meristematic cells capable of specialisation in response to hormones from growth centres; totipotential.

toxaspire (tŏk′săspīr) *n.* [Gk. *toxon*, bow; L. *spira*, coil.] A spiral spicule of rather more than one revolution.

toxic (tŏk′sĭk) *a.* [Gk. *toxikon*, poison.] *Pert.*, caused by, or of the nature of a poison; poisonous.

toxicant,—any poison or toxic agent.

toxicity (tŏksĭs′ĭtĭ) *n.* [Gk. *toxikon*, poison.] The nature of a poison; the virulence of a poison or of a poisonous agency.

toxicology (tŏk′sĭkŏl′öjĭ) *n.* [Gk. *toxikon*, poison; *logos*, discourse.] The science treating of poisons and their effects.

toxiferous (tŏksĭf′ërŭs) *a.* [Gk. *toxikon*, poison; L. *ferre*, to carry.] Holding or carrying poison; toxicophorous.

toxigenic (tŏksĭjĕn'ĭk) *a.* [Gk. *toxicon*, poison; *-genes*, producing.] Producing a poison; toxicogenic.

toxiglossate (tŏk'sĭglŏs'āt) *a.* [Gk. *toxikon*, poison; *glossa*, tongue.] Having hollow lateral radula teeth conveying poisonous secretion of salivary glands, as certain carnivorous marine gastropods.

toxin (tŏk'sĭn) *n.* [Gk. *toxikon*, poison.] Any poison derived from a plant or animal: phytotoxin or zootoxin.

toxoid (tŏk'soid) *n.* [Gk. *toxikon*, poison; *eidos*, form.] A toxin deprived of its toxic but not of its antigenic capacity; anatoxin.

toxon (tŏk'sŏn) *n.* [Gk. *toxon*, bow.] A toxa or bow-shaped spicule.

toxophores (tŏk'söfōrz) *n. plu.* [Gk. *toxikon*, poison; *pherein*, to carry.] The poisoning qualities of toxin molecules; *cf.* haptophores.

trabant (trăbănt') *n.* [Ger. *Trabant*, satellite.] Short chromosome segment constricted from the rest; satellite, *q.v.*

trabeculae (trăbĕk'ūlē) *n. plu.* [L. *trabecula*, little beam.] Primordial lamellae of agarics; plates of sterile cells extending across sporangium of pteridophytes; a row of cells bridging a cavity; two curved bars of cartilage embracing hypophysis cerebri of embryo; small fibrous bands forming imperfect septa or framework of organs.

trabecular (trăbĕk'ūlăr) *a.* [L. *trabecula*, little beam.] *Pert.* or of nature of a trabecula; having a cross-barred framework; trabeculate.

trabs cerebri,—corpus callosum.

trace-elements,—elements occurring in minute quantities as natural constituents of living organisms or tissues, as Ag, Cd, Co, Cu, Fe, Li, Mn, Ni, Pb, Sr, V.

tracer-elements,—isotopes used for tracing chemical elements and compounds in living tissue; tracers.

trachea (trăkē'ă, trā'këă) *n.* [L.L. *trachia*, windpipe.] The windpipe; a respiratory tubule of insects and other arthropods; spiral or annular vascular tissue of plants; wood-vessel.

tracheal (trăkē'ăl, trā'këăl) *a.* [L.L. *trachia*, windpipe.] *Pert.*, resembling, or having tracheae; tracheate, *appl.* tissue, as of xylem; *appl.* ectodermal cavities opening into pneumatophore of certain Siphonophora.

tracheal gills,—small wing-like respiratory outgrowths from the abdomen of aquatic larvae of insects.

tracheary,—tracheal, tracheate.

tracheate (trā'këāt) *a.* [L.L. *trachia*, windpipe.] Having tracheae; trachean.

tracheid (trăk'ëĭd) *n.* [L.L. *trachia*, windpipe.] One of the cells with spiral thickening or bordered pits, conducting water and solutes, and forming woody tissue.

tracheidal cells,—pericycle cells resembling tracheids.

trachein (trăk'ëĭn) *n.* [L.L. *trachia*, windpipe.] Colloid substance of tracheal air sacs, contracting or expanding according to degree of moisture, in certain buoyant insect larvae.

trachelate (trăk'ēlāt) *a.* [Gk. *trachelos*, neck.] Narrowed, as in neck-formation.

trachelomastoid (trăk'ēlömăs'toid) *a.* [Gk. *trachelos*, neck; *mastos*, breast; *eidos*, form.] *Pert.* neck region and mastoid process; *appl.* muscle, longissimus capitis.

trachenchyma (trăkĕng'kĭmă) *n.* [L. *trachia*, windpipe; Gk. *engchyma*, infusion.] Tracheal vascular tissue.

tracheobronchial (trăk'ëöbrŏng'kĭăl) *a.* [L. *trachia*, windpipe; Gk. *brongchos*, bronchial tube.] *Appl.* lymph-glands; *appl.* a syrinx formed of lower end of trachea and upper bronchi.

tracheole (trăk'ëōl) *n.* [L. *trachia*, windpipe.] An ultimate branch of tracheal system.

tracheophyte (trăk'ëöfīt) *n.* [L.L. *trachia*, windpipe.] Any vascular plant, a pteridophyte or a spermatophyte.

trachychromatic (trăk'ĭkrōmăt'ĭk) *n.* [Gk. *trachys*, rugged; *chroma*, colour.] Staining or stained deeply. *Opp.* amblychromatic.

trachyglossate (trăk'ĭglŏs'āt) *a.* [Gk. *trachys*, rough; *glossa*, tongue.] With rasping or toothed tongue.

tract (trăkt) *n.* [L. *trahere*, to draw.] A region or area or system considered as a whole, as alimentary tract; a band, bundle, or system of nerve fibres.

tractellum (trăktĕl'ŭm) *n.* [L. *trahere*, to draw.] A flagellum of forward end of Mastigophora, or of zoospores, with circumductory motion.

tragus (trā'gŭs) *n.* [Gk. *tragos*, goat.] A small pointed eminence in front of concha of ear; its hair.

trama (trā'mă, trâmâ) *n.* [L. *trama*, woof.] A central core of interwoven hyphae of a fungal gill or conidiophore.

tramal (trām'ăl) *a.* [L. *trama*, woof.] In, from, or *pert.* trama.

transad (trăn'săd) *adv.* [L. *trans*, across; *ad*, to.] *Appl.* organisms of the same or closely related species which have become separated by an environmental barrier, as European and American reindeer.

transamination (trăn'sămĭnā'shŭn) *n.* [L. *trans*, across; Gk. *ammoniakon*, resinous gum.] Transfer of amino (NH_2) groups to another molecule.

transapical (trăn'săp'ĭkăl) *a.* [L. *trans*, across; *apex*, summit.] *Appl.* transverse axis and plane of diatom valve.

transect (trăn'sĕkt) *n.* [L. *trans*, across; *secare*, to cut.] A line, strip, or profile, as of vegetation, chosen for study and charting.

transection (trănsĕk'shŭn) *n.* [L. *trans*, across; *sectio*, a cut.] Cross section; section across a longitudinal axis.

transeptate (trănsĕp'tāt) *a.* [L. *trans*, across; *septum*, partition.] Having transverse partitions or septa.

transformation (trăns'fôrmā'shŭn) *n.* [L. *transformare*, to change in shape.] Change of form, as in metamorphosis; metabolism.

transfusion tissue,—tissue of gymnosperm leaves, consisting of parenchymatous and tracheidal cells.

transgenation,—point mutation or genovariation.

transilient (trănsĭl'ĭĕnt) *a.* [L. *transilire*, to leap over.] *Appl.* nerve fibres connecting brain convolutions not adjacent. *n.* A mutation.

transitional (trănsĭsh'ŏnăl) *a.* [L. *transire*, to go across.] *Appl.* epithelium occurring in ureters and urinary bladder, renewing itself by mitotic division of third and innermost layer of cells.

translocation (trăns'lŏkā'shŭn) *n.* [L. *trans*, across; *locus*, place.] Removal to a different place or habitat; diffusion, as of food material; change in position of a chromosome segment to another part of the same chromosome or of a different chromosome.

translocation quotient,—ratio of chemical content of shoot to that of root, a measure of mobility or relative translocation, *e.g.* of manganese.

transmedian (trănsmē'dĭăn) *a.* [L. *trans*, across; *medius*, middle.] *Pert.* or crossing the middle plane; *appl.* muscles.

transmutation theory,—theory that one species can evolve from another.

transpalatine (trănspăl'ătĭn) *n.* [L. *trans*, across; *palatus*, the palate.] A cranial bone of crocodiles, connecting pterygoid with jugal and maxilla.

transpinalis (trănspīnā'lĭs) *n.* [L. *trans*, across; *spina*, spine.] A muscle connecting transverse processes of vertebrae.

transpiration (trănspĭrā'shŭn) *n.* [L. *trans*, across; *spirare*, to breathe.] Exhalation of vapour through pores or stomata.

transplant (trănsplânt', trănzplănt') *v.* [L. *trans*, across; *plantare*, to plant.] To transfer tissue from one part to another part of the body of the same or that of another individual. (trăns′plânt, trănz′-plănt) *n.* Tissue transferred to another part ; graft.

transpyloric plane, — upper of imaginary horizontal planes dividing abdomen into artificial regions.

transudate (trănsū′dāt) *n.* [L. *trans*, beyond ; *sudare*, to sweat.] Any substance which has oozed through a membrane or pores.

transversal (trănsvĕr′săl) *a.* [L. *transversus*, across.] Lying across or between, as a transversal wall.

transverse (trănsvĕrs′) *a.* [L. *transversus*, across.] Lying across or between, as artery, colon, ligament, process ; heterotropous.

transversum (trănsvĕr′sŭm) *n.* [L. *transversus*, across.] In most reptiles, a cranial bone extending from pterygoid to maxilla.

transversus (trănsvĕr′sŭs) *n.* [L. *transversus*, across.] A transverse muscle, as of abdomen, thorax, pinna, tongue, foot, perinaeum.

trapeziform (trăpē′zĭfôrm) *a.* [Gk. *trapezion*, small table ; L. *forma*, shape.] Trapezium-shaped.

trapezium (trăpē′zĭŭm) *n.* [Gk. *trapezion*, small table.] The first carpal bone, at base of first metacarpal ; greater multangular bone ; portion of pons Varolii.

trapezius (trăpē′zĭŭs) *n.* [Gk. *trapezion*, small table.] A broad, flat, triangular muscle of neck and shoulders.

trapezoid (trăpē′zoid, trăp′ëzoid) *a.* [Gk. *trapezion*, small table ; *eidos*, form.] Trapezium-shaped ; *appl.* ligament, nucleus, ridge. *n.* Lesser multangular bone.

traumatic (trômăt′ĭk) *a.* [Gk. *trauma*, wound.] *Pert.*, or caused by, a wound or other injury.

traumatin (trô′mătĭn) *n.* [Gk. *trauma*, wound.] Substance occurring in injured plant cells, which is capable of causing uninjured cells to divide; wound hormone; $C_{11}H_{17}O_4N$.

traumatonasty (trô′mătönăs′tĭ) *n.* [Gk. *trauma*, wound ; *nastos*, close pressed.] Curvature response to stimulus of wounding.

traumatotropic (trô′mătötrŏp′ĭk) *a.* [Gk. *trauma*, wound ; *trope*, turning.] *Appl.* curvature of plant organ in response to a wounding influence ; traumatropic.

traumatropism (trômăt′röpĭzm) *n.* [Gk. *trauma*, wound ; *trope*, turn.] Curving of plant parts in response to wounds.

traumotaxis (trô′mötăk′sĭs) *n.* [Gk. *trauma*, wound ; *taxis*, arrangement.] Reaction after wounding, as in nuclei and protoplasts.

trefoil (trē′foil) *n.* [L. *trifolius*, three-leaved.] Flower or leaf with three lobes.

tremelloid (trĕm′ĕloid) *a.* [L. *tremere*, to tremble.] Gelatinous in substance or appearance.

trephocyte (trĕf′ösīt) *n.* [Gk. *trephein*, to nourish ; *kytos*, hollow.] A cell nourishing adjacent cells ; nurse cell ; sustentacular cell.

trephones (trëfōnz′) *n. plu.* [Gk. *trephein*, to nourish.] Nutritive substances formed on breaking down of cells and which stimulate cell-division.

triactinal (trīăk′tĭnăl) *a.* [Gk. *tria*, three ; *aktis*, ray.] Three-rayed.

triadelphous (trī′ădĕl′fŭs) *a.* [Gk. *tria*, three ; *adelphos*, brother.] Having stamens united by their filaments into three bundles.

triaene (trī′ēn) *n.* [Gk. *triaina*, trident.] A somewhat trident-shaped spicule.

triandrous (trīăn′drŭs) *a.* [Gk. *tria*, three ; *aner*, man.] Having three stamens.

triangle (trīăng′gl) *n.* [L. *triangularis*, three-sided.] A three-sided structure or area.

triangularis (trī′ăngūlā′rĭs) *n.* [L. *triangularis*, three-cornered.] Muscle from mandible to lower lip, which pulls down corner of mouth, depressor anguli oris ; muscle and tendinous fibres between dorsal surface of sternum and costal cartilages, transversus thoracis, which assists expiration.

trianthous (trīăn'thŭs) *a.* [Gk. *tria*, three; *anthos*, flower.] Having three flowers.

triarch (trī'ârk) *n.* [Gk. *tria*, three; *arche*, beginning.] Having three xylem bundles uniting to form the woody tissue of root.

triarticulate (trī'ârtĭk'ūlāt) *a.* [L. *tres*, three; *articulus*, joint.] Three-jointed.

Triassic (trīăs'ĭk) *a.* [Gk. *tria*, three.] *Appl.* the early period of the Mesozoic era.

triaster (trīăs'tĕr) *n.* [Gk. *tria*, three; *aster*, star.] Three chromatin masses resulting from tripolar mitosis, as in cancer cells.

triaxon (trīăk'sŏn) *n.* [Gk. *tria*, three; *axis*, axle.] A sponge spicule with three axes.

tribe (trīb) *n.* [L. *tribus*, tribe.] In classification, a subdivision of a family and differing in minor characters from other tribes.

triboloid (trĭb'ŏloid) *a.* [Gk. *tribolos*, burr; *eidos*, form.] Like a burr; prickly; echinulate.

triboluminescence (trĭb'ŏloomĭnĕs'ĕns) *n.* [Gk. *tribein*, to rub; L. *luminescere*, to grow light.] Luminescence produced by friction.

tribracteate (trībrăk'tēăt) *a.* [L. *tres*, three; *bractea*, thin plate of metal.] With three bracts.

trica (trī'kă) *n.* [F. *tricoter*, to knit.] A lichen apothecium with ridged spherical surface.

tricarpellary (trīkâr'pĕlărĭ) *a.* [Gk. *tria*, three; *karpos*, fruit.] With three carpels.

tricentric (trīsĕn'trĭk) *a.* [Gk. *tria*, three; *kentron*, centre.] Having three centromeres, *appl.* chromosomes.

triceps (trī'sĕps) *n.* [L. *tres*, three; *caput*, head.] *Appl.* a muscle with three heads or insertions.

trichidium (trĭkĭd'ĭŭm) *n.* [Gk. *thrix*, hair; *idion*, *dim.*] A sterigma.

trichilium (trĭkĭl'ĭŭm) *n.* [Gk. *thrix*, hair; *ile*, crowd.] A pad of matted hairs at base of certain leaf petioles.

trichites (trĭk'īts) *n. plu.* [Gk. *thrix*, hair.] Fine rod-like structures found in oral basket of certain infusoria; silicious spicules in certain sponges; hypothetical amylose crystals constituting a starch granule.

trichoblast (trĭk'ŏblăst) *n.* [Gk. *thrix*, hair; *blastos*, bud.] A cell, of plant epidermis, which develops into a root-hair.

trichobothrium (trĭk'ŏbŏth'rĭŭm) *n.* [Gk. *thrix*, hair; *bothros*, pit.] A conical protuberance with sense-hair, on each side of anal segment in certain myriopods; a vibratory sense-hair or setula in spiders.

trichocarpous (trĭk'ŏkâr'pŭs) *a.* [Gk. *thrix*, hair; *karpos*, fruit.] With hairy fruits.

trichocutis (trĭk'ŏkū'tĭs) *n.* [Gk. *thrix*, hair; L. *cutis*, skin.] Cutis of a stipe, formed by coherent hairs or filaments of trichoderm.

trichocyst (trĭk'ŏsĭst) *n.* [Gk. *thrix*, hair; *kystis*, bladder.] An oval or spindle-shaped protrusible body found in ectoplasm of infusoria.

trichoderm (trĭk'ŏdĕrm) *n.* [Gk. *thrix*, hair; *derma*, skin.] A filamentous outer layer of pileus and stipe of agarics. *Cf.* epitrichoderm.

trichodragmata (trĭk'ŏdrăg'mătă) *n. plu.* [Gk. *thrix*, hair; *dragma*, sheaf.] Straight, fine hair-like spicules in bundles.

trichogen (trĭk'ŏjĕn) *n.* [Gk. *thrix*, hair; *-genes*, producing.] A hair- or bristle-producing cell, in insects.

trichogyne (trĭk'ŏjĭnē) *n.* [Gk. *thrix*, hair; *gyne*, woman.] An elongated hair-like receptive cell at end of carpogonium of Thallophyta.

trichohyalin (trĭk'ŏhī'ălĭn) *n.* [Gk. *thrix*, hair; *hyalos*, glass.] A substance resembling eleidin, in granules in Huxley's layer of hair-follicle.

trichoid (trĭk'oid) *a.* [Gk. *thrix*, hair; *eidos*, form.] Hair-like; *appl.* a type of tactile sensilla in insects.

trichome (trĭk'ōm) *n.* [Gk. *trichoma*, growth of hair.] An outgrowth of plant epidermis, either hairs or scales; a hair tuft; a filamentous thallus; trichoma.

trichophore (trĭk′öfōr) *n*. [Gk. *thrix*, hair; *pherein*, to bear.] A group of cells bearing trichogyne; chaetigerous sac of annelids.

trichosiderin (trĭk′ösĭdērĭn) *n*. [Gk. *thrix*, hair; *sideros*, iron.] Iron-containing red pigment isolated from human red hair.

trichosis (trĭkō′sĭs) *n*. [Gk. *thrix*, hair.] Distribution of hair; abnormal hair growth.

trichospore,—zoospore, *q.v.*

trichothallic (trĭk′öthăl′ĭk) *a*. [Gk. *thrix*, hair; *thallos*, young shoot.] Having a filamentous thallus, as certain algae; *appl*. growth of filament by division of intercalary meristematic cells.

trichotomous (trĭkŏt′ömŭs) *a*. [Gk. *tricha*, threefold; *tome*, cutting.] Divided into three branches.

trichroic (trīkrō′ĭk) *a*. [Gk. *tria*, three; *chros*, colour.] Showing three different colours when seen in three different aspects.

trichromatic (trī′krōmăt′ĭk) *a*. [Gk. *tria*, three; *chroma*, colour.] Able to perceive the three primary colours; trichromic.

tricipital (trīsĭp′ĭtăl) *a*. [L. *tres*, three; *caput*, head.] Having three heads or insertions, as triceps.

tricoccous (trīkŏk′ŭs) *a*. [Gk. *tria*, three; *kokkos*, kernel.] *Appl*. a three-carpel fruit.

triconodont (trīkō′nödŏnt) *a*. [Gk. *tria*, three; *konos*, cone; *odous*, tooth.] *Appl*. tooth with three crown prominences in a line parallel to jaw axis.

tricostate (trīkŏs′tāt) *a*. [L. *tres*, three; *costa*, rib.] With three ribs.

tricotyledonous (trī′kŏtĭlē′dönŭs) *a*. [Gk. *tria*, three; *kotyledon*, cup-like hollow.] With three cotyledons.

tricrotic (trīkrŏt′ĭk) *a*. [Gk. *tria*, three; *krotein*, to beat.] Having a triple beat in the arterial pulse.

tricrural (trīkroor′ăl) *a*. [L. *tres*, three; *crus*, leg.] With three branches.

tricuspid (trīkŭs′pĭd) *a*. [L. *tres*, three; *cuspis*, point.] Three-pointed; *appl*. triangular valve of heart.

tricuspidate (trīkŭs′pĭdāt) *a*. [L. *tres*, three; *cuspis*, point.] Having three points; *appl*. leaf.

tridactyl (trīdăk′tĭl) *a*. [Gk. *tria*, three; *daktylos*, finger.] Having three digits; with three jaws, *appl*. pedicellariae; tridactyle.

tridentate (trīdĕn′tāt) *a*. [L. *tridens*, three-pronged.] Having three tooth-like divisions.

tridynamous (trīdĭn′ămŭs) *a*. [Gk. *tria*, three; *dynamis*, power.] With three long and three short stamens.

trifacial (trīfā′shĭăl) *a*. [L. *tres*, three; *facies*, face.] *Appl*. fifth cranial nerve, the trigeminal.

trifarious (trīfā′rĭŭs) *a*. [L. *trifarius*, of three sorts.] In groups of three; of three kinds; in three rows; having three surfaces.

trifid (trī′fĭd) *a*. [L. *trifidus*, three-forked.] Cleft to form three lobes.

triflagellate (trīflăj′ēlāt) *a*. [L. *tres*, three; *flagellum*, whip.] Having three flagella.

trifoliate (trīfō′lĭăt) *a*. [L. *tres*, three; *folium*, leaf.] Having three leaves growing from same point.

trifoliolate (trīfō′lĭölāt) *a*. [L. *tres*, three; *dim*. of *folium*, leaf.] With three leaflets growing from same point.

trifurcate (trīfŭr′kāt) *a*. [L. *trifurcatus*, three-forked.] With three forks or branches.

trigamma (trīgăm′ă) *n*. [Gk. *tria*, three; γ, gamma.] Three-pronged forked wing venation in Lepidoptera.

trigamous (trĭg′ămŭs) *a*. [Gk. *tria*, three; *gamos*, marriage.] *Appl*. flower-head with staminate, pistillate, and hermaphrodite flowers.

trigeminal (trījĕm′ĭnăl) *a*. [L. *trigeminus*, triplet.] Consisting of, or *pert*., three structures; *appl*. fifth cranial nerve, with ophthalmic, maxillary, and mandibular divisions; *appl*. arrangement of pairs of pores in three rows in ambulacra of some echinoids.

trigeneric (trījĕnĕr'ĭk) *a.* [L. *tres*, three; *genus*, race.] *Pert.* or derived from three genera; *appl.* hybrids.

trigenic (trījĕn'ĭk) *a.* [Gk. *tria*, three; *genos*, descent.] *Pert.* or controlled by three genes.

trigon (trī'gŏn) *n.* [Gk. *tria*, three; *gonia*, angle.] Triangle of cusps of upper jaw molar teeth.

trigonal (trĭg'ŏnăl) *a.* [Gk. *trigonos*, triangular.] Ternary or triangular when *appl.* symmetry with three parts to a whorl; *appl.* three-sided stems.

trigone (trīgōn) *n.* [Gk. *trigonon*, triangle.] Also trigonum,—a small triangular space, as olfactory trigone, trigonum vesicae, etc.

trigonid (trĭg'ōnĭd) *n.* [Gk. *trigonon*, triangle.] Triangle of cusps of lower molar teeth.

trigonum (trĭg'ōnŭm) *n.* [Gk. *trigonon*, triangle.] A trigone; os trigonum, posterior process of talus forming a separate ossicle.

trigynous (trĭj'ĭnŭs) *a.* [Gk. *tria*, three; *gyne*, woman.] Having three styles.

triheterozygote (trīhĕt'ĕrōzī'gōt) *n.* [Gk. *tria*, three; *heteros*, other; *zygotos*, yoked together.] An organism heterozygous for three genes.

trijugate (trī'joogāt) *a.* [L. *tres*, three; *jugum*, yoke.] Having three pairs of leaflets.

trilabiate (trīlā'bĭāt) *a.* [L. *tres*, three; *labium*, lip.] With three lips.

trilacunar (trī'lăkū'năr) *a.* [L. *tres*, three; *lacuna*, cavity.] With three lacunae; having three leaf-gaps, *appl.* nodes.

trilobate (trī'lŏbāt) *a.* [Gk. *tria*, three; *lobos*, lobe.] Three-lobed.

trilocular (trīlŏk'ūlăr) *a.* [L. *tres*, three; *loculus*, compartment.] Having three cells or loculi.

trilophodont (trīlŏf'ŏdŏnt) *a.* [Gk. *tria*, three; *lophos*, crest; *odous*, tooth.] Having three-crested teeth.

trilophous (trīlŏf'ŭs) *a.* [Gk. *tria*, three; *lophos*, crest.] *Appl.* rayed spicule with three rays branched or ridged.

trimerous (trĭm'ĕrŭs) *a.* [Gk. *tria*, three; *meros*, part.] Composed of three or multiples of three, as parts of flower.

trimitic (trīmĭt'ĭk) *a.* [Gk. *tria*, three; *mitos*, thread.] Having three kinds of hyphae: supporting, connective, and reproductive. *Cf.* dimitic.

trimonoecious (trīmŏnē'sĭŭs) *a.* [Gk. *tria*, three; *monos*, alone; *oikos*, house.] With male, female, and hermaphrodite flowers on the same plant.

trimorphism (trīmôr'fĭzm) *n.* [Gk. *tria*, three; *morphe*, form.] Occurrence of three distinct forms or forms of organs in one life-cycle or in one species; trimorphous condition.

trinervate (trīnĕr'vāt) *a.* [L. *tres*, three; *nervus*, sinew.] Having three veins or ribs running from base to margin of leaf.

trinomial (trīnō'mĭăl) *a.* [L. *tres*, three; *nomen*, name.] *Appl.* names consisting of three terms; *cf.* binomial.

triod (trī'ŏd) *n.* [Gk. *triodos*, meeting of three roads.] A three-rayed or triactinal spicule in sponges.

trioecious (trīē'sĭŭs) *a.* [Gk. *tria*, three; *oikos*, house.] Producing male, female, and hermaphrodite forms on different plants; trioikous.

triosseum (trīŏs'ēŭm) *a.* [L. *tres*, three; *ossa*, bones.] *Appl.* foramen, the opening between coracoid, clavicle, and scapula.

triovulate (trīōv'ūlāt) *a.* [L. *tres*, three; *ovum*, egg.] Having three ovules.

tripartite (trīpâr'tīt, trĭp'ărtīt) *a.* [L. *tres*, three; *partitus*, separated.] Divided into three lobes, as a leaf.

tripetalous (trīpĕt'ălŭs) *a.* [Gk. *tria*, three; *petalon*, leaf.] Having three petals.

triphyllous (trīfĭl'ŭs, trĭf'ĭlŭs) *a.* [Gk. *tria*, three; *phyllon*, leaf.] Three-leaved; trifoliate.

tripinnate (trīpĭn'āt) *a.* [L. *tres*, three; *pinna*, feather.] Thrice pinnate; divided pinnately three times.

tripinnatifid (trīpĭnăt'ĭfĭd) *a.* [L. *tres*, three; *pinna*, feather; *findere*, to cleave.] Divided three times in a pinnatifid manner.

tripinnatisect (trīpĭnăt'ĭsĕkt) *a.* [L. *tres*, three; *pinna*, feather; *secare*, to cut.] Thrice pinnatisect; three times lobed with divisions nearly to midrib.

triplechinoid,—*see* diadematoid.

triple-nerved,—*appl.* a leaf with three prominent veins.

triplex (trĭp'lĕks) *a.* [L. *triplex*, three-fold.] Having three dominant genes, in polyploidy.

triplicostate (trĭp'lĭkŏs'tāt) *a.* [L. *triplus*, triple; *costa*, rib.] Having three ribs.

triploblastic (trĭp'löblăs'tĭk) *a.* [Gk. *triploos*, triple; *blastos*, bud.] With three primary germinal layers, epiblast, mesoblast, hypoblast.

triplocaulescent (trĭp'lökôlĕs'ënt) *a.* [L. *triplus*, triple; *caulis*, stalk.] Having axes of the third order.

triploid (trĭp'loid) *a.* [Gk. *triploos*, threefold.] With treble the normal number of gametic chromosomes. *n.* An organism with three haploid chromosome sets.

triplostichous (trĭplŏs'tĭkŭs) *a.* [Gk. *triploos*, threefold; *stichos*, row.] Arranged in three rows, as of cortical cells on small branches of Chara; *appl.* eyes with preretinal, retinal, and postretinal layers, as of larval scorpion.

tripod (trī'pŏd) *n.* [Gk. *tria*, three; *pous*, foot.] A tripod-shaped or three-legged spicule.

tripolar (trīpō'lăr) *a.* [Gk. *tria*, three; *polos*, axis.] *Appl.* division of chromatin to three poles in diseased cells instead of normal two poles, in mitosis.

tripolite (trĭp'ölīt) *n.* [*Tripolis* in North Africa; Gk. *lithos*, stone.] Siliceous deposit formed mainly of frustules of diatoms; diatomaceous earth, infusorial earth, kieselguhr.

tripton (trĭp'tŏn) *n.* [Gk. *triptos*, pounded.] Non-living seston, *q.v.*

tripus (trĭp'ŭs) *n.* [L. *tripus*, tripod.] Posterior Weberian ossicle, adjoining air-bladder; trifurcation of coeliac artery into left or coronary gastric, hepatic, and splenic arteries, tripus Halleri.

triquetrous (trĭkwĕt'rŭs) *a.* [L. *triquetrus*, three-cornered.] *Appl.* stem with three angles and three concave faces; *appl.* three-cornered or wedge-shaped bone.

triquetrum (trĭkwĕt'rŭm) *n.* [L. *triquetrum*, triangle.] The cuneiform carpal bone; triquetral or Wormian bone.

triquinate (trīkwī'nāt) *a.* [L. *tres*, three; *quini*, five each.] Divided into three, with each lobe again divided into five.

triradial (trīrā'dĭăl) *a.* [L. *tres*, three; *radius*, ray.] Having three branches as radii from one centre; triradiate; *appl.* orbital sulcus.

trisepalous (trīsĕp'ălŭs) *a.* [Gk. *tria*, three; F. *sépale*, sepal.] Having three sepals.

triseptate (trīsĕp'tāt) *a.* [L. *tres*, three; *septum*, partition.] Having three partitions or septa.

triserial (trīsē'rĭăl) *a.* [L. *tres*, three; *series*, row.] Arranged in three rows; trifarious; having three whorls.

trisomic (trīsō'mĭk) *a.* [Gk. *tria*, three; *soma*, body.] *Pert.*, or having, three homologous chromosomes.

trisporous (trīspō'rŭs) *a.* [Gk. *tria*, three; *sporos*, seed.] Having three spores; trisporic.

tristachyous (trīstă'kĭŭs) *a.* [Gk. *tria*, three; *stachys*, ear of corn.] With three spikes.

tristichous (trĭs'tĭkŭs) *a.* [Gk. *tria*, three; *stichos*, row.] Arranged in three vertical rows.

tristyly (trīstī'lĭ) *n.* [Gk. *tria*, three; *stylos*, pillar.] The condition of having short, medium-length and long styles.

triternate (trītĕr'nāt) *a.* [L. *tres*, three; *terni*, three each] Thrice ternately divided.

tritibial (trītĭb'ĭăl) *n.* [L. *tres*, three; *tibia*, shin.] Compound ankle-bone formed when centrale unites with talus.

tritoblasts (trĭt'öblăsts) *n. plu.* [Gk. *tritos*, third; *blastos*, bud.] A generation of Neosporidia produced by deutoblasts and in turn giving rise to teloblasts.

tritocerebrum (trĭt'ösĕr'ēbrŭm) *n.* [Gk. *tritos*, third; L. *cerebrum*, brain.] Third lobe of insect brain indicated during development; part of brain of higher Crustacea, consisting of antennal nerve centres; also tritocerebron.

tritocone (trĭt'ökōn) *n.* [Gk. *tritos*, third; *konos*, cone.] Premolar cusp.

tritonymph (trĭt'önĭmf) *n.* [Gk. *tritos*, third; *nymphe*, chrysalis.] Developmental stage or instar following the deutonymph in Acaridae.

tritor (trī'tŏr) *n.* [L. *tritor*, grinder.] Grinding surface of a tooth.

tritosternum (trĭt'östĕr'nŭm) *n.* [Gk. *tritos*, third; *sternon*, chest.] Sternite of third segment of prosoma or first segment of podosoma in Acarina.

tritozooid (trī'tözō'oid) *n.* [Gk. *tritos*, third; *zoon*, animal; *eidos*, form.] A zooid of third generation.

tritubercular (trītūbĕr'kūlăr) *a.* [L. *tres*, three; *tuberculum*, small hump.] *Appl.* molar teeth with three cusps; tricuspid.

trituberculy (trītūbĕr'kūlĭ) *n.* [L. *tres*, three; *tuberculum*, small hump.] Theory of molar tooth development.

triungulin (trīŭng'gūlĭn) *n.* [L. *tres*, three; *ungula*, claw.] Small, six-legged larva of Strepsiptera and Cantharidae; triungulus.

trivalent (trīv'ălĕnt) *n.* [L. *tres*, three; *valere*, to be strong.] Association of three chromosomes held together by chiasmata between diplotene and metaphase of first division in meiosis. *a. Appl.* amboceptor which can bind three different complements.

trivium (trĭv'ĭŭm) *n.* [L. *trivium*, cross-road.] The three rays of starfish farthest from madreporite; *cf.* bivium.

trizoic (trīzō'ĭk) *a.* [Gk. *tria*, three; *zoon*, animal.] *Appl.* protozoan spore containing three sporozoites.

trochal (trō'kăl) *a.* [Gk. *trochos*, wheel.] Wheel-shaped; *appl.* anterior disc of Rotifera.

trochantellus (trŏk'ăntĕl'ŭs) *n.* [Gk. *trochanter*, runner.] A segment of leg between trochanter and femur, in some insects.

trochanter (trökăn'tĕr) *n.* [Gk. *trochanter*, runner.] *Appl.* processes or prominences at upper end of thigh-bone—greater (major), lesser (minor), and third (tertius); small segment of leg between coxa and femur, in insects and spiders.

trochanteric fossa,—a deep depression on medial surface of neck of femur.

trochantin (trökăn'tĭn) *n.* [Gk. *trochanter*, runner.] A small sclerite at base of coxa of insect leg; sclerite for articulation of mandible in Orthoptera; lesser trochanter.

trochate (trŏk'āt) *a.* [Gk. *trochos*, wheel.] Having a wheel-like structure; wheel-shaped; trochiferous, trochiform.

trochite (trō'kīt) *n.* [Gk. *trochos*, wheel.] Segment or joint of stem of Crinoidea.

trochlea (trŏk'lēă) *n.* [Gk. *trochilia*, pulley.] A pulley-like structure through which a tendon passes, as of humerus, femur, orbit.

trochlear (trŏk'lēăr) *a.* [Gk. *trochilia*, pulley.] Shaped like a pulley; *pert.* trochlea; *appl.* nerve, pathetic or fourth cranial nerve to superior oblique muscle of eye.

trochoblasts (trŏk'öblăsts) *n. plu.* [Gk. *trochos*, wheel; *blastos*, bud.] Portions of segmenting egg destined to become prototroch of a trochosphere.

trochoid (trō'koid) *a.* [Gk. *trochos*, wheel; *eidos*, form.] Wheel-shaped; capable of rotating motion, as a pivot-joint.

trochophore (trŏk'ōfōr), **trochosphere** (trŏk'ŏsfēr) *n.* [Gk. *trochos*, wheel; *sphaira*, globe.] Free-swimming pelagic larval stage of many worms and some molluscs.

trochus (trŏk'ŭs) *n.* [Gk. *trochos*, wheel.] Inner, anterior, coarser ciliary zone of rotifer disc; *cf.* cingulum.

tropeic (trŏp'ēĭk) *a.* [Gk. *tropis*, keel.] Keel-shaped; cariniform.

trophallaxis (trŏfăl'ăksĭs) *n.* [Gk. *trophe*, nourishment; *allaxis*, interchange.] Interchange of food between larvae and imagines in certain insects; reciprocal feeding.

trophamnion (trŏfăm'nĭŏn) *n.* [Gk. *trophe*, nourishment; *amnion*, foetal membrane.] Sheath around developing egg of some insects, and passing nourishment to the embryo.

trophectoderm (trŏfĕk'tōdĕrm) *n.* [Gk. *trophe*, nourishment; *ektos*, outside; *derma*, skin.] Outer layer of mammalian blastocyst; trophoblast, *q.v.*

trophi (trō'fī) *n. plu.* [Gk. *trophe*, nourishment.] Hard chitinous chewing organs of rotifers; mouth-parts of insects; mandibles and maxillae collectively.

trophic (trŏf'ĭk) *a.* [Gk. *trophe*, nourishment.] *Pert.*, or connected with, nutrition; *appl.* nerves, stimuli, enlargement, etc.; *appl.* hormones influencing activity of endocrine glands and growth, as those secreted by the anterior lobe of the hypophysis; *appl.* nucleus: trophonucleus, *q.v.*

trophidium (trŏfĭd'ĭŭm) *n.* [Gk. *trophe*, brood; *idion*, *dim.*] The first larval stage of certain ants.

trophifer, trophiger (trŏf'ĭfĕr, -jĕr) *n.* [Gk. *trophe*, nourishment; L. *ferre*, *gerere*, to carry.] Postero-lateral region of insect head with which mouth-parts articulate.

trophoblast (trŏf'ōblăst) *n.* [Gk. *trophe*, nourishment; *blastos*, bud.] The outer layer of cells of epiblast, or of morula; trophoderm, *q.v.*

trophochromatin (trŏf'ōkrō'mătĭn) *n.* [Gk. *trophe*, nourishment; *chroma*, colour.] Vegetative chromatin, or that which regulates metabolism and functions; *cf.* idiochromatin.

trophochrome (trŏf'ōkrōm) *a.* [Gk. *trophe*, nourishment; *chroma*, colour.] *Appl.* cells with secretory granules giving staining reaction for mucus; mucoserous, muco-albuminous.

trophochromidia (trŏf'ōkrōmĭd'ĭă) *n. plu.* [Gk. *trophe*, nourishment; *chroma*, colour.] Vegetative chromidia; *cf.* idiochromidia.

trophocyst (trŏf'ōsĭst) *n.* [Gk. *trophe*, nourishment; *kystis*, bag.] Primordial structure giving rise to a sporangiophore, as in Pilobolus.

trophocytes (trŏf'ōsīts) *n. plu.* [Gk. *trophe*, nourishment; *kytos*, hollow.] Fat-cells used as food, in insect development.

trophoderm (trŏf'ōdĕrm) *n.* [Gk. *trophe*, nourishment; *derma*, skin.] Outer layer of chorion; trophectoderm with a mesodermal cell layer.

trophodisc (trŏf'ōdĭsk) *n.* [Gk. *trophe*, nourishment; *diskos*, plate.] Female gonophore of certain Hydrozoa.

trophogone (trŏfōgō'nē) *n.* [Gk. *trophe*, nourishment; *gone*, seed.] A nutritive organ in Ascomycetes, considered as an antheridium which has lost its normal function.

trophology (trŏfŏl'ōjĭ) *n.* [Gk. *trophe*, nourishment; *logos*, discourse.] The science of nutrition.

trophonemata (trŏf'ōnē'mătă) *n. plu.* [Gk. *trophe*, nourishment; *nema*, thread.] Uterine villi or hair-like projections which transfer nourishment to embryo through spiracle of elasmobranchs; villi.

trophont (trŏfŏnt) *n.* [Gk. *trephein*, to feed; *on*, being.] Growth stage in Holotricha.

trophonucleus (trŏf'ōnū'klēŭs) *n.* [Gk. *trophe*, nourishment; L. *nucleus*, kernel.] Larger nucleus of binuclear protozoa, regulating metabolism and growth; macronucleus, meganucleus; *cf.* kinetonucleus.

trophophore (trŏfōfōr) *n.* [Gk. *trophe*, nourishment; *pherein*, to bear.] In sponges, an internal bud or group of cells destined to become a gemmule.

trophoplasm (trŏf′öplăzm) *n.* [Gk. *trophe*, nourishment; *plasma*, mould.] Vegetative or nutritive part of cell, *opp.* kinoplasm; *cf.* idioplasm.

trophoplast (trŏf′öplăst) *n.* [Gk. *trophe*, nourishment; *plastos*, moulded.] A cell, nucleated or not; a plastid.

trophosome (trŏf′ösōm) *n.* [Gk. *trophe*, nourishment; *soma*, body.] The nutritive polypoid persons of a hydroid colony.

trophospongia (trŏf′öspŭn′jĭă) *n.* [Gk. *trophe*, nourishment; *spongia*, sponge.] Spongy vascular layer of mucous membrane between uterine wall and trophoblast.

trophospongium (trŏf′öspŭn′jĭŭm) *n.* [Gk. *trophe*, nourishment; *spongia*, sponge.] Canalisation of nerve cells, canaliculi occupied by branching processes of neuroglia cells.

trophotaeniae (trŏf′ötē′nĭē) *n. plu.* [Gk. *trophe*, nourishment; *tainia*, ribbon.] Embryonic rectal processes, for absorption of nutritive substances from ovarian fluid, in Goodeidae and certain other fishes.

trophotaxis (trŏf′ötăk′sĭs) *n.* [Gk. *trophe*, nourishment; *taxis*, arrangement.] Response to stimulation by an agent which may serve as food.

trophothylax (trŏf′öthī′lăks) *n.* [Gk. *trophe*, nourishment; *thylax*, sack.] Food-pocket on first abdominal segment of certain ant larvae.

trophotropism (trŏf′ötrōpĭzm) *n.* [Gk. *trophe*, nourishment; *trope*, turn.] Tendency of an organism to turn towards a food supply.

trophozoite (trŏf′özō′īt) *n.* [Gk. *trophe*, nourishment; *zoon*, animal.] The adult stage of a sporozoan.

trophozooid (trŏf′özō′oid) *n.* [Gk. *trophe*, nourishment; *zoon*, animal; *eidos*, form.] A nutritive zooid of free-swimming tunicate colonies.

tropibasic (trŏpĭbā′sĭk) *a.* [Gk. *trope*, turn; *basis*, base.] *Appl.* chondrocranium with small hypophysial fenestra and common trabecula; *cf.* platybasic.

tropic (trŏp′ĭk) *a.* [Gk. *trope*, turn.] *Pert.* tropism; *appl.* movement or curvature in response to a directional or unilateral stimulus.

tropine (trō′pĭn) *n.* [Gk. *trope*, turn.] Opsonin.

tropism (trŏp′ĭzm) *n.* [Gk. *trope*, turn.] Tendency of an organism to react in a certain way to a certain kind of stimulus; a tendency to move towards (positive) or away from (negative) the source of a stimulus; growth curvature movement; movement in response to stimuli, in sessile animals; *cf.* taxis.

tropocollagen (trŏpökŏl′ăjĕn) *n.* [Gk. *tropos*, mode; *kolla*, glue; *gennaein*, to produce.] A particle which unites with others to form a collagen.

tropophil (trŏp′öfĭl) *a.* [Gk. *tropos*, turn; *philos*, loving.] Tolerating alternating periods of cold and warmth, or of moisture and dryness; adapted to seasonal changes; *appl.* vegetation; tropophilous.

tropophyte (trŏp′öfīt) *n.* [Gk. *tropos*, turn; *phyton*, plant.] A changing plant, or one which is more or less hygrophilous in summer and xerophilous in winter; a plant growing in the tropics.

tropotaxis (trŏp′ötăk′sĭs) *n.* [Gk. *tropos*, turn; *taxis*, arrangement.] Movement leading to equal stimulation of symmetrically placed sense organs; symmetrical orientation.

true ribs,—ribs which are directly connected with sternum.

true soil,—solum.

trumpet hyphae,—elongated cells with enlarged ends in contact with those of adjoining cells, and comparable to sieve tubes, as in medulla of thallus in Laminaria.

truncate (trŭng'kāt) *a.* [L. *truncatus*, cut off.] Terminating abruptly, as if tapering end were cut off.

truncus arteriosus,—most anterior region of amphibian, or foetal, heart, through which blood is driven from ventricle.

trunk (trŭngk') *n.* [Fr. *tronc*, from *truncus*, stem of tree.] Main stem of tree; body exclusive of head and extremities; main stem of a vessel or nerve; truncus; proboscis, as of elephant.

trunk legs,—pereiopods of decapods, thoracic locomotory legs.

tryma (trī'mă) *n.* [Gk. *tryme*, hole.] A drupe with separable rind and two-valved endocarp with spurious dissepiments, as walnut.

trypanomonad (trĭp'ănömŏn'ăd) *a.* [Gk. *trypan*, to bore; *monas*, unit.] *Appl.* phase in development of trypanosome while in its invertebrate host; crithidial.

trypanorhynchus (trĭp'ănörĭng'kŭs) *n.* [Gk. *trypan*, to bore; *rhyngchos*, snout.] A spiniferous protrusible proboscis accompanying each phyllidium in certain Cestoidea.

trypsin (trĭp'sĭn) *n.* [Gk. *tryein*, to rub down; *pepsis*, digesting.] Proteolytic enzyme of pancreatic juice; similar enzyme of various plants and animals.

trypsinogen (trĭpsĭn'öjĕn) *n.* [Gk. *tryein*, to rub down; *pepsis*, digesting; *-genes*, producing.] Substance secreted by cells of pancreas converted into trypsin by enterokinase of succus entericus.

tryptic (trĭp'tĭk) *a.* [Gk. *tryein*, to rub down; *pepsis*, digesting.] Produced by, or *pert.*, trypsin.

tryptophane (trĭp'töfān) *n.* [Gk. *tryein*, to rub down; *pepsis*, digesting; *phainein*, to appear.] An amino-acid derivative elaborated in plants and essential for nutrition of animals; $C_{11}H_{12}O_2N_2$.

tuba (tū'bă) *n.* [L. *tuba*, trumpet.] A salpinx or tube, as tuba acustica or auditiva, the Eustachian tube; tuba uterina, Fallopian tube.

tubal,—*pert.* a tuba or tube.

tubar (tū'băr) *a.* [L. *tubus*, pipe.] Consisting of an arrangement of tubes, or forming a tube, as *appl.* system and skeleton in sponges.

tubate (tū'bāt) *a.* [L. *tubus*, pipe.] Tube-shaped; tubular; tubiform.

tube (tūb) *n.* [L. *tubus*, pipe.] Any tubular structure; cylindrical structure, as protective enveloping case of many animals; a mollusc siphon.

tube-feet,—organs connected with the water vascular system in various echinoderms, for locomotion, also modified for sensory, food-catching, and respiratory functions.

tuber (tū'bĕr) *n.* [L. *tuber*, knob.] Thickened fleshy underground stem with surface buds; rounded protuberance.

tuber cinereum,—hollow protuberance of grey matter between optic chiasma and corpora mamillaria of hypothalamus; tuber anterius.

tuber vermis,—part of superior vermis of cerebellum, continuous laterally with inferior semilunar lobules.

tubercle (tū'bĕrkl) *n.* [L. *tuberculum*, small hump.] A small rounded protuberance; root-swelling or nodule; a bulbil; rib-knob; a cusp; tuberculum.

tuberculate (tūbĕr'kūlāt) *a.* [L. *tuberculum*, small hump.] *Pert.* resembling, or having tubercles.

tuberculose (tūbĕr'kūlōs) *a.* [L. *tuberculum*, small hump.] Having many tubercles.

tuberiferous (tū'bĕrĭf'ĕrŭs) *a.* [L. *tuber*, hump; *ferre*, to bear.] Bearing or producing tubers.

tuberiform (tū'bĕrĭfôrm) *a.* [L. *tuber*, hump; *forma*, shape.] Resembling or shaped like a tuber; tuberoid.

tuberosity (tū'bĕrŏs'ĭtĭ) *n.* [L. *tuber*, hump.] Rounded eminence on a bone, as for muscle attachment.

tuberous (tū'bĕrŭs) *a.* [L. *tuber*, hump.] Covered with or having many tubers; tuberose.

tube-tonsil,—lymphoid tissue near pharyngeal opening of auditory tube.

tubicolous (tūbĭk'ölŭs) *a.* [L. *tubus*, tube; *colere*, to inhabit.] Inhabiting a tube.

tubicorn (tū'bĭkôrn) *a.* [L. *tubus*, tube; *cornu*, horn.] With hollow horns.

tubifacient (tū'bĭfā'shĭënt) *a.* [L. *tubus*, tube; *faciens*, making.] Tube-making, as some worms.

tubiflorous,—tubuliflorous.

tubilingual (tū'bĭlĭng'gwăl) *a.* [L. *tubus*, tube; *lingua*, tongue.] Having a tubular tongue, adapted for sucking.

tubiparous (tūbĭp'ărŭs) *a.* [L. *tubus*, tube; *parere*, to beget.] Secreting tube-forming material; *appl.* glands.

tubo-ovarian (tū'böōvā'rĭăn) *a.* [L. *tubus*, pipe; *ovarium*, ovary.] Of or *pert.* oviduct and ovary.

tubotympanic (tū'bötĭmpăn'ĭk) *a.* [L. *tubus*, pipe; *tympanum*, drum.] *Appl.* recess between first and third visceral arches, from which are derived the tympanic cavity and Eustachian tube.

tubular (tū'būlăr) *a.* [L. *tubulus*, small tube.] Having the form of a tube or tubule; tubiform, tubuliform; containing tubules; *appl.* dentine: orthodentine

tubulate (tū'būlāt) *a.* [L. *tubulus*, small tube.] Tubiform; tubular; tubuliferous.

tubule (tū'būl) *n.* [L. *tubulus*, small tube.] Any small hollow, cylindrical structure; tubulus.

tubuli,—*plu.* of tubulus.

tubuli contorti,—the convoluted seminiferous tubules.

tubuli recti,—straight tubules connecting seminiferous tubules and rete testis.

tubuliferous (tū'būlĭf'ërŭs) *a.* [L. *tubulus*, small tube; *ferre*, to carry.] Having a tubule or tubules.

tubuliflorous (tū'būlĭflō'rŭs) *a.* [L. *tubulus*, small tube; *flos*, flower.] Having florets with tubular corolla.

tubuliform (tū'būlĭfôrm) *a.* [L. *tubulus*, small tube; *forma*, shape.] Tube-shaped; *appl.* certain spinning glands.

tubulose (tū'būlōs) *a.* [L. *tubulus*, small tube.] Having, or composed of, tubular structures, as an aster head, a tubipore coral; hollow and cylindrical.

tubulus (tū'būlŭs) *n.* [L. *tubulus*, small tube.] A hymeneal pore; cylindrical ovipositor; a tubule. *Plu.* Any small tubular structures, as tubuli lactiferi, recti, seminiferi.

tumid (tū'mĭd) *a.* [L. *tumidus*, swollen.] Swollen; turgid.

tundra (toon'dră) *n.* [Russ.] Treeless region with permanently frozen subsoil.

tunic (tūn'ĭk), *n.* [L. *tunica*, coating.] An investing membrane or tissue, as those of bulbs, eye, kidney, ovary, testis, arteries, etc.

tunica,—a tunic; apical meristematic cells giving rise to protoderm.

tunica albuginea,—*see* albuginea.

tunicate (tū'nĭkāt) *a.* [L. *tunica*, coating.] Provided with a tunic or test; *appl.* bulbs with numerous concentric broad layers; enveloped in tough test or mantle. *n.* A sea-squirt or other form of Urochorda.

tunicine (tū'nĭsĭn) *n.* [L. *tunica*, coating.] A substance related to cellulose, in tunic of ascidians; tunicin; animal cellulose.

tunicle (tū'nĭkl) *n.* [L. *tunicula*, little coat.] A natural covering; integument.

tunnel of Corti [*A. Corti*, Italian histologist]. Triangular tunnel enclosed by two rows of pillars of Corti and basilar membrane.

turacin (tū'răsĭn) *n.* [*Turaco*, an African bird.] A water-soluble red plumage pigment containing copper, in turaco and other Musophagidae.

turacoverdin (tū'răkövër'dĭn) *n.* [*Turaco*; F. *vert*, green.] A green feather pigment containing iron, in certain plantain-eaters or Musophagidae.

turbinal (tŭr'bĭnăl) *a.* [L. *turbo*, whirl.] Spirally rolled or coiled, as bone or cartilage.

turbinate (tŭr'bĭnāt) *a.* [L. *turbo*, whirl.] Top-shaped; *appl.* pileus; *appl.* shells; *appl.* certain nasal bones, or conchae nasales.

turbinulate (tŭrbĭn'ūlāt) *a.* [*Dim.* of L. *turbo*, whirl.] Shaped like a small top ; *appl.* certain apothecia.

turgescence (tŭrjĕs'ĕns) *n.* [L. *turgescere*, to swell.] The process of distention of living cell tissue, due to increased internal pressure ; the turgescent condition ; turgor, turgidity.

turgor (tŭr'gŏr) *n.* [L. *turgere*, to swell.] Distention of cells or tissues due to internal pressure ; rigidity of plant tissue due to inflation of cells with water.

turio (tū'rĭö), **turion** (tū'rĭŏn) *n.* [L. *turio*, shoot.] Young scaly shoot budded off from underground stem ; winter-bud, as of Hydrocharis.

tutamen (tūtā'mĕn) *n.* [L. *tutamen*, protection.] Means of protection ; a protective structure, as eye-lid. *Plu.* tutamina.

tychocoen (tĭk'ösēn) *n.* [Gk. *tyche*, chance ; *koinos*, common.] Those members of a biocoenosis which thrive under different habitat conditions. *Opp.* eucoen.

tycholimnetic (tĭk'ölĭmnĕt'ĭk) *a.* [Gk. *tyche*, chance ; *limne*, marshy lake.] Temporarily attached to the bed of a lake and at other times floating ; *appl.* certain fresh-water organisms.

tychopotamic (tĭk'öpötăm'ĭk) *a.* [Gk. *tyche*, chance ; *potamos*, river.] Thriving only in backwaters, *appl.* potamoplankton.

tylhexactine (tĭl'hĕksăk'tĭn) *n.* [Gk. *tylos*, knob ; *hex*, six ; *aktis*, ray.] A hexactine spicule with rays ending in knobs.

tylosis (tĭlō'sĭs) *n.* [Gk. *tylos*, callus.] Development of irregular cells in a cell cavity ; a cellular intrusion into vessel through pits of parenchyma cells ; a callosity ; callus formation.

tylosoid (tī'lösoid) *n.* [Gk. *tylos*, knob ; *eidos*, form.] A resin duct filled with parenchymatous cells.

tylostyle (tī'löstīl) *n.* [Gk. *tylos*, knob ; *stylos*, pillar.] Spicule pointed at one end, knobbed at other.

tylotate (tĭlō'tāt) *a.* [Gk. *tylotos*, knobbed.] With a knob at each end.

tylote (tĭlōt', tī'lōt) *n.* [Gk. *tylotos*, knobbed.] A slender dumbbell-shaped spicule.

tylotic (tĭlŏt'ĭk) *a.* [Gk. *tylos*, callus.] Affected by tylosis.

tylotoxea (tī'lötŏk'sëă) *n.* [Gk. *tylos*, knob ; *oxys*, sharp.] A tylote with one sharp end, directed towards surface of sponge.

tylus (tī'lŭs) *n.* [Gk. *tylos*, knob.] A medial protuberance on head of certain Hemiptera.

tymbal,—timbal, *q.v.*

tympanic (tĭmpăn'ĭk) *a.* [Gk. *tympanon*, drum.] *Pert.* tympanum.

tympanohyal (tĭm'pănöhī'ăl) *n.* [Gk. *tympanon*, drum ; *hyoeides*, Y-shaped.] *Pert.* tympanum and hyoid ; part of hyoid arch embedded in petro-mastoid.

tympanum (tĭm'pănŭm) *n.* [Gk. *tympanon*, drum.] The epiphragm of mosses ; the drum-like cavity constituting middle ear ; drum of ear ; membrane of auditory organ on tibia, metathorax, or abdomen of insect ; inflatable air-sac on neck of some Tetraoninae.

type (tīp) *n.* [L. *typus*, pattern.] Sum of characteristics common to a large number of individuals, serving as a ground for classification ; a primary model ; the actual specimen described as the original of a new genus or species.

type locality,—the locality in which the holotype or other type used for designation of a species was found.

type number,—the most frequently occurring chromosome number in a taxonomic group ; modal number.

typhlosole (tĭf'lösōl) *n.* [Gk. *typhlos*, blind ; *solen*, channel.] Median dorsal longitudinal fold of intestine projecting into lumen of gut of some invertebrates.

typical (tĭp'ĭkăl) *a.* Gk. *typos*, pattern.] *Appl.* specimen conforming to type or primary example ; exhibiting in marked degree the essential characteristics of genus or species.

typogenesis (tī'pöjĕn'ĕsĭs) *n.* [Gk. *typos*, pattern; *genesis*, descent.] Phase of rapid type-formation in phylogenesis; quantitative or 'explosive' evolution.

typology (tīpŏl'öjĭ) *n.* [Gk. *typos*, pattern; *logos*, discourse.] The study of types, as of constitutional types.

typolysis (tīpŏl'ĭsĭs) *n.* [Gk. *typos*, pattern; *lysis*, loosing.] Phase preceding extinction of type; phylogerontic stage.

typonym (tī'pönĭm) *n.* [Gk. *typos*, pattern; *onyma*, name.] A name designating or based on a type specimen or type species.

typostasis (tīpŏst'ăsĭs, tīpöstā'sĭs) *n.* [Gk. *typos*, pattern; *stasis*, halt.] Relative absence of type formation, a static phase in phylogenesis.

tyramine (tī'rămĭn) *n.* [Gk. *tyros*, cheese; *ammoniacum*, resinous gum.] A substance causing rise of arterial pressure, formed by bacterial action on tyrosine; also secreted by Cephalopoda; $C_8H_{11}ON$.

tyrosine (tī'rösĭn) *n.* [Gk. *tyros*, cheese.] An amino-acid synthesised in plants, and utilised in animals, as in formation of melanin, adrenaline, and thyroxine; $C_9H_{11}O_3N$.

Tyson's glands [*E. Tyson*, English anatomist]. Sebaceous glands round the corona of the glans penis.

U

ula (ū'lă) *n.plu.* [Gk. *oula*, the gums.] The gums; gingivae.

uletic (ūlĕt'ĭk) *a.* [Gk. *oulon*, gum.] *Pert.* the gums; gingival.

uliginous (ūlĭj'ĭnŭs) *a.* [L. *uliginosus*, oozy.] Swampy; growing in swampy soil; uliginose; paludicole.

ulna (ŭl'nă) *n.* [L. *ulna*, elbow.] A long bone on medial side of forearm parallel with radius.

ulnar (ŭl'năr) *a.* [L. *ulna*, elbow.] *Pert.* ulna; *appl.* artery, nerve, veins, bone, ligaments.

ulnar nervure,—radiating or cross nervure in wing of insects.

ulnare (ŭlnā'rē) *n.* [L. *ulna*, elbow.] Bone, in proximal row of carpals, lying at distal end of ulna.

ulnocarpal (ŭlnökâr'păl) *a.* [L. *ulna*, elbow; *carpus*, wrist.] *Pert.* ulna and carpus.

ulnoradial (ŭlnörā'dĭăl) *a.* [L. *ulna*, elbow; *radius*, radius.] *Pert.* ulna and radius.

uloid (ū'loid) *a.* [Gk. *oule*, scar; *eidos*, form.] Resembling a scar.

ulotrichous (ūlŏt'rĭkŭs) *a.* [Gk. *oulos*, woolly; *thrix*, hair.] Having woolly or curly hair.

ultimate cell,—tip cell, *q.v.*

ultimobranchial bodies, — pair of gland rudiments derived from fifth pharyngeal pouches, which later degenerate and disappear; postbranchial or suprapericardial bodies.

umbel (ŭm'bĕl) *n.* [L. *umbella*, *dim.* of *umbra*, shade.] An arrangement of flowers or of polyps springing from a common centre and forming a flat or rounded cluster.

umbella (ŭmbĕl'ă) *n.* [L. *umbella*, sun-shade.] An umbel; umbrella of jelly-fish.

umbellate (ŭm'bĕlāt) *a.* [L. *umbella*, shade.] Arranged in umbels.

umbellet,—umbellule.

umbelliferous (ŭm'bĕlĭf'ĕrŭs) *a.* [L. *umbella*, shade; *ferre*, to carry.] Producing umbels.

umbelliform (ŭmbĕl'ĭfôrm) *a.* [L. *umbella*, shade; *forma*, shape.] Shaped like an umbel.

umbelligerous (ŭm'bĕlĭj'ĕrŭs) *a.* [L. *umbella*, shade; *gerere*, to carry.] Bearing flowers or polyps in umbellate clusters.

umbellula (ŭmbĕl'ūlă) *n.* [L.L. *umbellula*, *dim.* of *umbella*, shade.] A large cluster of polyps at tip of elongated stalk of rachis; umbellule, *q.v.*

umbellulate (ŭmbĕl'ūlāt) *a.* [L.L. *umbellula*, small umbel.] Arranged in umbels and umbellules.

umbellule (ŭm'bĕlūl) *n.* [L.L. *umbellula*, small umbel.] A small or secondary umbel.

umbilical (ŭm'bĭlī'kăl, ŭmbĭl'ĭkăl) *a.* [L. *umbilicus*, navel.] *Pert.* navel, or umbilical cord ; *appl.* arteries, veins, tissues, vesicle, plane, etc. ; omphalic.

umbilical cord,—navel cord connecting embryo with placenta ; funicle or prolongation by which ovule is attached to placenta.

umbilicate (ŭmbĭl'ĭkāt) *a.* [L. *umbilicus*, navel.] Having a central depression ; navel-like ; omphaloid.

umbilicus (ŭm'bĭlī'kŭs) *n.* [L. *umbilicus*, navel.] The navel, central abdominal depression at place of attachment of umbilical cord ; hilum ; basal depression of certain spiral shells ; an opening near base of feather ; a structure for attachment of thallus in certain lichens.

umbo (ŭm'bō) *n.* [L. *umbo*, shield-boss.] A protuberance like boss of a shield ; swollen point of a cone scale ; convexity of tympanic membrane at point of attachment of manubrium mallei ; beak or older part of bivalve shell ; a prothoracic projection in certain insects.

umbonal (ŭm'bönăl) *a.* [L. *umbo*, shield-boss.] *Pert.* an umbo.

umbonate (ŭm'bönāt) *a.* [L. *umbo*, shield-boss.] Having a conical or rounded protuberance.

umbones,—*plu.* of umbo.

umbraculiferous (ŭmbrăk'ūlĭf'ërŭs) *a.* [L. *umbraculum*, sun-shade.] Bearing an umbrella-like organ or structure.

umbraculiform (ŭmbrăk'ūlĭfôrm) *a.* [L. *umbraculum*, sun-shade ; *forma*, shape.] Shaped like an expanded umbrella.

umbraculum (ŭmbrăk'ūlŭm) *n.* [L. *umbraculum*, sun-shade.] Any umbrella-like structure ; pigmented fringe of iris, in certain ungulates ; pupillary appendage, in amphibians.

umbraticolous (ŭm'brătĭk'ölŭs) *a.* [L. *umbraticola*, one who likes the shade.] Growing in a shaded habitat ; skiophilous.

umbrella (ŭmbrĕl'ă) *n.* [L. *umbella*, sun-shade.] The contractile disc of a jelly-fish ; web between arms of certain Octopoda.

uncate (ŭng'kāt) *a.* [L. *uncus*, hook.] Hooked ; hamate.

unciferous (ŭnsĭf'ërŭs) *a.* [L. *uncus*, hook ; *ferre*, to carry.] Bearing hooks or hook-like processes.

unciform (ŭn'sĭfôrm) *a.* [L. *uncus*, hook ; *forma*, shape.] Shaped like a hook or barb ; *appl.* process of ethmoid bone. *n.* Unciform bone or os hamatum or uncinatum of wrist.

uncinate (ŭn'sĭnāt) *a.* [L. *uncinus*, hook.] Unciform ; hook-like ; *appl.* fasciculus associating temporal and frontal lobes of brain ; *appl.* process, of ribs of birds ; process of ethmoid, of head of pancreas ; *appl.* decurrent lamellae of agarics.

uncinus (ŭnsī'nŭs) *n.* [L. *uncinus*, hook.] Small hooked, or hook-like, structure ; a crotchet ; one of small hooks found on segments of many worms ; a hook-like structure found in certain infusorians ; a marginal tooth of gastropods.

unconditioned,—*appl.* inborn reflex, *opp.* conditioned or acquired reflex.

uncus (ŭng'kŭs) *n.* [L. *uncus*, hook.] Hook-shaped anterior extremity of hippocampal gyrus ; hooked head of malleus of rotifers ; hook-like or bifid process on dorsal portion of ninth abdominal segment of male Lepidoptera ; uncinate hair.

undate (ŭn'dāt) *a.* [L. *undare*, to rise in waves.] Wavy ; undose ; undulating.

under-wing,—one of posterior wings of any insect.

undose (ŭn'dōs) *a.* [L. *undosus*, billowy.] Having undulating and nearly parallel depressions which run linto one another and resemble ripple-marks ; undate.

undulating membrane,—a membrane formed by fusion of cilia, for wafting food to the mouth in ciliates ; a protoplasmic membrane between body and part of flagellum in flagellates.

unequally pinnate,—odd pinnate, imparipinnate, pinnate with single terminal leaflet.

ungual (ŭng'gwăl) *a.* [L. *unguis*, nail.] *Pert.* or having a nail or claw ; *appl.* phalanges bearing claws or nails.

unguicorn,—dertrotheca, *q.v.*

unguiculate (ŭnggwĭk'ūlāt) *a.* [L. *unguiculus*, little nail.] Clawed ; *appl.* petals with narrowed stalk-like portion below.

unguis (ŭng'gwĭs) *n.* [L. *unguis*, claw.] A nail or claw ; narrow stalk-like portion of some petals ; a chitinous hook on foot of insect ; distal joint, the crochet or fang, of arachnid chelicerae ; lacrimal bone ; the calcar avis, *q.v.*

unguitractor (ŭng'wĭtrăk'tŏr) *n.* [L. *unguis*, claw ; *tractus*, pull.] A median plate of pretarsus for attachment of retractor or flexor muscle of claw, in insects.

ungula (ŭng'gūlă) *n.* [L. *ungula*, hoof.] Hoof ; unguis of petal.

ungulate (ŭng'gūlāt) *a.* [L. *ungula*, hoof.] Hoofed ; hoof-like.

unguligrade (ŭng'gūlĭgrād') *a.* [L. *ungula*, hoof ; *gradus*, step.] Walking upon hoofs.

uniascal (ū'nĭăs'kăl) *a.* [L. *unus*, one ; Gk. *askos*, bag.] Containing a single ascus ; *appl.* locules.

uniaxial (ū'nĭăk'sĭăl) *a.* [L. *unus*, one; *axis*, axis.] With one axis; monaxial.

unibranchiate (ū'nĭbrăng'kĭāt) *a.* [L. *unus*, one ; Gk. *brangchia*, gills.] Having one gill.

unicapsular (ū'nĭkăp'sūlăr) *a.* [L. *unus*, one ; *capsula*, small case.] Having only one capsule.

unicell (ū'nĭsĕl') *n.* [L. *unus*, one ; *cellula*, cell.] A unicellular organism ; protophyton, or protozoon.

unicellular (ū'nĭsĕl'ūlăr) *a.* [L. *unus*, one ; *cellula*, cell.] Having only one cell, or consisting of one cell.

uniciliate (ū'nĭsĭl'ĭāt) *a.* [L. *unus*, one ; *cilium*, eyelash.] Having one cilium or flagellum.

unicorn (ū'nĭkôrn) *a.* [L. *unus*, one ; *cornu*, horn.] Having a single horn-like spine ; *appl.* shells.

unicostate (ū'nĭkŏs'tāt) *a.* [L. *unus*, one ; *costa*, rib.] Having a single prominent mid-rib, as certain leaves.

unicotyledonous (ū'nĭkŏtĭlē'dŏnŭs) *a.* [L. *unus*, one ; Gk. *kotyle*, cup.] Having a single cotyledon ; monocotyledonous.

unicuspid (ū'nĭkŭs'pĭd) *a.* [L. *unus*, one ; *cuspis*, point of spear.] Having one tapering point, as a tooth.

unidactyl (ū'nĭdăk'tĭl) *a.* [L. *unus*, one ; Gk. *daktylos*, finger.] Having one digit only ; monodactylous.

uniembryonate (ū'nĭĕm'brĭŏnāt) *a.* [L. *unus*, one ; Gk. *embryon*, foetus.] Having one embryo only.

unifacial (ū'nĭfā'shăl) *a.* [L. *unus*, one ; *facies*, face.] Having one face or chief surface.

unifactorial (ū'nĭfăktō'rĭăl) *a.* [L. *unus*, one ; *facere*, to make.] *Pert.* or controlled by a single gene ; monogenic.

uniflagellate (ū'nĭflăj'ĕlāt) *a.* [L. *unus*, one ; *flagellum*, whip.] Having only one flagellum.

uniflorous (ū'nĭflō'rŭs) *a.* [L. *unus*, one ; *flos*, flower.] Bearing only one flower.

unifoliate (ū'nĭfō'lĭāt) *a.* [L. *unus*, one ; *folium*, leaf.] With one leaf.

unifoliolate (ū'nĭfō'lĭōlāt) *a.* [L. *unus*, one ; *foliolum*, *dim.* of *folium*, leaf.] Having one leaflet only.

uniforate (ūnĭf'ŏrāt) *a.* [L. *unus*, one ; *foratus*, pierced.] Having only one opening.

unigeminal (ū'nĭjĕm'ĭnăl) *a.* [L. *unus*, one ; *geminus*, twin-born.] *Appl.* arrangement of pore-pairs in one row, in ambulacra of some echinoids.

unigenesis,—monogenesis.

unihumoral (ū'nĭhū'mŏrăl) *a.* [L. *unus*, one ; *humor*, fluid.] Activated by only one neurohumor, *appl.* certain chromatophores.

unijugate (ū'nĭjoog'āt) *a.* [L. *unus*, one ; *jugum*, yoke.] *Appl.* pinnate leaf having one pair of leaflets.

unilabiate (ū'nĭlā'bĭāt) *a.* [L. *unus*, one ; *labium*, lip.] With one lip or labium.

unilacunar (ū'nĭlăkū'năr) *a.* [L. *unus*, one ; *lacuna*, cavity,] With one lacuna ; having one leaf-gap, *appl.* nodes.

unilaminate (ū'nĭlăm'ĭnāt) *a.* [L. *unus*, one ; *lamina*, layer.] Having one layer only ; *appl.* tissues.

unilateral (ū'nĭlăt'ĕrăl) *a.* [L. *unus*, one ; *latus*, side.] Arranged on one side only.

unilocular (ū'nilŏk'ūlăr) *a.* [L. *unus*, one ; *loculus*, compartment.] One-celled ; having one compartment only ; *appl.* ovaries ; *appl.* Foraminifera.

unimucronate (ū'nĭmū'krŏnāt) *a.* [L. *unus*, one ; *mucro*, sharp point.] Having a single sharp point or tip ; *appl.* leaves, etc.

uninucleate (ū'nĭnū'klēāt) *a.* [L. *unus*, one ; *nucleus*, nucleus.] Having one nucleus ; uninuclear.

uniovular (ūnĭô'vūlâr) *a.* [L. *unus*, one ; *ovum*, egg.] *Pert.* a single ovum ; monozygotic ; *appl.* twinning.

uniparous (ūnĭp'ărŭs) *a.* [L. *unus*, one ; *parere*, to beget.] Producing one offspring at a birth ; having a cymose inflorescence with one axis at each branching.

unipennate (ū'nĭpĕn'āt) *a.* [L. *unus*, one ; *penna*, feather.] *Appl.* muscle having its tendon of insertion extending along one side.

unipetalous (ū'nĭpĕt'ălŭs) *a.* [L. *unus*, one ; Gk. *petalon*, leaf.] Having one petal ; monopetalous.

unipolar (ū'nĭpō'lăr) *a.* [L. *unus*, one ; *polus*, pole.] Having one pole only ; *appl.* some nerve-cells.

unipotent (ūnĭp'ŏtĕnt) *a.* [L. *unus*, one ; *potens*, powerful.] *Appl.* cells which can develop into cells of one kind only ; unipotential, *opp.* totipotent.

uniramous (ū'nĭrā'mŭs) *a.* [L. *unus*, one ; *ramus*, branch.] Having one branch ; *appl.* crustacean appendage lacking an exopodite ; *appl.* antennule.

unisepalous,—monosepalous.

uniseptate (ū'nĭsĕp'tāt) *a.* [L. *unus*, one ; *septum*, hedge.] Having one septum or dividing partition.

uniserial (ūnĭsē'rĭăl) *a.* [L. *unus*, one ; *series*, rank.] Arranged in one row or series ; *appl.* certain ascospores ; *appl.* fins with radials on one side of basalia ; uniseriate, *appl.* medullary rays ; *appl.* thecae of graptolites.

uniserrate (ū'nĭsĕr'āt) *a.* [L. *unus*, one ; *serra*, saw.] Having only one row of serrations on edge.

uniserrulate (ū'nĭsĕr'ūlāt) *a.* [L. *unus*, one ; *serrula*, *dim.* of *serra*, saw.] Having one row of small serrations on edge.

unisetose (ū'nĭsē'tōs) *a.* [L. *unus*, one ; *seta*, bristle.] Bearing one bristle.

unisexual (ū'nĭsĕk'sūăl) *a.* [L. *unus*, one ; *sexus*, sex.] Of one or other sex ; distinctly male or female ; diclinous ; gonochoristic.

unispiral (ū'nĭspī'răl) *a.* [L. *unus*, one ; *spira*, coil.] Having one spiral only.

unistrate (ū'nĭstrāt) *a.* [L. *unus*, one ; *stratum*, layer.] Having only one layer ; unistratose.

univalent (ūnĭv'ălĕnt, ū'nĭvā'lĕnt) *a.* [L. *unus*, one ; *valere*, to be strong.] *Appl.* a single unpaired chromosome.

univalve (ū'nĭvălv') *n.* [L. *unus*, one ; *valvae*, folding doors.] A shell consisting of one piece or valve, as a gastropod shell.

universal donor,—person with blood of group O, or four, whose blood may be transfused into, or whose skin may be grafted on to, a member of any other group, without harmful reaction.

universal recipient,—person with blood of group AB, or one, into whom blood may be transfused from a member of any other group, without harmful reaction.

universal veil,—tissue enveloping pileus and stipe in angiocarpic Agaricales and Boletales, separated later from the pileus and forming the volva ; velum universale.

univoltine (ū'nĭvŏl'tĭn) *a.* [L. *unus*, one ; It. *volta*, time.] Producing one brood in the season, as certain silkworms, coccids.

unpaired (ŭn'pārd) *a.* [L. *un*, not ; *par*, equal.] Situated in median line of body, consequently single.

urachus (ū'răkŭs) *n.* [Gk. *ouron*, urine; *echein*, to hold.] The median umbilical ligament; fibrous cord extending from apex of bladder to umbilicus.

urate (ū'rāt) *n.* [Gk. *ouron*, urine.] A salt of uric acid; *appl.* excretory cells in fat-body of insects lacking Malpighian tubules.

urceolate (ŭr'sēōlāt) *a.* [L. *urceolus*, small pitcher.] Urn- or pitcher-shaped; *appl.* apothecium; *appl.* calyx or corolla; *appl.* shells of various protozoa; having an urceolus.

urceolus (ŭrsē'ōlŭs) *n.* [L. *urceolus*, small pitcher.] Any pitcher-shaped structure; the external tube of certain rotifers.

urea (ū'rēă) *n.* [Gk. *ouron*, urine.] Carbamide, a crystalline excretory substance, chief organic constituent of urine; $CO(NH_2)_2$.

uredia,—*plu.* of uredium.

uredial (ūrē'dĭăl) *a.* [L. *uredo*, blight.] *Appl.* or *pert.* the summer stage of rust fungi; uredinial.

urediniospore,—uredospore.

uredinium (ū'rēdĭn'ĭŭm) *n.* [L. *uredo*, blight.] In rusts, the sorus bearing uredospores.

urediospore,—uredospore.

uredium (ūrē'dĭŭm) *n.* [L. *uredo*, blight.] A sorus bearing summer-spores in rust fungi; uredinium.

uredo (ūrē'dō) *n.* [L. *uredo*, blight.] Summer stage of rust fungi.

uredobuds,—uredospores.

uredogonidium,—uredospore.

uredosorus (ūrē'dōsō'rŭs) *n.* [L. *uredo*, blight; Gk. *soros*, heap.] A group of developing uredospores.

uredospores (ūrē'dōspōrz) *n. plu.* [L. *uredo*, blight; Gk. *sporos*, seed.] Reddish summer-spores borne on sporophore of rust fungi; uredobuds.

ureotelic (ū'rēōtĕl'ĭk) *a.* [Gk. *ouron*, urine; *telos*, end.] Excreting nitrogen as urea; *appl.* mammals; *cf.* uricotelic.

ureter (ūrē'tĕr) *n.* [Gk. *oureter*, ureter.] Duct conveying urine from kidney to bladder or cloaca.

urethra (ūrē'thră) *n.* [Gk. *ourethra*, from *ouron*, urine.] Duct leading off urine from bladder, and in male conveying semen in addition.

uric acid,—end-product of nucleic acid katabolism in mammals, main nitrogenous constituent of urine in reptiles and birds; trioxypurine, $C_5H_4N_4O_3$.

uricase,—an enzyme of kidney and liver, also of some fungi, causing oxidation of uric acid to allantoin and carbon dioxide; uric acid oxidase.

uricolytic (ū'rĭkōlĭt'ĭk) *a.* [Gk. *ouron*, urine; *lyein*, to loose.] Decomposing uric acid; *appl.* index, the ratio between nitrogen excreted as allantoin to that present in urine as uric acid.

uricotelic (ū'rĭkōtĕl'ĭk) *a.* [Gk. *ouron*, urine; *telos*, end.] Excreting nitrogen as uric acid; *appl.* birds; *cf.* ureotelic.

urinary (ū'rĭnărĭ) *a.* [L. *urina*, urine.] *Pert.* urine; *appl.* organs including kidneys, ureters, bladder, and urethra.

urine (ū'rĭn) *n.* [L. *urina*, urine.] A fluid excretion from kidneys in mammals, a solid or semisolid excretion in birds and reptiles.

uriniparous (ū'rĭnĭp'ărŭs) *a.* [L. *urina*, urine; *parere*, to bring forth.] Urine-producing; *appl.* tubules in cortical portion of kidney.

urinogenital (ū'rĭnōjĕn'ĭtăl) *a.* [L. *urina*, urine; *gignere*, to beget.] *Pert.* urinary and genital systems.

urinogenital ridge,—a paired ridge from which urinary and genital systems are developed.

urinogenital sinus,—bladder or pouch in connection with urinary and genital systems in many animals.

urite (ū'rīt) *n.* [Gk. *oura*, tail.] An abdominal segment in arthropods; anal cirrus in polychaetes.

urn (ŭrn) *n.* [L. *urna*, jar.] An urn-shaped structure; the base of a pyxis in lichens; theca or capsule of mosses; one of the ciliate bodies floating in coelomic fluid of annulates.

urobilin (ū'rōbī'lĭn) *n.* [Gk. *ouron*, urine; L. *bilis*, bile.] A brown pigment of urine; stercobilin; $C_{33}H_{44}O_6N_4$.

urocardiac ossicle,—a short stout bar forming part of gastric mill in certain Crustacea.

urochord (ū'rōkôrd) *n.* [Gk. *oura*, tail; *chorde*, cord.] The notochord when confined to caudal region, as in tunicates.

urochrome (ū'rōkrōm) *n.* [Gk. *ouron*, urine; *chroma*, colour.] A yellowish pigment to which ordinary colour of urine is due.

urocoel (ū'rōsēl) *n.* [Gk. *ouron*, urine; *koilos*, hollow.] An excretory organ in Mollusca.

urocyst (ū'rōsĭst) *n.* [Gk. *ouron*, urine; *kystis*, bladder.] The urinary bladder; vesica urinaria.

urodaeum (ū'rōdē'ŭm) *n.* [Gk. *ouron*, urine; *odaios*, way.] The part or chamber of cloaca into which ureters and genital ducts open.

urodelous (ū'rōdē'lŭs) *a.* [Gk. *oura*, tail; *delos*, visible.] With persistent tail.

urogastric (ū'rōgăs'trĭk) *a.* [Gk. *oura*, tail; *gaster*, stomach.] *Pert.* the posterior portion of the gastric region in certain crustaceans.

urogenital,—urinogenital, *q.v.*

urohyal (ū'rōhīăl) *n.* [Gk. *oura*, tail; *hyoeides*, Y-shaped.] A median bony element in hyoid arch below hypohyals; basibranchiostegal.

uromere (ū'rōmēr) *n.* [Gk. *oura*, tail; *meros*, part.] An abdominal segment in Arthropoda.

uromorphic (ū'rōmôr'fĭk) *a.* [Gk. *oura*, tail; *morphe*, shape.] Like a tail; uromorphous.

uroneme (ū'rōnēm) *n.* [Gk. *oura*, tail; *nema*, thread.] A tail-like structure of some ciliate Protozoa.

uropatagium (ū'rōpătāj'ĭŭm) *n.* [Gk. *oura*, tail; L. *patagium*, border.] Membrane stretching from one femur to the other in bats; podical plate of insects.

urophan (ū'rōfăn) *n.* [Gk. *ouron*, urine; *phanai*, to show.] Any ingested substance found chemically unchanged in urine. *a.* Uropharic.

uropod (ū'rōpŏd) *n.* [Gk. *oura*, tail; *pous*, foot.] An abdominal appendage in Crustacea.

uropore (ū'rōpōr) *n.* [Gk. *ouron*, urine; *poros*, passage.] Opening of excretory duct in Acarina.

uroporphyrin (ū'rōpôr'fĭrĭn) *n.* [Gk. *ouron*, urine; *porphyra*, purple.] A brownish-red iron-free product of haem metabolism, a pigment of urine.

uropygial (ū'rōpĭj'ĭăl) *a.* [Gk. *orros*, end of os sacrum; *pyge*, rump.] *Pert.* uropygium; *appl.* oil gland.

uropygium (ū'rōpĭj'ĭŭm) *n.* [Gk. *orros*, end of os sacrum; *pyge*, rump.] The hump at end of bird's trunk, containing caudal vertebrae, and supporting tail feathers; also uropyge.

uropyloric (ū'rōpīlŏr'ĭk) *a.* [Gk. *oura*, tail; *pyle*, gate.] *Pert.* posterior portion of crustacean stomach.

urorectal (ū'rōrĕk'tăl) *a.* [L. *urina*, urine; *rectus*, straight.] *Appl.* embryonic septum, which ultimately divides intestine into anal and urinogenital parts.

urorubin (ū'rōroob'ĭn) *n.* [Gk. *ouron*, urine; L. *ruber*, red.] The red pigment of urine.

urosacral (ū'rōsā'krăl) *a.* [Gk. *oura*, tail; *sacrum*, sacred.] *Pert.* caudal and sacral regions of the vertebral column.

urosome (ū'rōsōm) *n.* [Gk. *oura*, tail; *soma*, body.] Tail region of fish; abdomen of arthropod.

urostege (ū'rōstēj) *n.* [Gk. *oura*, tail; *stege*, roof.] Ventral tail-plate of serpent; urostegite.

urosteon (ūrŏs'tēŏn) *n.* [Gk. *oura*, tail; *osteon*, bone.] Median ossification on the back portion of the keel-bearing part of the sternum in birds.

urosternite (ū'rōstĕr'nīt) *n.* [Gk. *oura*, tail; *sternon*, breast.] Ventral plate of arthropodan abdominal segment.

urosthenic (ū'rōsthĕn'ĭk) *a.* [Gk. *oura*, tail; *sthenos*, strength.]

Having tail strongly developed for propulsion.

urostyle (ū′röstīl) *n.* [Gk. *oura*, tail; *stylos*, pillar.] An unsegmented bone, posterior part of vertebral column of anurous amphibians; hypural bone in fishes.

uroxanthin (ū′rözăn′thĭn) *n.* [Gk. *ouron*, urine; *xanthos*, yellow.] A yellow pigment of normal urine.

urticant (ŭr′tĭkănt) *a.* [L. *urtica*, nettle.] Nettling; stinging; *appl.* thread-cells.

urticarial (ŭrtĭkā′rĭăl) *a.* L. *urtica*, nettle.] Nettling; urticant; *appl.* hairs, as of some caterpillars.

urticator (ŭr′tĭkātör) *n.* [L. *urtica*, nettle.] A nettling or stinging cell; a nematocyst.

use inheritance,—transmission of acquired characteristics.

uterine (ū′tërīn) *a.* [L. *uterus*, womb.] *Pert.* uterus; *appl.* artery, vein, plexus, glands, etc. of mammals.

uterine bell,—muscular bell-like structure in female of certain thread-worms, communicating with coelom and uterus.

uterine crypts,—depressions in uterine mucosa, for accommodation of chorionic villi.

uteroabdominal (ū′tëröăbdŏm′ĭnăl) *a.* [L. *uterus*, womb; *abdomen*, stomach.] *Pert.* uterus and abdominal region.

uterosacral (ū′tërösā′krăl) *a.* [L. *uterus*, womb; *sacrum*, sacred.] *Appl.* two ligaments of sacro-genital folds attached to sacrum.

uterovaginal (ū′tërövăj′ĭnăl, -văjī′-năl) *a.* [L. *uterus*, womb; *vagina*, vagina.] *Pert.* uterus and vagina.

uterovesical (ū′tërövĕs′ĭkăl) *a.* [L. *uterus*, womb; *vesicula*, vesicle.] *Pert.* uterus and bladder.

uterus (ū′tërŭs) *n.* [L. *uterus*, womb.] The organ in female mammals in which the embryo develops and is nourished before birth; an enlarged portion of oviduct modified to serve as a place for development of young or of eggs.

uterus masculinus,—median sac, vestigial Müllerian duct in male, attached to dorsal surface of urinogenital canal; utriculus prostaticus, vesica prostatica, sinus pocularis, Weber's organ.

utricle (ū′trĭkl) *n.* [L. *utriculus*, small bag.] Utriculus; former term for ascus; bladder-like pericarp of certain fungi; an air-bladder of aquatic plants; membranous indehiscent one-celled fruit; protoplasm enveloping a vacuole; membranous sac of ear-labyrinth; uterus masculinus.

utricular (ūtrĭk′ūlăr) *a.* [L. *utriculus*, small bag.] Containing vessels like small bags; *appl.* modification of laticiferous tissue.

utriculiform (ūtrĭk′ūlĭfôrm) *a.* [L. *utriculus*, small bag; *forma*, shape.] Shaped like a utricle or small bladder.

utriculus,—utricle, *q.v.*

utriform (ū′trĭfôrm) *a.* [L. *uter*, leather bottle; *forma*, shape.] Bladder-shaped, with a shallow constriction.

uva (ū′vă) *n.* [L. *uva*, grape.] Pulpy indehiscent fruit with central placenta, such as the grape.

uvea (ū′vëă) *n.* [L. *uva*, grape.] Pigmented epithelium covering posterior surface of iris; pars iridica retinae.

uvette (ūvĕt′) *n.* [F. from L. *uva*, grape.] The glandular junction of the two demanian vessels whence duct passes to exterior.

uvula (ū′vūlă) *n.* [L.L. *dim* of L. *uva*, grape.] Part of inferior vermis of cerebellum; conical pendulous process from soft palate; small elevation in mucous membrane of urinary bladder, caused by prostate.

V

vaccine (văk′sēn, -ĭn) *n.* [L. *vacca*, cow.] An attenuated living culture of a pathogenic organism, as those used against smallpox and other diseases.

vacuolar (văk'ūōlăr) *a.* [L. *vacuus*, empty.] *Pert.* or like a vacuole.

vacuolated (văk'ūōlā'tĕd) *a.* [L. *vacuus*, empty.] Containing vacuoles.

vacuole (văk'ūōl) *n.* [L. *vacuus*, empty.] One of spaces in cell protoplasm containing air, sap, or partially digested food.

vacuolisation (văk'ūōlĭzā'shŭn) *n.* [L. *vacuus*, empty.] The formation of vacuoles; appearance or formation of drops of clear fluid in growing or ageing cells; vacuolation.

vacuome (văk'ūōm) *n.* [L. *vacuus*, empty.] The vacuolar system of a single cell.

vagal (vā'găl) *a.* [L. *vagus*, wandering.] *Pert.* the vagus.

vagile (văj'ĭl) *a.* [L. *vagus*, wandering.] Freely motile; able to migrate.

vagina (văjī'nă) *n.* [L. *vagina*, sheath.] A sheath or sheath-like tube; expanded sheath-like portion of leaf-base; canal leading from uterus to external opening of genital canal.

vaginae mucosae,—mucous sheaths lessening friction of tendons gliding in fibro-osseous canals, as in hand or foot.

vaginal (văj'ĭnăl, văjī'năl) *a.* [L. *vagina*, sheath.] *Pert.* or supplying vagina; *appl.* arteries, nerves, etc.

vaginal process,—projecting lamina on inferior surface of petrous portion of temporal; a lamina on sphenoid.

vaginate (văj'ĭnāt) *a.* [L. *vagina*, sheath.] Invested by a sheath.

vaginervose (vā'jĭnĕr'vōs) *a.* [L. *vagus*, wandering; *nervus*, sinew.] With irregularly-arranged veins.

vaginicolous (văj'ĭnĭk'ōlŭs) *a.* [L. *vagina*, sheath; *colere*, to inhabit.] *Appl.* certain infusorians which build and inhabit sheaths or cases.

vaginiferous (văj'ĭnĭf'ĕrŭs) *a.* [L. *vagina*, sheath; *ferre*, to carry.] Vaginate; invested by a sheath.

vaginipennate (văj'ĭnĭpĕn'āt) *a.* [L. *vagina*, sheath; *penna*, feather.] Having wings protected by a sheath.

vaginula (văjĭn'ūlă) *n.* [L. *vaginula*, *dim.* of *vagina*, sheath.] A small sheath; sheath surrounding basal portion of sporogonium in mosses.

vagus (vā'gŭs) *n.* [L. *vagus*, wandering.] The pneumogastric or tenth cranial nerve; visceral accessory nervous system in insects.

vallate (văl'āt) *a.* [L. *vallatus*, surrounded by a rampart.] With a rim surrounding a depression; *appl.* papillae with taste-buds on back part of tongue; circumvallate.

vallecula (vălĕk'ūlă) *n.* [L.L. *dim.* of L. *vallis*, valley.] A depression or groove.

vallecular canal,—one of canals in cortical tissue of stem of horse-tails.

valleculate (vălĕk'ūlāt) *a.* [L.L. *dim.* of L. *vallis*, valley.] Grooved.

Valsalva,—*see* sinuses of Valsalva.

valval (văl'văl) *a.* [L. *valva*, fold.] *Appl.* view of diatom when one whole valve is next the observer; valvar.

valvate (văl'vāt) *a.* [L. *valva*, fold.] Hinged at margin only; meeting at edges; opening by or furnished with valves; *pert.* valves.

valve (vălv) *n.* [L. *valva*, fold.] Any of various structures which permit flow in one direction, but are capable of closing tube or vessel and preventing backward flow; any of pieces formed by a capsule on dehiscence; lid-like structure of certain anthers; flowering glume or lemma; one of pieces forming shell of diatom; any of pieces which form shell in certain molluscs, barnacles, etc.; one of pieces forming sheath of ovipositor or of clasper in certain insects.

valve of Thebesius [*A. C. Thebesius*, German anatomist]. Valve of the coronary sinus in right atrium; thebesian valve, valvula sinus coronarii cordis.

valve of Vieussens [*R. Vieussens*, French anatomist]. Thin layer of white matter extending between superior peduncles of cerebellum; anterior medullary velum; Willis' valve.

valvelet (vălv'lĕt), **valvula** (văl'vūlă) *n.* [L. *valvula, dim.* of *valva*, fold.] A small fold or valve.

valvifer (văl'vĭfĕr) *n.* [L. *valva*, fold; *ferre*, to bear.] One of the sclerites or coxites at base of valves of ovipositor in certain insects.

valvulae conniventes, — circular, spiral, or bifurcated folds of mucous membrane found in alimentary canal from duodenum to ileum, affording increased area for secretion and absorption; Kerckring's valves, plicae circulares.

valvular (văl'vūlăr) *a.* [L. *dim.* of *valva*, fold.] *Pert.*, or like, a valve or valves; *appl.* dehiscence of certain capsules and anthers.

valvule (văl'vūl) *n.* [L. *dim.* of *valva*, fold.] A valvula; upper palea of grasses.

vane (vān) *n.* [A.S. *fana*, small flag.] The vexillum or web of a feather, consisting of barbs, etc.

vannal (văn'ăl) *a.* [L. *vannus*, fan.] *Pert.* vannus; *appl.* veins.

vannus (văn'ŭs) *n.* [L. *vannus*, fan.] Fan-like posterior lobe of hind wing in some insects; anal lobe.

variant (vā'rĭănt) *n.* [L. *varians*, changing.] An individual or species deviating in some character or characters from type.

variate (vā'rĭāt) *n.* [L. *variare*, to change.] The variable quantity in variation; a character variable in quality or magnitude.

variation (vā'rĭā'shŭn) *n.* [L. *variare*, to change.] Divergence from type in certain characteristics.

varicellate (văr'ĭsĕl'āt) *a.* [L. *varix*, dilatation.] *Appl.* shells with small or indistinct ridges.

varices (văr'ĭsēz) *n. plu.* [L. *varix*, dilatation.] Prominent ridges across whorls of various univalve shells, showing previous position of outer lip.

variole (vā'rĭōl) *n.* [L. *varius*, various.] A small pit-like marking found on various parts in insects; a foveola.

varix,—*sing.* of varices.

vas (văs) *n.*, **vasa** (vā'să) *plu.* [L. *vas*, vessel.] A small vessel, duct, or canal, blind tube.

vasa afferentia,—lymphatic vessels entering lymph nodes.

vasa deferentia, — ducts leading from testes to penis, exterior, urinogenital canal, or cloaca; deferent ducts.

vasa efferentia, — ductules leading from testis to vas deferens; lymphatic vessels leading from lymph nodes.

vasa vasorum,—nutrient vessels for the larger arteries and veins.

vasal (vā'săl) *a.* [L. *vas*, vessel.] *Pert.* or connected with a vessel.

vascular (văs'kūlăr) *a.* [L. *vasculum*, small vessel.] *Pert.*, consisting of, or containing vessels adapted for transmission or circulation of fluid.

vascular areas, — scattered areas developed between endoderm and mesoderm of yolk-sac, beginnings of primitive blood-vessels.

vascular bundle,—a group of special cells consisting of two parts, xylem or wood portion and phloem or bast portion; many have in addition a thin strip of cambium separating the two parts.

vascular cylinder,—stele.

vascular tissue,—specially modified plant-cells, usually consisting of either tracheal or sieve cells, for circulation of sap.

vascular tunic, — choroid, ciliary body, and iris.

vasculum (văs'kūlŭm) *n.* [L. *vasculum*, small vessel.] A pitcher-shaped leaf or ascidium; a small blood-vessel.

vasifactive (văs'ĭfăk'tĭv) *a.* [L. *vas*, vessel; *facere*, to make.] Producing new blood-vessels.

vasiform (văs'ĭfôrm) *a.* [L. *vas*, vessel; *forma*, shape.] Functioning as or resembling a duct; vascular.

vasoconstrictor (văs'ökŏnstrĭk'tŏr) *a.* [L. *vas*, vessel; *constringere*, to draw tight.] Causing constriction of blood vessels.

vasodentine (văs'ödĕn'tĭn) *n.* [L. *vas*, vessel; *dens*, tooth.] A variety of dentine permeated by blood-vessels.

vasodilatin (văs'ödīlā'tĭn) *n.* [L. *vas*, vessel; *dilatus*, separated.] Product of protein disintegration corresponding in properties with histamine.

vasodilator (văs'ödīlā'tŏr) *a.* [L. *vas*, vessel; *dilatus*, separated.] Relaxing or enlarging the vessels.

vasoformative,—vasifactive, *q.v.*

vasoganglion (văs'ögăng'glĭŏn) *n.* [L. *vas*, vessel; Gk. *gangglion*, little tumour.] A compact plexus of blood-vessels or rete mirabile representing reduced hyoidean gill, as in certain fishes.

vasohypertonic, — vasoconstrictor, *q.v.*

vasohypotonic,—vasodilator, *q.v.*

vasoinhibitory,—vasodilator, *q.v.*

vasomotion (văs'ömō'shŭn) *n.* [L. *vas*, vessel; *movere*, to move.] A change in calibre of blood-vessel.

vasomotor (văs'ömō'tŏr) *a.* [L. *vas*, vessel; *movere*, to move.] *Appl.* nerves supplying muscles in wall of blood-vessels and regulating calibre of blood-vessels, through containing both vasoconstrictor and vasodilator fibres.

vasopressin (văs'öprĕs'ĭn) *n.* [L. *vas*, vessel; *pressus*, pressure.] A hormone of posterior lobe of pituitary gland which stimulates plain muscle, constricting arteries and raising blood pressure; β hypophamine; pitressin.

vastus (văs'tŭs) *n.* [L. *vastus*, immense.] A division of quadriceps muscle of thigh.

Vater's ampulla [*A. Vater*, German anatomist]. Dilation of the united common bile-duct and pancreatic duct.

Vater's corpuscles,—Pacinian corpuscles, *q.v.*

V-chromosomes, — chromosomes with two arms; mediocentric chromosomes.

vector (vĕk'tŏr) *n.* [L. *vector*, bearer.] A carrier, as many invertebrate hosts, of pathogenic organisms; any agent transferring a parasite to a host.

vegetal pole,—that side of a blastula at which megameres collect; the lower more slowly segmenting portion of a telolecithal egg, *opp.* animal pole.

vegetative (vĕj'ëtā'tĭv) *a.* [L. *vegetare*, to enliven.] *Appl.* stage of growth in plants, *opp.* reproductive period; assimilative, *appl.* fungi; *appl.* foliage shoots, *opp.* flower or reproductive shoots; *appl.* reproduction by bud-formation or other asexual method in plants and animals; *appl.* nervous system, the autonomic nervous system.

vegetative cone,—the apical point.

vegetative nucleus,—macronucleus, meganucleus, trophic nucleus, trophonucleus: pollen tube nucleus.

vegetative pole,—vegetal pole, *q.v.*

veil (vāl) *n.* [L. *velum*, covering.] Velum; calyptra; indusium.

veins (vānz) *n. plu.* [L. *vena*, vein.] Branched vessels which convey blood to heart; ribs or nervures of insect wing; ridges between lamellae of agarics; branching ribs or strands of vascular tissue of leaf.

velamen (vēlā'mĕn) *n.* [L. *velamen*, covering.] A membrane; sheath of tracheids at apex of aerial roots of orchids; a specialised moisture-absorbing tissue; velamentum.

velaminous (vēlăm'ĭnŭs) *a.* [L. *velamen*, covering.] Having a velamen; *appl.* roots.

velangiocarpy (vēlăn'jĭökârpĭ) *n.* [L. *velum*, covering; Gk. *anggeion*, vessel; *karpos*, fruit.] The enclosure of a fungal fruit-body by an early-formed veil or velum.

velar (vē'lăr) *a.* [L. *velum*, covering.] *Pert.* or situated near a velum.

velarium (vēlā'rĭŭm) *n.* [L. *velarium*, awning.] Velum of certain Cubomedusae, which differs from a true velum in containing endodermic canals; margin of umbrella, including tentacles, in Scyphozoa.

velate (vē'lāt) *a.* [L. *velum*, covering.] Veiled; covered by a velum.

veliger (vē'lĭjĕr) *n.* [L. *velum*, covering; *gerere*, to carry.] Second stage in larval life of certain molluscs when head bears a velum.

vellus (vĕl′ŭs) *n.* [L. *vellus*, fleece.] The stipe of certain fungi; hair replacing primary hair or lanugo.

velum (vē′lŭm) *n.* [L. *velum*, covering.] A membrane or structure similar to a veil; in Hydromedusae and certain jelly-fishes, the annular membrane projecting inwards from margin of bell; membrane in connection with buccal cavity in lancelet; flap-like structure for closing off choanae from mouth cavity in Crocodilia; membrane-like structure bordering oral cavity of certain ciliates; ciliated swimming organ of veliger larva; mass of tissue stretching from stipe to pileus in certain thallophytes; membrane partly covering opening of fovea in Isoëtes.

velutinous (vĕlū′tĭnŭs) *a.* [It. *velluto*, velvet.] Velvety; covered with very fine, dense, short upright hairs.

velvet (vĕl′vĕt) *n.* [M.E. *veluet*, velvet.] Soft vascular skin which covers antlers of deer during growth.

vena (vē′nă) *n.* [L. *vena*, vein.] A vein, or vessel by which blood is carried from body to heart.

venae,—*plu.* of vena.

venation (vĕnā′shŭn) *n.* [L. *vena*, vein.] System or disposition of veins or nervures; nervation.

venin (vĕn′ĭn) *n.* [L. *venenum*, poison.] A toxic substance of snake venom.

veniplex (vē′nĭplĕks) *n.* [L. *vena*, vein; *plexus*, interwoven.] A plexus of veins.

venomosalivary (vĕn′ömösăl′ĭvărĭ) *a.* [L. *venenum*, poison; *salivare*, to salivate.] *Pert.* salivary glands of which the secretion is poisonous.

venomous (vĕn′ömŭs) *a.* [L. *venenum*, poison.] Having poison-glands; able to inflict a poisonous wound.

venose (vē′nōs) *a.* [L. *vena*, vein.] With many and prominent veins.

venous (vē′nŭs) *a.* [L. *vena*, vein.] *Pert.* veins; *appl.* blood returning to heart after circulation in body.

vent (vĕnt) *n.* [L. *findere*, to cleave.] The anus; cloacal or anal aperture in lower vertebrates; *appl.* feather: an under tail covert.

venter (vĕn′tĕr) *n.* [L. *venter*, belly.] The abdomen; lower abdominal surface; protuberance, as of muscle; smooth concave surface; swollen basal portion of archegonium.

ventrad (vĕn′trăd) *adv.* [L. *venter*, belly; *ad*, to.] Towards lower or abdominal surface, *opp.* dorsad.

ventral (vĕn′trăl) *a.* [L. *venter*, belly.] *Pert.* or situated on lower or abdominal surface; *pert.* or designating that surface of a petal, etc., that faces centre or axis of flower; *appl.* lower surface of flattened ribbon-like thalli; *pert.* a venter.

ventrianal (vĕn′trĭā′năl) *a.* [L. *venter*, belly; *anus*, anus.] *Appl.* plate formed by fused ventral and anal sclerites, in certain Acarina.

ventricle (vĕn′trĭkl) *n.* [L. *ventriculus*, *dim.* of *venter*, belly.] A cavity or chamber, as in heart or brain; *appl.* fusiform fossa of larynx; gizzard of birds; mid-gut or chylific ventricle of insects; ventriculus.

ventricose (vĕn′trĭkōs) *a.* [L. *venter*, belly.] Swelling out in the middle, or unequally; *appl.* corolla, spores, stipe; *appl.* shells.

ventricular (vĕntrĭk′ūlăr) *a.* [L. *ventriculus*, belly.] *Pert.* a ventricle; *appl.* ligaments and folds of larynx; *appl.* septum and valves in heart.

ventriculus, — the stomach; a ventricle.

ventrodorsal (vĕn′trödôr′săl) *a.* [L. *venter*, belly; *dorsum*, back.] Extending from ventral to dorsal surface.

ventrolateral (vĕn′trölăt′ĕrăl) *a.* [L. *venter*, belly; *latus*, side.] At side of ventral region; ventral and lateral.

venule (vĕn′ūl) *n.* [L. *venula*, *dim.* of *vena*, vein.] Small vein of leaf or of insect wing; small vessel conducting venous blood from capillaries to vein.

venulose (vĕn′ūlōs) *a.* [L. *venula*, veinlet.] Having numerous small veins.

vermian (vĕr'mĭăn) *a.* [L. *vermis*, worm.] Worm-like; *pert.* vermis.

vermicular (vĕrmĭk'ūlăr) *a.* [*Dim.* of L. *vermis*, worm.] Resembling a worm in appearance or movement.

vermiculate (vĕrmĭk'ūlāt) *a.* [*Dim.* of L. *vermis*, worm.] Marked with numerous sinuate fine lines or bands of colour or by irregular depressed lines.

vermiculation (vĕr'mĭkūlā'shŭn) *n.* [*Dim.* of L. *vermis*, worm.] Worm-like or peristaltic movement; fine wavy markings.

vermicule (vĕr'mĭkūl) *n.* [*Dim.* of L. *vermis*, worm.] Motile or ookinete stage of some Sporozoa; a small worm-like structure.

vermiform (vĕr'mĭfôrm) *a.* [L. *vermis*, worm; *forma*, shape.] Shaped like a worm; *appl.* certain Protista and numerous structures, especially appendix; *appl.* body, a scolecite; *appl.* cells, plasmatocyte-like blood-cells in insects.

vermis (vĕr'mĭs) *n.* [L. *vermis*, worm.] Annulated median portion of cerebellum; central portion of cerebellum in birds and reptiles.

vernacular (vĕrnăk'ūlăr) *n.* [L. *vernaculus*, indigenous.] The local or native name of a plant or animal, *opp.* Latin or scientific name.

vernalin (vĕrnā'lĭn) *n.* [L. *vernalis*, of the spring.] A substance, or hormone, believed to control temperature effect in vernalisation, and possibly concerned in the formation of florigen.

vernalisation (vĕr'nălīzā'shŭn) *n.* [L. *vernalis*, of the spring.] A method of inducing the plant embryo to complete part of its development independently of its rate of growth; theory of plant development based upon sequence of mutually independent phases; first developmental phase, preceding photostage, of annual and some perennial herbaceous plants; thermophase; jarovization.

vernalised (vĕr'nălīzd) *a.* [L. *vernalis*, of the spring.] *Appl.* plant which has completed part of its development before sowing.

vernation (vĕrnā'shŭn) *n.* [L. *vernatio*, sloughing.] The arrangement of leaves within a bud; *cf.* prefoliation.

vernicose (vĕr'nĭkōs) *a.* [F. *vernis*, varnished.] Having a varnished appearance; glossy.

vernix caseosa,—shed flakes of epidermis mixed with sebaceous secretions gradually coating the skin during second half of human foetal life.

verruca (vĕrū'kă, -oo-) *n.* [L. *verruca*, wart.] A wart-like projection; a wart-like apothecium; one of small wart-like projections surrounding base of polyps in many Alcyonaria; one of the blister-like evaginations of body wall in some sea-anemones; a cuticular protuberance tufted with bristles, as in larval insects.

verruciform (vĕrū'sĭfôrm, -oo-) *a.* [L. *verruca*, wart; *forma*, shape.] Wart-shaped.

verrucose (vĕr'ūkōs) *a.* [L. *verrucosus*, warty.] Covered with wart-like projections.

verruculose (vĕrū'kūlōs) *a.* [L. *verrucula*, small wart.] Covered with minute wart-like excrescences.

versatile (vĕr'sătĭl) *a.* [L. *versatilis*, turning around.] Swinging freely, *appl.* anthers; capable of turning backwards and forwards, *appl.* bird's toe.

versicoloured (vĕr'sĭkŭl'ërd) *a.* [L. *versicolor*, changing colour.] Variegated in colour; capable of changing colour.

Verson's glands,—ecdysial glands, *q.v.*

vertebra (vĕr'tĕbră) *n.* [L. *vertebra*, turning joint.] Any of the bony or cartilaginous segments that make up the backbone; one of the ossicles in an ophiuroid arm.

vertebra prominens,—seventh cervical vertebra.

vertebral (vĕr′tĕbrăl) *a.* [L. *vertebra*, vertebra.] *Pert.* spinal column; *appl.* various structures situated near or connected with spinal column, or with any structure likened to spinal column.

vertebrarterial canal,—canal formed by foramina in transverse processes of cervical vertebrae or between cervical rib and vertebra.

vertebrate (vĕr′tĕbrāt) *a.* [L. *vertebra*, vertebra.] Having a backbone or spinal column.

vertebration (vĕr′tĕbrā′shŭn) *n.* [L. *vertebra*, vertebra.] Division into segments or parts resembling vertebrae.

vertebropelvic (vĕr′tĕbrōpĕl′vĭk) *a.* [L. *vertebra*, vertebra; *pelvis*, basin.] *Appl.* ligaments: the iliolumbar, sacrospinous, and sacrotuberous ligaments.

vertex (vĕr′tĕks) *n.* [L. *vertex*, top.] Top of head; highest point of skull; region between compound eyes in insects.

vertical (vĕr′tĭkăl) *a.* [L. *vertex*, top.] Standing upright; lengthwise, in direction of axis; *pert.* vertex of head.

vertical margin, — limit between frons and occiput in Diptera.

verticil (vĕr′tĭsĭl) *n.* [L. *verticillus*, *dim.* of *vertex*, whirl.] An arrangement of flowers, inflorescences or other structures about the same point on the axis.

verticillaster (vĕr′tĭsĭlăs′tĕr) *n.* [L. *verticillus*, small whorl; *aster*, star.] A much condensed cyme with appearance of whorl, but in reality arising in axils of opposite leaves.

verticillate (vĕrtĭs′ĭlāt) *a.* [L. *verticillus*, small whorl.] Disposed in verticils; whorled; *Appl.* antennae whose joints are surrounded, at equal distances, by stiff hairs.

veruculate (vĕrŭk′ūlāt) *a.* [L. *veruculum*, skewer.] Rod-shaped and pointed.

verumontanum (vĕr′oomŏntā′nŭm) *n.* [L. *veru*, spit; *montanum*, mountainous.] Ridge on floor of urethra, with small elevation where seminal ducts enter the colliculus seminalis; urethral crest.

vesica (vēsī′kă) *n.* [L. *vesica*, bladder.] Bladder.

vesica fellea,—gall-bladder.

vesica prostatica,—prostatic utricle, sinus pocularis, uterus masculinus, *q.v.*, or Weber's organ.

vesica urinaria,—urinary bladder.

vesical (vĕs′ĭkăl) *a.* [L. *vesica*, bladder.] *Pert.* or in relation with bladder; *appl.* arteries, etc.

vesicle (vĕs′ĭkl) *n.* [L. *vesicula*, *dim.* of *vesica*, bladder.] Small globular or bladder-like air space in tissues; small cavity or sac usually containing fluid; a hyphal swelling in mycorrhiza; hollow prominence on shell or coral; one of three primary cavities of brain.

vesicula (vēsĭk′ūlă) *n.* [L. *vesicula*, small bladder.] A small bladder-like cyst or sac; a vesicle.

vesicula seminalis,—a sac in which spermatozoa complete their development and are stored.

vesicular (vēsĭk′ūlăr) *a.* [L. *vesicula*, small bladder.] Composed of or marked by presence of vesicle-like cavities; bladder-like.

vesicular gland,—a gland in tissue underlying epidermis in plants and containing essential oils.

vesicular ovarian follicle, — Graafian follicle, *q.v.*

vesiculase (vēsĭk′ūlās) *n.* [L. *vesicula*, small bladder.] An enzyme from secretion of prostate gland, capable of coagulating contents of seminal vesicles.

vespertine (vĕs′pĕrtĭn) *a.* [L. *vespertinus*, of the evening.] Blossoming or active in the evening; crepuscular.

vespoid (vĕs′poid) *a.* [L. *vespa*, wasp; Gk. *eidos*, like.] Wasp-like.

vessel (vĕs′ĕl) *n.* [L. *vascellum*, *dim.* of *vas*, vessel.] Any tube or canal with properly defined walls in which fluids, such as blood, lymph, etc., circulate; continuous tube formed by superposition of numerous cells.

vestibular (vĕstĭb'ūlăr) *a.* [L. *vestibulum*, porch.] *Pert.* a vestibule; *appl.* artery, bulb, fissure, gland, nerve, etc.

vestibulate (vĕstĭb'ūlăt) *a.* [L. *vestibulum*, porch.] In the form of a passage between two channels; resembling, or having, a vestibule.

vestibule (vĕs'tĭbūl) *n.* [L. *vestibulum*, porch.] Vestibulum; a cavity leading into another cavity or passage, as cavity of ear-labyrinth; space between labia minora containing opening of urethra; portion of ventricle directly below opening of aortic arch; cavity leading to larynx; nasal cavity; posterior chamber of bird's cloaca; small tubular or grooved depression leading to mouth in most infusorians; space within circle of tentacles in endoproctan polyzoans; pit leading to pore or stoma of leaf.

vestige (vĕs'tĭj) *n.* [L. *vestigium*, trace.] A small degenerate or imperfectly developed organ or part which may have been complete and functional in some ancestor.

vestigial (vĕstĭj'ĭăl) *a.* [L. *vestigium*, trace.] Small and imperfectly developed.

vestiture (vĕs'tĭtūr) *n.* [L. *vestitus*, garment.] A body covering, as of scales, feathers, etc.

veterinary(vĕt'ĕrĭnărĭ) *a.* [L. *veterinus*, *pert.* beasts of burden.] *Pert.* science and art of treating diseases of animals.

vexilla,—*plu.* of vexillum.

vexillary vĕk'sĭlărĭ) *a.* [L. *vexillum*, standard.] *Pert.* a vexillum; *appl.* type of imbricate aestivation in which upper petal is folded over others; vexillar.

vexillate (vĕk'sĭlăt) *a.* [L. *vexillum*, standard.] Bearing a vexillum.

vexillum (vĕksĭl'ŭm) *n.* [L. *vexillum*, standard.] Standard or upper petal in papilionaceous flower; vane of feather.

via (vī'ă, vē'ă) *n.* [L. *via*, way.] A way or passage.

viable (vī'ăbl) *a.* [F. *vie*, life.] Capable of living; capable of developing and surviving parturition.

viatical (vīăt'ĭkăl) *a.* [L. *via*, way.] *Appl.* plants growing by the roadside.

vibraculum (vĭbrăk'ūlŭm) *n.* [L. *vibrare*, to quiver.] Modified whip-like avicularium for defensive purposes, in Polyzoa; vibracularium.

vibratile (vĭb'rătĭl) *a.* [L. *vibrare*, to quiver.] Oscillating; *appl.* antennae of insects.

vibratile corpuscles, — corpuscles closely resembling sperms found in coelomic fluid of starfish.

vibrioid (vĭb'rĭoid) *a.* [L. *vibrare*, to quiver; Gk. *eidos*, like.] Like a vibrio, a bacterium with thread-like appendages and a vibratory motion.

vibrioid body,—a slender cylindrical body found in superficial cytoplasmic layer of certain algae and fungi.

vibrissa (vībrĭs'ă) *n.* [L. *vibrissa*, nostril-hair.] A hair growing on nostril or face of animals, as whiskers of cat, acting often as tactile organ; a feather at base of bill or around eye; one of paired bristles near upper angles of mouth cavity in Diptera; one of the sensitive hairs of an insectivorous plant, as of Dionaea.

vicariation (vī'kārĭā'shŭn) *n.* [L. *vicarius*, deputy.] The separate occurrence of corresponding species, as reindeer and caribou, in corresponding but separate environments.

vicinism (vĭs'ĭnĭzm) *n.* [L. *vicinus*, neighbour.] Tendency to variation due to proximity of related forms.

Vicq-d'Azyr, bundles of [*F. Vicq-d'Azyr*, French comparative anatomist]. The thalamomamillary fasciculus.

villi,—*plu.* of villus.

villiform (vĭl'ĭfôrm) *a.* [L. *villus*, shaggy hair; *forma*, shape.] Having form or appearance of velvet; *appl.* dentition.

villose, (vĭl'ōs), **villous** (vĭl'ŭs) *a.* [L. *villus*, shaggy hair.] Pubescent; having villi or covered with villi.

villus (vĭl'ŭs) *n.* [L. *villus*, shaggy hair.] Trophonema or one of minute vascular processes on small intestine lining ; one of processes on chorion through which nourishment passes to embryo ; pacchionian body, *q.v.*, of arachnoid ; invagination, into joint-cavity, of a synovial membrane ; fine straight process on epidermis of plants.

vimen (vī'mĕn) *n.* [L. *vimen*, osier.] Long slender shoot or branch. *Plu.* vimina.

vinculum (vĭng'kūlŭm) *n.*, **vincula** (vĭng'kūlă) *plu.* [L. *vinculum*, bond.] Slender tendinous bands ; accessory connecting bands of fibres, as vincula brevia ; band uniting two main tendons of foot in birds ; sternal region of ninth segment in Lepidoptera.

viosterol, — irradiated ergosterol, vitamin D_2 preparation influencing calcium and phosphorus assimilation.

viral (vī'răl) *a.* [L. *virus*, poison.] *Pert.*, consisting of, or due to a virus.

virescence (vĭrĕs'ĕns) *n.* [L. *virescere*, to grow green.] Production of green colouring matter in petals instead of usual pigment.

virescent,—turning greenish or green.

virgate (vĕr'gāt) *a.* [L. *virga*, rod.] Rod-shaped ; striped.

virgula (vĕr'gūlă) *n.* [L. *dim.* of *virga*, rod.] A small rod, axis of graptolite ; a paired or bilobed structure or organ at oral sucker in certain trematodes.

virgulate (vĕr'gūlāt) *a.* [L. *virgula*, little rod.] With or like a small rod or twig ; having minute stripes.

viridant (vĭr'ĭdănt) *a.* [L. *viridare*, to make green.] Becoming or being green.

viroids (vī'roidz) *n. plu.* [L. *virus*, poison ; Gk. *eidos*, form.] Ultramicroscopic entities or symbionts theoretically existing in living organisms, and able to give rise to viruses by mutation ; *cf.* neovirus, palaeovirus.

virose (vī'rōs) *a.* [L. *virosus*, poisonous.] Containing a virus ; virous.

virulin,—aggressin, *q.v.*

virus (vī'rŭs) *n.* [L. *virus*, poisonous liquid.] One of the nucleoprotein-like entities able to pass through bacteria-retaining filters, having many characteristics of living organisms and recognised by their toxic or pathogenic effects in plants and animals.

viscera (vĭs'ĕră) *n. plu.* [L. *viscera*, bowels.] The internal organs contained in various cavities of body.

visceral (vĭs'ĕrăl) *a.* [L. *viscera*, bowels.] *Pert.* viscera ; *appl.* to numerous structures and organs.

visceral arches,—a series of arches developed in connection with mouth and pharynx.

visceral clefts,—a series of furrows or clefts in neck region between successive visceral arches.

viscerocranium (vĭs'ĕrōkrā'nĭŭm) *n.* [L. *viscera*, bowels ; *cranium*, skull.] Jaws and visceral arches ; *cf.* neurocranium.

visceromotor (vĭs'ĕrōmō'tŏr) *a.* [L. *viscera*, bowels ; *movere*, to move.] Carrying motor impulses to viscera.

viscin (vĭs'ĭn) *n.* [L. *viscum*, mistletoe.] Sticky substance obtained from various plants, especially from berries of mistletoe ; $C_{10}H_{24}O_4$.

viscosity (vĭskŏs'ĭtĭ) *n.* [L. *viscosus*, viscous.] Internal friction in fluids due to adherence of particles to one another.

viscus,—*sing.* of viscera.

visual purple,—porphyropsin, rhodopsin, *q.v.*

visual red,—a retinal pigment noticed in the tench.

visual violet,—iodopsin, *q.v.*

visual white,—the product of visual yellow irradiated by ultra-violet rays ; leucopsin.

visual yellow,—a pigment formed by the action of light upon visual purple ; a retinal pigment in certain fish; xanthopsin.

vital capacity,—of lungs, the sum of complemental, tidal, and supplemental air.

vital force,—form of energy manifested in living phenomena when considered distinct from chemical, physical, and mechanical forces; élan vital; *cf.* horme.

vital functions,—functions of body on which life depends.

vitalism (vī′tălĭzm) *n.* [L. *vita*, life.] Belief of vitalists, that phenomena exhibited in living organisms are due to a special force distinct from physical and chemical forces.

vitamers (vī′tămĕrz) *n. plu.* [L. *vita*, life; Gk. *meros*, part.] Compounds having a chemical structure and physiological effects similar to those of natural vitamins.

vitamins (vī′tămĭnz) *n. plu.* [L. *vita*, life; *ammoniacum*, resinous gum.] Accessory food factors deficiency or excess of which causes disease; *cf.* deficiency diseases.

vitazyme (vī′tăzīm) *n.* [L. *vita*, life; *zyme*, leaven.] An enzyme having vitamins as part of its chemical structure.

vitellarium (vĭt′ĕlā′rĭŭm) *a.* [L. *vitellus*, yolk.] A yolk gland in flatworms and many rotifers; part of an ovariole.

vitelligenous (vĭt′ĕlĭj′ĕnŭs) *a.* [L. *vitellus*, yolk; *gignere*, to beget.] Producing yolk; *appl.* cells in ovary of many insects; also vitellogenous, vitellogene.

vitellin (vĭtĕl′ĭn) *n.* [L. *vitellus*, yolk.] The phosphoprotein of egg-yolk; ovovitellin; similar or related substance in seeds.

vitelline (vĭtĕl′ēn) *a.* [L. *vitellus*, yolk.] *Pert.* yolk, or yolk-producing organ; *appl.* artery, vein, duct, gland, membrane; yolk-coloured.

vitelloduct (vĭtĕl′ödŭkt) *n.* [L. *vitellus*, yolk; *ductus*, led.] Albuminiferous canal, duct conveying vitellus from yolk gland into oviduct.

vitellogen (vĭtĕl′öjĕn) *n.* [L. *vitellus*, yolk; *gignere*, to produce.] Yolk gland; vitellarium, *q.v.*

vitellophags (vĭtĕl′öfăgz) *n. plu.* [L. *vitellus*, yolk; Gk. *phagein*, to eat.] Isolated cells forming hypoblast of crustacean and insect egg.

vitellose (vĭtĕl′ōs) *n.* [L. *vitellus*, yolk.] A substance formed in digestion of yolk.

vitellus (vĭtĕl′ŭs) *n.* [L. *vitellus*, yolk.] Yolk of ovum or egg.

vitrella (vĭtrĕl′ă) *n.* [L. *vitrum*, glass.] A crystalline cone cell of an invertebrate eye.

vitreodentine (vĭt′rēödĕn′tĭn) *n.* [L. *vitreus*, glassy; *dens*, tooth.] A very hard variety of dentine; also vitrodentine.

vitreous (vĭt′rēŭs) *a.* [L. *vitreus*, glassy.] Hyaline; transparent; *appl.* humour or body, the clear jelly-like substance in inner chamber of eye; *appl.* membrane, the innermost layer of dermic coat of hair-follicle.

vitreum (vĭt′rēŭm) *n.* [L. *vitreus*, glassy.] Vitreous humour of the eye; vitrina.

vitrification (vĭt′rĭfĭkā′shŭn) *n.* [L. *vitrum*, glass; *facere*, to make.] Condition of cells or organisms instantaneously frozen but able to resume all vital activities on being thawed out.

vitrina,—vitreum.

vitta (vĭt′ă) *n.*, **vittae** (vĭt′ē) *plu.* [L. *vitta*, band or fillet.] Oil receptacles in pericarp of Umbelliferae; a longitudinal ridge in diatoms; a band of colour.

vittate (vĭt āt) *a.* [L. *vittatus*, with a fillet.] Having ridges, stripes, or bands lengthwise.

vivification (vĭv′ĭfĭkā′shŭn) *n.* [L. *vivus*, living; *facere*, to make.] One of series of changes in assimilation by which proteid material which has been taken up by cell is able to exhibit phenomena of living protoplasm.

viviparity (vĭv′ĭpăr′ĭtĭ) *n.* [L. *vivus*, alive; *parere*, to beget.] Condition of bringing young forth alive; or of multiplying by means of shoots or bulbils; vivipary.

viviparous (vĭvĭp′ărŭs) *a.* [L. *vivus*, living; *parere*, to beget.] Bringing forth young alive ; *cf.* oviparous, ovoviviparous ; germinating while still attached to parent plant ; exhibiting vivipary, as certain tropical plants.

vocal (vō′kăl) *a.* [L. *vox*, voice.] *Pert.* voice or utterance of sounds.

vocal cords,—folds of mucous membrane projecting into larynx.

volar (vō′lăr) *a.* [L. *vola*, palm of hand.] *Pert.* palm of hand or sole of foot.

Volkmann's canals [*A. W. Volkmann*, German physiologist]. Simple canals piercing circumferential or periosteal lamellae of bone, for blood-vessels, and joining Haversian canal system.

voltine (vŏl′tĭn) *a.* [It. *volta*, time.] *Pert.* number of broods in a year, as of silkworms.

voluble (vŏl′ūbl) *a.* [L. *volvere*, to roll.] Twining spirally.

voluntary (vŏl′ŭntărĭ) *a.* [L. *voluntas*, will.] Subject to or regulated by the will ; *appl.* striped muscles and their action.

volute (vŏlūt′) *a.* [L. *volvere*, to roll.] Rolled up ; spirally twisted.

volutin grains,—ribonucleic acid granules formed in cytoplasm and representing a food-material which is absorbed by the nucleus in growth and formation of chromatin ; metachromatic bodies.

volution (vŏlū′shŭn) *n.* [L. *volvere*, to roll.] Spiral twist of a shell or of cochlea.

volva (vŏl′vă) *n.* [L. *volva*, wrapper.] Tissue enveloping the sporophore of some Agaricales and Boletales, the universal veil ; universal veil after becoming detached from pileus and limited to lower part of stipe.

volvate (vŏl′vāt) *a.* [L. *volva*, wrapper.] Provided with a volva.

vomer (vō′mĕr) *n.* [L. *vomer*, ploughshare.] A bone in nasal region.

vomerine (vō′mĕrĭn) *a.* [L. *vomer*, plough-share.] *Pert.* vomer ; *appl.* teeth.

vomeronasal (vō′mĕrōnā′zăl) *a.* [L. *vomer*, ploughshare ; *nasus*, nose.] *Appl.* cartilage and organ in region of vomer and nasal cavity ; *cf.* Jacobson's cartilage and organ.

vomeropalatine (vō′mĕrōpăl′ătĭn) *n.* [L. *vomer*, ploughshare ; *palatum*, palate.] Fused vomer and palatine, in some ganoids and amphibians.

von Baer's law [*K. E. von Baer*, German biologist]. Recapitulation theory, *q.v.*

vortex (vôr′tĕks) *n.* [L. *vortex*, vortex.] Spiral arrangement of muscle fibres at apex of heart ; spiral arrangement of hairs.

vulva (vŭl′vă) *n.* [L. *vulva*, vulva.] The external female genitalia or pudendum ; recess of third ventricle, between columns of fornix ; epigynum, *q.v.*

vulviform (vŭl′vĭfôrm) *a.* [L. *vulva*, vulva ; *forma*, shape.] Like a cleft with projecting lips ; shaped like a vulva.

vulvouterine (vŭl′vōū′tĕrĭn) *a.* [L. *vulva*, vulva ; *uterus*, womb.] *Pert.* vulva and uterus.

vulvovaginal (vŭl′vōvăj′ĭnăl) *a.* [L. *vulva*, vulva ; *vagina*, sheath.] *Pert.* vulva and vagina.

W

Wagner's corpuscles [*R. Wagner*, German physiologist]. Tactile corpuscles ; Meissner's corpuscles.

Waldeyer's tonsillar ring (*H. W. G. von Waldeyer*, German anatomist]. *See* tonsillar ring.

Wallace's Line [*A. R. Wallace*, English naturalist]. Imaginary line, separating Australian and Oriental zoogeographical regions, between Bali and Lombok, between Celebes and Borneo, and then eastward of Philippines.

Wallerian degeneration [*A. V. Waller*, English physiologist]. Degeneration of nerve fibres following section, produced distally to the injury.

wandering cells,—amoeboid cells of mesogloea ; cercids ; migratory leucocytes of areolar tissue ; planocytes.

wandering resting cells,—macrophages in connective tissue; clasmatocytes, histiocytes, rhagiocrine cells.

Warburg's factor [*O. H. Warburg*, German physiologist]. A respiratory enzyme, cytochrome oxidase; intracellular oxidation catalyst.

Warburg's yellow enzyme,—*see* yellow enzyme.

warm-blooded,—*appl.* animals which have a fairly high and constant temperature above that of surrounding medium; homoiothermal.

warning colours, — conspicuous colours assumed by many animals to warn off enemies.

wart (wôrt) *n.* [A.S. *wearte*, wart.] A dry excrescence formed on skin; firm glandular protuberance; verruca, *q.v.*

water-cells, — specialised cells in stomach of camel, for storage of fluid.

water culture,—experimental raising of plants in water to see effects of different nutrient solutions; *cf.* hydroponics.

water-gland,—structure in mesophyll of leaves regulating water excretion through stomata.

water-pore,—minute ciliated opening through actinal wall of disc of Antedon; opening at apex of leaf-vein for excretion of water.

water stomata,—pores on surfaces of leaves for excretion of water; hydathodes.

water-tube,—ciliated branched tube connected with ring-vessel and coelom or with gill-structures.

water vascular system,—system of canals circulating watery fluid throughout body of Echinoderma; also applied to excretory system of Platyhelminthes.

wattle (wôtl) *n.* [M.E. *watel*, bag.] Fleshy process under throat of cock or turkey, and of certain reptiles; tassel or appendix colli; barbel. [A.S. *watel*, interwoven twigs.] Acacia.

wax (wăks) *n.* [A.S. *weax*, wax.] A substance soluble in fat solvents, produced by plants to reduce transpiration, and by animals, as by honey-bees and scale-insects.

wax-hair,—a filament of wax extruded through pore of the wax-gland, as in certain scale insects.

wax-pocket,—one of the paired wax-secreting glands on abdomen of worker bee.

W-chromosome, — the X-chromosome when female is the heterozygous sex.

web (wĕb) *n.* [A.S. *webbe*, web.] Membrane stretching from toe to toe, as in frog and swimming birds; vexillum; network of threads spun by spiders.

Weberian apparatus [*E. H. Weber*, German physiologist]. An apparatus found in Cypriniformes, and including Weberian ossicles, a chain of four small bones stretching on each side from a membranous fenestra of atrium to air-bladder.

Weber's law,—inference that, within limits, equal relative differences between two stimuli of the same kind are equally perceptible.

Weber's line [*M. Weber*, Dutch zoologist]. Imaginary line separating islands with a preponderant Indo-Malayan fauna from those with a preponderant Papuan fauna.

Weber's organ [*M. I. Weber*, German anatomist]. Uterus masculinus, *q.v.*

wedge-and-groove suture,—schindylesis.

wedge bones,—small infravertebral ossifications at junction of two vertebrae, often present in lizards.

weismannism (vīs′mănĭzm) *n.* [*A. F. L. Weismann*, German biologist]. The teaching of Weismann in connection with evolution and heredity, dealing chiefly with continuity of germ-plasm, and non-transmissibility of acquired characters.

Weismann's gland,—ring gland, *q.v.*

Wharton's duct [*T. Wharton*. English anatomist]. The duct of the submaxillary gland; submaxillary duct.

Wharton's jelly,—the gelatinous core of the umbilical cord.

wheel organ, — locomotory ciliated ring or trochal disc of Rotifera; specialised ciliated epithelial structure in buccal cavity of Cephalochorda.

whirl,—whorl, *q.v.*

white blood cell,—leucocyte.

white body,—so-called optic gland of molluscs, a large soft body of unknown function.

white commissure,—anterior commissure, a transverse band of white fibres forming floor of median ventral fissure of spinal cord.

white matter,—tracts of medullated fibres in brain and spinal cord.

white yolk spheres,—minute vesicles forming a flask-shaped plug in centre of egg-yolk, and fine layers alternating with yellow yolk.

whorl (hwôrl) *n.* [A.S. *hweorfan*, to turn.] The spiral turn or volution of a univalve shell; circle of flowers, parts of a flower, or leaves, arising from one point; a verticil.

wild type,—the typical form or genotype of an organism as found in nature, *opp.* mutant.

Willis's circle [*T. Willis*, English anatomist]. Arterial circle, an anastomosis in subarachnoid space at base of brain.

wilting coefficient,—percentage of moisture in soil when wilting takes place.

wind-fertilisation,—fertilisation of plants by pollen carried by wind; wind-pollination, anemophily.

wing (wĭng) *n.* [M.E. *winge*, wing.] One of two lateral petals in a papilionaceous flower; lateral expansion on many seeds; any broad membranous expansion; large lateral process of sphenoid; fore-limb modified for flying, in pterodactyls, birds and bats; flight organ of insects; ala.

wing coverts,—tectrices, *q.v.*

winged stem,—stem having photosynthetic expansions.

wing-pad,—undeveloped wing of insect pupae.

wing petal,—lateral petal in papilionaceous flowers.

wing quills,—remiges, *q.v.*

wing sheath,—elytrum of insects.

Winslow's foramen [*J. B. Winslow*, Danish anatomist]. Epiploic foramen.

winter bud,—dormant bud, protected by hard scales during winter.

winter egg,—egg of many fresh-water forms, provided with thick shell which preserves it as it lies quiescent during winter; *cf.* summer egg.

Wirsung's duct [*J. G. Wirsung*, Bavarian surgeon]. The main pancreatic duct.

wisdom teeth,—four molar teeth which complete permanent set in man, erupting late.

wolf tooth,—a small premolar tooth at front of premolar series, occasionally present in horses.

Wolffian (vŏl'fĭăn) *a.* [*C. F. Wolff*, German embryologist]. *Appl.* certain structures first discovered by Wolff.

Wolffian body, — embryonic mesonephros arising as a series of tubules.

Wolffian duct, — duct of mesonephros.

Wolffian ridges,—ridges which appear on either side of middle line of early embryo, and upon which limb-buds are formed.

Wolfring's glands [*E. F. Wolfring*, Polish ophthalmologist]. Tubulo-alveolar glands near proximal end of tarsi of eyelids, with ducts opening on conjunctiva.

wood (wood) *n.* [A.S. *wudu*, wood.] The hard substance of a tree stem, xylem of vascular bundles.

wood vessel,—an element of tracheal tissue, a long tubular structure formed by cell-fusion.

Woolner's tubercle [*T. Woolner*, British sculptor]. Darwinian tubercle, *q.v.*

worker, — non-fertile female in a colony of social insects.

worm (wŭrm) *n.* [A.S. *wyrm*, worm.] A general name, of no scientific value, used to designate any of the flatworms, roundworms, polychaetes, or oligochaetes ; lytta, as of dog ; vermis.

Wormian bones [*O. Worm* or *Wormius*, Danish anatomist]. Sutural bones, *q.v.*

Woronin bodies, — metachromatic bodies in protoplasm of certain hyphal cells, as in Discomycetes.

Woronin hypha,—a hypha inside coil of perithecial hyphae and giving rise to ascogonia, as in Sphaeriales ; scolecite.

wound cambium,—cambium forming protective tissue at site of an injury.

wound hormones,—substances produced in wounded cells, said to act as stimulus to renewed growth near the wounds ; *cf.* traumatin.

***w*-substance,**—a pituitary hormone, secreted by pars tuberalis and inducing contraction of chromatophores.

X

xanthein (zăn'thēĭn) *n.* [Gk. *xanthos*, yellow.] A water-soluble yellow colouring matter of cell-sap.

xanthin (zăn'thĭn) *n.* [Gk. *xanthos*, yellow.] Yellow colouring matter in flowers.

xanthine (zăn'thĭn) *n.* [Gk. *xanthos*, yellow.] Dioxy-purine found in muscle, liver, pancreas, spleen, urine also in certain plants ; $C_5H_4N_4O_2$

xanthocarpous (zăn'thōkâr'pŭs) *a.* [Gk. *xanthos*, yellow ; *karpos*, fruit.] Having yellow fruits.

xanthodermic (zăn'thōdĕr'mĭk) *a.* [Gk. *xanthos*, yellow ; *derma*, skin.] Having a yellowish skin.

xanthodont (zăn'thōdŏnt) *a.* [Gk. *xanthos*, yellow ; *odous*, tooth.] Having yellow-coloured incisors ; *appl.* certain rodents.

xantholeucite (zăn'thōloo'sīt) *n.* [Gk. *xanthos*, yellow ; *leukos*, white.] Leucoplast of an etiolated plant.

xantholeucophore (zăn'thōlook'-ōfōr), *n.* [Gk. *xanthos*, yellow ; *leukos*, white ; *pherein*, to bear.] Yellow pigment-bearing cell ; xanthophore, *q.v.*

xanthophane (zăn'thōfān) *n.* [Gk. *xanthos*, yellow ; *phainein*, to appear.] A yellow chromophane.

xanthophore (zăn'thōfōr) *n.* [Gk. *xanthos*, yellow ; *pherein*, to bear.] A yellow chromatophore ; lipophore.

xanthophyll (zăn'thōfĭl) *n.* [Gk. *xanthos*, yellow ; *phyllon*, leaf.] A yellow colouring matter found in plastids, as in autumn leaves ; lutein ; $C_{40}H_{56}O_2$.

xanthoplast (zăn'thōplăst) *n.* [Gk. *xanthos*, yellow ; *plastos*, formed.] A yellow plastid or chromatophore.

xanthopous (zăn'thōpŭs) *a.* [Gk. *xanthos*, yellow ; *pous*, foot.] Having a yellow stem.

xanthopsin (zănthŏp'sĭn) *n.* [Gk. *xanthos*, yellow ; *opsis*, sight.] Yellow pigment of insect eyes ; visual yellow, *q.v.*

xanthopterine (zăn'thŏp'tĕrĭn) *n.* [Gk. *xanthos*, yellow ; *pteron*, wing.] Yellow pigment of wing of lemon butterfly and of integument of wasps, etc. ; possibly precursor of anti-anaemia vitamin M ; $C_{19}H_{18}O_6N_{16}$.

xanthosomes (zăn'thōsōmz) *n. plu.* [Gk. *xanthos*, yellow ; *soma*, body.] Amber-coloured excretory granules in foraminifera.

xanthospermous (zăn'thōspĕr'mŭs) *a.* [Gk. *xanthos*, yellow ; *sperma*, seed.] Having yellow seeds.

X-bodies,—protein-like inclusions in cells affected by a virus.

X-chromosome, — sex-chromosome, single in the heterogametic sex, paired in the homogametic sex.

xenarthral (zĕnâr'thrăl) *a.* [Gk. *xenos*, strange ; *arthron*, joint.] Having additional articular facets on dorso-lumbar vertebrae.

xenia (zē'nĭă) *n.* [Gk. *xenios*, hospitable.] Appearances in seed, fruit, or maternal tissues, of characters belonging to male parent.

xeniobiosis (zĕnĭŏbīō'sĭs) *n.* [Gk. *xenios*, hospitable ; *bioun*, to live.] Hospitality, in ant colonies.

xenoecic (zĕnē'sĭk) *a.* [Gk. *xenos*, host ; *oikos*, house.] Living in the empty shell of another organism.

xenogamy (zĕnŏg'ămĭ) *n.* [Gk. *xenos*, strange ; *gamos*, marriage.] Cross-fertilisation.

xenogenesis (zĕnŏjĕn'ĕsĭs) *n.* [Gk. *xenos*, strange ; *genesis*, descent.] Heterogenesis.

xenogenous (zĕnŏj'ĕnŭs) *a.* [Gk. *xenos*, strange ; *genos*, descent.] Originating outside the organism ; caused by external stimuli ; exogenous.

xenology (zĕnŏl'ŏjĭ) *n.* [Gk. *xenos*, host ; *logos*, discourse.] The study of hosts in relation to the life-history of parasites ; *cf.* definitive host, intermediate host.

xenomixis (zĕn'ŏmĭk'sĭs) *n.* [Gk. *xenos*, strange ; *mixis*, mingling.] Union of sex elements of different lineage ; exomixis.

xenomorphosis (zĕnŏmôr'fōsĭs) *n.* [Gk. *xenos*, strange ; *morphosis*, a shaping.] Heteromorphosis.

xenophya (zĕn'ŏfī'ă) *n. plu.* [Gk. *xenos*, stranger ; *phyein*, to grow.] Foreign bodies deposited in interspaces of certain Sarcodina, or used in formation of shells of certain protozoa ; *cf.* autophya.

xenoplastic (zĕn'ŏplăs'tĭk) *a.* [Gk. *xenos*, stranger ; *plastos*, formed.] *Appl.* graft established in a different host ; *cf.* heteroplastic.

xerantic (zērăn'tĭk) *a.* [Gk. *xeransis*, parching.] Drying up ; withering, parched, exsiccant.

xerarch (zē'rârk) *a.* [Gk. *xeros*, dry ; *arche*, beginning.] *Appl.* seres progressing from xeric towards mesic conditions.

xeric (zē'rĭk) *a.* [Gk. *xeros*, dry.] Characterised by a scanty supply of moisture ; tolerating, or adapted to, arid conditions. *Opp.* hygric.

xerochasy (zē'rŏkā'sĭ) *n.* [Gk. *xeros*, dry ; *chasis*, separation.] Dehiscence of seed vessels when induced by aridity ; *cf.* hygrochasy.

xeromorphic (zērŏmôr'fĭk) *a.* [Gk. *xeros*, dry ; *morphe*, form.] Structurally modified so as to retard transpiration ; *appl.* characters of xerophytes.

xeromorphy, — xeromorphic condition.

xerophilous (zērŏf'ĭlŭs) *a.* [Gk. *xeros*, dry ; *philein*, to love.] Able to withstand drought ; *appl.* plants adapted to a limited water supply ; xerophil.

xerophobous (zērŏf'ŏbŭs) *a.* [Gk. *xeros*, dry ; *phobos*, fear.] Not tolerating drought.

xerophyte (zē'rŏfīt) *n.* [Gk. *xeros*, dry ; *phyton*, plant.] A xerophilous plant ; a plant growing in desert or alkaline or physiologically dry soil ; a xerophil.

xerophyton (zē'rŏfī'tŏn) *n.* [Gk. *xeros*, dry ; *phyton*, plant.] A plant inhabiting dry land.

xeropoium (zē'rŏpoi'ŭm) *n.* [Gk. *xeros*, dry ; *poa*, grass.] Steppe vegetation.

xerosere (zē'rŏsēr) *n.* [Gk. *xeros*, dry ; L. *serere*, to put in a row.] A plant succession originating on dry soil.

xerotherm (zē'rŏthĕrm) *n.* [Gk. *xeros*, dry ; *therme*, heat.] A plant surviving in conditions of drought and heat.

***x*-generation**, — gametophyte ; *2x*, sporophyte generation.

xiphihumeralis (zĭf'ĭhūmĕrā'lĭs) *n.* [Gk. *xiphos*, sword ; L. *humerus*, shoulder.] A muscle extending from xiphoid cartilage to humerus.

xiphiplastron (zĭf'ĭplăs'trŏn) *n.* [Gk. *xiphos*, sword ; F. *plastron*, breastplate.] Fourth lateral plate in plastron of Chelonia.

xiphisternum (zĭf'ĭstĕr'nŭm) *n.* [Gk. *xiphos*, sword ; L. *sternum*, breastbone.] The posterior segment or ensiform process of sternum ; metasternum.

xiphoid (zĭf'oid) *a.* [Gk. *xiphos*, sword ; *eidos*, shape.] Sword-shaped ; ensiform ; xiphioid.

xiphoid process,—last segment of sternum; xiphisternum; tail or telson of Limulus.

xiphophyllous (zĭf′öfĭl′ŭs) *a.* [Gk. *xiphos*, sword; *phyllon*, leaf.] Having sword-shaped leaves.

X-organ,—small compact or sac-like incretory organ found on eye-stalk of certain Crustacea.

xylary (zī′lărĭ) *a.* [Gk. *xylon*, wood.] *Pert.* xylem; *appl.* fibres, procambium, etc.; xyloic.

xylem (zī′lĕm) *n.* [Gk. *xylon*, wood.] Lignified portion of vascular bundle.

xylem-canal,—narrow tubular space replacing central xylem in demersed stem of some aquatic plants.

xylem-parenchyma,—short lignified cells surrounding vascular cells or produced with other xylem cells toward the end of the growing season.

xylem-ray,—ray or plate of xylem between two medullary rays.

xylocarp (zī′lökârp) *n.* [Gk. *xylon*, wood; *karpos*, fruit.] A hard woody fruit.

xylochrome (zī′lökrōm) *n.* [Gk. *xylon*, wood; *chroma*, colour.] Wood dye or pigment of tannin, produced before death of wood-cells.

xylogen (zī′löjĕn) *n.* [Gk. *xylon*, wood; *-genes*, producing.] The forming wood in a bundle; lignin, *q.v.*

xyloic (zī′löĭk) *a.* [Gk. *xylon*, wood.] *Pert.* xylem; *appl.* procambium that gives rise to xylem; xylary.

xyloid (zī′loid) *a.* [Gk. *xylon*, wood; *eidos*, shape.] Woody, or resembling wood in structure; ligneous.

xyloma (zīlō′mă) *n.* [Gk. *xylon*, wood.] A hardened mass of mycelium which gives rise to spore-bearing structures in certain fungi; a tree tumour.

xylophagous (zīlŏf′ăgŭs) *a.* [Gk. *xylon*, wood; *phagein*, to eat.] Wood-eating; *appl.* certain molluscs, insects, fungi; xylophilous.

xylophilous (zīlŏf′ĭlŭs) *a.* [Gk. *xylon*, wood; *philein*, to love.] Preferring wood; growing on wood.

xylophyte (zī′löfit) *n.* [Gk. *xylon*, wood; *phyton*, plant.] A woody plant.

xylostroma (zī′löstrō′mă) *n.* [Gk. *xylon*, wood; *stroma*, bedding.] The felt-like mycelium of certain wood-destroying fungi.

xylotomous (zīlŏt′ömŭs) *a.* [Gk. *xylon*, wood; *temnein*, to cut]. Able to bore or cut wood.

X-zone,—transitory region of inner adrenal cortex.

Y

yarovization,—jarovization, vernalisation, *q.v.*

Y-cartilage,—cartilage joining ilium, ischium and pubes in the acetabulum.

Y-chromosome,—the sex-chromosome which pairs with the X-chromosome in the heterogametic sex.

yelk,—yolk.

yellow body,—corpus luteum.

yellow cartilage,—a cartilage with matrix pervaded by yellow or elastic connective tissue fibres.

yellow cells,—chloragogen cells surrounding gut of Annelida; cells occurring in intestine of Turbellaria; in Radiolaria, symbiotic algae or zoochlorellae; zooxanthellae; chromo-argentaffin cells.

yellow enzyme,—a combination of riboflavine, a protein, and phosphoric acid, essential in cellular respiration; yellow oxidation catalyst; cytoflavin.

yellow spot,—macula lutea of retina.

Y-granules,—granules, microchemically allied to yolk, found in male germ cells; yolk granules.

Y-ligament,—iliofemoral ligament.

yolk (yōk) *n.* [A.S. *geoloca*, yellow part.] Inert, or non-formative, nutrient material in ovum; vitellus; suint or greasy substance of fleece.

yolk-duct,—vitelline duct.

yolk-epithelium, — epithelium surrounding yolk-sac.

yolk-gland,—a gland in connection with reproductive system by which egg is furnished with a supply of food-material; vitellarium.

yolk-nucleus or **vitelline body,**—cytoplasmic body appearing in ovarian egg; Balbiani's body or nucleus.

yolk-plates,—parallel lamellae into which deutoplasm may be split up in amphibians and many fishes.

yolk-plug,—mass of yolk-cells filling up blastopore, as in frog.

yolk-pyramids,—certain cells formed in segmenting egg of crayfish.

yolk-sac,—membranous sac attached to embryo and containing yolk which passes to intestine through vitelline duct and acts as food for developing embryo.

yolk-spherules,—remains of neighbouring cells or of pseudo-cells found in ovum.

yolk-stalk,—a short stalk or strand containing ducts and connecting yolk-sac with embryo.

ypsiliform (ĭp′sĭlĭfôrm) *a.* [Gk. *Y*, upsilon; L. *forma*, shape.] *Y*-shaped; *appl.* germinal spot at a certain stage in its development; ypsiloid.

ypsiloid (ĭp′sĭloid) *a.* [Gk. *Y*, upsilon; *eidos*, form.] *Y*-shaped; *appl.* cartilage anterior to pubis in salamanders, for attachment of muscles used in breathing.

Y-shaped ligament of Bigelow,—the iliofemoral ligament.

Z

zalambdodont (zălăm′dŏdŏnt) *a.* [Gk. *za*, very; *lambda*, λ; *odous*, tooth.] *Appl.* insectivores with narrow molar teeth with V-shaped transverse ridges.

Z-chromosome,—the Y-chromosome when female is the heterozygous sex.

Z-disc,—intermediate disc; Krause's membrane; Dobie's line, telophragma, plasmophore.

zeaxanthin (zē′ăzăn′thĭn) *n.* [Gk. *zea*, corn; *xanthos*, yellow.] The yellow carotenoid pigment of maize, or of yolk; xanthophyll or lutein, $C_{40}H_{56}O_2$.

Zeis, glands of,—sebaceous glands associated with eyelashes.

zero (zē′rō) *n.* [Ar. *cifrun*, cipher.] The origin of graduation.

zero, physiological, — point of adaptation to temperature.

zeugopodium (zū′gŏpō′dĭŭm) *n.* [Gk. *zeugos*, joined; *pous*, foot.] Forearm; shank.

Zinn, zonule of [*J. G. Zinn*, German anatomist]. Zonula ciliaris.

zoaea,—zoëa, *q.v.*

zoanthella (zōănthĕl′ă) *n.* [Gk. *zoon*, animal; *anthos*, flower.] Type of zoanthid larva with transverse girdle of cilia.

zoanthina (zōăn′thĭnă) *n.* [Gk. *zoon*, animal; *anthinos*, of flowers.] Type of zoanthid larva with longitudinal band of cilia.

zoarium (zōā′rĭŭm) *n.* [*Dim.* of Gk. *zoon*, animal.] All the individuals of a polyzoan colony; a polypary.

zodiophilous,—zoophilous, *q.v.*

zoëa (zōē′ă) *n.* [Gk. *zoe*, life.] Early larval form of certain decapod crustaceans.

zoëaform (zōē′ăfôrm) *a.* [Gk. *zoe*, life; L. *forma*, shape.] Shaped like a zoëa; also zoaeaform.

zoecial, zoecium,—*see* zooe-.

zoetic (zōĕt′ĭk) *a.* [Gk. *zoe*, life.] Of or *pert.* life.

zoic (zō′ĭk) *a.* [Gk. *zoikos*, *pert.* life.] Containing remains of organisms and their products, *opp.* azoic. [Gk. *zoon*, animal.] *Pert.* animals or animal life.

zoid (zō′ĭd) *n.* [Gk. *zoon*, animal; *idion*, *dim.*] A zoospore; a sporozoite formed by division of sporoblasts of Haemosporidia.

zoidiogamic (zōĭd′ĭögăm′ĭk) *a.* [Gk. *zoon*, animal; *idion*, *dim.*; *gamos*, marriage.] *Appl.* plants fertilised by spermatozoids carried by water.

zoidiogamy (zōĭdĭŏg′ămĭ) *n.* [Gk. *zoon*, animal; *idion*, *dim.*; *gamos*, marriage.] Fertilisation by motile spermatozoids or antherozoids.

zoidophore (zō'ĭdŏfōr) *n.* [Gk. *zoon*, animal ; *idion*, *dim.* ; *pherein*, to bear.] A spore mother cell or sporoblast formed by segmentation of oocyte in Haemosporidia.

zona (zō'nă) *n.* [L. *zona*, girdle.] A zone, band, or area.

zona arcuata,—inner part of basilar membrane, supporting spiral organ of Corti.

zona fasciculata,—radially arranged columnar cells in suprarenal cortex below zona glomerulosa.

zona glomerulosa,—rounded groups of cells forming external layer of suprarenal cortex beneath capsule.

zona granulosa,—granular zone around ovum in Graafian follicle, formed by cells of membrana granulosa ; discus proligerus.

zona orbicularis,—circular fibres of capsule of hip-joint, around neck of femur.

zona pectinata, — outer division of basilar membrane of cochlea.

zona pellucida,—thick transparent membrane surrounding ovum ; zona striata.

zona radiata,—radially striated inner egg-envelope, as in Polychaeta ; membrane with radially arranged pores receiving cell processes from corona radiata, *q.v.*

zona reticularis or **reticulata,**—inner layer of suprarenal cortex.

zona striata,—zona pellucida.

zona tecta,—zona arcuata.

zonal (zō'năl) *a.* [L. *zonalis*, *pert.* zone.] Of or *pert.* a zone.

zonal symmetry,—metamerism, *q.v.*

zonal view,—view of diatom when the girdle is seen.

zonality (zōnăl'ĭtĭ) *n.* [L. *zona*, girdle.] Zonal distribution; zonal character.

zonary (zō'nărĭ) *a.* [L. *zona*, girdle.] *Appl.* placenta with villi arranged in a band or girdle.

zonate (zō'nāt) *a.* [L. *zona*, girdle.] Zoned or marked with rings ; arranged in a single row, as some tetraspores.

zonation (zōnā'shŭn) *n.* [L. *zona*, girdle.] Arrangement or distribution in zones.

zone (zōn) *n.* [Gk. *zone*, girdle.] An area characterised by similar fauna or flora ; a belt or area to which certain species are limited ; stratum or set of beds characterised by typical fossil or set of fossils ; an area or region of the body ; zona.

zonite (zō'nīt) *n.* [Gk. *zone*, girdle.] A body segment of Diplopoda.

zonociliate (zō'nŏsĭl'ĭāt) *a.* [Gk. *zone*, girdle ; L. *cilium*, eyelash.] Banded with cilia, as certain annelid larvae.

zonoid (zō'noid) *a.* [Gk. *zone*, girdle ; *eidos*, form.] Like a zone.

zonolimnetic (zō'nŏlĭmnĕt'ĭk) *a.* [Gk. *zone*, girdle ; *limne*, pool.] Of or *pert.* a certain zone in depth ; *appl.* fresh-water plankton.

zonoplacental (zō'nŏplăsĕn'tăl) *a.* [L. *zona*, girdle ; *placenta*, cake.] Having a zonary placenta.

zonula ciliaris (zō'nūlă sĭlĭā'rĭs) *n.* [L. *zonula*, *dim.* of *zona*, girdle ; *cilium*, eyelash.] The hyaloid membrane forming suspensory ligament of lens of eye ; zonule of Zinn.

zonule (zō'nūl) *n.* [L. *zonula*, *dim.* of *zona*, girdle.] A little zone, belt, or girdle ; zonula.

zooamylon (zō'ŏăm'ĭlŏn) *n.* [Gk. *zoon*, animal ; *amylon*, starch.] Food reserve in refractile bodies of cytoplasm, as in protozoa ; paramylon, paraglycogen.

zooanthellae (zō'ŏănthĕl'ē) *n. plu.* [Gk. *zoon*, animal ; *anthos*, flower.] Cryptomonads symbiotic with certain marine protozoa.

zooapocrisis (zō'ŏăpŏk'rĭsĭs) *n.* [Gk. *zoon*, animal ; *apokrisis*, answer.] The response of animals to their environmental conditions as a whole.

zoobenthos (zō'ŏbĕn'thŏs) *n.* [Gk. *zoon*, animal ; *benthos*, depths of sea.] The fauna of the sea-bottom, or of the bottom of inland waters.

zoobiotic (zō'ŏbīŏt'ĭk) *a.* [Gk. *zoon*, animal ; *bios*, life.] Parasitic on an animal, as some fungi.

zooblast (zō'öblăst) *n.* [Gk. *zoon*, animal; *blastos*, bud.] An animal cell.

zoocaulon (zō'ökôl'ŏn) *n.* [Gk. *zoon*, animal; *kaulos*, stalk.] Zoodendrium.

zoochlorellae (zō'öklörĕl'ē) *n. plu.* [Gk. *zoon*, animal; *chloros*, green.] Symbiotic green algae living in various animals, *e.g.* in Sarcodina, Radiolaria, Hydra.

zoochoric (zō'ökō'rĭk) *a.* [Gk. *zoon*, animal; *chorein*, to spread.] Dispersed by animals, *appl.* plants.

zoocoenocyte (zō'ösē'nösīt) *n.* [Gk. *zoon*, animal; *koinos*, common; *kytos*, hollow.] A coenocyte bearing cilia, in certain algae; synzoospore.

zoocyst (zō'ösĭst) *n.* [Gk. *zoon* animal; *kystis*, sac.] A sporocyst.

zoocytium (zō'ösĭt'ĭŭm) *n.* [Gk. *zoon*, animal; *kytos*, hollow.] In certain Infusoria, the common gelatinous and often branched matrix.

zoodendrium (zō'ödĕn'drĭŭm) *n.* [Gk. *zoon*, animal; *dendron*, tree.] The tree-like branched stalk of certain colonial infusorians.

zoodynamics (zō'ödĭnăm'ĭks) *n.* [Gk. *zoon*, animal; *dynamis*, power.] The physiology of animals.

zooecial (zōē'sĭăl) *a.* [Gk. *zoon*, animal; *oikos*, house.] *Pert.* or resembling a zooecium.

zooecium (zōē'sĭŭm) *n.* [Gk. *zoon*, animal; *oikos*, house.] A chamber or sac enclosing a polyzoan nutritive zooid.

zooerythrin (zō'öĕrĭth'rĭn) *n.* [Gk. *zoon*, animal; *erythros*, red.] Red pigment found in plumage of various birds.

zoofulvin (zō'öfŭl'vĭn) *n.* [Gk. *zoon*, animal; L. *fulvus*, yellow.] Yellow pigment found in plumage of various birds.

zoogamete (zō'ögămēt') *n.* [Gk. *zoon*, animal; *gametes*, spouse.] A motile gamete or planogamete.

zoogamy (zōŏg'ămĭ) *n.* [Gk. *zoon*, animal; *gamos*, marriage.] Sexual reproduction in animals.

zoogenesis (zō'öjĕn'ësĭs) *n.* [Gk. *zoon*, animal; *genesis*, descent.] The origin of animals; ontogeny and phylogeny of animals.

zoogenous (zōŏj'ënŭs) *a.* [Gk. *zoon*, animal; *gennaein*, to produce.] Produced or caused by animals.

zoogeography (zō'öjēŏg'răfĭ) *n.* [Gk. *zoon*, animal; *ge*, earth; *graphein*, to write.] The science of distribution of animals on the earth.

zoogloea (zō'öglē'ă) *n.* [Gk. *zoon*, animal; *gloia*, glue.] A mass of bacteria embedded in a mucilaginous matrix, frequently forming an iridescent film; zooglea.

zoogonidangium (zō'ögŏnĭdăn'jĭŭm) *n.* [Gk. *zoon*, animal; *gonos*, offspring; *idion*, *dim.*; *anggeion*, vessel.] A cell which produces zoospores or zoogonidia, in algae.

zoogonidium (zō'ögŏnĭd'ĭŭm) *n.* [Gk. *zoon*, animal; *gonos*, offspring; *idion*, *dim.*] One of motile spores formed in gonidangium of algae.

zoogonous (zōŏg'önŭs) *a.* [Gk. *zoon*, animal; *gonos*, offspring.] Viviparous.

zooid (zō'oid) *n.* [Gk. *zoon*, animal; *eidos*, like.] A member of a compound animal organism; an individual or person in a coelenterate or polyzoan colony; posterior genital and non-sexual region formed in many polychaetes.

zoolith (zō'ölĭth) *n.* [Gk. *zoon*, animal; *lithos*, stone.] A fossil animal.

zoology (zōŏl'öjĭ) *n.* [Gk. *zoon*, animal; *logos*, discourse.] The science dealing with structure, functions, behaviour, history, classification, and distribution of animals.

zoöme (zō'ōm) *n.* [Gk. *zoon*, animal.] Animals considered as an ecological unit.

zoomorphosis (zō'ömôr'fōsĭs) *n.* [Gk. *zoon*, animal; *morphosis*, a forming.] Formation of structures in plants owing to animal agents, as production of galls.

zoon (zō'ŏn) *n.* [Gk. *zoon*, animal.] An individual developed from an egg.

zoonerythrin (zō'ŏnĕrĭth'rĭn) *n.* [Gk. *zoon*, animal ; *erythros*, red.] Red lipochrome pigment found in various animals ; zooerythrin, *q.v.*

zoonite (zō'ŏnīt) *n.* [Gk. *zoon*, animal.] A body segment of an articulated animal.

zoonomy (zōŏn'ŏmĭ) *n.* [Gk. *zoon*, animal ; *nomos*, law.] The laws dealing with animal life.

zoonosis (zōŏn'ŏsis) *n.* [Gk. *zoon*, animal ; *nosos*, disease.] Disease of animals ; animal disease transmitted to man. *Cf.* zoosis.

zooparasite (zō'ŏpăr'ăsīt) *n.* [Gk. *zoon*, animal ; *parasitos*, parasite.] Any parasitic animal.

zoopherin,—nutritional factor X, related to erythrotin or vitamin B_{12}.

zoophilous (zōŏf'ĭlŭs) *a.* [Gk *zoon*, animal ; *philein*, to love.] *Appl.* plants adapted for pollination by animals other than insects.

zoophobic (zōŏfŏb'ĭk) *a.* [Gk. *zoon*, animal ; *phobos*, fear.] Shunning, or shunned by, animals ; *appl.* plants protected by spines, hairs, secretions, etc.

zoophyte (zō'ŏfīt) *n.* [Gk. *zoon*, animal ; *phyton*, plant.] An animal resembling a plant in appearance or growth.

zooplankton (zō'ŏplăng'ktŏn) *n.* [Gk. *zoon*, animal ; *plangktos*, wandering.] Animal plankton.

zooplasm (zō'ŏplăzm) *n.* [Gk. *zoon*, animal ; *plasma*, mould.] Living substance which depends on the products of other living organisms for nutritive material.

zoosis (zō'ŏsĭs) *n.* [Gk. *zoon*, animal.] Any disease produced by animals ; *cf.* zoonosis.

zoosperm (zō'ŏspĕrm) *n.* [Gk. *zoon*, animal ; *sperma*, seed.] A spermatozoid ; a zoospore.

zoosphere (zō'ŏsfēr) *n.* [Gk. *zoon*, animal ; *sphaira*, globe.] Biciliate zoospore of algae.

zoosporangiophore (zō'ŏspŏrăn'-jĭŏfōr) *n.* [Gk. *zoon*, animal ; *sporos*, seed ; *anggeion*, vessel ; *phoros*, bearing.] Structure bearing zoosporangia, as in mildew fungi.

zoosporangium (zō'ŏspŏrăn'jĭŭm) *n.* [Gk. *zoon*, animal ; *sporos*, seed ; *anggeion*, vessel.] A sporangium in which zoospores develop.

zoospore (zō'ŏspōr) *n.* [Gk. *zoon*, animal ; *sporos*, seed.] A swarm-cell, flagellate or amoeboid, in many protozoa ; a motile protoplast in certain algae ; swarm-spore of certain fungi.

zoosporocyst (zō'ŏspŏr'ŏsĭst) *n.* [Gk. *zoon*, animal ; *sporos*, seed ; *kystis*, bladder.] Zoosporangium of certain saprophytic Phycomycetes.

zoosterols (zōŏstĕr'ŏlz) *n. plu.* [Gk. *zoon*, animal ; *stereos*, solid ; L. *oleum*, oil.] Animal sterols, as cholesterol, coprosterol, etc.

zootaxy (zō'ŏtăksĭ) *n.* [Gk. *zoon*, animal ; *taxis*, arrangement.] The classification of animals.

zootechnics (zō'ŏtĕk'nĭks) *n.* [Gk. *zoon*, animal ; *techne*, craft.] Science applied to the art of breeding, rearing, and utilising animals ; zootechny.

zoothecium,—zoocytium, *q.v.*

zoothome (zō'ŏthōm) *n.* [Gk. *zoon*, animal ; *thomos*, heap.] Any group of individuals in a living coral.

zootomy (zōŏt'ŏmĭ) *n.* [Gk. *zoon*, animal ; *temnein*, to cut.] Dissection or anatomy of animals other than man.

zootoxin (zō'ŏtŏk'sĭn) *n.* [Gk. *zoon*, animal ; *toxikon*, poison.] Any toxin or poison produced by animals.

zootrophic (zō'ŏtrŏf'ĭk) *a.* [Gk. *zoon*, animal ; *trephein*, to nourish.] Heterotrophic ; holozoic, *q.v.*

zootype (zō'ŏtīp) *n.* [Gk. *zoon*, animal ; *typos*, pattern.] Representative type of animal.

zooxanthellae (zō'ŏzănthĕl'ē) *n. plu.* [Gk. *zoon*, animal ; *xanthos*, yellow.] Yellow or brown cells or symbiotic unicellular algae living in various animals.

zooxanthin (zō'ŏzăn'thĭn) *n.* [Gk. *zoon*, animal ; *xanthos*, yellow.] Yellow pigment found in plumage of certain birds.

zoozygosphere,—planogamete, *q.v.*

zoozygospore (zōōzī'gōspōr) *n.* [Gk. *zoon*, animal; *zygon*, yoke; *sporos*, seed.] A motile zygospore.

Zuckerkandl's bodies [*E. Zuckerkandl*, Austrian anatomist]. Chromaffin tissue or paraganglia lying on each side of foetal abdominal aorta; aortic bodies.

zygantrum (zĭgăn'trŭm) *n.* [Gk. *zygon*, yoke; *antron*, cave.] A fossa on posterior surface of neural arch of vertebrae of snakes and certain lizards; *cf.* zygosphene.

zygapophysis (zī'găpŏf'ĭsĭs) *n.* [Gk. *zygon*, yoke; *apophysis*, process of a bone.] One of processes of a vertebra by which it articulates with adjacent vertebrae.

zygobranchiate (zī'gōbrăng'kĭăt) *a.* [Gk. *zygon*, yoke; *brangchia*, gills.] Having gills symmetrically placed and renal organs paired; *appl.* an order of Gastropoda.

zygocardiac ossicles,—paired lateral ossicles in gastric mill of Crustacea.

zygodactyl (zī'gōdăk'tĭl) *a.* [Gk. *zygon*, yoke; *daktylos*, digit.] Having two toes pointing forward, two backward, as in parrots.

zygodont (zī'gōdŏnt) *a.* [Gk. *zygon*, yoke; *odous*, tooth.] Having molar teeth in which the four tubercles are united in pairs.

zygogamy (zĭgŏg'ămĭ) *n.* [Gk. *zygon*, yoke; *gamos*, marriage.] The union of similar cells, as of unicellular organisms or of isogametes; isogamy.

zygogenetic (zĭg'ōjĕnĕt'ĭk) *a.* [Gk. *zygon*, yoke; *genesis*, origin.] Produced by fertilisation, *opp.* parthenogenetic; zygogenic.

zygoid (zī'goid) *a.* [Gk. *zygon*, yoke; *eidos*, form.] Diploid; *appl.* parthenogenesis.

zygolysis (zĭgŏl'ĭsĭs) *n.* [Gk. *zygon*, yoke; *lysis*, loosing.] Separation of a pair, as of allelomorphs.

zygoma (zĭgō'mă) *n.* [Gk. *zygoma*, yoke.] The bony arch of the cheek; arcus zygomaticus.

zygomatic (zĭg'ōmăt'ĭk) *a.* [Gk. *zygoma*, yoke.] Malar; *pert.* zygoma; *appl.* arch, bone, fossa, processes, muscle, nerve.

zygomaticofacial (zĭg'ōmăt'ĭkōfā'-sĭăl) *a.* [Gk. *zygoma*, yoke; L. *facies*, face.] *Appl.* foramen on malar surface of zygomatic for passage of nerve and vessels; *appl.* branch of zygomatic or temporomalar nerve.

zygomaticotemporal (zĭg'ōmăt'ĭkō-tĕm'pōrăl) *a.* [Gk. *zygoma*, yoke; L. *tempora*, temples.] *Appl.* suture, foramen, nerve, etc., at temporal surface of zygomatic bone.

zygomaticus,—muscle from zygomatic bone to angle of mouth.

zygomelous (zĭgŏm'ēlŭs) *a.* [Gk. *zygon*, yoke; *melos*, limb.] Having paired appendages; *appl.* fins; *opp.* azygomelous.

zygomite (zī'gōmīt) *n.* [Gk. *zygon*, yoke; *mitos*, thread.] One of a pair of conjugated filaments.

zygomorphic (zĭg'ōmôr'fĭk), *a.* [Gk. *zygon*, yoke; *morphe*, shape.] Bilaterally symmetrical, with only one plane of symmetry; zygomorphous, monosymmetrical.

zygonema (zĭg'ōnē'mă) *n.* [Gk. *zygon*, yoke; *nema*, thread.] Chromosome thread during amphitene or zygotene.

zygoneury (zĭg'ōnū'rĭ) *n.* [Gk. *zygon*, yoke; *neuron*, nerve.] In certain Gastropoda, having a connective between pleural ganglion and ganglion on visceral branch of opposite side.

zygophase (zī'gōfāz) *n.* [Gk. *zygon*, yoke; *phasis*, aspect.] The diploid phase of a life-cycle; diplophase; *cf.* gamophase.

zygophore (zī'gōfōr) *n.* [Gk. *zygon*, yoke; *pherein*, to bear.] A conjugating hypha in certain fungi.

zygophyte (zī'gōfīt) *n.* [Gk. *zygon*, yoke; *phyton*, plant.] A plant with two similar reproductive cells which unite in fertilisation.

zygopleural (zĭg'ōploor'ăl) *a.* [Gk. *zygon*, yoke; *pleuron*, side.] Bilaterally symmetrical.

zygopodium (zī'göpō'dĭŭm) *n.* [Gk. *zygon*, yoke; *pous*, foot.] Forearm; shank.

zygosis (zĭgō'sĭs) *n.* [Gk. *zygosis*, a joining.] Conjugation; union of gametes.

zygosome,—mixochromosome, *q.v.*

zygosperm (zī'göspĕrm) *n.* [Gk. *zygon*, yoke; *sperma*, seed.] Zygospore.

zygosphene (zī'gösfēn) *n.* [Gk. *zygon*, yoke; *sphen*, wedge.] An articular process on anterior surface of neural arch of vertebrae of snakes and certain lizards, which fits into zygantrum.

zygosphere (zī'gösfēr) *n.* [Gk. *zygon*, yoke; *sphaira*, globe.] A gamete which conjugates with a similar one to form a zygospore.

zygosporangium (zī'göspörăn'jĭŭm) *n.* [Gk. *zygon*, yoke; *sporos*, seed; *anggeion*, vessel.] A sporangium in which zygospores are formed.

zygospore (zī'göspōr) *n.* [Gk. *zygon*, yoke; *sporos*, seed.] A zygote; a cell, or resting spore, formed by conjugation of similar reproductive cells.

zygosporocarp (zī'göspŏr'ökârp) *n.* [Gk. *zygon*, yoke; *sporos*, seed; *karpos*, fruit.] A fruit-body in which zygospores are produced.

zygosporophore (zī'göspŏr'öfōr) *n.* [Gk. *zygon*, yoke; *sporos*, seed; *pherein*, to bear.] Zygophore, *q.v.*; suspensor in Mucorineae.

zygotaxis (zĭg'ötăk'sĭs) *n.* [Gk. *zygon*, yoke; *taxis*, arrangement.] Tendency towards conjugation between two specialised hyphae in certain fungi; zygotactism; mutual attraction between gametes of the opposite sex.

zygote (zī'gōt) *n.* [Gk. *zygotos*, yoked.] Cell formed by union of two gametes or reproductive cells; fertilised ovum.

zygotene (zī'götēn) *n.* [Gk. *zygon*, yoke; *tainia*, band.] Prophase stage of meiosis where spireme threads are uniting in pairs; pairing threads.

zygotic (zĭgŏt'ĭk) *a.* [Gk. *zygotos*, yoked.] *Pert.* a zygote; *appl.* mutation occurring immediately after fertilisation; *appl.* number, somatic, *opp.* gametic, number of chromosomes, 2*n*.

zygotoblast (zĭgō'töblăst') *n.* [Gk. *zygotos*, yoked; *blastos*, bud.] A sporozoite produced by segmentation of zygotomere in Haemamoebae.

zygotoid (zĭgō'toid) *n.* [Gk. *zygotos*, yoked; *eidos*, form.] Product of union of two gametoids, as in mucorine fungi.

zygotomere (zĭgō'tömēr) *n.* [Gk. *zygotos*, yoked; *meros*, part.] A cell formed by segmentation of zygote in Haemamoebae.

zygotonucleus (zĭgō'tönū'klëŭs) *n.* [Gk. *zygotos*, yoked; L. *nucleus*, kernel.] A nucleus formed by fusion of two gametonuclei.

zygotropism (zĭgŏt'röpĭzm) *n.* [Gk. *zygon*, yoke; *trope*, turn.] The growth of zygophores towards each other; *cf.* zygotaxis.

zygozoospore (zī'gözō'öspōr) *n.* [Gk. *zygon*, yoke; *zoon*, animal; *sporos*, seed.] A motile cell formed by union of two similar cells.

zymase (zī'mās) *n.* [Gk. *zyme*, leaven.] A complex of enzymes occurring in plants and acting on sugars, with production of carbon dioxide and alcohol.

zymin (zī'mĭn) *n.* [Gk. *zyme*, leaven.] An enzyme or ferment.

zymocont (zī'mökŏnt) *n.* [Gk. *zyme*, leaven; *kontos*, pole.] Rod-shaped chondriosome of a pancreatic cell.

zymo-excitor,—a substance activating a zymogen, *e.g.* hydrochloric acid, which activates pepsin

zymogen (zī'möjĕn) *n.* [Gk. *zyme*, leaven; *-genes*, producing.] A substance capable of being transformed into a ferment, *i.e.* precursor of an enzyme; proenzyme; proferment; a zymogenic organism.

zymogenesis (zī'möjĕn'ĕsĭs) *n.* [Gk. *zyme*, leaven; *genesis*, origin.] The production of an enzyme by a zymogen activated by a kinase.

zymogenic (zī'mōjĕn'ĭk) *a.* [Gk. *zyme*, leaven; *-genes*, producing.] Enzyme-producing; *appl.* certain cells of gastric gland tubule; *appl.* micro-organisms, as bacteria.

zymohydrolysis (zī'mōhīdrŏl'ĭsĭs) *n.* [Gk. *zyme*, leaven; *hydor*, water; *lysis*, breaking down.] Hydrolysis due to the action of an enzyme; enzymatic hydrolysis.

zymolysis (zīmŏl'ĭsĭs) *n.* [Gk. *zyme*, leaven; *lysis*, loosing.] Decomposition by the action of enzymes.

zymophore (zī'mōfōr) *n.* [Gk. *zyme*, leaven; *phoros*, bearing.] The active portion of an enzyme, bearing the ferment.

zymoprotein (zī'mōprōtēin) *n.* [Gk. *zyme*, leaven; *proteion*, first.] Any of the proteins having catalytic capacity.

zymosis (zīmō'sĭs) *n.* [Gk. *zymosis*, fermentation.] Fermentation; reactions induced by an enzyme or enzymes.

zymosthenic (zī'mōsthĕn'ĭk) *a.* [Gk. *zyme*, leaven; *sthenein*, to be strong.] Enhancing the activity of an enzyme.

zymotic (zīmŏt'ĭk) *a.* [Gk. *zymotikos*, causing fermentation.] *Pert.* or caused by fermentation; *appl.* diseases induced by infection.

PRINTED IN GREAT BRITAIN BY
OLIVER AND BOYD LTD.
EDINBURGH

0 [illegible]